Teacher's Edition

HBJ ALGEBRA 1

Arthur F. Coxford

Joseph N. Payne

Harcourt Brace Jovanovich, Publishers

New York   Chicago   San Francisco   Atlanta   Dallas   *and*   London

CONTENTS

Printed in the United States of America   ISBN 0-15-353875-9

DESCRIPTION OF THE PROGRAM

Textbook

Pages M-2 through M-11 describe, both verbally and pictorially, the features of the student textbook: a skills lesson, a problem solving and applications lesson, optional features (*Computer Applications, Calculator Applications, Puzzles, Consumer Applications, Career Applications*), and the approach to review and testing (*Review Capsules*, in-chapter *Reviews, Chapter Summary, Chapter Objectives and Review, Review of Word Problems, Cumulative Reviews*, and *Preparing for College Entrance Tests*).

Tests

The four components of the spirit duplicating master version of the testing program (Chapter Tests, Cumulative Tests, Preparing for College Entrance Tests, and a Placement Test) are described on page M-8. The answers for these tests apear on pages M-122 through M-126.

Skills Practice Book

This title, which is available as spirit duplicating masters and as a paperback, is described on page M-9.

Computer Programming

Page M-9 describes a typical lesson from the paperback publication *Computer Programming and Algebra 1*. A separate *Solution Key* is available for this title, upon request.

Copying Masters

Permission to reproduce the 63 pages of copying masters that are included in the Teacher's Manual is granted to users of *HBJ Algebra 1*. Page M-10 describes these unique copying masters (16 pages of *Quizzes*, 14 pages of *Chapter Tests*, 17 pages of survey tests and additional practice on whole numbers, decimals, fractions, per cent, and metric measures, and 16 pages of additional practice for the *Preparing for College Entrance Tests*).

Annotated Pages

The four basic components that appear in the margin of the annotated textbook pages for each lesson are described on page M-11 (the *Quick Quiz, Additional Examples, Additional Answers*, and a three-level *Assignment Guide*). The textbook page, which is reduced approximately ten per cent, contains annotated answers to the exercises. Answers that cannot be annotated are listed under *Additional Answers* in the margin.

Solution Key

Detailed solutions are provided in the paperback *Solution Key*. In addition to receiving a copy of the *Teacher's Edition*, upon request, each teacher will receive a copy of the *Solution Key*, upon request.

The Lesson

Review Capsules
These exercises review prior-taught skills that will be used in the lesson that follows. The exercises are referenced to those pages where the skill was presented.

Examples
Side comments within Examples help the students to understand the procedure.

_____ **REVIEW CAPSULE FOR SECTION 3–5** _____

Combine like terms. (Pages 60–63)

1. $7x + 9x + 2$ **2.** $8y + y - 9$ **3.** $4a + 2a - a$ **4.** $8a + (-3a) - 9$
5. $6t - 5t + 1$ **6.** $-6y - y + 9y$ **7.** $-32 + 4r - 9r$ **8.** $-7 - 10b + 15b$

3–5 Solving Equations: Like Terms

In solving equations, you sometimes have to combine like terms. Usually it is better to do this first. Then you apply the addition and multiplication properties for equations.

EXAMPLE 1 Solve and check: $9m - 2m + 6 = 27$

Solution: $9m - 2m + 6 = 27$ ◄─── **Combine 9m and 2m.**
         $7m + 6 = 27$ ◄─── $9m - 2m = (9 - 2)m = 7m$
         $7m = 21$
         $m = 3$
Check: $9m - 2m + 6 = 27$ ◄─── **Replace m with 3.**
     $9(3) - 2(3) + 6 \stackrel{?}{=} 27$
     $27 - 6 + 6 \stackrel{?}{=} 27$
     $27 \stackrel{?}{=} 27$ Yes ✔   **Solution set: {3}**

Sometimes it is helpful to use parentheses to group the like terms.

EXAMPLE 2 Solve and check: $t + (3t - 9) + t + (3t - 9) = 62$

Solution: $t + (3t - 9) + t + (3t - 9) = 62$ ◄─── **Group the like terms.**
   $(t + 3t + t + 3t) + [(-9) + (-9)] = 62$ ◄─── **Combine like terms.**
         $8t + (-18) = 62$ ◄─── $t + 3t + t + 3t = 8t$
         $8t = 80$
         $t = 10$
Check: $t + (3t - 9) + t + (3t - 9) = 62$ ◄─── **Replace t with 10.**
   $10 + (3 \cdot 10 - 9) + 10 + (3 \cdot 10 - 9) \stackrel{?}{=} 62$
     $10 + 21 + 10 + 21 \stackrel{?}{=} 62$
     $62 \stackrel{?}{=} 62$ Yes ✔   **Solution set: {10}**

When parentheses within an equation indicate multiplication, use the distributive postulate to multiply. For example,

$$-2(x - 5) = -2(x) + (-2)(-5)$$
$$= -2x + 10$$

Then you combine like terms and solve for the variable.

EXAMPLE 3 Solve and check: $4x - 3(x - 2) = 41$

Solution: $4x - 3(x - 2) = 41$ ◄─── **Write $-3(x - 2)$ as $+(-3)(x - 2)$.**
     $4x + (-3)(x - 2) = 41$
   $4x + (-3)(x) + (-3)(-2) = 41$ ◄─── **By the distributive postulate**
       $4x - 3x + 6 = 41$
         $x + 6 = 41$ ◄─── **Solve for x.**
   $x + 6 + (-6) = 41 + (-6)$
         $x = 35$
Check: $4x - 3(x - 2) = 41$ ◄─── **Replace x with 35.**
   $4(35) - 3(35 - 2) \stackrel{?}{=} 41$
     $140 - 3(33) \stackrel{?}{=} 41$
     $140 - 99 \stackrel{?}{=} 41$
     $41 \stackrel{?}{=} 41$ Yes ✔   **Solution set: {35}**

The following procedure summarizes the steps for solving equations.

Procedure

Steps for Solving Equations
1 Remove parentheses by using the distributive postulate.
2 Combine like terms.
3 Use the addition property for equations.
4 Use the multiplication property for equations.
5 Check the equation.

CLASSROOM EXERCISES

Use the distributive property to find each product.

1. $9(x - 1)$ **2.** $2(5x + 3)$ **3.** $7(-2x - 1)$ **4.** $8(3x - 10)$
5. $-2(x + 1)$ **6.** $-3(x - 7)$ **7.** $-5(x - 1)$ **8.** $-2(x - 5)$

Solve and check.

9. $3a + a = 8$ **10.** $6a - a + 3 = 15$ **11.** $7b + 3b - b = 16$
12. $2(x + 3) = 9$ **13.** $3(x - 5) = 21$ **14.** $-2(-3 - 4x) = -10$

WRITTEN EXERCISES

A   Use the distributive postulate to find each product.

1. $2(x - 3)$ **2.** $4(x - 4)$ **3.** $3(2x + 1)$ **4.** $3(2x - 1)$
5. $4(5x - 7)$ **6.** $4(2b - 3)$ **7.** $4(b - 6)$ **8.** $2(9 - b)$

98   *Chapter 3*

Use the distributive postulate to find each product.

9. $-4(x - 9)$ **10.** $-2(y - 3)$ **11.** $-4(5 - n)$ **12.** $-5(y - 6)$
13. $-4(3 - x)$ **14.** $-1(5 - m)$ **15.** $-1(9 - 4m)$ **16.** $-2(m - 4)$

Solve and check each equation.

17. $7x - 3x = 8$ **18.** $5n - 2n = 12$ **19.** $3y + 2y - 4y = 6$
20. $8m - 2m + 7 = 19$ **21.** $15 = 7x - 2x$ **22.** $16 = 8a + 7a + a$
23. $2n - 5n = 12$ **24.** $-3n - 4n = -21$ **25.** $-5x - 4x + 3 = 12$
26. $7 - x + 2x = 7$ **27.** $2(x - 3) = -10$ **28.** $2(x - 5) = -8$
29. $2(x - 5) = 4$ **30.** $3(2x + 1) = -15$ **31.** $3(2x - 1) = 9$
32. $4(5x - 7) = 12$ **33.** $2(5 - 3n) = -14$ **34.** $4(7 - 2x) = 4$
35. $-7b + 4(2b - 3) = 16$ **36.** $2x + 3(x + 5) = 0$ **37.** $-3x + 6(x - 4) = 9$
38. $2y + 4(y - 5) = 4$ **39.** $2a - 5(a - 6) = 3$ **40.** $2b + 4(b - 6) = 12$
41. $-4(x - 9) + 5 = 1$ **42.** $2(9 - b) - 8 = 0$ **43.** $6m - 15m = 3$
44. $2b + 6b = 12$ **45.** $2(x - 6) = 3$ **46.** $-3(y + 5) = 10$
47. $b - 2(4 - b) = -5$ **48.** $x - 4(3 - x) = 0$ **49.** $5 - 2(m + 2) = 9$

B
50. $6 - (m - 4) = 18$ **51.** $-2 - (5 + 3m) = 20$ **52.** $-8 - (9 - 4m) = 15$
53. $\frac{1}{2}x + \frac{3}{4}x = 2\frac{1}{2}$ **54.** $0.04x + 0.96x = 4.80$ **55.** $1.6a + 2.4 - 7 = 3$

C
In Exercises 56–57, give the reason for each step of each proof. In these proofs, all variables represent real numbers.

56. If $ac = bc$ and $c \neq 0$, then $a = b$.

Statements	Reasons
1. $ac = bc$	**1.** Given
2. $(ac)\left(\frac{1}{c}\right) = bc\left(\frac{1}{c}\right)$	**2.** ?
3. ?	

57. If $a + c = b + c$, then $a = b$.

Statements	Reasons
1. $a + b = b + c$	**1.** Given
2. $(a + c) + (-c) =$ $b + c + (-c)$	**2.** ?
3. $a + [c + (-c)] =$ $b + c$	**2.** ?

Procedure
The ideas and steps presented in a given lesson are summarized for the student.

Classroom Exercises
These exercises help to determine how well students understand the lesson before proceeding with the homework assignment.

Written Exercises
The graded exercises are designed to meet the needs of a wide range of student abilities. The **C** exercises will challenge the more able students.

Problem Solving and Applications Lesson

Each *Problem Solving and Applications* lesson is directly related to the algebraic content presented in the given chapter. This begins in Chapter 1 with *Using Formulas*. (See pages 12-16.) The applications cover a wide range of practical and mathematical topics.

Translating Words to Symbols
Careful attention is paid to developing the skill of translating word expressions to algebraic expressions.

Using Tables Organizing the information given in a word problem helps students in using Condition 2 to write an equation or inequality for the problem.

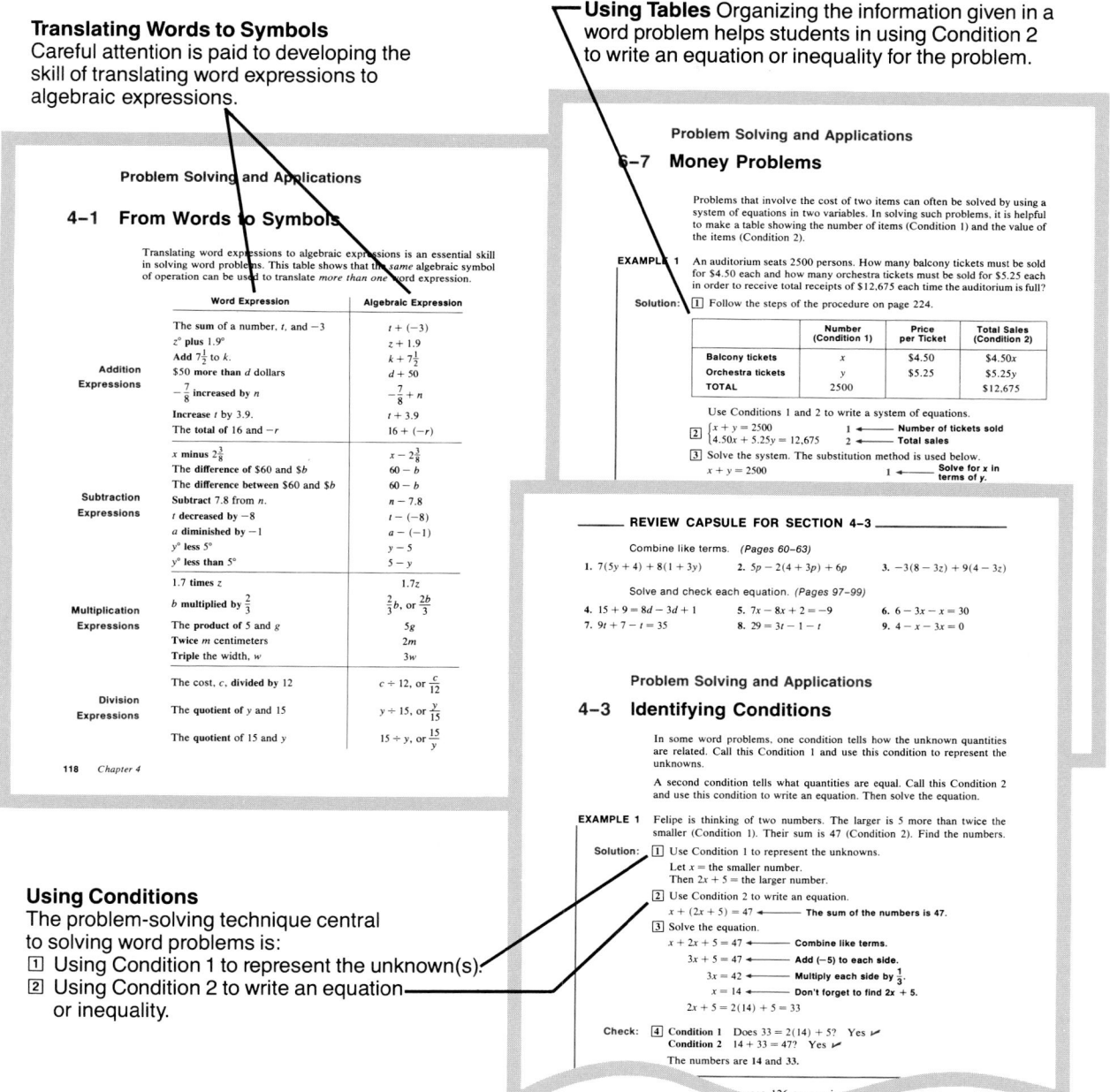

Problem Solving and Applications

4–1 From Words to Symbols

Translating word expressions to algebraic expressions is an essential skill in solving word problems. This table shows that the *same* algebraic symbol of operation can be used to translate *more than one* word expression.

	Word Expression	Algebraic Expression
	The sum of a number, t, and -3	$t + (-3)$
	$z°$ plus $1.9°$	$z + 1.9$
	Add $7\frac{1}{2}$ to k.	$k + 7\frac{1}{2}$
Addition Expressions	$\$50$ more than d dollars	$d + 50$
	$-\frac{7}{8}$ increased by n	$-\frac{7}{8} + n$
	Increase t by 3.9.	$t + 3.9$
	The total of 16 and $-r$	$16 + (-r)$
	x minus $2\frac{3}{8}$	$x - 2\frac{3}{8}$
	The difference of $\$60$ and $\$b$	$60 - b$
	The difference between $\$60$ and $\$b$	$60 - b$
Subtraction Expressions	Subtract 7.8 from n.	$n - 7.8$
	t decreased by -8	$t - (-8)$
	a diminished by -1	$a - (-1)$
	$y°$ less $5°$	$y - 5$
	$y°$ less than $5°$	$5 - y$
	1.7 times z	$1.7z$
Multiplication Expressions	b multiplied by $\frac{2}{3}$	$\frac{2}{3}b$, or $\frac{2b}{3}$
	The product of 5 and g	$5g$
	Twice m centimeters	$2m$
	Triple the width, w	$3w$
	The cost, c, divided by 12	$c \div 12$, or $\frac{c}{12}$
Division Expressions	The quotient of y and 15	$y \div 15$, or $\frac{y}{15}$
	The quotient of 15 and y	$15 \div y$, or $\frac{15}{y}$

118   Chapter 4

Using Conditions
The problem-solving technique central to solving word problems is:
① Using Condition 1 to represent the unknown(s).
② Using Condition 2 to write an equation or inequality.

Problem Solving and Applications

6–7   Money Problems

Problems that involve the cost of two items can often be solved by using a system of equations in two variables. In solving such problems, it is helpful to make a table showing the number of items (Condition 1) and the value of the items (Condition 2).

EXAMPLE 1   An auditorium seats 2500 persons. How many balcony tickets must be sold for $\$4.50$ each and how many orchestra tickets must be sold for $\$5.25$ each in order to receive total receipts of $\$12,675$ each time the auditorium is full?

Solution: ① Follow the steps of the procedure on page 224.

	Number (Condition 1)	Price per Ticket	Total Sales (Condition 2)
Balcony tickets	x	$\$4.50$	$\$4.50x$
Orchestra tickets	y	$\$5.25$	$\$5.25y$
TOTAL	2500		$\$12,675$

Use Conditions 1 and 2 to write a system of equations.

② $\begin{cases} x + y = 2500 & 1 \longleftarrow \text{Number of tickets sold} \\ 4.50x + 5.25y = 12,675 & 2 \longleftarrow \text{Total sales} \end{cases}$

③ Solve the system. The substitution method is used below.
$x + y = 2500$ 1 $\longleftarrow$ **Solve for x in terms of y.**

―――― **REVIEW CAPSULE FOR SECTION 4–3** ――――

Combine like terms.   *(Pages 60–63)*

1. $7(5y + 4) + 8(1 + 3y)$ 2. $5p - 2(4 + 3p) + 6p$ 3. $-3(8 - 3z) + 9(4 - 3z)$

Solve and check each equation. *(Pages 97–99)*

4. $15 + 9 = 8d - 3d + 1$ 5. $7x - 8x + 2 = -9$ 6. $6 - 3x - x = 30$
7. $9t + 7 - t = 35$ 8. $29 = 3t - 1 - t$ 9. $4 - x - 3x = 0$

Problem Solving and Applications

4–3   Identifying Conditions

In some word problems, one condition tells how the unknown quantities are related. Call this Condition 1 and use this condition to represent the unknowns.

A second condition tells what quantities are equal. Call this Condition 2 and use this condition to write an equation. Then solve the equation.

EXAMPLE 1   Felipe is thinking of two numbers. The larger is 5 more than twice the smaller (Condition 1). Their sum is 47 (Condition 2). Find the numbers.

Solution: ① Use Condition 1 to represent the unknowns.
Let $x = $ the smaller number.
Then $2x + 5 = $ the larger number.
② Use Condition 2 to write an equation.
$x + (2x + 5) = 47$ $\longleftarrow$ **The sum of the numbers is 47.**
③ Solve the equation.
$x + 2x + 5 = 47$ $\longleftarrow$ **Combine like terms.**
$3x + 5 = 47$ $\longleftarrow$ **Add (-5) to each side.**
$3x = 42$ $\longleftarrow$ **Multiply each side by $\frac{1}{3}$.**
$x = 14$ $\longleftarrow$ **Don't forget to find $2x + 5$.**
$2x + 5 = 2(14) + 5 = 33$

Check: ④ **Condition 1**   Does $33 = 2(14) + 5$?   Yes ✔
Condition 2 $14 + 33 = 47$?   Yes ✔
The numbers are 14 and 33.

page 126 summari―

Optional Features

Computer Applications in the BASIC language are directly related to the algebraic content presented in the given chapter.

Each lesson opens with the statement of a **Problem** which is then followed by the **Program.**

Each lesson contains an **Analysis** of the steps in the program.

COMPUTER APPLICATIONS

BASIC: SOLVING ABSOLUTE VALUE EQUATIONS

Problem: *Write a program which solves equations of the form $|Ax + B| = C$. Include the possibilities that the solution set may be all real numbers or may be the empty set.*

```
100 PRINT "FOR THE EQUATION !AX + B! = C,"
110 PRINT "WHAT ARE A, B, AND C";
120 INPUT A, B, C
130 IF C < 0 THEN 250
140 IF C = 0 THEN 200
150 IF A = 0 THEN 230
160 LET X1 = (C - B)/A
170 LET X2 = (-C - B)/A
180 PRINT "SOLUTIONS ARE ";X1;" AND ";X2
190 GOTO 280
200 LET X = -B/A
210 PRINT "SOLUTION IS ";X
220 GOTO 280
230 IF B = C THEN 270
240 IF B = -C THEN 270
250 PRINT "NO SOLUTION"
260 GOTO 280
270 PRINT "ALL REAL NUMBERS ARE SOLUTIONS."
280 PRINT
290 PRINT "ANY MORE EQUATIONS TO SOLVE (1=YES, 0=NO)";
300 INPUT Z
310 IF Z = 1 THEN 120
320 END
```

The following is the output from a sample run of the program above.

Output:
```
RUN
FOR THE EQUATION !AX + B! = C,
WHAT ARE A, B, AND C? -3,9,15
SOLUTIONS ARE -2  AND  8

ANY MORE EQUATIONS TO SOLVE (1=YES, 0=NO)? 1
? 2,8,0
SOLUTION IS -4

ANY MORE EQUATIONS TO SOLVE (1=YES, 0=NO)? 1
?0,6,8
NO SOLUTION
```

268   Computer Applications

```
ANY MORE EQUATIONS TO SOLVE (1=YES, 0=NO)? 1
? 0,-8,8
ALL REAL NUMBERS ARE SOLUTIONS.

ANY MORE EQUATIONS TO SOLVE (1=YES, 0=NO)? 0
READY
```

Analysis

Statements 130, 250: An absolute value expression cannot equal a negative number. Thus if $C < 0$, there is no solution.

Statements 140, 200–210: If $C = 0$, the equation has only one solution.

Statements 150, 230–250: If $A = 0$, the formulas in statements 160 and 170 cannot be used. Instead, if $|B| = C$, any real number is a solution. But if $|B| \neq C$, no real number is a solution.

Statements 160–180: If the computer reaches statement 160, then $C > 0$ and $A \neq 0$. The equation has two solutions, as the following steps show.

$$|Ax + B| = C$$
$$Ax + B = C \quad \text{or} \quad Ax + B = -C$$
$$Ax = C - B \quad \text{or} \quad Ax = -C - B \quad \leftarrow \text{Subtract } B \text{ from both sides.}$$
$$x = \frac{C - B}{A} \quad \text{or} \quad x = \frac{-C - B}{A} \quad \leftarrow \text{Divide both sides by } A.$$

EXERCISES

A Write each equation in the form $|Ax + B| = C$. Then use the program on page 268 to solve the equation.

1. $|x - 1| = 5$
2. $|x + 3| - 7 = 0$
3. $|2x| = 24$
4. $35 = |4x - 1|$
5. $|4 - x| = 44$
6. $|15 + 5x| = 55$
7. $0 = |6 - 2x|$
8. $100 = |-5x|$
9. $|4x + 2| + 8 = 0$
10. $|10 + 8x| = 0$
11. $0 = |80 - 10x| - 8$
12. $9 = |3x - 1| + 9$

Write a BASIC program for each problem.

13. Given the coordinates of a point, decide whether the point is in the solution set of the following system of inequalities.
$$\begin{cases} x \leq 0 \\ 2x + y \geq 6 \\ 4x + y < 3 \end{cases}$$

B

14. Solve inequalities of the form $|Ax + B| < C$.

15. Solve inequalities of the form $|Ax + B| > C$.

Solving Absolute Value Equations   **269**

The **Output** from a sample run of the program is included in most lessons.

The **Exercises** are graded in order to provide experiences with the computer for <u>all</u> students.

The *Puzzles* are designed as diversions for <u>all</u> students.

Calculator Applications are included in most chapters. Each is an application of algebraic content.

Puzzle

Here are some brain teasers for you to solve.

1. Two riders race on a circular track. Rider A can circle the track in 6 minutes, and Rider B in 4 minutes. From the beginning of the race, how many minutes will it be before Rider B overtakes Rider A?
2. If a hen and a half lays an egg and a half in a day and a half, how many eggs will six hens lay in six days?
3. It takes a clock 2 seconds to strike 3 o'clock. How long will it take to strike 12 o'clock?

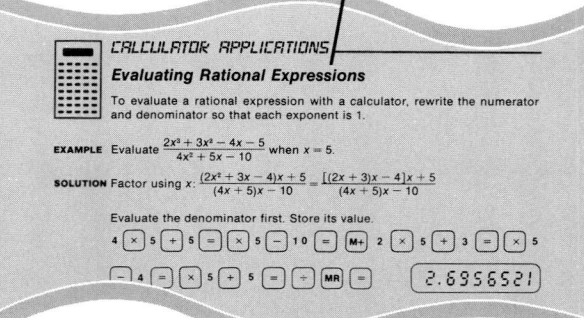

CALCULATOR APPLICATIONS

Evaluating Rational Expressions

To evaluate a rational expression with a calculator, rewrite the numerator and denominator so that each exponent is 1.

EXAMPLE Evaluate $\dfrac{2x^3 + 3x^2 - 4x - 5}{4x^2 + 5x - 10}$ when $x = 5$.

SOLUTION Factor using x: $\dfrac{(2x^2 + 3x - 4)x + 5}{(4x + 5)x - 10} = \dfrac{[(2x + 3)x - 4]x + 5}{(4x + 5)x - 10}$

Evaluate the denominator first. Store its value.

$4 \boxed{\times} 5 \boxed{+} 5 \boxed{=} \boxed{\times} 5 \boxed{-} 10 \boxed{=} \boxed{M+} 2 \boxed{\times} 5 \boxed{+} 3 \boxed{=} \boxed{\times} 5$

$\boxed{-} 4 \boxed{=} \boxed{\times} 5 \boxed{+} 5 \boxed{=} \boxed{\div} \boxed{MR} \boxed{=} \quad \boxed{2.6956521}$

Optional Features

Each of Chapters 1-13 contains either a *Career Application* or a *Consumer Application.* Each type is an application of the content of the related chapter.

Career Applications
Each illustrates the need for mathematics in a wide range of career areas.

Exercises
Each *Career Application* and *Consumer Application* contains a set of exercises.

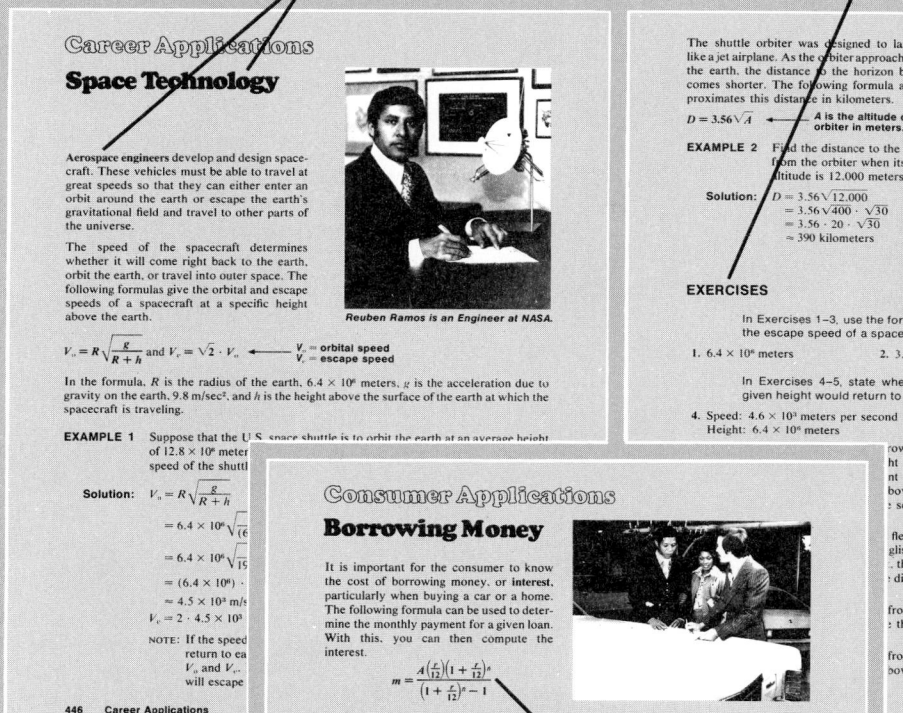

Career Applications
Space Technology

Aerospace engineers develop and design space-craft. These vehicles must be able to travel at great speeds so that they can either enter an orbit around the earth or escape the earth's gravitational field and travel to other parts of the universe.

The speed of the spacecraft determines whether it will come right back to the earth, orbit the earth, or travel into outer space. The following formulas give the orbital and escape speeds of a spacecraft at a specific height above the earth.

Reuben Ramos is an Engineer at NASA.

$$V_o = R\sqrt{\frac{g}{R+h}} \text{ and } V_e = \sqrt{2} \cdot V_o \qquad \begin{array}{l} V_o = \text{orbital speed} \\ V_e = \text{escape speed} \end{array}$$

In the formula, R is the radius of the earth, 6.4×10^6 meters, g is the acceleration due to gravity on the earth, 9.8 m/sec², and h is the height above the surface of the earth at which the spacecraft is traveling.

EXAMPLE 1 Suppose that the U.S. space shuttle is to orbit the earth at an average height of 12.8×10^6 meters. . . .
speed of the shuttle. . . .

Solution: $V_o = R\sqrt{\frac{g}{R+h}}$

$= 6.4 \times 10^6 \sqrt{(6\ldots}$

$= 6.4 \times 10^6 \sqrt{15\ldots}$

$= (6.4 \times 10^6) \cdot \ldots$

$\approx 4.5 \times 10^3 \text{ m/s}$

$V_e = 2 \cdot 4.5 \times 10^3 \ldots$

NOTE: If the speed . . . return to ea . . .
V_o and V_e . . . will escape . . .

446 **Career Applications**

The shuttle orbiter was designed to land like a jet airplane. As the orbiter approaches the earth, the distance to the horizon becomes shorter. The following formula approximates this distance in kilometers.

$D = 3.56\sqrt{A}$ ◄── **A is the altitude of the orbiter in meters.**

EXAMPLE 2 Find the distance to the horizon from the orbiter when its altitude is 12,000 meters.

Solution: $D = 3.56\sqrt{12,000}$
$= 3.56\sqrt{400} \cdot \sqrt{30}$
$= 3.56 \cdot 20 \cdot \sqrt{30}$
$\approx 390 \text{ kilometers}$

12,000 m A ── 390 km

EXERCISES

In Exercises 1–3, use the formulas on page 446 to find the orbital speed and the escape speed of a spacecraft at the given height above the earth.

1. 6.4×10^6 meters 　　 2. 3.2×10^6 meters 　　 3. 9.6×10^6 meters

In Exercises 4–5, state whether a spacecraft with the given speed at the given height would return to earth, orbit the earth, or travel into outer space.

4. Speed: 4.6×10^3 meters per second
Height: 6.4×10^6 meters

5. Speed: 4.8×10^3 meters per second
Height: 1.92×10^7 meters

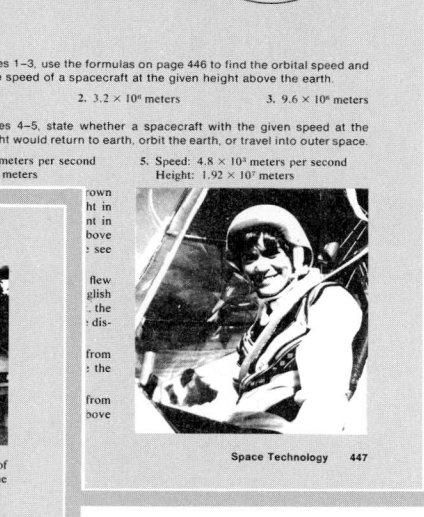

[. . . rown . . . ht in . . . nt in . . . bove . . . see . . . flew . . . glish . . . the . . . dis- . . . from . . . the . . . from . . . bove]

Space Technology 447

Consumer Applications
Borrowing Money

It is important for the consumer to know the cost of borrowing money, or **interest**, particularly when buying a car or a home. The following formula can be used to determine the monthly payment for a given loan. With this, you can then compute the interest.

$$m = \frac{A\left(\frac{r}{12}\right)\left(1 + \frac{r}{12}\right)^n}{\left(1 + \frac{r}{12}\right)^n - 1}$$

EXAMPLE Mr. and Mrs. Jones want to borrow $5000 to buy a car. The annual rate of interest is 14% and the loan is to be paid back over 48 months. Find **a.** the monthly payment **b.** the total interest.

Solution: **a.** $A = \$5000; r = 0.14; n = 48$

$m = \frac{5000\left(\frac{0.14}{12}\right)\left(1 + \frac{0.14}{12}\right)^{48}}{\left(1 + \frac{0.14}{12}\right)^{48} - 1}$ ◄── $\frac{0.14}{12} = 0.0117$

$= \frac{5000(0.0117)(1.0117)^{48}}{(1.0117)^{48} - 1}$ ◄── Use a calculator.

$= \$136.73$

b. Total Interest = Total of Payments − Cash Price of Car
$= (48 \times 136.73) - 5000$
$= 6563.04 - 5000$
$= \$1563.04 \text{ interest}$

EXERCISES

In Exercises 1–5, compute the missing amounts.

	Amount Borrowed	Rate	Months	Monthly Payments	Total Cost	Total Interest
1.	$ 3,000	12.5%	36	?	?	?
2.	$10,000	13%	48	?	?	?
3.	$15,000	12%	96	?	?	?
4.	$20,000	13.5%	120	?	?	?
5.	$ 2,000	18%	24	?	?	?

Borrowing Money 399

Consumer Applications
College-bound students are not often afforded the opportunity to study consumer-related applications.

This consumer topic relates directly to the major topic of the chapter—applications of rational expressions.

Review and Testing

Review

Each chapter is divided into two or three parts. Each part is followed by a *Review*. Each set of exercises in the *Review* is referenced to the related section.

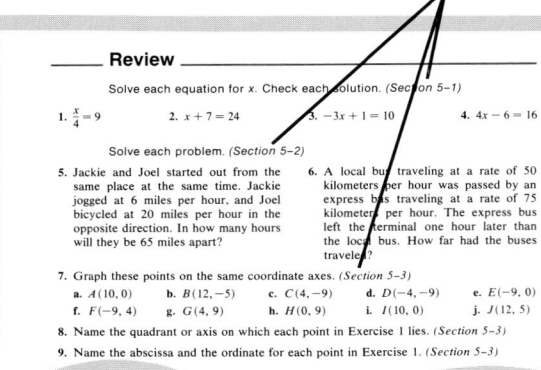

Review

Solve each equation for x. Check each solution. *(Section 5-1)*

1. $\frac{x}{4} = 9$ 2. $x + 7 = 24$ 3. $-3x + 1 = 10$ 4. $4x - 6 = 16$

Solve each problem. *(Section 5-2)*

5. Jackie and Joel started out from the same place at the same time. Jackie jogged at 6 miles per hour, and Joel bicycled at 20 miles per hour in the opposite direction. In how many hours will they be 65 miles apart?

6. A local bus traveling at a rate of 50 kilometers per hour was passed by an express bus traveling at a rate of 75 kilometers per hour. The express bus left the terminal one hour later than the local bus. How far had the buses traveled?

7. Graph these points on the same coordinate axes. *(Section 5-3)*

   a. $A(10, 0)$ b. $B(12, -5)$ c. $C(4, -9)$ d. $D(-4, -9)$ e. $E(-9, 0)$
   f. $F(-9, 4)$ g. $G(4, 9)$ h. $H(0, 9)$ i. $I(10, 0)$ j. $J(12, 5)$

8. Name the quadrant or axis on which each point in Exercise 1 lies. *(Section 5-3)*

9. Name the abscissa and the ordinate for each point in Exercise 1. *(Section 5-3)*

Puzzle

Additional Practice

The *Additional Practice* exercises that appear after each Chapter Test in Chapters 1-13 are provided for those students who did not perform well on the formal Chapter Test. Each set of exercises is referenced to the related section.

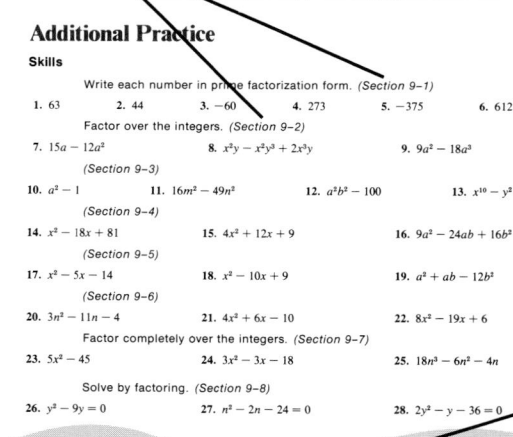

Additional Practice

Skills

Write each number in prime factorization form. *(Section 9-1)*

1. 63   2. 44   3. -60 4. 273   5. -375 6. 612

Factor over the integers. *(Section 9-2)*

7. $15a - 12a^2$ 8. $x^2y - x^2y^3 + 2x^3y$ 9. $9a^2 - 18a^3$

(Section 9-3)

10. $a^2 - 1$ 11. $16m^2 - 49n^2$ 12. $a^2b^2 - 100$ 13. $x^{10} - y^2$

(Section 9-4)

14. $x^2 - 18x + 81$ 15. $4x^2 + 12x + 9$ 16. $9a^2 - 24ab + 16b^2$

(Section 9-5)

17. $x^2 - 5x - 14$ 18. $x^2 - 10x + 9$ 19. $a^2 + ab - 12b^2$

(Section 9-6)

20. $3n^2 - 11n - 4$ 21. $4x^2 + 6x - 10$ 22. $8x^2 - 19x + 6$

Factor completely over the integers. *(Section 9-7)*

23. $5x^2 - 45$ 24. $3x^2 - 3x - 18$ 25. $18n^3 - 6n^2 - 4n$

Solve by factoring. *(Section 9-8)*

26. $y^2 - 9y = 0$ 27. $n^2 - 2n - 24 = 0$ 28. $2y^2 - y - 36 = 0$

Chapter Tests

The *Chapter Tests* parallel those in the Teacher's Manual and those in the *Tests: Duplicating Masters* (see page M-8).

Chapter Summary

This item appears at the end of each chapter. It lists the **Important Terms** and **Ideas** of the chapter.

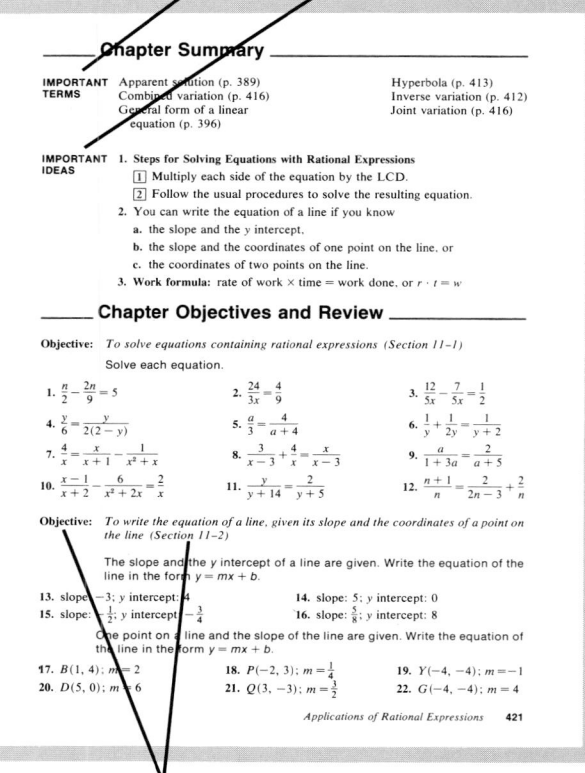

Chapter Summary

IMPORTANT TERMS

Apparent solution (p. 389)
Combined variation (p. 416)
General form of a linear equation (p. 396)
Hyperbola (p. 413)
Inverse variation (p. 412)
Joint variation (p. 416)

IMPORTANT IDEAS

1. Steps for Solving Equations with Rational Expressions
   1 Multiply each side of the equation by the LCD.
   2 Follow the usual procedures to solve the resulting equation.

2. You can write the equation of a line if you know
   a. the slope and the y intercept.
   b. the slope and the coordinates of one point on the line, or
   c. the coordinates of two points on the line.

3. **Work formula:** rate of work × time = work done, or $r \cdot t = w$

Chapter Objectives and Review

Objective: *To solve equations containing rational expressions (Section 11-1)*

Solve each equation.

1. $\frac{n}{2} - \frac{2n}{9} = 5$ 2. $\frac{24}{3x} = \frac{4}{9}$ 3. $\frac{12}{5x} - \frac{7}{5x} = \frac{1}{2}$

4. $\frac{y}{6} = \frac{y}{2(2-y)}$ 5. $\frac{a}{3} = \frac{4}{a+4}$ 6. $\frac{1}{y} + \frac{1}{2y} = \frac{1}{y+2}$

7. $\frac{4}{x} = \frac{x}{x+1} - \frac{1}{x^2+x}$ 8. $\frac{3}{x-3} + \frac{4}{x} = \frac{x}{x-3}$ 9. $\frac{a}{1+3a} = \frac{2}{a+5}$

10. $\frac{x-1}{x+2} - \frac{6}{x^2+2x} = \frac{2}{x}$ 11. $\frac{y}{y+14} = \frac{2}{y+5}$ 12. $\frac{n+1}{n} = \frac{2}{2n-3} + \frac{2}{n}$

Objective: *To write the equation of a line, given its slope and the coordinates of a point on the line (Section 11-2)*

The slope and the y intercept of a line are given. Write the equation of the line in the form $y = mx + b$.

13. slope: -3; y intercept: 4   14. slope: 5; y intercept: 0
15. slope: $\frac{1}{2}$; y intercept: $-\frac{3}{4}$ 16. slope: $\frac{5}{8}$; y intercept: 8

One point on a line and the slope of the line are given. Write the equation of the line in the form $y = mx + b$.

17. $B(1, 4)$; $m = 2$ 18. $P(-2, 3)$; $m = \frac{1}{4}$ 19. $Y(-4, -4)$; $m = -1$
20. $D(5, 0)$; $m = 6$ 21. $Q(3, -3)$; $m = \frac{3}{2}$ 22. $G(-4, -4)$; $m = 4$

Applications of Rational Expressions **421**

Chapter Objectives and Review

The objectives for each chapter are listed at the end of each chapter. Each objective is referenced to the related section and is followed by a set of exercises on the objective.

Chapter Test

Solve and check each equation.

1. $5 + z = 23$ 2. $9k = -72$ 3. $t - (-4.3) = 0$

4. $\frac{r}{7} = 6$ 5. $x - 3\frac{1}{4} = 11$ 6. $-\frac{1}{9}y = 1\frac{2}{3}$

7. $\frac{1}{3}p - 4 = -2$ 8. $14w + 6 = 13$ 9. $\frac{v}{15} - 9 = -16$

10. $7a + 11a = 9$ 11. $6b - 4b + 3 = 11$ 12. $5(-3c - 8) = 35$

13. $12d - 3(d - 1) = 15$ 14. $6 = 3 - (f + 7)$ 15. $\frac{3}{4}g + 7 + \frac{1}{4}g = 7$

16. A broker's weekly wage, W, amounted to \$390.52. Use the formula $W = \$370 + 0.02A$ to find A, the broker's total amount of weekly sales.

17. The angles of a triangle measure b, $2b + 20$, and $b + 20$. Find the measure of each angle. Use the formula $A + B + C = 180°$, where A, B, and C represent the measures of the angles of the triangle.

18. Paul bought boots at a "30% off" sale. The original price was \$42. How much did he save?

...ive even integers whose sum is 70.

...tegers whose sum is 17?

Review and Testing

Review of Word Problems
Each *Review of Word Problems* that appears at the end of Chapters 4, 7, 11, and 13 is cumulative. Each word problem is referenced to the related section in the text.

Preparing for College Entrance Tests
This feature appears at the end of Chapters 4, 7, 11, and 13. Each of the eight focuses on a specific type of problem-solving situation found on College Entrance tests. Each Example illustrates a technique for solving the given type.

Review of Word Problems: Chapters 1–7

1. A family's phone bill for December was $32.50 more than the phone bill for November. Phone service for the two months cost a total of $89.30. How much was the December bill? *(Section 4–3)*
2. Two trains 700 kilometers apart start at the same time and travel toward each other. One travels at a rate of 80 kilometers per hour and the other at a rate of 95 kilometers per hour. In how many hours will they meet? *(Section 5–2)*

The sales tax rate for a certain state is 6%. Use this information in Exercises 3–5. *(Section 5–6)*

3. Make a table to show the amount of tax, t, for sales, s, of $100, $200 and $300.
4. Use the ordered pairs from the table in Exercise 3 to graph the function. Assume that the graph is linear.
5. Use the graph in Exercise 4 to determine the tax on $250.
6. The distance between two cities on a map varies directly with the actual distance between the cities. If 2.5 centimeters on the map represent 50 kilometers, what distance does 6 centimeters represent? *(Section 5–10)*
7. Robert drove from Dallas to Chicago and then from Chicago to Nashville. He drove 1387 miles in all. The distance from Dallas to Chicago is 34 miles greater than twice the distance from Chicago to Nashville. How far is it from Dallas to Chicago? *(Section 6–4)*
8. The sum of the digits of a two-digit number is 10. When 54 is added to the number, the result is the original number with its digits reversed. Find the number. *(Section 6–5)*
9. The regular admission price at the movies is $4.50. Admission for senior citizens is $3.50. One evening, 284 tickets were sold for a total of $1226. How many tickets were sold to senior citizens? *(Section 6–7)*
10. A 3% salt solution is mixed with an 8% salt solution. How many milliliters of each are needed to obtain 800 milliliters of a 5% solution? *(Section 6–8)*

A wholesale bakery makes large and small loaves of rye bread. The profit on a large loaf is 10 cents, and the profit on a small loaf is 8 cents. No more than 300 loaves of rye bread are bak[ed] least 150 small loaves and at [...] Use this information in Exerci[ses ...]

11. Let x represent the number of small loa[ves ...] large loaves of rye bread produced eac[h ...] the total daily profit.
12. Write a system of inequalities that sho[ws ...]
13. Graph the system of inequalities you w[rote ...] ordinates of the vertices of the polygo[n ...]
14. What is the maximum possible daily p[rofit ...]

274   *Review of Word Problems: Chapters 1[–7]*

Preparing for College Entrance Tests

Instead of solving a given equation, it is sometimes easier to try each of the given "solutions" to see which one makes the equation true.

REMEMBER: Watch for clues that will enable you to eliminate one or more of the possibilities without extensive calculations.

EXAMPLE: Which of the following numbers is in the solution set for $3x^2 - 14x + 16 = 0$?
    (a) 4   (b) 2   (c) −4   (d) −8

Think: If $3x^2 - 14x + 16 = 0$, then $3x^2 = 14x - 16$.
But $3x^2$ is positive. Therefore, $14x - 16$ must be positive.
Thus, $14x - 16 > 0$, or $14x > 16$ and $x > 1$.
This eliminates choices (c) and (d). Test choices (a) and (b).

Solution: Test (a): $3(4)^2 - 14(4) + 16 = 8 \neq 0$ ←——— **4 is not a solution.**
           Test (b): $3(2)^2 - 14(2) + 16 = 0$ ←——— **2 is a solution.**   **Answer: b**

Choose the best answer. Choose *a, b, c,* or *d.*
1. Which of the following numbers is in the solution set for $x^2 + 13x + 12 = 0$?
    (a) −4   (b) −1   (c) 1   (d) 6
2. Which of the following numbers is in the solution set for $x^2 - 14x + 24 = 0$?
    (a) −12   (b) −2   (c) 2   (d) 8
3. Which of the following numbers is in the solution set for $2x^2 + 11x + 12 = 0$?
    (a) −4   (b) −1   (c) 2   (d) 4
4. Which of the following numbers is in the solution set for $3x^2 + 4x - 4 = 0$?
    (a) −4   (b) −2   (c) $\frac{1}{3}$ (d) 4
5. Which of the following numbers is in the solution set for $x^2 + 16x - 36 = 0$?
                       (c) 4   (d) 6
  [...s]olution set for $6x^2 - 23x - 4 = 0$?
                     (c) $\frac{1}{2}$ (d) 4

  [H]INT: $\frac{1+x}{2}$ must equal 0.)

            (c) 0   (d) 1

            (c) 0   (d) 1

Preparing for College Entrance Tests   **505**

Cumulative Review: Chapters 5–7

Choose the best answer. Choose *a, b, c,* or *d.*
1. Solve for l: $P = 2l + 2w$
    a. $l = P - w$ b. $l = \frac{P}{2} - w$ c. $l = \frac{(2w - P)}{2}$ d. $l = P - 2w - 2$
2. Two cars leave the same place at the same time. One is traveling east at an average rate of 80 kilometers per hour and the other is traveling west at an average rate of 60 kilometers per hour. In how many hours will they be 1120 kilometers apart?
    a. 8   b. 16   c. 4   d. 3
3. In which quadrant is the graph of $P(-6, 8)$ located?
    a. I   b. II   c. III   d. IV
4. Which point is <u>not</u> on the line parallel to the x axis and 3 units below it?
    a. $A(-3, 0)$ b. $B(0, -3)$ c. $C(-3, -3)$ d. $D(18, -3)$
5. Pencils cost 10¢ each or 3 for 25¢. Which number <u>cannot</u> be in the range of this function?
    a. 30¢   b. 50¢   c. 60¢   d. $1.00
6. Which of the following is a correct description of this set of ordered pairs:
            $\{(0, 7)(-8, 6)(9, -7)(0, -8)\}$
    a. Function   b. Relation, not a function
    c. Function, not a relation   d. Neither a function nor a relation
7. What is the slope of the line containing the points $A(-2, 7)$ and $B(3, -8)$?
    a. 3   b. −3   c. −1   d. 1
8. What is the slope of the graph of $2x + y = 7$?
    a. −2   b. 2   c. 7   d. $\frac{7}{2}$
9. If y varies directly as x and $y = 8$ when x is 16, find y when $x = 2$.
    a. −4   b. 4   c. 1   d. −1
10. Seventeen liters of gasoline cost $4.76. How much will 32 liters cost?
    a. $28.00   b. $9.52   c. $13.72   d. $8.96
11. Which points are <u>not</u> on the graph of either line? $\begin{cases} x + y = 10 \\ x - y = 5 \end{cases}$
    a. $A(17, -7)$ b. $B(12, 7)$ c. $C(12, -7)$ d. $D(-20, 30)$
12. Which point is a solution of this system? $\begin{cases} 2x + y = 17 \\ x - 3y = 5 \end{cases}$
    a. $A(8, 1)$ b. $B(-8, 1)$ c. $C(-8, -1)$ d. $D(8, -1)$
  [...] has no solutions?
    $\begin{cases} 2x - 3y = 8 \\ ... \end{cases}$ c. $\begin{cases} 8y - 5x = 7 \\ ... \end{cases}$

Cumulative Reviews
A *Cumulative Review* appears after Chapters 4, 7, 11, and 13. The chapters being reviewed are indicated in the title. The one after Chapter 13 reviews Chapters 1-13, the essential content of first-year algebra.

Additional Practice
The *Teacher's Manual* contains 16 pages of additional exercises for the *Preparing for College Entrance Tests*. (See pages M-104 through M-119.)

Cumulative Tests
Preparing for College Entrance Tests
See page M-8 for a description.

Tests: Duplicating Masters

This publication is available as bound spirit duplicating masters.

Chapter Tests
A test for each chapter is included.
NOTE: The *Teacher's Manual* also contains an equivalent form
of each Chapter Test.

Cumulative Tests
Preparing for College Entrance Tests: Chapters 8-13
Two cumulative tests for this feature are included.
One covers the content of Chapters 1-7
and one covers the content of Chapters 8-13.

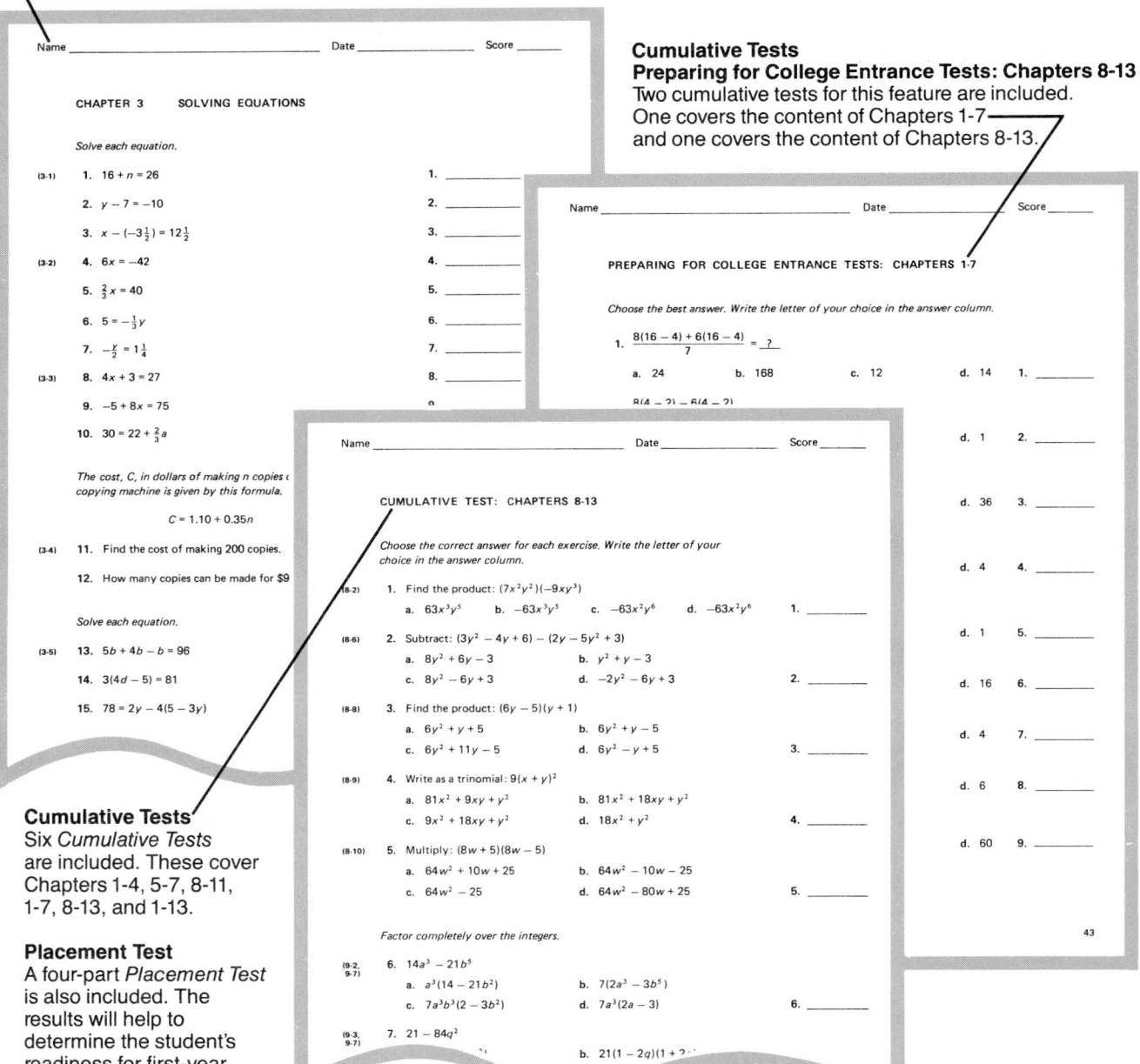

Cumulative Tests
Six *Cumulative Tests*
are included. These cover
Chapters 1-4, 5-7, 8-11,
1-7, 8-13, and 1-13.

Placement Test
A four-part *Placement Test*
is also included. The
results will help to
determine the student's
readiness for first-year
algebra.

Computer Programming and Algebra 1

Student Booklet
This paperback publication consists of computer applications in the BASIC language. Each is directly related to the content in the textbook.

Each computer application parallels those contained in the textbook. (See page M-4.)

Skills Practice Book
The 112-page *Skills Practice Book* provides additional exercises for each section (lesson) in Chapters 1-13 of the textbook.

NOTE: Each page is clearly referenced to the related section.

BASIC: Solving Equations

Problem: *Write a program which solves equations of the form*
$Ax + B = Cx + D.$

Program:
```
100 PRINT
110 PRINT "FOR THE EQUATION AX + B = CX + D,"
120 PRINT "WHAT ARE A, B, C, AND D";
130 INPUT A, B, C, D
140 IF A = C THEN 180
150 LET X = (D - B)/(A - C)
160 PRINT "X = ";X
170 GOTO 220
180 IF B = D THEN 210
190 PRINT "NULL SET"
200 GOTO 220
210 PRINT "ALL REAL NUMBERS ARE SOLUTIONS."
220 PRINT
230 PRINT "ANY MORE EQUATIONS (1=YES, 0=NO)";
240 INPUT Z
250 IF Z=1 THEN 100
260 PRINT
270 END
```

The following is the output from a sample run of the program above.

Output: RUN
```
FOR THE EQUATION AX + B = CX + D,
WHAT ARE A, B, C, AND D? 4,3,2,7
X = 2
```

EXERCISES

A   Use Program 4A to solve these equations. If necessary, first convert the equation to the form $Ax + B = Cx + D$.

1. $8x - 13 = 2x + 56$ 2. $8x - 20 = -32 - 7x$ 3. $11 - 2x - 16$
4. $4x + 12 = 7x + 3$ 5. $-16 - 3x = 5x + 16$ 6. $-5x + 2 = -9$
7. $4(x + 2) = 4x - 9$ 8. $5x - 13 = 6x - 18$ 9. $-3(x - 8) = 2$

10. Rewrite Program 4A using READ and DATA statements. Print the output in five labeled columns: A, B, C, D, and SOLUTION. For example, for the data used in the sample run above, the output would be the following.

```
A     B     C     D     SOLUTION

4     3     2     7     X = 2
3    -9     5     6     X = -7.5
2     3     2     5     NULL SET
1     8     1     8     ALL REAL NUMBERS
```

B   Write a BASIC program for each problem.

8. Solve inequalities of the form $Ax + B < Cx + D$.
9. Solve inequalities of the form $Ax + B > Cx + D$.

BASIC: Solving Equations   13

2-7 DIVISION OF REAL NUMBERS   (Pages 68-71)

Divide.

Example: $-14 \div \frac{1}{2}$ Solution: $-14 \div \frac{1}{2} = -14 \cdot 2$
$$= -28$$

1. $-48 \div 3$ _____   2. $36 \div (-9)$ _____   3. $-54 \div (-9)$ _____
4. $75 \div 15$ _____   5. $-96 \div (-3)$ _____   6. $45 \div (-15)$ _____
7. $0 \div (-7)$ _____   8. $-15 \div (-3)$ _____   9. $18 \div (-2)$ _____
10. $-42 \div 6$ _____   11. $50 \div (-5)$ _____   12. $-144 \div (-12)$ _____
13. $-95 \div (-5)$ _____   14. $30 \div (-6)$ _____   15. $52 \div 13$ _____
16. $-72 \div (-12)$ _____   17. $56 \div (-7)$ _____   18. $0 \div (-15)$ _____
19. $-1.5 \div (-0.3)$ _____   20. $2.4 \div (-1.2)$ _____   21. $-1.44 \div (0.3)$ _____
22. $-15 \div \frac{3}{5}$ _____   23. $-\frac{3}{4} \div (-12)$ _____   24. $18 \div (-\frac{6}{7})$ _____
25. $-\frac{3}{8} \div (-\frac{3}{4})$ _____   26. $\frac{4}{5} \div (-\frac{3}{10})$ _____   27. $\frac{5}{6} \div \frac{4}{9}$ _____

The temperatures in Exercises 28-30 are in Celsius degrees.
Find the mean temperature for the week. Round your answers to the nearest tenth.

28.

Sun.	Mon.	Tues.	Wed.	Thurs.	Fri.	Sat.
−4.0°	−2.1°	1.3°	8.2°	−3.0°	−0.5°	−0.6°

_____

29.

Sun.	Mon.	Tues.	Wed.	Thurs.	Fri.	Sat.
−1.1°	−0.6°	0.3°	−1.2°	−2.3°	−0.7°	−0.4°

_____

30.

Sun.	Mon.	Tues.	Wed.	Thurs.	Fri.	Sat.
−1.5°	2.0°	−2.1°	−1.6°	−0.2°	1.4°	0.6°

_____

31. A company reported the following profits (positive amounts) and losses (negative amounts) for six months. Find the average profit or loss.

Jan.	Feb.	March	April	May	June
$53,080	$12,425	−$6240	−$3465	−$12,476	$7946

_____

OPERATIONS WITH REAL NUMBERS   15

Skills Practice Book
Paperback and Duplicating Masters
This title is available in two versions.

1. The paperback version is accompanied by an annotated *Teacher's Edition*.

2. The answers for the duplicating masters version are overprinted on the masters and will not reproduce.

Solution Key
A complete solution for each exercise is provided in the paperback *Solution Key*.

Teacher's Manual

Permission to reproduce the 16 pages of *Quizzes,* 14 pages of *Chapter Tests,* 16 pages of additional practice for the *Preparing for College Entrance Tests,* and 17 pages of additional practice on *Review of Essential Skills* is granted to users of *HBJ Algebra 1.*

Quizzes
The *Quiz* section in the Teacher's Manual contains a *Quiz* for each Review in the student textbook.

Chapter Tests
This section of the *Teacher's Manual* contains a test for each chapter.

Additional Practice
Preparing for College Entrance Tests
Each of the *Preparing for College Entrance Tests* in the student textbook is supplemented by two pages of additional practice. (See pages M-104 through M-119.) Each is referenced to the related page in the textbook.

QUIZ FOR SECTIONS 4-1 THROUGH 4-6

Represent each word expression by an algebraic expression.

1. The product of n and -7
2. 8.7 less than twice r

Write an equation to represent each word sentence.

3. When 11 is decreased by twice a certain number, n, the result is 3.
4. When the q number, c, ar the result is 2

5. Doris bought two pairs of shoes. She started with \$95 and after her shoe purchase. If one pair of shoes cost \$5 mo other, what was the cost of each pair?
6. The sum of two numbers is 97. Twice the smaller is 10 l larger. What are the numbers?
7. The perimeter of a tirangle is 61 cm. One side is 4 cm lon smallest side, and the third side is 9 cm longer than the smal the length of the smallest side?
8. Mr. Hill is now five times as old as his daughter, Katherine. Mr. Hill will be only twice Katherine's age. How old is Kathe

Solve and check.

9. $9a + 24 - 2a = 5a + 4$
10. $3x - 5(x + 7)$

QUIZ FOR SECTIONS 4-7 THROUGH 4-9

Complete each statement. Use

1. If $-2 > 9y$, then $2 \underline{\ ?\ } -9y$
2. If $6t < 2$, then $6t - 3 \underline{\ ?\ } -1$.

Solve each inequality.

3. $3 - 2m < 15$
4. $13y + 1.0 > 9$

Solve and graph each inequality

6. $-12r \geq 120$
7. $3m <$
9. Ed's three quiz grades were 84, 90, and 92. What is the lowest grade he can receive on the next quiz in order to have an average greater than 90?

Copyright © 1983 by Harcourt Brace
notice, permission to reproduce is gra

PREPARING FOR COLLEGE ENTRANCE TESTS
(Page 277)

*Choose the best answer. Circle **a, b, c,** or **d**.*

1. If $x > 0$, which of the following *must* be true?
   a. $\dfrac{x}{2} < \dfrac{x}{3}$
   b. $-2x < -3x$
   c. $x - 2 < x - 3$
   d. $2 - x < 3 - x$

2. If $y < 0$, which of the following *must* be true?
   a. $y > \dfrac{y}{2}$
   b. $y > 2y$
   c. $y > \dfrac{2}{y}$
   d. $y - 2 > 2 - y$

3. If $m > 0$ and $m \neq 1$, which of the following *must* be true?
   a. $\dfrac{1}{m} > \dfrac{1}{m^2}$
   b. $\dfrac{1}{m} > \dfrac{1}{m+1}$
   c. $m^2 > m$
   d. $\dfrac{1}{m^2} > \dfrac{1}{m^2 - 1}$

4. If $n < 0$, which of the following *must* be true?
   a. $\dfrac{1}{n^2} > \dfrac{1}{n}$
   b. $\dfrac{1}{n} > \dfrac{1}{n-1}$
   c. $\dfrac{1}{n^2+1} > \dfrac{1}{n^2}$
   d. $\dfrac{1}{n} > \dfrac{n+1}{n}$

5. If $a < 0$, which of the following *must* be true?
   a. $a^3 > a^5$
   b. $a^2 > a^3$
   c. $a^4 > a^2$
   d. $a^5 > a^4$

PRACTICE 4: PER CENT

Write a per cent for each decimal.

1. 0.16
2. 0.03
3. 0.40
4. 0.785
5. 0.008
6. 1.085

Write a decimal for each per cent.

7. 17%
8. 9%
9. 20%
10. $12\frac{1}{2}\%$
11. $85\frac{3}{4}\%$
12. $9\frac{1}{4}\%$

13. 125%
14. 240%
15. $\frac{1}{2}\%$
16. $\frac{1}{4}\%$
17. $3\frac{1}{8}\%$
18. $12\frac{2}{3}\%$

Write a per cent for each fraction.

19. $\frac{3}{10}$
20. $\frac{4}{5}$
21. $\frac{3}{4}$
22. $\frac{1}{3}$
23. $\frac{1}{8}$
24. $\frac{5}{6}$

Find each answer.

25. 12% of 650 = $\underline{\ ?\ }$
26. 5% of 92 = $\underline{\ ?\ }$
27. 8% of 98 = $\underline{\ ?\ }$

28. $33\frac{1}{3}\%$ of 96 = $\underline{\ ?\ }$
29. 125% of 80 = $\underline{\ ?\ }$
30. 0.4% of 16 = $\underline{\ ?\ }$

31. 1% of 350 = $\underline{\ ?\ }$
32. $87\frac{1}{2}\%$ of 480 = $\underline{\ ?\ }$
33. 4.2% of 800 = $\underline{\ ?\ }$

34. $\underline{\ ?\ }\%$ of 40 = 16
35. $\underline{\ ?\ }\%$ of 96 = 24
36. $\underline{\ ?\ }\%$ of 20 = 17

37. $\underline{\ \ \ }\%$ of 72 = 18
38. $\underline{\ ?\ }\%$ of 40 = 12
39. $\underline{\ ?\ }\%$ of 64 = 48

40. $\underline{\ ?\ }\%$ of 18 = 27
41. $\underline{\ ?\ }\%$ of 144 = 60
42. $\underline{\ ?\ }\%$ of 90 = 72

$\underline{\ ?\ }$ = 2
44. 12% of $\underline{\ ?\ }$
$\underline{\ ?\ }$ = 7

Additional Practice
Review of Essential Skills
This section contains 5 Survey Tests and 5 Practice sets of exercises on Whole Numbers, Decimals, Fractions, Per Cent, and Metric Measures.

Annotated Teacher's Edition

Quick Quiz
Each section (lesson) contains a *Quick Quiz*. This pre-lesson activity is designed to determine the readiness of the class for the given section.

Assignment Guide
The *Written Exercises* are accompanied by a three-level *Assignment Guide*. A *Suggested Timetable of Assignments* chart for each chapter (see pages M-29 through M-40) and a *Master Timetable* (see page M-28) are also provided.

Teaching Suggestions p. M-20

Quick Quiz
Solve and graph.
1. $-5x \geq -20$
  Ans: {all real numbers less than or equal to 4}

2. $-7 < 4x - 3 < 5$
  Ans: {all real numbers greater than -1 and less than 2}

Additional Examples
Example 1
Graph: $y < 3x + 2$
Ans:

Example 2
Graph: $2x - 4y > 8$
Ans:

254

OBJECTIVE: To graph linear inequalities on the coordinate plane

7–2 Graphing Linear Inequalities

The graph of a linear equation separates the coordinate plane into three sets of points: the points in the two **half-planes** and the points on the line. Thus, every point on the coordinate plane is either in one of the half-planes or on the line.

The equation of the line graphed at the right is $y = \frac{3}{2}x - 3$. Thus, the coordinates of every point in the plane make one of these sentences true.

$$y = \frac{3}{2}x - 3 \qquad y > \frac{3}{2}x - 3 \qquad y < \frac{3}{2}x - 3$$

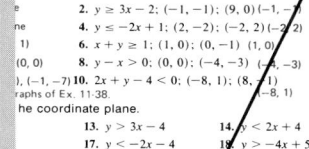
Half-plane

The graph of an inequality that uses > or < *does not include* the graph of the related equation. To show this, the graph of the related equation is dashed.

EXAMPLE 1 Graph $y > 2x - 1$.

Solution:
1. Draw the graph of $y = 2x - 1$ as a dashed line.
2. To identify the half-plane for which $y > 2x - 1$, test a point in each half-plane.

Try $(0, 1)$.	Try $(3, 0)$.
$1 > 2(0) - 1$?	$0 > 2(3) - 1$?
$1 > -1$? Yes ✔	$0 > 5$? No

3. Shade the half-plane containing $(0, 1)$.

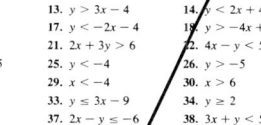
$y > 2x - 1$

Since the graph of $y > 2x - 1$ *does not include* the graph of the related equation, the graph is an **open half-plane**.

The graph of an inequality that uses ≥ or ≤ *includes* the graph of the related equation. To show this, the graph of the related equation is a solid line. This line is the **edge** or **boundary** of the half-plane.

EXAMPLE 2 Graph $3x - 4y \leq 12$.

Solution:
1. Draw the graph of $3x - 4y = 12$ as a **solid** line.
2. To identify the half-plane for which $3x - 4y < 12$, test a point in each half-plane.

Try $(0, 0)$.	Try $(3, -2)$.
$3(0) - 4(0) < 12$?	$3(3) - 4(-2) < 12$?
$0 < 12$? Yes ✔	$9 + 8 < 12$? No

3. Shade the half-plane containing $(0, 0)$.

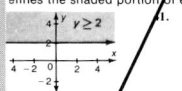
$3x - 4y \leq 12$

254 Chapter 7

$- 4y \leq 12$ includes the edge or boundary of the half-closed half-plane.

given point belongs to the graph of the given

$3x - 4$; $(2, 3)$ Yes   3. $x \geq 6$; $(-1, 5)$ No
$-\frac{1}{2}x + 1$; $(-4, 3)$ Yes   6. $3x - y \leq 5$; $(0, -5)$ Yes

given points, if any, belong to the graph of the
    2. $y \geq 3x - 2$; $(-1, -1)$; $(9, 0)(-1, -$
    4. $y \leq -2x + 1$; $(2, -2)$; $(-2, 2)(-2, 2)$
)   6. $x + y \geq 1$; $(1, 0)$; $(0, -1)$; $(1, 0)$
(0, 0)   8. $y - x > 0$; $(0, 0)$; $(-4, -3)$ $(-4, -3)$
), $(-1, -7)$ 10. $2x + y - 4 < 0$; $(-8, 1)$; $(8, -1)$
raphs of Ex. 11-38.
he coordinate plane.
    13. $y > 3x - 4$ 14. $y < 2x + 4$
    17. $y < -2x - 4$ 18. $y > -4x + 5$
    21. $2x + 3y > 6$ 22. $4x - y < 5$
-5 25. $y < -4$ 26. $y > -5$
    29. $x < -4$ 30. $x > 6$
5 33. $y \leq 3x - 9$ 34. $y \geq 2$
    37. $2x - y \leq -6$ 38. $3x + y < 5$

efines the shaded portion of each plane.

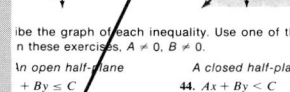

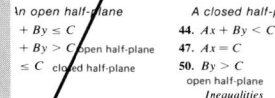

ibe the graph of each inequality. Use one of the
n these exercises, $A \neq 0, B \neq 0$.

An open half-plane   A closed half-plane
$+ By \leq C$ 44. $Ax + By < C$
$+ By > C$ open half-plane   47. $Ax = C$
$\leq C$ closed half-plane   50. $By > C$
    open half-plane
    Inequalities **255**

Assignment Guide
Minimal
Day 1 p. 255: 1-21 odd
Day 2 p. 255: 22-38 even
Average p. 255: 1-41 odd
Above Average p. 255:
3, 6, 9, . . . 39, 41-50

Additional Answers
Written Exercises
Each graph in Exercises 11-30 is an open half-plane. The location of each half-plane with respect to the related dashed line is given along with two points for the line.
11. Above; $(0, -3)$, $(1, -2)$
12. Below; $(0, 3)$, $(1, 4)$
13. Left; $(0, -4)$, $(1, -1)$
14. Right; $(-1, 2)$, $(0, 4)$
15. Right; $(0, 0)$, $(1, -3)$
16. Left; $(0, 0)$, $(1, -4)$
17. Left; $(0, -4)$, $(1, -6)$
18. Right; $(0, 5)$, $(1, 1)$
19. Above; $(0, 1)$, $(1, 3)$
20. Below; $(0, -2)$, $(1, -1)$
21. Above; $(0, 2)$, $(3, 0)$
22. Left; $(0, -5)$, $(1, -1)$
23. Above; $(0, 4)$, $(2, 4)$
24. Below; $(0, -5)$, $(2, -5)$
25. Below; $(0, -4)$, $(2, -4)$
26. Above; $(0, -5)$, $(2, -5)$
27. Left; $(8, 0)$, $(8, 2)$
28. Right; $(-6, 0)$, $(-6, -2)$
29. Left; $(-4, 0)$, $(-4, 2)$
30. Right; $(6, 0)$, $(6, 2)$
Each graph in Exercises 31-37 is a closed-half plane. The graph is described in the same manner as in Exercises 11-30.
31. Above; $(0, -4)$, $(2, -1)$
32. Left; $(0, -5)$, $(1, -3)$
33. Right; $(1, -6)$, $(0, -9)$
34. Above; $(0, 2)$, $(2, 2)$
35. Below; $(0, -5)$, $(2, -5)$
36. Above; $(0, 4)$, $(1, 3)$
37. Left; $(0, 6)$, $(1, 8)$
38. Open half-plane to the left of the line through $(0, 5)$ and $(1, 2)$
43. Closed half-plane
44. Open half-plane
45. Closed half-plane
47. Straight line

255

Additional Examples
Each example in the textbook is supplemented by *Additional Examples* that can be used by the teacher in the following ways.
1. As an alternate to the textbook Example.
2. As exercises to be used after presenting the textbook Example.

Additional Answers
Answers that cannot be annotated on the textbook page are listed in the margin.

Solution Key
Detailed solutions are provided in the paperback *Solution Key*. In addition to receiving a copy of the *Teacher's Edition*, upon request, each teacher will also receive a copy of the *Solution Key*, upon request.

OVERVIEW: HBJ ALGEBRA 1

Philosophy

A major concern of a course in first-year algebra is a program of instruction that accommodates the wide range of student abilities and interests. Within a given class there are those students who enter the course with deficiencies in the essential prerequisite skills. On the other end of the continuum, there are those students who need to be challenged in order to preserve their interest in mathematics. Clearly, most students in first-year algebra would be classified as "average students."

Pedagogy

With this understanding of the make-up of a class in first-year algebra, the authors have structured a three-level approach to instruction.

Basic: This course is designed for students with deficiencies in the prerequisite skills. As the *Suggested Timetables of Assignments* (see pages M-29 through M-40) illustrate, the **A**-level Written Exercises in Chapters 1–10 and in Chapter 12 (less certain sections) were especially designed for the "basic-level" student.

Average: Since most of these students will elect geometry or second-year algebra to satisfy the minimal requirement for college entrance, the **A**- and **B**-level exercises in Chapters 1–13 (less certain sections) define the "average" course of study. However, certain portions of the *Review of Essential Skills* (particularly fractions and per cent) and the *Skills Practice Book* along with the *Additional Practice* will benefit many of these students.

Above Average: Students at this level should be able to complete Chapters 1–14 with the emphasis on the **B**- and **C**-level exercises and the *More Challenging Problems*.

CONTENT

Problem Solving and Applications

The authors' concern for this issue is evidenced by a cursory examination of the Table of Contents. A primary goal of algebra is the use of mathematical ideas in solving work problems—problems ranging from everyday applications to the sciences. It is the belief of many educators that students will have a more complete understanding of the skills and concepts of algebra if they have the opportunity to apply these skills to problem-solving situations. Thus, each *Problem Solving and Applications* lesson immediately follows the related skills lesson(s).

The unique problem-solving technique used by the authors focuses on

(**1**) identifying the conditions within the verbal statement of the problem and

(**2**) translating these conditions into the equations or inequalities needed to solve the problem (see pages 125–128).

In addition to the *Problem Solving and Applications* lessons, the authors have included Applications within the Written Exercises of skills lessons (see Exercises 46–53 on page 54 and Exercises 53–58 on pages 57 and 58). These exercises are direct applications of the skill(s) presented in the related lesson.

The *Review of Word Problems* found at the end of Chapters 4, 7, 11, and 13 gives the student the opportunity to solve word problems in a mixed-practice setting. This review reflects the authors' concern for continual review and maintenance of problem-solving techniques.

Optional Applications

Each chapter contains other forms of applications that may be considered optional, such as *Computer Applications*, *Calculator Applications*, and *Consumer* and *Career* lessons. In each instance, the application is directly related to the content of the chapter.

Review of Essential Skills

The lack of success in first-year algebra for many students is directly related to their deficiencies with the prerequisite skills—the operations using whole numbers, decimals, fractions, and per cent. Although work with these prerequisite skills is included within the textbook, some students may require additional practice. Thus, 17 pages of copying masters that contain survey tests and additional practice on these skills plus metric measures can be found on pages M-84 through M-100.

Exercises

The heart of any mathematics textbook is the quality and quantity of the exercises. Of particular importance is the need for graded exercises to meet the wide range of student abilities and interests. Thus, the Written Exercises are graded **A, B,** and **C**. The *Skills Practice Book* contains additional **A**-type exercises for each lesson in Chapters 1–13.

Preparing for College Entrance Tests

Many educators believe that attention to preparation for college entrance tests will be most beneficial to students if it is handled in an on-going fashion. The inclusion of *Preparing for College Entrance Tests* at the end of Chapters 4, 7, 11, and 13 allows teachers the opportunity to do exactly this. Not only is each item in each test presented in a multiple-choice format, but each item also reflects the type of problem that appears on college entrance tests. The Example that is provided focuses on a specific type of problem-solving situation. Because practice is important, 16 pages of copying masters are provided on pages M-104 through M-119.

> NOTE: The two *Preparing for College Entrance Tests* that appear in the *Tests: Duplicating Masters* are cumulative tests. The first covers the content of Chapters 1–7, and the second covers the content of Chapters 8–13.

Proof

In *HBJ Algebra 1*, work with deductive proof is reserved for the **C** exercises (see Exercises 80–86 on pages 54 and 55 and Exercises 115 and 116 on page 67). Content related to proof is also included in Chapter 14, which is optional (see pages 527–536).

CHAPTER 1:   USES OF ALGEBRA

OVERVIEW

Four themes are basic to the first chapter: (1) the concept of variable; (2) evaluation of algebraic expressions; (3) identifying whole, integral, rational, irrational, and real numbers; and (4) properties of the operations on real numbers. All of algebra requires mastery of these basic concepts and the related skills.

SECTION-BY-SECTION COMMENTARY

Section 1-1 (pages 2-4)
The concept of variable is used to write algebraic expressions for familiar quantitative ideas. Emphasize that operations within parentheses are performed before other operations.

Section 1-2 (pages 5-8)
Replacing variables with numbers continues the development of the meaning of "variable." Show students that the conventions for order of operations give unambiguous meaning to numerical expressions.

Section 1-3 (pages 9-11)
Formulas for familiar relationships are used in finding values of a variable for given numerical replacements of the other variables.

Section 1-4 (pages 12-16)
Formulas are used to solve problems related to such topics as consumer affairs and geometry. Students not only evaluate formulas but also write formulas to express familiar quantitative relationships.

Section 1-5 (pages 18-21)
The concept of the solution set of an open sentence is fundamental to solving all equations and inequalities. Emphasize that an open sentence must have a replacement set before its truth or falsehood for particular values of the variable can be determined.

Section 1-6 (pages 22-24)
Negative numbers are shown here with a raised dash, to avoid confusion with the operation of subtraction. In the next chapter, the transition is made to the lower dash. Practical uses of positive and negative numbers are easy to find (see Exercises 25-55).

Section 1-7 (pages 25-29)
The one-to-one correspondence between real numbers and points on a line will be used later in graphing numbers, equations, and inequalities.

Section 1-8 (pages 30-33)
The postulates for real numbers, together with the inverse postulates in the next chapter, will form the basis for almost all the algebraic manipulations in the year ahead. To help students remember the names of the postulates, refer to them throughout the course.

COMMENTARY: OPTIONAL FEATURES

Calculator Applications (page 21)
This feature can be used with Section 1-2 (pages 5-8) or Section 1-3 (pages 9-11), as it is an application of the calculator to evaluating expressions and formulas.

Consumer Applications (page 17)
Because this feature is an application of formulas to finding the cost of operating and maintaining a car, it can be used with Section 1-4 (pages 12-16).

Computer Applications (pages 34-36)
This feature is an application of computer programming to evaluating the expressions and formulas. Thus, it can be used with Section 1-2 (pages 5-8).

CHAPTER 2:   OPERATIONS WITH REAL NUMBERS

OVERVIEW

The purpose of this chapter is to give students practice with all four operations on positive and negative numbers. Reviewing earlier rules after learning a new one will help students distinguish when each rule is used. After addition and subtraction are studied, these skills are applied to combining like terms. When multiplication and division have been introduced, students use all four operations in evaluating expressions and in preparation for solving equations.

SECTION-BY-SECTION COMMENTARY

Section 2-1 (pages 44-46)
The meaning and the symbol for opposite are developed. The lower dash can now be used to denote negative numbers, but it is worth emphasizing that an expression such as "$-x$" does *not* necessarily denote a negative number.

Section 2-2 (pages 47-50)
The additive inverse postulate and the concept of absolute value are fundamental for developing operations on positive and negative numbers. The intuitive idea of absolute value as distance from 0 underscores that it is always nonnegative.

Section 2-3 (pages 51-55)
Gain and loss provide intuitive motivation for adding positive and negative numbers.

Section 2-4 (pages 56-58)
The rule for subtracting a number, by adding its opposite, can be illustrated with examples on the number line. We know that $8 - 3 = 5$, and 3 is 5 units to the left of 8 on the number line. Similarly, $7 - (-3) = 10$, and -3 is 10 units to the left of 7 on the number line.

Section 2-5 (pages 60-63)
Adding and subtracting positive and negative numbers, together with the distributive postulate, provide the justification for combining like terms. Review the identity property for multiplication to help students see the variable y as $1 \cdot y$.

Section 2-6 (pages 64-67)
Patterns are used to motivate theorems for products of positive and negative numbers. In multiplying two or more numbers, have students first decide whether the product will be positive or negative.

Section 2-7 (pages 68-71)
From the rules for multiplication, we obtain similar rules for division. Division is applied to averages of such naturally positive and negative quantities as temperatures or profits and losses.

Section 2-8 (pages 72-74)
This section prepares students for using the addition and multiplication properties of equations in Chapter 3. A summary of all the rules for operations on positive and negative numbers will be useful here.

COMMENTARY: OPTIONAL FEATURES

Calculator Applications (page 50)
Because this feature is an application of the calculator to evaluating powers, it can be used after Section 1-3 (pages 9-11)

Consumer Applications (page 59)
This feature can be used with Section 2-4 (pages 56-58), as it is an application of addition and subtraction of real numbers.

Computer Applicatons (pages 75-76)
This lesson is an application of the computer to using formulas. Thus, it can be used after Section 1-4 (pages 12-16).

CHAPTER 3:   SOLVING EQUATIONS

OVERVIEW

The two major properties used in solving equations, the addition and multiplication properties, are taught in the first two sections. Checking the solutions of all equations serves two purposes: to determine whether any errors were made in solving, and to underscore the meaning of *solution* as a number that makes an equation true. To minimize errors, students are encouraged to think of $a - b$ as a plus the opposite of b. Equations are applied to a variety of word problems.

SECTION-BY-SECTION COMMENTARY

Section 3-1 (pages 84-85)
The intuitive idea of keeping a two-sided balance level makes the addition property for equations easier to understand. The goal of getting the variable alone on one side is stressed.

Section 3-2 (pages 86-88)
The key goal of getting the variable alone on one side is again stressed in using the multiplication property for equations. Students will need help in interpreting $\frac{x}{a}$ as $\frac{1}{a} \cdot x$.

Section 3-3 (pages 89-91)
When both the addition property and the multiplication property are needed to solve an equation, the work is usually easier and much less prone to error if the addition property is used *first*.

Section 3-4 (pages 94-96)
Methods of solving equations are applied to problems involving formulas. Having students express formulas in words with everyday language will help make them more meaningful.

Section 3-5 (pages 97-99)
The skill of combining terms by appling the distributive postulate, learned in Chapter 2, is now applied in solving equations. Continued emphasis on checking will help identify errors with signs or in combining terms incorrectly.

Sections 3-6 (pages 100-102)
In moving from formulas to equations, the variables in a formula, such as $A + B + C = 180°$, are first replaced by *expressions*. After the resulting equation is solved for the variable, the values of A, B, and C are determined.

Section 3-7 (pages 103-106)
Distinguishing clearly between the three types of per cent problems is fundamental. Be sure students can do this with numerical examples before attempting to solve word problems.

Section 3-8 (pages 107-109)
A brief review of Section 1-1 (Algebraic Expressions) may help in preparing to write equations for word problems.

COMMENTARY: OPTIONAL FEATURES

Calculator Applications (page 91)
This feature can be used with Section 3-3 (pages 89-91), as it is an application of the calculator to checking equations.

Calculator Applications (page 106)
Because this feature is an application of the calculator to per cent increase and decrease, it can be used with Section 3-7 (pages 103-106).

Consumer Applications (pages 92-93)
This lesson applies the skills of using formulas and multiplying positive and negative numbers. Thus, it can be used after Section 1-4 (pages 12-16).

Computer Applications (pages 110-111)
Because this lesson is an application of the computer to solving the equation $ax + b = c$, it can be used with Section 3-3 (pages 89-91).

CHAPTER 4: EQUATIONS AND INEQUALITIES

OVERVIEW

This chapter emphasizes the skills essential for problem solving. The key problem-solving strategy of identifying conditions to write equations is introduced in Section 4-3 and applied often later in the book. Solving equations with the variable on both sides and solving inequalities are taught in the latter part of the chapter.

SECTION-BY-SECTION COMMENTARY

Section 4-1 (pages 118-121)
This section provides practice in recognizing the many ordinary and mathematical words used to express addition, subtraction, multiplication, and division. It extends the work on writing expressions begun in Chapter 1.

Section 4-2 (pages 122-124)
Algebraic expressions involving more than one operation are used to write equations for a variety of verbal statements. The equations are solved by the techniques of Chapter 3. This lesson provides valuable preparation for the applications presented in later sections, such as age and measurement problems.

Section 4-3 (pages 125-128)
By clearly identifying Condition 1, which is used to represent the unknowns, and Condition 2, which is used to write an equation, students will avoid much confusion with word problems. Emphasize the usefulness of this procedure.

Section 4-4 (pages 129-132)
Measurement problems relate to many familiar topics, such as aviation, sports, and surveying.

Section 4-5 (pages 133-134)
Emphasize that all terms with the variable must be on one side of the equation *before* the methods of Chapter 3 can be applied to solving it. The Classroom Exercises provide practice in finding the term to be added to both sides of the equation.

Section 4-6 (pages 135-137)
A table is helpful for organizing the data for age problems. Taking the time to identify Conditions 1 and 2 will pay off.

Section 4-7 (pages 140-142)
Relate the addition property for inequalities to the addition property for equations. Because inequalities are frequently satisfied by many real numbers, a number line is an efficient way to represent the solution set.

Section 4-8 (pages 143-145)
A common error is failing to reverse the inequality sign when multiplying each side of an inequality by a negative number. In solving certain inequalities (see Exercises 25-27), the distributive property must be used before the multiplication property.

Section 4-9 (pages 146-148)
Condition 1 is used to represent the unknowns, and Condition 2 is used to write an inequality for a problem. Then the techniques for solving inequalities are applied. Averages (arithmetic means) provide a practical application of inequalities.

COMMENTARY: OPTIONAL FEATURES

Calculator Aplications (page 121)
This feature applies the calculator to computations involving exponents. Thus, it can be used after Section 1-3.

Calculator Applications (page 145)
This feature applies the calculator to checking inequalities. Thus, it can be used with Section 4-7.

Career Applications (pages 138-139)
Because this feature is an application of the skill of evaluating a formula, it can be used after Section 1-4.

Computer Applications (pages 149-150)
Because this lesson is an application of computer programming to solving inequalities, it can be used with Section 4-8.

CHAPTER 5:   GRAPHING RELATIONS AND FUNCTIONS

OVERVIEW

The major goal of this chapter is understanding and graphing linear equations. The slope–intercept equation of a line and direct variation are important special cases of linear equations. The skill of solving equations for a variable in terms of the other variables, taught in Section 5-1, is an extension of the work in Chapter 4 and a preparation for expressing linear equations in different forms.

SECTION-BY-SECTION COMMENTARY

Section 5-1 (pages 162-164)
The methods used in Chapter 3 to solve an equation are based on the addition and multiplication properties. The same properties are used now to solve equations such as $p = 2 + 2w$ for a variable in terms of the other variables.

Section 5-2 (pages 165-168)
Distance/rate/time problems provide one of the most useful applications of algebra. Organizing data in a table helps keep track of all the information.

Section 5-3 (pages 169-172)
Having students graph points such as (2, 5) and (5, 2) on the same coordinate axes will reinforce for them the difference between abscissa and ordinate. Use the basic vocabulary of graphing frequently to help them master these terms.

Section 5-4 (pages 176-180)
Students are familiar with many relations that can be described mathematically. Thinking of these relations as sets of ordered pairs allows relations and functions to be represented graphically (Section 5-5).

Section 5-5 (pages 181-184)
Point out that, although we graph a linear equation in two variables by plotting only a few solutions, every such equation has an infinite number of solutions. The graph represents *all* the solutions.

Section 5-6 (pages 185-188)
In employing graphs to estimate the coordinates of points other than those already plotted, we make use of the fact that a linear equation has an infinite number of solutions.

Section 5-7 (pages 189-193)
As a useful classroom exercise, start with a linear equation such as $3x + y = 6$ and find four ordered pairs that satisfy the equation. Use these ordered pairs in different combinations to find the slope of the graph. Verify that the value of the slope is always the same.

Section 5-8 (pages 194-196)
The slope–intercept form of a linear equation immediately tells the slope and y intercept of its graph. These quantities frequently provide an efficient way of graphing the equation.

Section 5-9 (pages 197-200)
Direct variation is treated as a special case of the linear function, $y = mx + b$, when $b = 0$.

Section 5-10 (pages 201-203)
A wide variety of physical phenomena relate to direct variation. In each problem, the approach is the same: find the constant of variation, k, and use k to write an equation for the direct variation.

COMMENTARY: OPTIONAL FEATURES

Calculator Applications (pages 193, 200)
These features can be used with Section 5-5 (pages 181-184) and Section 5-9 (pages 197-200), respectively.

Career Applications (pages 174-175)
As this feature applies the skill of reading ordered pairs to navigation, it can be used with Section 5-3.

Computer Applications (pages 204-205)
This lesson can be used with Section 5-10, as it applies computer programming to direct variation.

CHAPTER 6: SYSTEMS OF SENTENCES

OVERVIEW

The background work with linear equations in Chapter 5 is used to develop the skill of solving systems of equations. The graphical, addition, and substitution methods are taught. The four Problem Solving and Applications sections demonstrate the wide ap-plicability of this skill. In each of these sections, the problem-solving strategy is the same: represent the two unknown quantities with different variables, identify Conditions 1 and 2, and then express each condition with an equation.

SECTION-BY-SECTION COMMENTARY

Section 6-1 (pages 212-216)
In this section, emphasize the meaning of solution set. While each of the two equations has an infinite num-ber of ordered pairs that satisfy it, the major goal is to find the single ordered pair that satisfies both equa-tions, if there is such a pair.

Section 6-2 (pages 217-219)
With the addition method, it is possible to find solu-tions more precisely than with the graphical method. This section deals with systems that can be solved by simple addition, without multiplication.

Section 6-3 (pages 220-222)
When multiplication must be used with the addition method, determine first whether it is sufficient to mul-tiply only one equation by some number. Choosing the simplest way of applying the addition method will minimize errors.

Section 6-4 (pages 223-225)
Students frequently find it easier to write two equa-tions, as is done in this section, than to use one condi-tion to represent the unknowns, as they did in

Chapters 3 and 4. Contrasting the two methods will prove beneficial.

Section 6-5 (pages 226-228)
Digit problems will help students deepen their under-standing of place value.

Section 6-6 (pages 232-233)
Help students recognize systems of equations that are readily solved by the substitution method. If one equa-tion has a variable alone on one side or can easily be put in such a form, the substitution method is appro-priate.

Section 6-7 (pages 234-237)
A table helps organize the data for money problems. In Example 1, the table clearly distinguishes the num-ber of tickets from the total sales. In Example 2, it separates the amounts invested from the interest.

Section 6-8 (pages 238-241)
Again, a table helps organize the data for mixture problems. In Example 1, it distinguishes the number of kilograms from the total value. In Example 2, it sepa-rates the amounts of fertilizer from the amounts of ni-trogen.

COMMENTARY: OPTIONAL FEATURES

Calculator Applications (page 229)
Because it is an application of the calculator to check-ing solutions of systems of equations, this feature can be used with Section 6-3 (pages 220-222).

Consumer Applications (pages 230-231)
This feature applies the skills of operations with integers and interpreting graphs to the topic of saving en-ergy. Thus, it can be used after Section 5-6 (pages 185-188).

Computer Applications (pages 242-243)
This lesson can be used with Section 6-3 (pages 220-222), as it applies computer programming to solv-ing systems of equations.

CHAPTER 7: INEQUALITIES

OVERVIEW

Understanding of graphical concepts is deepened through the study of inequalities in this chapter. These concepts are applied to linear programming, which can be covered in greater depth in the next algebra course. The last two sections, on absolute value equations, produce interesting solutions and interesting graphs. The extra attention to inequalities and graphing in this chapter will be highly beneficial to students who take more advanced mathematics courses such as Algebra 2 or calculus.

SECTION-BY-SECTION COMMENTARY

Section 7-1 (pages 250-253)
The emphasis in this section is on expressing inequalities such as $x \geq 5$ as or statements, and inequalities such as $-6 < x < 2$ as and statements. Stress the relation of or to union of sets and the relation of and to intersection.

Section 7-2 (pages 254-255)
To identify the half-plane that satisfies a linear inequality, it is enough to test *one* point not on the graph of the corresponding equation. However, testing two points, one on each side of the line, will minimize errors and will reinforce the fact that *all* points on one side of the line satisfy the inequality while *no* points on the other side satisfy it.

Section 7-3 (pages 256-258)
Relate the graphing of systems of inequalities to graphing a system of two equations (Section 6-1). Care in graphing each inequality is essential.

Section 7-4 (pages 259-261)
The simple linear programming Example, which has a common-sense solution, shows an important application of systems of inequalities. A central idea is that the maximum or minimum value occurs at a vertex of the polygonal region.

Section 7-5 (pages 264-265)
The crucial idea in this section is that an absolute value equation can be written as two simpler equations with the connective or. Checking *all* solutions reinforces the idea that an absolute value equation is equivalent to a compound sentence.

Section 7-6 (pages 266-267)
In graphing an absolute value equation such as $y = |x|$, find more than two or three pairs of numbers that satisfy the absolute value equation. More points will make the shape of the graph easier to see.

COMMENTARY: OPTIONAL FEATURES

Calculator Applications (page 258)
This feature can be used with Section 7-3 (pages 256-258), as it is an application of the calculator to graphing systems of inequalities.

Consumer Applications (pages 262-263)
This feature applies the skills of finding per cents and solving linear equations to the topic of saving energy. Thus, it can be used after Section 3-5.

Computer Applications (pages 268-269)
Because it is an application of computer programming to solving absolute value equations, this lesson can be used with Section 7-5 (pages 264-265).

CHAPTER 8: EXPONENTS AND POLYNOMIALS

OVERVIEW

The major goal of the chapter is to become skillful with finding products of polynomials. The postulates for real numbers, the definition of exponent, and the properties of exponents provide the methods of finding products. The special cases treated in Sections 8-8, 8-9, and 8-10 are aimed at performing certain multiplications more efficiently. There are many applications of finding products to geometry.

SECTION-BY-SECTION COMMENTARY

Section 8-1 (pages 280-282)
Writing large numbers in exponential form and evaluating monomial expressions lay the groundwork for the following lessons. Note that Example 2, on page 281, is a preview of the Multiplication Theorem for Exponents.

Section 8-2 (pages 283-284)
Encourage students to use a simple example, such as $x^2 \cdot x^3 = x^5$, to help recall the Multiplication Theorem for Exponents. Emphasize the necessity of having the *same base* to apply this theorem.

Section 8-3 (pages 285-287)
Again, encourage students to use simple examples, such as **a, b, c,** and **d** on page 285, to help them recall Theorems 8.2 and 8.3.

Section 8-4 (pages 288-289)
The Division Theorem for Exponents depends on the definition of exponent. The condition in Theorem 8-4 that $a \geq b$ will be removed in the next section, after negative exponents are defined.

Section 8-5 (pages 290-293)
Negative integral exponents are defined so that the Divison Theorem will continue to hold when the exponent in the denominator is larger than the exponent in

the numerator. A useful application of positive and negative exponents is scientific notation.

Section 8-6 (pages 296-298)
This section extends the previous work on combining like terms.

Section 8-7 (pages 299-301)
Multiplication of polynomials depends on the distributive postulate, applied one or more times, and on the properties of exponents. The special products taught in subsequent lessons are derived with the methods of this section.

Section 8-8 (pages 302-303)
The FOIL method is an easily remembered way of multiplying binomials. "FOIL," of course, contains the first letters of First, Outer, Inner, and Last.

Section 8-9 (pages 304-305)
This section deals with two special and frequently encountered products. The goal is increased facility in finding products.

Section 8-10 (pages 306-307)
The special product $(a + b)(a - b)$ is frequently encountered in algebra. It is also useful in finding the products of certain numbers, as Example 2 demonstrates.

COMMENTARY: OPTIONAL FEATURES

Calculator Applications (page 287)
Since this feature is an application of the calculator to evaluating expressions with exponents, it can be used with Section 8-3 (pages 285-287).

Career Applications (pages 294-295)
This feature applies the skills of using scientific nota-

tion and evaluating expressions with exponents to the career area of physics. Thus, it can be used with Section 8-5 (pages 290-293).

Computer Applications (pages 308-309)
As this lesson applies computer programming to squaring binomials, it can be used with Section 8-9.

CHAPTER 9: FACTORING POLYNOMIALS

OVERVIEW

This chapter concentrates on finding factors of polynomials. Special factorizations, such as factoring the difference of two squares or factoring a perfect square trinomial, correspond to the special products covered in Chapter 8. The major check of a factorization is to multiply the factors to see whether the original polynomial is obtained.

SECTION-BY-SECTION COMMENTARY

Section 9-1 (pages 316-318)
Factoring integers, recognizing prime numbers, and expressing numbers in prime-factorization form set the stage for factoring polynomials and identifying prime polynomials.

Section 9-2 (pages 319-321)
Finding common factors is related to multiplying polynomials by monomials. Stress finding the common monomial factor such that no common factor remains in the terms of the polynomial.

Section 9-3 (pages 322-323)
Factoring the difference of two squares is related to finding the product of the sum and difference of two numbers. Exercises 29–31 provide some appealing applications of this type of factorization.

Section 9-4 (pages 326-328)
Factoring a perfect square trinomial is related to squaring the sum or the difference of two numbers. Emphasize that the sign of the middle term of a perfect square trinomial determines the operation (addition or subtraction) in the binomial factors.

Section 9-5 (pages 329-331)
In this section, the coefficient of the squared term is always 1. This allows students to concentrate on the middle and last terms. Success with this section is critical for the next one.

Section 9-6 (pages 332-334)
Factoring general trinomials requires trial and error procedures. Encourage students to check their work by multiplying the factors to obtain the original polynomial.

Section 9-7 (pages 335-336)
All patterns for factoring are used in this section. The emphasis should be on first finding any common factors, then looking at the resulting polynomial factor for special patterns.

Section 9-8 (pages 337-338)
Factoring is very useful in solving quadratic equations. Point out that when the constant term in a quadratic equation is 0, one solution of the equation is 0.

Section 9-9 (pages 339-342)
Skill in solving quadratic equations is used with applications to integers and to geometry, especially area.

COMMENTARY: OPTIONAL FEATURES

Calculator Applications (page 318)
As this feature is an application of the calculator to finding prime numbers, it can be used with Section 9-1.

Calculator Applications (page 328)
This feature applies the calculator and the skill of finding a common monomial factor to calculating certain numerical sums. Thus, it can be used with Section 9-2.

Consumer Applications (page 325)
This feature applies the skills of evaluating a formula and using exponents to the topic of nutrition. Thus, it can be used after Section 8-1.

Computer Applications (pages 343-344)
Because this lesson is an application of computer programming to factoring the difference of two squares, it can be used with Section 9-3.

CHAPTER 10: RATIONAL EXPRESSIONS

OVERVIEW

Pointing out the similarities between operations on rational expressions and arithmetic of fractions will enhance students' understanding. Factoring of polynomials is an essential skill for simplifying and performing arithmetic on rational expressions.

SECTION-BY-SECTION COMMENTARY

Section 10-1 (pages 350-353)
Proportions are examples of direct variation, which was introduced in Section 5-9. Proportions are especially useful in science.

Section 10-2 (pages 354-356)
Investment and mixture problems, which were solved by systems of equations in two variables in Sections 6-7 and 6-8, are solved here with a single equation in one variable. As before, organizing the information in a table will help in writing the equation.

Section 10-3 (pages 357-359)
The key idea for simplifying rational expressions is to divide numerator and denominator by the same *factor*, *not* the same term. For many simplifications, polynomials must first be factored, using the methods of Chapter 9.

Section 10-4 (pages 362-364)
Multiplying rational expressions is usually straightforward; where difficulties may arise is in simplifying the answer. As Example 2 shows, it is frequently easier to simplify *before* multiplying.

Section 10-5 (pages 365-367)
Simplifying is as important in division of rational expressions as in multiplication. However, it is important to take the reciprocal of the divisor *before* any simplifying is done.

Section 10-6 (pages 368-369)
Finding a least common denominator is an essential skill for adding and subtracting rational expressions with unlike denominators (Section 10-7).

Section 10-7 (pages 370-373)
Like numerical fractions, rational expressions can be added or subtracted only when they have like denominators. Some teachers may wish to omit Example 3 and the corresponding exercises.

Section 10-8 (pages 374-375)
Mixed expressions are not basically different from the additions and subtractions in Section 10-7. The new idea in this section is to write a polynomial as a rational expression with a denominator of 1.

Section 10-9 (pages 376-378)
Students may doubt the necessity of including all terms with zero coefficients in the dividend of a polynomial division problem. Point out the parallel with the part played by zero in long division of numbers, for example, in dividing 1207 by 95.

COMMENTARY: OPTIONAL FEATURES

Calculator Applications (page 367)
Because this feature is an application of the calculator to evaluating rational expressions, it can be used with Section 10-3 (pages 357-359).

Career Applications (pages 360-361)
This feature applies the skills of calculating a per cent and solving a proportion to the topic of chemistry.

Thus, it can be used with Section 10-1 (pages 350-353).

Computer Applications (pages 379-380)
This lesson can be used with Section 10-7 (pages 370-373), as it is an application of computer programming to adding fractions.

CHAPTER 11: APPLICATIONS OF RATIONAL EXPRESSIONS

OVERVIEW

The chapter begins with the key skill of solving equations with rational expressions. The content of Section 11-1 is essential for the rest of the chapter. Equations with rational expressions are applied in the remaining lessons: using slope to write the equation of a line, number problems, distance/rate/time problems, work problems, and inverse and joint variation. Skill in finding the least common denominator (Section 10-6) will be important throughout the chapter.

SECTION-BY-SECTION COMMENTARY

Section 11-1 (pages 388-391)
In solving equations with rational expressions, checking all solutions serves not only to identify errors but also to eliminate apparent solutions. Carefully noting all excluded values of the variable will also help eliminate apparent solutions.

Section 11-2 (pages 392-394)
Review the slope–intercept form of a linear equation (Section 5-8). Using the slope and the coordinates of a point to write the equation of a line results in an equation with rational expressions.

Section 11-3 (pages 395-397)
When using two points to write the equation of a line, we first compute the slope of the line. Then we can use the slope either to write a proportion, as in Example 1, or to find the y intercept, as in Example 2. The equation obtained can be written in general form if desired.

Section 11-4 (pages 400-402)
Number problems involving fractions (Example 1) and reciprocals (Example 2) are solved by writing equations with rational expressions. Again, the strategy of identifying Conditions 1 and 2 helps in representing the unknowns and in writing an equation.

Section 11-5 (pages 403-406)
Distance/rate/time problems were encountered earlier, in Section 5-2. Here, problems that lead to equations with rational expressions can be solved.

Section 11-6 (pages 407-411)
Work problems lead to rational expressions for rate of work or the part of a job completed. An equation involving rational expressions is written and solved with the techniques of Section 11-1.

Section 11-7 (pages 412-415)
Inverse variation, like direct variation, has many practical applications. Contrast the two types of variation to help students distnguish between them.

Section 11-8 (pages 416-418)
Geometry and the physical sciences provide many examples of joint variation. When a problem involves both direct and inverse variation, an equation with rational expressions will result.

COMMENTARY: OPTIONAL FEATURES

Calculator Applications (page 398)
As this feature is an application of the calculator to equations with rational expressions, it can be used with Section 11-1 (pages 388-391).

Consumer Applications (page 399)
This feature applies the skills of evaluating a formula involving rational expressions and of using exponents to the topic of consumer loans. Thus, it can be used with Section 11-1 (pages 388-391).

Computer Applications (pages 419-420)
This lesson is an application of computer programming to writing the equation of a line. Thus, it can be used with Section 11-2 (pages 392-394).

CHAPTER 12:   RADICALS

OVERVIEW

The work on radicals in this chapter is essential for solving quadratic equations in Chapter 13. The major emphasis is on square roots, although other roots (cube, fourth, etc.) and rational number exponents are discussed as well. Two useful applications of radicals, the Pythagorean Theorem and the Distance Formula, give geometric meaning to irrational square roots.

SECTION-BY-SECTION COMMENTARY

Section 12-1 (pages 432-433)
Many students are already familiar with the concept of square root, but that of principal square root will be new to most. Emphasize that radical expressions involving variables always denote the principal square root.

Section 12-2 (pages 434-436)
Approximating an irrational square root between consecutive integers will give students a feeling for how large or small such a number is. Tables or calculators give closer approximations.

Section 12-3 (pages 437-438)
Radicals are simplified by first finding the largest perfect square factor of the radicand. Then Theorem 12-1, on products on square roots, is applied.

Section 12-4 (pages 439-442)
The Pythagorean Theorem provides additional use for radicals. Theorems 12-2 and 12-3 together form an "if and only if" theorem.

Section 12-5 (pages 443-445)
The Distance Formula is a simple application of the Pythagorean Theorem. Understanding its derivation will help students remember it.

Section 12-6 (pages 448-449)
Multiplication of square root radicals uses Theorem 12-1 (page 437). Radicals should be simplified *before* multiplying, if possible.

Section 12-7 (page 450-453)
Relate division of square root radicals to multiplication (Section 12-6). Although an expression with a radical in the denominator is not incorrect, denominators are usually rationalized to make it easier to find decimal approximations, as shown on page 452.

Section 12-8 (pages 454-456)
Relating addition and subtraction of radicals to combining like terms will help students avoid the common error of adding numbers under the radical signs. Simplification of radicals is often needed to recognize when radicals can be combined.

Section 12-9 (pages 457-459)
Emphasize the need to check all apparent solutions of radical equations.

Section 12-10 (pages 460-462)
Show students that the definition of rational exponent is reasonable. It means that the properties of integral exponents also hold for rational exponents.

COMMENTARY: OPTIONAL FEATURES

Calculator Applications (page 449)
This feature is an application of the calculator to multiplying radicals (Section 12-6).

Calculator Applications (page 462)
This feature is an application of the calculator to evaluating formulas with radicals. Thus, it can be used with Section 12-3 (pages 437-438).

Career Applications (page 446-447)
Because this feature applies the skill of evaluating a formula with radicals to space technology, it can be used with Section 12-3 (pages 437-438).

Computer Applications (pages 463-464)
This lesson applies computer programming to the approximation of square roots (Section 12-2).

CHAPTER 13:   QUADRATIC FUNCTIONS AND EQUATIONS

OVERVIEW

Two major ideas are developed in this chapter: (1) the solution of quadratic equations, and (2) the nature of quadratic functions (whose zeros are solutions of quadratic equations). Applications are included for quadratic equations and quadratic functions. An especially interesting application, maximum and minimum, is a precursor to calculus. Sections 13-1 through 13-4 deal with solving quadratic equations; Sections 13-5 through 13-8 deal more with quadratic functions. Some teachers may wish to begin with Section 13-5, on graphing quadratic functions, and then approach Sections 13-1 through 13-4 from the viewpoint of finding the zeros of a quadratic function.

SECTION-BY-SECTION COMMENTARY

Section 13-1 (pages 470-471)
When taking the square root of each side of a quadratic equation, both positive and negative square roots must be considered to obtain all solutions.

Section 13-2 (pages 472-474)
Completing the square prepares for the development of the quadratic formula in Section 13-3.

Section 13-3 (pages 475-477)
While not all students will be able to derive the quadratic formula independently, they should be able to follow the development. This formula should be memorized by all students.

Section 13-4 (pages 478-481)
With the knowledge of how to solve quadratic equations, a wider range of applied problems can be undertaken.

Section 13-5 (pages 484-485)
The important idea is that all quadratic functions have parabolas as graphs. Point out that the zeros of a quadratic function are solutions of a quadratic equation.

Section 13-6 (pages 486-488)
Since the discriminant of a quadratic equation is a square root, reviewing when a square root is rational, when it is zero, and when it is not a real number will help students remember the nature of roots as an extension of previous knowledge.

Section 13-7 (pages 489-492)
The maximum or minimum value of a quadratic function occurs at the turning point, or vertex, of the parabola. Students who later study calculus will learn to find maximum and minimum values for many types of functions.

Section 13-8 (pages 492-493)
The procedure for graphing quadratic inequalities is very similar to the one used to graph linear inequalities: Graph the corresponding quadratic equation and test points inside and outside the graph.

COMMENTARY: OPTIONAL FEATURES

Calculator Applications (page 488)
This feature is an application of the calculator to evaluating irrational solutions of equations. Therefore it can be used with Section 13-3 (pages 475-477).

Career Applications (pages 482-483)
This feature applies the skills of reading a table and evaluating a formula with square roots to the career area of meteorology. Thus it can be used with Section 13-1 (pages 470-471).

Computer Applications (pages 494-495)
Because this lesson is an application of computer programming to solving quadratic equations, it can be used with Section 13-3 (pages 475-477).

CHAPTER 14:   OTHER APPLICATIONS OF ALGEBRA

OVERVIEW

The major purpose of the chapter is as a preparation for a next mathematics course in geometry. Sections 14-1 through 14-3 deal with complementary and supplementary angles, the sum of the angles of a triangle, and similar triangles. The similar triangle work provides the necessary background for the trigonometric ratios discussed in Section 14-4 through 14-6. The trigonometric ratios are practical, especially for students who may enter a technical field, and may be useful whether or not students proceed to geometry. With the introductory work in Section 14-3 on similarity, Sections 14-4 through 14-6 could be done independently of the rest of the chapter. Sections 14-7 through 14-9 provide a deeper acquaintance with logic and proof, which will play important parts in geometry and second-year algebra.

SECTION-BY-SECTION COMMENTARY

Section 14-1 (pages 508-509)
As the Example on page 509 shows, geometry and algebra are not unrelated fields. Algebra can be a useful tool in geometry.

Section 14-2 (pages 510-512)
The Triangle-Sum Theorem and the Pythagorean Theorem can be used to obtain algebraic solutions to certain geometric problems.

Section 14-3 (pages 513-515)
The major idea in this section is that for similar triangles, corresponding sides are proportional. Exercises 3-6 give practical applications of similarity. Review the concept of proportion (Section 10-1).

Section 14-4 (pages 516-519)
The tangent is the first of the three trigonometric ratios applied to right triangles. Memorizing the definition will make problem solving proceed more smoothly.

Section 14-5 (pages 520-523)
The sine and cosine ratios for right triangles involve the hypotenuse and one other side. Mastery of the definitions of the three trigonometric ratios is essential for the next section, in which students must decide which ratio to use.

Section 14-6 (pages 524-526)
Sketching a triangle will help in choosing the trigonometric ratio to use in solving a problem. The Classroom Exercises provide practice in deciding which ratio is appropriate.

Section 14-7 (pages 527-530)
Clock arithmetic is used to make the field postulates, which are quite abstract for many students, understandable. To see whether a set of elements with operations defined is a field, begin by checking the closure, identity, and inverse postulates.

Section 14-8 (pages 531-533)
The major emphasis is on determining when a conditional statement is true and when false. To help understand the distinction between a conditional and its converse, examine several true conditionals whose converses are false.

Section 14-9 (pages 534-536)
Direct proof will play an important part in geometry and second-year algebra. Students who take more advanced mathematics courses will also meet indirect proof.

MASTER TIMETABLE

Overview   The following *Master Timetable* for three levels of ability is coordinated with the *Suggested Timetables of Assignments* that appear on pages M-29 through M-40 and the *Assignment Guide* that appears in the margin of the annotated pages. Note that the total number of days for each chapter includes additional days for review and testing for each level.

The *Master Timetable*, the *Suggested Timetables of Assignments*, and the *Assignment Guide* should be considered as guidelines only.

MASTER TIMETABLE

Chapter	Basic Sections	Days	Average Sections	Days	Above Average Sections	Days
1	All	13	All	10	All	10
2	All	17	All	13	All	11
3	All	19	All	15	All	10
4	O (9)	13	All	11	All	11
5	All	15	All	14	All	13
6	All	14	All	13	All	11
7	O (3–6)	5	O (6)	9	All	9
8	All	20	All	15	All	14
9	All	19	All	14	All	12
10	All	18	All	15	All	14
11	Omit		O (7, 8)	9	All	11
12	O (2, 4–5, 9–10)	11	O (2, 10)	16	All	15
13	Omit		O (7, 8)	12	All	14
14	Omit		Omit		All	11
Cumulative Reviews		6		4		4
Total		**170**		**170**		**170**

SUGGESTED TIMETABLES OF ASSIGNMENTS

The *Suggested Timetable of Assignments* for each chapter is structured for three levels of ability: **Basic, Average,** and **Above Average.**

Basic Course

The Basic timetable outlines a minimal course. The assignments for this level are drawn from the **A**–type exercises only. Further, certain sections (lessons) are indicated as optional and can be omitted without affecting the continuity.

Since students at this level require more practice than the average or above average student, additional exercises for each lesson in Chapters 1–13 are provided in the *Skills Practice Book.*

Average Course

The *Suggested Timetable of Assignments* for the Average Course is the standard course in first-year algebra. The assignments for this level are drawn from both the **A**– and **B**–type exercises. If additional exercises are needed for any section in Chapters 1–13, see the comment above regarding the *Skills Practice Book.*

Above Average Course

The *Suggested Table of Assignments* for this level outlines a program for the above average student. The assignments for this level are drawn from the **A, B,** and **C** exercises with an emphasis on the **B**– and **C**–type exercises.

CHAPTER 1:   USES OF ALGEBRA

Section	Pages	Basic	Average	Above Average
1–1	2-4	Odds 1-45	Odds 1-51	Odds 17-45 All 46-52
1–2	5-8	Day 1: Odds 1-39 Day 2: All 40-53	Odds 1-63	3, 6, 9, $\cdots$, 51 Evens 54-64 All 65-68
1–3	9-11	Evens 2-42	Evens 2-62	Odds 13-47 All 48-62
1–4	12-16	All 1-24	Odds 1-49	3, 6, 9, $\cdots$, 36 Odds 37-55
1–5	18-21	All 1-30	Evens 2-50	3, 6, 9, $\cdots$, 42 Evens 52-62
1–6	22-24	All 1-12 Odds 13-53	Odds 1-63	Odds 1-53 All 54-63
1–7	25-29	Evens 2-50	Evens 2-62	3, 6, 9, $\cdots$, 63 All 64-82
1–8	30-33	Day 1: All 1-20 Day 2: Evens 22-62	Evens 2-62 All 63-65	3, 6, 9, $\cdots$, 60 All 63-72
Review and Testing		3 days	2 days	2 days
Total Days		**13**	**10**	**10**

CHAPTER 2: OPERATIONS WITH REAL NUMBERS

Section	Pages	Basic	Average	Above Average
2-1	44-46	Day 1: Odds 1-31 All 33-40 Day 2: All 41-60	Day 1: All 1-40 Day 2: All 41-60 Odds 61-75	Odds 13-75 All 77-84
2-2	47-50	Day 1: Odds 1-65 Day 2: All 68-91	Day 1: Odds 1-51 All 52-67 Day 2: All 68-101	Day 1: Odds 1-79 Day 2: All 80-106
2-3	51-55	Day 1: Odds 1-45 Day 2: All 46-53	Day 1: Odds 1-53 Day 2: All 54-79	3, 6, 9, ···, 45 Odds 47-85
2-4	56-58	Day 1: All 1-30 Day 2: All 31-56	Odds 1-75	4, 8, 12, ···, 52 Evens 54-90
2-5	60-63	Evens 2-62	3, 6, 9, ···, 63 Evens 64-80	4, 8, 12, ···, 60 Evens 64-98
2-6	64-67	Day 1: All 1-28 Day 2: All 29-56	3, 6, 9, ···, 54 Evens 58-110	4, 8, 12, ···, 92 Evens 96-116
2-7	68-71	Day 1: All 1-24 Day 2: All 25-38	Odds 1-45	Odds 5-45 All 46-54
2-8	72-74	Odds 1-81	3, 6, 9, ···, 81 Evens 82-100	4, 8, 12, ···, 80 All 82-101
Review and Testing		3 days	2 days	2 days
Total Days		**17**	**13**	**11**

CHAPTER 3:   SOLVING EQUATIONS

Section	Pages	Basic	Average	Above Average
3–1	84-85	Day 1: All 1-10 Day 2: All 11-30	Evens 2-48	Evens 2-40 All 41-52
3–2	86-88	Day 1: All 1-15 Day 2: All 16-35	Evens 2-50	Evens 6-50 All 51-54
3–3	89-91	Day 1: All 1-20 Day 2: Odds 21-47	Odds 1-51	3, 6, 9, $\cdots$, 48 All 49-57
3–4	94-96	Day 1: All 1-4 Day 2: All 5-10	Day 1: All 1-8 Day 2: All 9-16	Evens 2-16
3–5	97-99	Day 1: All 1-16 Day 2: Odds 17-49	Day 1: All 1-30 Day 2: All 31-55	Odds 9-55 All 57-62
3–6	100-102	Day 1: Evens 2-12 Day 2: All 13-17	Day 1: All 1-14 Day 2: All 15-20	Evens 2-20 All 21-24
3–7	103-106	Day 1: All 1-12 Day 2: Odds 13-25	Day 1: Evens 2-18 Day 2: Odds 19-31	3, 6, 9, $\cdots$, 30 All 31-36
3–8	107-109	Day 1: All 1-5 Day 2: All 6-12	Day 1: All 1-12 Day 2: All 13-22	All 5-24
Review and Testing		3 days	2 days	2 days
Total Days		**19**	**15**	**10**

CHAPTER 4: EQUATIONS AND INEQUALITIES

Section	Pages	Basic	Average	Above Average
4-1	118-121	Evens 2-58	Evens 2-64	Evens 16-58 All 59-64
4-2	122-124	Odds 1-31	Odds 1-39	3, 6, 9, ···, 24 All 27-40
4-3	125-128	Day 1: All 1-15 Day 2: All 16-22	Evens 2-28	Evens 2-28 All 29-32
4-4	129-132	Day 1: All 1-7 Day 2: All 8-14	Odds 1-19	Odds 5-19 All 20-23
4-5	133-134	Odds 1-27	Odds 1-45	Odds 1-57
4-6	135-137	Evens 2-12	Evens 2-18	Evens 2-12 All 13-18
4-7	140-142	Odds 1-17	Odds 1-31	Odds 11-31 All 33-43
4-8	143-145	All 1-25	Evens 2-48	Evens 10-62
4-9	146-148	Omit	Odds 1-15	Odds 1-15 All 16-18
Review and Testing		3 days	2 days	2 days
Total Days		**13**	**11**	**11**

		Basic	Average	Above Average
		All 1-23	Evens 2-38	Evens 6-38 All 39-44
	-168	Day 1: All 1-5 Day 2: All 6-11	Day 1: All 1-8 Day 2: All 9-15	Day 1: All 3-11 Day 2: All 12-16
5-	169-172	Odds 1-25	Odds 1-41	3, 6, 9, ···, 39 All 42-48
5-4	176-180	Evens 2-28	Evens 2-36	Evens 8-28 All 30-37
5-5	181-184	All 1-20	Odds 1-39	Odds 1-49
5-6	185-188	All 1-19	All 1-33	All 6-36
5-7	189-193	Odds 1-25	Odds 1-39	Odds 1-33 All 35-39
5-8	194-196	Evens 2-30	Evens 2-40	Evens 2-36 All 37-42
5-9	197-200	Day 1: All 1-14 Day 2: All 15-30	Day 1: All 1-24 Day 2: All 25-35	Evens 2-30 All 31-39
5-10	201-203	All 1-6	Evens 2-14	All 5-14
Review and Testing		3 days	2 days	2 days
Total Days		15	14	13

CHAPTER 6:   SYSTEMS OF SENTENCES

Section	Pages	Basic	Average	Above Average
6-1	212-216	All 1-30	Odds 1-39 All 40-46	3, 6, 9, ···, 39 All 40-55
6-2	217-219	Evens 2-18	Evens 2-24	3, 6, 9, ···, 18 All 19-24
6-3	220-222	Odds 1-21	Odds 1-33	3, 6, 9, ···, 21 Odds 23-43
6-4	223-225	All 1-10	Evens 2-18	3, 6, 9, 12, 14, 15, 17, 18, 21, 22
6-5	226-228	All 1-8	Odds 1-13	Odds 5-13 All 15-20
6-6	232-233	Day 1: All 1-8 Day 2: All 9-15	Day 1: All 1-12 Day 2: All 14-25	Day 1: Odds 1-19 Day 2: All 20-30
6-7	234-237	Day 1: All 1-5 Day 2: All 6-10	Day 1: All 1-8 Day 2: All 9-12	Evens 2-10, 11, 12
6-8	238-241	Day 1: All 1-4 Day 2: All 5-9	Day 1: All 1-7 Day 2: All 8-12	Evens 2-10, 11, 12
Review and Testing		3 days	2 days	2 days
Total Days		**14**	**13**	**11**

CHAPTER 7:   INEQUALITIES

Section	Pages	Basic	Average	Above Average
7-1	250-253	Day 1: All 1-18 Day 2: Evens 20-36 All 37-42	Day 1: Evens 2-36 Day 2: All 37-51	3, 6, 9, ···, 39 All 40-51
7-2	254-255	Day 1: Odds 1-19 Day 2: Evens 22-38	Odds 1-41	3, 6, 9, ···, 39 All 41-50
7-3	256-258	Omit	Day 1: All 1-12 Day 2: All 13-20	Day 1: Evens 2-12 All 13-16 Day 2: All 17-24
7-4	259-261	Omit	All 1-13	All 1-18
7-5	264-265	Omit	Evens 2-30	3, 6, 9, ···, 30 All 31-38
7-6	266-267	Omit	Omit	Odds 1-19, 21, 25, 29, 33, 35
Review and Testing		1 day	2 days	2 days
Total Days		**5**	**9**	**9**

CHAPTER 8: EXPONENTS AND POLYNOMIALS

Section	Pages	Basic	Average	Above Average
8-1	280-282	Day 1: All 1-29 Day 2: All 30-59	Odds 1-63	Odds 1-51 All 52-64
8-2	283-284	Odds 1-45	Odds 1-45 All 47-52	3, 6, 9, ···, 51 All 53-64
8-3	285-287	Day 1: All 1-27 Day 2: Evens 28-64	Day 1: Evens 2-50 Day 2: All 51-71	Day 1: Evens 2-64 Day 2: All 65-68
8-4	288-289	Day 1: All 1-15 Day 2: All 16-28	Day 1: All 1-20 Day 2: All 21-36	Day 1: All 1-28 Day 2: All 29-36 Odds 37-47
8-5	290-293	Day 1: All 1-32 Day 2: Odds 33-65	Odds 1-69	3, 6, 9, ···, 69 All 70-77
8-6	296-298	Day 1: All 1-13 Evens 14-18 Day 2: All 20-41	Day 1: All 1-19 Day 2: Evens 20-40 All 42-46	Evens 2-50
8-7	299-301	Day 1: All 1-20 Day 2: Odds 21-57	Odds 1-65	3, 6, 9, ···, 69 Odds 71-79
8-8	302-303	Day 1: All 1-23 Day 2: All 24-45	Odds 1-45, 55, 56	3, 6, 9, ···, 45 All 46-58
8-9	304-305	Evens 2-42	Evens 2-42, 43, 46, 50	3, 6, 9, ···, 42 All 43-52
8-10	306-307	Odds 1-33	Odds 1-33 All 34-37	3, 6, 9, ···, 36 All 38-43
Review and Testing		3 days	2 days	2 days
Total Days		**20**	**15**	**14**

CHAPTER 9: FACTORING POLYNOMIALS

Section	Pages	Basic	Average	Above Average
9-1	316-318	Evens 2-42	Evens 2-58	3, 6, 9, $\cdots$, 42 All 43-58
9-2	319-321	Day 1: All 1-34 Day 2: All 35-55	3, 6, 9, $\cdots$, 33 Odds 35-75	4, 8, 12, $\cdots$, 56 Odds 59-83 All 85-88
9-3	322-323	Day 1: All 1-20 Day 2: All 21-31	Odds 1-19 All 21-31	Odds 9-31 All 32-38
9-4	326-328	Day 1: All 1-16 Day 2: All 17-40	All 1-16 Evens 18-40	Evens 2-30 All 31-46
9-5	329-331	Day 1: All 1-15 Day 2: Evens 16-50	Evens 2-30 33, 36, 39, $\cdots$, 54	3, 6, 9, $\cdots$, 51 All 52-56
9-6	332-334	Day 1: All 1-10 Day 2: Odds 11-33	Day 1: All 1-20 Day 2: Odds 21-45	5, 10, 15, $\cdots$, 30 All 35-46
9-7	335-336	Day 1: All 1-20 Day 2: All 21-40	Day 1: Evens 2-40 Day 2: All 41-54	Day 1: Evens 2-48 Day 2: All 51-70
9-8	337-338	Odds 1-27	Odds 1-41	3, 6, 9, $\cdots$, 42 All 43-48
9-9	339-342	Day 1: All 1-10 Day 2: All 11-18	Day 1: Evens 2-18 Day 2: All 19-24	3, 6, 9, $\cdots$, 24, 25, 26
Review and Testing		3 days	2 days	2 days
Total Days		**19**	**14**	**12**

CHAPTER 10: RATIONAL EXPRESSIONS

Section	Pages	Basic	Average	Above Average
10–1	350-353	Day 1: All 1-18 Day 2: All 20-34	Day 1: Evens 2-32 Day 2: All 33-40	Day 1: Evens 10-32 All 34-36 Day 2: All 37-50
10–2	354-356	Day 1: All 1-5 Day 2: All 6-10	Evens 2-14	3, 6, 9 All 11-16
10–3	357-359	Day 1: All 1-26 Day 2: all 27-44	Evens 2-56	3, 6, 9, ···, 52 All 53-61
10–4	362-364	Day 1: All 1-16 Day 2: All 17-30	Day 1: Odds 1-29 Day 2: All 31-43	4, 8, 12, ···, 28 Odds 31-47
10–5	365-367	Day 1: All 1-18 Day 2: All 19-30	Day 1: All 1-22 Day 2: All 23-30 Odds 31-37	Day 1: All 1-27 Day 2: All 28-38 Odds 39-43
10–6	368-369	Evens 2-34	Evens 2-38	Evens 2-34 All 35-38
10–7	370-373	Day 1: All 1-18 Day 2: Odds 19-57	Day 1: Odds 1-57 Day 2: All 58-72	Day 1: 3, 6, 9, ···, 57 Odds 59-71 Day 2: All 73-81
10–8	374-375	Evens 2-24	Evens 2-32	3, 6, 9, ···, 33 Evens 34-44
10–9	376-378	Odds 1-23	Odds 1-31	3, 6, 9, ···, 30 All 32-41
Review and Testing		3 days	2 days	2 days
Total Days		**18**	**15**	**14**

CHAPTER 11: APPLICATIONS OF RATIONAL EXPRESSIONS

Section	Pages	Basic	Average	Above Average
11-1	388-391	Omit	Day 1: Evens 2-26 Day 2: Evens 28-42	Evens 2-48
11-2	392-394	Omit	Odds 1-29	Odds 1-37
11-3	395-397	Omit	Odds 1-27	Odds 1-33, 34
11-4	400-402	Omit	Evens 2-18	Evens 2-18, 19, 20
11-5	403-406	Omit	All 1-8	Evens 2-16
11-6	407-411	Omit	All 1-10	3, 6, 9, 15 All 16-20
11-7	412-415	Omit	Omit	Day 1: Evens 2-32 Day 2: All 33-44
11-8	416-418	Omit	Omit	Odds 1-17
Review and Testing	—		2 days	2 days
Total Days	—		**9**	**11**

CHAPTER 12:   RADICALS

Section	Pages	Basic	Average	Above Average
12–1	432-433	Evens 2-40	Day 1: All 1-40 Day 2: All 41-60	Day 1: All 1-48 Day 2: All 49-72
12–2	434-436	Omit	Omit	Evens 2-42
12–3	437-438	Day 1: All 1-25 Day 2: All 26-48	Day 1: Odds 1-17 All 19-36 Day 2: All 37-60	3, 6, 9, ⋯, 60 All 61-66
12–4	439-442	Omit	Evens 2-32	3, 6, 9, ⋯, 30 All 33-41
12–5	443-445	Omit	Odds 1-27	Odds 1-21 All 22-28
12–6	448-449	Day 1: All 1-16 Day 2: all 17-32	Day 1: All 1-24 Day 2: All 25-48	3, 6, 9, ⋯, 30 All 33-54
12–7	450-453	Day 1: All 1-15 Day 2: Evens 16-50	Day 1: All 1-30 Day 2: Evens 32-50 All 51-62	Day 1: Evens 2-50 Day 2: All 51-74
12–8	454-456	Day 1: All 1-15 Day 2: All 16-30	Day 1: All 1-30 Day 2: All 31-49	3, 6, 9, ⋯, 51 All 52-63
12–9	457-459	Omit	Day 1: Evens 2-30 Day 2: All 31-46	Day 1: All 1-36 Day 2: All 37-52
12–10	460-462	Omit	Omit	3, 6, 9, ⋯, 54 All 56-65
Review and Testing		2 days	2 days	2 days
Total Days		**11**	**16**	**15**

CHAPTER 13:   QUADRATIC FUNCTIONS AND EQUATIONS

Section	Pages	Basic	Average	Above Average
13-1	470-471	Omit	Day 1: Evens 2-32 Day 2: Evens 34-48	Day 1: 3, 6, 9, ···, 30 Evens 32-48 Day 2: All 49-64
13-2	472-474	Omit	Day 1: All 1-12 Odds 13-39 Day 2: All 40-54	Day 1: Odds 1-53 Day 2: All 55-66
13-3	475-477	Omit	Day 1: Odds 1-27 Day 2: All 28-45	Day 1: Odds 1-39 Day 1: All 40-56
13-4	478-481	Omit	Day 1: All 1-7, 11, 14 Day 2: All 15-20	Day 1: Evens 2-16 Day 2: All 17-22
13-5	484-485	Omit	Odds 1-27	3, 6, 9, 12 Odds 13-33
13-6	486-488	Omit	Evens 2-24	Evens 2-28 All 29-32
13-7	489-491	Omit	Omit	Odds 1-27
13-8	492-493	Omit	Omit	3, 6, 9, ···, 27, 29, 31
Review and Testing	—		2 days	2 days
Total Days	—		**12**	**14**

CHAPTER 14:   OTHER APPLICATIONS OF ALGEBRA

Section	Pages	Basic	Average	Above Average
14-1	508-509	Omit	Omit	All 1-14
14-2	510-512	Omit	Omit	Evens 1-10 All 11-14
14-3	513-515	Omit	Omit	All 1-6
14-4	516-519	Omit	Omit	Odds 1-31
14-5	520-523	Omit	Omit	All 1-20 Odds 21-33
14-6	524-526	Omit	Omit	All 1-9
14-7	527-530	Omit	Omit	All 1-12
14-8	531-533	Omit	Omit	All 1-24
14-9	534-536	Omit	Omit	Odds 1-27
Review and Testing	—		—	2 days
Total Days	—		—	**11**

QUIZZES

The *Quizzes* on pages M-42 through M-57 parallel the *Reviews* that appear in the textbook. The answers for the *Quizzes* begin on page M-58.

Permission to reproduce pages M-42 through M-57 is granted to users of *HBJ Algebra I*.

QUIZ FOR SECTIONS 1-1 THROUGH 1-5

Write an algebraic expression for each word description.

1. The cost of 5 boxes of cereal at n dollars per box.

2. The discount, d, subtracted from the list price, p.

3. The average speed driving 500 kilometers in h hours.

Evaluate.

4. $18 - 3 \cdot 4$

5. $21 \div (15 - 2 \cdot 4)$

6. Evaluate $70 + 5x - 9y$, when $x = 2$ and $y = 5$.

7. Find A in $A = 2(a + b)$ when a is 12 inches and b is 36 inches.

Find the solution set for each sentence. The replacement set is $\{0, 1, 2, 5, 10\}$.

8. $x + 7 = 9$

9. $x^2 = x$

10. $x + 3 > 10$

QUIZ FOR SECTIONS 1-6 THROUGH 1-8

Represent each of the following by a positive or negative rational number.

1. A bank withdrawal of $18.30

2. A climb of 300 meters

Classify each statement as true, T, or false, F. When a statement is false, tell why it is false.

3. $\{0\} \subset Ir$

4. $N \subset Ir$

5. $Q \subset N$

6. Identify $\sqrt{\frac{49}{36}}$ as rational or irrational. Give a reason for your answer.

7. Replace n with the smallest possible whole number to make a true statement:
$$10 < \sqrt{112} < n.$$

Name the postulate illustrated by each sentence.

8. $7 \cdot 4 + 7 \cdot 3 = 7(4 + 3)$

9. $6 \cdot 7 + 4 \cdot 7 = 6 \cdot 7 + 7 \cdot 4$

10. Evaluate: $30 - 2(5 - 3)$.

QUIZ FOR SECTIONS 2-1 THROUGH 2-4

Write without parentheses.

1. $-(3-4)$

2. $-(-300)$

Solve.

3. $|x| = 4$

4. $r = |-1.6|$

5. $1 \cdot m = -|-8|$

Use $<$, $=$, or $>$ to compare the numbers.

6. $|16|$? -10

7. $|-7|$? 3

8. $|-4.6|$? $|4.6|$

Evaluate.

9. $|-3| + |3|$

10. $|-1.6| - |-1|$

11. $7 + -8$

Add or subtract as indicated.

12. $-15 + (-3)$

13. $28 + (-15)$

14. $(8-13) - 5$

15. $-4.6 + 9.2 - 5.8$

QUIZ FOR SECTIONS 2-5 THROUGH 2-8

Simplify.

1. $5m - 2m$

2. $1.9 - 8x + 15x$

3. $6x + 5 - 4x + 7y$

Multiply or divide as indicated.

4. $3(-8)$

5. $-30 \div 2$

6. $-0.3(-0.2)$

7. $-50 \div (-0.1)$

8. $\left(-\frac{3}{4}\right)^2$

9. $-12 \div \frac{2}{3}$

Evaluate each expression for $a = -1$, $b = 3$, and $c = -6$.

10. $ab - ac$

11. $bc + abc$

12. $(6a - 3b) \div 2$

By what number would you multiply each expression or what number would you add to each expression to obtain a?

13. $-3a$

14. $-7 + a$

15. $\frac{a}{8}$

QUIZ FOR SECTIONS 3-1 THROUGH 3-4

Solve and check each equation.

1. $m - 9 = -3$
2. $\frac{1}{4} + r = 7\frac{1}{2}$
3. $-7b = 18$
4. $\frac{m}{6} = 12$

5. $\frac{7}{2}t = \frac{35}{2}$
6. $2m + 7 = 17$
7. $23 = 9x - 22$
8. $12 + \frac{2}{3}r = 16$

9. The formula $d = rt$ relates distance, d, rate, r, and time, t. Find r when $d = 750$ miles and $t = 10$ hours.

10. The formula $C = 0.22 + 0.07(n - 3)$ relates the cost of a phone call, C, to the number of minutes, n, that a person talks. Find the cost of a phone call that lasts 17 minutes.

QUIZ FOR SECTIONS 3-5 THROUGH 3-7

Solve and check each equation.

1. $7y - 2y = 30$
2. $-7m + 3m - 9m = -26$

3. $8 - 7(m - 6) = 1$
4. $\frac{1}{2}x - \frac{1}{4}x = 15 - 2\frac{3}{4}$

In Exercises 5-6, use the formula $A + B + C = 180°$.

5. One angle of a triangle has a measure of 20°. The measures of the other two angles can each be represented by $4x$. Find the measures of the remaining two angles.

6. The measure of one angle of a triangle is 18°. The measure of another angle is 37°. Find the measure of the third angle.

Solve.

7. What per cent of 15 is 12?

8. Of Harry's books, 30% are novels. If Harry has 90 novels, how many books does he have altogether?

9. Find three consecutive integers whose sum is 0.

10. Find three consecutive odd integers whose sum is −69.

QUIZ FOR SECTIONS 4-1 THROUGH 4-6

Represent each word expression by an algebraic expression.

1. The product of n and -7

2. 8.7 less than twice r

Write an equation to represent each word sentence.

3. When 11 is decreased by twice a certain number, n, the result is 3.

4. When the quotient of a certain number, c, and 5 is increased by 6, the result is 20.

5. Doris bought two pairs of shoes. She started with $95 and had $20 left after her shoe purchase. If one pair of shoes cost $5 more than the other, what was the cost of each pair?

6. The sum of two numbers is 97. Twice the smaller is 10 less than the larger. What are the numbers?

7. The perimeter of a tirangle is 61 cm. One side is 4 cm longer than the smallest side, and the third side is 9 cm longer than the smallest. What is the length of the smallest side?

8. Mr. Hill is now five times as old as his daughter, Katherine. In 18 years, Mr. Hill will be only twice Katherine's age. How old is Katherine now?

Solve and check.

9. $9a + 24 - 2a = 5a + 4$

10. $3x - 5(x + 7) = 5x$

QUIZ FOR SECTIONS 4-7 THROUGH 4-9

Complete each statement. Use $<$ or $>$.

1. If $-2 > 9y$, then $2 \underline{\ ?\ } -9y$.

2. If $6t < 2$, then $6t - 3 \underline{\ ?\ } -1$.

Solve each inequality.

3. $3 - 2m < 15$

4. $13y + 1.0 > 9y - 0.6$

5. $x - 3(2x + 2) - 2 \leq 4(3 + x)$

Solve and graph each inequality.

6. $-12r \geq 120$

7. $3m < 4(2m - 5)$

8. $2t + 3 \geq 5(9 - t)$

9. Ed's three quiz grades were 84, 90, and 92. What is the lowest grade he can receive on the next quiz in order to have an average greater than 90?

10. Teresa is paid $180 per week plus $12 for each garment she sells. If she wishes to earn at least $350 per week, how many garments must she sell?

QUIZ FOR SECTIONS 5-1 THROUGH 5-3

Solve each equation for x.

1. $ax = 15$

2. $x - c = b$

3. The formula for the perimeter of a parallelogram is $P = 2(a + b)$, where a and b represent the lengths of the sides. Solve the formula for b.

4. The formula for the volume of a circular cylinder is $A = \pi r^2 h$. Solve the formula for h.

Solve each problem.

5. Molly plans to switch cars with her parents, but they live in different cities. They decide to meet part way, have lunch, and exchange cars. Molly left City A, where she lives, and averaged 80 kilometers per hour. Her parents left City B at the same time and average 85 kilometers per hour. If the cities are 660 kilometers apart, how many hours will it take them to meet?

6. On a hiking trip from home to the top of a mountain, Jacques averaged 8 km/hr. On the hike back home, he averaged 12 km/hr. He took two hours longer on his hike to the mountain top than on his return trip. How long did it take him to hike to the top of the mountain?

7. Graph these points on the same axes.

$A(-5, 0)$ $B(-7, -8)$ $C(-3, 8)$ $D(1, -8)$ $F(-1, 0)$

8. Name the quadrant or axis on which each point in Exercise 7 lies.

9. Name the ordinate of $P(-1, 0)$.

10. Name the abscissa of $Q(-7, -8)$.

QUIZ FOR SECTIONS 5-4 THROUGH 5-6

In Exercises 1-3, use the relation $\{(-5, 0), (6, -8), (-8, 6), (7, -8), (-5, 12)\}$

1. Give the range of the relation.

2. Give the domain of the relation.

3. Is the relation a function? Give a reason for your answer.

4. Complete this table showing ordered pairs that satisfy $x + 4y = 20$.

x	-4	0	4	18
y	?	?	?	?

Graph each linear equation in the coordinate plane.

5. $y = x$ 6. $2x + y = 8$ 7. $y = -5$

Sound travels in air at approximately $\frac{1}{5}$ mile per second. That is, $d = \frac{1}{5}t$, where t is time in seconds and d is distance traveled in miles. Use this information in Exercises 8-10.

8. Write three ordered pairs for this function.

9. Use the ordered pairs to graph the function.

10. Use the graph to estimate the distance that a thunderclap travels in 6.5 seconds.

QUIZ FOR SECTIONS 5-7 THROUGH 5-10

Find the slope of the line containing the given points.

1. $P(-1, 1); Q(0, 3)$ 2. $R(-7, 5); S(3, -9)$ 3. $A(-4, 6); B(8, 1)$

Write each equation in the form $y = mx + b$. Then give the slope and y intercept of its graph.

4. $7x = y + 9$ 5. $3x - 4y = 24$

6. Use the slope and y intercept you obtained in Exercise 5 to graph the equation.

In Exercises 7-8, determine whether the relation between the variables is that of direct variation. Explain your answer.

7. The total cost, T, of n twenty-cent postage stamps

8. The total cost, C, of a refrigerator repair which took h hours if the charge is $25 per hour plus $20 for the trip from the store to your home.

9. If y varies directly as x and $y = 15$ when $x = 3$, what is y when $x = 7.5$?

10. Marko is building a fence around a rectangular field that is 500 feet long and 200 feet wide. It took him 6 hours to build 50 feet of fence. At this rate, how long will it take him to finish?

QUIZ FOR SECTIONS 6-1 THROUGH 6-5

Solve each system by graphing.

1. $\begin{cases} x = -3 \\ y - x = 2 \end{cases}$

2. $\begin{cases} 2x + y = 12 \\ y = 2x + 4 \end{cases}$

Write one, none, or infinitely many to describe the number of solutions for each system.

3. $\begin{cases} y = 7x + 9 \\ y = -7x - 9 \end{cases}$

4. $\begin{cases} x + y = 12 \\ 4y = 48 - 4x \end{cases}$

5. $\begin{cases} \frac{1}{2}x = y - 3 \\ 2y - x = 5 \end{cases}$

Solve each system.

6. $\begin{cases} x - y = 11 \\ 2x + y = 16 \end{cases}$

7. $\begin{cases} a + 3b = 7 \\ -a + b = 5 \end{cases}$

8. $\begin{cases} 3x - 5y = 15 \\ x + 2y = 5 \end{cases}$

9. The sum of the digits of a two-digit number is 12. The number is 18 more than the number obtained by reversing the digits. Find the number.

10. At a sale, Marge bought four tires and a battery for $170. Mario bought 2 tires and a battery for $100. What was the price of a battery?

QUIZ FOR SECTIONS 6-6 THROUGH 6-8

Use the substitution method to solve each system.

1. $\begin{cases} 3b + 4a = 6 \\ a - b = 5 \end{cases}$

2. $\begin{cases} 3r = 4s \\ r - s = 1 \end{cases}$

3. $\begin{cases} 3x - 4y = -2 \\ 2x - 4 = 0 \end{cases}$

4. Thirty members of a club bought tickets to a concert. Some were orchestra tickets at $18 apiece, and some were balcony tickets at $14 apiece. The total cost of the tickets was $492. How many tickets of each type did they buy?

5. Solution A, which is 8% iodine, is mixed with Solution B, which is 12% iodine, to obtain 360 grams of a solution that is 11% iodine. How many grams of each solution are used?

QUIZ FOR SECTIONS 7-1 THROUGH 7-4

Write each compound sentence as two simple sentences joined by or or and.

1. $3x - 7 \geq 6.4$
2. $0 < 2x < 12$
3. $-2 < p < 3$
4. Write without or: $y > -1$ or $y = -1$
5. Write without and: $z > 3$ and $z < 10$

Solve and graph each inequality.

6. $-6x \geq 30$
7. $8(y - 2) \geq -4$
8. $10 < x + 2 < 16$

Graph each inequality in the coordinate plane.

9. $3x - y < 6$
10. $y \geq x + 2$
11. Solve by graphing: $\begin{cases} x + 2y \geq 6 \\ x - y \leq -5 \end{cases}$

Rafael sells mixtures of cashews and peanuts. The cashews sell for $3.50 per pound, and the peanuts sell for $1.50 per pound. Each day he can sell at most 6 pounds of cashews and at most 5 pounds of peanuts. He sells at most 7 pounds of nuts each day. Use this information for Exercises 12-15.

12. Let x represent the number of pounds of cashews sold and y represent the number of pounds of peanuts sold. Write an expression for the total amount Rafael makes selling cashews and peanuts.

13. Write a system of inequalities that shows the constraints on x and y.

14. Graph the system of inequalities you wrote in Exercise 13.

15. How many pounds of each type of nut should Rafael sell in order to make the maximum amount of money?

QUIZ FOR SECTIONS 7-5 THROUGH 7-6

Solve and check each equation.

1. $|-2x| = 6$
2. $|t + 3| = 1$
3. $|y - 5| - 2 = 2$
4. $3 = |7d - 1|$
5. $|x + 4| = 3$
6. $|5 - 2(r - 6)| = 10$

Graph each equation on the coordinate plane.

7. $x - |y| = 4$
8. $y = |x| + 3$
9. $x = |2y| + 1$
10. $y = -|x| + 1$

QUIZ FOR SECTIONS 8-1 THROUGH 8-5

Find the value when a = −1, b = −2, and c = 3.

1. abc **2.** ab^2c **3.** $a^2b^2c^2$ **4.** $(2abc)^2$ **5.** $a^{46}b^2$

Find each product.

6. $y^3 \cdot y$ **7.** $(4a^2)(-3a^3)$ **8.** $10^5 \cdot 10^2$

Simplify. No denominator equals zero.

9. $(4^3)^2$ **10.** $(-2x)^3$ **11.** $(-3ab^2)^3$

12. $\dfrac{z^9}{z^3}$ **13.** $\left(\dfrac{x^3}{y}\right)^2$ **14.** $\dfrac{6r^4s^5}{(3r)(2s)^2}$

Simplify. No variable equals zero.

15. $\left(-\frac{1}{3}\right)^{-3}$ **16.** $\left(\frac{2}{5}\right)^{-2}$ **17.** $4p^{-4}$

Write each number in scientific notation.

18. 3 millionths   **19.** 5 million   **20.** 0.0024

QUIZ FOR SECTIONS 8-6 THROUGH 8-10

Add or subtract as indicated.

1. $(x + y) + (-2y)$

2. $(r - 3s) + (8s - 5r)$

3. $3t - (6t + 7)$

4. $5m - 7n + 6 - (4n - 17m + 9)$

5. $(a^5 + a^2b - b^4) + (a^5 - ab + 3b^4)$

Multiply.

6. $3(2 + 5x)$ **7.** $x(xy - x^2)$ **8.** $3t(2t - 5)$

9. $(z + 1)(z + 2)$ **10.** $(b - 1)(3b + 2)$ **11.** $(t + 2)(6t - 1)$

Write the square of each binomial as a trinomial.

12. $(x + 3)^2$ **13.** $(5t - 4)^2$

Multiply.

14. $(6t - 1)(6t + 1)$ **15.** $(2 + q)(2 - q)$

QUIZ FOR SECTIONS 9-1 THROUGH 9-3

Determine whether the second number is a factor of the number in parentheses. Answer Yes or No.

1. $(2^7 \cdot 3^4 \cdot 5); 40$ **2.** $(2^7 \cdot 3^4 \cdot 5); 2^6 \cdot 25$ **3.** $(3^5 \cdot 5); 45$

Write each number in prime-factorization form.

4. 72   **5.** 729   **6.** 363

Factor over the integers. If a polynomial cannot be factored over the integers, write Prime.

7. $a + 7b$ **8.** $7a + 7b$ **9.** $8x + 4y - 12$

10. $b^2 - 4z^2$ **11.** $16 - r^2$ **12.** $3(m - 3) + t(m - 3)$

Factor each polynomial over the rational numbers.

13. $\dfrac{a^2}{36} - \dfrac{b^2}{16}$ **14.** $\dfrac{1}{25} - q^2$ **15.** $x^2y^2 - w^2z^2$

QUIZ FOR SECTIONS 9-4 THROUGH 9-9

Factor completely over the integers.

1. $x^2 - 7x + 6$ **2.** $y^2 - 14y + 49$ **3.** $5t^2 - 45$

4. $3x^2 + 6x + 6$ **5.** $6r^2 - 19r + 10$ **6.** $a^2b^2 - 4c^4$

Solve by factoring.

7. $2x^2 = 32$ **8.** $x^2 + 2x = 0$ **9.** $a^2 - a = 6$

10. Steve has a rectangular garden with area 60 square meters. The length of the garden is 7 meters more than the width. What are the length and width of the garden?

QUIZ FOR SECTIONS 10-1 THROUGH 10-3

Solve each proportion.

1. $\dfrac{5}{x} = \dfrac{1}{11}$

2. $\dfrac{10}{3} = \dfrac{x}{22.5}$

3. $\dfrac{4}{y} = \dfrac{5}{y+6}$

4. In sandlot baseball, Jessica pitched five games and allowed 18 hits. At this rate, how many hits would she allow in 20 games?

5. Mr. Peluso has $9000 invested, part at a yearly interest rate of 10% and the rest at a yearly interest rate of 8%. His total yearly interest is $770. How much is invested at each amount?

6. A fruit juice drink consists of 25% grapefruit juice and 75% orange juice. How much pure grapefruit juice must be added to 80 ounces of the mixture to make a drink that is 40% grapefruit juice?

Simplify. No denominator equals zero.

7. $\dfrac{75}{100}$

8. $\dfrac{15d}{20d}$

9. $\dfrac{21b^2c^5}{30ab^3c^2}$

10. $\dfrac{5a + 10b}{a^2 + ab - 2b^2}$

QUIZ FOR SECTIONS 10-4 THROUGH 10-9

Multiply or divide as indicated. Write each answer in simplest form.

11. $\dfrac{x^3y^2z}{xy^5} \cdot \dfrac{xy^6}{z^2}$

2. $\dfrac{2a - 2b}{a + b} \cdot \dfrac{a^2 - b^2}{a^2 - 2ab + b^2}$

3. $\dfrac{r^2 - 9}{15} \div \dfrac{r - 3}{5}$

4. $\dfrac{x^2 - 5x}{3x - 3} \div \dfrac{x^2 - 4x - 5}{x - 1}$

5. Find the LCD of rational expressions having denominators $x^2 - x - 12$ and $x^3 + 3x^2$.

Add or subtract as indicated. Write each answer in simplest form.

6. $\dfrac{9t - 4}{3} - \dfrac{18t + 5}{3}$

7. $\dfrac{7a + 5}{2a + 7} + \dfrac{3a - 8}{2a + 7}$

8. $6 + \dfrac{5}{b - 7}$

9. $\dfrac{2}{9 - x^2} - \dfrac{x}{2x + 6}$

10. Divide $(a^3 - 7a^2 + 6a + 5)$ by $(a - 2)$.

QUIZ FOR SECTIONS 11-1 THROUGH 11-3

Solve each equation.

1. $\dfrac{n}{8} - \dfrac{n}{12} = 5$

2. $\dfrac{a-3}{4} + \dfrac{5}{6} = \dfrac{3a+1}{12}$

3. $\dfrac{10}{x} + \dfrac{3}{x-2} = \dfrac{5}{x}$

One point on a line and the slope of the line are given. Write the equation of the line in the form $y = mx + b$.

4. $C(-4, 2); m = \frac{1}{4}$

5. $T(1, 0); m = 2$

6. $P(-6, 4); m = -3$

Determine the equation of the line passing through the given points. Write the equation in the form $y = mx + b$.

7. $S(0, 3); T(11, 2)$

8. $A(4, -11); B(-2, 7)$

Determine the equation of the line passing through the given points. Write the equation in general form.

9. $R(-3, 1); M(4, 5)$

10. $Q(2, 1); P(3, -4)$

QUIZ FOR SECTIONS 11-4 THROUGH 11-8

1. What number must be added to both the numerator and the denominator of the fraction $\frac{7}{9}$ to make a fraction equal to $\frac{15}{16}$?

2. One number is three times another. The sum of their reciprocals is $5\frac{1}{3}$. What are the numbers?

3. On a 3000-mile trip, a plane has a 60-mph headwind. On the return trip it has a 60-mph tailwind, and it takes only $\frac{2}{3}$ as long to make the trip. What is the speed of the plane in still air?

4. It takes Lynn 8 hours to mow a field with a regular power mower. Jack can mow the same field using a tractor mower in 5 hours. If Lynn and Jack work together, how long will it take them to mow the field?

Determine whether each of the following is an example of inverse variation. Answer <u>Yes</u> or <u>No</u>. Give a reason for each answer.

5. $x = 7y$

6. $x = \dfrac{7}{y}$

7. If y varies inversely as x and $x = 8$ when $y = 16$, find x when $y = 80$.

8. The number of days needed to cement a lot varies inversely as the number of people working. It takes 8 people 12 days to do the job. How long would it take 10 people to do it?

9. Using k as the constant of variation, write a formula for this statement: T varies jointly as w and s.

10. If A varies jointly as b and h, and $A = 10$ when $b = 6$ and $h = 5$, find A when $b = 7$ and $h = 9$.

M-53

QUIZ FOR SECTIONS 12-1 THROUGH 12-5

Simplify.

1. $-\sqrt{900}$

2. $\left(\sqrt{18.4}\right)^2$

3. $5\sqrt{63a^3}$

4. Express $2.\overline{43}$ in the form $\frac{a}{b}$.

5. Determine the consecutive integers x and y such that $x < \sqrt{71} < y$.

Simplify. Assume that all variables represent positive real numbers.

6. $\sqrt{48x^2}$

7. $15\sqrt{360}$

8. The sides of a rectangle are 5 cm and 12 cm. Find the length of a diagonal.

9. Do three straight sticks 5 feet, 3 feet, and 7 feet long form a right triangle if arranged to form a triangle?

10. Find the distance between $P(6, -2)$ and $Q(-3, 1)$. Simplify your answer.

QUIZ FOR SECTIONS 12-6 THROUGH 12-10

Multiply and simplify. Variables represent positive numbers.

1. $\sqrt{18} \cdot \sqrt{6}$

2. $3\sqrt{32} \cdot 5\sqrt{45}$

3. $\sqrt{2c} \cdot \sqrt{2cd}$

Simplify. Variables represent positive real numbers.

4. $\dfrac{2}{\sqrt{7}}$

5. $\sqrt{\dfrac{5}{6}}$

6. $\dfrac{\sqrt{16x^2y}}{\sqrt{2y}}$

Add or subtract as indicated.

7. $5\sqrt{2} - 8\sqrt{2} + 3\sqrt{7} - 8\sqrt{7}$ **8.** $3\sqrt{8} - 4\sqrt{2} + 5\sqrt{12} - 8\sqrt{3}$ **9.** $\sqrt{x^3} + 8\sqrt{x^3}$

Solve and check each equation. If an apparent solution does not check in the original equation, give the solution set as ϕ.

10. $\sqrt{x + 5} = 8$

11. $\sqrt{8x + 5} = 3\sqrt{x}$

12. $3 + \sqrt{x} = 8$

Simplify.

13. $64^{\frac{1}{2}}$

14. $(-27)^{\frac{1}{3}}$

15. $\left(\frac{1}{32}\right)^{\frac{1}{5}}$

QUIZ FOR SECTIONS 13-1 THROUGH 13-4

Solve each equation. Irrational solutions may be left in simplified radical form.

1. $(x - 5)^2 = 0$ **2.** $x^2 + 8 = 20$ **3.** $(2x - 3)^2 = 49$

Solve by completing the square. Irrational solutions may be left in simplified radical form.

4. $x^2 + x - 5 = 0$ **5.** $3x^2 - 5x = 2$

Use the quadratic formula to solve each equation. Irrational solutions may be left in simplified radical form.

6. $2x^2 - 5x = 1$ **7.** $4t^2 - 6t + 1 = 0$

The area A of a parallelogram is given by A = bh, where b is the length of a base and h is the height. A certain parallelogram has area 270 square centimeters. The base of the parallelogram is 3 centimeters more than the height. Use this information in Exercises 8-9.

8. Represent the base and height of the parallelogram in terms of a single variable. Write an equation to represent the area.

9. Find the base of the parallelogram.

10. The sum of the squares of two consecutive positive odd integers is 130. Find the integers.

QUIZ FOR SECTIONS 13-5 THROUGH 13-8

1. Graph the quadratic function $y = 4 - x^2$.

2. Determine the zeros of the function $y = 4 - x^2$.

Without solving, give the nature of the solutions of each equation.

3. $x^2 + 7x + 7 = 0$ **4.** $5x^2 - 3x + 1 = 0$ **5.** $9x^2 - 30x + 25 = 0$

In Exercises 6-8, use the function y = x² - 2x - 10.

6. Write the equation of the axis of symmetry.

7. Write the coordinates of the vertex, and tell whether it is a maximum or a minimum point.

8. Sketch the parabola.

9. Lars has 225 feet of fence to make a rectangular yard for his dog. Find the length and width of the rectangle that will give the maximum area.

10. Graph the inequality $y < x^2 - 2$.

QUIZ FOR SECTIONS 14-1 THROUGH 14-3

1. The measure of $\angle A$ is $\frac{4}{5}$ the measure of its complement. Find the measure of $\angle A$.

2. Find the supplement of $\angle A$ in Exercise 1.

3. The figure at the right shows the path Felicia took around a pond, from A to C. The measure of $\angle B$ is 20° less than 3 times the measure of $\angle A$. The measure of $\angle C$ is 30° more than the measure of $\angle A$. Find the measure of each angle.

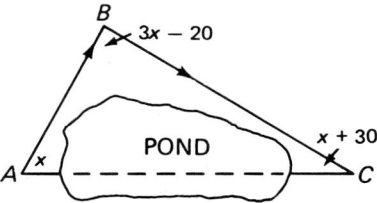

4. Two ropes, each 18 meters long, extend from the top of a flagpole to the ground. The distance between the ends of the ropes is 20 meters. Find the height of the flagpole. Leave your answer in simplest radical form.

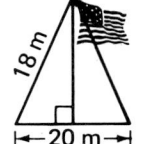

5. Matteo's height is 2 meters. At a time when he casts a shadow 3 meters long, a tree casts a shadow 16 meters long. How tall is the tree?

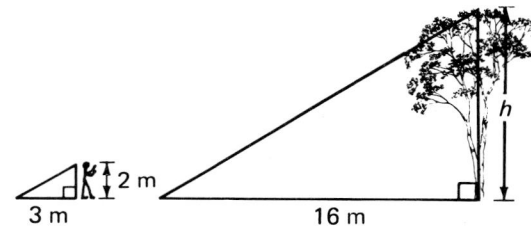

QUIZ FOR SECTIONS 14-4 THROUGH 14-6

*In Exercises 1–4, use the right triangle ABC,
shown at the right, to find the required value.*

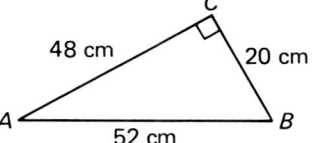

1. cos *B*   **2.** tan *A*

3. sin *A*   **4.** sin *B*

In Exercises 5–6, tell which trigonometric ratio could be used to find x.

5.

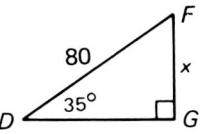

6.

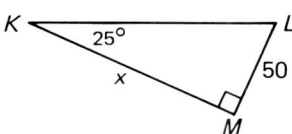

In Exercises 7–10, use the table below.

Angle	Sin	Cos	Tan
40°	.6428	.7660	.8391
45°	.7071	.7071	1.0000
50°	.7660	.6428	1.1918

7. Find sin *P*.

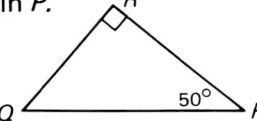

8. Find tan *Y*.

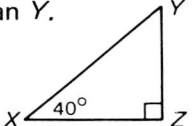

9. Find cos *S*.

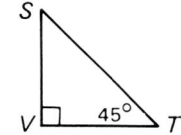

10. A tree casts a shadow 18 meters long. From the end of this shadow, the angle of elevation to the top of the tree is 40°. Find the height of the tree to the nearest meter.

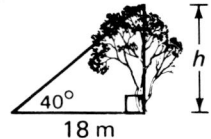

QUIZ FOR SECTIONS 14-7 THROUGH 14-9

1. Use the multiplication table for a four-hour clock, shown at the right, to name the inverse element for 2, such that $2 \times n = 1$.

x	0	1	2	3
0	0	0	0	0
1	0	1	2	3
2	0	2	0	2
3	0	3	2	1

2. Combine the following two statements to form a true conditional.

A figure is a square; a figure has four sides.

3. Write the converse of the conditional you wrote in Exercise 2.

4. When is the converse in Exercise 3 false?

5. Write a direct proof of the following statement: $2n + n = 3n$

ANSWERS: QUIZZES

Sections 1-1 through 1-5 1. $5n$ 2. $p - d$ 3. $\dfrac{500}{h}$ 4. 6 5. 3 6. 35 7. 96 inches 8. $\{2\}$ 9. $\{0, 1\}$
10. $\{10\}$

Sections 1-6 through 1-8 1. -18.30 2. 300 3. F; 0 is a rational number. 4. F; all natural numbers, N, are rational
numbers. 5. F; some elements of Q, such as $\frac{2}{3}$ and 0.03, are not elements of N. 6. Rational; $\sqrt{\frac{49}{36}} = \frac{7}{6}$, which is a
rational number 7. $n = 11$ 8. Distributive postulate 9. Commutative postulate for multiplication 10. 26

Sections 2-1 through 2-4 1. 1 2. 300 3. $x = 4$ or $x = -4$ 4. $r = 1.6$ 5. $m = -8$ 6. $>$ 7. $>$ 8. $=$ 9. 6
10. 0.6 11. -1 12. -18 13. 13 14. -10 15. -1.2

Sections 2-5 through 2-8 1. $3m$ 2. $7x + 1.9$ 3. $2x + 7y + 5$ 4. -24 5. -15 6. 0.06 7. 500 8. $\frac{9}{16}$
9. -18 10. -9 11. 0 12. $-7\frac{1}{2}$ 13. $-\frac{1}{3}$ 14. 7 15. 8

Sections 3-1 through 3-4 1. $m = 6$ 2. $r = 7\frac{1}{4}$ 3. $b = 2\frac{4}{7}$ 4. $m = 72$ 5. $t = 5$ 6. $m = 5$ 7. $x = 5$ 8. $r = 24$
9. 75 mph 10. $1.20

Sections 3-5 through 3-7 1. $y = 6$ 2. $m = 2$ 3. $m = 7$ 4. $x = 49$ 5. $80°; 80°$ 6. $125°$ 7. 80% 8. 300
9. $-1, 0, 1$ 10. $-25, -23, -21$

Sections 4-1 through 4-6 1. $-7n$ 2. $2r - 8.7$ 3. $11 - 2n = 3$ 4. $\dfrac{c}{5} + 6 = 20$ 5. one pair: $35; other pair: $40
6. smaller: 29; larger: 68 7. 16 cm 8. 6 years old 9. $a = -10$ 10. $x = -5$

Sections 4-7 through 4-9 1. $<$ 2. $<$ 3. $\{$all real numbers greater than $-6\}$ 4. $\{$all real numbers greater than $-0.4\}$
5. $\{$all real numbers greater than or equal to $-2\frac{2}{9}\}$

6. $\{$all real numbers less than or equal to $-10\}$

7. $\{$all real numbers greater than 4$\}$

8. $\{$all real numbers greater than or equal to 6$\}$ 9. 94 10. 15

Sections 5-1 through 5-3 1. $x = \dfrac{15}{a}$ 2. $x = b + c$ 3. $b = \dfrac{P - 2a}{2}$, or $b = \dfrac{P}{2} - a$ 4. $h = \dfrac{A}{\pi r^2}$ 5. 4 hr 6. 6 hr
7. Start at the origin and make the moves given for each point. A: left 5; B: left 7, down 8; C: left 3, up 8; D: right 1,
down 8; F: left 1 8. A: on the x axis; B: Quadrant III; C: Quadrant II; D: Quadrant IV; F: on the x axis 9. 0 10. -7

Sections 5-4 through 5-6 1. $\{0, -8, 6, 12\}$ 2. $\{-5, 6, -8, 7\}$ 3. No; two ordered pairs, $(-5, 0)$ and $(-5, 12)$ have
the same first element. 4. $6; 5; 4; \frac{1}{2}$ 5. The line through $(-2, -2)$ and $(2, 2)$. See the graph on page M-61. 6. The
line through $(2, 4)$ and $(4, 0)$. See the graph on page M-61. 7. The line through $(-2, 5)$ and $(2, 5)$. See the graph on page
M-61. 8. Answers may vary. For example, $\{(0, 0), (5, 1), (10, 2)\}$ 9. See the graph on page M-61. 10. About 1.3 mi

Sections 5-7 through 5-10 1. 2 2. $-\frac{7}{5}$ 3. $-\frac{5}{12}$ 4. $y = 7x - 9$; slope: 7; y intercept: -9 5. $y = \frac{3}{4}x - 6$; slope: $\frac{3}{4}$;
y intercept: -6 6. The line through $(0, -6)$ and $(4, -3)$; see the graph on page M-61. 7. Yes; T is always 0.20 times n.
8. No; the equation, $C = 25h + 20$, which describes the relation involves addition as well as multiplication by a constant.
9. 37.5 10. 168 hr

Sections 6-1 through 6-5   1. $(-3, -1)$; see the graph on page M-61.   2. $(2, 8)$; see the graph on page M-61.   3. One   4. Infinitely many   5. None   6. $(9, -2)$ 7. $(-2, 3)$ 8. $(5, 0)$ 9. 75   10. \$30

Sections 6-6 through 6-8   1. $(3, -2)$ 2. $(3, 4)$ 3. $(2, 2)$ 4. Orchestra: 18; balcony: 12   5. Solution A: 90 g; Solution B: 270 g

Sections 7-1 through 7-4   1. $3x - 7 > 6.4$ <u>or</u> $3x - 7 = 6.4$ 2. $0 < 2x$ <u>and</u> $2x < 12$ 3. $-2 < p$ <u>and</u> $p < 3$ 4. $y \geq -1$
5. $3 < z < 10$

6. {all real numbers less than or equal to -5}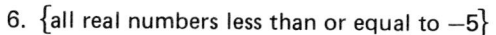

7. {all real numbers greater than or equal to $1\frac{1}{2}$}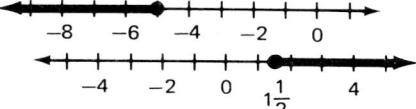

8. {all real numbers greater than 8 and less than 14}

9. The open half-plane to the left of the line through $(0, -6)$ and $(2, 0)$; see the graph on page M-61.   10. The closed half-plane above the line through $(-2, 0)$ and $(0, 2)$; see the graph on page M-61.   11. See the graph on page M-61.
12. $3.50x + 1.50y$ 13. $x \leq 6$ and $y \leq 5$ and $x + y \leq 7$ and $x \geq 0$ and $y \geq 0$.   14. Vertices of polygonal region: $(0, 0)$; $(0, 5)$; $(2, 5)$; $(6, 1)$; $(6, 0)$; see the graph on page M-61.   15. Cashews: 6 lb; peanuts: 1 lb

Sections 7-5 through 7-6   1. $x = -3$ <u>or</u> $x = 3$ 2. $t = -2$ <u>or</u> $t = -4$ 3. $y = 9$ <u>or</u> $y = -1$ 4. $d = \frac{2}{7}$ <u>or</u> $d = \frac{4}{7}$
5. $x = -\frac{3}{5}$ <u>or</u> $x = -\frac{12}{5}$ 6. $r = 3\frac{1}{2}$ <u>or</u> $r = 13\frac{1}{2}$ 7. Two rays with their initial point at $(4, 0)$; one ray also contains $(6, 2)$, and the other ray also contains $(6, -2)$. See the graph on page M-62.   8. Two rays with their initial point at $(0, 3)$; one ray also contains $(-2, 5)$, and the other ray also contains $(2, 5)$. See the graph on page M-62.   9. Two rays with their initial point at $(1, 0)$; one ray also contains $(5, 2)$, and the other ray also contains $(5, -2)$. See the graph on page M-62.
10. Two rays with their initial point at $(0, 1)$; one ray also contains $(2, -1)$, and the other ray also contains $(-2, -1)$. See the graph on page M-62.

Sections 8-1 through 8-5   1. 6   2. -2 3. 36   4. 144   5. 4   6. y^4 7. $-12a^5$ 8. 10^7, or 10,000,000   9. 4^6, or 4096   10. $-8x^3$ 11. $-27a^3b^6$ 12. z^6 13. $\frac{x^6}{y^2}$ 14. $\frac{r^3s^3}{2}$ 15. -27 16. $\frac{25}{4}$ 17. $\frac{4}{p^4}$ 18. 3×10^{-6} 19. 5×10^6 20. 2.4×10^{-3}

Sections 8-6 through 8-10   1. $x - y$ 2. $-4r + 5s$ 3. $-3t - 7$ 4. $22m - 11n - 3$ 5. $2a^5 + a^2b - ab + 2b^4$
6. $6 + 15x$ 7. $x^2y - x^3$ 8. $6t^2 - 15t$ 9. $z^2 + 3z + 2$ 10. $3b^2 - b - 2$ 11. $12t^2 + 11t - 2$ 12. $x^2 + 6x + 9$
13. $25t^2 - 40t + 16$ 14. $36t^2 - 1$ 15. $4 - q^2$

Sections 9-1 through 9-3   1. Yes   2. No   3. Yes   4. $2^3 \cdot 3^2$ 5. 3^6 6. $3 \cdot 11^2$ 7. Prime   8. $7(a + b)$
9. $4(2x + y - 3)$ 10. $(b + 2z)(b - 2z)$ 11. $(4 + r)(4 - r)$ 12. $(m - 3)(t + 3)$ 13. $\left(\frac{a}{6} + \frac{b}{4}\right)\left(\frac{a}{6} - \frac{b}{4}\right)$
14. $(\frac{1}{5} + q)(\frac{1}{5} - q)$ 15. $(xy + wz)(xy - wz)$

Sections 9-4 through 9-9   1. $(x - 6)(x - 1)$ 2. $(y - 7)(y - 7)$, or $(y - 7)^2$ 3. $5(t + 3)(t - 3)$ 4. $3(x^2 + 2x + 2)$
5. $(3r - 2)(2r - 5)$ 6. $(ab + 2c^2)(ab - 2c^2)$ 7. $x = -4$ <u>or</u> $x = 4$ 8. $x = -2$ <u>or</u> $x = 0$ 9. $x = -2$ <u>or</u> $x = 3$
10. Length: 12 m; width: 5 m

Sections 10-1 through 10-3   1. $x = 55$ 2. $x = 75$ 3. $y = 24$ 4. 72   5. 10%: \$2500; 8%: \$6500   6. 20 oz   7. $\frac{3}{4}$
8. $\frac{3}{4}$ 9. $\frac{7c^3}{10ab}$ 10. $\frac{5}{a - b}$

Sections 10-4 through 10-9   1. $\dfrac{x^3y^3}{z}$ 2. 2   3. $\dfrac{r+3}{3}$ 4. $\dfrac{x}{3x+3}$ 5. $x^2(x+3)(x-4)$ 6. $-3t-3$ 7. $\dfrac{10a-3}{2a+7}$

8. $\dfrac{6b-37}{b-7}$ 9. $\dfrac{-x^2+3x-4}{2(x+3)(x-3)}$ 10. $a^2-5a-4+\dfrac{-3}{a-2}$

Sections 11-1 through 11-3   1. $n=120$ 2. $\{$all real numbers$\}$ 3. $x=\dfrac{5}{4}$ 4. $y=\dfrac{1}{4}x+3$ 5. $y=2x-2$

6. $y=-3x-14$ 7. $y=-\dfrac{1}{11}x+3$ 8. $y=-3x+1$ 9. $-4x+7y=19$ 10. $5x+y=11$

Sections 11-4 through 11-8   1. 23   2. $\dfrac{1}{4};\dfrac{3}{4}$ 3. 300 mph   4. $3\dfrac{1}{13}$ hr   5. No; it does not have the same form as

$xy=k$, or $y=\dfrac{k}{x}$.   6. Yes; it has the same form as $y=\dfrac{k}{x}$.   7. $1\dfrac{3}{5}$ 8. $9\dfrac{3}{5}$ days   9. $T=ksw$ 10. 21

Sections 12-1 through 12-5   1. -30 2. 18.4   3. $15\,|a|\,\sqrt{7a}$ 4. $\dfrac{241}{99}$ 5. $x=8; y=9$ 6. $4x\sqrt{3}$ 7. $90\sqrt{10}$

8. 13 cm   9. No   10. $3\sqrt{10}$

Sections 12-6 through 12-10   1. $6\sqrt{3}$ 2. $180\sqrt{10}$ 3. $2c\sqrt{d}$ 4. $\dfrac{2\sqrt{7}}{7}$ 5. $\dfrac{\sqrt{30}}{6}$ 6. $2x\sqrt{2}$ 7. $-3\sqrt{2}-\sqrt{7}$

8. $2\sqrt{2}+2\sqrt{3}$ 9. $9x\sqrt{x}$ 10. $x=59$ 11. $x=5$ 12. $x=25$ 13. 8   14. -3 15. $\dfrac{1}{2}$

Sections 13-1 through 13-4   1. $x=5$ 2. $x=\pm2\sqrt{3}$ 3. $x=-2$ or $x=5$ 4. $x=\dfrac{-1-\sqrt{21}}{2}$ or $x=\dfrac{-1+\sqrt{21}}{2}$

5. $x=-\dfrac{1}{3}$ or $x=2$ 6. $x=\dfrac{5-\sqrt{33}}{4}$ or $x\,\dfrac{5+\sqrt{33}}{4}$ 7. $t=\dfrac{3-\sqrt{5}}{4}$ or $t=\dfrac{3+\sqrt{5}}{4}$ 8. Let $x=$ the height of the

parallelogram and $x+3=$ the length of a base of the parallelogram; $(x+3)x=270$.   9. 18 cm   10. 7 and 9

Sections 13-5 through 13-8   1. The parabola opening downward with vertex at $(0, 4)$ and passing through $(-2, 0)$ and $(2, 0)$; See the graph on page M-62.   2. -2 and 2   3. Two distinct real solutions   4. No real solutions   5. Exactly one real solution   6. $x=1$ 7. $(1, -11)$; minimum point   8. The parabola opening upward with vertex at $(1, -11)$ and passing through $(0, -10)$ and $(2, -10)$; see the graph on page M-62.   9. Length: $56\dfrac{1}{4}$ ft; width: $56\dfrac{1}{4}$ ft   10. The set of points outside the parabola, opening upward, with vertex at $(0, -2)$ and passing through $(-2, 2)$ and $(2, 2)$; see the graph on page M-62.

Sections 14-1 through 14-3   1. $40°$ 2. $140°$ 3. A: $34°$; B: $82°$; C: $64°$ 4. $2\sqrt{51}$ m   5. $10\dfrac{2}{3}$ m

Sections 14-4 through 14-6   1. $\dfrac{5}{13}$ 2. $\dfrac{5}{12}$ 3. $\dfrac{5}{13}$ 4. $\dfrac{12}{13}$ 5. $\sin 35°$ 6. $\tan 35°$ 7. .7660   8. .8391   9. .7071
10. 15 m

Sections 14-7 through 14-9   1. There is no inverse element for 2 such that $2 \times n = 1$.   2. If a figure is a square, then the figure has four sides <u>or</u> if a figure is not a square, then the figure is not a square.   3. If a figure has four sides, then the figure is a square; if a figure is not a square, then the figure does not have four sides.   4. When the figure has four sides and the figure is not a square.   5. Hypothesis: n is a real number; Conclusion: $2n+n=3n$.

5. Statements	Reasons
1. n is a real number.	1. Given
2. $2n+n=(2+1)n$	2. Distributive postulate
3. $(2+1)n=3n$	3. Addition
4. $2n+n=3n$	4. Substitution

QUIZ FOR SECTIONS 5-4 THROUGH 5-6

Page M-47, Ex. 5

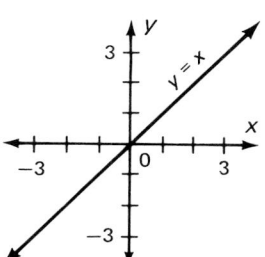

Page M-47, Ex. 6

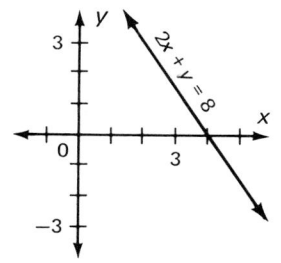

Page M-47, Ex. 7

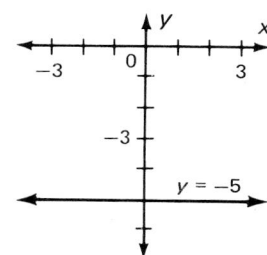

Page M-47, Ex. 9

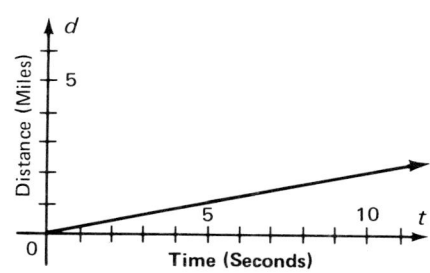

QUIZ FOR SECTIONS 5-7 THROUGH 5-10

Page M-47, Ex. 6

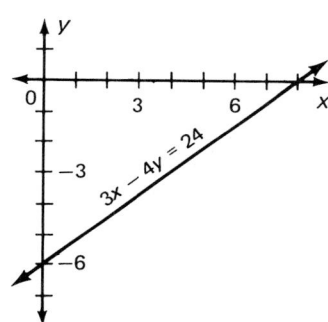

Page M-48, Ex. 1

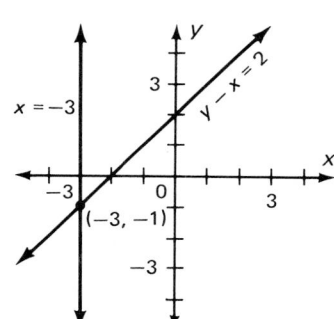

Page M-48, Ex. 2

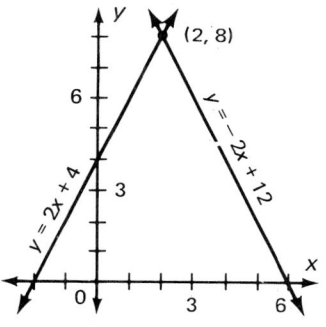

QUIZ FOR SECTIONS 7-1 THROUGH 7-4

Page M-49, Ex. 9

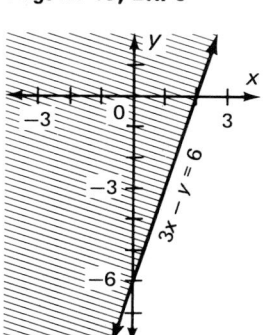

Page M-49, Ex. 10

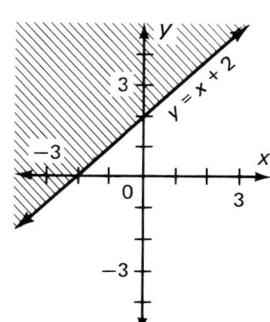

Page M-49, Ex. 11

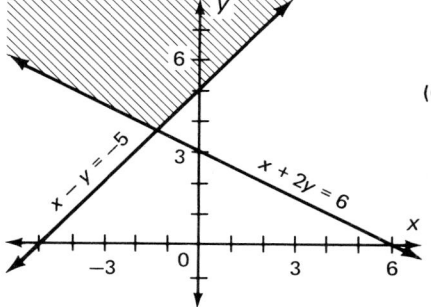

Page M-49, Ex. 14

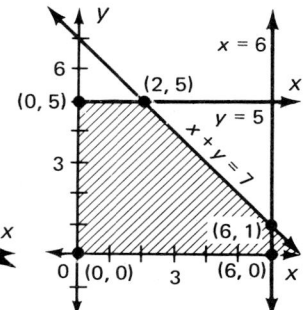

QUIZ FOR SECTIONS 7-5 THROUGH 7-6

Page M-49, Ex. 7

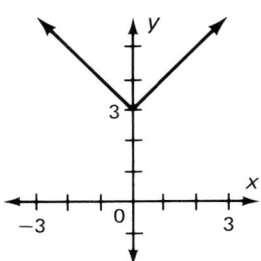

Page M-49, Ex. 8

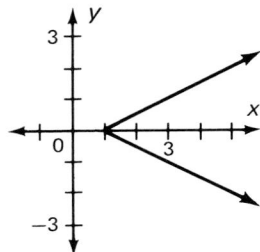

Page M-49, Ex. 9

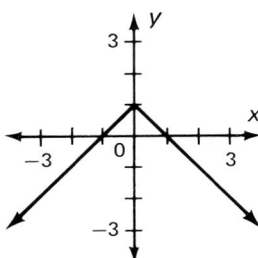

Page M-49, Ex. 10

QUIZ FOR SECTIONS 13-5 THROUGH 13-8

Page M-55, Ex. 1

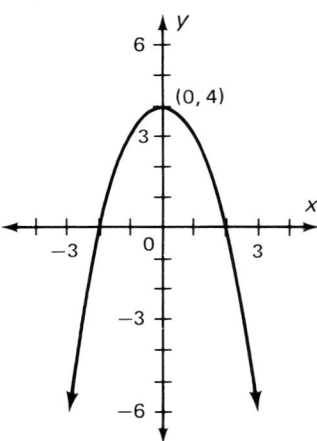

Page M-55, Ex. 8

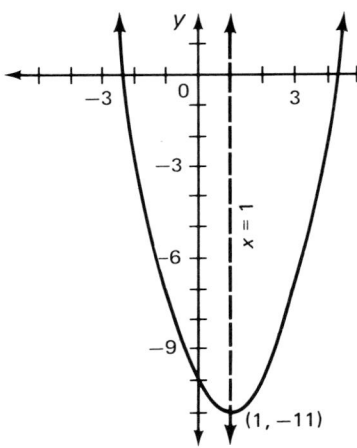

Page M-55, Ex. 10

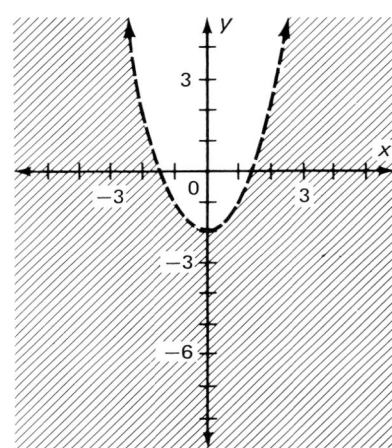

CHAPTER TESTS

Pages M-64 through M-77 contain a test for each chapter in the textbook. The answers for the tests begin on page M-78.

Permission to reproduce pages M-64 through M-77 is granted to users of *HBJ Algebra 1*.

The *Tests: Duplicating Masters* contains a parallel form of each chapter test, six cumulative tests, and two cumulative *Preparing for College Entrance Tests*. The answers for these tests begin on page M-121.

CHAPTER 1 TEST   USES OF ALGEBRA

Write an algebraic description for each word description.

(1-1) **1.** The cost of t liters of orange juice at 89¢ per liter

2. The monthly rent, r, subtracted from $1286

3. The cost of one ticket if p tickets cost $15

Find the value of each numerical expression.

(1-1,   **4.** $48 - (60 \div 12)$ **5.** $\dfrac{9(12-7)}{9+6}$ **6.** $4[6(8-3) \div 10]$
1-2)

Evaluate for the given values of the variables.

7. $6p - 3w$, for $p = 8$ and $w = 6$

8. $\frac{2}{3}m + \frac{3}{5}t$, for $m = 12$ and $t = 15$

Find B for each formula. The replacement set for t is {2, 4, 6}.

(1-3)   **9.** $B = 4t$ **10.** $B = \dfrac{8+t}{3}$

Evaluate.

11. 3^3 **12.** $\left(\dfrac{3}{4}\right)^2$

(1-4)   **13.** Use the formula $U = P \div n$ to find U when $P = \$1.81$ and $n = 106$ grams. Round the answer to the nearest tenth of a cent.

14. Use the formula $A = \frac{1}{2}h(b + c)$ to find A when $h = 6$ meters, $b = 5$ meters, and $c = 8$ meters.

Find the solution set. The replacement set for x is {2, 3, 4}.

(1-5)   **15.** $x + 9 = 12$ **16.** $5x > 15$

Classify each sentence as true, $\underline{T}$, or false, $\underline{F}$.

(1-6)   **17.** Every counting number is an integer.

18. $\frac{8}{9}$ is a rational number.

Represent each of the following by a positive or negative rational number.

19. A raise in pay of $2.50 per hour

20. A descent to 100 feet below sea level

Identify each number as rational, Q, or irrational, Ir.

(1-7)   **21.** $\sqrt{11}$ **22.** $-1\frac{1}{8}$ **23.** $3.1087395 \cdots$

Name the postulate illustrated by each sentence.

(1-8)   **24.** $18(5 + 9) = (5 + 9)18$ **25.** $81 + (3 + 29) = (81 + 3) + 29$

CHAPTER 2 TEST OPERATIONS WITH REAL NUMBERS

(2-1) **1.** Write without parentheses: $-(-q)$

2. Use $<$ or $>$ to compare the numbers: -22 _?_ $-(-22)$

(2-2) **3.** Write the additive inverse of -1.

4. Evaluate: $|8| + |-20|$

5. Solve: $-|-7| = x$

Add.

(2-3) **6.** $-13 + 8$

7. $-5\frac{1}{5} + (-4\frac{2}{5})$

8. $8.6 + 3.7 + (-2.2)$

Use positive and negative numbers to represent this problem. Then find the sum.

9. Jeff had \$125 in his checking account. He made a deposit of \$40 and wrote checks for \$62.80 and \$13.98. How much was left in the account?

Subtract.

(2-4) **10.** $-12 - (-8)$

11. $-8.9 - 4.7$

12. At midnight the temperature was $3°C$. Six hours later, the temperature was $-1°C$. How much did the temperature change?

13. Evaluate $x - y + z$ when $x = -8$, $y = -2$, and $z = 24$.

Combine like terms.

(2-5) **14.** $10t - 18 + 8t$

15. $8ab - 4b + 9a - 7ab$

16. Find the sum of the areas of these two figures.

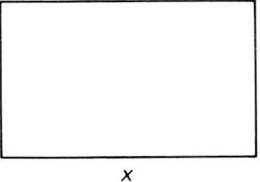
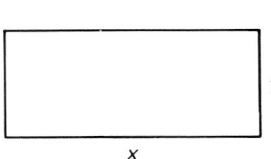

Multiply or divide as indicated.

(2-6) **17.** $\frac{1}{3}(-6)(5)$

18. $(-8)(-1)(-9)$

(2-7) **19.** $-84 \div 21$

20. $-\frac{8}{9} \div (-\frac{2}{3})$

21. $-3.2 \div 0.8$

22. Simplify: $8(-3) \div (-\frac{3}{4})$

(2-8) **23.** Evaluate $x^2 + y^2 + z$ when $x = -10$, $y = 5$, and $z = 0$.

24. By what number would you multiply $\frac{1}{8}t$ to obtain t?

25. What number would you add to $x + (-8 + 13)$ to obtain x?

Solve each equation.

(3-1) **1.** $18 + n = 48$ **2.** $y + 18 = -20$ **3.** $x - 8 = -20$

(3-2) **4.** $8x = -48$ **5.** $\frac{7}{2}y = 84$

6. $\frac{3}{5}x = 40$ **7.** $\frac{x}{3} = -1\frac{2}{3}$

(3-3) **8.** $8x + 4 = 36$ **9.** $-6 + 12x = 78$ **10.** $40 = 18 + \frac{1}{2}a$

The weekly earnings, E, of a salesperson who is paid a base salary of $305 and a 2% commission on the amount of sales, S, is given by this formula.

$$E = 305 + 0.02S$$

(3-4) **11.** One week, the salesperson's total sales were $4000. Find the total earnings.

12. The salesperson's total earnings for a certain week amounted to $415. What were the total sales?

Solve each equation.

(3-5) **13.** $8b - 3b + b = 30$ **14.** $16 = 4(3a - 2)$ **15.** $2y - 4(6 - 2y) = 36$

Solve each problem.

(3-6) **16.** The sum of the measures of two angles is 90°. The measure of one of these angles is $3t$. The measure of the second angle is twice the first. Find the measure of each angle.

(3-7) **17.** Average monthly heating costs for the Meyer family amount to $92. By lowering the thermostat 1°, they saved 9% of this amount. How much did they save?

18. At a sale, the cost of a pair of shoes was reduced from $42.00 to $33.60. What was the per cent of discount?

(3-8) **19.** Find two consecutive integers such that five times the smaller equals four times the larger.

20. The sum of three consecutive odd integers is 51. What are the integers?

CHAPTER 4 TEST   EQUATIONS AND INEQUALITIES

Represent each word expression by an algebraic expression.

(4-1) **1.** The product of b and 6   **2.** t increased by $\frac{3}{4}$

3. b less 18   **4.** The quotient of 8 and y

Solve each problem.

5. The Garcia family spent a total of $2500 for a vacation that lasted d days. Represent the average cost per day.

(4-2) **6.** Three times the number of voters decreased by 110 is 116,890. Find the number of voters.

(4-3) **7.** One number is 9 more than twice a second number. The sum of the numbers is 123. Find the numbers.

8. Together, Sarah and Linda earned $571. Linda earned $5 less than three times the amount Sarah earned. How much did Linda earn?

(4-4) **9.** The length of a rectangle is 9 centimeters more than the width. The perimeter is 62 centimeters. Find the length and the width.

Solve each equation.

(4-5) **10.** $5b - 6 = 8b - 15$ **11.** $\frac{1}{3}x + 9 = x + 3$

12. $-5(r - 8) = 3r - 16$

(4-6) **13.** Tony's present age is 5 times his brother's present age. In 9 years, Tony will be twice as old as his brother will be then. How old is each now?

Solve and graph each inequality.

(4-7) **14.** $y - 3 > 2$ **15.** $1.6 > x - 0.2$ **16.** $15y < 3(3y - 2) + 12$

(4-8) **17.** $\frac{1}{8}t > 2$ **18.** $68 - 8a < 9a$ **19.** $39 > -6t - 7t$

(4-9) **20.** Several pipe sections, each 8 meters long, are to be joined to form a pipe greater than 126 meters long. What is the least number of pipe sections that will be needed?

M-67

Solve each equation for x.

(5-1) **1.** $b + x = c + d$ **2.** $4x - b = 3c$

(5-2) **3.** A freight train leaves a station and travels at an average rate of 45 miles per hour. Two hours later, a passenger train leaves the same station, traveling at an average rate of 60 miles per hour. In how many hours will the passenger train overtake the freight train?

Name the quadrant in which each point lies.

(5-3) **4.** $(-8, 2)$ **5.** $P(x, y)$ where $x < 0$ and $y > 0$

(5-4) **6.** Give the domain and range of this relation.

$$\{(1, 6), (2, 12), (2, 18), (3, 24)\}$$

Determine whether each relation is a function. Answer Yes or No.

7. $\{(1, 15), (2, 30), (3, 45), (4, 60)\}$ **8.** $\{(-3, 0), (-1, 1), (0, 5), (3, 5)\}$

Graph each linear equation in the coordinate plane.

(5-5) **9.** $y = 3x - 4$ **10.** $y = \frac{1}{4}x$ **11.** $x + 1 = 0$

The basic fee for renting a certain piano is $55 plus an additional $35 for each month of rental. Refer to this information in Exercises 12-14.

(5-6) **12.** Complete the table.

Number of months (m)	1	2	3
Cost (C)	?	?	?

13. Use the ordered pairs in Exercise 12 to graph the function. Assume that it is linear.

14. Use the graph in Exercise 13 to estimate the cost of renting the piano for 6 months.

(5-7) **15.** Find the slope of the line containing the points $Q(-2, -5)$ and $V(-3, 8)$.

Find the slope and y intercept of the graph of each equation.

(5-8) **16.** $3x + y = 6$ **17.** $3y - 2x = 15$

(5-9) **18.** P varies directly as s and $P = 32$ when $s = 5$. Find k.

19. If y varies directly as x and $y = 1$ when $x = 8$, find y when $x = 12$.

(5-10) **20.** On a scale drawing, 3 centimeters represents 75 meters. How many meters will 18.4 centimeters represent?

CHAPTER 6 TEST   SYSTEMS OF SENTENCES

Solve each system by graphing.

(6-1)　**1.** $\begin{cases} x + y = 5 \\ x - y = 3 \end{cases}$ 　　　　　　 **2.** $\begin{cases} x + y = 4 \\ 2x - y = 2 \end{cases}$

Write <u>one</u>, <u>none</u>, or <u>infinitely many</u> to describe the number of solutions for each system.

3. $\begin{cases} y - 5 = -x \\ 3x + 3y = 15 \end{cases}$ 　　 **4.** $\begin{cases} 3x - 2y = 8 \\ 4x + 5y = 20 \end{cases}$ 　　 **5.** $\begin{cases} y = \frac{1}{3}x + 9 \\ y = \frac{1}{3}x - 7 \end{cases}$

Solve by the addition method.

(6-2)　**6.** $\begin{cases} 2x + y = 19 \\ x - y = 2 \end{cases}$ 　　　　　 **7.** $\begin{cases} 3x + 5y = 11 \\ 2x - 5y = -26 \end{cases}$

(6-3)　**8.** Use multiplication with the addition method to solve this system.

$$\begin{cases} 5x + 2y = 4 \\ 3x + 4y = -6 \end{cases}$$

Solve by the substitution method.

(6-6)　**9.** $\begin{cases} y = 3x \\ x + y = 20 \end{cases}$ 　　　　　 **10.** $\begin{cases} 2x + 6y = 11 \\ x + 4y = 5 \end{cases}$

Write a system of equations in two variables for each problem. Then solve.

(6-4)　**11.** The sum of two numbers is 68. Five times the smaller is 4 more than 3 times the larger. Find the numbers.

(6-5)　**12.** The tens digit of a two-digit number is 3 times the units digit. The difference of the digits is 6. What is the number?

13. The sum of the digits of a two-digit number is 11. When 27 is added to the number, the result is the original number with its digits reversed. Find the number.

(6-7)　**14.** Five hundred tickets were sold for a concert. Adult tickets cost $4.20 and student tickets cost $1.80. Total receipts amounted to $1260. How many of each type of ticket were sold?

(6-8)　**15.** A 30–kilogram mixture of coffee is made from two brands. Brand A sells at $2.55 per kilogram. Brand B sells at $3.75 per kilogram. The mixture will sell at $3.25 per kilogram. How many kilograms of each brand must be used?

M-69

CHAPTER 7 TEST   INEQUALITIES

Write each compound sentence as two single sentences joined by or or and.

(7-1)   **1.** $8x \geq 10$

2. $12 < 4x < 8$

Solve each inequality. Graph the solution set on a number line.

3. $7x \leq 21$

4. $-8 < y + 2 < 5$

Graph each inequality in the coordinate plane.

(7-2)   **5.** $x + y > 2$

6. $y \geq 4x - 4$

(7-3)   **7.** Solve by graphing: $\begin{cases} x + y < 8 \\ x - y > 3 \end{cases}$

Refer to this information in Exercises 8-12.

A manufacturer makes two models of reading lamps. The profit on Model A is $15 per lamp and the profit on Model B is $20 per lamp. The manufacturer can produce no more than 200 lamps per week. To meet the market demand, at least 50 Model A lamps and at least 100 Model B lamps must be available for sale each week.

(7-4)   **8.** Let x represent the number of Model A lamps produced per week and let y represent the number of Model B lamps produced per week. Write an expression to represent the total weekly profit.

9. Write a system of 5 inequalities that shows the constraints on x and y.

10. Graph the system of inequalities from Exercise 9.

11. State the coordinates of the vertices (corners) of the polygonal region graphed in Exercise 10.

12. What is the manufacturer's maximum possible weekly profit?

Solve and check each equation.

(7-5)   **13.** $|8y| = 16$

14. $|5m + 8| = 23$

(7-6)   **15.** Graph in the coordinate plane: $y = |3x|$

CHAPTER 8 TEST   EXPONENTS AND POLYNOMIALS

Evaluate when a = −1, b = 3, and c = −5.

(8-1)   **1.** $a^{24}c^3$ **2.** a^5b^2c

Find each product.

(8-2)   **3.** $10^2 \cdot 10^2 \cdot 10^3$ **4.** $(6rt^2)(-5r^5t^3)$

Simplify. No denominator equals zero.

(8-3)   **5.** $(y^3)^5$ **6.** $(3a^3b^2)^3$

(8-4)   **7.** $\dfrac{32x^3y^8z^2}{4xy^5z}$ **8.** $\dfrac{8bc(3a^2b^3)}{-6ab^2}$

(8-5)   **9.** $a^{-3}b^0$ **10.** $\left(-\frac{3}{4}\right)^{-2}$

Write each number in scientific notation.

11. 438,000,000   **12.** 0.00087

Add or subtract as indicated.

(8-6)   **13.** $(8x^2 - 3xy + 4y^2) + (x^2 - 2xy - 2y^2)$

14. $(a + b - c) + (-a + b - c)$

15. $(3b - 4c) - (8b + 3c)$

16. $(4x + 3y) - (6x - 9 - y)$

Multiply.

(8-7)   **17.** $6a^2(3a^2 + 4a - 8)$ **18.** $(4x - y)(3x + 4y)$

(8-8)   **19.** $(x - 4)(x - 7)$ **20.** $(3r + 2)(r - 1)$

21. $(8y - 1)(3y + 5)$ **22.** $(a^2 + 4)(a^2 - 3)$

Write the square of each binomial as a trinomial.

(8-9)   **23.** $\left(t + \frac{1}{8}\right)^2$ **24.** $(6a - 3b)^2$

(8-10)   **25.** Write as a binomial: $(5a - 8)(5a + 8)$

CHAPTER 9 TEST   FACTORING POLYNOMIALS

Write each number in prime-factorization form.

(9-1)   **1.** 56   **2.** 111

Factor over the integers.

(9-2)   **3.** $12a + 12b$ **4.** $x^3y^2 + xy^2 + x^3y$

(9-3)   **5.** $t^2 - 25$ **6.** $64q^2 - 1$

(9-4)   **7.** $a^2 + 8a + 16$ **8.** $1 - 12x + 36x^2$

(9-5)   **9.** $r^2 + 9r + 20$ **10.** $x^2 + 10xy + 24y^2$

            11. $a^2 - 11a + 8$ **12.** $t^2 - 15t + 54$

(9-6)   **13.** $5b^2 + 8b + 3$ **14.** $2x^2 + 13x - 7$

            15. $2p^2 - 13p + 15$ **16.** $2y^2 + 5y - 12$

Factor completely over the integers.

(9-7)   **17.** $3x^2 + 12x - 36$ **18.** $8x^2 - 8y^2$

            19. $2t^2 - 12t - 80$ **20.** $s(s - 4)(s + 1) + 9(s + 1)$

Solve by factoring.

(9-8)   **21.** $x^2 = 49$ **22.** $t^2 - 9t = 0$ **23.** $q^2 + 2q = 15$

Solve each problem.

(9-9)   **24.** Find two consecutive even integers whose product is 440.

            25. A rose garden is 3 meters longer than it is wide. Its area is 88 square meters. Find the length and width of the garden.

CHAPTER 10 TEST   RATIONAL EXPRESSIONS

Solve each proportion.

(10-1) **1.** $\dfrac{x}{13} = \dfrac{9}{39}$

2. $\dfrac{r+8}{6} = \dfrac{r-3}{8}$

3. In a mixture of concrete, the ratio of sand to cement is 2:5. How many bags of cement are needed to mix with 15 bags of sand?

(10-2) **4.** Pierre has the same amount of money invested at a yearly interest rate of 13% as at a yearly interest rate of 15%. Total interest for the year amounted to $420. How much is invested at each rate?

5. A pharmacist has a 50% peroxide solution and a 10% peroxide solution. How many liters of each will be needed to make 100 liters of a 20% peroxide solution?

Simplify. No denominator equals zero.

(10-3) **6.** $\dfrac{8x + 8y}{40(x+y)}$

7. $\dfrac{x^2 - x}{x^2 + x - 2}$

8. $\dfrac{r^2 + r - 6}{r^2 - 9}$

Multiply or divide. Express each answer in simplest form.

(10-4) **9.** $\dfrac{6a^2}{x} \cdot \dfrac{x^2}{18a}$

10. $\dfrac{2r+1}{r-3} \cdot \dfrac{r^2 - 9}{4r+2}$

11. $\dfrac{p-1}{p^2 - 49} \cdot \dfrac{p^2 + 3p - 28}{3 - 3p}$

(10-5) **12.** $\dfrac{ab}{x^2} \div \dfrac{ab}{xy}$

13. $\dfrac{c^2 - 2cd + d^2}{x+y} \div \dfrac{c-d}{x^2 - y^2}$

14. $\dfrac{q^2 + 5q + 4}{16 - q^2} \div (q^2 - q - 2)$

Add or subtract as indicated. Write answers in simplest form.

(10-6, **15.** $\dfrac{12}{x-2} + \dfrac{6x}{x-2}$
10-7,
10-8)

16. $\dfrac{6x-1}{x+5} - \dfrac{4x-4}{x+5}$

17. $\dfrac{y+4}{y^2 - 16} + \dfrac{y-2}{y+4}$

18. $6 - \dfrac{3}{a-2}$

19. $b - 1 - \dfrac{1}{b+1}$

(10-9) **20.** Divide $(a^3 + 9a^2 + 17a - 12)$ by $(a + 4)$.

M-73

Solve each equation.

(11-1)   **1.** $\dfrac{5x}{3} + \dfrac{3}{5} = \dfrac{10x}{5}$ **2.** $\dfrac{4}{x-3} = \dfrac{5}{x}$ **3.** $\dfrac{1}{x} + \dfrac{2}{x-2} = \dfrac{1}{2x}$

A point on a line and the slope of the line are given. Write an equation of the line in the form $y = mx + b$.

(11-2)   **4.** $A(2, 3)$; $m = -6$ **5.** $P(4, -4)$; $m = \dfrac{4}{3}$

Write an equation of the line passing through the given points. Write the equation in the form $y = mx + b$.

(11-3)   **6.** $T(3, 4)$; $Q(4, 5)$ **7.** $N(-5, -6)$; $S(-4, -3)$

(11-4)   **8.** When the same number is added to both the numerator and denominator of $\dfrac{4}{7}$, the resulting fraction equals $\dfrac{4}{5}$. Find the number.

(11-5)   **9.** Ruth drove her car a distance of 330 kilometers in the same time it took Karl to drive 270 kilometers. Ruth's rate of speed was 10 kilometers per hour faster than Karl's. Find the speeds of each.

(11-6)   **10.** It takes Luis 20 minutes to complete a certain job. It takes Bob 30 minutes to complete the same job. How long would it take both boys working together to complete the job?

(11-7)   **11.** If y varies inversely as x, and $y = 12$ when $x = 8$, write an equation that shows how x and y are related.

(11-8)   **12.** If a varies inversely as b and $a = 120$ when $b = \dfrac{1}{4}$, find b when $a = 160$.

13. The number of trees in a row in an apple orchard varies inversely as the distance between each pair of trees. If the trees are 40 feet apart, there are 30 trees per row. Find the number of trees per row when the trees are 50 feet apart.

(11-9)   **14.** Given that y varies directly as x and inversely as w, and $y = 35$ when $x = 70$ and $w = 8$, find y when $x = 21$ and $w = 12$.

15. The area of a triangle varies jointly as the base and the height. A triangle with a base of 13 inches and a height of 20 inches has an area of 130 square inches. Find the area when the base is 9 inches and the height is 16 inches.

CHAPTER 12 TEST   RADICALS

Simplify.

(12-1)   **1.** $\pm\sqrt{81}$ **2.** $\sqrt{25d^6}$ **3.** $-\sqrt{121x^8y^4z^2}$

(12-2)   **4.** Write $0.\overline{39}$ in the form $\dfrac{a}{b}$.

Simplify. All variables represent positive real numbers.

(12-3)   **5.** $\sqrt{48}$ **6.** $8\sqrt{84b^3}$ **7.** $\sqrt{75a^5b^7}$

(12-4)   **8.** The lengths of the legs of a right triangle are 10 and 24. Find the length of the hypotenuse, the longest side.

   9. A ladder 25 feet long leans against a building and reaches a ledge. The foot of the ladder is 15 feet from the building. What is the distance from the ground to the ledge?

(12-5)   **10.** Find the distance between $P(-1,-2)$ and $Q(-6,-14)$.

Simplify. All variables represent positive real numbers.

(12-6)   **11.** $\sqrt{10}\cdot\sqrt{12}$ **12.** $(8\sqrt{2})(-4\sqrt{6})$ **13.** $\sqrt{a^3b}\cdot\sqrt{b^3c}$

(12-7)   **14.** $2\sqrt{\dfrac{18}{96}}$ **15.** $\dfrac{6\sqrt{3}}{\sqrt{12}}$ **16.** $\dfrac{\sqrt{32x^3}}{\sqrt{8x}}$

   17. Rationalize the denominator and simplify: $\dfrac{2\sqrt{3}}{\sqrt{2}}$

Add or subtract as indicated.

(12-8)   **18.** $8\sqrt{5}+10\sqrt{5}-5\sqrt{5}$ **19.** $2\sqrt{128}-9\sqrt{50}-3\sqrt{98}$

Simplify.

   20. $\sqrt{5}\,(2\sqrt{3}-\sqrt{10})$ **21.** $(8-\sqrt{5})(8+\sqrt{5})$

(12-9)   **22.** Solve for y: $10-2\sqrt{y}=4$

Simplify.

(12-10)   **23.** $(49)^{\frac{1}{2}}$ **24.** $-(\frac{1}{64})^{\frac{1}{3}}$ **25.** $27^{\frac{2}{3}}$

M-75

Solve by factoring or by taking the square root.

(13-1)   **1.** $t^2 - 100 = 0$ **2.** $(r + 1)^2 = 4$

Solve by completing the square. Write irrational solutions in simplest radical form.

(13-2)   **3.** $y^2 - 4y = 60$ **4.** $8a^2 - 16a - 32 = 0$

Solve by using the quadratic formula. Write irrational solutions in simplest radical form.

(13-3)   **5.** $3x^2 + 8x + 5 = 0$ **6.** $y^2 - 5y = 15$

Use a quadratic equation to represent the conditions of each problem. Then solve the equation.

(13-4)   **7.** The sum of a positive number and its square is 210. Find the number.

   8. In a school auditorium, the number of seats in each row is 3 less than the number of rows. The auditorium has 700 seats in all. How many rows are there?

In Exercises 9-11:
a. *Graph the function.*
b. *Give the zeros of the function.*

(13-5)   **9.** $y = x^2 - 4$ **10.** $y = x^2 - 2x + 1$ **11.** $y = x^2 - x - 6$

Without solving, give the nature of the solutions of each equation.

(13-6)   **12.** $x^2 + 2x - 48 = 0$ **13.** $5 - b = -2b^2$

   14. $t^2 + 12t = 36$ **15.** $3x^2 + 6x - 7 = 0$

Exercises 16-19 refer to the parabola $y = x^2 - 4x$.

(13-7)   **16.** Write the equation of the axis of symmetry.

   17. Write the coordinates of the vertex.

   18. Give the maximum or minimum point of the graph of the parabola. Tell whether the point is a maximum or a minimum.

   19. Sketch the parabola.

(13-8)   **20.** Graph this inequality: $y < x^2 - 1$

CHAPTER 14 TEST   OTHER APPLICATIONS OF ALGEBRA

(14-1)   **1.** The measure of an angle is $\frac{2}{3}$ the measure of its complement. Find the measure of the angle, of its complement, and of its supplement.

(14-2)   **2.** In triangle ABC, the measure of angle A is $20°$ less than the measure of angle B. The measure of angle C is $35°$ more than the measure of angle B. Find the measure of each angle.

3. A TV antenna is supported by two guy wires that form an isosceles triangle with the ground. Each guy wire is 13 meters long. The two wires are anchored at points 10 meters apart. Find the height, h, of the antenna.

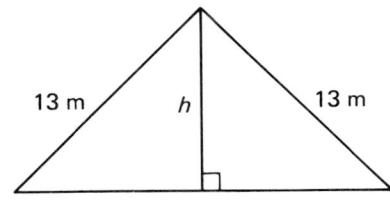

(14-3)   **4.** The triangles shown at the right are similar. Find a.

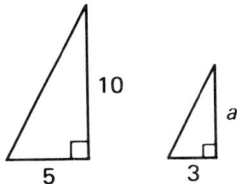

In Exercises 6-10, refer to right triangle ABC.
Express each answer as a fraction in lowest terms.

(14-4,   **5.** $\sin A$ **6.** $\cos A$

14-5)   **7.** $\tan A$ **8.** $\cos B$

          9. $\sin B$ **10.** $\tan B$

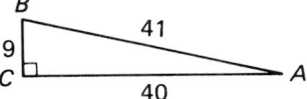

(14-6)   **11.** From a given point, the measure of the angle of elevation to the top of a tree is $50°$. The distance from the point to the center of the base of the tree is 30 meters. Find the height of the tree.

12. In right triangle ABC, C is the right angle and the measure of angle B is $70°$. Find the length of the side adjacent to angle B if the length of the hypotenuse is 100 meters. ($\sin 70° = .9397$; $\cos 70° = .3420$)

(14-7)   **13.** Construct a multiplication table for a "four-hour clock." Use the table to determine the multiplicative inverse of 3.

(14-8)   **14.** Write this definition as a condition and its converse.

A right angle is an angle whose measure is $90°$.

15. Combine these two statements to form a true conditional.

$1 + 6 = 8; 4 + 5 = 9$

(14-9)   **16.** Prove: $3(6a) = 18a$

ANSWERS: CHAPTER TESTS

Chapter 1   1. $89t$ cents   2. $(1286 - r)$ dollars   3. $\frac{p}{15}$ dollars   4. 3   5. 3   6. 12   7. 30   8. 17   9. $B = 8$; $B = 16$; $B = 24$ 10. $B = 3\frac{1}{3}$; $B = 4$; $B = 4\frac{2}{3}$ 11. 27   12. $\frac{9}{16}$ 13. $0.017   14. 39 square meters   15. $\{3\}$ 16. $\{4\}$ 17. T   18. T   19. 2.50   20. -100 21. Ir   22. Q   23. Ir   24. Commutative postulate for multiplication   25. Associative postulate for addition

Chapter 2   1. q 2. $<$ 3. 1   4. 28   5. $x = -7$ 6. -5 7. $-9\frac{3}{5}$ 8. 10.1   9. $125 + 40 - 62.80 - 13.98$; $88.22   10. -4 11. -13.6 12. $4°$ 13. 18   14. $18t - 18$ 15. $9a + ab - 4b$ 16. $5x$ square units   17. -10 18. -72 19. -4 20. $1\frac{1}{3}$ 21. -4 22. 32   23. 125   24. 8   25. -5

Chapter 3   1. $n = 30$ 2. $y = -38$ 3. $x = -12$ 4. $x = -6$ 5. $y = 24$ 6. $x = 66\frac{2}{3}$ 7. $x = -5$ 8. $x = 4$ 9. $x = 7$ 10. $a = 44$ 11. $385   12. $5500   13. $b = 5$ 14. $a = 2$ 15. $y = 6$ 16. $30°$; $60°$ 17. $8.28   18. 20%   19. 4; 5   20. 15; 17; 19

Chapter 4   1. $6b$ 2. $t + \frac{3}{4}$ 3. $b - 18$ 4. $\frac{8}{y}$ 5. $\frac{2500}{d}$ dollars   6. 39,000   7. 38; 85   8. $427   9. Length: 20 cm, width: 11 cm   10. $b = 3$ 11. $x = 9$ 12. $r = 7$ 13. Tony: 15 years old; brother: 3 years old   20. 16

14. $y > 5$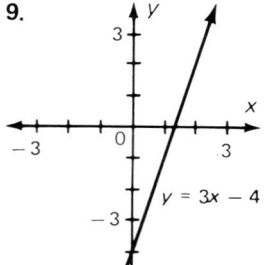

15. $x < 1.8$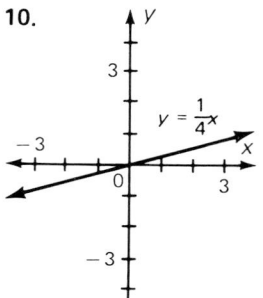

16. $y < -1$

17. $t > 16$

18. $a > 4$

19. $t > -3$

Chapter 5   1. $x = c + d - b$ 2. $x = \frac{b + 3c}{4}$ 3. 6 hours after the passenger train leaves or 8 hours after the freight train leaves.   4. Quadrant II   5. Quadrant II   6. Domain: $\{1, 2, 3\}$; range: $\{6, 12, 18, 24\}$ 7. Yes   8. Yes   9-11. See the graphs below.   12. C: $90; $125; $160   13. See the graph below.   14. $265   15. -13 16. Slope: -3; y intercept: 6   17. Slope: $\frac{2}{3}$; y intercept: 5   18. $\frac{32}{5}$ or $6\frac{2}{5}$ 19. $1\frac{1}{2}$ 20. 460

9.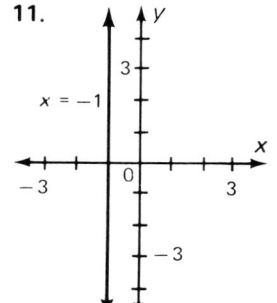

10.

11.

13.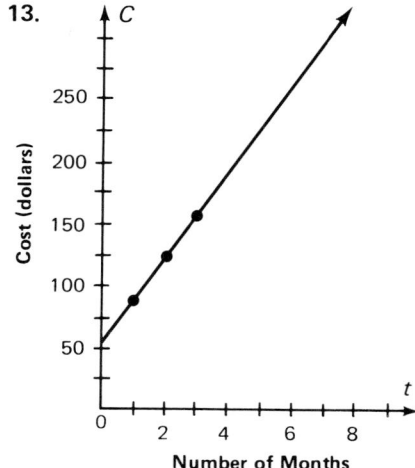

Chapter 6   1. (4, 1); see the graph below.   2. (2, 2); see the graph below.   3. Infinitely many   4. One   5. None
6. (7, 5)   7. (−3, 4)   8. (2, 3)   9. (5, 15)   10. $(7, -\frac{1}{2})$ 11. $\begin{cases} x + y = 28 \\ 5x = 3y + 4 \end{cases}$; smaller number: 26; larger number: 42

12. $\begin{cases} t = 3u \\ t - u = 6 \end{cases}$; 93   13. $\begin{cases} t + u = 11 \\ 10t + u + 27 = 10u + t \end{cases}$; 47;   14. $\begin{cases} x + y = 500 \\ 4.20x + 1.80y = 1260 \end{cases}$; adult tickets: 150; student

tickets: 350   15. $\begin{cases} x + y = 30 \\ 2.55x + 3.75y = 30(3.25) \end{cases}$; Brand A: 12.5 kilograms; Brand B: 17.5 kg

1.
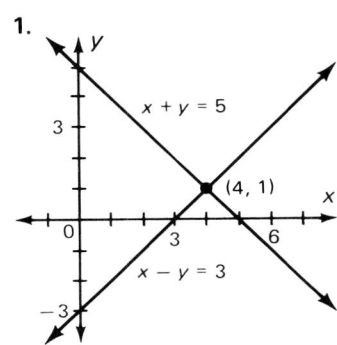

2.
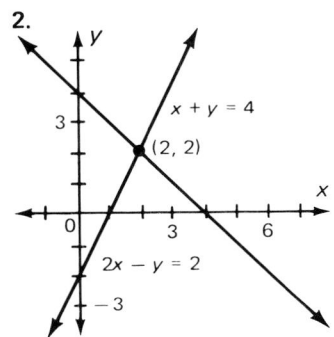

Chapter 7   1. $8x > 10$ or $8x = 10$ 2. $12 < 4x$ and $4x < 8$ 3. $x < 3$ or $x = 3$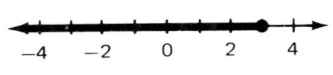
4. $-10 < y < 3$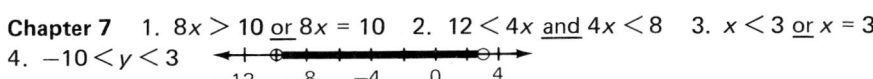

5.
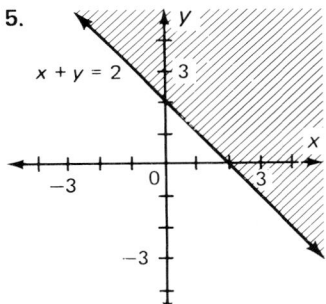

6.
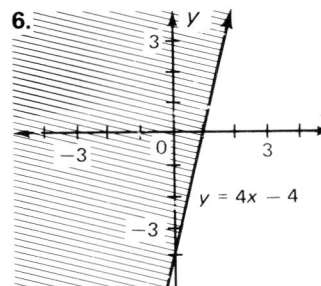

7.
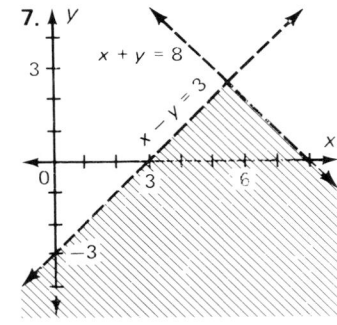

8. $15x + 20y$ 9. $\begin{cases} x \geq 0 \\ y \geq 0 \\ x + y \leq 200 \\ x \geq 50 \\ y \geq 100 \end{cases}$

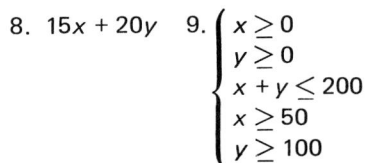

10.
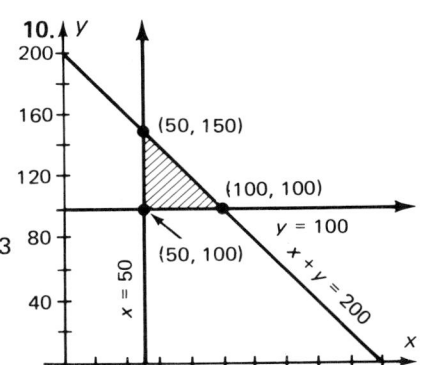

15.
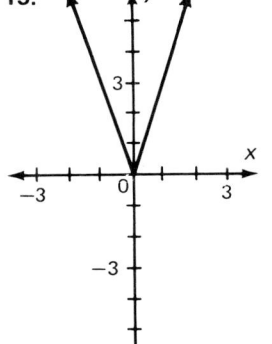

11. (50, 100); (50, 150); (100, 100)
12. $3750   13. $y = -2$ or $y = 2$ 14. $m = -6\frac{1}{5}$ or $m = 3$

Chapter 8 1. -125 2. 45 3. 10^7 4. $-30r^6t^5$ 5. y^{15} 6. $27a^9b^6$ 7. $8x^2y^3z$ 8. $-4ab^2c$ 9. $\dfrac{1}{a^3}$ 10. $\dfrac{16}{9}$

11. 4.38×10^8 12. 8.7×10^{-4} 13. $9x^2 - 5xy + 2y^2$ 14. $2b - 2c$ 15. $-5b - 7c$ 16. $-2x + 4y + 9$
17. $18a^4 + 24a^3 - 48a^2$ 18. $12x^2 + 13xy - 4y^2$ 19. $x^2 - 11x + 28$ 20. $3r^2 - r - 2$ 21. $24y^2 + 37y - 5$
22. $a^4 + a^2 - 12$ 23. $t^2 + \frac{1}{4}t + \frac{1}{64}$ 24. $36a^2 - 3ab + 9b^2$ 25. $25a^2 - 64$

Chapter 9 1. $2^3 \cdot 7$ 2. $3 \cdot 37$ 3. $12\,(a + b)$ 4. $xy(x^2y + y^2 + x^2)$ 5. $(t + 5)(t - 5)$ 6. $(8q + 1)(8q - 1)$
7. $(a + 4)^2$ 8. $(1 - 6x)^2$ 9. $(r + 5)(r + 4)$ 10. $(x + 6y)(x + 4y)$ 11. Prime 12. $(t - 9)(t - 6)$
13. $(5b + 3)(b + 1)$ 14. $(2x - 1)(x + 7)$ 15. $(2p - 3)(p - 5)$ 16. $(2y - 3)(y + 4)$ 17. $3(x + 6)(x - 2)$
18. $8(x + y)(x - y)$ 19. $2(t - 10)(t + 4)$ 20. $(s + 1)\,[s(s - 4) + 9]$ or $(s + 1)(s^2 - 4s + 9)$ 21. $x = -7$ or $x = 7$
22. $t = 0$ or $t = 9$ 23. $q = -5$ or $q = 3$ 24. -22 and 20 or 20 and 22 25. length: 11 meters; width: 8 meters

Chapter 10 1. $x = 3$ 2. $r = -41$ 3. 6 4. $\$1500$ 5. 50%: 25 liters; 10%: 75 liters 6. $\frac{1}{5}$ 7. $\dfrac{x}{x + 2}$

8. $\dfrac{r - 2}{r - 3}$ 9. $\dfrac{ax}{3}$ 10. $\dfrac{r + 3}{2}$ 11. $\dfrac{p - 4}{-3(p - 7)}$ 12. $\dfrac{y}{x}$ 13. $(c - d)(x - y)$ 14. $-\dfrac{1}{q - 4}$ 15. $\dfrac{6x + 12}{x - 2}$ 16. $\dfrac{2x + 3}{x + 5}$

17. $\dfrac{y^2 - 5y + 12}{y^2 - 16}$ 18. $\dfrac{6a - 15}{a - 2}$ 19. $\dfrac{b^2 - 2}{b + 1}$ 20. $a^2 + 5a - 3$

Chapter 11 1. $x = 1\frac{4}{5}$ 2. $x = 15$ 3. $x = \frac{2}{5}$ 4. $y = -6x + 15$ 5. $y = \frac{4}{3}x - \frac{28}{3}$ 6. $y = x + 1$ 7. $y = 3x + 9$
8. 8 9. Ruth: 55 km/h; Karl: 45 km/h 10. 12 minutes 11. $xy = 96$ 12. $\frac{3}{16}$ 13. 24 14. $23\frac{1}{4}$
15. 72 square inches

Chapter 12 1. ± 9 2. $5|d^3|$ 3. $-11x^4y^2\,|z|$ 4. $\frac{13}{33}$ 5. $4\sqrt{3}$ 6. $16b\sqrt{21b}$ 7. $5a^2b^3\sqrt{3ab}$ 8. 26 9. 20 feet
10. $\sqrt{185}$ 11. $2\sqrt{30}$ 12. $-64\sqrt{3}$ 13. $ab^2\sqrt{ac}$ 14. $\frac{1}{2}\sqrt{3}$ 15. 3 16. $2x$ 17. $\sqrt{6}$ 18. $13\sqrt{5}$ 19. $-50\sqrt{2}$
20. $2\sqrt{15} - 5\sqrt{2}$ 21. 59 22. $y = 9$ 23. 7 24. $-\frac{1}{4}$ 25. 9

Chapter 13 1. $t = -10$ or $t = 10$ 2. $r = -3$ or $r = 1$ 3. $y = -6$ or $y = 10$ 4. $a = 1 - \sqrt{5}$ or $a = 1 + \sqrt{5}$
5. $x = -1\frac{2}{3}$ or $x = -1$ 6. $y = \dfrac{5 - \sqrt{85}}{2}$ or $y = \dfrac{5 + \sqrt{85}}{2}$ 7. -15 or 14 8. 28 9a. See the graph below. b. $-2, 2$
10a. See the graph below. b. 1 11a. See the graph below. b. $-2, 3$ 12. Two distinct real solutions 13. No real
solutions 14. One distinct real solution 15. Two distinct real solutions 16. $x = 2$ 17. $(2, -4)$ 18. $(2, -4)$;
minimum

9. a.
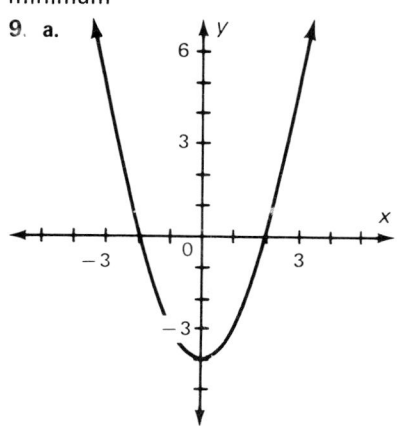

10. a.
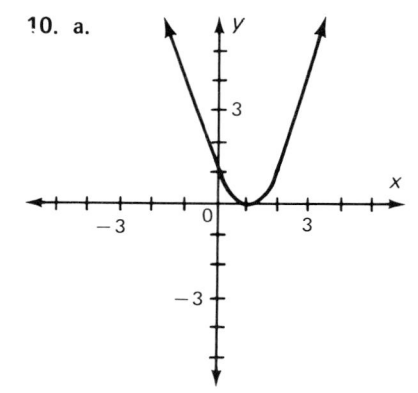

11. a.
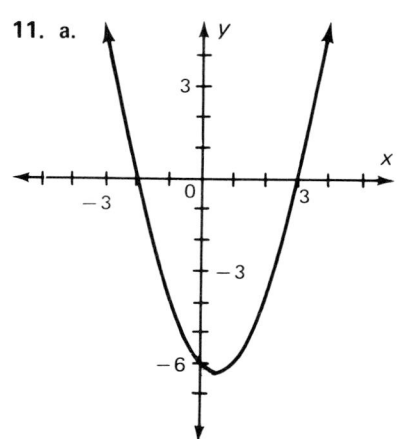

19.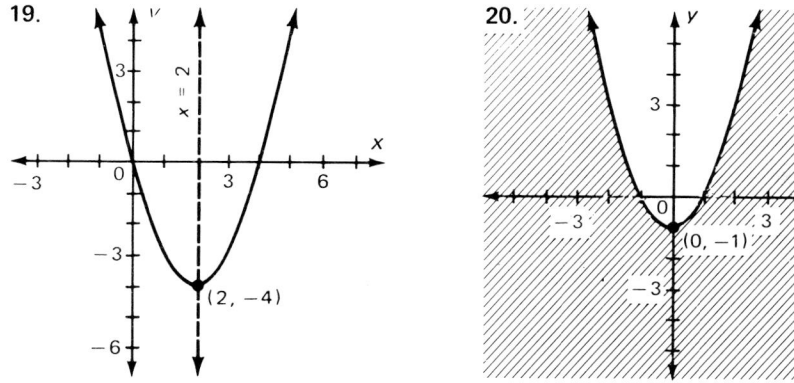

20.

Chapter 14   **1.** angle: $36°$; complement: $54°$; supplement: $144°$ **2.** A: $35°$; B: $55°$; C: $90°$ **3.** 12 meters   **4.** 6
5. $\frac{9}{41}$ **6.** $\frac{40}{41}$ **7.** $\frac{9}{40}$ **8.** $\frac{9}{41}$ **9.** $\frac{40}{41}$ **10.** $\frac{40}{9}$ or $4\frac{4}{9}$ **11.** About 36 meters   **12.** About 34 meters   **13.** 3   **14.** Conditional: If an angle is a right angle, then its measure is $90°$. Converse: If the measure of an angle is $90°$, then the angle is a right angle.   **15.** If $1 + 6 = 8$, then $4 + 5 = 9$ <u>or</u> if $1 + 6 = 8$, then $4 + 5 \neq 9$ <u>or</u> if $1 + 6 \neq 8$, then $4 + 5 = 9$.   **16.** Hypothesis: a is a real number. Conclusion: $3(6a) = 18a$. Proof: 1. a is a real number. (Given). 2. $3(6a) = (3 \cdot 6)a$ (Associative postulate for multiplication).   3. $(3 \cdot 6)a = 18a$ (Multiplication).   4. $3(6a) = 18a$ (Substitution).

REVIEW OF ESSENTIAL SKILLS

Survey Tests

1. Whole Numbers
   Operations — Rounding — Estimation
2. Decimals
   Operations — Rounding — Estimation
3. Fractions
   Operations — Rounding — Estimation
4. Per Cent
   Operations — Rounding — Estimation
5. Metric Measures
   Units of Length — Units of Mass — Units of Capacity

Practice

1. Whole Numbers
   Operations — Rounding — Estimation
2. Decimals
   Operations — Rounding — Estimation
3. Fractions
   Operations — Rounding — Estimation
4. Per Cent
   Operations — Rounding — Estimation
5. Metric Measures
   Units of Length — Units of Mass — Units of Capacity

The *Review of Essential Skills* is designed for those students in first-year algebra who have difficulties with the essential skills that are a prerequisite for first-year algebra: whole numbers, decimals, fractions, per cent, and metric measures. It consists of two parts: a survey test and a corresponding practice exercises. The five survey tests can be used to determine which students require additional practice. Answers for the *Review of Essential Skills* begin on page M-101.

SURVEY TEST 1: WHOLE NUMBERS

Add.

1.
$$\begin{array}{r} 8 \\ 7 \\ +9 \\ \hline \end{array}$$

2.
$$\begin{array}{r} 19 \\ 72 \\ +57 \\ \hline \end{array}$$

3.
$$\begin{array}{r} 3074 \\ 969 \\ +\ \ 83 \\ \hline \end{array}$$

4. $918 + 407 + 21 + 5829$

Subtract.

5.
$$\begin{array}{r} 56 \\ -\ 9 \\ \hline \end{array}$$

6.
$$\begin{array}{r} 80 \\ -62 \\ \hline \end{array}$$

7.
$$\begin{array}{r} 907 \\ -458 \\ \hline \end{array}$$

8. $573 - 88$

9. $9078 - 4739$

Multiply.

10.
$$\begin{array}{r} 57 \\ \times\ 8 \\ \hline \end{array}$$

11.
$$\begin{array}{r} 97 \\ \times 30 \\ \hline \end{array}$$

12.
$$\begin{array}{r} 709 \\ \times\ 39 \\ \hline \end{array}$$

13. 6095×87

14. 480×63

Divide.

15. $7\overline{)238}$

16. $34\overline{)238}$

17. $148 \div 7$

18. $2244 \div 9$

19. $19{,}530 \div 8$

20. $20\overline{)708}$

21. $24\overline{)11{,}045}$

22. $252\overline{)10{,}836}$

Rounding and Estimation

Round each number as indicated.

23. 14; nearest 10

24. 288; nearest hundred

25. 65; nearest 10

26. 7109; nearest thousand

Choose the letter of the response that gives the best estimate.
Choose a, b, or c.

27. $85 + 32 + 71$ a. $80 + 30 + 70$ b. $90 + 40 + 80$ c. $90 + 30 + 70$

28. $3997 - 1214$ a. $4000 - 1000$ b. $3000 - 2000$ c. $4000 - 2000$

29. 195×206 a. 100×300 b. 200×200 c. 200×300

30. $89 \div 31$ a. $80 \div 40$ b. $90 \div 45$ c. $90 \div 30$

SURVEY TEST 2: DECIMALS

Add.

1. $\begin{array}{r} 4.7 \\ +3.8 \\ \hline \end{array}$

2. $\begin{array}{r} 0.57 \\ 0.38 \\ +0.94 \\ \hline \end{array}$

3. $\begin{array}{r} 51.169 \\ 3.285 \\ +398.426 \\ \hline \end{array}$

4. $12.9 + 189.68 + 8.07$

Subtract.

5. $\begin{array}{r} 8.3 \\ -6.7 \\ \hline \end{array}$

6. $\begin{array}{r} 0.58 \\ -0.09 \\ \hline \end{array}$

7. $\begin{array}{r} 8.032 \\ -5.97 \\ \hline \end{array}$

8. $60.53 - 15.6$

9. $50 - 0.333$

Multiply.

10. $\begin{array}{r} 9.5 \\ \times\ 7 \\ \hline \end{array}$

11. $\begin{array}{r} 39 \\ \times\ 0.8 \\ \hline \end{array}$

12. $\begin{array}{r} 0.492 \\ \times\ 0.12 \\ \hline \end{array}$

13. 458.2×0.32

14. 0.0513×0.007

Divide.

15. $7\overline{)18.9}$

16. $0.06\overline{)0.5874}$

17. $128 \div 0.04$

18. $820.8 \div 0.9$

19. $0.08\overline{)680.6}$

20. $10\overline{)49}$

21. $76.7 \div 100$

22. $317.2 \div 1000$

Rounding and Estimation

Round each number as indicated.

23. 9.53; nearest whole number

24. 7.05; nearest tenth

25. 0.084; nearest hundredth

26. 1.8036; nearest thousandth

Choose the letter of the response that gives the best estimate.
*Choose **a, b,** or **c.***

27. $8.2 + 19.8 + 34.9$ **a.** $8 + 19 + 34$ **b.** $8 + 20 + 35$ **c.** $10 + 20 + 30$

28. $68.07 - 12.96$ **a.** $68 - 13$ **b.** $68 - 12$ **c.** $70 - 10$

29. 3.9×12.01 **a.** 3×12 **b.** 4×10 **c.** 4×12

30. $89.6 \div 3$ **a.** $90 \div 3$ **b.** $9 \div 3$ **c.** $87 \div 3$

SURVEY TEST 3:   FRACTIONS

Write each fraction in lowest terms.

1. $\frac{4}{10}$ **2.** $\frac{12}{16}$ **3.** $\frac{9}{21}$ **4.** $\frac{1200}{36{,}000}$

Write a mixed number in lowest terms for each of the following.

5. $\frac{11}{6}$ **6.** $\frac{19}{12}$ **7.** $\frac{36}{24}$ **8.** 15.8   **9.** 7.25

Write a decimal for each fraction.

10. $\frac{3}{5}$ **11.** $\frac{9}{10}$ **12.** $\frac{7}{8}$ **13.** $\frac{12}{5}$ **14.** $\frac{11}{50}$

Add or subtract as indicated.

15. $\begin{array}{r} \frac{3}{8} \\ + \frac{10}{16} \\ \hline \end{array}$ **16.** $\begin{array}{r} \frac{3}{5} \\ + \frac{4}{7} \\ \hline \end{array}$ **17.** $\begin{array}{r} \frac{11}{12} \\ - \frac{3}{8} \\ \hline \end{array}$ **18.** $\begin{array}{r} 5\frac{2}{5} \\ - 1\frac{4}{5} \\ \hline \end{array}$

19. $\frac{1}{6} + \frac{3}{4}$ **20.** $3\frac{3}{10} + 5\frac{5}{8}$ **21.** $4\frac{1}{3} - 2\frac{5}{9}$ **22.** $4 - 1\frac{7}{8}$

Multiply or divide as indicated.

23. $\frac{2}{7} \times \frac{3}{5}$ **24.** $\frac{4}{7} \times \frac{5}{12}$ **25.** $15 \times \frac{3}{4}$ **26.** $12 \times 2\frac{1}{5}$

27. $\frac{5}{12} \div \frac{7}{8}$ **28.** $4\frac{1}{2} \div \frac{3}{8}$ **29.** $5\frac{1}{4} \div 3$ **30.** $13 \div \frac{1}{4}$

Rounding and Estimation

Round each fraction to the nearest whole number.

31. $\frac{7}{8}$ **32.** $\frac{1}{12}$ **33.** $29\frac{2}{3}$ **34.** $5\frac{1}{4}$ **35.** $1\frac{1}{2}$

Choose the letter of the response that gives the best estimate.
Choose a, b, or c.

36. $12\frac{3}{4} + 8\frac{1}{6}$ **a.** $13 + 8$ **b.** $12 + 8$ **c.** $10 + 10$

37. $28\frac{11}{12} - 9\frac{4}{5}$ **a.** $30 - 10$ **b.** $29 - 10$ **c.** $29 - 9$

38. $15\frac{1}{8} \times \frac{19}{20}$ **a.** 16×1 **b.** 15×19 **c.** 15×1

39. $2\frac{5}{6} \div \frac{7}{8}$ **a.** $3 \div 1$ **b.** $2 \div 1$ **c.** $2 \div 2$

SURVEY TEST 4: PER CENT

Write a per cent for each decimal.

1. 0.64

2. 0.07

3. 0.40

4. 1.02

5. 0.005

Write a decimal for each per cent.

6. 42%

7. 3%

8. 10%

9. 125%

10. $3\frac{1}{2}$%

Write a per cent for each fraction.

11. $\frac{3}{5}$

12. $\frac{1}{4}$

13. $\frac{8}{10}$

14. $\frac{2}{3}$

15. $\frac{7}{8}$

Find each answer.

16. 24% of 780 = __?__

17. 3% of 38 = __?__

18. 162% of 70 = __?__

19. __?__ % of 35 = 14

20. __?__ % of 96 = 12

21. __?__ % of 72 = 27

22. 6% of __?__ = 3

23. 160% of __?__ = 50

24. $15\frac{1}{2}$% of __?__ = 465

Rounding and Estimation

Round each per cent as indicated.

25. 16.5%; nearest whole per cent

26. $66\frac{2}{3}$%; nearest whole per cent

27. $37\frac{1}{2}$%; nearest ten per cent

28. 52.4%; nearest ten per cent

Choose the letter of the response that gives the best estimate.
*Choose **a**, **b**, or **c**.*

29. 25% of $399

a. 0.20 × $400

b. 0.30 × $400

c. $\frac{1}{4}$ × $400

30. 12% of $1600

a. $\frac{1}{8}$ × $1600

b. $\frac{1}{10}$ × $1600

c. $\frac{1}{5}$ × $1600

31. $33\frac{1}{3}$% of 295.76

a. $\frac{1}{2}$ × 300

b. $\frac{3}{10}$ × 300

c. $\frac{1}{3}$ × 300

32. $18\frac{3}{4}$% of 10,000

a. $\frac{1}{10}$ × 10,000

b. $\frac{1}{5}$ × 10,000

c. $\frac{1}{8}$ × 10,000

33. 30% of 118.27

a. 0.30 × 120

b. 0.30 × 110

c. $\frac{1}{3}$ × 120

SURVEY TEST 5: METRIC MEASURES

For Exercises 1-4, choose the most suitable unit of measure.
Choose a, b, or c.

1. Length of a pencil   a. millimeter   b. meter   c. centimeter

2. Thickness of a dime   a. millimeter   b. centimeter   c. meter

3. Capacity of a teaspoon   a. milliliter   b. liter   c. kiloliter

4. Weight of an automobile   a. milligram   b. gram   c. kilogram

For Exercises 5-8, choose the most suitable measure.
Choose a, b, c, or d.

5. Thickness of 50 sheets of loose-leaf paper in millimeters
      a. 50 mm   b. 500 mm   c. 0.5 mm   d. 5 mm

6. Height of Niagara Falls in meters
      a. 58 m   b. 5.8 m   c. 580 m   d. 5800 m

7. Weight of a pro football player in kilograms
      a. 12.8 kg   b. 1280 kg   c. 128 kg   d. 1.28 kg

8. Capacity of a can of fruit juice in milliliters
      a. 3.54 mL   b. 354 mL   c. 35.4 mL   d. 3540 mL

For Exercises 9-12, choose the equivalent measure.
Choose a, b, c, or d.

9. 7.8 meters   a. 780 km   b. 0.0078 km   c. 78 mm   d. 78 cm

10. 1800 millimeters   a. 1.8 m   b. 0.018 km   c. 18,000 cm   d. 1.8 cm

11. 84.5 liters   a. 8.45 kL   b. 84,500 mL   c. 8450 mL   d. 84.5 kL

12. 1.6 kilograms   a. 160 g   b. 16 g   c. 1600 g   d. 16,000 g

13. The highway distance from Chicago to Pittsburgh is 728 kilometers. Write this distance in meters.

14. A water pitcher holds 1900 milliliters. Write this capacity in liters.

15. A box of cereal weighs 340 grams. What is this weight in kilograms?

PRACTICE 1: WHOLE NUMBERS

Add.

1.	8	2.	28	3.	927	4.	108	5.	1085	6.	4806
	7		14		348		567		247		7329
	+4		+63		+569		+924		+96		+6194

7. $24 + 5 + 19$ 8. $38 + 164 + 96$ 9. $309 + 75 + 54$ 10. $49 + 3096 + 287$

Subtract.

11.	86	12.	90	13.	432	14.	765	15.	408	16.	7283
	−9		−24		−9		−76		−129		−5647

17. $37 - 19$ 18. $324 - 76$ 19. $603 - 247$ 20. $6002 - 2865$

Multiply.

21.	47	22.	729	23.	508	24.	4276	25.	593	26.	6008
	✕ 8		✕ 6		✕ 7		✕ 9		✕ 72		✕ 47

27. 52×34 28. 46×87 29. 308×29 30. 690×56

31. $(75)(84)$ 32. $(476)(100)$ 33. $907 \cdot 58$ 34. 6007×19

Divide.

35. $6\overline{)168}$ 36. $8\overline{)1784}$ 37. $9\overline{)2736}$ 38. $28\overline{)532}$

Divide. Write each remainder as a fraction in lowest terms.

39. $384 \div 9$ 40. $2516 \div 7$ 41. $4078 \div 8$ 42. $24{,}046 \div 6$

43. $18\overline{)708}$ 44. $24\overline{)1382}$ 45. $72\overline{)10{,}314}$ 46. $208\overline{)113{,}828}$

Rounding

Rules: To round a whole number, look at the <u>digit</u> to the <u>right</u> of the place to which you are rounding.

1. If the digit is **less than 5**, round **down**.

2. If the digit is **5 or greater than 5**, round **up**.

Examples: **a.** **7** rounded to the nearest <u>ten</u> is **10.**

        b. **112** rounded to the nearest <u>hundred</u> is **100.**

        c. **6806** rounded to the nearest <u>thousand</u> is **7000.**

        d. **38,653** rounded to the nearest <u>ten</u> is **38,650.**

        e. **38,653** rounded to the nearest <u>hundred</u> is **38,700.**

        f. **38,653** rounded to the nearest <u>thousand</u> is **39,000.**

Round to the nearest ten.

47. 72   **48.** 89   **49.** 427   **50.** 893   **51.** 5445   **52.** 6358

Round to the nearest hundred.

53. 562   **54.** 448   **55.** 906   **56.** 8439   **57.** 6752   **58.** 998

Round to the nearest thousand.

59. 6208   **60.** 3647   **61.** 8529   **62.** 7500   **63.** 12,548   **64.** 68,492

Estimation

You can use rounding to estimate answers.

Choose the letter of the response that gives the best estimate.
*Choose **a, b,** or **c.***

65. $75 + 92 + 48$ **a.** $70 + 90 + 40$ **b.** $80 + 90 + 50$ **c.** $70 + 90 + 50$

66. $406 + 712 + 894$ **a.** $400 + 700 + 900$ **b.** $400 + 700 + 800$ **c.** $500 + 800 + 900$

67. $803 - 689$ **a.** $900 - 600$ **b.** $800 - 600$ **c.** $800 - 700$

68. $6508 - 4078$ **a.** $6500 - 4000$ **b.** $6000 - 4000$ **c.** $6500 - 4100$

69. 32×28 **a.** 35×30 **b.** 30×30 **c.** 35×25

70. 482×811 **a.** 500×800 **b.** 400×800 **c.** 500×900

71. $1887 \div 98$ **a.** $2000 \div 100$ **b.** $1500 \div 100$ **c.** $1900 \div 100$

72. $3556 \div 39$ **a.** $4000 \div 40$ **b.** $3600 \div 40$ **c.** $3000 \div 30$

PRACTICE 2: DECIMALS

Add.

1.	2.	3.	4.	5.	6.
3.6	7.8	0.25	6.76	65.08	5.08
+ 4.9	+ 4.7	0.56	8.68	29.76	267.94
		+ 0.84	+ 2.09	+ 35.92	+ 86.47

7. $0.374 + 0.968$ 8. $14.8 + 9.06 + 186.9$ 9. $15.76 + 208.49 + 9.06$

Subtract.

10.	11.	12.	13.	14.	15.
9.2	0.86	12.62	86.06	6.182	44.83
− 4.7	− 0.58	− 9.75	− 57.29	− 3.287	− 19.7

16. $8.03 − 5.9$ 17. $24.5 − 13.38$ 18. $0.3 − 0.186$ 19. $253 − 19.87$

Multiply.

20.	21.	22.	23.	24.	25.
6.2	87	5.9	46	623	6.37
✕ 7	✕ 0.6	✕ 12	✕ 0.28	✕ 4.7	✕ 5.3

26. 0.008×0.92 27. 42.8×100 28. 7.03×0.78 29. 0.089×40.6

Divide.

30. $8\overline{)194.4}$ 31. $9\overline{)63.576}$ 32. $24\overline{)114.72}$ 33. $0.07\overline{)0.5824}$

34. $112 \div 0.04$ 35. $319.2 \div 0.42$ 36. $0.4032 \div 8.4$ 37. $76.2 \div 0.12$

38. $38 \div 10$ 39. $709 \div 10$ 40. $43.6 \div 10$ 41. $6 \div 100$

42. $73 \div 100$ 43. $187.5 \div 100$ 44. $56 \div 1000$ 45. $28.72 \div 1000$

Rounding

Rules: To round a decimal, look at the <u>digit</u> to the <u>right</u> of the place to which you are rounding.

1. If the digit is **less than 5**, round **down**.
2. If the digit is **5 or greater than 5**, round **up**.

Examples: a. 8.**63** rounded to the nearest tenth is 8.**6**.

   b. 0.0**18** rounded to the nearest hundredth is 0.0**2**.

   c. **64**.8054 rounded to the nearest whole number is **65**.

   d. 64.**8**054 rounded to the nearest tenth is 64.**8**.

   e. 64.8**0**54 rounded to the nearest hundredth is 64.8**1**.

   f. 64.80**5**4 rounded to the nearest thousandth is 64.80**5**.

Round to the nearest whole number.

46. 86.5   **47.** 79.6   **48.** 426.47   **49.** 0.81   **50.** 35.09

Round to the nearest tenth.

51. 8.64   **52.** 4.08   **53.** 12.055   **54.** 0.987   **55.** 65.045

Round to the nearest hundredth.

56. 5.683   **57.** 14.649   **58.** 0.396   **59.** 19.445   **60.** 0.005

Round to the nearest thousandth.

61. 0.1261   **62.** 3.0587   **63.** 0.4064   **64.** 0.1999   **65.** 7.0096

Estimation

You can use rounding to estimate answers.

Choose the letter of the response that gives the best estimate.
Choose **a, b,** *or* **c.**

66. 8.75 + 9.10   **a.** 8 + 9   **b.** 9 + 9   **c.** 9 + 10

67. 6.71 + 2.15   **a.** 7 + 2   **b.** 6 + 2   **c.** 5 + 2

68. 0.93 − 0.56   **a.** 1 − 0.5   **b.** 1 − 0.6   **c.** 0.9 − 0.6

69. 68.07 − 13.98   **a.** 70 − 10   **b.** 70 − 20   **c.** 68 − 14

70. 473 × 0.64   **a.** 473 × 1   **b.** 500 × 0.6   **c.** 400 × 0.6

71. 87.3 ÷ 4.8   **a.** 90 ÷ 5   **b.** 80 ÷ 4   **c.** 87 ÷ 5

PRACTICE 3:   FRACTIONS

Write in lowest terms.

1. $\frac{8}{12}$ **2.** $\frac{15}{18}$ **3.** $\frac{9}{24}$ **4.** $\frac{8}{28}$ **5.** $\frac{14}{21}$

6. $\frac{12,000}{17,000}$ **7.** $\frac{1500}{21,000}$ **8.** $\frac{24,000}{3600}$ **9.** $\frac{12,000,000}{33,000}$ **10.** $\frac{192,000}{39,000,000}$

Write a mixed number for each of the following.
Write your answer in lowest terms.

11. $\frac{12}{7}$ **12.** $\frac{18}{13}$ **13.** $\frac{22}{5}$ **14.** 15.8   **15.** 2.125

Write as a decimal.

16. $\frac{5}{8}$ **17.** $\frac{7}{16}$ **18.** $\frac{11}{4}$ **19.** $\frac{23}{8}$ **20.** $\frac{85}{32}$

Add or subtract as indicated. Write your answer in lowest terms.

21. $\begin{array}{r} \frac{5}{6} \\ + \frac{7}{12} \\ \hline \end{array}$ **22.** $\begin{array}{r} \frac{13}{16} \\ + \frac{5}{8} \\ \hline \end{array}$ **23.** $\begin{array}{r} \frac{2}{5} \\ + \frac{3}{4} \\ \hline \end{array}$ **24.** $\begin{array}{r} 3\frac{1}{4} \\ - 1\frac{7}{8} \\ \hline \end{array}$ **25.** $\begin{array}{r} 5\frac{1}{6} \\ - 2\frac{3}{4} \\ \hline \end{array}$

26. $\frac{1}{8} + \frac{5}{12}$ **27.** $\frac{19}{24} - \frac{5}{8}$ **28.** $4\frac{5}{12} - 3\frac{13}{16}$ **29.** $6\frac{7}{8} + 3\frac{5}{6}$

Multiply or divide as indicated.

30. $\frac{1}{5} \times \frac{3}{4}$ **31.** $\frac{5}{6} \times \frac{3}{2}$ **32.** $\frac{5}{16} \div \frac{3}{4}$ **33.** $1\frac{5}{6} \div \frac{1}{3}$ **34.** $2\frac{1}{2} \times \frac{2}{3}$

35. $\frac{2}{5} \times 45$ **36.** $2\frac{3}{4} \times 16$ **37.** $2\frac{7}{8} \div \frac{1}{4}$ **38.** $3\frac{1}{6} \div 4\frac{5}{6}$ **39.** $6\frac{2}{3} \div 2$

40. $14 \div \frac{7}{8}$ **41.** $27 \div \frac{9}{16}$ **42.** $33 \div 1\frac{3}{8}$ **43.** $58 \div 3\frac{5}{8}$ **44.** $16 \div \frac{2}{3}$

Rounding

Rules: **1.** If a fraction is **less than** $\frac{1}{2}$, round **down** to the nearest whole number.

        2. If a fraction is **greater than or equal to** $\frac{1}{2}$, round **up** to the nearest whole number.

Examples: **a.** $\frac{4}{5}$ rounded to the nearest whole number is **1**.

b. $5\frac{1}{4}$ rounded to the nearest whole number is **5**.

c. $7\frac{9}{16}$ rounded to the nearest whole number is **8**.

d. $15\frac{1}{2}$ rounded to the nearest whole number is **16**.

e. $2\frac{1}{6}$ rounded to the nearest whole number is **2**.

Round to the nearest whole number.

45. $\frac{7}{8}$ **46.** $\frac{5}{6}$ **47.** $\frac{1}{9}$ **48.** $4\frac{5}{8}$ **49.** $7\frac{2}{5}$ **50.** $3\frac{3}{4}$

51. $2\frac{5}{12}$ **52.** $13\frac{7}{10}$ **53.** $6\frac{4}{5}$ **54.** $12\frac{15}{16}$ **55.** $19\frac{2}{3}$ **56.** $3\frac{9}{10}$

Estimation

Choose the letter of the response that gives the best estimate.
Choose a, b, or c.

57. $3\frac{1}{4} + 5\frac{3}{8} + 1\frac{15}{16}$ **a.** $3 + 5 + 1$ **b.** $3 + 6 + 2$ **c.** $3 + 5 + 2$

58. $50\frac{9}{16} + 49\frac{7}{8} + 89\frac{5}{6}$ **a.** $51 + 50 + 90$ **b.** $50 + 49 + 89$ **c.** $40 + 40 + 80$

59. $8\frac{7}{8} - 2\frac{1}{4}$ **a.** $8 - 2$ **b.** $8 - 3$ **c.** $9 - 2$

60. $114\frac{2}{3} - 79\frac{5}{6}$ **a.** $115 - 80$ **b.** $110 - 75$ **c.** $115 - 75$

61. $5\frac{1}{4} \times 2\frac{2}{3}$ **a.** 5×3 **b.** 5×4 **c.** 6×2

62. $7\frac{5}{8} \times 5\frac{1}{8}$ **a.** 8×5 **b.** 7×5 **c.** 7×10

63. $19\frac{7}{12} \div 5\frac{1}{8}$ **a.** $20 \div 5$ **b.** $19 \div 5$ **c.** $15 \div 5$

64. $192\frac{1}{8} \div 3\frac{5}{7}$ **a.** $190 \div 4$ **b.** $192 \div 4$ **c.** $192 \div 3$

65. $\frac{11}{12} \div \frac{19}{20}$ **a.** $2 \div 1$ **b.** $2 \div \frac{1}{2}$ **c.** $1 \div 1$

66. $89 \div 3\frac{1}{3}$ **a.** $89 \div 3$ **b.** $90 \div 3$ **c.** $100 \div 3$

PRACTICE 4: PER CENT

Write a per cent for each decimal.

1. 0.16　　**2.** 0.03　　**3.** 0.40　　**4.** 0.785　　**5.** 0.008　　**6.** 1.085

Write a decimal for each per cent.

7. 17%　　**8.** 9%　　**9.** 20%　　**10.** $12\frac{1}{2}$%　　**11.** $85\frac{3}{4}$%　　**12.** $9\frac{1}{4}$%

13. 125%　　**14.** 240%　　**15.** $\frac{1}{2}$%　　**16.** $\frac{1}{4}$%　　**17.** $3\frac{1}{8}$%　　**18.** $12\frac{2}{3}$%

Write a per cent for each fraction.

19. $\frac{3}{10}$　　**20.** $\frac{4}{5}$　　**21.** $\frac{3}{4}$　　**22.** $\frac{1}{3}$　　**23.** $\frac{1}{8}$　　**24.** $\frac{5}{6}$

Find each answer.

25. 12% of 650 = _?_　　**26.** 5% of 92 = _?_　　**27.** 8% of 98 = _?_

28. $33\frac{1}{3}$% of 96 = _?_　　**29.** 125% of 80 = _?_　　**30.** 0.4% of 16 = _?_

31. 1% of 350 = _?_　　**32.** $87\frac{1}{2}$% of 480 = _?_　　**33.** 4.2% of 800 = _?_

34. _?_ % of 40 = 16　　**35.** _?_ % of 96 = 24　　**36.** _?_ % of 20 = 17

37. ——% of 72 = 18　　**38.** _?_ % of 40 = 12　　**39.** _?_ % of 64 = 48

40. _?_ % of 18 = 27　　**41.** _?_ % of 144 = 60　　**42.** _?_ % of 90 = 72

43. 8% of _?_ = 2　　**44.** 12% of _?_ = 48　　**45.** 20% of _?_ = 7

46. 25% of _?_ = 60　　**47.** 45% of _?_ = 36　　**48.** 0.5% of _?_ = 2

49. 120% of _?_ = 57.6　　**50.** 16.5% of _?_ = 79.2　　**51.** $12\frac{1}{2}$% of _?_ = 9

52. _?_ % of 90 = 120　　**53.** $16\frac{2}{3}$% of 144 = _?_　　**54.** $83\frac{1}{3}$% of _?_ = 55

55. _?_ % of 288 = 16　　**56.** $33\frac{1}{3}$% of _?_ = 15　　**57.** $187\frac{1}{2}$% of 16 = _?_

Rounding

Rule: To round per cents, apply the rules for rounding whole numbers, decimals, and fractions.

Examples: **a.** 72.5% rounded to the nearest whole per cent is **73%**.

b. $33\frac{1}{3}$% rounded to the nearest whole number is **33%**.

c. 86.3% rounded to the nearest ten per cent is **90%**.

d. 4.62% rounded to the nearest tenth of a per cent is **4.6%**.

Round to the nearest whole per cent.

58. 15.6% **59.** 4.45% **60.** $23\frac{1}{2}$% **61.** $74\frac{3}{4}$% **62.** 0.62%

Round to the nearest ten per cent.

63. 48.3% **64.** 8.9% **65.** $17\frac{5}{8}$% **66.** $66\frac{2}{3}$% **67.** 326.4%

Round to the nearest tenth of a per cent.

68. 8.65% **69.** 14.73% **70.** 0.16% **71.** 0.345% **72.** 19.33%.

Estimation

Choose the letter of the response that gives the best estimate. Choose **a, b,** *or* **c.**

73. 20% of $897.60 **a.** $\frac{1}{4}$ × $900 **b.** $\frac{1}{4}$ × $800 **c.** $\frac{1}{5}$ × $900

74. $66\frac{2}{3}$% of $1785 **a.** $\frac{1}{6}$ × $1800 **b.** $\frac{2}{3}$ × $1800 **c.** $\frac{4}{5}$ × $1800

75. 59% of 2095 **a.** $\frac{1}{2}$ × 3000 **b.** $\frac{4}{5}$ × 2000 **c.** 0.60 × 2000

76. $12\frac{1}{2}$% of 512 **a.** $\frac{1}{12}$ × 512 **b.** $\frac{1}{10}$ × 512 **c.** $\frac{1}{8}$ × 512

77. 39% of 289 **a.** 0.40 × 290 **b.** 0.40 × 280 **c.** $\frac{1}{3}$ × 300

PRACTICE 5: METRIC SYSTEM

Units of Length

The **basic unit of length** in the metric system is the **meter**. The following table shows how other metric units of length are related to the meter.

Units of Length	Prefix	Meaning
1 millimeter (mm) = 0.001 meter (m)	milli-	$\frac{1}{1000}$, or 0.001
1 centimeter (cm) = 0.01 meter	centi-	$\frac{1}{100}$, or 0.01
1 decimeter (dm) = 0.1 meter	deci-	$\frac{1}{10}$, or 0.1
1 dekameter (dam) = 10 meters	deka-	10
1 hectometer (hm) = 100 meters	hecto-	100
1 kilometer (km) = 1000 meters	kilo-	1000

Examples:
1. To change to a smaller metric unit, multiply by 10, by 100, by 1000, and so on.

2. To change to a larger metric unit, divide by 10, by 100, by 1000, and so on.

   — Larger to Smaller —
   a. 75 km = 75 × 1000 = 75,000 m

   b. 255 mm = 255 ÷ 1000 = 0.255 m
   — Smaller to Larger —

   c. 165 cm = 165 ÷ 100 = 1.65 m

   d. 165 cm = 165 × 10 = 1650 mm

The actual sizes of the centimeter and the millimeter are shown on the metric ruler below.

The **millimeter** is suitable for measuring the thickness of a pad of writing paper.

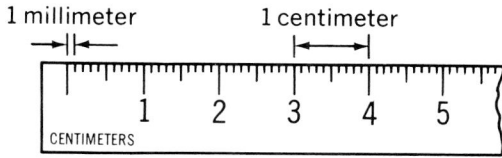

The **centimeter** is suitable for measuring the length and width of a sheet of paper.

The **meter** is suitable for measuring the height of a building.

The **kilometer** is suitable for measuring the distance between two cities.

EXERCISES

Complete the table. First check whether you multiply or divide. Then check the number by which you multiply or divide. The first one is done for you.

	From	To	Multiply	Divide	By 10	By 100	By 1000
1.	centimeters	meters		✔		✔	
2.	centimeters	millimeters					
3.	meters	kilometers					
4.	kilometers	meters					
5.	decimeters	millimeters					
6.	centimeters	dekameters					

Choose the equivalent measure. Choose a, b, c, or d.

7. The length of a race is 1500 meters. This is equivalent to
   a. 150 km b. 150,000 cm c. 0.15 km d. 15 cm

8. The bore of an automobile cylinder is 79.5 millimeters. This is equivalent to
   a. 795 cm b. 7.95 cm c. 0.795 m d. 0.00795 km

9. A calculator is 7.5 millimeters thick. This is equivalent to
   a. 75 cm b. 0.075 m c. 750 dm d. 0.75 cm

10. The width of some camera film is 3.5 centimeters. This is equivalent to
    a. 0.35 dm b. 3500 m c. 350 mm d. 0.035 dam

11. The length of scotch tape on a roll is 27.9 meters. This is equivalent to
    a. 279 dam b. 0.279 km c. 279 dm d. 2790 mm

12. The airline distance from New York to Paris is 5852 kilometers. This is equivalent to
    a. 585.2 km b. 5,852,000 m c. 5.852 m d. 58,520 dam

13. The thickness of a pad of paper is 1.4 centimeters.
    This is equivalent to
    a. 1.4 dm b. 0.0014 dam c. 0.14 dam d. 14 km

Units of Mass

The **basic unit of mass** (weight) in the metric system is the **gram** (g). The other most commonly used units are the **kilogram** (kg) and the **milligram** (mg).

A nickel weighs about 5 grams. Most aspirin tablets weigh 325 milligrams each. A 250-pound football lineman weighs about 113 kilograms.

The following table shows how other metric units of mass are related to the gram.

1 milligram (mg) = 0.001 gram	1 dekagram (dag) = 10 grams
1 centigram (cg) = 0.01 gram	1 hectogram (hg) = 100 grams
1 decigram (dg) = 0.1 gram	1 kilogram (kg) = 1000 grams
	1 metric ton (t) = 1000 kilograms

Choose the most suitable unit of measure.
Choose **a, b,** *or* **c.**

1. Contact lens   **a.** milligram   **b.** gram   **c.** kilogram

2. Airline luggage   **a.** milligram   **b.** gram   **c.** kilogram

3. One serving of cereal   **a.** milligram   **b.** gram   **c.** kilogram

4. Outboard motor for boat   **a.** milligram   **b.** gram   **c.** kilogram

Choose the equivalent measure. Choose **a, b, c,** *or* **d.**

5. 325 grams   **a.** 32.5 kg   **b.** 3250 kg   **c.** 0.325 kg   **d.** 3.25 kg

6. 14.3 kilograms   **a.** 143 g   **b.** 14,300 g   **c.** 1430 g   **d.** 1.43 g

7. 1850 milligrams   **a.** 185 g   **b.** 1.85 g   **c.** 18.5 g   **d.** 18,500 g

8. 25,000 kilograms   **a.** 2.5 t   **b.** 0.25 t   **c.** 2500 t   **d.** 25 t

Choose the most suitable measure. Choose **a, b, c,** *or* **d.**

9. Automobile   **a.** 100 kg   **b.** 2 t   **c.** 5000 g   **d.** 1,000 mg

10. Baseball   **a.** 142 g   **b.** 3500 mg   **c.** 1.2 kg   **d.** 500 g

11. Algebra book   **a.** 85 g   **b.** 8500 mg   **c.** 850 g   **d.** 8.5 kg

Units of Capacity

The **basic unit of capacity** in the metric system is the **liter** (L). The other most commonly used units are the **milliliter** (mL) and the **kiloliter** (kL).

A quart of milk is about 946 milliliters. A small glass of orange juice is about 125 milliliters. The fuel tank on a compact car holds about 50 liters. A family-size swimming pool holds about 75 kiloliters of water.

The following table shows how other metric units of capacity are related to the liter.

1 milliliter (mL) = 0.001 liter   1 dekaliter (daL) = 10 liters

1 centiliter (cL) = 0.01 liter   1 hectoliter (hL) = 100 liters

1 deciliter (dL) = 0.1 liter   1 kiloliter (kL) = 1000 liters

Choose the most suitable unit of measure. Choose **a, b**, *or* **c.**

1. A bottle of cough syrup   **a.** milliliter   **b.** liter   **c.** kiloliter

2. Capacity of a picnic jug   **a.** milliliter   **b.** liter   **c.** kiloliter

3. Container of fruit juice
   concentrate   **a.** milliliter   **b.** liter   **c.** kiloliter

4. Amount of water used by a
   large hotel in a year   **a.** milliliter   **b.** liter   **c.** kiloliter

Choose the equivalent measure. Choose **a, b, c**, *or* **d.**

5. 325 milliliters   a. 3.25 L   b. 32.5 L   c. 3250 L   d. 0.325 L

6. 45.6 liters   a. 4.56 mL   b. 45,600 mL   c. 4560 mL   d. 0.0456 mL

7. 8.25 kiloliters   a. 8250 L   b. 0.00825 L   c. 82.5 L   d. 825 L

8. 90.5 liters   a. 90,500 kL   b. 9.05 kL   c. 0.0905 kL   d. 9050 kL

Choose the most suitable measure. Choose **a, b, c**, *or* **d.**

9. Engine size of a car   a. 500 mL   b. 2.8 L   c. 1.9 kL   d. 14.5 L

10. Half-filled bathtub   a. 25 kL   b. 1000 mL   c. 750 L   d. 160 L

11. Cup of cocoa   a. 250 mL   b. 0.5 L   c. 30 mL   d. 800 mL

ANSWERS: REVIEW OF ESSENTIAL SKILLS

Page M-84   **Survey Test 1**

1. 24   2. 148   3. 4126   4. 7175   5. 47   6. 18   7. 449   8. 485   9. 4339   10. 456   11. 2910   12. 27,651
13. 530,265   14. 30,240   15. 34   16. 7   17. $21\frac{1}{7}$ 18. $249\frac{1}{3}$ 19. $2441\frac{1}{4}$ 20. $35\frac{2}{5}$ 21. $460\frac{5}{24}$ 22. 43
23. 10   24. 300   25. 70   26. 7000   27. c   28. a   29. b   30. c

Page M-85   **Survey Test 2**

1. 8.5   2. 1.89   3. 452.880   4. 210.65   5. 1.6   6. 0.49   7. 2.062   8. 44.93   9. 49.667   10. 66.5   11. 31.2
12. 0.05904   13. 146.624   14. 0.0003591   15. 2.7   16. 9.79   17. 3200   18. 912   19. 8507.5   20. 4.9
21. 0.767   22. 0.3172   23. 10   24. 7.1   25. 0.08   26. 1.804   27. b   28. a   29. c   30. a

Page M-86   **Survey Test 3**

1. $\frac{2}{5}$ 2. $\frac{3}{4}$ 3. $\frac{3}{7}$ 4. $\frac{1}{30}$ 5. $1\frac{5}{6}$ 6. $1\frac{7}{12}$ 7. $1\frac{1}{2}$ 8. $15\frac{4}{5}$ 9. $7\frac{1}{4}$ 10. 0.6   11. 0.9   12. 0.875   13. 2.4
14. 0.22   15. 1   16. $1\frac{6}{35}$ 17. $\frac{13}{24}$ 18. $3\frac{3}{5}$ 19. $\frac{11}{12}$ 20. $8\frac{37}{40}$ 21. $1\frac{7}{9}$ 22. $2\frac{1}{8}$ 23. $\frac{6}{35}$ 24. $\frac{5}{21}$ 25. $11\frac{1}{4}$
26. $26\frac{2}{5}$ 27. $\frac{10}{21}$ 28. 12   29. $1\frac{3}{4}$ 30. 52   31. 1   32. 0   33. 30   34. 5   35. 2   36. a   37. b   38. c
39. a

Page M-87   **Survey Test 4**

1. 64%   2. 7%   3. 40%   4. 102%   5. 0.5%   6. 0.42   7. 0.03   8. 0.10   9. 1.25   10. 0.035   11. 60%
12. 25%   13. 80%   14. $66\frac{2}{3}$%   15. $87\frac{1}{2}$%   16. 187.2   17. 1.14   18. 113.4   19. 40   20. 12.5   21. 37.5
22. 50   23. 31.25   24. 3000   25. 17%   26. 67%   27. 40%   28. 50%   29. c   30. a   31. c   32. b   33. a

Page M-88   **Survey Test 5**

1. c   2. a   3. a   4. c   5. d   6. a   7. c   8. b   9. b   10. a   11. b   12. c   13. 728,000 m   14. 1.9 L
15. 0.34 kg

Page M-89   **Practice 1**

1. 19   2. 105   3. 1844   4. 1599   5. 1428   6. 18,329   7. 48   8. 298   9. 438   10. 3432   11. 77   12. 66
13. 423   14. 689   15. 279   16. 1636   17. 18   18. 248   19. 356   20. 3137   21. 376   22. 4374   23. 3556
24. 38,484   25. 42,696   26. 282,376   27. 1768   28. 4002   29. 8932   30. 38,640   31. 6300   32. 47,600
33. 52,606   34. 114,133   35. 28   36. 223   37. 304   38. 19   39. $42\frac{2}{3}$ 40. $359\frac{3}{7}$ 41. $509\frac{3}{4}$ 42. $4007\frac{2}{3}$
43. $39\frac{1}{3}$ 44. $57\frac{7}{12}$ 45. $143\frac{1}{4}$ 46. $547\frac{1}{4}$ 47. 70   48. 90   49. 430   50. 890   51. 5450   52. 6360   53. 600
54. 400   55. 900   56. 8400   57. 6800   58. 1000   59. 6000   60. 4000   61. 9000   62. 8000   63. 13,000
64. 68,000   65. b   66. a   67. c   68. c   69. b   70. a   71. c   72. b

Page M-91   **Practice 2**

1. 8.5   2. 12.5   3. 1.65   4. 17.53   5. 130.76   6. 359.49   7. 1.342   8. 210.76   9. 233.31   10. 13.9
11. 0.28   12. 2.87   13. 28.77   14. 2.895   15. 25.13   16. 2.13   17. 11.12   18. 0.114   19. 233.13   20. 43.4
21. 52.2   22. 70.8   23. 12.88   24. 2928.1   25. 33.761   26. 0.00736   27. 4280   28. 5.4834   29. 3.6134
30. 24.3   31. 7.064   32. 4.78   33. 8.32   34. 2800   35. 760   36. 0.048   37. 635   38. 3.8   39. 70.9
40. 4.36   41. 0.06   42. 0.73   43. 1.875   44. 0.056   45. 0.02872   46. 87   47. 80   48. 426   49. 1   50. 35
51. 8.6   52. 4.1   53. 12.1   54. 1.0   55. 65.0   56. 5.68   57. 14.65   58. 0.40   59. 19.45   60. 0.01
61. 0.126   62. 3.059   63. 0.406   64. 0.200   65. 7.010   66. b   67. a   68. c   69. c   70. a   71. a

Page M-93   **Practice 3**

1. $\frac{2}{3}$ 2. $\frac{5}{6}$ 3. $\frac{3}{8}$ 4. $\frac{2}{7}$ 5. $\frac{2}{3}$ 6. $\frac{12}{17}$ 7. $\frac{1}{14}$ 8. $6\frac{2}{3}$ 9. $363\frac{7}{11}$ 10. $\frac{8}{1625}$ 11. $1\frac{5}{7}$ 12. $1\frac{5}{13}$ 13. $4\frac{2}{5}$
14. $15\frac{4}{5}$ 15. $2\frac{1}{8}$ 16. 0.625   17. 0.4375   18. 2.75   19. 2.875   20. 2.65625   21. $1\frac{5}{12}$ 22. $1\frac{7}{16}$ 23. $1\frac{3}{20}$
24. $1\frac{3}{8}$ 25. $2\frac{5}{12}$ 26. $\frac{13}{24}$ 27. $\frac{1}{6}$ 28. $\frac{29}{48}$ 29. $10\frac{17}{24}$ 30. $\frac{3}{20}$ 31. $1\frac{1}{4}$ 32. $\frac{5}{12}$ 33. $5\frac{1}{2}$ 34. $1\frac{2}{3}$ 35. 18
36. 44   37. $11\frac{1}{2}$ 38. $\frac{19}{29}$ 39. $3\frac{1}{3}$ 40. 16   41. 48   42. 24   43. 16   44. 24   45. 1   46. 1   47. 0   48. 5
49. 7   50. 4   51. 2   52. 14   53. 7   54. 13   55. 20   56. 4   57. c   58. a   59. c   60. a   61. a   62. a
63. a   64. b   65. c   66. b

Page M-95   **Practice 4**

1. 16%   2. 3%   3. 40%   4. 78.5%   5. 0.8%   6. 108.5%   7. 0.17   8. 0.09   9. 0.2   10. 0.125   11. 0.8575
12. 0.0925   13. 1.25   14. 2.4   15. 0.005   16. 0.0025   17. 0.03125   18. $0.12\overline{6}$ 19. 30%   20. 80%   21. 75%
22. $33\frac{1}{3}$%   23. $12\frac{1}{2}$%   24. $83\frac{1}{3}$%   25. 78   26. 4.6   27. 7.84   28. 32   29. 100   30. 0.064   31. 3.5   32. 420
33. 33.6   34. 40   35. 25   36. 85   37. 25   38. 30   39. 75   40. 150   41. $41\frac{2}{3}$ 42. 80   43. 25   44. 400
45. 35   46. 240   47. 80   48. 400   49. 48   50. 480   51. 72   52. $133\frac{1}{3}$ 53. 24   54. 66   55. $5\frac{5}{9}$ 56. 45
57. 30   58. 16%   59. 4%   60. 24%   61. 75%   62. 1%   63. 50%   64. 10%   65. 20%   66. 70%   67. 330%
68. 8.7%   69. 14.7%   70. 0.2%   71. 0.3%   72. 19.3%   73. c   74. b   75. c   76. c   77. a

Page M-97   **Practice 5**

1. Divide by 100.   2. Multiply by 10.   3. Divide by 1000.   4. Multiply by 1000.   5. Multiply by 100.
6. Divide by 1000.   7. b   8. b   9. d   10. a   11. c   12. b   13. b

Page M-99   **Units of Mass**

1. a   2. c   3. b   4. c   5. c   6. b   7. b   8. d   9. b   10. d   11. c

Page M-100   **Units of Capacity**

1. a   2. b   3. a   4. c   5. d   6. b   7. a   8. c   9. b   10. d   11. a

ADDITIONAL PRACTICE

PREPARING FOR COLLEGE ENTRANCE TESTS

Pages M-104 through M-119 contain two pages of additional practice for each of the eight *Preparing for College Entrance Tests* that appear in the textbook. Each is referenced to the related pages in the text. The answers for these exercises begin on page M-120.

Permission to reproduce pages M-104 through M-119 is granted to users of *HBJ Algebra 1*.

Choose the best answer. Circle **a, b, c,** *or* **d.**

1. $\dfrac{16(23 - 8) - 11(23 - 8)}{5} = \underline{\ ?\ }$

    a. 3   **b.** 4   **c.** 5   **d.** 15

2. $\dfrac{9(16 + 14) - 13(16 + 14)}{4} = \underline{\ ?\ }$

    a. −30   **b.** −20   **c.** −4   **d.** 30

3. $\dfrac{6(35 - 17) - (35 - 17)}{18} = \underline{\ ?\ }$

    a. 0   **b.** 5   **c.** 6   **d.** 18

4. $\dfrac{14(12 + 2) - 2(12 + 2)}{14} = \underline{\ ?\ }$

    a. −14   **b.** −1   **c.** 12   **d.** 14

5. $\dfrac{21(42 - 28) - 27(42 - 28)}{-6} = \underline{\ ?\ }$

    a. −14   **b.** 6   **c.** 14   **d.** 24

6. $\dfrac{3(16 - 9) + 4(16 - 9)}{14} = \underline{\ ?\ }$

    a. 7   **b.** $3\frac{1}{2}$ **c.** 1   **d.** $\frac{1}{2}$

7. $\dfrac{20(1.6 + 2.4) - 4(1.6 + 2.4)}{16} = \underline{\ ?\ }$

    a. 0.25   **b.** 4   **c.** 5   **d.** 16

8. $\dfrac{16(4.5 + 7.5) + 14(4.5 + 7.5)}{6} = \underline{\ ?\ }$

    a. 10   **b.** 12   **c.** 30   **d.** 60

9. $\dfrac{48\left(\frac{2}{3} - \frac{1}{3}\right) - 16\left(\frac{2}{3} - \frac{1}{3}\right)}{16} = \underline{\ ?\ }$

    a. $15\frac{2}{3}$ **b.** $\frac{2}{3}$ **c.** $\frac{1}{3}$ **d.** $-4\frac{2}{3}$

10. $\dfrac{40\left(\frac{5}{8} + \frac{3}{8}\right) - 8\left(\frac{5}{8} + \frac{3}{8}\right)}{16} = \underline{\ ?\ }$

    a. 2   **b.** 3   **c.** 8   **d.** 16

11. $6(22 - 8) + 5(22 - 8) - 10(22 - 8) = \underline{\ ?\ }$

    a. −14   **b.** 0   **c.** 14   **d.** 28

M-104

12. $-(62 + 38) + 18(62 + 38) - 17(62 + 38) = \underline{\ ?\ }$

 a. -100 **b.** -90 **c.** 0 **d.** 100

13. $2(6.4 - 2.4) - 5(6.4 - 2.4) + (6.4 - 2.4) = \underline{\ ?\ }$

 a. -8 **b.** -4 **c.** 4 **d.** 8

14. $-18(\frac{3}{4} - \frac{1}{4}) + 18(\frac{3}{4} - \frac{1}{4}) + \frac{3}{4} - \frac{1}{4} = \underline{\ ?\ }$

 a. 1 **b.** $\frac{1}{2}$ **c.** 0 **d.** $-\frac{1}{2}$

15. $6(3 - \frac{1}{2}) - 4(3 - \frac{1}{2}) - 3 + \frac{1}{2} = \underline{\ ?\ }$

 a. $3\frac{1}{2}$ **b.** $2\frac{1}{2}$ **c.** $-2\frac{1}{2}$ **d.** $-3\frac{1}{2}$

16. $\frac{1}{2}(59 - 35) - (59 - 35) + \frac{1}{2}(59 - 35) = \underline{\ ?\ }$

 a. -24 **b.** 0 **c.** 12 **d.** 24

17. $\dfrac{45 + 45 + 45 + 45 + 45}{5} = \underline{\ ?\ }$

 a. 5 **b.** 9 **c.** 45 **d.** 80

18. $\dfrac{56 + 56 + 56 + 56 + 56 + 56}{12} = \underline{\ ?\ }$

 a. 112 **b.** 56 **c.** 36 **d.** 28

19. $\dfrac{36 + 36 + 36 + 36}{12} = \underline{\ ?\ }$

 a. 12 **b.** 36 **c.** 45 **d.** 111

20. $\dfrac{\frac{2}{3} + \frac{2}{3} + \frac{2}{3} + \frac{2}{3} + \frac{2}{3} + \frac{2}{3}}{2} = \underline{\ ?\ }$

 a. 2 **b.** 3 **c.** 6 **d.** 8

21. $\dfrac{4.8 + 4.8 + 4.8}{48} = \underline{\ ?\ }$

 a. 3 **b.** 1.06 **c.** 0.96 **d.** 0.3

22. $\dfrac{0.1 + 0.1 + 0.1 + 0.1 + 0.1}{2.5} = \underline{\ ?\ }$

 a. 5 **b.** 0.2 **c.** 1.25 **d.** 2

23. $(66 - 49) - (76 - 49) = \underline{\ ?\ }$

 a. -10 **b.** -98 **c.** -108 **d.** -142

24. $(-12.3 - 6.4) - (-12.3 - 6.4) = \underline{\ ?\ }$

 a. -37.4 **b.** -24.6 **c.** -12.8 **d.** 0

M-105

PREPARING FOR COLLEGE ENTRANCE TESTS

Choose the best answer. Circle **a, b, c,** *or* **d.** (Page 160)

1. If $4x + 2 = 10$, what is the value of $2x + 1$?
   - **a.** 2
   - **b.** 4
   - **c.** 5
   - **d.** 10

2. If $6y + 6 = 24$, what is the value of $y + 1$?
   - **a.** $\frac{2}{3}$
   - **b.** 3
   - **c.** 4
   - **d.** 18

3. If $3n - 15 = -3$, what is the value of $n - 5$?
   - **a.** -3
   - **b.** -1
   - **c.** $-\frac{1}{3}$
   - **d.** 4

4. If $18 - 9b = 3$, what is the value of $2 - b$?
   - **a.** $\frac{1}{3}$
   - **b.** $1\frac{2}{3}$
   - **c.** 3
   - **d.** 27

5. If $4p + 6 = -8$, what is the value of $2p + 3$?
   - **a.** -16
   - **b.** -4
   - **c.** $-3\frac{1}{2}$
   - **d.** -2

6. If $8t - 12 = 2$, what is the value of $2t - 3$?
   - **a.** 8
   - **b.** $1\frac{3}{4}$
   - **c.** $\frac{1}{2}$
   - **d.** $-\frac{1}{2}$

7. If $2z + 18 = \frac{1}{2}$, what is the value of $z + 9$?
   - **a.** 9
   - **b.** $1\frac{2}{3}$
   - **c.** $\frac{1}{2}$
   - **d.** $\frac{1}{4}$

8. If $12x + 16 = 4$, what is the value of $3x + 4$?
   - **a.** -1
   - **b.** $\frac{1}{4}$
   - **c.** 1
   - **d.** 4

9. If $18n + 18 = 27$, what is the value of $n + 1$?
   - **a.** $\frac{1}{2}$
   - **b.** $\frac{2}{3}$
   - **c.** $1\frac{1}{2}$
   - **d.** 9

10. If $6q - 4 = 0$, what is the value of $3q - 2$?
    - **a.** -2
    - **b.** 0
    - **c.** 2
    - **d.** 4

11. If $\frac{1}{2}x + 1 = \frac{1}{4}$, what is the value of $x + 2$?
    - **a.** 8
    - **b.** $\frac{1}{2}$
    - **c.** $\frac{1}{8}$
    - **d.** $-1\frac{1}{2}$

12. If $s - \frac{1}{3} = -6$, what is the value of $3s - 1$?
    - **a.** -18
    - **b.** $-5\frac{2}{3}$
    - **c.** -2
    - **d.** $-\frac{1}{2}$

13. If $w - 1\frac{1}{2} = 12$, what is the value of $8w - 12$?

    a. -12 **b.** -96 **c.** 48 **d.** 96

14. If $t + 0.4 = -2$, what is the value of $5t + 2$?

    a. 10 **b.** -10 **c.** 2 **d.** 3

15. If $\frac{a}{6} = 4$, what is the value of $\frac{a}{4}$?

    a. $\frac{1}{6}$ **b.** $\frac{1}{4}$ **c.** 6 **d.** 24

16. If $\frac{3c}{9} = 8$, what is the value of $\frac{3c}{8}$?

    a. $\frac{1}{9}$ **b.** $\frac{1}{3}$ **c.** 3 **d.** 9

17. If $\frac{6m}{2} = 3$, what is the value of $2m$?

    a. 2 **b.** 1 **c.** $\frac{2}{3}$ **d.** $\frac{1}{2}$

18. If $\frac{8p}{12} = 10$, what is the value of $\frac{4}{5}p$?

    a. 3 **b.** 6 **c.** 12 **d.** 25

19. If $\frac{12r}{2} = 3$, what is the value of $4r$?

    a. 8 **b.** 4 **c.** 3 **d.** 2

20. If $\frac{9n}{3} = -6$, what is the value of $\frac{3}{2}n$?

    a. -3 **b.** -1 **c.** 1 **d.** 3

21. If $\frac{4x}{-14} = -10$, what is the value of $\frac{2}{5}x$?

    a. -14 **b.** -7 **c.** 7 **d.** 14

22. If $\frac{4p}{3} = 16$, what is the value of $\frac{1}{4}p$?

    a. 4 **b.** 3 **c.** 12 **d.** $5\frac{1}{3}$

23. If $\frac{9r}{-5} = 12$, what is the value of $\frac{3}{4}r$?

    a. -5 **b.** -9 **c.** $-2\frac{2}{5}$ **d.** 5

24. If $\frac{n}{6} = 0.1$, what is the value of $10n$?

    a. $\frac{1}{6}$ **b.** 0.6 **c.** 6 **d.** 60

Choose the best answer. Circle **a, b, c,** *or* **d.**

1. If $x > 0$, which of the following *must* be true?

a. $\dfrac{x}{2} < \dfrac{x}{3}$ b. $-2x < -3x$ c. $x - 2 < x - 3$ d. $2 - x < 3 - x$

2. If $y < 0$, which of the following *must* be true?

a. $y > \dfrac{y}{2}$ b. $y > 2y$ c. $y > \dfrac{2}{y}$ d. $y - 2 > 2 - y$

3. If $m > 0$ and $m \neq 1$, which of the following *must* be true?

a. $\dfrac{1}{m} > \dfrac{1}{m^2}$ b. $\dfrac{1}{m} > \dfrac{1}{m+1}$ c. $m^2 > m$ d. $\dfrac{1}{m^2} > \dfrac{1}{m^2 - 1}$

4. If $n < 0$, which of the following *must* be true?

a. $\dfrac{1}{n^2} > \dfrac{1}{n}$ b. $\dfrac{1}{n} > \dfrac{1}{n-1}$ c. $\dfrac{1}{n^2+1} > \dfrac{1}{n^2}$ d. $\dfrac{1}{n} > \dfrac{n+1}{n}$

5. If $a < 0$, which of the following *must* be true?

a. $a^3 > a^5$ b. $a^2 > a^3$ c. $a^4 > a^2$ d. $a^5 > a^4$

6. If $t > 0$ and $t \neq 3$, which of the following *must* be true?

a. $\dfrac{3}{t} > \dfrac{3}{t-3}$ b. $\dfrac{3}{t+3} > \dfrac{3}{t}$ c. $\dfrac{t+3}{3} > \dfrac{t}{3}$ d. $\dfrac{t-3}{3} > \dfrac{t}{4}$

7. If $x > 3$, which of the following *must* be true?

a. $\dfrac{3+x}{3} < \dfrac{3x}{3}$ b. $\dfrac{3+x}{3} < \dfrac{3+x}{x}$ c. $\dfrac{3x}{x} < \dfrac{3+x}{3}$ d. $\dfrac{3x}{3} < \dfrac{3x}{x}$

8. If $p > 0$, which of the following *must* be true?

a. $\dfrac{2 + (p-2)}{2} < \dfrac{2 - (p+2)}{2}$ b. $\dfrac{2 + (p+2)}{2} < \dfrac{2 - (p-2)}{2}$

c. $\dfrac{2 - (p-2)}{2} < \dfrac{2 + (p-2)}{2}$ d. $\dfrac{2 - (p+2)}{2} < \dfrac{2 - (p-2)}{2}$

9. If $q < 0$, which of the following *must* be true?

a. $\dfrac{1-q}{2} > \dfrac{q+1}{2}$ b. $\dfrac{-q-1}{2} > \dfrac{q+1}{2}$

c. $\dfrac{q-1}{2} > \dfrac{-q-1}{2}$ d. $\dfrac{q-1}{2} > \dfrac{1-q}{2}$

10. If $w > 1$, which of the following *must* be true?

a. $\dfrac{w}{w-1} < \dfrac{w-1}{w}$

b. $\dfrac{1-w}{w} < \dfrac{w}{w-1}$

c. $\dfrac{w}{1-w} < \dfrac{1-w}{w}$

d. $\dfrac{w-1}{w} < \dfrac{1-w}{w}$

11. If $z > 2$, which of the following *must* be true?

a. $\dfrac{1}{2-z} > \dfrac{-1}{z-2}$

b. $\dfrac{1}{z-2} > \dfrac{1}{2-z}$

c. $\dfrac{1}{2-z} > \dfrac{-1}{2-z}$

d. $\dfrac{1}{z-2} > \dfrac{-1}{2-z}$

12. If $c < -2$, which of the following *must* be true?

a. $2 \cdot c \cdot c \cdot c > 2 \cdot 2 \cdot 2 \cdot c$

b. $2 \cdot 2 \cdot c \cdot c > c \cdot c \cdot c \cdot c$

c. $2 \cdot c \cdot c \cdot c > c \cdot c \cdot c \cdot c$

d. $2 \cdot 2 \cdot c \cdot c > 2 \cdot c \cdot c \cdot c$

13. If $d > 0$, which of the following *must* be true?

a. $d(d-1) > -d(d-1)$

b. $-d(d+1) > -d(d-1)$

c. $d(d+1) > d(d-1)$

d. $-d(d+1) > d(d-1)$

14. If $h < 0$, which of the following *must* be true?

a. $(h+1)(h+2) > 0$

b. $(h-1)(h-2) > 0$

c. $(h+1)(h-2) > 0$

d. $(h-1)(h+2) > 0$

15. If $k < 0$, which of the following *must* be true?

a. $|x+3| < |x| + 3$

b. $|3x| < 3|x|$

c. $|x-3| < |x| - 3$

d. $|3-x| < 3 - |x|$

16. If $p < 0$, which of the following *must* be true?

a. $p^2 < |p^2|$

b. $\dfrac{p}{p} < \left|\dfrac{p}{p}\right|$

c. $p + p < |p + p|$

d. $p - p < |p - p|$

17. If $y > 0$, which of the following *must* be true?

a. $\dfrac{-y}{y} = \left|\dfrac{-y}{y}\right|$

b. $y - (-y) = y - |-y|$

c. $y(-y) = y|-y|$

d. $y + (-y) = y - |-y|$

18. If $|a| = -a$ and $a \neq 0$, which of the following *must* be true?

a. $a > 0$

b. $\dfrac{a}{|a|} = 1$

c. $a + 2 < 0$

d. $a|a| = -a^2$

19. If $y^2 > 4$, which of the following *must* be true?

a. $y > 2$

b. $|y+2| > 2$

c. $|y| > 2$

d. $(y+2)^2 > 4$

20. If $|x| < 1$ and $x \neq 0$, which of the following *must* be true?

    a. $|x| < x^2$ **b.** $x^2 < 1$ **c.** $\dfrac{1}{x} < x$ **d.** $x < x^2$

21. If p is a positive integer, which of the following *must* be true?
(HINT: An even integer is divisible by 2.)

    a. $p + 2$ is an even integer.   **b.** $\dfrac{p}{2}$ is an even integer.

    c. $2p$ is an even integer.   **d.** $2p + 1$ is an even integer.

22. If p is a positive integer, which of the following *must* be true?
(HINT: An odd integer is not divisible by 2.)

    a. $p + 1$ is an odd integer.   **b.** $2p + 1$ is an odd integer.
    c. $3p$ is an odd integer.   **d.** $3p + 1$ is an odd integer.

23. If r is a positive integer, which of the following *must* be true?
    a. $r + 1$ is divisible by 3.   **b.** $r + 3$ is divisible by 3.
    c. $3r + 1$ is divisible by 3.   **d.** $3(r + 1)$ is divisible by 3.

24. If s is a positive integer, which of the following *must* be true?

    a. $\dfrac{s + 8}{2}$ is divisible by 4.   **b.** $\dfrac{8s}{4}$ is divisible by 4.

    c. $\dfrac{8(s + 1)}{2}$ is divisible by 4.   **d.** $2s + 4$ is divisible by 4.

25. If t is an odd integer, which of the following *must* be true?

    a. $\dfrac{t + 3}{2}$ is an odd integer.   **b.** $t + 2$ is an odd integer.

    c. $\dfrac{t - 2}{2}$ is an odd integer.   **d.** $2t - 2$ is an odd integer.

26. If v is an even integer, which of the following *must* be true?

    a. $2(v - 1)$ is an even integer.   **b.** $\dfrac{v - 6}{3}$ is an even integer.

    c. $\dfrac{2v + 3}{2}$ is an even integer.   **d.** $\dfrac{2(v + 1)}{2}$ is an even integer.

27. If $a > 0$ and $b < 0$, which of the following *must* be true?

    a. $ab > 0$ **b.** $a + b > 0$ **c.** $\dfrac{a}{b} > 0$ **d.** $a - b > 0$

28. If $x > 0$ and $y > 0$, which of the following *must* be true?

    a. $xy > x + y$ **b.** $xy > \dfrac{x}{y}$ **c.** $x + y > x - y$ **d.** $x + y > \dfrac{x}{y}$

29. If $m < 0$ and $n < 0$, which of the following *must* be true?

   a. $\dfrac{m}{n} > 0$ b. $m + n > m - n$ c. $mn > \dfrac{1}{mn}$ d. $m - n > mn$

30. If $p > 0$ and $p > q$, which of the following *must* be true?

   a. $q < 0$ b. $p - q > 0$ c. $q^2 < p^2$ d. $p + q > 0$

31. If $r < 0$ and $r < s$, which of the following *must* be true?

   a. $s - r > 0$ b. $rs > 0$ c. $r + s > 0$ d. $\dfrac{s}{r} > 0$

32. If $\dfrac{a}{b} < 0$, which of the following *must* be true?

   a. $a < 0$ b. $b < 0$ c. $ab < 0$ d. $a + b < 0$

33. If $c < d$ and $c + d < 0$, which of the following *must* be true?

   a. $d < 0$ b. $c < 0$ c. $d > 0$ d. $c > 0$

34. If $m > n$ and $mn > 0$, which of the following *must* be true?

   a. $m > 0$ b. $n < 0$ c. $m - n > 0$ d. $m + n < 0$

35. If $x^2 > y^2$, which of the following *must* be true?

   a. $x > y$ b. $|x| > |y|$ c. $y^2 > xy$ d. $xy > x^2$

36. If $|x + y| > 1$, which of the following *must* be true?

   a. $x + y > 1$ b. $|x| + y > 1$ c. $x + |y| > 1$ d. $|x| + |y| > 1$

37. If $|a| = |b|$, which of the following *must* be true?

   a. $a = b$ b. $a^2 = b^2$ c. $ab = a^2$ d. $a^3 = b^3$

38. If $|xy| > xy$, which of the following *must* be true?

   a. $x < 0$ b. $y < 0$ c. $xy < 0$ d. $x + y < 0$

39. If $|x + y| > x + y$, and $x > y$, which of the following *must* be true?

   a. $x < 0$ b. $|y| < |x|$ c. $xy < |xy|$ d. $y < 0$

40. If $x^2 < |x|$ and $y^2 < |y|$, which of the following *must* be true?

   a. $xy < 1$ b. $x + y < 1$ c. $x - y < 1$ d. $\dfrac{x}{y} < 1$

41. If $|s| < |t|$ and $s + t < 0$, which of the following *must* be true?

   a. $t > 0$ b. $t < 0$ c. $s > 0$ d. $s < 0$

42. If $|xy| < x$, which of the following *must* be true?

   a. $x > 0$ b. $y > 0$ c. $x > y$ d. $xy > 0$

Choose the best answer. Circle **a, b, c,** *or* **d.**

1. If $c + d = 10$ and $c - d = 4$, find $c^2 - d^2$.

    a. 9   **b.** 16   **c.** 40   **d.** 46

2. If $m - n = -3$ and $m + n = 13$, find $m^2 - n^2$.

    a. −160   **b.** −40   **c.** −39   **d.** −16

3. If $x + 3y = 10$ and $x - 3y = -2$, find $x^2 - 9y^2$.

    a. −308   **b.** −20   **c.** 88   **d.** 96

4. If $2a - b = 21$ and $2a + b = 27$, find $4a^2 - b^2$.

    a. −153   **b.** 135   **c.** 540   **d.** 567

5. If $p + q = 2\frac{1}{2}$ and $p - q = 1\frac{1}{2}$, find $p^2 - q^2$.

    a. $3\frac{3}{4}$ **b.** $3\frac{1}{2}$ **c.** $2\frac{1}{4}$ **d.** $1\frac{1}{2}$

6. If $s^2 - t^2 = 12$ and $s - t = 2$, find $s + t$.

    a. 6   **b.** 10   **c.** 12   **d.** 24

7. If $a^2 - b^2 = 9$ and $a + b = 4$, find $a - b$.

    a. 1   **b.** $2\frac{1}{4}$ **c.** 5   **d.** 36

8. If $x + y = 4$ and $x^2 - y^2 = 6$, find $x - y$.

    a. −2   **b.** $\frac{2}{3}$ **c.** $1\frac{1}{2}$ **d.** 24

9. If $9p^2 - 16q^2 = 5$ and $3p - 4q = 1$, find $3p + 4q$.

    a. $\frac{1}{5}$ **b.** 5   **c.** 8   **d.** 17

10. If $m^2 - n^2 = 0$ and $m - n = 2$, find $m + n$.

    a. 2   **b.** 1   **c.** $\frac{1}{2}$ **d.** 0

11. If $c + d = 3$ and $c^2 - d^2 = 9$, find $c - d$.

    a. 0   **b.** 3   **c.** 6   **d.** 27

12. If $3r + 2s = -8$ and $9r^2 - 4s^2 = -28$, find $3r - 2s$.

    a. $-3\frac{1}{2}$ **b.** −1   **c.** $-\frac{1}{2}$ **d.** $3\frac{1}{2}$

13. If $2c + 9d = -5$ and $2c - 9d = 15$, find $4c^2 - 81d^2$.

    a. -3 **b.** 75   **c.** 3   **d.** -75

14. If $(r + s)^2 = 9$ and $rs = -4$, find $r^2 + s^2$.

    a. 17   **b.** 5   **c.** 1   **d.** 13

15. If $p + q = -6$ and $pq = 8$, find $p^2 + q^2$.

    a. 14   **b.** -14 **c.** 2   **d.** 20

16. If $(a + b)^2 = 8$ and $ab = 4$, find $a^2 + b^2$.

    a. 0   **b.** 1   **c.** 2   **d.** 4

17. If $m + n = 7$ and $mn = 6$, find $m^2 + n^2$.

    a. -5 **b.** 1   **c.** 37   **d.** 43

18. If $(x - y)^2 = 25$ and $xy = 50$, find $x^2 + y^2$.

    a. $\frac{1}{2}$ **b.** 2   **c.** 75   **d.** 125

19. If $p - q = 6$ and $2pq = 144$, find $p^2 + q^2$.

    a. 180   **b.** 108   **c.** -108 **d.** -282

20. If $c - d = -2$ and $cd = 48$, find $c^2 + d^2$.

    a. -92 **b.** 52   **c.** 92   **d.** 100

21. If $ab = \frac{1}{3}$ and $a + b = 1\frac{1}{3}$, find $a^2 + b^2$.

    a. $\frac{2}{3}$ **b.** $1\frac{1}{3}$ **c.** $1\frac{1}{9}$ **d.** $2\frac{2}{3}$

22. If $mn = 12$ and $m^2 + n^2 = 40$, find $(m + n)^2$.

    a. 64   **b.** 52   **c.** 28   **d.** 16

23. If $c^2 + d^2 = 26$ and $cd = 5$, find $(c - d)^2$.

    a. 36   **b.** 31   **c.** 21   **d.** 16

24. If $x^2 + y^2 = 70$ and $(x + y)^2 = 36$, find xy.

    a. 17   **b.** -17 **c.** -34 **d.** -68

25. If $g^2 + h^2 = 82$ and $(g - h)^2 = 100$, find gh.

    a. 18   **b.** 9   **c.** 36   **d.** -9

26. If $(j + k)^2 = 0$ and $j^2 + 2jk = -25$, find k^2.

    a. 50   **b.** 25   **c.** -5 **d.** -50

Choose the best answer. Circle **a, b, c,** *or* **d.**

1. If a farmer plows a acres in d days, how many days will it take to plow b acres?

   a. $\dfrac{ab}{d}$ **b.** $\dfrac{bd}{a}$ **c.** $\dfrac{d}{ab}$ **d.** $\dfrac{a}{bd}$

2. If a machine produces p plastic plates in h hours, how many plates can it produce in k hours?

   a. $\dfrac{ph}{k}$ **b.** $\dfrac{kh}{p}$ **c.** $\dfrac{h}{pk}$ **d.** $\dfrac{pk}{h}$

3. A car travels x miles in y hours. At that rate, how many miles will the car travel in 10 hours?

   a. $10xy$ **b.** $\dfrac{10x}{y}$ **c.** $\dfrac{10y}{x}$ **d.** $\dfrac{xy}{10}$

4. If Louis earns d dollars in h hours, how many hours will it take him to earn \$500?

   a. $\dfrac{500d}{h}$ **b.** $\dfrac{500}{dh}$ **c.** $\dfrac{500h}{d}$ **d.** $\dfrac{dh}{500}$

5. If Tina addresses x envelopes in y hours, how many envelopes can she address in 8 hours?

   a. $\dfrac{8x}{y}$ **b.** $\dfrac{8y}{x}$ **c.** $\dfrac{8}{xy}$ **d.** $8xy$

6. If k kilograms of roast beef feed c customers, how many customers can be fed with $10k$ kilograms of roast beef?

   a. $10k$ **b.** $\dfrac{10k^2}{c}$ **c.** $\dfrac{c}{10}$ **d.** $10c$

7. If ℓ liters of paint cost d dollars, how many dollars must be paid for 5ℓ liters?

   a. $5d$ **b.** 5ℓ **c.** $\dfrac{5\ell^2}{d}$ **d.** $\dfrac{d}{5}$

8. A machine uses x liters of oil every d days. How many liters of oil will it use in $d + 7$ days?

   a. $\dfrac{xd}{d+7}$ **b.** $x + \dfrac{7}{d}$ **c.** $x(d+7)$ **d.** $x + \dfrac{7x}{d}$

9. Each bus can seat p passengers. How many passengers can be seated on n buses?

    a. $\dfrac{n}{p}$ **b.** pn **c.** $\dfrac{p}{n}$ **d.** $p + n$

10. A factory produces t tractors per week. How many weeks will it take to produce 500 tractors?

    a. $\dfrac{500}{t}$ **b.** $500 + t$ **c.** $\dfrac{t}{500}$ **d.** $500t$

11. A corporation's annual report is p pages long. How many pages are there in 2000 copies of the report?

    a. $2000 + p$ **b.** $\dfrac{p}{2000}$ **c.** $2000p$ **d.** $\dfrac{2000}{p}$

12. If a bus makes 12 round trips each day to the airport, how many round trips does it make in w weeks?

    a. $\dfrac{12}{7w}$ **b.** $84w$ **c.** $\dfrac{7w}{12}$ **d.** $12w$

13. A water treatment plant purifies g gallons of water per minute. How many hours are required for 120,000 gallons of water to be purified?

    a. $\dfrac{7{,}200{,}000}{g}$ **b.** $\dfrac{20{,}000}{g}$ **c.** $\dfrac{120{,}000}{g}$ **d.** $\dfrac{2000}{g}$

14. An airline makes s scheduled flights per week. At that rate, how many flights does the airline make in 2 years?

    a. $104s$ **b.** $52s$ **c.** $\dfrac{104}{s}$ **d.** $\dfrac{52}{s}$

15. For nonzero numbers a, b, and c, $8a = 4b$ and $2b = c$. Then $\dfrac{a}{c} = \underline{\ ?\ }$

    a. $\dfrac{1}{4}$ **b.** $\dfrac{1}{2}$ **c.** $\dfrac{1}{1}$ **d.** $\dfrac{4}{1}$

16. For nonzero numbers p, q, and r, $5p = 3q$ and $6q = 7r$. Then $\dfrac{p}{r} = \underline{\ ?\ }$

    a. $\dfrac{18}{35}$ **b.** $\dfrac{7}{10}$ **c.** $\dfrac{7}{5}$ **d.** $\dfrac{10}{7}$

17. For nonzero numbers r, s, and t, $18r = 12s$ and $4s = 7t$. Then $\dfrac{r}{t} = \underline{\ ?\ }$

    a. $\dfrac{8}{21}$ **b.** $\dfrac{7}{9}$ **c.** $\dfrac{6}{7}$ **d.** $\dfrac{7}{6}$

18. For nonzero numbers x, y, and z, $3x = 9y$ and $6y = 8z$. Then $\dfrac{x}{z} = \underline{\ ?\ }$

    a. $\dfrac{1}{8}$ **b.** $\dfrac{9}{4}$ **c.** $\dfrac{4}{1}$ **d.** $\dfrac{8}{1}$

Choose the best answer. Choose **a, b, c,** *or* **d.**

1. Which of the following numbers is in the solution set for $x^2 + 12x + 20 = 0$?

    a. -4 **b.** -2 **c.** 4 **d.** 5

2. Which of the following numbers is in the solution set for $3x^2 - 11x + 6 = 0$?

    a. -6 **b.** -2 **c.** 1 **d.** 3

3. Which of the following numbers is in the solution set for $4x^2 + 23x + 15 = 0$?

    a. -15 **b.** -5 **c.** 1 **d.** 3

4. Which of the following numbers is in the solution set for $3x^2 - 10x + 8 = 0$?

    a. -8 **b.** -4 **c.** 2 **d.** 4

5. Which of the following numbers is in the solution set for $x^2 + x - 12 = 0$?

    a. -4 **b.** -1 **c.** 12 **d.** 24

6. Which of the following numbers is in the solution set for $3x^2 + 8x - 3 = 0$?

    a. -3 **b.** $-\frac{1}{3}$ **c.** 1 **d.** 3

7. Which of the following numbers is in the solution set for $12x^2 - 11x + 2 = 0$?

    a. -2 **b.** $-\frac{1}{3}$ **c.** $\frac{1}{4}$ **d.** 2

8. Which of the following numbers is in the solution set for $24x^2 + 17x + 3 = 0$?

    a. -3 **b.** $-\frac{1}{3}$ **c.** $\frac{1}{8}$ **d.** 3

9. Which of the following numbers is in the solution set for $16x^2 - 18x - 9 = 0$?

    a. -9 **b.** -3 **c.** $\frac{1}{3}$ **d.** $\frac{3}{2}$

10. Which of the following numbers is in the solution set for $2x^2 - 3x - 2 = 0$?

    a. -2 **b.** -1 **c.** $\frac{1}{2}$ **d.** 2

11. Which of the following numbers is in the solution set for $4x^2 - 27x + 18 = 0$?

    a. -3 **b.** $-\frac{1}{2}$ **c.** $\frac{3}{4}$ **d.** 3

12. Which of the following numbers is in the solution set for $30x^2 - 7x - 2 = 0$?

    a. $-\frac{1}{6}$ **b.** $-\frac{1}{15}$ **c.** $\frac{2}{5}$ **d.** 2

13. If $\dfrac{3}{4 + \dfrac{x-2}{3}} = \dfrac{3}{4}$, what is the value of x?

    a. −2   **b.** 0   **c.** 2   **d.** 3

14. If $\dfrac{3 + \dfrac{x+1}{3}}{6} = \dfrac{1}{2}$, what is the value of x?

    a. −3   **b.** −1   **c.** 0   **d.** 2

15. If $\dfrac{3}{2 + \dfrac{x-1}{2}} = 1$, what is the value of x?

    a. 0   **b.** 1   **c.** 2   **d.** 3

16. If $\dfrac{6}{4 - \dfrac{6}{x}} = 2$, what is the value of x? (HINT: $\dfrac{6}{x}$ must equal 1.)

    a. −6   **b.** −2   **c.** 3   **d.** 6

17. If $\dfrac{1}{1 + \dfrac{2x+1}{3}} = \dfrac{1}{2}$, what is the value of x?

    a. 0   **b.** $\frac{1}{2}$ **c.** 1   **d.** 3

18. If $\dfrac{1}{1 - \dfrac{x+2}{2}} = \dfrac{1}{2}$, what is the value of x?

    a. −4   **b.** −2   **c.** 2   **d.** 4

19. If $\dfrac{2}{3} + \dfrac{x+1}{3} = 1$, what is the value of x? (HINT: $\dfrac{x+1}{3}$ must equal $1 - \dfrac{2}{3}$.)

    a. −1   **b.** 0   **c.** 1   **d.** 2

20. If $\dfrac{1}{2} + \dfrac{2}{x-2} = 1$, what is the value of x?

    a. 0   **b.** 3   **c.** 4   **d.** 6

21. If $\dfrac{2}{4 + \dfrac{x+1}{x}} = \dfrac{1}{2}$, what is the value of x?

    a. −2   **b.** −1   **c.** 1   **d.** 2

Choose the best answer. Circle **a, b, c,** *or* **d.**

1. If x is an integer, which of the following *must* be integers?

I. $3x$　　　　　II. $\dfrac{x}{3}$　　　　　III. $x - 3$

a. I only　　　**b.** III only　　　**c.** I and II only　　　**d.** I and III only

2. If $\sqrt{a}$ is an integer, which of the following *must* be integers?

I. $\sqrt{a + 9}$　　　　　II. $\sqrt{9a}$　　　　　III. $\sqrt[9]{a}$

a. II only　　　**b.** I and III only　　　**c.** II and III only　　　**d.** I, II, and III

3. If d is an integer, which of the following *must* be integers?

I. 2^d　　　　　II. $(2^d)^d$　　　　　III. $(d^2)^d$

a. I only　　　**b.** II only　　　**c.** I and III only　　　**d.** II and III only

4. If q is a negative integer, which of the following numbers *must* be negative?

I. 3^q　　　　　II. q^3　　　　　III. $\sqrt[3]{q}$

a. I only　　　**b.** II only　　　**c.** I and II only　　　**d.** II and III only

5. If $\sqrt{b}$ is a rational number, which of the following *must* be rational numbers?

I. $\frac{1}{4}\sqrt{b}$　　　　II. $\frac{1}{4} + \sqrt{b}$　　　　III. $\sqrt{\frac{1}{4}b}$

a. I and II only　　　**b.** I and III only　　　**c.** II and III only　　　**d.** I, II, and III

6. If $\sqrt{m}$ is an irrational number, which of the following *must* be irrational?

I. $3\sqrt{m}$　　　　　II. $\sqrt{3m}$　　　　　III. $\sqrt{\dfrac{m}{3}}$

a. I only　　　**b.** II only　　　**c.** III only　　　**d.** None of these

7. If $y > 0$, which of the following statements *must* be true?

I. $y > \sqrt{y}$　　　　　II. $y^2 > y$　　　　　III. $y^2 > \sqrt{y}$

a. I only　　　**b.** II only　　　**c.** III only　　　**d.** None of these

8. If $k \neq 0$, which of the following statements *must* be true?

I. $\sqrt{k - k} = 0$　　　　II. $\sqrt{\dfrac{k}{k}} = 1$　　　　III. $\sqrt{k^2} = k$

a. I only　　　**b.** I and II only　　　**c.** I and III only　　　**d.** II and III only

9. If r is a positive integer, which of the following statements *must* be true?

I. $2^r \cdot 2^r = (2^r)^r$　　　II. $r^2 \cdot r^2 = (r^2)^2$　　　III. $2^r + 2^r = 2^{r+1}$

a. II only　　　**b.** III only　　　**c.** I and II only　　　**d.** II and III only

10. If x, y, and z are negative integers, which of the following statements *must* be true?

I. $x(y + z) < 0$
II. $x + y + z < 0$
III. $x(y - z) < 0$

a. I only
b. II only
c. I and III only
d. II and III only

11. If a and b are positive integers, and $a < b$, which of the following statements *must* be true?

I. $a^a < b^b$
II. $a^b < b^b$
III. $a^b < b^a$

a. I only
b. II only
c. I and II only
d. I, II, and III

12. If c and d are negative integers, and $c < d$, which of the following statements *must* be true?

I. $c^c < d^d$
II. $c^d < d^d$
III. $c^d < d^c$

a. I only
b. II only
c. III only
d. None of these

13. If $z < 0$, which of the following decrease(s) as z decreases?

I. $3z$
II. $\dfrac{3}{z}$
III. $\dfrac{z}{3}$

a. I only
b. I and II only
c. I and III only
d. II and III only

14. If $w > 1$, which of the following decrease(s) as w increases?

I. $w^2 - w$
II. $w - w^2$
III. $w - \sqrt{w}$

a. II only
b. III only
c. I and II only
d. II and III only

15. If $y < -1$, which of the following increase(s) as y decreases?

I. $\dfrac{1}{1 - y}$
II. $\dfrac{1 - y}{y}$
III. $\dfrac{y}{1 - y}$

a. II only
b. I and II only
c. I and III only
d. II and III only

16. If $p > 0$, which of the following decrease(s) as p increases?

I. $\dfrac{1}{4} + p$
II. $\dfrac{1}{p} + 4$
III. $\dfrac{p}{4} + 1$

a. I only
b. II only
c. III only
d. None of these

17. Which of the following statements are true?

I. $\sqrt{1 + \frac{9}{16}} > \sqrt{1} + \sqrt{\frac{9}{16}}$
II. $\sqrt{1 + \frac{16}{9}} > \sqrt{1} + \sqrt{\frac{16}{9}}$

III. $\sqrt{1 + \frac{16}{9}} > \sqrt{1} + \sqrt{\frac{9}{16}}$

a. I only
b. II only
c. III only
d. None of these

Page M-104 1. d 2. a 3. b 4. c 5. c 6. b 7. b 8. d 9. b 10. a 11. c 12. c 13. a 14. b
15. b 16. b 17. c 18. d 19. a 20. a 21. d 22. b 23. a 24. d

Page M-106 1. c 2. c 3. b 4. a 5. b 6. c 7. d 8. c 9. c 10. b 11. b 12. a 13. d 14. b
15. c 16. d 17. a 18. c 19. d 20. a 21. d 22. b 23. a 24. c

Page M-108 1. d 2. b 3. b 4. a 5. b 6. c 7. a 8. d 9. a 10. c 11. b 12. d 13. c 14. b
15. a 16. c 17. d 18. d 19. c 20. b 21. c 22. b 23. d 24. c 25. b 26. a 27. d 28. c 29. a
30. b 31. a 32. c 33. b 34. c 35. b 36. d 37. b 38. c 39. d 40. a 41. b 42. a

Page M-112 1. c 2. c 3. b 4. d 5. a 6. a 7. b 8. c 9. b 10. d 11. b 12. d 13. d 14. a
15. d 16. a 17. c 18. d 19. a 20. d 21. c 22. a 23. d 24. b 25. d 26. b

Page M-114 1. b 2. d 3. b 4. c 5. a 6. d 7. a 8. d 9. b 10. a 11. c 12. b 13. d 14. a
15. a 16. b 17. d 18. c

Page M-116 1. b 2. d 3. b 4. c 5. a 6. a 7. c 8. b 9. d 10. d 11. c 12. a 13. c 14. b
15. d 16. d 17. c 18. a 19. b 20. d 21. b

Page M-118 1. d 2. c 3. b 4. d 5. d 6. a 7. d 8. b 9. d 10. b 11. c 12. d 13. c 14. a
15. a 16. b 17. d

ANSWERS TO TESTS: DUPLICATING MASTERS

The following appear in the *Tests: Duplicating Masters.*

1. Chapter Test

A parallel form of each chapter test that appears on pages M-64 through M-77 of the Teacher's Manual is included.

2. Cumulative Tests

Six cumulative tests are included. These cover Chapters 1–4, 5–7, 8–11, 1–7, 8–13, and 1–13.

3. Cumulative **Preparing for College Entrance Tests**

Two cumulative Preparing for College Entrance Tests are included. These cover Chapters 1–7 and 8–13.

4. Placement Test

This four-part test is designed to determine the student's readiness for first-year algebra. A complete description of the Placement Test is included in the *Tests: Duplicating Masters.*

The answers for these tests can be found on pages M-122 through M-126.

ANSWERS TO TESTS: DUPLICATING MASTERS

Chapter 1   1. $1.39g$ 2. $6.95t$ 3. $276.89 - c$ 4. 18   5. 4   6. 6   7. 9   8. 16   9. 6; 12; 18
10. $2\frac{1}{2}$; $3\frac{1}{2}$; $4\frac{1}{2}$ 11. 32   12. $\frac{8}{27}$ 13. \$2400   14. 180 m^3 15. $\{3\}$ 16. $\{5\}$ 17. F   18. T
19. -12.69 20. 10   21. Q   22. Q   23. Ir   24. Commutative postulate for addition   25. Distributive
postulate

Chapter 2   1. 7   2. $<$ 3. $<$ 4. 18   5. $a = 7$ 6. -5 7. $-10\frac{1}{2}$ 8. -0.5 9. a. $19 + (-6) + 2$
b. on the 15th floor   10. 2   11. -11.8 12. $36°$ 13. 8   14. $2t + 8$ 15. $6xy + 4y$ 16. $21a$ 17. -20
18. 60   19. -1 20. $1\frac{1}{2}$ 21. -3 22. 18   23. 325   24. $-\frac{8}{5}$ 25. 36

Chapter 3   1. $n = 10$ 2. $y = -3$ 3. $x = 16$ 4. $x = -7$ 5. $x = 60$ 6. $y = -15$ 7. $y = -2\frac{1}{2}$ 8. $x = 6$
9. $x = 10$ 10. $a = 12$ 11. \$71.10   12. 25   13. $b = 12$ 14. $d = 8$ 15. $y = 7$ 16. $30°$; $60°$; $90°$
17. 1800   18. 15%   19. 3; 4   20. -41; -40; -39

Chapter 4   1. $\frac{x}{6}$ 2. $3a$ 3. $s + \frac{4}{5}$ 4. $9 - x$ 5. $\frac{3200}{k}$ 6. \$205   7. smaller; 34; larger: 41   8. Joan: \$64;
Theresa: \$70   9. width: 6 cm; length: 30 cm   10. $b = \frac{2}{3}$ 11. $x = 20$ 12. $a = 5$ 13. Angela: 8 yr old;
brother: 2 yr old
14. {all real numbers greater than 0}

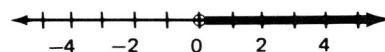

15. {all real numbers less than 4}

16. {all real numbers greater than -5}

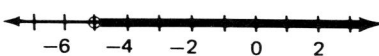

17. {all real numbers greater than -3}

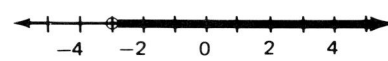

18. {all real numbers greater than 3}

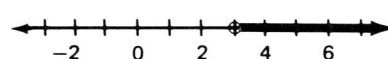

19. {all real numbers greater than -4}   20. 20

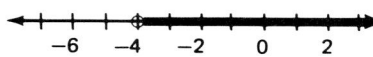

Chapter 5   1. $x = \dfrac{3c - b}{3}$, or $x = c - \dfrac{b}{3}$ 2. $w = \dfrac{P - 21}{2}$, or $w = \dfrac{P}{2} - l$ 3. 6 hr   4. Quadrant III   5. Quadrant IV   6. Domain: $\{1, 2, 3, 4\}$; Range: $\{25, 50, 75, 100\}$ 7. No   8. No   9.-10. See below for the graph.
11. \$6; \$12; \$18   12. See below for the graph.   13. \$9   14. \$19.50   15. $-\frac{1}{13}$ 16. Slope: $-\frac{2}{5}$; y intercept: 6
17. Slope: 4; y intercept: 3   18. $2\frac{1}{2}$ 19. 14   20. 195 m
9.-10.

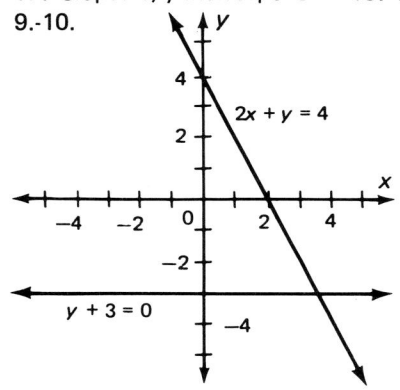

12.

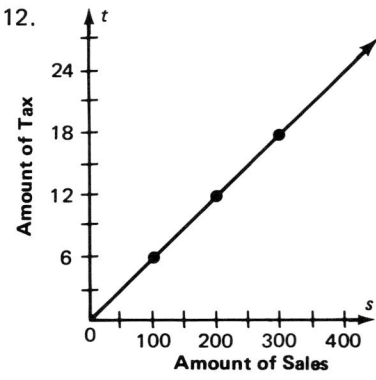

Chapter 6 1.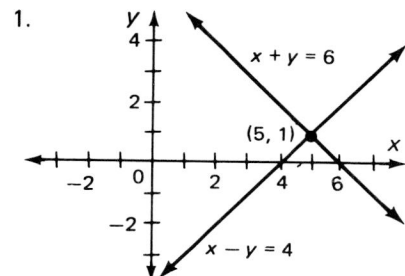

2.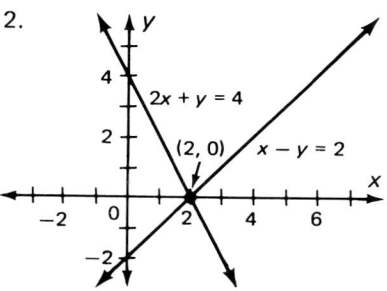

3. infinitely many 4. one 5. none 6. one 7. one 8. $\left\{\left(\frac{1}{3}, -4\right)\right\}$ 9. $\{(4, 8)\}$ 10. $\{(-1, 1)\}$

11. $\begin{cases} x + y = 58 \\ 3x = 2y - 1 \end{cases}$; smaller: 23; larger: 35 12. $\begin{cases} u = 2t \\ u - t = 3 \end{cases}$; 36 13. $\begin{cases} t + u = 13 \\ 10t + u + 45 = 10u + t \end{cases}$; 49

14. $\begin{cases} x + y = 39 \\ 0.15x + 0.20y = 6.95 \end{cases}$; 15¢ : 17; 20¢: 22

15. $\begin{cases} x + y = 20 \\ 5.50x + 6.50(20 - x) = 6.25(20) \end{cases}$; Brand A: 5 kg; Brand B: 15 kg

Chapter 7 1. $4x < 8$ or $4x = 8$ 2. $16 < 4t$ and $4t < 8$ 3. {all real numbers less than or equal to 4}; see below for the graph. 4. {all real numbers greater than −2 and less than 5}; see below for the graph. 5. See below for the graph. 6. See below for the graph. 7. See below for the graph.

8. $12x + 15y$

9. $\begin{cases} x \geq 0 \\ y \geq 0 \\ x + y \leq 300 \\ x \geq 75 \\ y \geq 100 \end{cases}$

10.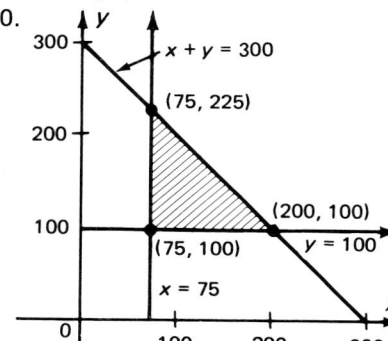

15.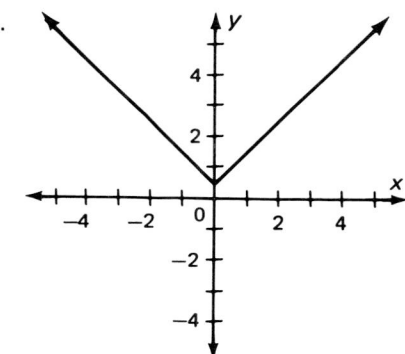

11. $(75, 100)$; $(75, 225)$; $(200, 100)$
12. $4275
13. $y = -3$ or $y = 3$
14. $q = -5\frac{2}{3}$ or $q = 3$

3.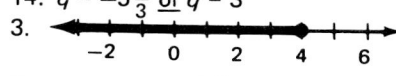

4.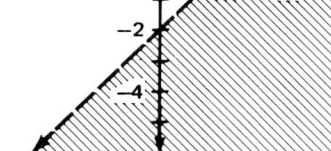

5.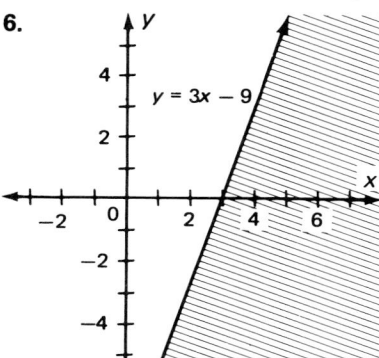

6.

7.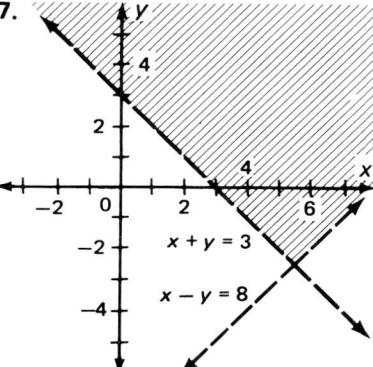

Chapter 8   1. 1500   2. −16,200   3. 10^8, or 100,000,000   4. $−24r^5t^4$ 5. x^6 6. $16p^{12}r^8$ 7. $8x^2y^3z$

8. $−2b$ 9. $\dfrac{1}{r}$ 10. $−2$ 11. 3.18×10^5 12. 4.2×10^{-5} 13. $6xy − 3x + 3y$ 14. $2a^2 − 3ab + 9b^2$

15. $5t − c$ 16. $7x − 3y − 13z$ 17. $30t^4 + 10t^3 − 20t^2$ 18. $6f^2 + 7fg − 3g^2$ 19. $p^2 − 20p + 99$

20. $12y^2 − 28y − 5$ 21. $14q^2 + 59q − 18$ 22. $s^4 − 2s^2 − 15$ 23. $x^2 − \dfrac{3}{2}x + \dfrac{9}{16}$ 24. $25e^2 − 40ef + 16f^2$

25. $16c^2 − 9$

Chapter 9   1. $2^5 \cdot 3$ 2. $2^4 \cdot 3 \cdot 5$ 3. $12(2x + y)$ 4. $ab(a + b + b^2)$ 5. $(y + 12)(y − 12)$ 6. $(3 + q)(3 − q)$

7. $(r + 9)(r + 9)$, or $(r + 9)^2$ 8. $(2 − 3x)(2 − 3x)$, or $(2 − 3x)^2$ 9. $(p + 6)(p + 2)$ 10. $(s − 4)(s + 3)$

11. $(z − 4)(z − 3)$ 12. $(r + 5t)(r + 3t)$ 13. $(6x + 1)(2x + 1)$ 14. $(3y − 5)(y − 2)$ 15. $(2a − 1)(a + 5)$

16. $(3t − 1)(t − 5)$ 17. $21(r + t)(r − t)$ 18. $2(y + 10)(y − 4)$ 19. $5(p − 9)(p + 2)$ 20. $(a + 5)(a^2 − 3a + 11)$

21. $t = −6$ <u>or</u> $t = 6$ 22. $r = 0$ <u>or</u> $r = 3$ 23. $g = −6$ <u>or</u> $g = 4$ 24. 12; 13   25. length: 11m; width: 9m

Chapter 10   1. $p = 6$ 2. $s = 13$ 3. $73\dfrac{1}{3}$ ft/sec   4. \$800 at each rate   5. 18 oz   6. 2   7. $\dfrac{1}{a + b}$ 8. $\dfrac{d + 5}{d + 1}$

9. $\dfrac{4}{c^2f}$ 10. $4t − 16$ 11. $\dfrac{3y − 18}{y − 2}$ 12. $\dfrac{b}{a}$ 13. $\dfrac{6}{p^2}$ 14. $\dfrac{−3}{2a^2 + 4a − 6}$ 15. $\dfrac{12a}{a − 1}$ 16. $\dfrac{−s + 6}{s + 1}$

17. $\dfrac{y^2 − 2y + 5}{(y + 2)(y − 2)}$ 18. $\dfrac{3y + x}{y}$ 19. $\dfrac{r^2 − 3}{r − 1}$ 20. $c^2 − 2c + 6$

Chapter 11   1. $x = −5$ 2. $x = 3$ 3. $r = −6$ 4. $y = −3x + 13$ 5. $y = \dfrac{3}{2}x − 7$ 6. $y = −x + 12$ 7. $y = x − 1$

8. 8   9. Susan: 50 km/hr; Erica: 45 km/hr   10. $1\dfrac{1}{5}$ hr   11. $rt = 60$ 12. $\dfrac{1}{5}$ 13. 36   14. $8\dfrac{1}{6}$ 15. 50 cm^3

Chapter 12   1. ± 8 2. $−3|c^5|$ 3. $9a^2|bc^3|$ 4. $\dfrac{23}{99}$ 5. $4\sqrt{10}$ 6. $12r^3\sqrt{2}$ 7. $12a^3b^4\sqrt{3a}$ 8. 20

9. $\sqrt{74}$ mi   10. $\sqrt{374}$ 11. $4\sqrt{3}$ 12. $48\sqrt{6}$ 13. $−ry^2\sqrt{r}$ 14. $\dfrac{20\sqrt{5}}{3}$ 15. 4   16. $2b\sqrt{3}$ 17. $\dfrac{4\sqrt{15}}{5}$

18. $6\sqrt{3}$ 19. $39\sqrt{2}$ 20. $5\sqrt{6} − 3\sqrt{2}$ 21. $−2$ 22. $x = 26$ 23. 12   24. $−\dfrac{1}{6}$ 25. 25

Chapter 13   1. $s = −13$ <u>or</u> $s = 13$ 2. $t = −3$ <u>or</u> $t = 5$ 3. $y = −8$ <u>or</u> $y = 10$ 4. $c = 1 − \sqrt{5}$ or $c = 1 + \sqrt{5}$

5. $x = \dfrac{−7 − \sqrt{33}}{4}$ <u>or</u> $x = \dfrac{−7 + \sqrt{33}}{4}$ 6. $t = \dfrac{−3 − \sqrt{13}}{3}$ <u>or</u> $t = \dfrac{−3 + \sqrt{13}}{3}$ 7. $x^2 = 10x − 21$; 3 or 7   8. 4 cm

9.a.
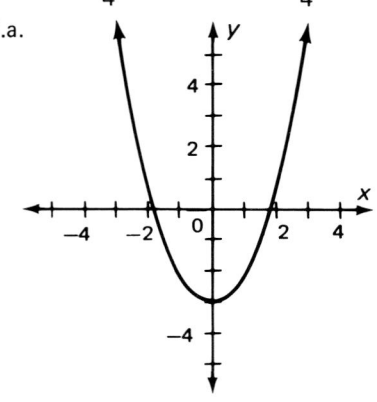

10.a.
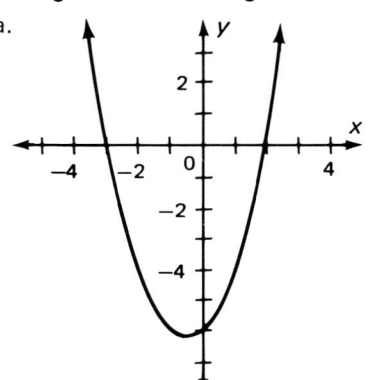

11.a.
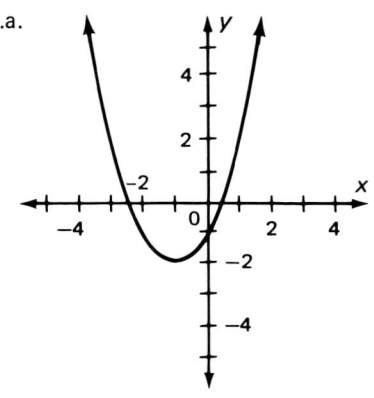

b. $\approx −1.7$ and ≈ 1.7 b. $−3$ and 2   b. $\approx −2.4$ and ≈ 0.4

12. Exactly one real solution.   13. No real solutions.   14. Two distinct, real solutions.   15. No real solutions.
16. $x = -1$ 17. $(-1, -1)$ 18. $(-1, -1)$; minimum

19.

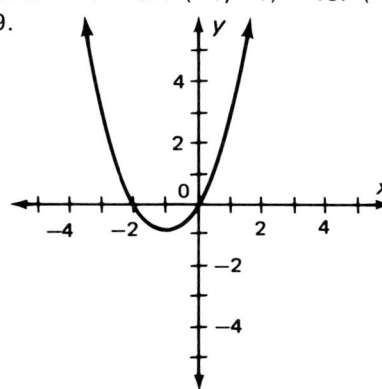

20.

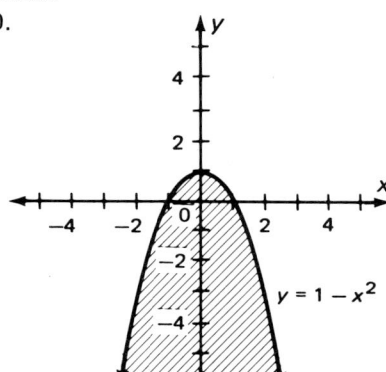

$y = 1 - x^2$

Chapter 14   1. angle: $40°$; complement: $50°$; supplement: $140°$ 2. $A: 76\frac{2}{3}°$; $B: 61\frac{2}{3}°$; $C: 41\frac{2}{3}°$ 3. $\sqrt{13}$ ft
4. $a = 4$ 5. $\frac{5}{13}$ 6. $\frac{12}{13}$ 7. $\frac{5}{12}$ 8. $\frac{12}{13}$ 9. $\frac{5}{13}$ 10. $\frac{12}{5}$, or $2\frac{2}{5}$ 11. ≈ 17 m   12. ≈ 87 m

13.

+	0	1	2
0	0	1	2
1	1	2	0
2	2	0	1

14. Conditional: If lines are parallel, then the lines have the same slope.
Converse: If lines have the same slope, then the lines are parallel.

15. If $\sqrt{3}$ is irrational, then 12 is an even number, <u>or</u>, if $\sqrt{3}$ is not irrational, then 12 is an even number, <u>or</u>, if $\sqrt{3}$ is not irrational, then 12 is not an even number.   16. Hypotheses: a and b are real numbers; conclusion: $8(a + b) + (-8b) = 8a$;
Proof: 1. a and b are real numbers. (Given) 2. $8(a + b) + (-8b) = 8 \cdot a + 8 \cdot b + (-8b)$ (Distributive postulate) 3. $8 \cdot a + 8 \cdot b + (-8b) = 8a + 8b + (-8b)$ (Multiplication)   4. $8a + 8b + (-8b) = 8a + [8b + (-8b)]$ (Associative for addition)
5. $8a + [8b + (-8b)] = 8a + 0$ (Additive inverse)   6. $8a + 0 = 8a$ (Identity for addition)   7. $8(a + b) + (-8b) = 8a$
(Substitution)

ANSWERS: CUMULATIVE TESTS

Chapters 1-4   1. c   2. b   3. a   4. b   5. d   6. d   7. a   8. c   9. d   10. b   11. b   12. b   13. b
14. c   15. a   16. c   17. b   18. d   19. a   20. a

Chapters 5-7   1. c   2. a   3. b   4. a   5. b   6. b   7. d   8. b   9. b   10. d   11. d   12. c   13. d
14. b   15. b   16. a   17. a   18. c   19. c   20. c

Chapters 1-7   1. d   2. c   3. d   4. c   5. d   6. c   7. a   8. c   9. b   10. b   11. b   12. b   13. b
14. d   15. b   16. a   17. c   18. d   19. d   20. a   21. d   22. c   23. d   24. b   25. b

Chapters 8-11   1. d   2. c   3. d   4. a   5. d   6. c   7. d   8. a   9. c   10. d   11. b   12. d   13. c
14. a   15. d   16. c   17. c   18. b   19. c   20. a

Chapters 8-13   1. b   2. c   3. b   4. b   5. c   6. b   7. b   8. a   9. b   10. b   11. c   12. b   13. d
14. c   15. b   16. c   17. d   18. c   19. d   20. b   21. a   22. c   23. c   24. a   25. c

Chapters 1-13   1. d   2. b   3. c   4. c   5. a   6. d   7. b   8. a   9. d   10. a   11. d   12. b   13. d
14. d   15. d   16. a   17. c   18. d   19. a   20. a   21. b   22. c   23. b   24. c   25. c

Preparing for College Entrance Tests: Chapters 1-7   1. a   2. c   3. d   4. c   5. c   6. a   7. a   8. d   9. c
10. b   11. c   12. c   13. b   14. a   15. b   16. b   17. a   18. b   19. d   20. b   21. a   22. d

Preparing for College Entrance Tests: Chapters 8-13   1. c   2. d   3. a   4. d   5. a   6. c   7. b   8. d   9. b
10. c   11. c   12. c   13. d   14. b   15. c   16. c   17. b   18. a   19. d   20. d   21. c

ANSWERS: PLACEMENT TEST

Part 1   1. 35   2. 10,318   3. 5378   4. 2609   5. 67,624   6. 297,783   7. 36   8. 497   9. 192.976
10. 938.7   11. $658.74   12. 614.68   13. 7.83   14. 75.168   15. 25.6   16. 0.0549   17. $\frac{3}{4}$ 18. $11\frac{3}{8}$
19. $\frac{1}{12}$ 20. $4\frac{15}{16}$ 21. $\frac{3}{5}$ 22. $4\frac{1}{2}$ 23. $\frac{1}{6}$ 24. $2\frac{2}{5}$ 25. 59   26. 68   27. 83   28. 9.5   29. 47.6   30. 225

Part 2   1. c   2. b   3. d   4. a   5. d   6. b   7. c   8. a   9. b   10. d   11. b   12. a   13. d   14. c
15. d   16. d   17. a   18. b   19. d   20. b

Part 3   1. b   2. a   3. b   4. c   5. d   6. a   7. d   8. b   9. c   10. c   11. b   12. a   13. c   14. d
15. a   16. c   17. c   18. d   19. a   20. b

Part 4   1. b   2. c   3. a   4. d   5. c   6. a   7. c   8. d   9. b   10. a   11. b   12. b   13. a   14. d
15. c   16. b   17. d   18. a

HBJ ALGEBRA 1

Arthur F. Coxford

Joseph N. Payne

Harcourt Brace Jovanovich, Publishers

New York   Chicago   San Francisco   Atlanta   Dallas   *and*   London

ABOUT THE AUTHORS

ARTHUR F.COXFORD
Professor of Mathematics Education
University of Michigan
Ann Arbor, Michigan

JOSEPH N. PAYNE
Professor of Mathematics Education
University of Michigan
Ann Arbor, Michigan

EDITORIAL ADVISORS

Mrs. Lou Baker
Mathematics Department Chairperson
Arlington High School
Arlington, Texas

Mrs. Alice Mitchell
Mathematics Supervisor
Campbell Union High School District
San Jose, California

Thomas Day
Mathematics Department Chairman
Farmington High School
Farmington, Connecticut

Donald Nutter
Chairman, Department of Mathematics
Firestone High School
Akron, Ohio

Mrs. Billy Dooley
Mathematics Teacher
Central High School
Columbia, Tennessee

Mrs. Emily Springer
Formerly Mathematics Department Chairperson
Stephen F. Austin Jr. High School
Amarillo, Texas

Mrs. Mary Heins
Mathematics Teacher
Coronado High School
El Paso, Texas

August J. Zarcone
Mathematics Instructor
College of DuPage
Glen Ellyn, Illinois

The contributions of **Brother Neal Golden, S.C.**, who wrote the
Computer Applications, are gratefully acknowledged.

Printed in the United States of America

ISBN 0–15–353870–8

Contents

UNIT IV   QUADRATIC EQUATIONS AND APPLICATIONS

PHOTO CREDITS

KEY: *t* top; *c* center; *b* bottom

pages 13, Monkmeyer; 25, National Park Service; 34, News Bureau, University of Pennsylvania; 35 *(t)*, HBJ Photo; *(c)*, HBJ Photo; *(b)*, American Telephone and Telegraph; 92 *(t)*, AGA Corporation; *(b)*, AGA Corporation; 93; Joe Barnell, Shostal; 138, HBJ Photo; 168 *(t)*, Schwinn; *(b)*, L. Druskis, Taurus; 201, L.L.T. Rhodes, Taurus; 202, Tom McHugh, Photo Researchers; 216, The Regina Company; 231, Freda Leinwand, Monkmeyer; 262, Clifford Hausner, Leo deWys; 263, David Forbert, Shostal; 294, NASA; 295, Chester Higgins, Jr., Photo Researchers; 325, HBJ Photo; 360, Ray Ellis, Photo Researchers; 361, Michal Heron, Monkmeyer; 399, H. Armstrong Roberts; 406, Focus on Sports; 446, NASA; 447, Randa Bishop, Contact; 459, John Colwell, Grant Heilman; 478, H. Armstrong Roberts; 482, Mimi Forsyth, Monkmeyer; 483, NASA.

Quick Quiz
Perform the indicated operations.
1. $5 + 0.302 + 12.6$
   Ans: 17.902
2. $3\frac{2}{3} + 5\frac{1}{5}$
   Ans: $8\frac{13}{15}$
3. $0.8 - 0.062$
   Ans: 0.738
4. $6\frac{1}{3} - 2\frac{3}{4}$
   Ans: $3\frac{7}{12}$
5. 5.25×0.005
   Ans: 0.02625
6. $4\frac{1}{2} \times 3\frac{1}{3} \times 2\frac{1}{5}$
   Ans: 33
7. $25\frac{2}{3} \times 9$
   Ans: 237
8. $232{,}468 \div 356$
   Ans: 653
9. $57.936 \div 0.32$
   Ans: 181.05
10. $5\frac{1}{2} \div 3\frac{2}{3}$
    Ans: $1\frac{1}{2}$

Additional Examples
Example 1
Give the meaning of each expression.
1. $5y$
   Ans: 5 multiplied by y
2. $\dfrac{x}{y}$
   Ans: x divided by y
3. $r + s$
   Ans: the sum of r and s
4. $12 - x$
   Ans: x subtracted from 12

Example 2
Write an algebraic expression for each word description.
1. The sum of x dollars and y cents
   Ans: $x + y$
2. The cost of x tokens at 75¢ each
   Ans: $75x$ cents

OBJECTIVES: To write algebraic expressions for word descriptions

1–1 Algebraic Expressions

To evaluate numerical expressions involving parentheses

The table below shows you how to find a person's distance in kilometers from the center of a storm by counting the number of seconds between a flash of lightning and the sound of thunder.

Number of Seconds	Distance in Kilometers from the Storm's Center
1	0.33×1, or 0.33
2	0.33×2, or 0.66
3	0.33×3, or 0.99
4	0.33×4, or 1.32
t	**$0.33 \times t$**

The expression,

$$0.33 \times t$$

is an *algebraic expression*. In the expression, the letter, t, is a **variable**. It represents the time in seconds. An **algebraic expression** contains at least one variable.

An expression such as $0.33 \times t$ can also be written as

$$0.33 \cdot t \quad \text{or} \quad 0.33(t) \quad \text{or} \quad 0.33t.$$

Each expression means "0.33 times the value of t."

EXAMPLE 1 Give the meaning of each expression.

   a. $10m$ b. $\dfrac{4}{x}$ c. $a + b$ d. $r - 18$

Solutions: a. $10m$ means **10 times m**, or the **product of 10 and m**, or **10 multiplied by m**.

   b. $\dfrac{4}{x}$ means **4 divided by x** or the **quotient of 4 and x**.

   c. $a + b$ means the **sum of a and b**, or **b added to a**.

   d. $r - 18$ means the **difference of r and 18**, or **18 subtracted from r**.

You can write an algebraic expression for a word description.

EXAMPLE 2 Write an algebraic expression for each word description.

   a. The sum of the principal, p, and the interest, i

   b. The cost of r stamps at 20¢ each

   c. The cost per liter if p liters of gasoline cost \$2.05

Solutions: a. $p + i$ b. $20 \cdot r$, or $20r$ cents   c. $2.05 \div p$, or $\dfrac{2.05}{p}$ dollars

2   *Chapter 1*

Expressions such as

$$18\tfrac{1}{2} + 16\tfrac{3}{4} \qquad 210 - 47 \qquad 18.6 \times 9.05 \qquad 21 \div \tfrac{1}{3}$$

are *numerical expressions*. They do not contain a variable. A **numerical expression** contains at least one of the operations of addition, subtraction, multiplication, and division. To find the value of a numerical expression when it contains parentheses, **do the work inside parentheses first.**

EXAMPLE 3 Find the value of each of the following.

    a. $(2 \cdot 5) + 6$ **b.** $18 - (12 \div 2)$

Solutions: **a.** $(2 \cdot 5) + 6 = 10 + 6$ **b.** $18 - (12 \div 2) = 18 - 6$
                              $= 16$ $= 12$

Additional Examples
Example 3
Find the value of the following.
 1. $8 + (4 \cdot 6)$ **Ans: 32**
 2. $27 -{}_{,}(15 \div 5)$ **Ans: 24**

CLASSROOM EXERCISES

With each algebraic expression in Exercises 1–6, match the letter of the corresponding phrase in a–f that gives its meaning.

1. $4n$ d   **a.** n divided by 4

2. $\dfrac{n}{4}$ a   **b.** 4 subtracted from n

3. $n - 4$ b   **c.** n subtracted from 4

4. $n + 4$ f   **d.** n multiplied by 4

5. $4 - n$ c   **e.** 4 divided by n

6. $\dfrac{4}{n}$ e   **f.** 4 added to n

Find the value of each of the following.

7. $(8 \cdot 2) + 18$ 34   **8.** $16 - (25 \div 5)$ 11   **9.** $(5 \div 5) + 6$ 7   **10.** $5 \cdot (10 - 6)$ 20

WRITTEN EXERCISES

A   Give the meaning of each of the following.

1. $q - 5$ **2.** $5 + q$ **3.** $5 - q$ **4.** $q + 5$ **5.** $5q$

6. $5 \div q$ **7.** $q \div 5$ **8.** $\dfrac{q}{5}$ **9.** rs **10.** $\dfrac{r}{s}$

11. $s - 4$ **12.** $b - a$ **13.** $16s$ **14.** $t + n$ **15.** $n \div t$

Write an algebraic expression for each word description.

16. The sum of the restaurant bill, b, and the tip, t $b + t$

17. The sum of the down payment, d, and the mortgage loan, l $d + l$

Uses of Algebra   **3**

Assignment Guide
Minimal pp. 3–4: 1–45 odd
Average pp. 3–4: 1–51 odd
Above Average pp. 3–4:
17–45 odd, 46–52

Additional Answers
Written Exercises
 1. 5 subtracted from q
 2. q added to 5
 3. q subtracted from 5
 4. 5 added to q
 5. q multiplied by 5
 6. 5 divided by q
 7. q divided by 5
 8. q divided by 5
 9. s multiplied by r
10. r divided by s
11. 4 subtracted from s
12. a subtracted from b
13. s multiplied by 16
14. n added to t
15. n divided by t

18. The amount borrowed, a, added to the finance charge, c $c + a$

19. The net income, i, added to the total deductions, d $d + i$

20. The amount of tax withheld, w, subtracted from the total tax owed, t $t - w$

21. The total number of days absent, a, subtracted from 180 $180 - a$

22. The number of hours of darkness, d, subtracted from 24 $24 - d$

23. The amount spent, s, subtracted from $150 $150 - s$

24. The cost of 2 tickets at d dollars per ticket $2d$

25. The cost of renting a boat for h hours at $4.50 per hour $4.50h$

26. The cost of g gallons of gasoline at $1.55 per gallon $1.55g$

27. The cost of 3 pounds of bananas at c cents per pound $3c$

28. The number of books you can buy for $25 if each book costs d dollars $\dfrac{25}{d}$

29. The number of times at bat, t, divided by 24, the number of hits $\dfrac{t}{24}$

30. The number of kilometers driven, k, divided by 80, the average speed in kilometers per hour $\dfrac{k}{80}$

31. The total weekly earnings, s, divided by 40, the total number of hours worked per week $\dfrac{s}{40}$

Find the value of each of the following.

32. $(12 - 8) + 3$ 7   33. $15 + (18 - 7)$ 26   34. $40 - (1 + 10)$ 29   35. $(20 - 9) - 2$

36. $(16 + 23) \div 3$ 13   37. $4 + (64 \div 4)$ 20   38. $21 - (80 \div 16)$ 16   39. $4 - (20 \div 5)$

40. $18 - (0 \cdot 150)$ 18   41. $0 \cdot (360 \div 12)$ 0   42. $(7 \cdot 15) + (3 \cdot 15)$

43. $(18 \cdot 6) - (10 \cdot 6)$ 48   44. $(41 + 9) \div (75 \div 15)$ 10   45. $(80 \div 10) \div (21 - 13)$

B

46. $36 - (12 \cdot \frac{1}{3}) - 1$ 31   47. $24 - (4 \div \frac{1}{2})$ 16   48. $28 + (0 \div 4) - (10 \div 2)$

Give the meaning of each of the following.

49. $\dfrac{a + b}{5}$ 50. $\dfrac{a - b}{5}$ 51. $9(a - b)$ 52. $9(b - a)$

REVIEW CAPSULE FOR SECTION 1–2

Write in lowest terms.

1. $\dfrac{8}{12}$ $\dfrac{2}{3}$ 2. $\dfrac{9}{36}$ $\dfrac{1}{4}$ 3. $\dfrac{18}{54}$ $\dfrac{1}{3}$ 4. $\dfrac{45}{60}$ $\dfrac{3}{4}$ 5. $\dfrac{12}{18}$ $\dfrac{2}{3}$ 6. $\dfrac{84}{96}$ $\dfrac{7}{8}$

Multiply. Write your answers in lowest terms.

7. $\dfrac{1}{2} \times \dfrac{1}{3}$ $\dfrac{1}{6}$ 8. $\dfrac{1}{4} \times \dfrac{4}{5}$ $\dfrac{1}{5}$ 9. $\dfrac{2}{3} \times \dfrac{2}{5}$ $\dfrac{4}{15}$ 10. $\dfrac{3}{8} \times 7$ $2\dfrac{5}{8}$ 11. $\dfrac{5}{6} \times 3\dfrac{1}{5}$ $2\dfrac{2}{3}$

Perform the indicated operations.

12. $8.35 + 0.62$ 8.97   13. $23.92 + 0.8 + 0.45$ 25.17   14. $9.6 + 12.07 + 15 + 23.967$

15. 6×0.9 5.4   16. 0.8×6.7 5.36   17. 0.072×42.6 3.0672   18. 10×19.06

19. 29×2.9 84.1   20. 1.6×0.04 0.064   21. 82.7×0.79 65.333   22. 18.8×100

23. $0.966 \div 7$ 0.138   24. $4.34 \div 0.7$ 6.2   25. $25.9 \div 0.74$ 35   26. $144 \div 3.2$

4 *Chapter 1*

OBJECTIVE: To evaluate algebraic expressions using the rules for order of operations and

1–2 Evaluating Expressions
grouping symbols

In Section 1–1, parentheses were used to help you in **evaluating** (finding the value of) an expression.

Two students evaluated this expression which has no parentheses.

$$2 \cdot 6 + 4 \cdot 5$$

First Student	Second Student
$2 \cdot 6 = 12$	$2 \cdot 6 = 12$
$12 + 4 = 16$	$4 \cdot 5 = 20$
$16 \cdot 5 = 80$ ← **The answer is incorrect.**	$12 + 20 = 32$ ← **Correct answer**

Only one answer can be correct. The first student did not apply the rules for order of operations. Mathematicians agreed to follow these rules so that expressions such as $2 \cdot 6 + 4 \cdot 5$ will have *exactly one value*.

Rules

> **Order of Operations**
> 1. Do all multiplications and divisions in order from left to right.
> 2. Do all additions and subtractions in order from left to right.

Problem	Procedure	Computation
$4 \cdot 7 + 9$	Multiply 4 and 7. Then add 9.	$4 \cdot 7 + 9 = 28 + 9$ $= 37$
$2 + 5 \cdot 6$	Multiply 5 and 6. Then add 2.	$2 + 5 \cdot 6 = 2 + 30$ $= 32$
$18 - 2 \cdot 5$	Multiply 2 and 5. Then subtract this from 18.	$18 - 2 \cdot 5 = 18 - 10$ $= 8$
$16 + 10 \div 2$	Divide 10 by 2. Then add 16.	$16 + 10 \div 2 = 16 + 5$ $= 21$

Parentheses, ( ), and brackets, [ ], are called **grouping symbols**. A fraction bar is also a grouping symbol.

Rules

> **Rules for Grouping Symbols**
> 1. Perform the operations within parentheses, or in the numerators or denominators.
> 2. When parentheses have been removed, or where there are no parentheses, follow the rules for order of operations.

Quick Quiz
Give the meaning of each of the following:
1. $6 - y$
   Ans: *y* subtracted from 6
2. $\dfrac{rs}{3}$
   Ans: The product of *r* and *s* divided by 3
Write an algebraic expression for each word description.
3. The sum of the cost, *b*, of a bicycle and the tax, *t*
   Ans: *b* + *t*
4. The cost of renting a car for *h* hours at \$15 per hour
   Ans: 15*h*
5. The number of books you can buy for \$54 if each book costs *x* dollars
   Ans: $\dfrac{54}{x}$

Uses of Algebra   **5**

Problem	Procedure	Computation
$3(5+6)$	Add 5 and 6. Then multiply by 3.	$3(5+6) = 3 \cdot 11$ $= 33$
$(2 \cdot 4) - 7$	Multiply 2 and 4. Then subtract 7.	$(2 \cdot 4) - 7 = 8 - 7$ $= 1$
$3 \cdot \dfrac{7-5}{6 \div 2}$	Subtract 5 from 7. Divide 6 by 2. Multiply by 3.	$3 \cdot \dfrac{7-5}{6 \div 2} = 3 \cdot \dfrac{2}{3}$ $= 2$

REMEMBER: $3(5+6)$ means $3 \cdot (5+6)$.

When an expression contains more than one grouping symbol, perform the operations within the innermost grouping symbols first. Then work towards the outermost grouping symbols.

EXAMPLE 1 Evaluate: $3 + [5 + 2(8 \div 4)]$

Solution: $3 + [5 + 2(\overline{8 \div 4})] = 3 + [5 + 2(2)]$ ◄———— **Next, evaluate 2(2).**
$= 3 + [5 + 4]$
$= 3 + 9 = 12$

You follow the same rules when evaluating algebraic expressions.

EXAMPLE 2 Evaluate $\dfrac{x-y}{4}$ for $x = 19$ and $y = 10$.

Solution: Replace x with 19 and y with 10.
$$\frac{x-y}{4} = \frac{19-10}{4}$$
$$= \frac{9}{4}, \text{ or } 2\frac{1}{4}$$

CLASSROOM EXERCISES

Evaluate.

1. $2 \cdot 3 + 4$ 10

2. $4 + 2 \cdot 5$ 14

3. $2 \cdot 7 + 2 \cdot 8$ 30

4. $2(5+1)$

5. $2 \cdot (5+6)$ 22

6. $28 - 3 \cdot 7$ 7

7. $15 - 2 \div 2$ 14

8. $15 - (2 \div 2)$

9. $10[4 + (7-1)5]$ 340

10. $75 - 6[6(8-6)]$ 3

11. $36 - [1 + (4 \div 4)3]$

12. Evaluate $30 - 2w$ for $w = 10$. 10

13. Evaluate $\dfrac{2m-n}{5}$ for $m = 8$ and $n = 3$.
  $2\frac{3}{5}$

14. Evaluate $\dfrac{2(a-3)}{5}$ for $a = 21$. $7\frac{1}{5}$

15. Evaluate $\dfrac{4(1-y)}{3}$ for $y = \frac{1}{4}$. 1

WRITTEN EXERCISES

A   Evaluate. Follow the rules for order of operations and for the use of grouping symbols. Express answers in lowest terms.

1. $7 \cdot 9 + 6$ 69
2. $8 + 3 \cdot 7$ 29
3. $6 \cdot (3 + 11)$ 84

4. $(6 + 3) \cdot 3$ 27
5. $4 + (2 \cdot 7)$ 18
6. $(4 + 2) \cdot 7$ 42

7. $8 \cdot 7 + 9 \div 9$ 57
8. $3 \cdot 7 + 4$ 25
9. $5 \cdot 7 - 12$ 23

10. $15 - 6 \div 2$ 12
11. $18 - 1 \cdot 6$ 12
12. $30 - 7 \cdot 0$ 30

13. $0 + 7\frac{1}{2} \cdot 0$ 0
14. $62 \cdot 4 - 3$ 245
15. $6 + 89 \cdot 2$ 184

16. $89 \cdot (2 + 6)$ 712
17. $5(2 \cdot 10)$ 100
18. $(5 \cdot 2) \cdot 10$ 100

19. $6 \cdot (15 \cdot 4)$ 360
20. $(6 \cdot 15) \cdot 4$ 360
21. $7(1 + 8) \div 9$ 7

22. $\frac{15 - 4}{3}$ $3\frac{2}{3}$
23. $\frac{6}{12 - 5}$ $\frac{6}{7}$
24. $\frac{8 - 3}{5 - 2}$ $1\frac{2}{3}$

25. $\frac{6 - 2 \cdot 1}{9}$ $\frac{4}{9}$
26. $\frac{4}{2 \cdot 7 + 5}$ $\frac{4}{19}$
27. $\frac{13 - 2 \cdot 6}{5 + 2 \cdot 3}$ $\frac{1}{11}$

28. $\frac{4(3 - 1)}{8}$ 1
29. $\frac{6}{2(7 + 1)}$ $\frac{3}{8}$
30. $\frac{2(7 - 3)}{3(4 + 5)}$ $\frac{8}{27}$

31. $2[3 + 2 \times (10 - 3)]$ 34
32. $3[15 - (5 + 3)]$ 21
33. $8[29 - (14 - 5)]$

34. $4[24 \div (6 + 2)]$ 12
35. $4[(24 \div 6) + 2]$ 24
36. $2[(11 \cdot 8) \div 4]$

37. $2[11 \cdot (8 \div 4)]$ 44
38. $8 \div [16 - 2(3 + 4)]$ 4
39. $8 \div [(16 - 2)3 + 4]$

Evaluate for the given values of the variables.

40. $50 + 2w$, for $w = 20$ 90
41. $100 + 3y$, for $y = 10$ 130

42. $100 - 5q$, for $q = 8$ 60
43. $2p + 2s$, for $p = 4$ and $s = 5$ 18

44. $2(a + b)$, for $a = 4$ and $b = 5$ 18
45. $2a + b$, for $a = 7$ and $b = 5$ 19

46. $\frac{8}{x - y}$, for $x = 10$ and $y = 6$ 2
47. $\frac{3r}{2s}$, for $r = 10$ and $s = 15$ 1

48. $\frac{3}{4}c + \frac{5}{7}d$, for $c = 12$ and $d = 14$ 19
49. $\frac{5}{6}m - \frac{2}{9}r$, for $m = 12$ and $r = 9$ 8

50. $2.3g + 0.7f$, for $g = 4$ and $f = 8$ 14.8
51. $3.7a - 2.1b$, for $a = 4.8$ and $b = 3.7$

52. $5r - 9.2s$, for $r = 2.8$ and $s = 0.6$ 8.48
53. $8.5s - 0.6t$, for $s = 5$ and $t = 0.5$ 42.2

B
54. $\frac{2(t - 1)}{t}$, for $t = 11$ $1\frac{9}{11}$
55. $\frac{a + 2b}{5}$, for $a = 10$ and $b = 2$ $2\frac{4}{5}$

56. $\frac{m + m + m}{3m}$, for $m = 0.1$ 1
57. $\frac{m \cdot m \cdot m}{m}$, for $m = 1.5$ 2.25

58. $\frac{3}{8}a + \frac{5}{6}b - \frac{3}{5}c$, for $a = \frac{1}{3}$, $b = \frac{8}{15}$, and $c = \frac{2}{3}$ $\frac{61}{360}$

Insert parentheses so that the result of the indicated operations will be the given answer.

59. $1 + 9 \cdot 2 + 7$ Answer: 90
60. $3 + 3 + 3 \cdot 3$ Answer: 21

Uses of Algebra   **7**

Assignment Guide
Minimal
Day 1 p. 7: 1–39 odd
Day 2 p. 7: 40–53
Average: pp. 7–8: 1–63 odd
Above Average: pp. 7–8: 3, 6, 9, ... 51, 54–64 even, 65–68

Additional Answers
33. 160
36. 44
39. $\frac{4}{23}$
51. 9.99
59. $(1 + 9) \cdot (2 + 7)$
60. $3 + [(3 + 3) \cdot 3]$

Insert parentheses so that the result of the indicated operations will be the given answer.

61. $2 \cdot 5 + 7 + 9$ Answer: 42   **62.** $56 \div 6 - 2 \cdot 1$ Answer: 14

63. $2 \cdot 12 \div 2 + 6$ Answer: 3   **64.** $34 + 2 \div 2 + 10$ Answer: 3

APPLICATIONS: Using Algebraic Expressions

C   Write an algebraic expression to represent each word description.

65. The cost of a service call for a plumber who charges a base fee of \$25 plus \$11 per hour for t hours $25 + 11t$

66. The total cost of p pounds of potatoes at 69¢ per pound and r pounds of chicken at 89¢ per pound $0.69p + 0.89r$

67. The amount in a savings account if the balance in the account is \$475 and \$15 is withdrawn per week for w weeks $475 - 15w$

68. The amount in a checking account after x weeks if the present balance is \$315 and \$20 is added per week $315 + 20x$

Puzzle

Look for a pattern in a–d below.

a. $25 \times 25 = 625$ **b.** $75 \times 75 = 5625$ **c.** $45 \times 45 = 2025$ **d.** $95 \times 95 = 9025$

Without using paper and pencil, find the value of each expression.

1. 35×35 1225   **2.** 55×55 3025   **3.** 65×65 4225   **4.** 85×85 7225

REVIEW CAPSULE FOR SECTION 1–3

Write a decimal for each per cent.

1. 8% 0.08   **2.** 2% 0.02   **3.** 12% 0.12   **4.** 128% 1.28   **5.** $4\frac{1}{2}$% 0.045   **6.** 0.5%

Place the decimal point in each product.

7. $0.23 \times 43.4 = 9982$ 9.982   **8.** $0.74 \times 39.5 = 29230$ 29.230   **9.** $0.56 \times 3.84 = 21504$

Multiply.

10. 0.1×0.1 0.01   **11.** 2.5×2.5 6.25   **12.** $\frac{1}{3} \times \frac{1}{3}$ $\frac{1}{9}$ **13.** $\frac{5}{8} \times \frac{5}{8} \times \frac{5}{8}$

Add or subtract as indicated. Write your answer in lowest terms

14. $\frac{5}{9} + \frac{3}{9}$ $\frac{8}{9}$ **15.** $\frac{5}{8} + \frac{7}{8}$ $1\frac{1}{2}$ **16.** $\frac{7}{8} + \frac{3}{4}$ $1\frac{5}{8}$ **17.** $\frac{3}{4} + \frac{5}{7}$

18. $6\frac{1}{3} + \frac{1}{6}$ $6\frac{1}{2}$ **19.** $7\frac{3}{5} + 2\frac{7}{10}$ $10\frac{3}{10}$ **20.** $4\frac{1}{2} + 8\frac{1}{4}$ $12\frac{3}{4}$ **21.** $12\frac{2}{5} + 4\frac{1}{8}$

22. $\frac{5}{6} - \frac{3}{5}$ $\frac{7}{30}$ **23.** $\frac{3}{4} - \frac{1}{5}$ $\frac{11}{20}$ **24.** $\frac{5}{8} - \frac{1}{3}$ $\frac{7}{24}$ **25.** $\frac{8}{9} - \frac{3}{7}$

26. $12\frac{1}{6} - 7\frac{5}{12}$ $4\frac{3}{4}$ **27.** $6\frac{5}{8} - 2\frac{1}{6}$ $4\frac{11}{24}$ **28.** $5\frac{3}{16} - 2\frac{5}{6}$ $2\frac{17}{48}$ **29.** $3\frac{1}{8} - 2\frac{7}{10}$

30. $5\frac{2}{3} - 1\frac{1}{4}$ $4\frac{5}{12}$ **31.** $3\frac{7}{8} - 2\frac{2}{3}$ $1\frac{5}{24}$ **32.** $14 - 9\frac{2}{3}$ $4\frac{1}{3}$ **33.** $6 - 3\frac{1}{12}$

OBJECTIVES: To evaluate formulas using replacement sets

1–3 Formulas and Replacement Sets

To evaluate numerical expressions involving exponents

Teaching Suggestions p. M-14

You can use this **formula** to find the amount of tax, T, on a purchase of p dollars in a state that has a 4% sales tax.

$$T = 0.04p$$

To find T, you replace p in the formula with the amount of a purchase.

In the formula, the letter p is a **variable**. It represents any number from a given **set** or collection of numbers called the **replacement set.**

NOTE: Any letter may be used to represent a variable.

EXAMPLE 1   Use the formula $T = 0.04p$ to find T when the replacement set for p is $\{\$15, \$31.50, \$42.75\}$.

Solutions:

Replace p with 15.

$T = 0.04p$

$T = 0.04(15)$

$T = 0.60$

Tax: **$0.60**

Replace p with 31.50.

$T = 0.04p$

$T = 0.04(31.50)$

$T = 1.26$

Tax: **$1.26**

Replace p with 42.75.

$T = 0.04p$

$T = 0.04(42.75)$

$T = 1.71$

Tax: **$1.71**

Quick Quiz
Evaluate:
1. $15 \div [12 - 3(1+2)]$
   Ans: 5
2. $33 \div [(8-6)3 + 5]$
   Ans: 3
3. $\dfrac{2x - y}{4}$ for $x = 9$ and $y = 6$
   Ans: 3
4. $\dfrac{3(r-2)}{s}$ for $r = 10$ and $s = 3$
   Ans: 8

Additional Example
Example 1
Use the formula $T = 0.05p$
to find T when the replacement
set for p is $\{22, 45.60, 52.06\}$
Ans: 1.1, 2.28, 2.6

The formula for the area of the square at the right can be written in two ways. In the formula, the variable s represents the length of a side of the square.

$$A = s \cdot s \qquad \text{or} \qquad A = s^2$$

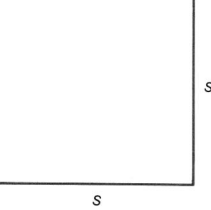

In $A = s^2$, the **exponent, 2,** shows that the **base,** s, is taken as a factor two times.

(Recall that since $35 = 7 \cdot 5$, 7 and 5 are *factors* of 35. Similarly, 35 and 1 are also *factors of 35* because $35 \cdot 1 = 35$.)

The following table illustrates the meaning of exponents.

Expression	Read	Exponent	Base	Meaning
3^2	3 squared	2	3	$3 \cdot 3$, or **9**
5^3	5 to the third power	3	5	$5 \cdot 5 \cdot 5$, or **125**
$\left(\dfrac{1}{6}\right)^4$	$\dfrac{1}{6}$ to the fourth power	4	$\dfrac{1}{6}$	$\dfrac{1}{6} \cdot \dfrac{1}{6} \cdot \dfrac{1}{6} \cdot \dfrac{1}{6}$, or $\dfrac{1}{1296}$
2^5	2 to the fifth power	5	2	$2 \cdot 2 \cdot 2 \cdot 2 \cdot 2$, or **32**
a^1	a to the first power	1	a	a
y^4	y to the fourth power	4	y	$y \cdot y \cdot y \cdot y$

Uses of Algebra   **9**

EXAMPLE 2 Use the formula $A = s^2$ to find A when the replacement set for s is $\{10, 2\frac{1}{2}\}$.

Solutions:

Replace s with 10.

$A = s^2$

$A = (10)^2$

$A = 10 \cdot 10$, or **100**

Replace s with $2\frac{1}{2}$.

$A = s^2$

$A = (2\frac{1}{2})^2$, or $\left(\frac{5}{2}\right)^2$

$A = \frac{5}{2} \cdot \frac{5}{2} = \frac{25}{4}$, or $6\frac{1}{4}$

NOTE: Area is measured in square units, such as square inches (in²), square feet (ft²), square centimeters (cm²), square meters (m²), and so on.

CLASSROOM EXERCISES

1. Use $T = 0.03p$ to find T when the replacement set for p is $\{\$18, \$24, \$40\}$.
   $0.54, $0.72, $1.20

Find each value.

2. 6^2 36
3. 4^3 64
4. 1^6 1
5. $(\frac{1}{5})^2$ $\frac{1}{25}$
6. $(\frac{2}{3})^3$ $\frac{8}{27}$
7. $(\frac{1}{2})^4$ $\frac{1}{16}$

8. The formula for the perimeter of a square is $P = 4s$. Find P when the replacement set for s is $\{\frac{1}{2}, 2, 9\}$. 2, 8, 36

Find R for each formula. The replacement set for t is $\{0, \frac{1}{4}, 3\}$.

9. $R = 2t$ $0, \frac{1}{2}, 6$
10. $R = t^2 + 1$
11. $R = \frac{16t}{2}$ 0, 2, 24
12. $R = \frac{t+1}{3}$

WRITTEN EXERCISES

A   Find T for each formula below. The replacement set for p is $\{\$20, \$50, \$100\}$.

1. $T = 0.04p$ $0.80, $2, $4
2. $T = 0.03p$ $0.60, $1.50, $3
3. $T = 0.05p$ $1, $2.50, $5
4. $T = 0.075p$

Find B for each formula. The replacement set for t is $\{1, 2, 3\}$.

5. $B = 4t$ 4, 8, 12
6. $B = t^2$ 1, 4, 9
7. $B = t - 1$ 0, 1, 2
8. $B = 2t - 1$

9. $B = 5 + t^2$ 6, 9, 14
10. $B = t + 2$ 3, 4, 5
11. $B = \frac{t}{3}$ $\frac{1}{3}, \frac{2}{3}, 1$
12. $B = \frac{t+1}{3}$

Find Q for each formula. The replacement set for n is $\{8, 10, 12\}$.

13. $Q = 2n$ 16, 10, 24
14. $Q = 2n - 1$ 15, 19, 23
15. $Q = 2n + 2$
16. $Q = 3n$

17. $Q = n + \frac{1}{2}$
18. $Q = 2n - \frac{1}{2}$
19. $Q = \frac{n}{2} + 7$ 11, 12, 13
20. $Q = 5(n - 3)$ 25, 35, 45

21. $Q = \frac{3+n}{2}$
22. $Q = 3n(5 + n)$ 312, 450, 612
23. $Q = n^3$ 512, 1000, 1728
24. $Q = \frac{n}{3} + \frac{2}{3}n$ 8, 10, 12

Evaluate.

25. 2^5 32
26. $(\frac{5}{9})^2$ $\frac{25}{81}$
27. $(0.1)^2$ 0.01
28. $(0.01)^2$
29. $(1.2)^2$

30. $(1.5)^2$ 2.25
31. $(0.04)^2$
32. $(\frac{3}{5})^3$ $\frac{27}{125}$
33. $(0.04)^3$
34. $(\frac{3}{4})^3$

35. $(\frac{2}{3})^4$ $\frac{16}{81}$
36. $(1.1)^2$ 1.21
37. $(1.02)^2$
38. 1^{25} 1
39. 10^5

In Exercises 40–43, use the formula $A = s^2$ to find A for each replacement set for s.

40. $\{10, 25, 50\}$ **41.** $\{\frac{1}{2}, \frac{1}{10}, \frac{3}{10}\}$ **42.** $\{1.2, 1.04, 0.05\}$ **43.** $\{0.15, 0.25, 1.43\}$

44. Find V in the formula $V = s^3$. The replacement set for s is $\{\frac{1}{3}, 0.5, 8\}$.

45. The formula $K = \frac{m}{1000}$ gives the number of kilometers in m meters. Find K if the replacement set for m is $\{\frac{1}{2}, 1, 100, 1000, 10{,}000\}$.

46. The formula $C = \frac{5}{9}(F - 32)$ relates the number of degrees on the Fahrenheit scale, F, to the corresponding number of degrees on the Celsius scale, C. Find C if the replacement set for F is $\{32, 68, 98.8, 212\}$. $0, 20, 37\frac{1}{9}, 100$

47. The formula $S = 180(n - 2)$ gives the sum of the measures of the angles of a polygon of n sides. Find S when the replacement set for n is $\{3, 4, 5, 6\}$.

B   If the replacement set for n is $\{0, 1, 2, 3\}$, which expressions represent even numbers only?

48. $3n$ No   **49.** $2n$ Yes   **50.** $2n + 1$ No   **51.** $3n + 1$ No   **52.** n^2 No

If the replacement set for t is $\{\frac{1}{2}, 0.25, 1\}$, give the least number represented by each algebraic expression.

53. t 0.25   **54.** $2(t + 3)$ 6.5   **55.** $2 - t$ 1   **56.** $t - t$ 0   **57.** $t \div 4$

58. t^2 **59.** $t \cdot t \cdot t$ **60.** $\frac{t}{2}$ 0.125   **61.** $\frac{1 - t}{4}$ 0   **62.** $\frac{t^3}{8}$

Puzzle

Name all the whole numbers 1–12, using six 6's, operation symbols, and parentheses only.

The first one is done below.

$$(6 + 6 + 6) \div (6 + 6 + 6) = 1$$

REVIEW CAPSULE FOR SECTION 1-4

Round each decimal to the nearest tenth.

1. 0.93 0.9   **2.** 1.09 1.1   **3.** 37.45 37.5   **4.** 0.507 0.5   **5.** 100.98

Divide. Round your answer to the nearest thousandth.

6. $1.92 \div 280$ 0.007   **7.** $4.59 \div 2.4$ 1.913   **8.** $250 \div 0.75$ 333.333   **9.** $1.09 \div 784$

Multiply. Express answers in lowest terms.

10. 3500×1.24 4340   **11.** 6000×1.36 8160   **12.** $72{,}000 \times 1.09$ **13.** $100{,}000 \times 1.84$
14. $\frac{5}{6} \times \frac{3}{5} \times \frac{10}{12}$ $\frac{5}{12}$ **15.** $1\frac{1}{2} \times 4\frac{3}{10} \times 8$ $51\frac{3}{5}$ **16.** $6\frac{4}{5} \times 17\frac{1}{8} \times \frac{1}{2}$

Uses of Algebra   **11**

Problem Solving and Applications

1-4 Using Formulas

Formulas use variables to show how quantities are related. To use a formula, you replace the known variables with given values (replacement set) in order to find the unknown variable.

EXAMPLE 1 The amount of money (A) in Ellen's savings account is given by the formula

$$A = P(1 + 0.06t).$$

In the formula, P is the **principal** (amount deposited) and t is the time in years that the principal has been in the account. Find A when $P = \$3500$ and $t = 4$ years.

Solution:

$A = P(1 + 0.06t)$ ◄——— **Write the formula.**

$A = 3500(1 + 0.06 \cdot 4)$ ◄——— **Replace P with 3500 and t with 4.**

$A = 3500(1 + 0.24)$

$A = 3500(1.24)$

$A = 4340$ The amount, A, in the account is **$4340**.

You can use a formula to find unit price. **Unit price** is the cost per gram, per ounce, and so on.

To find the unit price, U, of an item, divide the total price, P, by the number of units, n. That is,

$$U = P \div n \qquad \text{or} \qquad U = \frac{P}{n}.$$

EXAMPLE 2 A 305-gram can of soup costs 79¢. A 539-gram can of the same brand costs $1.09. Which is the better buy?

Solution: Find the unit price for each size. Round each unit price to the nearest tenth of a cent. Then compare the prices.

305-gram can: $U = \dfrac{P}{n}$ ◄— $P = 0.79$ / $n = 305$ 539-gram can: $U = \dfrac{P}{n}$ ◄— $P = 1.09$ / $n = 539$

$U = \dfrac{0.79}{305}$ $U = \dfrac{1.09}{539}$

$U = 0.003$ ◄— **0.3¢ per gram** $U = 0.002$ ◄— **0.2¢ per gram**

Since the **539-gram can** costs less per gram, it is the better buy.

Formulas can also be used to find the perimeter, area, and volume of geometric figures.

EXAMPLE 3 The volume, V, of this refrigerator car can be found by using the formula $V = lwh$. Find V when $l = 60$ feet, $w = 10\frac{1}{2}$ feet and $h = 12$ feet.

Solution: $V = lwh$ ← Replace l with 60, w with $10\frac{1}{2}$, and h with 12.

$V = 60 \cdot 10\frac{1}{2} \cdot 12$

$V = 60 \cdot \frac{21}{2} \cdot 12$

$V = 7560$

The volume is **7560 cubic feet.**

Additional Example
Example 3
A swimming pool is 180 feet wide, and 15 feet deep. Use the formula $V = lwh$ to find its volume.
Ans: 32,400 cubic feet

NOTE: Other cubic units of measure are cubic inches (in³), cubic yards (yd³), cubic centimeters (cm³), cubic meters (m³), and so on.

CLASSROOM EXERCISES

1. Use the formula $A = P(1 + 0.06t)$ to find A when $P = \$2500$ and $t = 2$ years. $2800
2. Use the formula in Exercise 1 to find A when $P = \$8000$ and $t = 3\frac{1}{4}$ years. $9560
3. Use the formula $U = P \div n$ to find U when $P = \$1.09$ and $n = 24$ ounces. Round your answer to the nearest tenth of a cent. $0.045, or 4.5¢
4. Use the formula $V = lwh$ to find V when $l = 10.5$ meters, $w = 4$ meters, and $h = 8.4$ meters. 352.8 m^3

WRITTEN EXERCISES

A   In Exercises 1–6, use the formula $A = P(1 + 0.06t)$ to find A.

1. $P = \$1500$; $t = 5$ years $1950
2. $P = \$780$; $t = 3$ years $920.40
3. $P = \$1000$; $t = 1$ year $1060
4. $P = \$1060$; $t = 1$ year $1123.60
5. $P = \$1123.50$; $t = 1$ year $1190.91
6. $P = \$1120$; $t = 1$ year $1187.20

In Exercises 7–12, use the unit price formula, $U = P \div n$, to find U for each value of P and n. Round each answer to the nearest tenth of a cent.

Product	Price (P)	Size (n)	Unit Price (U)	
7. Tuna	$1.92	280 grams	?	$0.007
8. String beans	$1.99	46 ounces	?	$0.043
9. Detergent	$4.59	2.4 liters	?	$1.913
10. Paper towels	$0.75	250 sheets	?	$0.003
11. Toothpaste	$0.99	8 ounces	?	$0.124
12. Mayonnaise	$1.09	784 grams	?	$0.001

Assignment Guide
Minimal pp. 13–14: 1–24
Average pp. 13–15: 1–50 odd
Above Average pp. 13–16
3, 6, 9, ... 36, 37–55 odd

Uses of Algebra   **13**

In Exercises 13–16, use the formula **U = P ÷ n** to determine the better buy. In each expression, assume that the items compared are the same brand.

13. A 473–milliliter bottle of vinegar for 43¢ or a 946–milliliter bottle for 75¢ 946-ml bottle

14. A 2–pound bag of flour for 61¢ or a 5–pound bag for $1.11 5-pound bag

15. A 16–ounce container of cottage cheese for $0.96 or a 24–ounce container for $1.38 24-oz container

16. A 50–gram jar of mustard for $1.09 or a 110–gram jar for $2.09 110-gram jar

In Exercises 17–24, use the formula **V = lwh** to find V for each value of l, w, and h.

17. $l = 4$ in, $w = 2\frac{1}{2}$ in, $h = 6$ in 60 in³

18. $l = 5\frac{1}{3}$ in, $w = 3\frac{1}{2}$ in, $h = 9$ in

19. $l = 18$ cm, $w = 5$ cm, $h = 24$ cm 2160 cm³

20. $l = 9.1$ cm, $w = 6.5$ cm, $h = 8$ cm

21. $l = 5\frac{1}{3}$ ft, $w = 3\frac{1}{2}$ ft, $h = 27$ ft 504 ft³

22. $l = 8\frac{1}{2}$ yd, $w = 5$ yd, $h = 12\frac{1}{3}$ yd

23. $l = 1.5$ m, $w = 0.8$ m, $h = 3$ m 3.6 m³

24. $l = 7.6$ cm, $w = 4.5$ cm, $h = 9$ cm

In Exercises 25–30, use the formula

$$A = \tfrac{1}{2}h(b + c)$$

to find the area of each trapezoid. Refer to the trapezoid at the right. (In a trapezoid, the bases are parallel.)

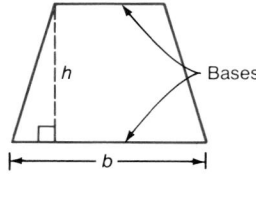

25. $h = 10$, $b = 15$, $c = 8$

26. $h = 2$, $b = 12$, $c = 5$

27. $h = 3$, $b = 4$, $c = 6$

28. $h = 5$, $b = 3$, $c = 2$

29. $h = 2$, $b = \frac{3}{4}$, $c = \frac{1}{4}$

30. $h = 4$, $b = \frac{1}{4}$, $c = \frac{1}{2}$

In Exercises 31–36, use the formula

$$p = 100\left(\frac{g - s}{g}\right)$$

to find the per cent of discount, p, on a purchase. In the formula, g represents the original price and s represents the sale price.

31. Original price: $40; sale price: $36 10%

32. Original price: $25; sale price: $20

33. Original price: $96; sale price: $64 $33\frac{1}{3}$%

34. Original price: $96; sale price: $72

35. Original price: $100; sale price: $70 30%

36. Original price: $48.96; sale price: $42.84 $12\frac{1}{2}$%

B   In Exercises 37–40, use the formula

$$A = P(1 + 0.075t)$$

to find A for each value of P and t. (HINT: Remember to express t in years.)

37. $P = \$3000$; $t = 6$ months $3112.50

38. $P = \$6500$; $t = 4$ months $6620.50

39. $P = \$10,000$; $t = 3$ years 9 months $12,812.50

40. $P = \$1000$; $t = 8$ months $1050

Additional Answers
18. 168 in³
20. 473.2 cm³
22. 524$\frac{1}{6}$ yd³
24. 307.8 cm³
25. 115 units²
26. 17 sq units
27. 15 sq units
28. 12$\frac{1}{2}$ sq units
29. 1 sq unit
30. 1$\frac{1}{2}$ sq units
32. 20%
34. 25%

The formula for the area of a circle with radius r is $A = \pi r^2$.
The formula for the circumference of a circle with radius r is $C = 2\pi r$.

Use these formulas in Exercises 41–44 to find the circumference and area of each circle with the given radius. Express your answers in terms of π.

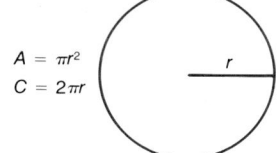

$A = \pi r^2$
$C = 2\pi r$

Example: $r = 10$ **Answers:** $C = 20\pi$; $A = 100\pi$

41. $r = 20$ **42.** $r = 9$ **43.** $r = 40$ **44.** $r = 4.2$

In Exercises 45–48, find the circumference and area of each circle with the given radius. Use 3.14 as an approximation for π.

45. $r = 10$ **46.** $r = 50$ **47.** $r = 100$ **48.** $r = 5.6$

Complete the table. Then write the formula. Exercise 49 is begun for you.

49. Tickets to a baseball game cost $3 each.

a.

n: number of tickets	1	2	3	4	5
C: cost of n tickets	$3	$6	$9	?	?

$12; $15

b. Cost = 3 · Number of Tickets, or $C =$ __?__ · n.   3

50. The amount of profit the Jones family can expect to make from selling their house is the difference between the amount offered for the house and $35,000, the amount they paid.

a.

a: amount offered	$60,000	$63,000	$65,000	$68,000
P: profit	$25,000	?	?	?

b. Profit = Amount offered − $35,000, or $P =$ __?__ − __?__ $a - 35,000$

51. To estimate the number of bricks needed for a wall, a bricklayer multiplies the area of the wall by 7.

a.

A: area in square feet	40	80	160	320
d: number of bricks	?	?	?	?

b. Bricks needed = 7 · Area, or $d =$ __?__ $7A$

52. The time in hours that it takes to travel d kilometers at an average rate of 86 kilometers per hour equals d divided by 86.

a.

d: distance in kilometers	774	1548	3096	6192
t: time in hours	?	?	?	?

b. Time = Distance ÷ 86, or __?__ = __?__ ÷ __?__ $t = d ÷ 86$

Uses of Algebra **15**

53. At the XYZ Tool Company, weekly earnings equal $340 plus $12.75 for each hour of overtime.

a.	h: hours of overtime	1	2	3	4	5
	E: weekly earnings	?	?	?	?	?

b. Weekly earnings = ___?___ + **$12.75h**, or $E =$ ___?___ $340; 340 + 12.75h

C
54. The total cost of a purchase in a state that has a 5% sales tax is the cost of the purchase plus the tax.

a.	c: cost of purchase	$5	$10	$15	$20	$25
	0.05c: tax	?	?	?	?	?
	T: total cost	?	?	?	?	?

b. Total cost = ___?___ + ___?___ , or $T =$ ___?___ $c + 0.05c; 1.05c$

55. When driving on dry pavement, a driver should stay 5.5 meters (one car length) distant from the car ahead for each 16 kilometers per hour of speed.

a.	r: rate in kilometers per hour	32	48	64	72	80
	F: following distance	?	?	?	?	?

b. Following distance = ___?___ $\cdot \left(\dfrac{\text{rate}}{16}\right)$, or $F =$ ___?___ $5.5; 5.5 \cdot \dfrac{r}{16}$

——————— **REVIEW CAPSULE FOR SECTION 1–5** ———————

Evaluate each expression for the given value of the variable. *(Pages 5–8)*

1. $3(x + 4) - 2$ when $x = 2$ 16

2. $14 - 2(y - 5)$ when $y = 7$ 10

3. $4(k - 5) + 5$ when $k = 5$ 5

4. $12 + 4(t + 1)$ when $t = 9$ 52

5. $2r + (r - 7)$ when $r = 12.5$ 30.5

6. $21t - 8$ when $t = 0.5$ 2.5

In Exercises 7–11, find Q for each formula. The replacement set for n is $\{0, 2, 4, 6, 8\}$. *(Pages 9–11)*

7. $Q = 4n + 1$ 1, 9, 17, 25, 33

8. $Q = 7n + 3$ 3, 17, 31, 45, 59

9. $Q = 100n + 1$

10. $Q = \dfrac{4n + 6}{4n + 3}$

11. $Q = \dfrac{8n + 12}{2}$ 6, 14, 22, 30, 38

12. $Q = \dfrac{2n + 1}{2n + 1}$ 1

16   *Chapter 1*

This lesson is optional. It applies the skills of operations with whole numbers and reading tables to consumer applications.

Consumer Applications

Yearly Driving Costs

Knowing the real cost for operating and maintaining a car may help the consumer save money and energy. To find the **yearly cost per mile**, use this formula.

$$\text{Cost per Mile} = \left(\begin{array}{c}\text{Total Fixed} \\ \text{Costs}\end{array} + \begin{array}{c}\text{Total Variable} \\ \text{Costs}\end{array} + \begin{array}{c}\text{Total Other} \\ \text{Costs}\end{array}\right) \div \begin{array}{c}\text{Total Miles} \\ \text{Driven}\end{array}$$

EXAMPLE   Samantha drives her car 25,000 miles per year. She listed the costs for operating her car last year. Compute the cost per mile.

FIXED COSTS	YEARLY TOTALS	
1. Depreciation	$2100	
2. Insurance	$ 700	
3. License, registration, taxes	$ 250	
4. Finance charges	$ 875	
5. TOTAL FIXED COSTS	$3925	← Line 1 + Line 2 + Line 3 + Line 4
VARIABLE COSTS		
6. Gas and oil per mile	$0.08	
7. Number of miles driven	24,000	← Line 6 × Line 7
8. Cost per year	$1920	
9. Maintenance	$ 325	
10. Tires (average yearly cost)	$ 40	
11. TOTAL VARIABLE COSTS	$2285	← Line 8 + Line 9 + Line 10
12. OTHER COSTS (car wash, tolls, parking fees, etc.)	$ 240	
13. TOTAL YEARLY DRIVING COSTS	$6450	← Line 5 + Line 11 + Line 12
14. COST PER MILE	$0.26875	← Line 13 ÷ Line 7

Thus, the cost per mile is **26.9¢.** ← **Rounded to the nearest tenth of a cent.**

EXERCISES

In Exercises 1–4, find the cost per mile to the nearest tenth of a cent.

	Total Fixed Costs	Total Variable Costs	Other Costs	Total Mileage	Total Yearly Driving Costs	Cost Per Mile
1.	$3416	$1825	$450	20,000	?	?
2.	$4650	$1975	$320.50	18,000	?	?
3.	$3829	$2120.50	$218.75	21,000	?	?
4.	$3118	$1865.70	$455.60	24,000	?	?

Additional Answers
1. $5691; 28.5¢
2. $6945.50; 38.6¢
3. $6168.25; 29.4¢
4. $5439.30

Yearly Driving Costs   17

Teaching Suggestions p. M-14

1–5   Sentences and Solution Sets

This table shows four different *mathematical sentences*.

Sentence	Read
$5 + 2 = 7$	Five plus two **equals** 7.
$8 > 5$	Eight **is greater than** five.
$15 + 6 < 25$	Fifteen plus six **is less than** twenty-five.
$17 \neq 4$	Seventeen **is not equal to** 4.

A mathematical sentence that contains the symbol "=" is an **equation.**

A sentence which contains a variable such as $3t - 5 = 22$, or any formula is also an equation. Such an equation is neither true nor false until you choose numbers to replace the variables. Equations that contain variables are **open sentences.**

When you find all the values for the variables that make a sentence true, you have found the *solution set.*

For example, when $t = 9$, $3t - 5 = 22$ is a true sentence. Thus, the solution set is $\{9\}$.

Definition

> The **solution set** of an open sentence is the set of numbers that makes the sentence true.

EXAMPLE 1   Find the solution set of $40 = 2n + 10$. The replacement set is $\{5, 10, 15\}$.

Solutions:

Replace n with 5.	Replace n with 10.	Replace n with 15.
$40 = 2n + 10$	$40 = 2n + 10$	$40 = 2n + 10$
$40 = 2(5) + 10$	$40 = 2(10) + 10$	$40 = 2(15) + 10$
$40 = 10 + 10$	$40 = 20 + 10$	$40 = 30 + 10$
$40 = 20$ **False**	$40 = 30$ **False**	$40 = 40$ **True**

Since 15 makes $40 = 2n + 10$ true, the solution set is $\{15\}$.

A mathematical sentence that uses $>$, $<$, or $\neq$ is an *inequality.*

Symbol	Meaning	Symbol	Meaning
$>$	is greater than	$<$	is less than

Symbol	Meaning
$\neq$	is not equal to

An inequality that contains a variable is also an open sentence.

EXAMPLE 2   Find the solution set of $x + 2 > 4$ where the replacement set is $\{2, 4, 6\}$.

Solutions:

Replace x with 2.	Replace x with 4.	Replace x with 6.
$x + 2 > 4$	$x + 2 > 4$	$x + 2 > 4$
$2 + 2 > 4$	$4 + 2 > 4$	$6 + 2 > 4$
$4 > 4$ **False**	$6 > 4$ **True**	$8 > 4$ **True**

Since 4 and 6 make $x + 2 > 4$ true, the solution set is $\{4, 6\}$.

When no number in the replacement set makes an open sentence true, the solution set is the **empty set,** or the **null set.** The symbol for the empty set is ϕ.

CLASSROOM EXERCISES

Classify each sentence as true, *T*, or false, *F*. When a sentence is false, tell why it is false.

1. $5 \cdot \frac{3}{8} = \frac{8}{3} \cdot 5$ $F; 1\frac{7}{8} \neq 13\frac{1}{3}$

2. $812 + 91 = 91 + 812$ T

3. $0 \cdot 491 < 0 \cdot 512$ $F; 0 = 0$

4. $597 - 0 = 597 + 0$ T

5. $(\frac{1}{5} + \frac{1}{3}) + \frac{5}{12} > \frac{1}{5} + (\frac{1}{3} + \frac{7}{12})$ $F; \frac{57}{60} < \frac{67}{60}$

6. $12\frac{1}{2} \cdot 1 = \frac{25}{2}$ T

Find the solution set of each sentence. The replacement set is $\{3, 5, 7, 9, 11\}$.

7. $x + 5 = 10$ $\{5\}$

8. $x + 5 > 10$ $\{7, 9, 11\}$

9. $x + 5 \neq 10$ $\{3, 7, 9, 11\}$

10. $x + 2x = 3x$ $\{3, 5, 7, 9, 11\}$

WRITTEN EXERCISES

Ⓐ   Classify each sentence as true, *T*, or false, *F*. When a sentence is false, tell why it is false.

1. $3 + 4 = 4 + 3$ T

2. $4 \cdot 3 = 3 \cdot 4$ T

3. $3 + (3 + 10) = (3 + 5) + 10$ $F; 16 \neq 18$

4. $(4 + \frac{1}{5}) + \frac{4}{5} > 4 + (\frac{1}{5} + \frac{4}{5})$ $F; 5 = 5$

5. $(2 \cdot 3) \cdot 5 < 2 \cdot (3 \cdot 6)$ T

6. $18 + 96 = 95 + 18$ $F; 114 \neq 113$

7. $632 + 49 = 49 + 632$ T

8. $0 \cdot 632 > 632$ $F; 0 < 632$

9. $0 + 632 = 632$ T

10. $1 \cdot 3\frac{1}{2} = 3\frac{1}{2}$ T

11. $12 + 44 < 43 + 12$ $F; 56 > 55$

12. $27 \cdot 9 > 9 \cdot 26$ T

Find the solution set for each sentence. The replacement set is $\{2, 4, 6, 8, 10\}$.

13. $x + 2 = 10$ $\{8\}$

14. $x + 2 < 10$ $\{2, 4, 6\}$

15. $x + 2 > 10$

16. $n \neq 3 + 5$ $\{2, 4, 6, 10\}$

17. $a + 2 = 2 + a$ $\{2, 4, 6, 8, 10\}$

18. $3x > 15$

19. $w + w = 8$ $\{4\}$

20. $t = 8$ $\{8\}$

21. $x \neq 2 + x$

22. $w + 5 = 7$ $\{2\}$

23. $2x < 8$ $\{2\}$

24. $x < 2$ ϕ

Uses of Algebra **19**

Additional Examples
Example 2
1. Find the solution set of $x - 3 > 8$ where the replacement set is $\{11, 12, 13\}$
   Ans: $\{12, 13\}$
2. Find the solution set of $x + 5 < 16$ where the replacement set is $\{6, 9, 12\}$
   Ans: $\{6, 9\}$

Assignment Guide
Minimal pp. 19–20: 1–30
Average pp. 19–20: 2–50 even
Above Average pp. 19–20: 3, 6, . . . 42, 52–62 even

Additional Answers
Written Exercises
15. $\{10\}$
18. $\{6, 8, 10\}$
21. $\{2, 4, 6, 8, 10\}$

Find the solution set. The replacement set is {0, 1, 2, 3, 4, 5}.

25. $x + 3 < 15$ {0, 1, 2, 3, 4, 5} **26.** $x + 2 < 10$ {0, 1, 2, 3, 4, 5} **27.** $10 + x = 15$

28. $10 + x > 30$ ϕ **29.** $x + 3 = x + 4$ ϕ **30.** $x + 1 < 5$

31. $3x > 9$ {4, 5} **32.** $x + 5 \neq 6$ {0, 2, 3, 4, 5} **33.** $25 < 2x + 3x$

Find the solution set. The replacement set is {0, 5, 10, 15, 20}.

34. $30 = 2l + 30$ {0} **35.** $4l + 70 = 150$ {20} **36.** $50 = 5w$

37. $6.2 + x > 9.8$ {5, 10, 15, 20} **38.** $2y - 10 < 15$ {0, 5, 10} **39.** $2a - a \neq 5$

40. $2m \cdot m = 0$ {0} **41.** $\frac{a^2}{5} = 45$ {15} **42.** $\frac{1}{2}x = 40$

Find the solution set for each sentence. The replacement set is {1, 2, 3, 4, 5, 6}.

43. $\frac{x}{2} = 1$ {2} **44.** $x^2 = 25$ {5} **45.** $x = x^2$ {1} **46.** $\frac{x}{10} < 1$

47. $x < 5 - 2$ {1, 2} **48.** $3x > \frac{x^2}{2}$ {1, 2, 3, 4, 5} **49.** $x^2 > 10$ {4, 5, 6} **50.** $\frac{6}{x} > 3$

C In Exercises 51–61, the replacement set for x and y is the set of whole numbers. Tell whether each sentence is true, T, or false, F, for all whole numbers. If the sentence is false, give an example that shows it is false.

51. $x + y = y + x$ T **52.** $(x + y) + x = x + (y + x)$ T

53. $x^2 > x + x$ **54.** $x^3 > x^2$ **55.** $1 \cdot x = x$ T **56.** $0 + y = y$ T

57. $x + y$ names one and only one whole number. T

58. xy names one and only one whole number. T

59. There is a whole number a such that $xa = 0$. T

60. There is a whole number a such that $x + a = x$. T

61. There is a whole number a such that $xa = 1$.

62. Is Exercise 53 true or false when the replacement set for x is the set of fractions? Give a reason for your answer. F; $(\frac{1}{2})^2 \not> \frac{1}{2} + \frac{1}{2}$

63. Is Exercise 54 true or false when the replacement set for x is the set of decimals? Give a reason for your answer. F; $(0.2)^3 \not> (0.2)^2$

Review

Write an algebraic expression for each word description. *(Section 1–1)*

1. The cost of 3 records at d dollars per record. $3d$

2. The number of miles, m, divided by 15, the number of gallons. $\frac{m}{15}$

Evaluate. *(Section 1–2)*

3. $4 \cdot 5 + 2$ 22 **4.** $15 - 1 \cdot 8$ 7 **5.** $\frac{3(8 - 5)}{4(2 + 8)}$ $\frac{9}{40}$ **6.** $12 \div [24 - 3(1 + 6)]$ 4

20 *Chapter 1*

Evaluate for the given values of the variables. *(Section 1–2)*

7. $80 - 8m$, for $m = 10$ 0

8. $(2a + b)$ for $a = 3$, $b = 5$ 11

Find *A* for each formula. The replacement set for *m* is $\{\frac{1}{2}, 4, 6\}$. *(Section 1–3)*

9. $A = 8 \cdot m + 6$
10, 38, 54

10. $A = \dfrac{2m + 4}{2}$
$\frac{5}{2}$, 6, 8

11. $A = m^3$
$\frac{1}{8}$, 64, 216

12. $A = 12(m + 2)$
30, 72, 96

Use the formula $A = \frac{1}{2}h(b + c)$ to find *A*. *(Section 1–4)*

13. $h = 10$, $b = 12$, $c = 15$

14. $h = 0.6$, $b = 0.03$, $c = 0.11$

15. $h = \frac{2}{3}$, $b = \frac{1}{3}$, $c = \frac{2}{3}$

Find the solution set. The replacement set is $\{1, 2, 3, 4, 5\}$. *(Section 1–5)*

16. $x + 7 < 10$ $\{1, 2\}$
17. $x - 3 \neq 1$
18. $\dfrac{x}{2} > 1$
19. $x^2 < 9$ $\{1, 2\}$

 **CALCULATOR APPLICATIONS** _____

Evaluating Expressions and Formulas

To evaluate expressions and formulas with a calculator, follow the rules for order of operations. It may be necessary to use the memory keys, M+ and MR.

EXAMPLE **a.** Use $C = \frac{5}{9}(F - 32)$ to find *C* when $F = 104$.

b. Evaluate: $9.35 - 4.062 \cdot 2.1 + 6.9$

SOLUTIONS a. First perform the operation in the parentheses.

$1\ 0\ 4\ \boxed{-}\ 3\ 2\ \boxed{\times}\ 5\ \boxed{\div}\ 9\ \boxed{=}$

b. Multiply first and store the product in the memory.

$4\ .\ 0\ 6\ 2\ \boxed{\times}\ 2\ .\ 1\ \boxed{=}\ \boxed{M+}\ 9\ .\ 3\ 5\ \boxed{-}\ \boxed{MR}\ \boxed{+}\ 6\ .\ 9\ \boxed{=}$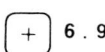

EXERCISES

Use the formula $C = \frac{5}{9}(F - 32)$ to find *C* for each value of *F*.

1. $F = 68$ 20
2. $F = 95$ 35
3. $F = 212$ 100
4. $F = 77$ 25
5. $F = 98.6$ 37
6. $F = \overset{45}{113}$

Evaluate each expression.

7. $6.04 + 2.72 \cdot 0.953 - 1.24$ 7.39216

8. $17.257 - 8.044 - 2.3 \cdot 3.64$ 0.841

9. $2.76 - 0.894 + 15.25 \div 1.90625$ 9.866

10. $0.026 \div 0.25 + 170 \div 1.6$ 106.354

_____ **REVIEW CAPSULE FOR SECTION 1–6** _____

Complete.

1. $\dfrac{1}{4} = \dfrac{?}{8}$ 2

2. $\dfrac{5}{?} = \dfrac{10}{12}$ 6

3. $\dfrac{3}{8} = \dfrac{?}{40}$ 15

4. $\dfrac{1}{14} = \dfrac{\overset{70}{5}}{?}$

5. $3\dfrac{3}{4} = \dfrac{?}{4}$ 15

6. $5\dfrac{3}{8} = \dfrac{?}{8}$ 43

7. $8\dfrac{4}{9} = \dfrac{?}{9}$ 76

8. $7\dfrac{5}{6} = \dfrac{?}{6}$
47

Quick Quiz
Find the solution set.
The replacement set is
{5, 7, 9, 11, 13}.
1. $x + 7 = 18$
   Ans: {**11**}
2. $n + 2 < 10$
   Ans: {**5, 7**}
3. $3t > 100$
   Ans: ϕ
4. $\frac{1}{3}p = 21$
   Ans: {**7**}
5. $z + 2z = 3z$
   Ans: {**5, 7, 9, 11, 13**}

OBJECTIVES: To identify elements which belong to the set of natural numbers

1–6 **Rational Numbers** and the set of rational numbers

To use positive and negative numbers to represent word statements

Some sets of numbers can be represented by listing their **elements** or **members**. The three dots mean that the numbers continue on indefinitely.

$$\text{Counting or natural numbers: } N = \{1, 2, 3, 4, \cdots\}$$

$$\text{Whole numbers: } W = \{0, 1, 2, 3, \cdots\}$$

The set of **integers** consists of the set of whole numbers and their **opposites**. The opposite of a positive integer is a **negative integer**. The opposite of a negative integer is a **positive integer**. For example, $^-2$ (read "negative 2") is the opposite of 2, and 3 is the opposite of $^-3$. The integer **0 is its own opposite**.

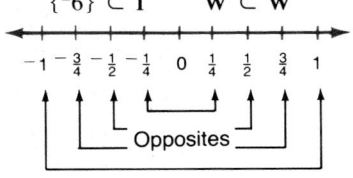

$$\text{Integers: } I = \{\cdots {}^-4, {}^-3, {}^-2, {}^-1, 0, 1, 2, 3, 4, \cdots\}$$

Since every number in the set of natural numbers is also a member of the set of integers, the set of natural numbers is a **subset** of the set of integers. The symbol $\subset$ means "is a subset of." Here are some subset relationships.

$$N \subset W \qquad W \subset I \qquad \{0\} \subset W \qquad \{^-6\} \subset I \qquad W \subset W$$

NOTE: **Every set is a subset of itself.**

Not all points on the number line represent integers. Numbers such as $^-1\frac{2}{3}$, $^-\frac{1}{3}$, $\frac{3}{2}$, $2\frac{5}{6}$, and so on, are **rational numbers**.

Definition

A **rational number** is a number that can be expressed in the form $\frac{a}{b}$, where a is an integer and b is a natural number.

Examples of rational numbers are given in the table below. Note that there are many ways of writing the same rational number:

Rational Number	Expressed as $\frac{a}{b}$	Some Other Names
4	$\frac{4}{1}$	$\frac{8}{2}, \frac{16}{4}, \frac{100}{25}, \cdots$
0	$\frac{0}{1}$	$\frac{0}{2}, \frac{0}{3}, \frac{0}{500}, \cdots$
0.73	$\frac{73}{100}$	$\frac{365}{500}, \frac{1460}{2000}, \frac{2190}{3000}, \cdots$
$^-5\frac{3}{4}$	$\frac{^-23}{4}$	$\frac{^-46}{8}, \frac{^-69}{12}, {}^-5\frac{6}{8}, \cdots$

22 *Chapter 1*

The **set of rational numbers,** Q, is made up of the positive rational numbers, the negative rational numbers, and zero.

Positive and negative rational numbers are used in various ways. One way is to show amounts above or below zero.

	Statement	Number
Temperature	32° above 0	32
	10° below 0	$^-10$
Elevation	150 meters above sea level	150
	100 meters below sea level	$^-100$

Positive and negative rational numbers can also be used to show both the amount and direction of change.

	Statement	Number
Football	Gain of 10 yards	10
	Loss of 3 yards	$^-3$
Money	Deposit of $30.75	30.75
	Withdrawal of $25	$^-25$

CLASSROOM EXERCISES

Use the words *natural number, whole number, integer,* or *rational number* to classify each number. More than one answer may be possible.

1. 0   2. $^-5$ 3. $\frac{2}{5}$ 4. $1\frac{1}{8}$ 5. $\frac{^-4}{5}$ 6. $^-1$

Write each number in the form $\frac{a}{b}$.

7. 0 $\frac{0}{1}$ 8. 1 $\frac{1}{1}$ 9. $16\frac{2}{3}$ $\frac{50}{3}$ 10. $^-0.25$ $-\frac{25}{100}$ 11. $^-5.2$ $-\frac{52}{10}$ 12. 15.9 $\frac{159}{10}$

WRITTEN EXERCISES

A   Classify each sentence as true, *T,* or false, *F.* When a sentence is false, tell why it is false.

1. $\frac{1}{3}$ is a natural number.

2. $^-\frac{1}{3}$ is an integer.

3. $12\frac{5}{6}$ is a rational number. *T*

4. 6.5 is a rational number. *T*

5. The opposite of 5 is $^-5$. *T*

6. Every counting number is an integer. *T*

7. Every integer is a rational number. *T*

8. There is at least one whole number that is not a natural number. *T*

Uses of Algebra   **23**

Additional Answers
Classroom Exercises
1. Whole number, integer, rational number
2. Integer, rational number
3. Rational number
4. Rational number
5. Rational number
6. Integer, rational number

Assignment Guide
Minimal pp. 23–24: 1–12, 13–53 odd
Average pp. 23–24: 1–63 odd
Above Average pp. 23–24: 1–53 odd, 54–63

Additional Answers
Written Exercises
1. *F*; fractions are not natural numbers.
2. *F*; fractions are not integers.

9. The number 0 is neither positive nor negative. *T*

10. The set of whole numbers is made up of the set of positive integers and 0. *T*

11. The set of rational numbers is made up of the negative integers, the positive integers, and zero.

12. The set of counting numbers is a subset of the rational numbers. *T*

Write each rational number in the form $\frac{a}{b}$, where a is an integer and b is a natural number.

13. 0.4 $\frac{4}{10}$ **14.** 0.75 $\frac{75}{100}$ **15.** 0.37 $\frac{37}{100}$ **16.** 0.24   **17.** $^-6\frac{1}{3}$ $-\frac{19}{3}$ **18.** $8\frac{2}{5}$ $\frac{42}{5}$

19. $3\frac{3}{4}$ $\frac{15}{4}$ **20.** $^-6\frac{8}{9}$ $\frac{62}{9}$ **21.** 67.25   **22.** $^-0.01$ **23.** 0 $\frac{0}{1}$ **24.** $^-100$ $\frac{-100}{1}$

Represent each of the following by a positive or negative rational number.

25. A temperature 6° above zero   6

26. A temperature 3° below zero -3

27. An elevation of 462 meters below sea level -462

28. An elevation of 6070 meters above sea level   6070

29. A deposit of $525 in a saving account   525

30. A deposit of $76.20 in a checking account   76.20

31. A withdrawal of $155 from a savings account -155

32. A loss of 7 yards on a football play -7

33. A gain of 12 yards on a football play   12

34. A velocity forward of 60 kilometers per hour   60

35. A velocity backward of 15 kilometers per hour -15

36. A stock loss of $\frac{1}{4}$ of a point $-\frac{1}{4}$

37. A jump upward of $4\frac{1}{2}$ feet $4\frac{1}{2}$

38. A stock gain of $3\frac{1}{8}$ points $3\frac{1}{8}$

39. A fall of 6 meters -6

40. A climb of 2000 feet   2000

41. A descent of 1 kilometer -1

42. A drop in temperature of 2° -2

43. Growth of $2\frac{3}{4}$ inches $2\frac{3}{4}$

44. A weight gain of $2\frac{1}{2}$ pounds $2\frac{1}{2}$

45. A weight loss of 31 pounds -31

46. A paycheck deduction of $3.15 -3.15

47. An income tax refund of $73.20

48. A team penalty of 15 yards -15

49. A debt of $250 -250

50. A temperature rise of 5.7°   5.7

51. A fall in temperature of 3.5° -3.5

52. A profit of $750   750

53. A loss of $315 -315

54. A salary increase of $2.50 per hour   2.50

55. A submarine dive of 500 feet -500

B   Classify each statement as true, *T*, or false, *F*. When a statement is false, tell why it is false.

56. N ⊂ W   *T*   **57.** I ⊂ W   *F*   **58.** N ⊂ I   *T*   **59.** W ⊂ N   *F*   **60.** N ⊂ N   *T*

61. Q ⊂ I   *F*   **62.** N ⊂ Q   *T*   **63.** Q ⊂ W   *F*   **64.** Q ⊂ Q   *T*   **65.** {0} ⊂ N   *F*

24   *Chapter 1*

Divide. Carry the division to five decimal places.

1. $2 \div 3$ 0.66666   2. $3 \div 11$ 0.27272   3. $2 \div 9$ 0.22222   4. $7 \div 12$ 0.58333   5. $1 \div 6$

Complete. Write a decimal for each fraction or mixed number.

6. $\frac{3}{5} = \frac{?}{100} = 0.6$ 60   7. $\frac{7}{10} = \frac{?}{100} = \underline{\ ?\ }$ 70, 0.7   8. $\frac{19}{20} = \frac{?}{100} = 0.95$ 95

9. $\frac{23}{50} = \frac{46}{?} = \underline{\ ?\ }$ 100; 0.46   10. $\frac{18}{25} = \frac{72}{?} = \underline{\ ?\ }$ 100; 0.72   11. $\frac{21}{4} = \frac{?}{100} = \underline{\ ?\ }$

12. $7\frac{1}{2} = 7 + 0.5 = \underline{\ ?\ }$ 7.5   13. $9\frac{3}{4} = 9 + \underline{\ ?\ } = 9.75$ 0.75   14. $8\frac{1}{5} = 8 + \underline{\ ?\ } = \underline{\ ?\ }$

OBJECTIVES: To identify irrational numbers and real numbers
To approximate values of irrational numbers using a Table of Square Roots

1–7   Real Numbers

Any rational number such as $\frac{1}{3}$ and $\frac{2}{11}$ can be represented by an infinite repeating decimal.

$$\frac{1}{3} = 0.333 \cdots = 0.\overline{3} \qquad\qquad\qquad \frac{2}{11} = 0.1818 \cdots = 0.\overline{18}$$

The bar indicates the digits that repeat.

Rational numbers such as 0.75 and 1.4 are **terminating decimals.** However, they can be written as infinite repeating decimals.

$$\frac{3}{4} = 0.75 = 0.75000 \cdots \qquad\qquad 1\frac{2}{5} = \frac{7}{5} = 1.4 = 1.4000 \cdots$$

Zero is the digit that repeats.

Irrational numbers can be represented by **infinite nonrepeating decimals.** This means that no matter how many digits are used in the decimal representation of an irrational number, the sequence of digits **never** repeats. Here are some examples of irrational numbers.

$1.4142135 \cdots \qquad 2.2360679 \cdots \qquad 3.4641016 \cdots \qquad 3.14114111411114 \cdots$

Irrational numbers may be positive or negative. For example, $^-1.4142135 \cdots$ is a negative irrational number. The number $1.4142135 \cdots$ can be written another way. That is,

$$1.4142135 \cdots = \sqrt{2} \longleftarrow \text{ Read: "the square root of 2."}$$

Taking the square root of a number is the inverse of squaring. For example,

$$\sqrt{16} = 4 \qquad \text{because} \qquad 4^2 = 4 \cdot 4 = 16.$$
$$\sqrt{225} = 15 \qquad \text{because} \qquad 15^2 = 15 \cdot 15 = 225.$$

For an irrational number such as $\sqrt{2}$, there is no positive integer whose square is 2. That is, there is no positive integer n, such that $n \cdot n = 2$.

Uses of Algebra   **25**

Teaching Suggestions p. M-14

Quick Quiz
Write each number in the form $\frac{a}{b}$, where a is an integer and b is a natural number.
1. 16.3
   Ans: $\frac{163}{10}$
2. $2\frac{3}{5}$
   Ans: $\frac{13}{5}$
Represent each of the following as a positive or negative rational number.
3. A temperature drop of 6.5°.
   Ans: $-6.5°$
4. A profit of $50
   Ans: 50
5. A stock loss of $1\frac{1}{4}$ points
   Ans: $-1\frac{1}{4}$

> For any positive integer n, $\sqrt{n}$ is either a positive integer (rational number) or an irrational number.

Additional Examples
Example 1
Tell whether each number
is rational or irrational.
Give a reason.
1. $\sqrt{15}$
   **Ans: Irrational; There is
   no positive integer n
   such that $n \cdot n = 15$.**
2. $\sqrt{169}$
   **Ans: Rational; $\sqrt{169} = 13$
   and 13 is a rational
   number.**

EXAMPLE 1 Tell whether n is rational or irrational. Give a reason for your answer.

$\sqrt{n}$	Rational or Irrational	Reason
a. $\sqrt{81}$	Rational	$\sqrt{81} = 9$ and 9 is a rational number.
b. $\sqrt{13}$	Irrational	There is no positive integer n such that $n \cdot n = 13$.
c. $\sqrt{7}$	Irrational	There is no positive integer n such that $n \cdot n = 7$.

Recall that any rational number can be represented in the form $\frac{a}{b}$, where a is an integer and b is a natural number. Irrational numbers *cannot* be represented in this way. Together, the set of rational numbers, Q, and the set of irrational numbers, Ir, form the set of real numbers.

> The set of rational numbers, Q, and the set of irrational numbers, Ir, make up the set of **real numbers, R.**

Every point on the number line can be associated with a real number.

A number associated with a point on the number line is called the **coordinate** of the point.

Example 2
Name the coordinate of each point.
1. The point 1 unit to the right of B
   Ans: $-\frac{1}{2}$
2. The point 3 units to the left of D
   Ans: $1\frac{1}{4}$
3. The point 2 units to the left of C
   Ans: $-\frac{1}{4}$
4. The point 4 units to the right of -2
   Ans: -1

EXAMPLE 2 Name the coordinates of A, B, C, and D.

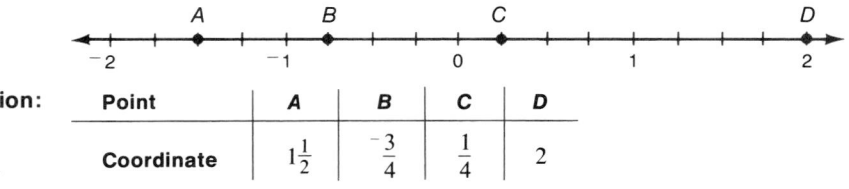

Solution:

Point	A	B	C	D
Coordinate	$1\frac{1}{2}$	$-\frac{3}{4}$	$\frac{1}{4}$	2

Every real number can also be associated with a point on the number line.

You will learn a geometric method of locating an irrational number on the number line when you study the Pythagorean Theorem on page 439.

However, you can use the Table of Square Roots on page 541 to find approximate values for some irrational numbers.

26   *Chapter 1*

EXAMPLE 3   Use the Table of Square Roots to find an approximate value for $\sqrt{10}$.

Solution: **1.** Find "10" in the No.–column.
2. Look directly to the right under the Square Root–column.

Number	Square	Square Root
10	100	3.162

3.162

Thus, $\sqrt{10} \approx 3.162$ ⟵ ≈ means "is approximately equal to."

Rounded to the nearest tenth, 3.162 = 3.2. Thus, on a number line, $\sqrt{10}$ is close to 3.2.

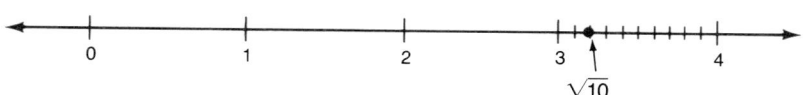

CLASSROOM EXERCISES

Identify each number as rational, Q, or irrational, Ir. Give a reason for each answer.

1. $\sqrt{5}$ Ir.   **2.** $\sqrt{49}$ Q   **3.** $\sqrt{21}$ Ir.   **4.** $\sqrt{18}$ Ir.   **5.** $\sqrt{144}$ Q   **6.** $\sqrt{51}$ Ir.

Name the sets to which each number belongs. More than one answer may be possible.

7. $\sqrt{1}$ **8.** $\sqrt{2}$ Ir., R   **9.** $0.\overline{3}$ Q, R   **10.** $\sqrt{\dfrac{9}{16}}$ Q, R   **11.** $^{-}1.5$ Q, R   **12.** $\sqrt{5}$ Ir., R

Use the Table of Square Roots on page 541 to find an approximate value for each number.

13. $\sqrt{19}$ 4.359   **14.** $\sqrt{97}$ 9.849   **15.** $\sqrt{101}$ 10.050   **16.** $\sqrt{63}$ 7.937   **17.** $\sqrt{149}$ 12.207   **18.** $\sqrt{135}$ 11.619

WRITTEN EXERCISES

A   Write a decimal for each fraction or mixed number. Use a bar to indicate the repeating, nonzero digits.

1. $\dfrac{2}{3}$ $0.\overline{6}$ **2.** $\dfrac{5}{9}$ $0.\overline{5}$ **3.** $\dfrac{16}{3}$ $5.\overline{3}$ **4.** $2\dfrac{1}{2}$ 2.5   **5.** $7\dfrac{3}{16}$ 7.1875   **6.** $\dfrac{8}{25}$

7. $1\dfrac{3}{8}$ 1.375   **8.** $4\dfrac{1}{12}$ $4.08\overline{3}$ **9.** $\dfrac{3}{20}$ 0.15   **10.** $\dfrac{^{-}6}{7}$ **11.** $\dfrac{^{-}3}{11}$ $-0.\overline{27}$ **12.** $\dfrac{5}{13}$

Identify each number as rational, Q, or irrational, Ir. Give a reason for each answer.

13. $\sqrt{7}$ Ir.   **14.** $\sqrt{64}$ Q   **15.** $\sqrt{11}$ Ir.   **16.** $\sqrt{17}$ Ir.   **17.** $\sqrt{625}$ Q   **18.** $\sqrt{19}$

19. $\sqrt{83}$ Ir.   **20.** $\sqrt{\dfrac{25}{9}}$ Q   **21.** $\sqrt{\dfrac{36}{16}}$ Q   **22.** $\sqrt{53}$ Ir.   **23.** $\sqrt{100}$ Q   **24.** $\sqrt{13}$

Uses of Algebra   **27**

Additional Examples
Example 3
Use the Table of Square Roots to find an approximate value for each number.
  1. $\sqrt{76}$ **Ans: 8.718**
  2. $\sqrt{34}$ **Ans: 5.831**
  3. $\sqrt{147}$ **Ans: 12.124**

Additional Answers
Classroom Exercises
  1. There is no positive integer n such that $n \cdot n = 5$.
  2. $\sqrt{49} = 7$, 7 is rational
  3. There is no positive integer n such that $n \cdot n = 21$.
  4. There is no positive integer n such that $n \cdot n = 11$.
  5. $\sqrt{144} = 12$, 12 is rational
  6. There is no positive integer n such that $n \cdot n = 51$.
  7. N, W, I, Q, R

Assignment Guide
Minimal pp. 27–28: 2–50 even
Average pp. 27–29: 2–62 even
Above Average pp. 27–29: 3, 6, 9, . . . 63, 64–82

Additional Answers
Written Exercises
  6. 0.32
  10. $-0.\overline{857142}$
  12. $0.\overline{384615}$
  13. There is no positive integer n such that $n \cdot n = 7$.
  14. $\sqrt{64} = 8$, 8 is rational
  15. There is no positive integer n such that $n \cdot n = 11$.
  16. There is no positive integer n such that $n \cdot n = 17$.
  17. $\sqrt{625} = 25$, 25 is rational
  18. There is no positive integer n such that $n \cdot n = 19$.
  19. There is no positive integer n such that $n \cdot n = 83$.
  20. $\sqrt{\dfrac{25}{9}} = \dfrac{5}{3}$, $\dfrac{5}{3}$ is rational
  21. $\sqrt{\dfrac{36}{16}} = \dfrac{6}{4}$, $\dfrac{6}{4}$ is rational
  22. There is no positive integer n such that $n \cdot n = 53$.
  23. $\sqrt{100} = 10$, 10 is rational
  24. There is no positive integer n such that $n \cdot n = 13$.

Copy this table. Then use a *check mark* (✔) to indicate the sets to which each number belongs. The first one is done for you.

		Integers	Rational Numbers	Irrational Numbers	Real Numbers
25.	-3.5		✔		✔
26.	$\frac{5}{6}$		√		√
27.	$\sqrt{3}$			√	√
28.	$0.\overline{524}$		√		√
29.	$3.4641016\cdots$			√	√
30.	$\frac{81}{3}$	√	√		√
31.	$\sqrt{121}$	√	√		√
32.	$1.\overline{26}$		√		√
33.	$\frac{3}{5}$		√		√
34.	$-2\frac{5}{6}$		√		√

Give the coordinate of the point named by each letter.

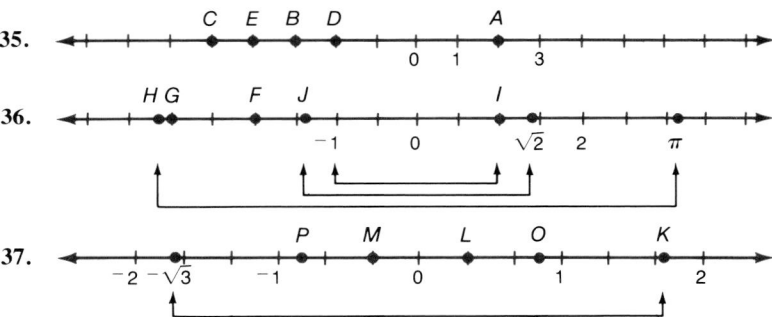

35.

36.

37.

Use the Table of Square Roots on page 541 to find an approximate value for each number.

38. $\sqrt{39}$ 6.245 **39.** $\sqrt{18}$ 4.243 **40.** $\sqrt{136}$ 11.662 **41.** $\sqrt{110}$ 10.488 **42.** $\sqrt{55}$

43. $\sqrt{17}$ 4.123 **44.** $\sqrt{40}$ 6.325 **45.** $\sqrt{80}$ 8.944 **46.** $\sqrt{139}$ 11.790 **47.** $\sqrt{76}$

48. Use your answer to Exercise 39 to graph the approximate position of $\sqrt{18}$ on a number line. Approximately 4.2 units to the right of the origin.

49. Use your answer to Exercise 43 to graph the approximate position of $\sqrt{17}$ on a number line. Approximately 4.1 units to the right of the origin.

50. Use your answer to Exercise 44 to graph the approximate position of $\sqrt{40}$ on a number line. Approximately 6.3 units to the right of the origin.

51. Use your answer to Exercise 47 to graph the approximate position of $\sqrt{76}$ on a number line. Approximately 8.7 units to the right of the origin.

28   *Chapter 1*

B Replace *n* with the smallest possible whole number to make a true statement.

52. $6 < \sqrt{39} < n$ 7

53. $7 < \sqrt{63} < n$ 8

54. $3 < \sqrt{12} < n$ 4

55. $15 < \sqrt{229} < n$ 16

56. $11 < \sqrt{140} < n$ 12

57. $8 < \sqrt{76} < n$ 9

Replace *x* with the largest possible number to make a true statement.

58. $x < \sqrt{223} < 15$ 14

59. $x < \sqrt{442} < 22$ 20

60. $x < \sqrt{189} < 14$

61. $x < \sqrt{627} < 26$ 25

62. $x < \sqrt{171} < 14$ 13

63. $x < \sqrt{1588} < 40$

The number π is an irrational number. It is the quotient of the circumference of a circle divided by the length of a diameter. To six decimal places,
$$\pi = 3.141592.$$

In Exercises 64–67, four approximations to π computed by ancient mathematicians are given. Divide to find the value of each approximation to six decimal places.

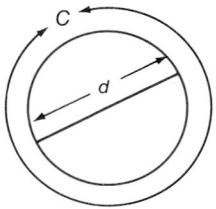

64. Archimedes (240 B.C.): $\pi = \frac{223}{71}$

65. Ptolemy (A.D. 150): $\pi = \frac{377}{120}$

66. Tsu Ch'ung–chik (A.D. 480): $\pi = \frac{355}{113}$

67. Bhāshara (A.D. 1150): $\pi = \frac{3927}{1250}$

68. Which of the approximations in Exercises 64–67 is closest to $\pi = 3.141592$?

Replace each __?__ with ⊂ or ⊄. (⊄ means "is not a subset of.")

69. I __?__ W   ⊄

70. Q __?__ R   ⊂

71. N __?__ Q   ⊂

72. R __?__ Q   ⊄

73. W __?__ N

74. I __?__ Q   ⊂

75. N __?__ W   ⊂

76. Q __?__ Ir   ⊄

77. I __?__ R   ⊂

78. Ir __?__ R

Choose from the box at the right the word or words that complete each statement. More than one answer may be possible.

| natural |
| whole |
| rational |
| irrational |
| real |

79. Every __?__ number is a real number.

80. Every rational number is a __?__ number.   real

81. Every irrational number is a __?__ number.   real

82. Every natural number is a __?__ number.   whole, rational, real

Puzzle

In Roman numerals, I stands for 1, and VII stands for 7. Therefore, $\frac{1}{7}$ can be written as $\frac{\text{I}}{\text{VII}}$ in Roman numerals.

Using straight lines for each digit, make $\frac{\text{I}}{\text{VII}}$ equal in value to 1 by changing the position of one line only.   Turn one line in VII horizontal to give $\frac{1}{\sqrt{1}} = 1$

1–8 Postulates For Real Numbers

Teaching Suggestions p. M-14

Quick Quiz

Indicate the set or sets to which each number belongs. Use I = {integers}, Q = {rational numbers}, Ir = {irrational numbers}, and R = {real numbers}.

1. $\sqrt{144}$ **Ans: I, Q, R**
2. $\sqrt{29}$ **Ans: Ir, R**
3. $4.\overline{3}$ **Ans: Q, R**
4. -3 **Ans: I, Q, R**
5. $\frac{98}{2}$ **Ans: I, Q, R**

Additional Examples
Example 1
Find a value of the variable that makes each equation true. Give a reason.

1. $6.2 + t = 6.2$
   Ans: $t = 0$; Ident. post. for add.
2. $\frac{1}{5} \cdot \frac{8}{9} = \frac{8}{9} \cdot x$
   Ans: $x = \frac{1}{5}$; Comm. post. for mult.
3. $120 + 62 = 62 + r$
   Ans: $r = 120$; Comm. post. for add.
4. $92.5 \cdot q = 92.5$
   Ans: $q = 1$; Ident. post. for mult.

The table illustrates four *postulates* that are true for all real numbers a and b. **Postulates** are statements that are accepted as true.

Name	In Symbols	Example
Commutative postulate for addition	$a + b = b + a$	$\frac{6}{7} + \frac{1}{2} = \frac{1}{2} + \frac{6}{7}$
Commutative postulate for multiplication	$a \cdot b = b \cdot a$	$\frac{6}{7} \cdot \frac{1}{2} = \frac{1}{2} \cdot \frac{6}{7}$
Identity postulate for addition	$a + 0 = 0 + a = a$	$3.5 + 0 = 0 + 3.5 = 3.5$
Identity postulate for multiplication	$a \cdot 1 = 1 \cdot a = a$	$1 \cdot \sqrt{2} = \sqrt{2} \cdot 1 = \sqrt{2}$

EXAMPLE 1 Use the postulates in the table to find a value of the variable that makes each equation true. Name the postulate that gives the reason for each answer.

a. $172 \cdot \frac{9}{7} = \frac{9}{7} \cdot x$ **b.** $15 + 0.3 = t + 15$ **c.** $\frac{3}{2} \cdot s = \frac{3}{2}$ **d.** $3 + z = 3$

Equation	Solution	Reason
a. $172 \cdot \frac{9}{7} = \frac{9}{7} \cdot x$	$x = 172$	Commutative postulate for multiplication
b. $15 + 0.3 = t + 15$	$t = 0.3$	Commutative postulate for addition
c. $\frac{3}{2} \cdot s = \frac{3}{2}$	$s = 1$	Identity postulate for multiplication
d. $3 + z = 3$	$z = 0$	Identity postulate for addition

The **Associative Postulates for addition and multiplication** allow you to regroup numbers. Remember that a, b, and c represent real numbers.

Name	In Symbols	Example
Associative postulate for addition	$a + (b + c) = (a + b) + c$	$7 + (5 + 8.1) = (7 + 5) + 8.1$
Associative postulate for multiplication	$a(bc) = (ab)c$	$7(5 \cdot 8.1) = (7 \cdot 5)8.1$

The **Distributive Postulate (multiplication over addition)** shows how to write a product as a sum.

Name	In Symbols	Example
Distributive postulate	$a(b + c) = ab + ac$	$9\left(3 + \frac{2}{3}\right) = 9 \cdot 3 + 9 \cdot \frac{2}{3}$

30 *Chapter 1*

The postulates for real numbers can be used to evaluate expressions. Recall that to evaluate an expression means to find its value.

EXAMPLE 2 Evaluate: **a.** $10(45 \cdot 6)$ **b.** $5\left(2 + \frac{1}{5}\right)$

Solutions: **a.** Use the associative postulate.

$10(45 \cdot 6) = (10 \cdot 45)6$ ◄——— **By the associative postulate**

$= 450 \cdot 6$

$= 2700$

b. Use the distributive postulate.

$5\left(2 + \frac{1}{5}\right) = 5(2) + 5\left(\frac{1}{5}\right)$

$= 10 + 1$

$= 11$

Additional Examples
Example 2
Evaluate:
1. 10 (51.7) **Ans: 3570**
2. 100 (16.9) **Ans: 14,400**
3. 21 $(3 + \frac{1}{7})$ **Ans: 66**
4. 18 $(\frac{1}{9} + 6)$ **Ans: 110**

The distributive postulate can also be expressed in this form.

$$(a + b)c = ac + bc$$

EXAMPLE 3 Use the distributive postulate to find $(45)8$.

Solution: First write 45 as $40 + 5$.

$45(8) = (40 + 5)8$

$= 40 \cdot 8 + 5 \cdot 8$ ◄——— **By the distributive postulate**

$= 320 + 40$

$= 360$

Example 3
Use the distributive postulate to find each of the following.
1. (39)6
 Ans: (30 + 9)6 = 234
2. (82)9
 Ans: (80 + 2)9 = 738

You already know that the sum of two real numbers is a real number and that the product of two real numbers is a real number. The following two postulates state this. Recall that

the symbol $\in$ means "is an element of."

For example,

$\sqrt{5} \in$ R means that $\sqrt{5}$ is an element of the set of real numbers.

Name	In Symbols	Examples
Closure postulate for addition	$(a + b) \in$ R	$0.05 + 1.65 = 1.70$ $\frac{3}{5} + \frac{1}{10} = \frac{7}{10}$
Closure postulate for multiplication	$(a \cdot b) \in$ R	$0.05 \cdot 1.65 = 0.0825$ $\frac{3}{5} \cdot \frac{1}{10} = \frac{3}{50}$

Uses of Algebra **31**

CLASSROOM EXERCISES

Name the postulate illustrated by each sentence.

1. $5 \cdot (20 + 3) = (5 \cdot 20) + (5 \cdot 3)$ dist. post.

2. $17 + 3\frac{1}{2} = 3\frac{1}{2} + 17$

3. $5\frac{1}{2} \cdot 6\frac{1}{2} = 6\frac{1}{2} \cdot 5\frac{1}{2}$ comm. post. for mult.

4. $4 + (2 + \frac{1}{2}) = (4 + 2) + \frac{1}{2}$

5. $0 + 62.9 = 62.9$ identity post. for add.

6. $3 \cdot (2 \cdot \frac{1}{2}) = (3 \cdot 2) \cdot \frac{1}{2}$

7. $0.\overline{9} \cdot 1 = 0.\overline{9}$ identity post. for mult.

8. $(98)12 = 90 \cdot 12 + 8 \cdot 12$ dist. post.

9. $x + \sqrt{5} = \sqrt{5} + x$ comm. post. for add.

10. $r \cdot \frac{1}{5} \cdot s = \frac{1}{5}rs$ comm. post. for mult.

11. $(0.5)(290)$ is a real number.
closure post. for mult.

12. $16.8 + 7.2$ is a real number.
closure post. for add.

WRITTEN EXERCISES

A   Name the postulate illustrated by each sentence.

1. $6 + 8 = 8 + 6$ comm. post. for add.

2. $(10 \cdot 5) \cdot 4 = 10 \cdot (5 \cdot 4)$

3. $3(10) = (10)3$ comm. post. for mult.

4. $8(2 + \frac{1}{2}) = (8 \cdot 2) + (8 \cdot \frac{1}{2})$ dist. post.

5. $(6 \cdot 0)5 = 6(0 \cdot 5)$ assoc. post. for mult.

6. $(1 + 3) + (6 \cdot 7) = (3 + 1) + (6 \cdot 7)$

7. $(6 \cdot 3) + (8 \cdot 2) = (8 \cdot 2) + (6 \cdot 3)$

8. $(6 + 0) + \frac{2}{3} = 6 + \frac{2}{3}$ identity post. for add.

9. $(6 + \frac{1}{3}) + (\frac{4}{3} \cdot 2) = (\frac{1}{3} + 6) + (\frac{4}{3} \cdot 2)$

10. $6 \cdot 1 = 6$ identity post. for mult.

11. $8(\frac{1}{2} + 3) = (8 \cdot \frac{1}{2}) + (8 \cdot 3)$ dist. post.

12. $(3 \cdot 4) + (3 \cdot 5) = 3 \cdot (4 + 5)$

13. $\frac{2}{3} + \frac{1}{2}$ is a real number. closure post. for add.

14. $7 \cdot \frac{1}{49}$ is a real number.

Use the postulates for real numbers to find a value of the variable that makes each equation true. Name the postulate that gives the reason for your choice.

15. $12 \cdot \frac{4}{5} = \frac{4}{5} \cdot n$ 12; comm. post. for mult.

16. $6(2 + x) = (6 \cdot 2) + (6 \cdot 1)$

17. $5 + 10 = a + 5$ 10; comm. for add.

18. $\frac{1}{6} \cdot (\frac{1}{5} \cdot \frac{1}{4}) = (c \cdot \frac{1}{5}) \cdot \frac{1}{4}$

19. $\frac{2}{3} + a = \frac{2}{3}$ 0; identity post. for add.

20. $9 + (3 + 1) = (b + 3) + 1$

Evaluate each expression.

21. $(2 + 29) + 1$ 32

22. $(18 + 6) + 14$ 38

23. $(5365 + 1150) + 1850$ 8365

24. $(879 + 13) + 21$ 913

25. $0.3(8 \cdot 10)$ 24

26. $\frac{1}{5}(3 \cdot 100)$ 60

27. $2(5 \cdot 19)$ 190

28. $25(4 \cdot 12)$

29. $250(4 \cdot 12)$ 12,000

30. $125(8 \cdot 65)$ 65,000

31. $4(26 \cdot 25)$ 2600

32. $0.5(362 \cdot 2)$

33. $3 \cdot (10 + 6)$ 48

34. $3 \cdot (20 + 9)$ 87

35. $2 \cdot (9 + \frac{1}{2})$ 19

36. $8 \cdot (200 + 6)$

37. $20 \cdot (40 + 7)$ 940

38. $\frac{3}{4} \cdot (3000 + 8)$ 2256

39. $10(4) + 10(6)$ 100

40. $3(15) + 3(9)$ 72

41. $8(3) + 8(4)$ 56

42. $6(0) + 6(1)$ 6

43. $67(8) + 67(2)$ 670

44. $86(97) + 86(3)$

45. $3(21)$ 63

46. $\frac{1}{4}(102)$ $25\frac{1}{2}$

47. $11(205)$ 2255

48. $9(1009)$ 9081

49. $5(86)$ 430

50. $9(1200)$ 10,800

51. $5(52)$ 260

52. $6(4\frac{2}{3})$ 28

32   *Chapter 1*

Name the postulate that gives the reason for each step.

53. $8 \cdot (5 \cdot 6) = (8 \cdot 5) \cdot 6$ __?__
$= 6 \cdot (8 \cdot 5)$ __?__ comm. post. mult.

54. $(3 \cdot 2) + (3 \cdot 7) = 3 \cdot (2 + 7)$ __?__
$= 3 \cdot (7 + 2)$ __?__

55. $a \cdot (b + c) = (ab) + (ac)$ __?__ dist. post.
$= (ba) + (ca)$ __?__ comm. post. mult.

56. $(b + c) \cdot a = a \cdot (b + c)$ __?__
$= (a \cdot b) + (a \cdot c)$ __?__
$= (b \cdot a) + (c \cdot a)$ __?__

57. A frame is $(3 + x)$ units long and 5 units wide.

$$\text{Area} = 5(3 + x) = 15 + \underline{\ \ ?\ \ }\ \ 5x$$

Find the area inside the frame when the replacement set for x is $\{7, 19, 265\}$. 50; 110; 1340

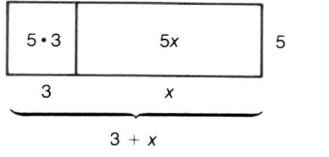

58. A frame is $(4 + x)$ units long and 6 units wide.

$$\text{Area} = 6(4 + x) = \underline{\ \ ?\ \ } + \underline{\ \ ?\ \ }\ \ 24 + 6x$$

Find the area inside the frame when the replacement set for x is $\{1.5, 6.2, 9.8\}$.
33; 61.2; 82.8

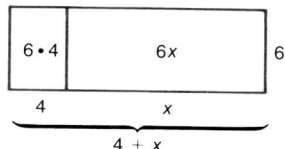

In Exercises 59–62, evaluate each expression.

59. $5 - (4 - 1)$ and $(5 - 4) - 1$ 2; 0

60. $30 - (10 - 6)$ and $(30 - 10) - 6$ 26; 14

61. $25 - (11 - 2)$ and $(25 - 11) - 2$ 16; 12

62. $2832 - (2762 - 13)$ and $(2832 - 2762) - 13$ 83; 57

B

63. Does the associative postulate hold for subtraction? (Refer to Exercises 59–62.) No

64. Does the commutative postulate hold for subtraction? Give an example to explain your answer. No; Examples will vary.

65. Does the commutative postulate hold for division? Give an example to explain your answer. No; Examples will vary.

C

Classify each sentence as true, *T*, or false, *F*. If a statement is false, give an example to show why it is false. Examples will vary in Ex. 66-71.

66. Division is distributive with respect to division. *F*

67. Division is distributive with respect to multiplication. *F*

68. Division is distributive with respect to subtraction. *F*

69. Subtraction is distributive with respect to addition. *F*

70. Addition is distributive with respect to addition. *F*

71. Subtraction is distributive with respect to subtraction. *F*

72. Multiplication is distributive with respect to subtraction. *T*

Uses of Algebra **33**

BASIC: COMPUTER PROGRAMMING STATEMENTS

This section is optional. Each computer applications lesson relates directly to a topic covered within the chapter. (See Section 1-2, pages 5–8)

The first electronic computer was completed in 1945 at the University of Pennsylvania. Named ENIAC ("Electrical Numerical Integrator and Computer"), it weighed almost 30 tons and filled the entire basement of a building.

Today, schools, businesses, and homes have microcomputers that sit on desk tops. The most common language for microcomputers is called BASIC (Beginners' All-Purpose Symbolic Instruction Code), which was created at Dartmouth College in 1965.

In BASIC, the following symbols are used for arithmetic operations.

Operation	BASIC Symbol
Addition	+
Subtraction	−
Multiplication	*
Division	/
Raising to a power	↑ or ∧

With regard to order of operations in BASIC, raising to a power is done first. Then follow the rules given on pages 5 and 6.

EXAMPLE 1   Find the value of $12 + 9 * 8 - 4 \uparrow 2 / 8$.

Solution: First raise to the power.

$$12 + 9 * 8 - 4\uparrow2/8 = 12 + 9 * 8 - 16/8 \quad \longleftarrow \text{ Now multiply and divide.}$$
$$= 12 + 72 - 2 \quad \longleftarrow \text{ Add and subtract.}$$
$$= 82$$

Unlike algebra, the multiplication symbol "*" must always be shown in BASIC. For example, $(5 + 3)2$ would *not* be correct in BASIC. It must be written as $(5 + 3) * 2$.

When writing an algebraic formula in BASIC, you do not use raised exponents or fractions. Note that in BASIC a variable is a capital letter. A formula in BASIC is a LET statement. However, the word LET is unnecessary in some forms of BASIC.

Algebraic Formula	Formula in BASIC
$y = 2x$	LET Y = 2 * X
$k = (a - 7)(b + 3)$	LET K = (A - 7) * (B + 3)
$m = \dfrac{a + b}{c - d}$	LET M = (A + B)/(C - D)
$z = x^2 + 2x - 3$	LET Z = X↑2 + 2*X - 3

To use the computer to solve a problem, the computer is given instructions in a step-by-step form called a **computer program.** Any computer program has four phases.

1. **Input:** A program and data are entered into the machine from a keyboard, a tape, or a diskette. Some computers also accept input from punched cards.

2. **Storage:** Anything entered into a computer goes into **memory.**

Picture part of the computer's memory as "boxes," where each box is named by a letter and each box can hold a number. For example,

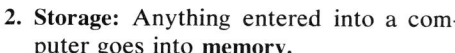

LET X = 10

puts a 10 in location X. Once numbers are in memory, they can be added, subtracted, multiplied and so on. Another way to put a number in memory is the INPUT command. For example,

INPUT X

takes a number typed on the keyboard and stores it in location X.

3. **Processing:** When told to RUN ("execute") a program, a computer does what the program tells it to do. It computes values and can make decisions based on these values.

4. **Output:** The results of a program are usually typed on a printer or shown on a television screen ("cathode ray tube" or "CRT"). Computers can also put answers on tapes or diskettes. To see the number stored in a location, you use the PRINT command.

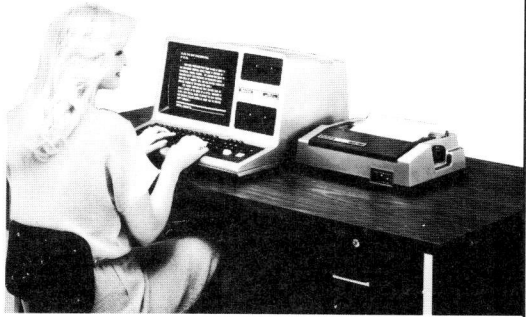

Computer Programming Statements **35**

The following example illustrates the use of LET, INPUT, and PRINT statements in a program.

Problem: *Write a program which accepts a baseball player's times at bat and number of hits, and prints the batting average. Use the following formula.*

Batting Average = Number of Hits ÷ Times at Bat

Program:
```
10   PRINT "HOW MANY TIMES AT BAT";
20   INPUT B                           ◄──────── B = Times at Bat
30   PRINT "HOW MANY HITS";
40   INPUT H                           ◄──────── H = Number of Hits
50   LET A = H / B                     ◄──────── Formula in BASIC
60   PRINT "BATTING AVERAGE = ";A
70   END
```

Statement 70 END tells the computer that there are no more lines in the program.

As shown in this program, the statements are numbered in multiples of 10. This allows you to insert additional statements later. To distinguish zero from the letter "O," some systems use the symbol Ø for zero.

EXERCISES

Ⓐ Find the value of each of the following BASIC formulas.

1. (5 - 1) * 10 40   **2.** 9 * 2↑2 36   **3.** 8.5 * 2/4 20

4. (2 - 10) * 2/4   **5.** (5 - 19)/7 * 3   **6.** ((7.2 + 0.9) * 2)/3
-4 -6 5.4

Write each formula as a BASIC LET statement.

7. $y = 3x - 5$ **8.** $p = 2(l + w)$ **9.** $z = -6x$

10. $r = 5(4s - k)$ **11.** $t = (r + s)(x - 8)$ **12.** $y = 2x^2 - 3x + 6$

13. $k = \dfrac{mn}{c + 2}$ **14.** $s = \dfrac{x - a}{3y}$ **15.** $r = -7 + \dfrac{b}{c - d}$

See the Solution Key for the answers to Ex. 16-19.

Write a BASIC program for each problem.

16. Given the number of wins and losses of a team, compute and print the winning percentage.

$$\frac{\text{Winning}}{\text{Percentage}} = \frac{\text{Number}}{\text{of Wins}} \div \frac{\text{Games}}{\text{Played}} \times 100$$

17. Given the number of hours worked and the rate per hour, compute and print a worker's weekly pay.

$$\frac{\text{Amount}}{\text{Earned}} = \frac{\text{Amount}}{\text{per Hour}} \times \frac{\text{Number}}{\text{of Hours}}$$

18. Given the number of miles a car has traveled and the number of gallons used, compute and print the average miles per gallon for the car.

$$\frac{\text{Miles}}{\text{per Gallon}} = \frac{\text{Number}}{\text{of Miles}} \div \frac{\text{Number}}{\text{of Gallons}}$$

19. Given the number of sides of a polygon, compute and print the sum of the measures of the angles of the polygon.

$$\frac{\text{Sum of}}{\text{Measures}} = 180 \times \frac{\text{Number}}{\text{of Sides}} - 360$$

36 *Computer Applications*

Review

Represent each of the following by a positive or negative rational number. *(Section 1–6)*

1. A weight loss of $12\frac{1}{2}$ pounds $-12\frac{1}{2}$

2. A fare increase of $1.25 1.25

Classify each statement as true or false. When a statement is false tell why it is false. *(Section 1–6)*

3. $I \subset I$ true

4. $Q \subset N$

5. $\{0\} \subset W$ true

6. $W \subset Q$ true

7. $N \subset I$

Identify each number as rational or irrational. Give a reason for each answer. *(Section 1–7)*

8. $\sqrt{16}$

9. $\sqrt{33}$

10. $\sqrt{\frac{9}{36}}$

11. $\sqrt{\frac{100}{49}}$

12. $\sqrt{18}$

13. $\sqrt{50}$

Replace n with the smallest possible whole number to make a true statement. *(Section 1–7)*

14. $13 < \sqrt{175} < n$ 14

15. $5 < \sqrt{30} < n$ 6

16. $12 < \sqrt{150} < n$ 13

Name the postulate illustrated by each sentence. *(Section 1–8)*

17. $5(9) = (9)5$

18. $7 + (8 + 6) = (8 + 6) + 7$

19. $4(2) + 4(9) = 4(2 + 9)$

Evaluate each expression. *(Section 1–8)*

20. $7 + (2 + 10)$ 19

21. $0.4(8 \cdot 6)$ 19.2

22. $\frac{2}{3}(75 + 9)$ 56

Chapter Summary

IMPORTANT TERMS

Algebraic expression (p. 2)
Associative postulate (p. 30)
Base (p. 9)
Closure postulate (p. 31)
Commutative postulate (p. 30)
Coordinate (p. 26)
Distributive postulate (p. 30)
Element (p. 22)
Empty set (p. 19)
Equation (p. 18)
Evaluating expressions (p. 5)
Exponent (p. 9)
Formula (p. 9)
Grouping symbols (p. 5)
Identity postulate (p. 30)
Inequality (p. 18)

Infinite nonrepeating decimal (p. 25)
Integer (p. 22)
Irrational number (p. 25)
Natural number (p. 22)
Numerical expression (p. 3)
Open sentence (p. 18)
Opposite (p. 22)
Postulate (p. 30)
Rational number (p. 22)
Real number (p. 26)
Replacement set (p. 9)
Solution set (p. 18)
Subset (p. 22)
Variable (p. 2)
Whole number (p. 22)

Uses of Algebra **37**

Additional Answers
4. False; Fractions and negative numbers are not natural numbers.
7. True
8. Rational
9. Irrational; There is no positive integer n such that $n \cdot n = 33$.
10. Rational
11. Rational
12. Irrational; There is no positive integer n such that $n \cdot n = 18$.
13. Irrational; There is no positive integer n such that $n \cdot n = 50$.
17. Comm. post. for mult.
18. Comm. post. for add.
19. Distributive postulate

1. **Order of Operations**

   $\boxed{1}$ Do all multiplications and divisions in order from left to right.

   $\boxed{2}$ Do all additions and subtractions in order from left to right.

2. **Rules for Grouping Symbols**

   $\boxed{1}$ Perform the operations within parentheses, or in the numerators or denominators, first.

   $\boxed{2}$ When the parentheses have been removed, or where there are no parentheses, follow the rules for order of operations.

3. When an expression contains more than one grouping symbol, perform the operations within the innermost grouping symbols first. Then work towards the outermost grouping symbols.

4. To use a formula, you replace the known variables with given values (replacement set) in order to find the unknown variables.

5. The symbol for the empty set is ϕ.

6. For any positive integer n, $\sqrt{n}$ is either a positive integer (rational number) or an irrational number.

7. Every point on the number line can be associated with a real number. Every real number can be associated with a point on the number line.

8. The number π is an irrational number.

9. The symbol $\in$ means "is an element of."

—— Chapter Objectives and Review ——

Objective: *To write algebraic expressions for word descriptions (Section 1–1)*

   Write an algebraic expression for each word description.

1. The cost of 5 tickets at x dollars per ticket. $5x$

2. The sum of the sale price, s, and the sales tax, t. $s + t$

3. The amount, a, spent on tires, divided by 4. $\dfrac{a}{4}$

4. The price of long–distance calls, d, subtracted from the total telephone bill, P.

   $P - d$

Objective: *To evaluate numerical expressions involving parentheses (Section 1–1)*

   Find the value of each numerical expression.

5. $(9 + 16) \div 5$ 5

6. $8 + (2 \times 12)$ 32

7. $40 \div (10 - 2)$ 5

8. $18 - (3 \div 3)$ 17

9. $(4 + 7) \times (60 \div 12)$ 55

10. $(3 - 3) \cdot (14 \div 2)$

    0

Objective: *To evaluate algebraic expressions using the rules for order of operations and grouping symbols (Section 1–2)*

11. $7 + 90 \div 10$ 16

12. $38 \cdot (7 - 3)$ 152

13. $\dfrac{18 \div 2}{3 \cdot 7 + 6}$ $\dfrac{1}{3}$

14. $\dfrac{7(8-4)}{2(10-8)}$ 7   **15.** $4[8+6\times(4+2)]$ 176   **16.** $11\div[(14-3)\div1]$
1

Evaluate for the given values of the variables.

17. $(18+7)w$, for $w=3$ 75   **18.** $6a-9b$, for $a=6$ and $b=4$ 0

19. $\dfrac{2r}{5m}$, for $r=20$ and $m=4$ 2   **20.** $3t-6.1f$, for $t=10.2$ and $f=3.9$
6.81

Objective: *To evaluate formulas using replacement sets (Section 1–3)*

Find R for each formula. The replacement set for b is $\{3, 5, 7\}$.

21. $R=0.07b$ **22.** $R=2b^2+5$ 23; 55; 103   **23.** $R=\dfrac{b+5}{2}$
   0.21; 0.35; 0.49
4; 5; 6

Objective: *To evaluate numerical expressions involving exponents (Section 1–3)*

24. 2^4 16   **25.** $\left(\dfrac{3}{8}\right)^2$ $\dfrac{9}{64}$ **26.** $(0.12)^2$ 0.0144   **27.** 1^{42} 1

Objective: *To use formulas to solve word problems (Section 1–4)*

28. Use the formula $V=lwh$ to find V when $l=3\frac{1}{2}$ feet, $w=2$ feet, and $h=4\frac{1}{2}$ feet.
$31\frac{1}{2}$ cubic feet

Objective: *To find the solution set of a sentence using a given replacement set (Section 1–5)*

Find the solution set for each sentence. The replacement set is $\{0, 3, 6, 9, 12\}$.

29. $x+6=9$ $\{3\}$ **30.** $4m+3>15$ $\{6, 9, 12\}$ **31.** $39<2y+y$ ϕ

Objective: *To identify elements which belong to the set of natural numbers, the set of rational numbers (Section 1–6)*

Classify each sentence as true, *T*, or false, *F*. When a sentence is false, tell why it is false.

32. The number 0 is a natural number. *F*; 0 is not a natural number

33. Every natural number is also an integer. *T*

34. The set of whole numbers is a subset of the set of integers. *T*

35. The opposite of ⁻7 is 7. *T*

36. 3.8 is an integer. *F*; decimals are not integers.

37. $2\frac{1}{5}$ is a rational number. *T*

38. ⁻0.07 can be written in the form $\dfrac{a}{b}$. *T*

Objective: *To use positive and negative rational numbers to represent word statements (Section 1–6)*

Represent each of the following by a positive or negative rational number.

39. A loss of 3 yards on a football play −3   **40.** A stock gain of $1\frac{3}{8}$ points $1\frac{3}{8}$

41. A rise in temperature of 10° 10   **42.** A paycheck deduction of $14.25
−14.25

Uses of Algebra   **39**

Objective: *To identify irrational numbers and real numbers (Section 1–7)*

Indicate the set or sets to which each number belongs. Use I = {Integers}, Q = {Rational Numbers}, Ir = {Irrational Numbers}, and R = {Real Numbers}.

43. $\sqrt{81}$ I, Q, R **44.** $^-1.3$ Q, R **45.** $\sqrt{7}$ Ir, R **46.** $1.\overline{37}$

47. $\frac{2}{11}$ Q, R **48.** $^-2\frac{1}{2}$ Q, R **49.** $8.3769138\cdots$ Ir, R **50.** $\frac{64}{4}$

Objective: *To identify the coordinates of points on the real number line (Section 1–7)*

Give the coordinate of the point named by each letter.

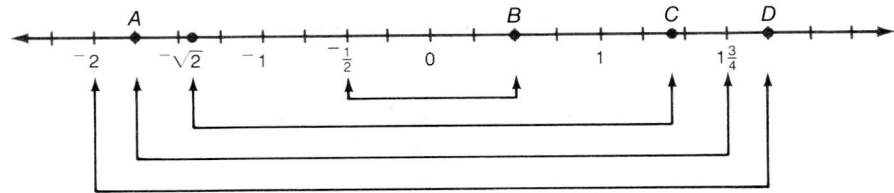

51. A $-1\frac{3}{4}$ **52.** B $\frac{1}{2}$ **53.** C $\sqrt{2}$ **54.** D 2

Objective: *To approximate values of irrational numbers using the Table of Square Roots (Section 1–7)*

Use the Table of Square Roots on page 541 to find an approximate value for each number.

55. $\sqrt{7}$ 2.646 **56.** $\sqrt{60}$ 7.746 **57.** $\sqrt{113}$ 10.630 **58.** $\sqrt{12}$
                                                                          3.464

Objective: *To identify the postulates for the addition and multiplication of real numbers (Section 1–8)*

Name the postulate illustrated by each sentence.

59. $7 + 3 = 3 + 7$ **60.** $121 \cdot 1 = 121$ **61.** $7 \cdot (10 \cdot 3) = (7 \cdot 10) \cdot 3$

Objective: *To use the postulates for real numbers (Section 1–8)*

Use the postulates for real numbers to find a value of the variable that makes each equation true. Name the postulate that gives the reason for your choice.

62. $9(x + 5) = (9 \cdot 2) + (9 \cdot 5)$ **63.** $\frac{3}{5} \cdot (\frac{1}{8} \cdot \frac{5}{9}) = (\frac{3}{5} \cdot t) \cdot \frac{5}{9}$

Evaluate each expression.

64. $21 \cdot (68 + 32)$ 2100 **65.** $\frac{5}{24} + (3\frac{1}{8} + 2\frac{2}{3})$ 6

_____ Chapter Test _____

A formal Chapter Test is provided in the Teacher's Manual. See p. M-64.

Write an algebraic expression for each word description.

1. The total coupon value, v, subtracted from the weekly food bill, b. $b - v$

2. The sum of a $1500 loan and the total interest, t. $1500 + t$

3. The cost of y record albums at $7.55 per album. $7.55y$

Find the value of each numerical expression.

4. $(3 + 14) \cdot 8$ 136

5. $(70 \div 10) + (8 - 3)$ 12

6. $\dfrac{9(19 - 15)}{33 + 11 + 7}$ $\dfrac{12}{17}$

7. $2[8 \cdot (11 - 2) \div 36]$ 4

Evaluate for the given values of the variables.

8. $17p - 3b$, for $p = 8$ and $b = 11$ 103

9. $\frac{1}{2}a + \frac{3}{4}c$, for $a = 16$ and $c = 4.8$ 11.6

10. Use the formula $M = 2x^2 - 3.1$ to find M when the replacement set for x is $\{2, 2.1\}$. 4.9; 5.72

11. Use the formula $A = \frac{1}{2}h(b + c)$ to find the area of a trapezoid when $b = 6.8$ meters, $c = 3.2$ meters, and $h = 7$ meters. 35

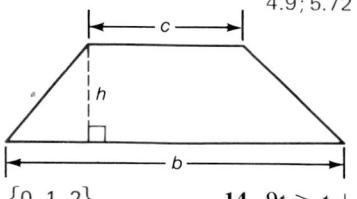

Find the solution set for each sentence. The replacement set is $\{0, 1, 2\}$.

12. $w + 11 = 13$ $\{2\}$

13. $r + 3 \neq r + 7$ $\{0, 1, 2\}$

14. $9t > t + 7$ $\{1, 2\}$

Classify each sentence as true, T, or false, F. When a sentence is false, tell why it is false.

15. $\frac{9}{5}$ is a rational number T

16. 0.3 is a natural number.

17. The opposite of 2 is $\frac{1}{2}$. F; The opposite of 2 is -2.

18. Every integer is also a rational number. T

19. Write the positive or negative rational number which represents a bank withdrawal of $105.10. -105.1

Indicate the set or sets to which each number belongs. Use I = {Integers}, Q = {Rational Numbers}, Ir = {Irrational Numbers}, and R = {Real Numbers}.

20. $\sqrt{21}$ Ir.; R

21. $-\sqrt{144}$ I; Q; R

22. $\sqrt{\dfrac{25}{121}}$ Q; R

23. $-1.0363987 \cdots$

24. Find the value of t in the following equation: $15(11 + 4) = (15 \cdot t) + (15 \cdot 4)$. Then name the postulate that gives the reason for your choice. 11; Dist. Post.

25. Evaluate: $73(47) + 73(53)$. 7300

Additional Answers

16. F; Natural numbers are not decimals.

23. Ir; R

Uses of Algebra **41**

Additional Practice

Skills You may wish to use all or some of these exercises, depending on how well students performed on the formal chapter test.

Find the value of each of the following. *(Sections 1–1, 1–2)*

1. $(7 \cdot 2) - 4$ 10
2. $6 + (49 \div 7)$ 13
3. $(11 + 7) \div 3$ 6
4. $(24 \div 2) \div (8 - 4)$

5. $\dfrac{11 - 9}{7 \cdot 3}$ $\frac{2}{21}$
6. $\dfrac{4(6 - 2)}{6 - 6 \div 3}$ 4
7. $\dfrac{4 \cdot 4 - 7}{7 + 10 \cdot 2}$ $\frac{1}{3}$
8. $4[(5 - 2) \div 3]$

Find *B* for each formula. The replacement set for *n* is {4, 5, 6}. *(Section 1–3)*

9. $B = 3n - 1$
10. $B = 8(n - 2)$
11. $B = n^2 + 3$
12. $B = n^3$

Find the solution set for each sentence. The replacement set is {1, 3, 5, 7, 9}. *(Section 1–5)*

13. $x + 3 = 12$ {9}
14. $x \neq 6 + 1$ {1, 3, 5, 9}
15. $10 + x > 14$ {5, 7, 9}
16. $9x < 7$ ϕ

Write each rational number in the form $\dfrac{a}{b}$, where *a* is an integer and *b* is a natural number. *(Section 1–6)*

17. 0.3 $\frac{3}{10}$
18. $^-0.25$ $-\frac{1}{4}$
19. $2\frac{1}{3}$ $\frac{7}{3}$
20. $^-6\frac{1}{6}$ $-\frac{37}{6}$
21. $^-38$ $-\frac{38}{1}$
22. 7.37

Identify each number as rational, Q, or irrational, Ir. Give a reason for each answer. *(Section 1–7)*

23. $\sqrt{5}$
24. $\sqrt{81}$ Q
25. $\sqrt{100}$ Q
26. $\sqrt{\frac{49}{4}}$ Q
27. $\sqrt{52}$
28. $\sqrt{12}$

Use the Table of Square Roots on page 541 to find an approximate value for each number. *(Section 1–7)*

29. $\sqrt{41}$
30. $\sqrt{23}$
31. $\sqrt{111}$
32. $\sqrt{54}$
33. $\sqrt{75}$
34. $\sqrt{32}$

Name the postulate illustrated by each sentence. *(Section 1–8)*

35. $\frac{1}{3} + 0 = \frac{1}{3}$
36. $2 \cdot (5 \cdot 7) = (2 \cdot 5) \cdot 7$
37. $11 + 4 = 4 + 11$

Applications

For Exercises 38 and 39 write an algebraic expression to represent each word description. *(Section 1–2)*

38. The cost of *t* gallons of gasoline at $1.15 per gallon. *c* = 1.15*t*

39. The total cost of *p* tickets at $12 per ticket and $7 for a program. *c* = 12*p* + 7

40. Use the formula $V = lwh$ to find the volume, *V*, of a rectangular garden pool where $l = 6$ meters, $w = 4$ meters, and $h = \frac{1}{2}$ meter. *(Section 1–4)*
12 cubic meters

41. Use the formula $A = \frac{1}{2}h(b + c)$ to find the area, *A*, of a car window where $h = 18$ inches, $b = 13$ inches, and $c = 17$ inches. *(Section 1–4)* 270 square inches

42   *Chapter 1*

CHAPTER

2 Operations with Real Numbers

2–1 Positive and Negative Numbers

On the number line below, 3 and ⁻3 are on *opposite sides* of 0, and 3 and ⁻3 are the *same distance* from 0.

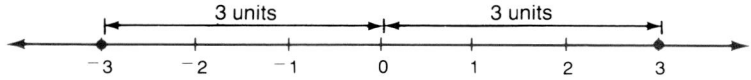

Hence, ⁻3 and 3 are **opposites**. That is,

3 is the opposite of ⁻3.
⁻3 is the opposite of 3.

These statements can be expressed in symbols by using a dash, —, to represent "the opposite of."

$$3 = - (^-3)$$
$$^-3 = -3$$

Since $^-3 = -3$, we will use the symbol for "the opposite of" to indicate a negative number. Thus, -3 can be read as "negative 3." It may be more appropriate to say "the opposite of" for the dash, —, in certain instances. Examples are shown in this table.

Example	Read	Meaning
$-(5)$	The opposite of 5.	-5
$-(-6)$	The opposite of negative 6.	6
$-(2)$	The opposite of 2.	-2
$-(-8\frac{1}{2})$	The opposite of negative $8\frac{1}{2}$.	$8\frac{1}{2}$
$-(-9.3)$	The opposite of negative 9.3.	9.3

Note that the number zero is its own opposite. That is,

$$0 = -0, \quad \text{and} \quad -0 = 0.$$

EXAMPLE 1 Write without parentheses.

a. $-(-5)$ **b.** $-(9.6 - 3.2)$

Solutions: **a.** $-(-5) = 5$ ⟵——— Think: **The opposite of negative 5 is 5.**

b. $-(9.6 - 3.2) = -(6.4)$ ⟵——— Think: **The opposite of 6.4 is negative 6.4.**
$$= -6.4$$

You can use the idea of opposites to solve equations.

EXAMPLE 2 Solve: $-x = 7$

Solution: $-x = 7$ ⟵——— Think: **The opposite of some number is 7.**

$x = -7$ Thus, the solution is -7.

You can use a number line to compare positive and negative numbers.

**For any two real numbers, the smaller is to
the left of the larger on the number line.**

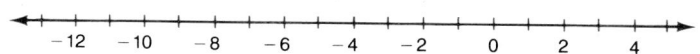

EXAMPLE 3   Use > or < to compare the numbers. Refer to the number line above.

a. $3 \underline{} -9$ b. $-11\frac{1}{2} \underline{} -7$ c. $0.5 \underline{} 0$

Solutions: a. $3 > -9$ ⟵———— **3 is to the right of −9**

b. $-11\frac{1}{2} < -7$ ⟵———— **$-11\frac{1}{2}$ is to the left of −7.**

c. $0.5 > 0$ ⟵———— **0.5 is to the right of 0.**

Additional Examples
Example 3
Use > or < to compare the
numbers.

1. $1 \underline{} -1$
   Ans: >
2. $-9 \underline{} -8$
   Ans: <
3. $\frac{1}{100} \underline{} 0$
   Ans: >

CLASSROOM EXERCISES

Write the opposite of each number.

1. 2 −2   2. −1 1   3. −7.8 7.8   4. 0 −0   5. $7\frac{1}{3}$ $-7\frac{1}{3}$ 6. $-\frac{5}{6}$ $\frac{5}{6}$

Write without parentheses.

7. $-(-\frac{1}{7})$ $\frac{1}{7}$ 8. $-(t)$ $-t$ 9. $-(\pi \cdot 0)$ -0 10. $-(9.1 + 6.7)$ -15.8

Solve for q.

11. $-q = 6$ $q = -6$ 12. $-q = -6$ $q = 6$ 13. $q = -(-6)$ $q = 6$ 14. $-q = -(-6)$ $q = -6$

Use > or < to compare the numbers.

15. $0 \underline{} -1$ >   16. $-0.5 \underline{} -3$ >   17. $-5 \underline{} -6$ >   18. $-12 \underline{} -11\frac{3}{4}$ <

WRITTEN EXERCISES

A   Write the opposite of each number.

1. 6 −6   2. −7 7   3. 9 −9   4. $-\sqrt{3}$ $\sqrt{3}$ 5. $-6\frac{1}{2}$ $6\frac{1}{2}$ 6. 0
7. 9.02 −9.02 8. −6.33 6.33   9. $-\frac{2}{3}$ $\frac{2}{3}$ 10. 5 −5   11. −9.001 9.001   12. $-\pi$

Write without parentheses.

13. $-(5)$ 5   14. $-(-9)$ 9   15. $-(3.14)$ −3.14 16. $-(-3.14)$ 3.14 17. $-\frac{5}{6}$ $\frac{5}{6}$
18. $-(-5)$ 5   19. $-(9)$ −9   20. $-(-0.9)$ 0.9 21. $-(0.9)$ −0.9 22. $-(-0)$ 0
23. $-(3.6 - 2.4)$ −1.2 24. $-(16 + 0)$ −16 25. $-(71 \cdot 0)$ −0 26. $-(\frac{1}{2} \cdot \frac{3}{4})$ $-\frac{3}{8}$ 27. $-(33 \div 11)$
28. $-(t)$ $-t$ 29. $-(-t)$ t   30. $-(r \cdot 0)$ −0 31. $-(-m)$ m 32. $-(-\pi)$ π

Solve.

33. $-x = 9$ $x = -9$ 34. $-m = -6$ $m = 6$ 35. $-x = 0$ $x = -0$ 36. $-y = 6\frac{1}{2}$
37. $-y = 3.25$ $y = -3.5$ 38. $-x = -\pi$ $x = \pi$ 39. $-a = -\frac{3}{4}$ $a = \frac{3}{4}$ 40. $-a = 1$

Assignment Guide
Minimal
Day 1 p. 45: 1–31 odd, 33–40
Day 2 p. 46: 41–60
Average
Day 1 pp. 45–46: 1–40
Day 2 pp. 45–46: 41–60,
61–75 odd
Above Average
pp. 45–46: 13–75 odd, 77–84

Additional Answers
Written Exercises
6. 0
12. π
27. −3
36. $y = -6\frac{1}{2}$
40. $a = -1$

Operations with Real Numbers   **45**

Additional Answers
Written Exercises
44. $>$
48. $>$
52. $<$
56. $<$
60. $>$
62. $-(-6) = 6$
63. $-20 = -(20)$
64. $400 = -(-400)$
65. $-(-200) = 200$
66. $3\frac{1}{2} = -(-3\frac{1}{2})$
67. $-1\frac{1}{4} = -(1\frac{1}{4})$
68. $-(2000) = -2000$
69. $-(-500) = 500$
70. $-6.5 = -(6.5)$
71. $-(2\frac{3}{4}) = -2\frac{3}{4}$
80. $x > 0$
84. $r < 6$

Use $<$ and $>$ to compare the numbers. Draw a number line if necessary.

41. $-5 \underline{\quad?\quad} 5$ $<$
42. $-15 \underline{\quad?\quad} -5$ $<$
43. $-8 \underline{\quad?\quad} 0.2$ $<$
44. $-12 \underline{\quad?\quad} -15$

45. $7 \underline{\quad?\quad} 5$ $>$
46. $-15 \underline{\quad?\quad} -20$ $>$
47. $0 \underline{\quad?\quad} -9$ $>$
48. $0 \underline{\quad?\quad} -8.6$

49. $6\frac{2}{3} \underline{\quad?\quad} -6$ $>$
50. $6.2 \underline{\quad?\quad} 6.3$ $<$
51. $-7.4 \underline{\quad?\quad} -7.5$ $>$
52. $-8\frac{2}{5} \underline{\quad?\quad} -8\frac{1}{5}$

53. $-(-6) \underline{\quad?\quad} 0$ $>$
54. $0 \underline{\quad?\quad} -(-5)$ $<$
55. $-(-\pi) \underline{\quad?\quad} 3$ $>$
56. $-(-\sqrt{3}) \underline{\quad?\quad} 3$

57. $-\sqrt{2} \underline{\quad?\quad} 2$ $<$
58. $-(-\sqrt{3}) \underline{\quad?\quad} (-\sqrt{2})$ $>$
59. $\sqrt{6} \underline{\quad?\quad} -(-\sqrt{7})$ $<$
60. $-(-3) \underline{\quad?\quad} 0$

APPLICATIONS: Using Opposites

B   Use algebraic symbols to represent each sentence.
The first one is done for you.

In Words		In Symbols

61. Depositing $27 in a checking account is the opposite of withdrawing $27. $27 = -(-27)$

62. The opposite of taking an elevator down 6 floors is taking an elevator up 6 floors. $\underline{\quad?\quad}$

63. A fall of 20° in temperature is the opposite of a rise of 20°. $\underline{\quad?\quad}$

64. An altitude of 400 meters above sea level is the opposite of a depth of 400 meters below sea level. $\underline{\quad?\quad}$

65. The opposite of owing $200 is having $200 in savings. $\underline{\quad?\quad}$

66. A weight gain of $3\frac{1}{2}$ pounds is the opposite of a weight loss of $3\frac{1}{2}$ pounds. $\underline{\quad?\quad}$

67. An investment loss of $1\frac{1}{4}$ per share is the opposite of an investment gain of $1\frac{1}{4}$ per share.

68. The opposite of a profit of $2000 is a loss of $2000. $\underline{\quad?\quad}$

69. The opposite of a loss of 500 meters in altitude is a gain in altitude of 500 meters. $\underline{\quad?\quad}$

70. A decrease in speed of 6.5 kilometers per hour is the opposite of an increase in speed of 6.5 kilometers per hour. $\underline{\quad?\quad}$

71. The opposite of growing $2\frac{3}{4}$ inches is shrinking $2\frac{3}{4}$ inches. $\underline{\quad?\quad}$

72. If a is a positive real number, is $-a$ positive or negative?   negative

73. If $-a$ is a positive real number, is a positive or negative?   negative

74. If $-a$ is a negative real number, is a positive or negative?   positive

75. If a is a positive real number, is $-(-a)$ positive or negative?   positive

76. If a is a negative real number, is $-(-a)$ positive or negative?   negative

C   Solve for the variable.

77. $-(-x) = 4$ $x = 4$
78. $-(-y) = 6$ $y = 6$
79. $-x = 0$ $x = 0$
80. $-x < 0$

81. $-x > 0$ $x < 0$
82. $-t > 4$ $t < -4$
83. $-t < 4$ $t > -4$
84. $-r > -6$

2–2 Additive Inverses and Absolute Value

Teaching Suggestions p. M-15

Quick Quiz
Write without parentheses.
1. $-(-5.6)$ **Ans: 5.6**
Solve for x.
2. $x = -(-21)$
Ans: $x = 21$
3. $-x = 1\frac{1}{2}$
Ans: $x = -1\frac{1}{2}$
Use $>$ or $<$ to compare the numbers.
4. -12 ___?___ -9
Ans: $<$
5. $-(-0.5)$ ___?___ 0
Ans: $>$

You can use a number line to show the following.

The sum of a number and its opposite is 0.

Arrows pointing to the right represent positive numbers. Arrows pointing to the left represent negative numbers.

Example	On the Number Line	Sum
a. $5 + (-5)$ Think: A gain of 5 followed by a loss of 5	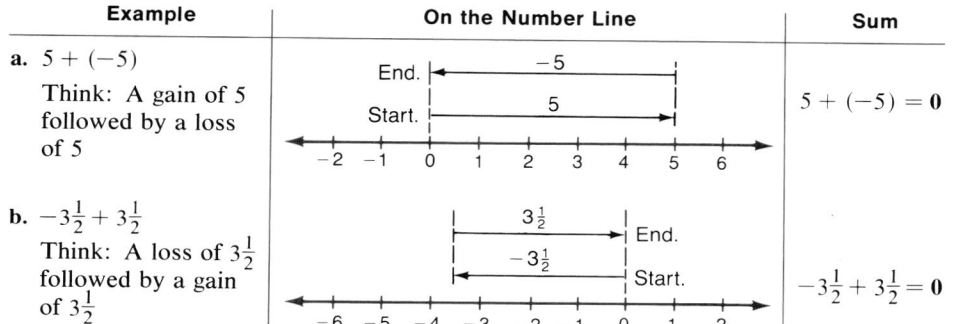	$5 + (-5) = 0$
b. $-3\frac{1}{2} + 3\frac{1}{2}$ Think: A loss of $3\frac{1}{2}$ followed by a gain of $3\frac{1}{2}$		$-3\frac{1}{2} + 3\frac{1}{2} = 0$

The Additive Inverse Postulate summarizes this property of real numbers.

Postulate

> **Additive Inverse Postulate**
>
> For any real number a, there is one and only one real number, $-a$, such that
>
> $$a + (-a) = 0.$$

Numbers that are opposites, such as 3 and -3, are **additive inverses of** each other because their sum is 0.

The number 0 is its own additive inverse.

Additive inverses are the same distance from 0 on the number line.

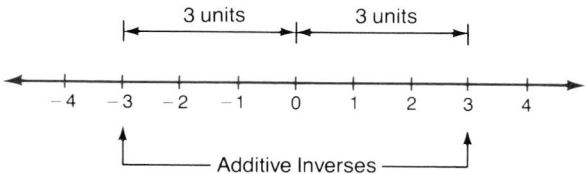

You use *absolute value notation* when you want to indicate distance, but not direction, from 0. The symbol for absolute value is $|\ |$.

Definition

> The **absolute value** of a real number x is the distance of x from 0. It is written $|x|$.

Operations with Real Numbers **47**

When $x = 0$, $|x| = 0$. For all other real numbers, $|x|$ is a positive real number.

Example	Meaning	Solution
$|-5|$	Distance of -5 from 0	$|-5| = 5$
$|8|$	Distance of 8 from 0	$|8| = 8$
$|-3\frac{1}{2}|$	Distance of $-3\frac{1}{2}$ from 0	$|-3\frac{1}{2}| = 3\frac{1}{2}$
$|0|$	Distance of 0 from 0	$|0| = 0$

Since $|x|$ is a positive real number for all real numbers x except 0, $-|x|$ is a negative real number.

Additional Examples
Example 1
Evaluate.
1. $-|-6|$
   Ans: -6
2. $-(-|101|)$
   Ans: 101
3. $-(|-2| + |5|)$
   Ans: -7
4. $|-21| - (-|5|)$
   Ans: 26

EXAMPLE 1 Evaluate: **a.** $-\left|-\frac{2}{3}\right|$ **b.** $-(|-5| + |-1|)$

Solutions: **a.** $\left|-\frac{2}{3}\right| = \frac{2}{3}$ ⟵——— **By the definition of absolute value**

So $-\left|-\frac{2}{3}\right| = -\frac{2}{3}$.

b. $(|-5| + |-1|) = (5 + 1) = 6$ ⟵——— **By definition**
So $-(|-5| + |-1|) = -6$.

To compare expressions such as $|-8|$ and $-|-10|$, first *evaluate each expression. Then compare the results.*

Example 2
Use > or < to compare the numbers.
1. $|-5|$ __?__ $|-12|$
   Ans: <
2. $|5|$ __?__ $|-12|$
   Ans: <
3. $-|-3|$ __?__ $-|-7|$
   Ans: >
4. $-|-3|$ __?__ $-|-2|$
   Ans: <

EXAMPLE 2 Use > or < to compare the numbers.

a. $|-8|$ __?__ $|-10|$ **b.** $-|-8|$ __?__ $-|-10|$

Solutions: **a.** $|-8| = 8$; $|-10| = 10$;   **b.** $-|-8| = -8$; $-|-10| = -10$;
and $8 < 10$ and $-8 > -10$
Thus, $|-8| < |-10|$.   Thus, $-|-8| > -|-10|$.

CLASSROOM EXERCISES

Write the additive inverse of each real number.

1. 6.5 $_{-6.5}$ **2.** -9 $_{9}$ **3.** $-m$ $_{m}$ **4.** $-(-9)$ $_{-9}$ **5.** $-(-0)$ $_{-0}$ **6.** $-(-t)$ $_{-t}$

Evaluate.

7. $|7|$ $_{7}$ **8.** $|-15|$ $_{15}$ **9.** $-|7|$ $_{-7}$ **10.** $-|-15|$ $_{-15}$ **11.** $|-(-3)|$ $_{3}$ **12.** $-|-(-\frac{1}{2})|$
$_{-\frac{1}{2}}$

Use > or < to compare the numbers.

13. $|10|$ $\underline{<\ ?}$ $|-12|$ **14.** $-|-\frac{1}{2}|$ $\underline{<\ ?}$ $|\frac{1}{3}|$ **15.** $|0|$ $\underline{>\ ?}$ $-|-1.5|$ **16.** $-|-7.3|$ $\underline{>\ ?}$ $-|8.4|$

48   *Chapter 2*

WRITTEN EXERCISES

A   Write the additive inverse of each number.

1. 6 -6 2. -7 7 3. $-3\frac{1}{5}$ $3\frac{1}{5}$ 4. 9 -9 5. -6.8

6. 7.09 -7.09 7. $-\pi$ π 8. $\sqrt{7}$ $-\sqrt{7}$ 9. $-\sqrt{2}$ $\sqrt{2}$ 10. $\sqrt{10}$

11. $-(-5)$ -5 12. $-(5)$ 5 13. $-(-4)$ -4 14. $-(-6.7)$ -6.7 15. $-(-0.9)$

    Complete.

16. $9 + \underline{\ ?\ } = 0$ -9 17. $-12 + \underline{\ ?\ } = 0$ 18. $-8.6 + \underline{\ ?\ } = 0$ 19. $15\frac{1}{2} + \underline{\ ?\ } = 0$

20. $8 + (-8) = \underline{\ ?\ }$ 0 21. $-\frac{1}{4} + \frac{1}{4} = \underline{\ ?\ }$ 22. $m + \underline{\ ?\ } = 0$ 23. $-r + \underline{\ ?\ } = 0$

24. $y + (-y) = \underline{\ ?\ }$ 0 25. $\underline{\ ?\ } + a = 0$ 26. $-(-t) + \underline{\ ?\ } = 0$ 27. $\underline{\ ?\ } + -(-x) = 0$

    Evaluate.

28. $|6|$ 6 29. $|-6|$ 6 30. $|-3\frac{1}{2}|$ $3\frac{1}{2}$ 31. $|-\pi|$ π 32. $|-19.5|$ 19.5 33. $|15|$

34. $|-18.5|$ 35. $|0|$ 0 36. $|-16|$ 16 37. $|-100|$ 100 38. $|695|$ 695 39. $|-462|$

40. $|-72.5|$ 41. $|22,000|$ 42. $|37.75|$ 43. $|-7.25|$ 44. $|-\sqrt{21}|$ $\sqrt{21}$ 45. $|\sqrt{5}|$

46. $|86.75|$ 47. $|-7.6|$ 7.6 48. $|-\sqrt{7}|$ $\sqrt{7}$ 49. $|\sqrt{7}|$ $\sqrt{7}$ 50. $-|19|$ -19 51. $-|-19|$

52. $|3| + |15|$ 18 53. $|-3| + |-9|$ 12 54. $|23| + |-18|$ 41 55. $|-1| + |14|$ 15

56. $|6| + |-8|$ 14 57. $|-4| + |8|$ 12 58. $|-9| + |9|$ 18 59. $|9| + |-12|$ 21

60. $|0| + |0|$ 0 61. $|\frac{1}{2}| + |\frac{2}{3}|$ $\frac{7}{6}$ 62. $|0.2| + |-0.37|$ 63. $|-235| + |16|$ 251

64. $-|3| + |3|$ 0 65. $-|\frac{1}{2}| + |\frac{1}{2}|$ 0 66. $|3.1| - |3.1|$ 0 X7. $|x| - |x|$ 0

    Use $>$, $=$, or $<$ to compare the numbers.

68. $|0.23| \underline{\ ?\ } |-3.7|$ $<$ 69. $|-6| \underline{\ ?\ } |6|$ $=$ 70. $|-\frac{1}{2}| \underline{\ ?\ } |\frac{1}{3}|$ $>$ 71. $|0.02| \underline{\ ?\ } |-0.001|$

72. $|0| \underline{\ ?\ } |-1|$ $<$ 73. $|-\frac{1}{6}| \underline{\ ?\ } |\frac{1}{7}|$ $>$ 74. $|-1| \underline{\ ?\ } |1|$ $=$ 75. $|0| \underline{\ ?\ } -|0|$ $=$

76. $|-3| \underline{\ ?\ } |-\frac{1}{4}|$ $>$ 77. $|-3| \underline{\ ?\ } |4|$ $<$ 78. $|-2| \underline{\ ?\ } |-2|$ $=$ 79. $|-5| \underline{\ ?\ } |-5|$ $=$

    Classify each equation as true, *T,* or false, *F.* When an equation is false, tell why it is false.

80. $|8| = 8$ T 81. $|-231| = 231$ T 82. $|-663| = |663|$ T 83. $|9| = 9$ T

84. $|-235| > |235|$ F 85. $|-35| > |35|$ F 86. $|-27| < |17|$ F 87. $|17.9| < |-17.9|$ F

88. $|-0.01| < |-0.001|$ 89. $|-\frac{1}{3}| < \frac{1}{4}$ F 90. $\frac{2}{3} < |-\frac{3}{4}|$ T 91. $|\frac{1}{8}| > -\frac{1}{7}$ T
      F

B   Solve.

92. $x = |-2|$ $x = 2$ 93. $|-7| = a$ $7 = a$ 94. $b = -|9|$ $b = -9$ 95. $-|2\frac{2}{3}| = y$

96. $|q| = 0$ $q = \pm 0$ 97. $|y| = 4$ $y = \pm 4$ 98. $|x| = |-1|$ $x = \pm 1$ 99. $-|x| + |-2| = 0$

    Complete each statement by writing $<$, $>$, or $=$.

100. If $x > 0$, then $|x| \underline{\ ?\ } 0$. $>$ 101. If $x < 0$, then $|x| \underline{\ ?\ } 0$. $>$

Operations with Real Numbers   **49**

Assignment Guide
Minimal
Day 1 p. 49: 1–65 odd
Day 2 p. 49: 68–91
Average
Day 1 p. 49: 1–51 odd, 52–67
Day 2 pp. 49–50: 69–101
Above Average
Day 1 p. 49: 1–79 odd
Day 2 pp. 49–50: 80–106

Additional Answers
5. 6.8
10. $-\sqrt{10}$
15. -0.9
17. 12
18. 8.6
19. $-15\frac{1}{2}$
21. 0
22. $-m$
23. r
25. $-a$
26. $-t$
27. $-x$
33. 15
34. 18.5
39. 462
40. 72.5
41. $22,000$
42. 37.75
43. 7.25
45. $\sqrt{5}$
46. 86.75
51. -19
62. 0.57
71. $>$
Reasons for Ex. 84–89
84. $|-235| = 235$, and $235 \not> 235$
85. $|-35| = 35$, and $35 \not> 35$
86. $|-27| = 27$, and $27 > 17$
87. $|-17.9| = 17.9$, and $17.9 \not< 17.9$
88. $|-0.01| = 0.01$ and $|-0.001| = 0.001$. Thus, $|-0.01| \not< |-0.001|$
89. $|-\frac{1}{3}| = \frac{1}{3}$, and $\frac{1}{3} > \frac{1}{4}$
95. $-2\frac{2}{3} = y$
99. $x = \pm 2$

c Classify each statement as true, *T,* or false, *F*. When a statement is false, tell why it is false.

102. If x is any real number, then $|x| = x$.   *F*
103. If y is any real number, then $|y| = |-y|$.   *T*
104. If x and y are real numbers and $x < y$, then $|x| < |y|$.   *F*
105. If x is any real number, then $-(-x) = x$.   *T*

CALCULATOR APPLICATIONS

Powers and Patterns

The power key, $\boxed{x^i}$ or $\boxed{y^x}$, on a scientific calculator simplifies the process of evaluating an expression that contains an exponent. If your calculator does not have a power key, you simply multiply. In either case, the answer may be too large for your calculator to express.

EXAMPLE Find 8^n for $n = 1, 2, 3, \cdots, 8$. Study the last digit of each product to see if you can discover a pattern. Predict the last digit for 8^9.

SOLUTION

$8^1 = 8$

$8^2 = 8\ \boxed{x^y}\ 2\ \boxed{=}$ 64

$8^3 = 8\ \boxed{x^y}\ 3\ \boxed{=}$ 512

$8^4 = 8\ \boxed{x^y}\ 4\ \boxed{=}$ 4096

$8^5 = 8\ \boxed{x^y}\ 5\ \boxed{=}$ 32768

$8^6 = 8\ \boxed{x^y}\ 6\ \boxed{=}$ 262144

$8^7 = 8\ \boxed{x^y}\ 7\ \boxed{=}$ 2097152

$8^8 = 8\ \boxed{x^y}\ 8\ \boxed{=}$ 16777216

Pattern of the last digits: 8, 4, 2, 6, 8, 4, 2, 6. Thus, the last digit for 8^9 is **8**.

EXERCISES

Predict the last digit for each of the following.

1. 8^{12} 6
2. 8^{16} 6
3. 8^{100} 6
4. 8^{101} 8
5. 6^{100} 6
6. 2^{27} 8
7. 2^{50} 4
8. 2^{99} 8

—————— REVIEW CAPSULE FOR SECTION 2–3 ——————

Add.

1. $76 + 39$ 115
2. $703 + 527$ 1230
3. $456 + 72 + 4998 + 39$ 5565
4. $0.44 + 0.32$ 0.76
5. $15.72 + 4.95$ 20.67
6. $12.19 + 2.5 + 14.306 + 27$ 55.996

Add. Write your answers in lowest terms.

7. $\frac{3}{6} + \frac{1}{6}$ $\frac{2}{3}$
8. $8 + \frac{3}{5}$ $8\frac{3}{5}$
9. $\frac{7}{8} + \frac{3}{4}$ $1\frac{5}{8}$
10. $\frac{1}{6} + \frac{1}{8}$
11. $12\frac{5}{8} + \frac{7}{8}$ $13\frac{1}{2}$
12. $3\frac{2}{3} + \frac{5}{6}$ $4\frac{1}{2}$
13. $7\frac{3}{5} + 9\frac{7}{10}$ $17\frac{3}{10}$
14. $6\frac{5}{8} + 9\frac{1}{3}$

OBJECTIVE: To add real numbers

2–3 Addition of Real Numbers

Teaching Suggestions p. M-15

You know that the sum of two positive numbers is a positive number. You can use a number line to show the following.

The sum of two negative numbers is a negative number.

Example	On the Number Line	Sum
a. $-3 + (-4)$ Think: A loss of 3 followed by a loss of 4	End. ⊢ -4 ⊣⊢ -3 ⊣ Start. $-8\ -7\ -6\ -5\ -4\ -3\ -2\ -1\quad 0\quad 1$	$-3 + (-4) = \mathbf{-7}$
b. $-2.5 + (-1.5)$ Think: A loss of 2.5 followed by a loss of 1.5	End. ⊢ -1.5 ⊣⊢ -2.5 ⊣ Start. $-8\ -7\ -6\ -5\ -4\ -3\ -2\ -1\quad 0\quad 1$	$-2.5 + (-1.5) = \mathbf{-4}$

You can use this procedure to find the sum of two positive numbers or of two negative numbers.

Procedure:

> To add two positive numbers or two negative numbers:
> 1. Determine whether the sum is positive or negative.
>   **a.** The sum of two positive numbers is positive.
>   **b.** The sum of two negative numbers is negative.
> 2. Add the absolute values of the numbers.

EXAMPLE 1   Add: $-6 + (-9)$

Solution: Follow the steps of the procedure.

> 1. $-6 + (-9) = -(\underline{\ ?\ })$ ◄——— **The sum is negative.**
> 2. $ = -(6 + 9)$
> $ = \mathbf{-15}$ ◄——— $|-6| = 6;\ |-9| = 9$

The procedure for adding negative numbers can be stated as a *theorem*. A **theorem** is a statement that can be proved from postulates and definitions.

Theorem 2–1

> **Sum of Two Negative Numbers**
> The sum of two negative numbers is the opposite of the sum of their absolute values.
> **If $x < 0$ and $y < 0$, then $x + y = -(|x| + |y|)$.**

Quick Quiz
Evaluate.
1. $|-5| + |6|$ **Ans: 11**
2. $-(|-3| + |4|)$ **Ans: -7**
3. $-|-\frac{1}{2}| + |-\frac{1}{2}|$ **Ans: 0**
Use $>$ or $<$ to compare the numbers.
4. $|-9|$ __?__ $-|-9|$
   Ans: $>$
5. $-|-1|$ __?__ $|0|$
   Ans: $<$

Additional Examples
Example 1
Add.
1. $-5 + (-11)$
   Ans: -16
2. $-6.2 + (-3.8)$
   Ans: -10

Operations with Real Numbers   **51**

You can also use a number line to find the sum of a positive and a negative number.

Example	On the Number Line	Sum
a. $5 + (-3)$ Think: A gain of 5 followed by a loss of 3.		$5 + (-3) = 2$
b. $-7 + 4$ Think: A loss of 7 followed by a gain of 4.		$-7 + 4 = -3$

Follow this procedure to find the sum of a positive and a negative number.

Procedure

To find the sum of a positive and a negative number:

1. Determine whether the sum is positive or negative.
   a. The sum is positive when the positive number has the greater absolute value.
   b. The sum is negative when the negative number has the greater absolute value.
2. Subtract the lesser absolute value from the greater absolute value.

Additional Examples
Example 2
Add.
1. $8 + (-12)$
   Ans: −4
2. $19 + (-35)$
   Ans: −16

EXAMPLE 2   Add: $8 + (-10)$

Solution: Follow the steps of the procedure.

$\boxed{1}$ $8 + (-10) = -(\underline{\;?\;})$ ◄────── **Since $|-10| > |8|$, the sum is negative.**
$\boxed{2}$ $\qquad\qquad = -(10 - 8)$ ◄────── $(|-10| - |8|)$
$\qquad\qquad\quad = -2$

Sometimes the positive number has the greater absolute value.

Example 3
Add.
1. $13 + (-1)$
   Ans: 12
2. $7 + (-6)$
   Ans: 1

EXAMPLE 3   Add: $20 + (-8)$

Solution: $\boxed{1}$ $20 + (-8) = (\underline{\;?\;})$
$\boxed{2}$ $\qquad\qquad = (20 - 8)$ ◄────── **Since $|20| > |-8|$, the sum is positive.**
$\qquad\qquad\quad = 12$ ◄────── $(|20| - |8|)$

The procedure can be stated as a theorem.

52   *Chapter 2*

Theorem 2–2

> **Sum of a Positive and a Negative Number**
> The sum of a positive number, x, and a negative number, y, is the difference of their absolute values. The sum is positive when x is farther from 0 and negative when y is farther from 0. That is,
> $$x + y = (|x| - |y|) \text{ when } |x| > |y|;$$
> $$x + y = -(|y| - |x|) \text{ when } |y| > |x|.$$

CLASSROOM EXERCISES

In Exercises 1–8, state whether each sum will be positive or negative.

1. $7 + (-15)$ Negative
2. $(-6) + (-4)$
3. $8 + (-9)$
4. $(-16) + 26$
5. $19 + 8$ Positive
6. $(-\frac{2}{3}) + (-\frac{1}{8})$ Negative
7. $(1\frac{1}{2}) + (-1\frac{1}{4})$ Positive
8. $-9.8 + 10.1$ Positive

Add.

9. $-6 + (-9)$ -15
10. $-12 + (-13)$ -25
11. $-\frac{1}{2} + (-\frac{1}{2})$ -1
12. $-2.3 + (-4.7)$
13. $-3 + 4$ 1
14. $-9 + 5$ -4
15. $9 + (-5)$ 4
16. $-12 + 18$ 6
17. $-4.6 + (-2.7)$ -7.3
18. $0.9 + (-9.4)$ -8.5
19. $-3\frac{2}{3} + 4\frac{1}{2}$ $\frac{5}{6}$
20. $-\frac{4}{5} + (-\frac{1}{4})$
21. $-40 + 15$ -25
22. $-8 + (-17)$ -25
23. $(-9) + 22$ 13
24. $-30 + (-11)$

WRITTEN EXERCISES

A Add.

1. $-3 + 6$ 3
2. $3 + 6$ 9
3. $(-3) + (-6)$
4. $3 + (-6)$ -3
5. $9 + (-6)$ 3
6. $(-9) + 6$
7. $2 + (-5)$ -3
8. $(-7) + (-2)$ -9
9. $(-4) + (-9)$
10. $7 + 5$ 12
11. $(-3) + 7$ 4
12. $(-10) + (-3)$
13. $6 + (-2)$ 4
14. $(-9) + (-6)$ -15
15. $8 + (-3)$ 5
16. $6 + 2$ 8
17. $(-10) + (-4)$ -14
18. $-8 + 3$ -5
19. $9 + 0$ 9
20. $0 + 9$ 9
21. $(-9) + 8$ -1
22. $7 + (-3)$ 4
23. $8 + (-7)$ 1
24. $(-3) + (-7)$
25. $9 + 6$ 15
26. $(-6) + 3$ -3
27. $5 + (-6)$ -1
28. $(-3) + 7$ 4
29. $(-9) + 0$ -9
30. $0 + (-9)$ -9
31. $2\frac{3}{4} + (-1\frac{1}{2})$ $1\frac{1}{4}$
32. $(-\frac{3}{5}) + (-\frac{2}{3})$ $-\frac{19}{15}$
33. $7 + 4\frac{1}{2}$ $11\frac{1}{2}$
34. $-9\frac{1}{3} + 6\frac{3}{4}$ $-2\frac{7}{12}$
35. $(-6\frac{5}{12}) + 8\frac{1}{6}$ $1\frac{3}{4}$
36. $8.6 + (-3.7)$
37. $(-4.5) + 2.4$ -2.1
38. $8.0 + (-3.2)$ 4.8
39. $(-6.0) + (-7.2)$
40. $8.2 + 6.4$ 14.6
41. $1.3 + (-0.7)$ 0.6
42. $2.4 + (-4.5)$
43. $(-3.7) + 8.6$ 4.9
44. $(-4.0) + 0.7$ -3.3
45. $(-1.6) + (-6.0)$

Operations with Real Numbers **53**

APPLICATIONS: Using Addition

In Exercises 46–53:

a. Use positive and negative numbers to represent each word description.

b. Find the sum.

46. An elevator on the 21st floor goes down 8 floors. Then it goes up 4 floors and the door opens. On what floor is the elevator now?

47. On three successive plays, a football team lost 4 yards, gained 5 yards, and gained 7 yards. What was the team's net gain in the three plays?

48. The temperature at 9 A.M. was 3°C. At noon, the temperature had risen 7°. By 5 P.M., it had fallen 4°, and by midnight, it had fallen another 6°. What was the midnight temperature?

49. The stock of HCJ Corporation opened in the morning at $52 per share. Two hours later, it lost $4. By closing time, it gained $2. What was its value at closing?

50. A plane was flying at an altitude of 12,000 meters. Then it dropped 3000 meters and rose 780 meters. What was the plane's new altitude?

51. Joann has $250 in her checking account. She wrote checks for $75 and $40 and made a deposit of $110. What was her new balance?

52. A submarine is cruising at a depth of 40 meters below the ocean's surface. The submarine then descends 15 meters and rises 18 meters. What is the submarine's new depth?

53. A company's loss during its first year of operation was $15,890. During its second and third years, it had profits of $5750 and $30,765. Find the net profit or loss over the three years.

B   Add.

54. $[5 + (-8)] + (-2)$ -5

55. $[5 + (-7)] + (-8)$ -10

56. $[-8 + 9] + [7 + (-5)]$

57. $[7 + 4] + [(-9) + 8]$ 10

58. $-12 + [37 + (-18)]$ 7

59. $2 + [37 + (-22)]$

Find the real number that can replace the variable to make a true sentence.

60. $y + 5 = 17$ 12

61. $q + 9 = 21$ 12

62. $n = -8 + 22$ 14

63. $-11 + 10 = n$ -1

64. $6 + y = -2$ -8

65. $10 + t = 1$ -9

66. $a + (-7) = -17$ -10

67. $u + (-3) = -5$ -2

68. $7 + c = 0$ -7

69. $z + (-1\frac{2}{5}) = 0$ $1\frac{2}{5}$

70. $-14 + u = 42$ 56

71. $-18 + r = 20$ 38

Evaluate each expression when $x = -10$, $y = 8$ and $q = -15$.

72. $x + y$ -2

73. $x + q$ -25

74. $y + q$ -7

75. $y + y$

76. $q + q$ -30

77. $x + y + q$ -17

78. $x + x + x$ -30

79. $q + q + x$

C

80. The following gives the steps for the proof of the following statement.

$$-14 + 8 = -6$$

Give the reasons for Steps 2, 3, and 4.

54   *Chapter 2*

Statements	Reasons
1. $-14 + 8 = [-6 + (-8)] + 8$	**1.** Theorem 2-1
2. $\quad = -6 + [(-8) + 8]$	**2.** __?__ Assoc. Post. for Add.
3. $\quad = -6 + \quad 0$	**3.** __?__ Additive Inv. Post.
4. $\quad = -6$	**4.** __?__ Identity Post. for Add.

81. Give the reasons for Steps 2, 3, and 4 in the following proof that $-11 + 17 = 6$.

Statements	Reasons
1. $-11 + 17 = -11 + (11 + 6)$	**1.** Renaming 17 as $11 + 6$
2. $\quad = (-11 + 11) + 6$	**2.** __?__ Assoc. Post. for Add.
3. $\quad = \quad 0 \quad + 6$	**3.** __?__ Additive Inverse Post.
4. $\quad = 6$	**4.** __?__ Identity Post. for Add.

82. To prove that $-4 + (-3) = -(4 + 3)$, you must show that $-4 + (-3)$ is the opposite of $(4 + 3)$, or that the sum of $-4 + (-3)$ and $(4 + 3)$ is 0. Give the reason why each statement in the following proof is true.

Statements	Reasons
1. $[-4 + (-3)] + (4 + 3) = -4 + [(-3) + 4] + 3$	**1.** __?__
2. $\quad = -4 + [4 + (-3)] + 3$	**2.** __?__
3. $\quad = (-4 + 4) + [(-3) + 3]$	**3.** __?__
4. $\quad = \quad 0 \quad + \quad 0$	**4.** __?__
5. $\quad = 0$	**5.** __?__

83. Once you know that the sum is 0, you know that $-4 + (-3)$ and $(4 + 3)$ are inverses. What part of the additive inverse postulate tells you that if $-4 + (-3)$ is the opposite of $(4 + 3)$, then $-4 + (-3)$ must be the same number as $-(4 + 3)$? Hence, $-4 + (-3) = -(4 + 3)$ is true. Theorem 2-1

Prove each of the following.

84. $-9 + (-15) = -24$ **85.** $-9 + 7 = -2$ **86.** $-9 + 17 = 8$

___

REVIEW CAPSULE FOR SECTION 2-4 _____

Subtract.

1. $66 - 45$ 21   **2.** $65 - 48$ 17   **3.** $603 - 245$ 358   **4.** $724 - 596$ 128

5. $6.2 - 0.8$ 5.4   **6.** $12.3 - 8.5$ 3.8   **7.** $10.47 + 3.64$ 6.83   **8.** $14 - 10.7$ 3.3

Subtract. Write your answers in lowest terms.

9. $\frac{9}{10} - \frac{2}{10}$ $\frac{7}{10}$ **10.** $15 - 5\frac{5}{8}$ $14\frac{3}{8}$ **11.** $\frac{3}{12} - \frac{1}{4}$ $\frac{0}{12}$ or 0   **12.** $\frac{3}{5} - \frac{1}{2}$ $\frac{1}{10}$

13. $3\frac{1}{6} - \frac{2}{3}$ $2\frac{1}{2}$ **14.** $6\frac{1}{2} - 3\frac{7}{8}$ $2\frac{5}{8}$ **15.** $3\frac{1}{8} - 2\frac{5}{6}$ $\frac{7}{24}$ **16.** $13\frac{5}{8} - 6\frac{11}{12}$ $6\frac{17}{24}$

Operations with Real Numbers   **55**

NOTE: In the first printing Ex. 7 should have read "$10.47 - 3.64$."

2-4 Subtraction of Real Numbers

Quick Quiz
Add.
1. $-10 + 8$ **Ans: −2**
2. $-5 + 7$ **Ans: 2**
3. $-18 + (-5)$
    Ans: −23
4. $6.3 + (-9.2)$
    Ans: −29
5. $-3\frac{1}{2} + (-5\frac{1}{4})$
    Ans: $-8\frac{3}{4}$

Note that the answers to each pair of the following problems are the same.

Subtraction: $10 - 3 = 7$	**Addition:** $10 + (-3) = 7$
Subtraction: $17 - 6.1 = 10.9$	**Addition:** $17 + (-6.1) = 10.9$
Subtraction: $\frac{3}{5} - \frac{1}{5} = \frac{2}{5}$	**Addition:** $\frac{3}{5} + \left(-\frac{1}{5}\right) = \frac{2}{5}$

Thus,

$10 - 3 = 10 + (-3)$ ◄───── NOTE: 3 and −3 are opposites.

$17 - 6.1 = 17 + (-16.1)$ ◄───── NOTE: 6.1 and −6.1 are opposites.

$\frac{3}{5} - \frac{1}{5} = \frac{3}{5} + \left(-\frac{1}{5}\right)$ ◄───── NOTE: $\frac{3}{5}$ and $-\frac{3}{5}$ are opposites.

This suggests that subtraction can be defined in terms of addition.

Definition

> **Subtraction of Real Numbers**
>
> To subtract a real number b from a real number a, add *the opposite of b* to a. That is,
>
> $$a - b = a + (-b)$$

EXAMPLE 1   Subtract: $3 - 7$

Solution: Write the subtraction problem as an addition problem.

$3 - 7 = 3 + (-7)$ ◄───── **Add the opposite of 7.**

$= -4$

You can use addition to check your answers.

Example 2
Subtract.
1. $-1.5 - (-2.9)$
    Ans: 1.4
2. $-6.2 - (-1.7)$
    Ans: −4.5

EXAMPLE 2   Subtract: $-5.1 - (-8.2)$

Solution: $-5.1 - (-8.2) = -5.1 + 8.2$ ◄───── **The opposite of (−8.2) is 8.2.**

$= 3.1$

Check: Does $3.1 + (-8.2) = -5.1$?   Yes ✔

To find the amount of change, **subtract the first value from the final value.**

EXAMPLE 3   The temperature was $-3°$ C. It is now $9°$ C. How much did the temperature change?

Solution: Subtract -3 (first value) *from* 9 (final value).

$9 - (-3) = 9 + 3$

$= 12$ The temperature changed **12°**.

CLASSROOM EXERCISES

Write an addition problem for each subtraction problem.

1. $6 - 3$ $6 + (-3)$
2. $0 - 9$ $0 + (-9)$
3. $-10 - 5$ $-10 + (-5)$
4. $-9 - 15$
5. $-5 - (-2)$ $-5 + 2$
6. $-5 - (-10)$ $-5 + 10$
7. $8 - (-4)$ $8 + 4$
8. $20 - (-7)$

Subtract.

9. $16 - (-7)$ 23
10. $14 - (-8)$ 22
11. $-9 - (-4)$ -5
12. $-18 - (-5)$
13. $-1.5 - 6.9$ -8.4
14. $-0.9 - (-0.1)$ -0.8
15. $\frac{3}{4} - \frac{1}{2}$ $\frac{1}{4}$
16. $-\frac{1}{3} - (-\frac{2}{3})$

WRITTEN EXERCISES

A   Write an addition problem for each subtraction problem.

1. $3 - 6$ $3 + (-6)$
2. $0 - 7$ $0 + (-7)$
3. $5 - (-9)$ $5 + 9$
4. $8 - (-3)$
5. $0 - (-2)$ $0 + 2$
6. $0 - (-6)$ $0 + 6$
7. $-5 - (-5)$ $-5 + 5$
8. $-3 - (-7)$
9. $-2 - 8$ $-2 + (-8)$
10. $-5 - (6)$ $-5 + (-6)$
11. $-3 - (-9)$ $-3 + 9$
12. $0 - (-8)$
13. $-2\frac{1}{2} - (-\frac{1}{2})$ $-2\frac{1}{2} + \frac{1}{2}$
14. $-5.4 - (-2.6)$

$-5.4 + 2.6$
15. $2.9 - 3.8$

$2.9 + (-3.8)$
16. $-6 - 2\frac{3}{4}$

Subtract.

17. $5 - 11$ -6
18. $6 - 8$ -2
19. $-4 - 5$ -9
20. $-5 - 1$
21. $-6 - 2$ -8
22. $-6 - 4$ -10
23. $4 - (-6)$ 10
24. $-6 - (-4)$
25. $-4 - 6$ -10
26. $-8 - 3$ -11
27. $-4 - 8$ -12
28. $-8 - 4$
29. $16 - (-15)$ 31
30. $24 - (-12)$ 36
31. $15 - 15$ 0
32. $9 - 9$ 0
33. $-9 - 10$ -19
34. $-10 - 10$
35. $-2.4 - 9.4$ -11.8
36. $-54 - 14$ -68
37. $-7.8 - 0$
38. $0 - 7.8$ -7.8
39. $\frac{1}{2} - (-\frac{1}{2})$ 1
40. $\frac{5}{3} - (-\frac{2}{3})$
41. $-54 - (-14)$ -40
42. $-64 - (-74)$ 10
43. $12.3 - 6.7$
44. $6.7 - 12.3$ -5.6
45. $12.3 - (-6.7)$ 19.0
46. $6.7 - (-12.3)$
47. $-12.3 - (-19)$ 6.7
48. $-6.7 - (12.3)$ -19.00
49. $-6.7 - (-12.3)$
50. $-12.3 - (-6.7)$ -5.6
51. $-\frac{1}{2} - (-\frac{1}{2})$ 0
52. $-\frac{3}{4} - (-\frac{3}{4})$ 0

APPLICATIONS: Using Subtraction

53. The temperature six hours ago was $-1°C$. It is now $11°C$. How much did the temperature change in the last six hours? 12°

54. The actual temperature is $20°F$. The wind chill temperature is $-15°$. How much colder than the actual temperature is the wind chill? $-35°$

55. A dolphin is swimming at a depth of 2 meters below the surface of a pool. It leaps to a height of 1 meter above the surface. Find the difference in height.

3 meters

56. The greatest recorded temperature change in one day in North America took place in Montana. The change was from $7°C$ to $-49°C$. Find the amount of change. $-56°$

Operations with Real Numbers   **57**

Additional Answers
Classroom Exercises
4. $-9 + (-15)$
8. $20 + 7$
12. -13
16. $\frac{1}{3}$

Assignment Guide
Minimal
Day 1 p. 57: 1–30
Day 2 pp. 57–58: 31–58
Average pp. 57–58: 1–75 odd
Above Average pp. 57–58
4, 8, 12, . . . 52, 54–90 even

Additional Answers
Written Exercises
4. $8 + 3$
8. $-3 + 7$
12. $0 + 8$
16. $-6 + (-2\frac{3}{4})$
20. -6
24. -2
28. -12
34. -20
37. -7.8
40. $\frac{7}{3}$
43. 5.6
46. 19.0
49. 5.6

57. The lowest temperature ever recorded in West Virginia was $-37°F$. The lowest temperature recorded in Wyoming was $-63°F$. Find the difference between the two temperatures. $-26°$

58. The highest point in Texas, Guadalupe Peak, is 2667 meters above sea level. The greatest known depth of the Atlantic Ocean (in the Puerto Rico trench) is 8648 meters below sea level. Find the difference between the points. 11,315 meters

B

59. $(2 - 10) - 3$ -11 **60.** $2 - (10 - 3)$ -5 **61.** $(3 - 7) - (2 - 9)$

62. $(5 - 2) - (-4 - 8)$ 15   **63.** $12 - (8 - 7)$ 11   **64.** $(-4 - 9) - 3$

65. $-\frac{2}{3} - \frac{1}{12} - (-\frac{1}{4})$ $-\frac{1}{2}$ **66.** $-1.8 - 0.12 - 0.36$ -2.28 **67.** $16 - 32 - 15 + 14$

Evaluate when $x = 12$, $y = -6$, and $q = -4$.

68. $y - x$ -18 **69.** $x - y$ 18   **70.** $y - q$ -2 **71.** $q - y$ 2

72. $x - y - y$ 24   **73.** $y - q - q$ 2   **74.** $q - y - y$ 8   **75.** $q - q$ 0

76. $x + y + q$ 2   **77.** $y + y + q$ -16 **78.** $q + q + x$ 4   **79.** $x + x + y + q$

C Classify each of the following as true, T, or false, F. When an equation is false, tell why it is false. The replacement set is the set of real numbers.

80. $-6 + (-2) = 4$ **81.** $-\frac{2}{3} - (-\frac{2}{3}) = \frac{1}{3}$ **82.** $-4 - (-2) = 2 - (-4)$

83. $0 = 0.24 - (-0.24)$ **84.** $8 - (-8) = 0$ **85.** $6 - 2 = 6 + (-2)$ T

86. $|8 - 2| = |2 - 8|$ T **87.** $|8 - 2| = |8| - |2|$ T **88.** $|2 - 8| = |2| - |8|$

89. $-3 + (-3) = -6$ T **90.** $a - b = a + (-b)$ T **91.** $|a - b| = |b - a|$ T

—— **Review** ————————————————

Write without parentheses. *(Section 2–1)*

1. $-(-1.5)$ 1.5   **2.** $-(600)$ -600 **3.** $-(16 + 21)$ -37 **4.** $-(9.2 - 5.6)$
-3.6

Use algebraic symbols to represent each sentence. *(Section 2–1)*

5. The opposite of losing 3 games is winning 3 games. $-(-3) = 3$

6. A rise of $15°$ in temperature is the opposite of a fall of $15°$. $15 = -(-15)$

Evaluate. *(Section 2–2)*

7. $|5| + |13|$ 18   **8.** $|-\sqrt{13}|$ $\sqrt{13}$ **9.** $|4| + |-3|$ 7   **10.** $-|1.6| + |1.6|$
0

Solve. *(Section 2–2)*

11. $x = |-6|$ $x = 6$ **12.** $m = -|8|$ $m = -8$ **13.** $|y| = 9$ **14.** $|a| = |-3|$
$y = 9$ or $y = -9$ $a = 3$ or $a = -3$

Add or subtract as indicated. *(Sections 2–3 and 2–4)*

15. $-5 + 2$ -3 **16.** $7 + (-12)$ -5 **17.** $[5 + 4] + [(-7) + 3]$
5

18. $(4 - 10) - 5$ -11 **19.** $-2.3 - 0.16 - 0.05$ -2.51 **20.** $10 - 26 - 8 + 16$ -8

Consumer Applications: Investing

When you buy shares of stock in a corporation, you become part owner of the corporation. Stock prices are listed each day in the business section of the newspaper. The prices are quoted (listed) in eighths of a dollar.

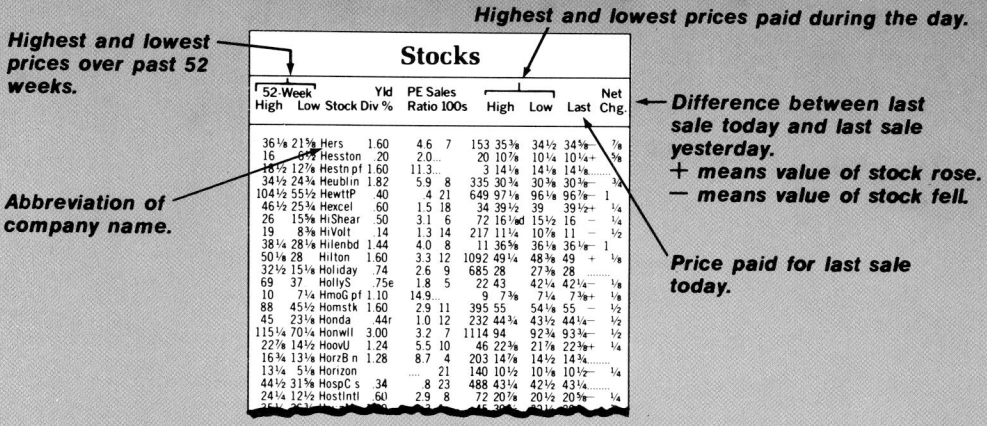

Highest and lowest prices over past 52 weeks.

Highest and lowest prices paid during the day.

Difference between last sale today and last sale yesterday.
+ means value of stock rose.
− means value of stock fell.

Abbreviation of company name.

Price paid for last sale today.

To find the amount of **profit** or **loss** on a stock sale, use this formula.

$$\text{Profit (Loss)} = \frac{\text{Amount Received}}{\text{for Stock}} - \frac{\text{Total Cost}}{\text{of Stock}}$$

EXAMPLE Bill Aikens bought 200 shares of stock at $40\frac{5}{8}$. The stockbroker charged $90.85 for a commission. A few months later, Bill sold the stock at $38\frac{7}{8}$. The broker charged $85.60 at that time. How much was Bill's profit or loss?

Solution:
1. Cost of stock: $200 \times \$40.625 + \$90.85 = \$8215.85$ ⟵ $40\frac{5}{8} = \$40.625$

2. Amount received: $200 \times \$38.875 - \$85.60 = \$7689.40$ ⟵ $38\frac{7}{8} = \$38.875$

3. Profit (Loss) = $\$7689.40 - \$8215.85 = -\$526.45$

Thus, Bill **lost $526.45** on the transaction.

EXERCISES

Find the amount of profit or loss on each transaction.

	Number of Shares	Buying Price	Broker's Commission	Selling Price	Broker's Commission	Profit (Loss)
1.	100	$36\frac{3}{8}$	$ 40.00	$38\frac{1}{8}$	$ 42.00	?
2.	200	$42\frac{7}{8}$	$ 90.50	$49\frac{5}{8}$	$ 92.80	?
3.	300	$26\frac{1}{8}$	$ 73.40	$20\frac{7}{8}$	$ 60.90	?
4.	1000	$31\frac{7}{8}$	$322.60	$27\frac{3}{8}$	$278.20	?

2-5 Combining Like Terms

Quick Quiz
Subtract.
1. $4 - 17$ **Ans: -13**
2. $12 - (-11)$ **Ans: 23**
3. $-8 - (-7)$ **Ans: -1**
4. $-\frac{5}{6} - \frac{1}{3}$ **Ans: $-\frac{7}{6}$, or $-1\frac{1}{6}$**
5. One hour ago, the temperature was $-2°C$. It is now $5°C$. How much did the temperature change?
Ans: $7°$

A **term** is a real number, a variable, or the product of real numbers and variables. Each of these is a *term*.

$$3x^2 \qquad \frac{1}{2}xy^3 \qquad \frac{4}{5}x^2 \qquad 7mn \qquad \frac{a}{2b}$$

$3x^2$ and $\frac{4}{5}x^2$ are *like terms*. **Like terms** have the same variables. In like terms, corresponding variables have the same exponents.

Terms	Like Terms	Reason
$3z$ and $5z$	Yes	Same variable, z, with same exponent, 1
$2y^2$ and $-3x^2$	No	Different variables
$3m^2n$ and $5mn$	No	Different exponents for m
9 and $4y$	No	The number, 9, has no variable

To **combine like terms** means to **add or subtract the like terms.**

To add or subtract like terms, you apply the distributive postulate. Then you add or subtract the numerical coefficients.

Term	Numerical Coefficient
$-7y$	-7
$16m^2n^2$	16
$1 \cdot q$ or q	1

Note carefully the last expression in the table.

$$q = 1 \cdot q = 1q$$

Similarly, $\qquad\qquad -q = -1 \cdot q = -1q$

Additional Examples
Example 1
Combine like terms.
1. $15t + 7t$
   Ans: $22t$
2. $10ab + 1ab$
   Ans: $11ab$

EXAMPLE 1 Combine like terms: $8x + x$

Solution: $8x + x = 8x + 1x$
$\qquad\qquad = (8 + 1)x$ ◀—— **By the distributive postulate**
$\qquad\qquad = 9x$

To subtract like terms, first write the subtraction as addition. Then proceed as in Example 1.

Example 2
Combine like terms.
1. $7y - 3y$
   Ans: $-10y$
2. $-15r - 1r$
   Ans: $-16r$

EXAMPLE 2 Combine like terms: $-3m - 7m$

Solution: $-3m - 7m = -3m + (-7m)$
$\qquad\qquad = [-3 + (-7)]m$ ◀—— **By the distributive postulate**
$\qquad\qquad = -10m$

When you combine like terms, you are **simplifying an algebraic expression.**

EXAMPLE 3 Simplify: $5t + 3r + 9t - 10r - 8$

Solution: $5t + 3r + 9t - 10r - 8 = (5t + 9t) + (3r - 10r) - 8$ ◄—— **By the commutative and associative postulates**

$$= 14t + (-7r) - 8$$

$$= 14t - 7r - 8$$

When you simplify an algebraic expression, the original expression and the simplified expression are equivalent. **Equivalent algebraic expressions** name the same number for all real–number replacements of the variable.

Substitution Principle

If two expressions are equivalent, you can always replace one with the other in a given expression.

CLASSROOM EXERCISES

Identify each pair of terms as *like terms* or *unlike terms*. Give a reason for each answer.

1. $2x$ and $3x$ Like terms

2. $9m$ and $6r$ Unlike terms

3. $\frac{1}{2}y$ and $2y^2$ Unlike terms

4. $-6m$ and $8m^2$ Unlike terms

5. $4xy$ and $7xy$ Like terms

6. $3a$ and $-11a$ Like terms

State the numerical coefficient of each term.

7. $2a$ 2

8. $-\frac{1}{2}x^2$ $-\frac{1}{2}$

9. $-0.05t$ -0.05

10. $\frac{2}{3}r^3$ $\frac{2}{3}$

11. t 1

12. y 1

Combine like terms.

13. $2x + 3x$ $5x$

14. $8y + y$ $9y$

15. $7m - 3m$ $4m$

16. $-9x - x$ $-10x$

WRITTEN EXERCISES

A Identify each pair of terms as *like terms* or *unlike terms*. Give a reason for each answer.

1. $4x, 7x$ Like

2. $8y, 4m$ Unlike

3. $9, 7y$ Unlike

4. $6a, -8$ Unlike

5. $x^2, 4x$ Unlike

6. $-7y, 2.5y$ Like

7. $-15m, 18n$ Unlike

8. $8r, -r$ Like

9. $4t, -8t$ Like

10. $0.4xy^2, 0.1xy^2$ Like

11. $3x^4, 5x^4$ Like

12. $3a^2b, 5ab^2$ Unlike

Combine like terms.

13. $8x + 2x$ $10x$

14. $7y + 13y$ $20y$

15. $15m + 6.2m$ $21.2m$

16. $5a^2 + 7a^2$ $12a^2$

17. $8mn + 6mn$ $14mn$

18. $3ab + 11ab$ $14ab$

Operations with Real Numbers **61**

19. $9x + x$ $10x$

20. $15y + y$ $16y$

21. $4m^2 + m^2$ $5m^2$

22. $3ab + ab$ $4ab$

23. $m + 19m$ $20m$

24. $a + 9a$ $10a$

25. $4y + (-12y)$ $-8y$

26. $m + (-16m)$ $-15m$

27. $-4.1y + (-2.3y)$ $-6.4y$

28. $-0.4x + (-0.6x)$ $-1.0x$

29. $-16t + (-t)$ $-17t$

30. $(-15x) + (-1x)$ $-16x$

31. $7m - 6m$ m

32. $9t - 3t$ $6t$

33. $12x - 9x$ $3x$

34. $8a - 5a$ $3a$

35. $4x - 1x$ $3x$

36. $9m - 1m$ $8m$

37. $-3a - 4a$ $-7a$

38. $-7b - 5b$ $-12b$

39. $-5m - (-8m)$ $3m$

40. $-3t - (-2t)$ $-t$

41. $-6r - (-1r)$ $-5r$

42. $-30q - (-1q)$ $-29q$

Simplify.

43. $3a + 2a + 4$ $5a + 4$

44. $8x + 3x + 9$ $11x + 9$

45. $15y + 6y + 3$

46. $4m + 7m - 5$ $11m - 5$

47. $6 + 2x + 4x$ $6x + 6$

48. $15 + 9y - 4y$

49. $5x + 7x - 6y$ $12x - 6y$

50. $4y - y + 8$ $3y + 8$

51. $5x - x - 15$

52. $4a - b - 7b$ $4a - 8b$

53. $2m + 7m - 8m$ m

54. $4a + 7a - 9a$ $2a$

55. $7x - x + 3y + 57$

56. $12x - 3y + x + 2y$ $13x - y$

57. $15xy - 2xy - 7xy + x$

58. $8rt + 3rt + t - 3t$ $11rt - 2t$

59. $4\frac{1}{2}xy + 7\frac{1}{3}xy + 2\frac{1}{4}xy$ $14\frac{1}{12}xy$

60. $19m - m - 3n + 2n$

61. $4.75r + 1.62r + r$ $7.37r$

62. $2.7m - 1.9m + m$ $1.8m$

63. $4.87 + 6.52q + q$

APPLICATIONS: Using Like Terms

B Find the sum of the areas of each group of figures.

64. Rectangle: $A = $ (length $\cdot$ width) $5b$

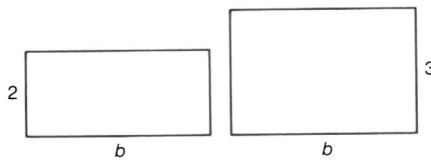

65. Parallelogram: $A = $ (base $\cdot$ height) $8h$

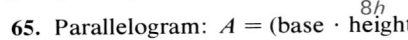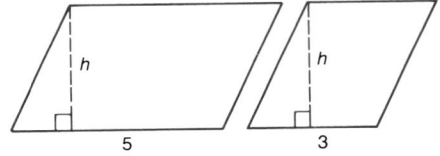

66. Triangle: $A = \frac{1}{2}$(base $\cdot$ height) $7b$

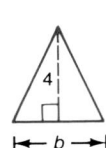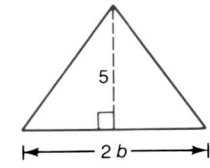

67. Rectangle: $A = $ (length $\cdot$ width) $w^2 + 5w + 25$

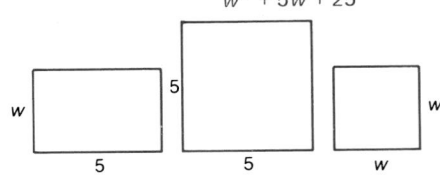

Classify each statement as true, *T*, or false, *F*. When a statement is false, give a numerical example to show why. This is called a **counterexample**.

For Exercises 68–77, counterexamples will vary.

68. $8x + x = 8x$ *F*

69. $3m + m = m^2$ *F*

70. $8 + 3x = 11x$ *F*

71. $8m - 2m + 5m = 11$ *F*

72. $m + m + m = m^3$ *F*

73. $4ab + a = 5ab$ *F*

62 *Chapter 2*

Classify each statement as true, *T*, or false, *F*. When a statement is false, give a numerical example to show why it is false.

74. $4(a + b) + 7(a + b) = 11(a + b)$ *T*

75. $2(m - n) + 7(m - n) = 9(m - n)$ *T*

76. $4x + x^2 = 5x^3$ *F*

77. $5x^2 + 2x^2 + 9x^2 = 21x^2$ *F*

In Exercises 78–81, write a formula for the area of each shaded region. Simplify the result. Use the formulas for the area of a rectangle and of a triangle (see Exercises 64 and 66 on page 62).

78.
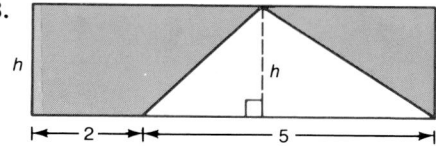

79.
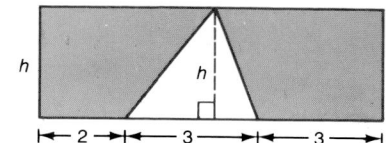

80.
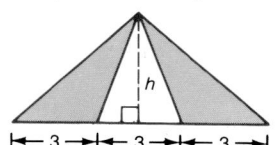

81.
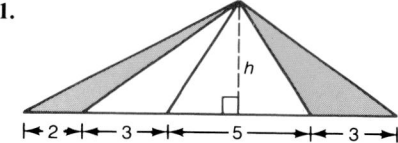

Additional Answers
Applications
78. $A = 7h - \frac{1}{2}(5h)$;
$A = \frac{9}{2}h$
79. $A = 8h - \frac{1}{2}(3h)$;
$A = \frac{13}{2}h$
80. $A = \frac{1}{2}(9h) - \frac{1}{2}(3h)$;
$A = 3h$
81. $A = \frac{1}{2}(13h) - \frac{1}{2}(8h)$;
$A = \frac{5}{2}h$
86. $7\frac{1}{2}x + 2\frac{1}{4}y + 13\frac{5}{6}z$
87. $4x - 4y$
88. $7x + 49y$
89. $-2x - 8y$

Simplify.

82. $3 \cdot 5a - 7 \cdot 3b - 3 \cdot 2a + 2 \cdot 9b$ $9a - 3b$

83. $\frac{5}{8}c - \frac{1}{4}d - \frac{3}{7}c + \frac{3}{5}d$ $\frac{11}{56}c + \frac{7}{20}d$

84. $7x - 3y + 2z - x + 4y + 6z$ $6x + y + 8z$

85. $2c - 1\frac{1}{2}d + 1\frac{1}{4}c - 2\frac{3}{4}c$ $\frac{1}{2}c - 1\frac{1}{2}d$

86. $5x - y + 3 \cdot 5z - 1\frac{1}{6}z + 2\frac{1}{2}x + 3\frac{1}{4}y$

87. $5(x - y) + 7(x - y) - 8(x - y)$

88. $3(x + 7y) - 5(x + 7y) + 9(x + 7y)$

89. $-5(2x + 8y) + 9(2x + 8y) - 5(2x + 8y)$

90. $6(x^2 + y^2) + 7(x^2 + y^2)$ $13x^2 + 13y^2$

91. $9(x^2 - y^2) - 3(x^2 - y^2)$ $6x^2 - 6y^2$

92. $3(a + b) + (a + b) + 9(a + b)$ $13a + 13b$

93. $-5(a - b) - (a - b) + 8(a - b)$
$2a - 2b$

C   Complete.

94. $ax + bx = (\underline{\ ?\ } + \underline{\ ?\ })x$ $(a + b)$

95. $mx - my = (\underline{\ ?\ } - \underline{\ ?\ })m$ $(x - y)$

96. $cr - dr = (\underline{\ ?\ } - \underline{\ ?\ })r$ $(c - d)$

97. $7r + 6r = (\underline{\ ?\ } + \underline{\ ?\ })r$ $(7 + 6)$

98. $a(x + y) + b(x + y) = (\underline{\ ?\ } + \underline{\ ?\ })(x + y)$ $(a + b)$

99. $c(x + y) - d(x + y) = (\underline{\ ?\ } - \underline{\ ?\ })(x + y)$ $(c - d)$

——————— **REVIEW CAPSULE FOR SECTION 2-6** ———————

Multiply.

1. 54×9 486

2. 84×27 2268

3. 703×428 300,884

4. 505×901
455,005

5. 0.7×0.8 0.56

6. 5.6×8.2 45.92

7. 4.059×1000 4059

8. 0.056×34.9
1.9544

Multiply. Write your answers in lowest terms.

9. $\frac{1}{4} \times \frac{4}{5}$ $\frac{1}{5}$

10. $\frac{2}{3} \times \frac{2}{5}$ $\frac{4}{15}$

11. $\frac{3}{8} \times 7$ $\frac{21}{8}$

12. $4\frac{3}{10} \times 8\frac{5}{16}$
$35\frac{119}{160}$

Operations with Real Numbers **63**

Quick Quiz
Combine like terms.
1. $7d + 34d$ **Ans: 41d**
2. $11ab - 13ab$ **Ans: −2ab**
3. $-14rt - (20rt)$
   Ans: 6rt
4. $x - 6 + 18x$
   Ans: 19x − 6
5. $17gt - (-6gt) + 9$
   Ans: 23gt + 9

OBJECTIVE: To multiply real numbers

2–6 Multiplication of Real Numbers

You already know that the product of two positive numbers is positive. You also know that the *product of a real number and zero is zero*. This is called the *Zero Multiplication Theorem*.

Theorem 2–3

Zero Multiplication Theorem
For any real number a, $a \cdot 0 = 0 \cdot a = 0$.

In Table 1, the first factor, 4, stays the same. The second factor decreases by 1 at each step.

If the pattern continues, what are the missing products?

$$4 \cdot 4 = 16 \qquad\qquad 4 \cdot (-1) = -4$$
$$4 \cdot 3 = 12 \qquad\qquad 4 \cdot (-2) = -8$$
$$4 \cdot 2 = 8 \qquad\qquad 4 \cdot (-3) = \underline{\ ?\ }$$
$$4 \cdot 1 = 4 \qquad\qquad 4 \cdot (-4) = \underline{\ ?\ }$$
$$4 \cdot 0 = 0$$

Table 1

The table suggests Theorem 2–4.

Theorem 2–4

Negative Product Theorem
The product of two real numbers is negative when one number is positive and the other is negative. That is, **for $a < 0$ and $b > 0$,** $$a \cdot b = -(|a| \cdot |b|).$$

Example 1 applies the Negative Product theorem.

EXAMPLE 1 Multiply: $-21 \cdot 9.2$

Solution: $-21 \cdot 9.2 = -(\ ?\ )$ ←——— **The product is negative.**
$$= -193.2$$

Additional Examples
Example 1
Multiply.
1. $-8 \cdot 3.7$
   Ans: −29.6
2. $12 \cdot (-11)$
   Ans: −132

Since multiplication of real numbers is commutative, you also know that the following is true.

$$4 \cdot (-2) = -2 \cdot 4 = -8$$

In Table 2 at the top of page 65, the first factor, (-4), stays the same. The second factor decreases by 1 at each step.

If the pattern continues, what are the missing products?

64   *Chapter 2*

$$-4 \cdot 3 = -12 \qquad\qquad -4 \cdot (-1) = 4$$
$$-4 \cdot 2 = -8 \qquad\qquad -4 \cdot (-2) = 8$$
$$-4 \cdot 1 = -4 \qquad\qquad -4 \cdot (-3) = ?$$
$$-4 \cdot 0 = 0 \qquad\qquad -4 \cdot (-4) = ?$$

Table 2

Table 2 suggests Theorem 2–5.

Theorem 2–5

> **Positive Product Theorem**
>
> The product of two real numbers is positive when both numbers are positive or when both numbers are negative. That is, **for $a < 0$ and $b < 0$, or for $a > 0$ and $b > 0$,**
> $$a \cdot b = |a| \cdot |b|.$$

Example 2 applies Theorem 2–5 in finding a product.

EXAMPLE 2 Multiply: $-18 \cdot \left(-\frac{2}{3}\right)$

Solution: $-18 \cdot \left(-\frac{2}{3}\right) = (\ ?\ )$ ◄——— **The product is positive.**

$= 12$ ◄——— $\overset{6}{\cancel{18}} \cdot \dfrac{2}{\underset{1}{\cancel{3}}} = 6 \cdot 2 = 12$

CLASSROOM EXERCISES

In Exercises 1–8, state whether each product is positive or negative.

1. $4 \cdot (-6)$ Negative **2.** $-3 \cdot 9$ Negative **3.** $-8 \cdot (-9)$ Positive **4.** $-6 \cdot (-1)$

5. $-9 \cdot 7$ Negative **6.** $12 \cdot \left(-\frac{1}{6}\right)$ Negative **7.** $(-18)(-3.7)$ Positive **8.** $200(-8.4)$

Multiply.

9. $7 \cdot (-8)$ -56 **10.** $13.6 \cdot 0$ 0 **11.** $(-9)(-8)$ 72 **12.** $\left(-\frac{1}{5}\right)(15)$ -3

13. $\frac{4}{5} \cdot 25$ 20 **14.** $(-1)(-1)$ 1 **15.** $(-80)(0)$ 0 **16.** $(-1.5)(100)$ -150

WRITTEN EXERCISES

A Multiply.

1. $6 \times (-3)$ -18 **2.** -5×2 -10 **3.** $2 \times (-5)$ -10 **4.** -2×5 -10

5. $5(-2)$ -10 **6.** $2(5)$ 10 **7.** $7(0)$ 0 **8.** $(-4)0$ 0

9. $-4 \cdot 3$ -12 **10.** $4 \cdot (-3)$ -12 **11.** $-\frac{3}{4} \cdot \frac{2}{3}$ $-\frac{1}{2}$ **12.** $\frac{1}{8} \cdot \left(-\frac{5}{6}\right)$ $-\frac{5}{48}$

Operations with Real Numbers **65**

Additional Examples
Example 2
Multiply.
1. $-24 \cdot \left(-\frac{5}{6}\right)$
  Ans: 20
2. $-3 \cdot (-45)$
  Ans: 135

Additional Answers
Classroom Exercises
4. Positive
8. Negative

Assignment Guide
Minimal
Day 1 pp. 65–66: 1–28
Day 2 p. 66: 29–56
Average pp. 65–66:
3, 6, 9, . . . 54, 58–110 even
Above Average pp. 65–67:
4, 8, 12, . . . 94, 96–116 even

13. $(-2)(-5)$ 10   14. $(-5)(-2)$ 10   15. $(-3)(5)$ -15 16. $(-4)(7)$ -28

17. $(-4)(-3)$ 12   18. $4(-7)$ -28 19. $(-2.5)(-0.1)$ 0.25   20. $(-\frac{1}{8})(-\frac{5}{6})$ $\frac{5}{48}$

21. $(-5)(-5)$ 25   22. $6 \cdot 3$ 18   23. $-6 \cdot 3$ -1.8 24. $-3 \cdot 6$ -18

25. $8 \cdot (-\frac{1}{4})$ -2 26. $12 \cdot 6$ 72   27. $12 \cdot (-6)$ -72 28. $-12 \cdot 6$ -72

29. $(-1)(5)$ -5 30. $8(-2.5)$ -20 31. $\frac{2}{3}(-12)$ -8 32. $3.8(-10)$ -38

33. $-62(100)$ -6200 34. $-17(28)$ -476 35. $2\frac{1}{5}(-\frac{3}{5})$ $-\frac{33}{25}$ 36. $33(-\frac{1}{3})$ -11

37. $8.1(0)$ 0   38. $-5(2.4)$ -12.0 39. $-7.2(\frac{1}{4})$ -1.8 40. $-6(-3)$ 18

41. $-4(-5)$ 20   42. $4(-5)$ -20 43. $-4(5)$ -20 44. $4(5)$ 20

45. $0(-2)$ 0   46. $-2(-9)$ 18   47. $7(-1)$ -7 48. $-48(-10)$ 480

49. $-1 \cdot (-1)$ 1   50. $-\frac{2}{3} \cdot (-\frac{3}{2})$ 1   51. $-0.5 \cdot (-12)$ 6.0   52. $-1.1 \cdot 3.4$

53. $(1)(-1)(1)$ -1 54. $2(-4)(5)$ -40 55. $(-5)(6)(2)$ -60 56. $(2)(3)(-1)$ -6

B

57. $\frac{1}{2}(-8)(5)$ -20 58. $(-0.1)(10)(10)$ -10 59. $(-0.1)(0.1)(0.1)$ 60. $\frac{1}{2}(-\frac{1}{2})(\frac{1}{2})$ $-\frac{1}{8}$

61. $(-2\frac{1}{2})(\frac{2}{5})(1)$ -1 62. $(4)(0)(-9)$ 0   63. $(3\frac{1}{2})(\frac{1}{2})(-2)$ $-\frac{7}{2}$ 64. $(4\frac{1}{5})(5)(-6)$

65. $(\frac{2}{3})(\frac{2}{3})(\frac{2}{3})$ $\frac{8}{27}$ 66. $(\frac{7}{5})(-\frac{7}{5})(2)$ $-\frac{98}{25}$ 67. $(\frac{8}{7})(-1)(\frac{7}{8})$ -1 68 $(10)(-\frac{1}{100})(2)$

69. $5(4)(-2)$ -40 70. $-5(4)(-2)$ 40   71. $-6(-5)(-4)$ -120 72. $5(-4)(-2)$

73. $6(-4)(-5)$ 120   74. $-8(-1)(2)$ 16   75. $3(0)(-5)$ 0   76. $5(-6)(-4)$

77. $-2(-2)(-2)$ -8 78. $(-3)^2$ 9   79. $(-4)^2$ 16   80. $(5)^2$ 25

81. $(-1)^2$ 1   82. $(1)^2$ 1   83. $(-1)^3$ -1 84. $(-1)^4$ 1

In Exercises 85–94, replace the __?__ with $<$, $=$, or $>$, to make true statements.

85. $2(-3)$ __?__ $-3(2)$ $=$ 86. $-6(-1)$ __?__ $-1(6)$ $>$

87. $-0.34(-6)$ __?__ $-0.17(-3)$ $>$ 88. $-\frac{3}{2}(\frac{1}{2})$ __?__ $-\frac{1}{2}(\frac{3}{2})$ $=$

89. $-6(0)$ __?__ $0(6)$ $=$ 90. $|4 \cdot 5|$ __?__ $|4| \cdot |5|$ $=$

91. $|-0.34 \cdot -2|$ __?__ $|-0.34| \cdot |-2|$ $=$ 92. $|0 \cdot 1|$ __?__ $|0| \cdot |1|$ $=$

93- $|0.2 \cdot 0.1|$ __?__ $|-0.2| \cdot |0.1|$ $=$ 94. $|\frac{2}{3} \cdot \frac{1}{2}|$ __?__ $|\frac{2}{3}| \cdot |\frac{1}{2}|$ $=$

In Exercises 95–110, evaluate each expression for $x = -3$, $y = -2$, and $p = 0$.

95. $2x$ -6 96. $3y$ -6 97. $-2x$ 6   98. $-7y$ 14

99. px 0   100. xy 6   101. $3xy$ 18   102. $5pxy$ 0

103. $3x + y$ -11 104. $2x + p$ -6 105. $2y + p$ -4 106. $4x + 7y$ -26

107. x^2 9   108. y^3 -8 109. px^2 0   110. x^2y^2 36

For each equation in Exercises 111–114, state whether the solution is positive, negative, or equal to zero.

111. $5x = -15$ 112. $-3x = 15$ 113. $-9x = -27$ 114. $3x = 0$ 0

Additional Answers
52. -3.74
59. -0.001
64. -126
68. $-\frac{1}{5}$
72. 40
76. 120
111. Negative
112. Negative
113. Positive

C The **Multiplication Property for Equations** states that if you multiply both sides of an equation by the same nonzero number, you obtain an equivalent equation. You can use this and other postulates to prove that $3(-4) = -12$ and to prove that $(-3)(-4) = 12$.

Complete the steps in each proof by supplying the missing reason or reasons.

115. Prove: $3(-4) = -12$

Statements	Reasons
1. $4 + (-4) = 0$	**1.** Additive inverse postulate
2. $3[4 + (-4)] = 3 \cdot 0$	**2.** Multiplication property for equations
3. $3[4 + (-4)] = 0$	**3.** __?__ Zero Multiplication Theorem
4. $3 \cdot 4 + 3(-4) = 0$	**4.** __?__ Distributive Postulate
5. Hence, $3 \cdot 4$ and $3(-4)$ are additive inverses.	**5.** Additive inverse postulate
6. $3(-4) = -(3 \cdot 4)$, or -12	**6.** Additive inverse postulate

116. Prove: $(-3)(-4) = 12$

Statements	Reasons
1. $4 + (-4) = 0$	**1.** __?__ Additive Inverse Postulate
2. $-3[4 + (-4)] = -3 \cdot 0$	**2.** Multiplication property for equations
3. $-3 \cdot 4 + (-3)(-4) = 0$	**3.** __?__ Distributive Postulate
4. $-12 + (-3)(-4) = 0$	**4.** __?__ Substitution Principle
5. Hence, -12 and $(-3)(-4)$ are additive inverses.	**5.** __?__ Additive Inverse Postulate
6. $(-3)(-4) = 12$	**6.** __?__ Additive Inverse Postulate.

―――――― **REVIEW CAPSULE FOR SECTION 2-7** ――――――

Divide.

1. $95 \div 19$ 5   **2.** $5913 \div 73$ 81   **3.** $3780 \div 756$ 5   **4.** $4606 \div 658$
5. $5.4 \div 6$ 0.9   **6.** $5.82 \div 0.6$ 9.7   **7.** $59.4 \div 1000$ 0.0594   **8.** $4.76 \div 0.068$

Divide. Write your answers in lowest terms.

9. $\frac{1}{9} \div \frac{1}{3}$ $\frac{1}{3}$ **10.** $\frac{7}{8} \div 4\frac{2}{3}$ $\frac{3}{16}$ **11.** $23 \div \frac{1}{4}$ 92   **12.** $8\frac{3}{5} \div 9\frac{1}{2}$
13. $15 \div \frac{9}{10}$ $\frac{50}{3}$ **14.** $12\frac{5}{8} \div 10\frac{5}{6}$ $\frac{303}{260}$ **15.** $6\frac{1}{2} \div 6\frac{1}{2}$ 1   **16.** $3\frac{3}{4} \div 2\frac{7}{10}$

Round each number to the nearest tenth.

17. 1.59 1.6   **8.** 0.42 0.4   **19.** 0.005 0.0   **20.** 21.35 21.4   **21.** 157.99
22. 7.03 7.0   **23.** 14.49 14.5   **24.** 76.13 76.1   **25.** 1.006 1.0   **26.** 0.019

2–7 Division of Real Numbers

Since division and multiplication are related, you can use multiplication to find the pattern for dividing positive and negative numbers.

Multiplication	Division
Since $5 \times 3 = 15$,	$15 \div 3 = 5$, and $15 \div 5 = 3$.
Since $-5 \times 3 = -15$,	$-15 \div 3 = -5$, and $-15 \div -5 = 3$.
Since $5 \times -3 = -15$,	$-15 \div 5 = -3$, and $-15 \div -3 = 5$.

Thus, the pattern for dividing positive and negative numbers is the same as the pattern for multiplying them.

> **Division of Real Numbers**
>
> 1. The quotient of two positive numbers is **positive**.
> 2. The quotient of two negative numbers is **positive**.
> 3. The quotient of a negative number and a positive number or of a positive number and a negative number is **negative**.

EXAMPLE 1 Tell whether the quotient is positive or negative.

    a. $-18 \div -6$ **b.** $16 \div -4$ **c.** $-20 \div 5$

Solutions: **a.** Positive ◄──── **By Rule 2**

            b. Negative ◄──── **By Rule 3**

            c. Negative ◄──── **By Rule 3**

Any two numbers whose product is 1 are called **reciprocals** or **multiplicative inverses** of each other. Thus,

$$3 \text{ and } \frac{1}{3} \text{ are reciprocals because } 3 \cdot \frac{1}{3} = 1;$$

$$-\frac{5}{8} \text{ and } \left(-\frac{8}{5}\right) \text{ are reciprocals because } -\frac{5}{8} \cdot \left(-\frac{8}{5}\right) = 1;$$

$$\frac{1}{6} \text{ and } 6 \text{ are reciprocals because } \frac{1}{6} \cdot 6 = 1.$$

Postulate

> **Multiplicative Inverse Postulate**
>
> For any real number a, $a \neq 0$, there exists one and only one real number $\frac{1}{a}$, such that $a \cdot \frac{1}{a} = 1$.

You can also divide by multiplying by the reciprocal of the divisor.

EXAMPLE 2 Divide: **a.** $24 \div (-6)$ **b.** $-24 \div (-\frac{5}{6})$

Solutions:

a. $24 \div (-6) = 24 \cdot \overset{\text{Reciprocals}}{-\frac{1}{6}}$

$= -4$

b. $-24 \div -\frac{5}{6} = -24 \cdot \overset{\text{Reciprocals}}{-\frac{6}{5}}$

$= \frac{144}{5}$, or $24\frac{4}{5}$

Recall that the quotient of zero and any number (except zero) is zero. **Division by zero is not defined.**

Finding an *arithmetic mean* (or *average*) involves finding a quotient. The **arithmetic mean** of a set of numbers, scores, and so on, is the sum of the elements in the set divided by the number of elements.

EXAMPLE 3 A city's low temperatures for one week are shown below. Find the mean low temperature for the week. Round your answer to the nearest tenth.

S	M	T	W	T	F	S
−2.5°C	−3.8°C	4.2°C	2.9°C	−2.8°C	−1.4°C	−3.2°C

Solution:

[1] Add the negative temperatures.

$-2.5 + (-3.8) + (-2.8) + (-1.4) + (-3.2) = -13.7$

[2] Add the positive temperatures: $4.2 + 2.9 = 7.1$

[3] Find the sum of the positive and negative temperatures. Then divide by 7, the number of temperatures.

$$\text{Mean} = \frac{-13.7 + 7.1}{7} = \frac{-6.6}{7} \approx -0.9$$

The mean low temperature is about **−0.9°C.**

Additional Examples
Example 2
Divide.
1. $125 \div (-5)$
   Ans: −25
2. $-18 \div (-\frac{2}{3})$
   Ans: 27
3. $96 \div (-12)$
   Ans: −8
4. $-56 \div (-\frac{8}{9})$
   Ans: 63

Example 3
A city's low temperatures for five days were: 8°C, −2.5°C, −1.7°C, 9.1°C, and 9.7°C. Find the mean low temperature for the five days. Round your answer to the nearest tenth.
Ans: 3.3°C

CLASSROOM EXERCISES

Tell whether the quotient is positive or negative.

1. $30 \div (-5)$ Negative **2.** $-110 \div 2$ Negative **3.** $-9 \div (-\frac{1}{3})$ Positive **4.** $80 \div 16$ Positive

Write the reciprocal of each number.

5. $7 \frac{1}{7}$ **6.** $\frac{1}{8}$ 8 **7.** $-\frac{2}{3}$ $-\frac{3}{2}$ **8.** -1 -1 **9.** 0 Undefined **10.** $2\frac{1}{4}$ $\frac{4}{9}$

Divide.

11. $9 \div 9$ 1 **12.** $9 \div (-9)$ −1 **13.** $-9 \div 9$ −1 **14.** $-9 \div (-9)$ 1 **15.** $-9 \div (-\frac{1}{9})$ 81

Operations with Real Numbers **69**

Assignment Guide
Minimal
Day 1 p. 70: 1–24
Day 2 pp. 70–71: 25–38
Average pp. 70–71: 1–45 odd
Above Average
pp. 70–71: 5–45 odd, 46–54

Additional Answers
Written Exercises
  8. −4
12. −120
16. −13
20. −6
24. 1.5
28. −324.1
32. $\frac{1}{3}$

WRITTEN EXERCISES

A   Tell whether the quotient is positive or negative.

1. −6 ÷ 2 Negative   **2.** −6 ÷ (−2) Positive   **3.** 6 ÷ (−2) Negative   **4.** 6 ÷ 2 Positive

Divide.

5. −20 ÷ 5 −4   **6.** −20 ÷ (−5) 4   **7.** 20 ÷ 5 4   **8.** 20 ÷ (−5)

9. 0 ÷ 5 0   **10.** 0 ÷ (−5) 0   **11.** 100 ÷ (−2) −50   **12.** −600 ÷ 5

13. −9 ÷ 9 −1   **14.** 6 ÷ 6 1   **15.** 4 ÷ (−4) −1   **16.** −91 ÷ 7

17. 48 ÷ (−8) −6   **18.** −56 ÷ (−1) 56   **19.** −12 ÷ $\frac{1}{3}$ −36   **20.** (−3) ÷ ($\frac{1}{2}$)

21. 0 ÷ (−24) 0   **22.** $\frac{-5}{8}$ ÷ $\frac{3}{2}$ $-\frac{5}{12}$ **23.** $\frac{-3}{7}$ ÷ ($\frac{-8}{21}$) $\frac{9}{8}$ **24.** −7.5 ÷ (−5)

25. −2.56 ÷ (−0.8) 3.2   **26.** $\frac{7}{10}$ ÷ 14 $\frac{1}{20}$ **27.** 12 ÷ ($\frac{-2}{3}$) −18   **28.** $\frac{-3241}{10}$

29. $\frac{785}{-100}$ −7.85   **30.** $\frac{-3.2}{-1000}$ 0.0032   **31.** −6$\frac{2}{3}$ ÷ 3$\frac{3}{4}$ $-\frac{16}{9}$ **32.** (−1$\frac{1}{2}$) ÷ (−4$\frac{1}{2}$)

APPLICATIONS: Using Positive and Negative Numbers

33. The Union Filter Corporation reported the following profit, shown as a positive amount, and loss, shown as a negative amount, for the last six months of a year. Find the average profit or loss for the 6 months. +$7,600

July	August	September	October	November	December
$55,800	$12,500	−$10,900	−$7,700	$16,700	−$20,800

34. A town's low temperatures for one week are recorded below. Find the mean low temperature for the week. Round your answer to the nearest tenth. −0.9°

S	M	T	W	T	F	S
−1.1°	−0.6°	0.3°	−1.2°	−2.3°	−0.7°	−0.4°

35. The table below shows the early arrivals, recorded as +, and the late arrivals, recorded as −, of a commuter train service for one week. Find the average number of minutes the train was early or late for the 5 working days. Round your answer to the nearest tenth of a minute. −0.8

M	T	W	T	F
+0.8	−1.5	−0.9	−2.6	On time

36. At the end of a year, the national inflation rate was 9.8%. The table below shows the change in rate for each of the first seven months of the following year. Find the average change for these seven months. +0.4%

J	F	M	A	M	J	J
−0.3%	−0.2%	+0.8%	+1.2%	−0.6%	+0.5%	+1.4%

37. The following table shows the change (in feet per second) in the average speed of a moving car over a five–minute interval. Find the mean change in the average speed between 9:01 and 9:06.   4

Time Interval	9:01–9:02	9:02–9:03	9:03–9:04	9:04–9:05	9:05–9:06
Change in Speed	+1.4	−0.4	+0.3	−0.1	+0.8

38. The following table shows the amount of gain and loss in the price of a stock over a five-day period. Find the average change over the five days. $-\frac{7}{20}$

M	T	W	T	F
$-1\frac{1}{4}$	$+\frac{3}{4}$	$-\frac{7}{8}$	$+\frac{1}{4}$	$-\frac{5}{8}$

B   Simplify.

39. $(3)(-5) \div (\frac{-24}{8})$ 5

40. $(-3)(-4)(-(\frac{-9}{-3}))$ −36

41. $\dfrac{(-51) \div (-17)}{-(3 \div \frac{-1}{3})}$

42. $\dfrac{(-4 \div 2) \div [(-3)(-4)(-2)]}{-6 \div (-8) \div (-2)}$ $-\frac{2}{9}$

43. $\dfrac{(-1)^2 - (-2)^3 + (-3)^2 - (-4)^2}{(-5)^2 - (-3)^2 + (-1)^3 - (-2)^2}$

44. $\dfrac{-100 - [12(-8 + 3)]}{3^2 + 4^2 + [-11(-5)]}$ $-\frac{1}{2}$

45. $\dfrac{[9^2 - (-3)(-7)] \div [40 \div (-2)]}{[(-3)^2 - 2^2] \div (3^2 - 2^2)}$

In Exercises 49–57, evaluate each expression for $x = -10$, $y = -15$, and $q = 0$.

46. $\dfrac{x + y}{-5}$ 5

47. $\dfrac{x - y}{-5}$ −1

48. $\dfrac{y + q}{15}$

49. $\dfrac{2x + q}{4}$ −5

50. $\dfrac{3y}{5}$ −9

51. $\dfrac{x^2 + y}{-5}$

52. $\dfrac{x^2 + y^2}{x}$ −32.5

53. $\dfrac{y^2 + q^2}{x}$ −22.5

54. $\dfrac{x^2 y^2 q^2}{x}$

―――――― **REVIEW CAPSULE FOR SECTION 2-8** ――――――

Write a fraction for each mixed number.

1. $6\frac{1}{2}$ $\frac{13}{2}$

2. $7\frac{3}{4}$ $\frac{31}{4}$

3. $-6\frac{1}{4}$ $-\frac{25}{4}$

4. $-9\frac{3}{4}$ $-\frac{39}{4}$

5. $1\frac{1}{10}$ $\frac{11}{10}$

6. $-3\frac{5}{8}$ $-\frac{29}{8}$

Multiply. Write your answer in lowest terms.

7. $\frac{2}{3} \cdot \frac{9}{4}$ $\frac{3}{2}$

8. $6\frac{1}{2} \cdot (-4)$ −26

9. $(-5\frac{1}{2})(-8\frac{1}{4})$ $\frac{363}{8}$

10. $(-3\frac{1}{2})(8\frac{1}{2})$ $-\frac{119}{4}$

Complete.

11. $-6 + 6 = \underline{\ ?\ }$ 0

12. $4\frac{1}{3} + (-4\frac{1}{3}) = \underline{\ ?\ }$ 0

13. $1.5 + \underline{\ ?\ } = 0$ −1.5

14. $-\frac{2}{3} + \underline{\ ?\ } = 0$ $\frac{2}{3}$

15. $9 \cdot \frac{1}{9} = \underline{\ ?\ }$ 1

16. $-\frac{3}{5} \cdot (-\frac{5}{3}) = \underline{\ ?\ }$ 1

17. $\underline{\ ?\ } \cdot (-\frac{1}{12}) = 1$ −12

18. $(-\frac{3}{4}) \cdot \underline{\ ?\ } = 1$ $-\frac{4}{3}$

Operations with Real Numbers   **71**

OBJECTIVE: To practice the skills needed to solve equations

2–8 Preparing to Solve Equations

Quick Quiz

Divide.

1. $115 \div (-115)$
   Ans: −1
2. $-\frac{1}{6} \div (-\frac{5}{12})$
   Ans: $\frac{2}{5}$
3. $-121.8 \div 3$
   Ans: −40.6
4. $306 \div (-9)$
   Ans: −34
5. The amount of gain or loss in the price of a stock for each of five days was $-\frac{3}{8}$, $+\frac{7}{8}$, $-\frac{1}{4}$, $+\frac{1}{4}$, and $-\frac{7}{8}$. Find the average change.
   Ans: $-\frac{3}{40}$

Additional Examples
Example 1
1. Evaluate.
   $r^2 + 2rt - t^2$ for $r = -1$ and $t = 3$. **Ans: −14**
2. Evaluate
   $y2 - x + 3$ for $y = 7$ and $x = -8$.
   Ans: 60

Example 2
1. Multiply. $-\frac{1}{4} \cdot 4y$
   Ans: $-y$
2. $-\frac{7}{16} \cdot (-\frac{16}{7}z)$
   Ans: z

Example 3
By what number would you multiply each expression to obtain t? Show that your answer is correct.
1. $-\frac{1}{5}t$ **Ans: −5**
   $(-\frac{1}{5}t)(-5) = (-\frac{1}{5} \cdot 5)t$
   $= 1 \cdot t = t$
2. $-3t$ **Ans: $-\frac{1}{3}$**
   $(-3t)(-\frac{1}{3}) = (-3 \cdot (-\frac{1}{3})t$
   $= 1 \cdot t = t$

The rules for addition, subtraction, multiplication, and division of real numbers are useful in evaluating algebraic expressions.

EXAMPLE 1 Evaluate $y^2 - xy + 3$ for $y = -2$ and $x = 3$.

Solution: $y^2 - xy + 3 = (-2)(-2) - (3)(-2) + 3$ ⟵ **Replace y with −2 and x with 3.**
$= 4 - (-6) + 3$ ⟵ $4 - (-6) = 4 + 6$
$= 4 + 6 + 3$
$= 13$

Examples 2, 3, and 4 will help you to sharpen the skills needed to solve equations.

Example 2 shows you how to find the product of a real number and an algebraic term having a numerical coefficient.

EXAMPLE 2 Multiply: **a.** $-\frac{1}{2} \cdot 2x$ **b.** $-\frac{3}{4} \cdot (-\frac{4}{3}x)$

Solutions: Use the associative postulate to group the real numbers.

a. The product will be negative.

$-\frac{1}{2} \cdot 2x = -(\frac{1}{2} \cdot 2)x$ ⟵ **By the associative postulate**
$= -1 \cdot x$
$= -x$

b. The product will be positive.

$-\frac{3}{4} \cdot (-\frac{4}{3}x) = (\frac{3}{4} \cdot \frac{4}{3})x$
$= 1 \cdot x$
$= x$

In Example 3, you use the fact that the product of a real number and its reciprocal (multiplicative inverse) is 1.

EXAMPLE 3 By what number would you multiply each expression to obtain y? Show that your answer is correct.

a. $-\frac{1}{4}y$ **b.** $-y$ ⟵ $-y = -1 \cdot y$

Solutions: Multiply by the reciprocal of the numerical coefficient.

a. Reciprocal of $-\frac{1}{4}$: −4

$-4 \cdot (-\frac{1}{4}y) = [-4 \cdot (-\frac{1}{4})] \cdot y$
$= 1 \cdot y$
$= y$

b. Reciprocal of −1: −1

$-1 \cdot (-1 \cdot y) = (-1 \cdot (-1)) \cdot y$
$= 1 \cdot y$
$= y$

72 Chapter 2

In Example 4, you use the Additive Inverse postulate which states that the sum of a real number and its opposite (additive inverse) is zero.

EXAMPLE 4   What number would you add to each expression to obtain x? Show that your answer is correct.

     a. $x + 9$ **b.** $x + (-6)$

Solutions: Add the opposite of the real numbers.

    a. Opposite of 9: -9 **b.** Opposite of -6: **6**

$$x + 9 + (-9) = x + [9 + (-9)] \qquad x + (-6) + 6 = x + (-6 + 6)$$
$$= x + 0 \qquad\qquad\qquad\qquad = x + 0$$
$$= x \qquad\qquad\qquad\qquad\qquad = x$$

CLASSROOM EXERCISES

Evaluate each expression for $x = -6$, $y = -4$, and $q = 6$.

1. $x + y$ -10 **2.** $y + q$ 2 **3.** $x - y$ -2 **4.** $y - q$ -10 **5.** x^2 36

6. $x \div y$ $\frac{3}{2}$ **7.** $q - x$ 12 **8.** y^2 16 **9.** $q^2 - xy$ 12 **10.** $y^2 - qx$ 52

By what number would you multiply each expression to obtain t?

11. $-4t$ $-\frac{1}{4}$ **12.** $\frac{7}{4}t$ $\frac{4}{7}$ **13.** $-\frac{2}{3}t$ $-\frac{3}{2}$ **14.** $-1 \cdot t$ -1 **15.** t 1

What number would you add to obtain z?

16. $z + 7$ -7 **17.** $z + (-9)$ 9 **18.** $-9 + z$ 9 **19.** $z + (-1)$ 1 **20.** $\frac{3}{5} + z$ $-\frac{3}{5}$

WRITTEN EXERCISES

A   Evaluate each expression for $x = -15$, $y = -10$, and $q = 0$.

1. $x + y$ -25 **2.** $y + q$ -10 **3.** $2x$ -30 **4.** $3y$ -30 **5.** xy

6. qy 0 **7.** x^2 225 **8.** y^2 100 **9.** $x^2 + y^2$ 325 **10.** $q^2 + y^2$

11. q^3 0 **12.** $x^2 + q^2$ 225 **13.** $q \cdot x \cdot y$ 0 **14.** x^2y -2250 **15.** $y - x$

16. $x - y$ -5 **17.** $x - y + q$ -5 **18.** $q - y$ 10 **19.** $q - x$ 15 **20.** $y^2 - x$

21. $\frac{x}{y^2}$ $\frac{3}{2}$ **22.** $\frac{y}{x}$ $\frac{2}{3}$ **23.** $\frac{q}{x}$ 0 **24.** $\frac{q}{y}$ 0 **25.** $\frac{x}{x}$ 1

Multiply.

26. $\frac{1}{3} \cdot 3y$ y **27.** $\frac{1}{4} \cdot 4y$ y **28.** $-\frac{1}{5} \cdot 5y$ $-y$ **29.** $-\frac{1}{6} \cdot 6y$ $-y$ **30.** $\frac{2}{3} \cdot \frac{3}{2}y$ y

31. $-\frac{2}{5} \cdot \frac{5}{2}y$ $-y$ **32.** $-\frac{5}{7} \cdot \frac{7}{5}y$ $-y$ **33.** $-\frac{5}{7} \cdot 7a$ **34.** $\frac{3}{5} \cdot (-5a)$ $-3a$ **35.** $-1 \cdot (-1a)$

36. $\frac{2}{3} \cdot (-3y)$ **37.** $\frac{5}{6} \cdot (-18b)$ **38.** $-1 \cdot \frac{4}{5}c$ **39.** $\frac{3}{8} \cdot (-q)$ $-\frac{3}{8}q$ **40.** $\frac{1}{2}(8x)$ $4x$

41. $-\frac{1}{2}(8x)$ $-4x$ **42.** $\frac{1}{2}(-8x)$ $-4x$ **43.** $-\frac{3}{5}(25p)$ **44.** $\frac{3}{5}(-25p)$ $-15p$ **45.** $-\frac{3}{5}(-25p)$

Operations with Real Numbers   **73**

Additional Examples
Example 4
What number would you add to each expression to obtain q? Show that your answer is correct.
1. $q + 12$
   Ans: -12
   $q + 12 + (-12) =$
   $q + [12 + (-12)] =$
   $q + 0 = q$
2. $q + (-27)$
   Ans: 27
   $q + (-27) + 27 =$
   $q + (-27 + 27) =$
   $q + 0 = q$

Assignment Guide
Minimal pp. 73–74: 1–81 odd
Average pp. 73–74: 3, 6, 9, . . . 81, 82–100 even
Above Average pp. 73–74: 4, 8, 12, . . . 80, 82–101

Additional Answers
Written Exercises
  5. 150
 10. 100
 15. 5
 20. 115
 33. $-5a$
 35. a
 36. $-2y$
 37. $-15b$
 38. $-\frac{4}{5}c$
 43. $-15p$
 45. $15p$

By what number would you multiply each expression to obtain y? In Exercises 46–55, show that your answer is correct.

46. $\frac{3}{5}y$ $\quad \frac{5}{3}$ **47.** $\frac{9}{7}y$ $\quad \frac{7}{9}$ **48.** $-7y$ $\quad -\frac{1}{7}$ **49.** $-8y$ $\quad -\frac{1}{8}$ **50.** $-\frac{1}{2}y$

51. $-\frac{1}{5}y$ $\quad -5$ **52.** $-\frac{2}{3}y$ $\quad -\frac{3}{2}$ **53.** $-\frac{2}{5}y$ $\quad -\frac{5}{2}$ **54.** $-\frac{9}{10}y$ $\quad -\frac{10}{9}$ **55.** $-\frac{3}{8}y$

56. $-1y$ $\quad -1$ **57.** $-y$ $\quad -1$ **58.** y $\quad 1$ **59.** $1y$ $\quad 1$ **60.** $2\frac{1}{2}y$

61. $3\frac{1}{4}y$ $\quad \frac{4}{13}$ **62.** $-7\frac{1}{4}y$ $\quad -\frac{4}{29}$ **63.** $-8\frac{1}{2}y$ $\quad -\frac{2}{17}$ **64.** $\frac{y}{2}$ $\quad 2$ **65.** $-\frac{y}{10}$

What number would you add to each expression to obtain x? In Exercises 66–73 and Exercises 82–89, show that your answer is correct.

66. $x + 10$ $\quad -10$ **67.** $x + 1$ $\quad -1$ **68.** $x + (-5)$ $\quad 5$ **69.** $x + (-9)$

70. $x + (-10)$ $\quad 10$ **71.** $x + (-4)$ $\quad 4$ **72.** $-6 + x$ $\quad 6$ **73.** $-12 + x$

74. $16 + x$ $\quad -16$ **75.** $21 + x$ $\quad -21$ **76.** $x + (12 - 4)$ $\quad -8$ **77.** $x + (-9 + 3)$

78. $(-12 + 5) + x$ $\quad 7$ **79.** $(-3 - 1) + x$ $\quad 4$ **80.** $(-9 - 17) + x$ $\quad 26$ **81.** $x + (8 - 13)$

B   **Example:** $x - 1 = x + (-1)$ Opposite of (-1): 1   Therefore, add **1.**

82. $x - 7$ $\quad$ add 7   **83.** $x - 15$ $\quad$ add 15   **84.** $x - 2$ $\quad$ add 2   **85.** $x - 23$

86. $x - 19$ $\quad$ add 19   **87.** $x - \frac{1}{5}$ $\quad$ add $\frac{1}{5}$ **88.** $x - (-1)$ $\quad$ add -1 **89.** $x - (-2)$

Evaluate each expression for $x = -20$, $y = -10$, and $q = -1$.

90. $2x + 3y$ $\quad -70$ **91.** $2x - y$ $\quad -30$ **92.** $x - 2y$ $\quad 0$ **93.** $2x + 3q$

94. $q - 2y$ $\quad 19$ **95.** $q - 3x$ $\quad 59$ **96.** $3xy$ $\quad 600$ **97.** $-5q^2x^2y$

98. $\frac{3x + y}{q}$ $\quad 70$ **99.** $\frac{y - x}{x}$ $\quad -\frac{1}{2}$ **100.** $\frac{2x + 3y}{-y}$ $\quad -7$ **101.** $\frac{3x - 7y}{qy}$ $\quad 1$

——— Review ———————————————————

Simplify. *(Section 2-5)*

1. $5 + 2a + 6a$ $\quad 5 + 8a$ **2.** $1.7x - x - 3.2x$ $\quad -2.5x$ $\frac{1}{4}x + \frac{1}{15}y$

3. $\frac{3}{4}x - \frac{1}{3}y - \frac{1}{2}x + \frac{2}{5}y$

Multiply. *(Section 2-6)*

4. $(-3)(-6)$ $\quad 18$ **5.** $\frac{3}{4}\left(-\frac{3}{4}\right)$ $\quad -\frac{9}{16}$ **6.** $(-0.2)(0.2)(0.2)$ $\quad -0.008$ **7.** $(-5)^2$ $\quad 25$

Divide. *(Section 2-7)*

8. $0 \div 7$ $\quad 0$ **9.** $-16 \div \frac{1}{4}$ $\quad -64$ **10.** $-9.8 \div (-7)$ $\quad 1.4$ $-8\frac{16}{23}$

11. $20 \div \left(-2\frac{3}{10}\right)$

By what number would you multiply each expression or what number would you add to each expression to obtain x? *(Section 2-8)*

12. $21 + x$ $\quad$ Add -21 **13.** $-\frac{1}{3}x$ $\quad$ Mult. by -3 **14.** $13x$ $\quad$ Mult. by $\frac{1}{13}$ **15.** $x + (12 - 8)$ $\quad$ Add -4

COMPUTER APPLICATIONS

BASIC: FORMULAS IN PROGRAMS

This lesson is optional. Each computer applications lesson relates directly to a topic covered within the given chapter or a previous chapter. (See Section 1–4, pages 12–16)

The program for the following problem uses REM (short for "remark") statements. REM statements are used to add explanatory comments to a program. The computer ignores REM statements when executing a program. They are intended for the people who read the program.

Problem: *Write a program which, given the total price of a purchase, p, and the number of units, n, computes and prints the unit price of each item. (See page 12.)* NOTE: Unit price was discussed in Example 2 on page 12.

```
100 REM   P = TOTAL PRICE
110 REM   N = NUMBER OF UNITS
120 REM   U = UNIT PRICE OF AN ITEM
130 REM
140 PRINT "WHAT IS THE TOTAL PRICE";
150 INPUT P
160 PRINT "HOW MANY UNITS";
170 INPUT N
180 LET U = P / N
190 PRINT "THE UNIT PRICE = $"; U
200 PRINT "ANY MORE CALCULATIONS (1 = YES, 0 = NO)";
210 INPUT Z
220 IF Z = 1 THEN 140
230 END
```

Analysis: Here is an explanation of the program above.

Statement 130: This is a "blank" remark separating the comments from the actual program which follows. REM statements may appear anywhere in a program.

Statements 140–150: When the computer comes to a PRINT statement, it displays the message in quotation marks on the screen or on a printer. The purpose of statement 140 is to "prompt" the person running the program to enter the appropriate number. Statement 150 causes the computer to print a question mark (?) and then wait for a number to be entered from the keyboard. When the user has typed a number and pressed the ENTER or RETURN key (depending on the machine), the computer stores the value entered as variable P.

Statements 160–170: These statements repeat the work of statements 140–150, but for the variable N (number of units).

Statement 180: Now that all values needed for the calculation have been entered, the LET statement gives the formula for computing the unit price. (See page 12.) In a LET statement the left side of the "=" sign must be only a variable. The right side, however, may contain any legitimate algebraic expression.

Formulas in Programs **75**

Statement 190: The computer will print the value of U it computed in statement 180. Notice that the last U in statement 190 is outside the quotation marks. This causes the *value* of the variable U to be printed rather than the letter "U."

Statements 200–230: Statement 200 asks the user if there is more data to be entered and gives a code for answering the question. Statement 210 accepts the "1" or "0" the person types and calls this value "Z". Then, in statement 220, the computer checks the value of Z. If Z = 1, there is more data to be entered and the computer is sent back to statement 140 to repeat the steps of the program. If Z is not 1, the computer ignores "THEN 140" in statement 220 and instead moves to 230 END. At this point the computer will stop executing the program. It then prints "READY", or a similar code word or symbol, and waits for further instructions.

EXERCISES See the Solution Key for the Answers to Ex. 10-15.

A   Run the program on page 75 for the following values.

1. $p = \$1.09$; $n = 24$ **2.** $p = \$1.99$; $n = 46$ **3.** $p = \$0.99$; $n = 9$

4. $p = \$3.10$; $n = 15$ **5.** $p = \$0.85$; $n = 50$ **6.** $p = \$1.59$; $n = 36$

7. $p = \$1.88$; $n = 25$ **8.** $p = \$4.51$; $n = 18$ **9.** $p = \$2.85$; $n = 19$

Write a BASIC program for each problem.

10. Given the length of a side, s, of a square, use the formula
$$A = s^2$$
to compute and print the area. (See page 9.)

11. Given the length, width, and height of a refrigerator car, use the formula
$$V = lwh$$
to compute and print the volume. (See page 13.)

12. Given the height and the lengths of the bases a and b of a trapezoid, use the formula
$$A = \tfrac{1}{2}(a + b)h$$
to compute and print the area. (See page 14.)

13. Compute and print the average of two given real numbers x and y. (See page 69.)

14. Given the length of a side of a square, use the formula
$$P = 4s$$
to compute and print the perimeter of the square. (See page 10.)

15. Given the length of the radius of a circle, use the formula
$$C = 2\pi r$$
to compute and print the circumference of the circle. Use $\pi = 3.14$. (See page 15.)

Chapter Summary

IMPORTANT IDEAS

1. For any two real numbers, the smaller is to the left of the larger on the number line.

2. **Additive Inverse Postulate:** For any real number a, there is one and only one real number, $-a$, such that $a + (-a) = 0$.

3. **Procedure for adding two numbers having like signs**

   $\boxed{1}$ Determine whether the sum is positive or negative.

      a. The sum of two positive numbers is positive.

      b. The sum of two negative numbers is negative.

   $\boxed{2}$ Add the absolute values of the numbers.

4. **Sum of Two Negative Numbers:** The sum of two negative numbers is the opposite of the sum of their absolute values.

   If $x < 0$ and $y < 0$, then $x + y = -(|x| + |y|)$.

5. **Procedure for finding the sum of a positive and negative number**

   $\boxed{1}$ Determine whether the sum is positive or negative.

      a. The sum is positive when the positive number has the greater absolute value.

      b. The sum is negative when the negative number has the greater absolute value.

   $\boxed{2}$ Subtract the lesser absolute value from the greater absolute value.

6. **Sum of a Positive and a Negative Number:** The sum of a positive number, x, and a negative number, y, is the difference of their absolute values. The sum is positive when x is farther from 0 and negative when y is farther from 0. That is,

$$x + y = (|x| - |y|) \text{ when } |x| > |y|$$
$$x + y = -(|y| - |x|) \text{ when } |y| > |x|.$$

7. **Substitution Principle:** If two expressions are equivalent, you can always replace one with the other in a given expression.

8. **Zero Multiplication Theorem:** For any real number a, $a \cdot 0 = 0 \cdot a = 0$.

9. **Negative Product Theorem:** The product of two real numbers is negative when one number is positive and the other number is negative. That is, for $a < 0$ and $b > 0$, $a \cdot b = -(|a| \cdot |b|)$.

Operations with Real Numbers   **77**

10. **Positive Product Theorem:** The product of two real numbers is positive when both numbers are positive or when both numbers are negative. That is, for $a < 0$ and $b < 0$, or for $a > 0$ and $b > 0$, $a \cdot b = |a| \cdot |b|$.

11. **Rules for Division of Real Numbers**
    $\boxed{1}$ The quotient of two positive numbers is positive.
    $\boxed{2}$ The quotient of two negative numbers is positive.
    $\boxed{3}$ The quotient of a negative number and a positive number, or of a positive number and a negative number, is negative.

12. **Multiplicative Inverse Postulate:** For any real number a, $a \neq 0$, there exists one and only one real number $\frac{1}{a}$, such that $a \cdot \frac{1}{a} = 1$.

13. Division by zero is not defined.

_____ **Chapter Objectives and Review** _____

Objective: _To write the opposite of a real number (Section 2–1)_

Write the opposite of each number.

1. 2 -2 **2.** -11 11   **3.** $-\sqrt{5}$ $\sqrt{5}$ **4.** 14.3 -14.3 **5.** $-6\frac{1}{2}$ $6\frac{1}{2}$ **6.** $-\pi$ π

Write without parentheses.

7. $-(-3.72)$ 3.72   **8.** $-(83.0)$ -83.0 **9.** $-(9.3 + 7.4)$ -16.7 **10.** $-(t)$ $-t$

Solve for x.

11. $-x = 7$ -7 **12.** $x = -(-8)$ 8   **13.** $-x = -\pi$ π **14.** $-x = 6\frac{2}{3}$ $-6\frac{2}{3}$

Objective: _To compare positive and negative numbers using > or < (Section 2–1)_

Use > or < to compare the numbers.

15. -14 _?_ 10 <   **16.** 6 _?_ -2 >   **17.** $-\sqrt{3}$ _?_ 1 <   **18.** $-(-4)$ _?_ 0 >

Objective: _To identify the additive inverse of a real number (Section 2–2)_

Write the additive inverse of each number.

19. -18 18   **20.** 37 -37 **21.** $-\sqrt{7}$ $\sqrt{7}$ **22.** $-(-2.31)$ -2.31 **23.** $\frac{1}{3}$ $-\frac{1}{3}$ **24.** $-(-2\frac{1}{8})$ $-2\frac{1}{8}$

Complete.

25. $7 + $ _?_ $= 0$ -7 **26.** $-3.2 + $ _?_ $= 0$ 3.2 **27.** _?_ $+ (-a) = 0$ a **28.** $-4\frac{1}{2} + 4\frac{1}{2} = $ _?_ 0

Objective: _To use absolute value notation (Section 2–2)_

Evaluate.

29. $|42{,}000|$ 42,000 **30.** $|-3| + |11|$ 14   **31.** $|236| + |-20|$ 256 **32.** $|4.21| - |2.33|$ 1.88

Use >, =, or < to compare the numbers.

33. $|0|$ __?__ $|-3|$ $<$ **34.** $|-5|$ __?__ $|5|$ $=$ **35.** $|-0.32|$ __?__ $|0.75|$ $<$ **36.** $|-\frac{3}{5}|$ __?__ $|-\frac{1}{2}|$
$>$

Objective: *To add real numbers (Section 2–3)*

Add.

37. $7 + 8$ 15   **38.** $(-11) + 4$ -7 **39.** $0 + (-1\frac{1}{2})$ $-1\frac{1}{2}$ **40.** $(-1.3) + (-2.5)$
-3.8

Use positive and negative numbers to represent each word description. Then find the sum.

41. The temperature at 7 P.M. was 5°C. By 5 A.M. it had dropped 7°. What was the temperature at 5 A.M.? $-2°$C

42. A plane was 12,500 meters high. It rose 725 meters and then dropped 785 meters. What was its new altitude?
12,440 meters

Objective: *To subtract real numbers (Section 2–4)*

Subtract.

43. $14 - 20$ -6 **44.** $-5 - 8$ -13 **45.** $\frac{3}{10} - (\frac{-1}{10})$ $\frac{2}{5}$ **46.** $-6.8 - (-8.1)$
1.3

47. The actual temperature is 25°F. The wind chill temperature is -12°F. How much colder than the actual temperature is the wind chill temperature?
37° colder

48. The actual temperature is 18°F. The wind chill temperature is -9°F. How much colder than the actual temperature is the wind chill temperature?
27° colder

Objective: *To combine like terms (Section 2–5)*

Combine like terms.

49. $3g + 11g$ $14g$ **50.** $9m - 17m$ $-8m$ **51.** $-26rt - (-2rt)$ $-24rt$ **52.** $16ab + (-5ab)$
$11ab$

Simplify.

53. $6x + 9x + 11$ **54.** $15y - 3y - 4$ **55.** $31n + 6mn - 2n$ **56.** $42x - 36 + 75x$

Objective: *To multiply real numbers (Section 2–6)*

Multiply.

57. $(-6)(4)$ -24 **58.** $(-19)(-1)(2)$ 38   **59.** $(0.2)(-3.1)$ -0.62 **60.** $-1\frac{1}{2} \cdot (-\frac{2}{3})$ 1

Objective: *To divide real numbers (Section 2–7)*

Divide.

61. $-14 \div 14$ -1 **62.** $117 \div (-9)$ -13 **63.** $(-\frac{2}{3}) \div (-\frac{1}{2})$ $1\frac{1}{3}$ **64.** $\frac{-7.38}{-100}$ 0.0738

65. The following table shows the amount of gain and loss in the price of a stock over a five–day period. Find the average change over the five days. $-\frac{23}{40}$

M	T	W	T	F
$-\frac{1}{8}$	$+\frac{7}{8}$	$-\frac{13}{4}$	$+\frac{1}{4}$	$-\frac{5}{8}$

Additional Answers
53. $15x + 11$
54. $12y - 4$
55. $29n + 6mn$
56. $117x - 36$

Operations with Real Numbers **79**

Objective: *To practice the skills needed to solve equations (Section 2–8)*

Evaluate each expression for $x = 7$, $y = -9$ and $z = \frac{1}{2}$.

66. $x + z$ $7\frac{1}{2}$ **67.** $y^2 + xz$ **68.** $(x - y)z$ 8 **69.** $xy - x^2$ -112 **70.** $y^2 + y$ 72

Multiply.

71. $\frac{1}{3} \cdot (-3m)$ $-m$ **72.** $-7 \cdot \frac{4}{7}t$ $-4t$ **73.** $-\frac{4}{9} \cdot (-81x)$ $-36x$ **74.** $-\frac{3}{4} \cdot 16p$ $-12p$ **75.** $\frac{1}{2} \cdot (-14x^2)$ $-7x^2$

By what number would you multiply each expression to obtain y?

76. $16y$ $\frac{1}{16}$ **77.** $-\frac{1}{9}y$ -9 **78.** $2\frac{1}{3}y$ $\frac{3}{7}$ **79.** $-7\frac{3}{4}y$ $-\frac{4}{31}$ **80.** $\frac{-y}{11}$ -11

What number would you add to each expression to obtain x?

81. $x + 11$ -11 **82.** $x - 8$ 8 **83.** $-4 + x$ 4 **84.** $15 + x$ -15 **85.** $(-1 + 6) + x$ -5

Chapter Test

A formal Chapter Test is provided in the Teacher's Manual. See p. M-65.

1. Write the additive inverse of $-(-19)$. -19 2. Solve for k when $-k = -(-10)$. $k = -10$

Evaluate.

3. $-(-617.25)$ 617.25 4. $|-(-1.2)|$ 1.2 5. $|-102|$ 102 6. $-|-\pi|$ $-\pi$

Use $>$, $=$, or $<$ to compare the numbers.

7. -19 __?__ -14 $<$ 8. 0.15 __?__ -0.13 $>$ 9. $|-9|$ __?__ $|9|$ $=$ 10. $-|21|$ __?__ $|50|$ $<$

Perform the indicated operations.

11. $(-4) + 11$ 7 **12.** $(-6.3) + (-1.9)$ -8.2 **13.** $-3 - (-12)$ 9

14. $(-\frac{2}{3})(-\frac{11}{2}) - 1$ $2\frac{2}{3}$ **15.** $15 \div (-\frac{5}{6})$ -18 **16.** $(-3.2) \div (-1.6)$

17. Myra has \$175 in her checking account. She wrote a check for \$169 and made a deposit of \$215. What was her new balance? \$221

18. The temperature was 14°C at noon. By 4 P.M. it had dropped to -2°C. How much did the temperature change during that time? 16°

Combine like terms.

19. $24gt - (-3gt) + 7$ $27gt + 7$ **20.** $4\frac{1}{2}cd - \frac{1}{2}c + \frac{1}{2}cd - 3$

21. A town's low temperatures for one week are recorded below. Find the mean low temperature for the week. -0.7°

S	M	T	W	T	F	S
$-1.3°$	$-0.5°$	$0.3°$	$-1.1°$	$-2.1°$	$-0.7°$	$0.5°$

22. Evaluate $t + mn$ for $t = 19$, $m = 7$, and $n = -1$. 12

23. Multiply: $(-\frac{14}{15})(-\frac{105}{7}r)$ $32\frac{2}{3}r$

24. By what number would you multiply $-\frac{8}{9}y$ to obtain y? $-\frac{9}{8}$

25. What number would you add to $(-11 - 15) + x$ to obtain x? 26

80 *Chapter 2*

Additional Practice

You may wish to use all or some of these exercises, depending on how well the students performed on the formal chapter test.

Skills

Write without parentheses. *(Section 2–1)*

1. $-(4)$ -4 **2.** $-(-4)$ 4 **3.** $-(3.1 - 0.1)$ -3 **4.** $-(34 \div 17)$ -2 **5.** $-(-x)$ x

Solve. *(Section 2–1)*

6. $-x = 5$ -5 **7.** $-m = 0$ 0 **8.** $-a = -\frac{1}{3}$ $\frac{1}{3}$ **9.** $-y = \pi$ π **10.** $-t = 3.72$

Use $<$ or $>$ to compare the numbers. *(Sections 2–1, 2–2)*

11. -4 __?__ 8 $<$ **12.** -9 __?__ -11 $>$ **13.** 0 __?__ -6 $>$ **14.** $-(-\sqrt{2})$ __?__ $\sqrt{5}$

15. $|-4|$ __?__ $|6|$ $<$ **16.** $|-\frac{1}{2}|$ __?__ $|-\frac{1}{4}|$ $>$ **17.** $|0.15|$ __?__ $|-0.9|$ $<$ **18.** $|-3|$ __?__ $|0|$ $>$

Evaluate. *(Section 2–2)*

19. $|3| + |-11|$ 14 **20.** $|-\sqrt{3}| - |\sqrt{3}|$ 0 **21.** $|7.8| - |-0.3|$ 7.5 **22.** $|t| - |-t|$ 0

Complete. *(Section 2–2)*

23. $9 + (-9) =$ __?__ 0 **24.** $-12 +$ __?__ $= 0$ **25.** $1.3 +$ __?__ $= 0$ -1.3 **26.** __?__ $- (-m) = 0$

Perform the indicated operations. *(Sections 2–3, 2–4, 2–6, 2–7)*

27. $8 + (-11)$ -3 **28.** $(-14) + (-5)$ **29.** $8.4 + (-0.2)$ 8.2 **30.** $(-5\frac{1}{3}) + 8\frac{5}{6}$

31. $13 - 13$ 0 **32.** $\frac{8}{3} - (-\frac{1}{3})$ 3 **33.** $-2 - (-7)$ 5 **34.** $4.8 - (-1.2)$

35. $3\frac{1}{5}(-\frac{1}{8})$ $-\frac{2}{5}$ **36.** $-1.3 \cdot 4.2$ **37.** $(-9)(7)(-2)$ 126 **38.** $(-10)^2$ 100

39. $14 \div (-2)$ -7 **40.** $-54 \div (-\frac{9}{10})$ **41.** $-7.2 \div 3.6$ -2 **42.** $\frac{-2.4}{100}$

Simplify. *(Section 2–5)*

43. $-7r - (-4r)$ $-3r$ **44.** $2.3n - 1.9n + 6$ $9.4n + 6$ **45.** $3bc + 9bc - 7b$

46. $-18t - t$ $-19t$ **47.** $24x - (-x)$ $25x$ **48.** $13b + (-b)$ $12b$

49. $6s - (-5s) + 10$ $11x + 10$ **50.** $-4q + (-9q) + 6r$ **51.** $4.3p - 6.2p - 7$

52. $14x - 5y - (-7x) + 6y$ **53.** $12a + 13a - (-2b) + b$ **54.** $24c - 16d - (-4d) + 6c$

Evaluate each expression for $x = 9$, $y = -3$, and $z = 0$. *(Section 2–8)*

55. zy 0 **56.** y^2 9 **57.** $x^2 + y^2$ 90 **58.** $x - y$ 12 **59.** $x \cdot y \cdot z$

Multiply. *(Section 2–8)*

60. $\frac{1}{4}(12x)$ $3x$ **61.** $-1(-3x)$ $3x$ **62.** $\frac{3}{8}(-16y)$ $-6y$ **63.** $(-g)(-3)$ $3g$ **64.** $\frac{5}{2}(-\frac{2}{5}a)$

By what number would you multiply each expression to obtain y? *(Section 2–8)*

65. $\frac{2}{3}y$ $\frac{3}{2}$ **66.** $\frac{8}{5}y$ $\frac{5}{8}$ **67.** $-3y$ $-\frac{1}{3}$ **68.** $-\frac{1}{2}y$ -2 **69.** $-3\frac{1}{3}y$

Operations with Real Numbers   **81**

Additional Answers
10. -3.72
14. $<$
24. 12
26. $-m$
28. -19
30. $3\frac{1}{2}$
34. 6
36. -5.46
40. 60
42. -0.024
45. $12bc - 7b$
50. $-13q + 6r$
51. $-1.9p - 7$
52. $21x + y$
53. $25a + 3b$
54. $30c - 12d$
59. 0
64. $-a$
69. $-\frac{3}{10}$

What number would you add to each expression to obtain x? *(Section 2–8)*

70. $x + 6$ -6 **71.** $x + (-3)$ 3 **72.** $x + (3 - 1)$ -2 **73.** $-11 + x$ 11 **74.** $14 + x$
-14

Applications

In Exercises 75 and 76, use algebraic symbols to represent each sentence. *(Section 2–1)*.

75. The opposite of a profit of $500 is a loss of $500. $-(500) = -500$

76. A fall of $10°$ in temperature is the opposite of a rise of $10°$. $-10 = -(10)$

77. On four successive plays, a football team lost 4 yards, lost 2 yards, gained 5 yards, and gained 3 yards. What was the team's net gain? *(Section 2–3)*

78. The stock of Hitec, Inc. cost $48 per share at 10 A.M. By noon it had gained $3, but went down $5 by closing. What was its value at closing? *(Section 2–3)*

79. The actual temperature is $15°F$. The wind chill temperature is $-20°F$. How much colder than the actual temperature is the wind chill temperature? *(Section 2–4)* 35° colder

80. The lowest temperature ever recorded in Nebraska was $-47°F$. The lowest temperature ever recorded in Nevada was $-50°F$. Find the difference between the two temperatures. *(Section 2–4)* 3°

In Exercises 81 and 82, find the sum of the areas of each pair of figures. *(Section 2–5)*

81. Rectangle: $A = $ length $\cdot$ width

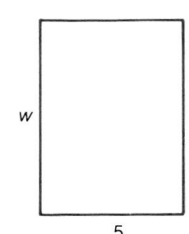 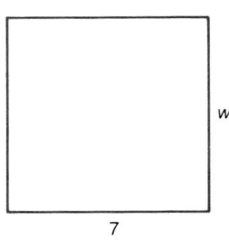

82. Triangle: $A = \frac{1}{2}$ (base $\cdot$ height)

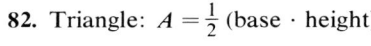
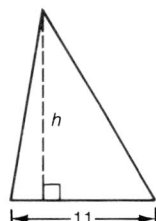 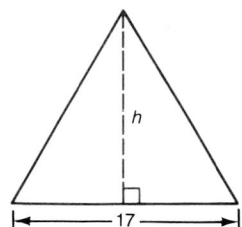

83. The table below shows a corporation's profit (+) and loss (−) over a six month period. Find the average profit or loss over the six months. *(Section 2–7)* $800 Loss

January	February	March	April	May	June
−$28,500	−$18,300	−$7,700	$12,500	$14,300	$22,900

84. The estimated highway MPG (miles per gallon) of a certain car is 35. On seven trips with this car, the driver calculated the difference between the actual MPG and the estimate (see the table below). Find the average difference for the seven trips. *(Section 2–7)* $\frac{5}{7}$ MPG

Trips	A	B	C	D	E	F	G
Difference	+2	−5	−6	+5	+7	−1	+3

3–1 Addition Property for Equations

Teaching Suggestions p. M-16

Quick Quiz
State the opposite of each expression.
1. -3 **Ans: 3**
2. 0 **Ans: 0**
3. 16 **Ans: -16**
4. $(3-2)$ **Ans: -1**
5. $-(-25)$ **Ans: -25**
6. $[8+(-8)]$ **Ans: 0**
7. $-[-(-3)]$ **Ans: 3**
8. $-|-12|$ **Ans: 12**
9. $|8-10|$ **Ans: -2**
10. $-|9-25|$ **Ans: 16**

Recall that an equation is a mathematical sentence that uses "=".

To solve equations, think of a balance. To keep the balance level, *whatever is added or subtracted from one side must be added or subtracted from the other.*

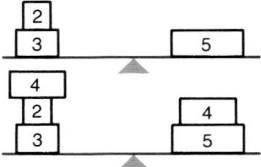

Property for Equations

Addition Property for Equations
Adding the same number to each side of an equation results in an equivalent equation.

Equivalent equations have the same solutions for the same replacement set. To solve an equation, you get the variable with a numerical coefficient of 1 alone on one side of the equation.

Additional Examples
Example 1
Solve and check.
1. $y + 18 = 7$
   Ans: $y = -11$
2. $a + 25 = 78$
   Ans: $a = 53$

EXAMPLE 1 Solve and check: $y + 21 = 8$

Solution: **Think:** What must be added to $y + 21$ to get y?

$$y + 21 = 8 \quad \longleftarrow \text{ Add } (-21) \text{ to each side.}$$
$$y + 21 + (-21) = 8 + (-21) \quad \longleftarrow \text{ Solve for } y.$$
$$y + \quad 0 \quad = \quad -13 \quad \longleftarrow \textbf{ } y \text{ is alone.}$$
$$y = -13$$

Check: Replace y with -13 in the original equation.
$$y + 21 = 8$$
$$-13 + 21 \overset{?}{=} 8$$
$$8 \overset{?}{=} 8 \quad \text{Yes } \;\;\; \text{The solution is } -13.$$

Always check your work by showing that the solution of the final equivalent equation also satisfies the original equation.

Example 2
Solve and check.
1. $x - 5\frac{2}{3} = 10$
   Ans: $x = 4\frac{1}{3}$
2. $-16 + x = 39$
   Ans: $x = 55$

EXAMPLE 2 Solve and check: $x - 3\frac{1}{2} = 8$

Solution: Write $x - 3\frac{1}{2} = 8$ as $x + (-3\frac{1}{2}) = 8$.

Think: What must be added to $x + (-3\frac{1}{2})$ to get x?

$$x + (-3\tfrac{1}{2}) = 8 \quad \longleftarrow \text{ Add } 3\tfrac{1}{2} \text{ to each side.}$$
$$x + (-3\tfrac{1}{2} + 3\tfrac{1}{2}) = 8 + 3\tfrac{1}{2} \quad \longleftarrow \text{ Solve for } x.$$
$$x + \quad 0 \quad = 11\tfrac{1}{2}$$
$$x = 11\tfrac{1}{2} \quad \longleftarrow \textbf{ } x \text{ is alone.}$$

Check: $x - 3\frac{1}{2} = 8$ ◄——— **Replace x with $11\frac{1}{2}$.**

$11\frac{1}{2} - 3\frac{1}{2} \overset{?}{=} 8$

$8 \overset{?}{=} 8$　Yes　✔　The solution is $11\frac{1}{2}$.

Unless otherwise stated, the replacement set for the variables in equations is the set of real numbers.

CLASSROOM EXERCISES

In each of Exercises 1–8, what number would you add to each side of the equation in order to get x?

1. $x + 2 = 11$　-2　　**2.** $6 + x = 13$　-6　　**3.** $x - 9 = 15$　9　　**4.** $x - 5.2 = 8$

5. $x - 6 = 14$　-6　　**6.** $4.5 = 2.1 + x$　-2.1　**7.** $x - (-9) = 8$　-9　**8.** $x - (-1.6) = 4$

Solve and check each equation.

9. $x + 6 = 8$　$x = 2$　**10.** $y + 9 = 41$　$y = 32$　**11.** $t - 11 = 13$　$t = 24$　**12.** $r - 25 = 63$

13. $18 = a + 5$　$a = 13$ **14.** $-11 = 3 + q$　　**15.** $x - (-1) = 52$　　**16.** $-13 = t - (-8)$

WRITTEN EXERCISES

A　　Solve and check each equation.

1. $x + 7 = 13$　$x = 6$　　**2.** $m + 3\frac{1}{2} = 7$　　**3.** $8 + n = 5$　$n = -3$　**4.** $11.2 + t = 3.7$

5. $y - 6 = 14$　$y = 20$　**6.** $x - 6\frac{1}{4} = 12\frac{1}{2}$　　**7.** $y - 4 = 13$　$y = 17$　**8.** $3 + y = 17$

9. $5.4 + n = -0.6$ $n = -6$ **10.** $-4 + y = 13$ $y = 17$ **11.** $-3 + y = -12$　　**12.** $5 = 28 + n$

13. $25 = x + 6$　$x = 19$　**14.** $2 + x = -1$　$x = -3$ **15.** $0.2 + t = 1.3$ $t = 1.1$ **16.** $-1.5 + r = 9.6$

17. $-8 + z = 30$ $z = 38$ **18.** $v - (-5) = 10$　　**19.** $m - (-3) = 1$　　**20.** $r - (-9) = -19$

21. $-8 + t = -13$ $t = -5$ **22.** $-12 + z = 1$　　**23.** $-15 + a = 0$ $a = 15$ **24.** $q - (-7) = 4\frac{1}{2}$

25. $r - (-4.6) = 8.1$　**26.** $s + 4.5 = 7.9$　　**27.** $z - 1.6 = 2$　　**28.** $y + 9.4 = 15$

29. $a + 4.22 = 7$　　**30.** $3.35 + x = 5$　　**31.** $8.91 + x = 11.09$　**32.** $-11.5 + r = 0$

33. $z - \frac{1}{4} = 1\frac{3}{4}$ $z = 2$ **34.** $t + \frac{3}{5} = \frac{9}{10}$ $t = \frac{3}{10}$ **35.** $\frac{1}{4} = \frac{3}{4} + c$ $c = -\frac{1}{2}$ **36.** $b + 1\frac{1}{2} = 2\frac{1}{8}$

37. $1 + r = 7\frac{1}{2}$ $r = 6\frac{1}{2}$ **38.** $\frac{7}{8} = q + \frac{3}{8}$ $q = \frac{1}{2}$ **39.** $y + 5 = 8\frac{1}{4}$ $y = 3\frac{1}{4}$ **40.** $6\frac{2}{3} = c + 4$

B

41. If $s + 9 = 11$, find the value of $7s$.　14

42. If $t + 8 = 11$, find the value of $\frac{1}{3}t$.

43. If $r - 1.5 = 3.5$, find the value of $r + 1$.　6

44. If $t - 6 = 21$, find the value of $\frac{1}{9}t$.

45. If $z - 1\frac{1}{4} = 5\frac{1}{2}$, find the value of $4z - 18$.　9

46. If $r - \frac{1}{5} = \frac{1}{4}$, find the value of $5r$.

47. If $2.8 + m = 3.7$, find the value of $1 - m$.　0.1

48. If $0.2 + p = 9$, find the value of $7p$.

C　　Solve and check.

49. $|x| - 1 = 3$　$-4, 4$　**50.** $-1 + |t| = 0$　$-1, 1$ **51.** $6 + |n| = 6$　$-6, 6$　**52.** $|s| + 9 = 18$

Solving Equations　**85**

Multiply. *(Pages 72–74)*

1. $\frac{1}{6}(6y)$ 2. $-\frac{1}{5}(5t) -t$ 3. $\frac{1}{3}(-3q) \ -q$ 4. $-\frac{1}{8}(-8t) \ t$ 5. $-\frac{1}{12}(-12n)$

Write the reciprocal (multiplicative inverse) of each number. *(Pages 68–71)*

6. $\frac{2}{3} \ \frac{3}{2}$ 7. $\frac{5}{8} \ \frac{8}{5}$ 8. $-\frac{1}{2} \ -2$ 9. $-\frac{3}{4} \ -\frac{4}{3}$ 10. $-9 \ -\frac{1}{9}$ 11. 7

By what number would you multiply each expression to obtain t? *(Pages 72–74)*

12. $2t \ \frac{1}{2}$ 13. $8t \ \frac{1}{8}$ 14. $-\frac{3}{4}t \ -\frac{4}{3}$ 15. $-\frac{1}{4}t \ -4$ 16. $\frac{5}{6}t \ \frac{6}{5}$ 17. $-t$

OBJECTIVE: To use the multiplication property for equations to solve equations

3–2 Multiplication Property for Equations

You can also obtain equivalent equations by multiplying each side of an equation by the same number (not zero).

$$5x = 35 \quad \text{is equivalent to} \quad \tfrac{1}{5} \cdot 5x = \tfrac{1}{5} \cdot 35, \quad \text{or} \quad x = 7.$$

$$\tfrac{2}{3}z = 6 \quad \text{is equivalent to} \quad \tfrac{3}{2} \cdot \tfrac{2}{3}z = \tfrac{3}{2} \cdot 6, \quad \text{or} \quad z = 9.$$

The examples suggest this property.

Property for Equations

Multiplication Property for Equations
Multiplying each side of an equation by the same *nonzero* number results in an equivalent equation.

Recall that to solve an equation, you try to get the variable with a numerical coefficient of 1 alone on one side of the equation.

EXAMPLE 1   Solve and check: $2x = 12$

Solution: **Think:** By what number must $2x$ be multiplied in order to get x?

$$2x = 12 \qquad \longleftarrow \text{ Multiply each side by } \tfrac{1}{2}.$$

$$\tfrac{1}{2} \cdot 2x = \tfrac{1}{2} \cdot 12 \longleftarrow \text{ Solve for } x.$$

$$\left(\tfrac{1}{2} \cdot 2\right)x = 6$$

$$x = 6 \longleftarrow \text{ } x \text{ is alone.}$$

Check: $2x = 12 \qquad \longleftarrow \text{ Replace } x \text{ with 6.}$

$$2(6) \overset{?}{=} 12$$

$$12 \overset{?}{=} 12 \quad \text{Yes} \ \checkmark \qquad \text{The solution is 6.}$$

86   *Chapter 3*

The number or numbers that satisfy an equation are also called the **solution set** of the equation. Thus, in Example 1, the solution set is $\{6\}$.

EXAMPLE 2 Solve and check: $-\frac{3}{4}y = 15$

Solution: **Think:** By what number must $-\frac{3}{4}y$ be multiplied in order to get y?

$$-\frac{3}{4}y = 15 \quad \longleftarrow \quad \textbf{Multiply each side by } -\frac{4}{3}.$$

$$-\frac{4}{3} \cdot \left(-\frac{3}{4}y\right) = -\frac{4}{3} \cdot 15$$

$$\left[-\frac{4}{3} \cdot \left(-\frac{3}{4}\right)\right] \cdot y = -\frac{4}{3} \cdot 15 \quad \longleftarrow \quad \left[-\frac{4}{3} \cdot \left(-\frac{3}{4}\right)\right] \cdot y = 1 \cdot y = y$$

$$y = -20 \quad \longleftarrow \quad \textbf{The left side is } y, \textbf{ or } 1 \cdot y.$$

Check: $-\frac{3}{4}y = 15 \quad \longleftarrow \quad \textbf{Replace } y \textbf{ with } (-20).$

$$-\frac{3}{4} \cdot (-20) \stackrel{?}{=} 15$$

$$15 \stackrel{?}{=} 15 \quad \text{Yes} \quad \checkmark \qquad \textbf{Solution set: } \{-20\}$$

Additional Examples
Example 2
Solve and check
1. $-\frac{2}{3}y = -12$
   Ans: $y = 18$
2. $\frac{5}{4}a = 20$
   Ans: $a = 16$

An expression such as $\frac{t}{4}$ means the same as $\frac{1}{4} \cdot t$. Thus, the numerical coefficient of $\frac{t}{4}$ is $\frac{1}{4}$.

EXAMPLE 3 Solve and check: $\frac{t}{4} = -9$

Solution: **Think:** By what number must $\frac{t}{4}$ be multiplied in order to get t?

$$\frac{t}{4} = -9 \quad \longleftarrow \quad \textbf{Multiply each side by 4.}$$

$$4 \cdot \frac{t}{4} = 4 \cdot (-9) \quad \longleftarrow \quad \frac{t}{4} = \frac{1}{4} \cdot t$$

$$\left(4 \cdot \frac{1}{4}\right) \cdot t = -36$$

$$t = -36 \quad \longleftarrow \quad \textbf{The left side is } t, \textbf{ or } 1 \cdot t.$$

Check: $\frac{t}{4} = -9 \quad \longleftarrow \quad \textbf{Replace } t \textbf{ with } -36.$

$$\frac{-36}{4} \stackrel{?}{=} -9$$

$$-9 \stackrel{?}{=} -9 \quad \text{Yes} \quad \checkmark \qquad \textbf{Solution set: } \{-36\}$$

Example 3
Solve and check
1. $\frac{w}{6} = -8$
   Ans: $w = -48$
2. $-16 = -\frac{b}{9}$
   Ans: $6 = 144$

REMEMBER: Always use the original equation to check your answers. Then write the solution set.

CLASSROOM EXERCISES

In each of Exercises 1–8, by what number would you multiply each side of the equation in order to get t alone on one side of the equation?

1. $3t = 9$ $\frac{1}{3}$
2. $12t = 1.2$ $\frac{1}{12}$
3. $-\frac{4}{5}t = 6$ $-\frac{5}{4}$
4. $\frac{2}{3}t = 20$
5. $\frac{t}{5} = 30$ 5
6. $-\frac{t}{27} = 1$ -27
7. $-t = 8$ -1
8. $2.1 = -t$

Solve and check each equation.

9. $3x = 21$ $x = 7$
10. $-8x = 148$ $x = -18\frac{1}{2}$
11. $\frac{1}{2}y = 8$ $y = 16$
12. $\frac{2}{3}q = 10$

13. $\frac{z}{6} = 10$ $z = 60$
14. $\frac{t}{5} = 0$ $t = 0$
15. $-\frac{4}{5}t = 16$ $t = -20$
16. $-\frac{3}{8}q = 12$

WRITTEN EXERCISES

A Solve and check each equation.

1. $2x = 8$ $x = 4$
2. $15y = 50$ $y = 3\frac{1}{3}$
3. $-12b = 24$ $b = -2$
4. $13t = -52$
5. $\frac{1}{4}x = 7$ $x = 28$
6. $-\frac{1}{2}y = 4$ $y = -8$
7. $-2.3s = 4.6$ $x = -2$
8. $2.1x = 105$
9. $\frac{n}{3} = 2$ $n = 6$
10. $\frac{y}{0.5} = 1$ $y = 0.5$
11. $\frac{2}{3}n = 12$ $n = 18$
12. $\frac{5}{6}n = 15$
13. $-9 = \frac{5}{4}v$ $v = -7\frac{1}{5}$
14. $12 = -\frac{3}{2}n$ $n = -8$
15. $-\frac{1}{4}x = 0$ $x = 0$
16. $5y = 0$
17. $\frac{t}{7} = -\frac{7}{2}$ $t = -24\frac{1}{2}$
18. $-\frac{30}{9} = \frac{5n}{3}$ $n = -2$
19. $-y = 6$ $y = -6$
20. $0 = -t$
21. $-r = \frac{1}{4}$ $r = -\frac{1}{4}$
22. $-\frac{1}{8} = -x$ $x = \frac{1}{8}$
23. $-\frac{1}{8} = 4n$ $n = -\frac{1}{32}$
24. $\frac{1}{2}y = 0$
25. $-0.25t = 8$ $t = -32$
26. $-0.1 = -8$ $x = 80$
27. $\frac{2}{3} = 5t$ $t = \frac{2}{15}$
28. $-1 = \frac{3}{4}t$
29. $\frac{y}{6} = \frac{2}{3}$ $y = 4$
30. $\frac{n}{2.4} = 0.2$ $n = 0.48$
31. $\frac{c}{0.01} = 0.75$
32. $\frac{t}{1.4} = 1$
33. $-\frac{2}{3}n = 1\frac{1}{9}$ $n = -1\frac{2}{3}$
34. $1.2x = -1.44$ $x = -1.2$
35. $-\frac{2}{9}x = -\frac{4}{3}$ $x = 6$
36. $\frac{4}{5} = -\frac{2}{15}u$
37. $-\frac{y}{2} = 1\frac{1}{4}$ $y = -2\frac{1}{2}$
38. $-\frac{a}{3} = 1\frac{2}{3}$ $a = -5$
39. $\frac{y}{3} = \frac{5}{9}$ $y = 1\frac{2}{3}$
40. $-\frac{c}{100} = 0.75$

B Complete.

41. If $2a + b = 10$, then $4a + 2b = $ ___?___ 20
42. If $3r + s = 5$, then $9r + 3s = $ ___?___ 15
43. If $q + 4p = 20$, then $5q + 20p = $ ___?___ 100
44. If $2x + 3 = 15$, then $8x + 12 = $ ___?___
45. If $6y + 5z = 21$, then $-(6y + 5z) = $ ___?___ -21
46. If $2w + z = 7$, then $-(2w + z) = $ ___?___ -7
47. If $9p = 111$, then $3p = $ ___?___ 37
48. If $8u = 124$, then $2u = $ ___?___ 31
49. If $2x = 88$, then $\frac{1}{4}x = $ ___?___ 11
50. If $5t = 120$, then $\frac{1}{2}t = $ ___?___ 12

C Classify each sentence as true, *T,* or false, *F.* When a sentence is false, tell why it is false.

51. For all real numbers x, $x + 2 = 3$.
52. For all real numbers x, $2x + 3x = 5x$.

53. For all real numbers x, $x + x = 1$.
54. For all real numbers, $\frac{x}{2} = \frac{1}{2}x$. *T*

88 *Chapter 3*

3–3   Using the Equation Properties

Teaching Suggestions p. M-16

The cost in dollars of taking students on a two-day skiing trip is given by

$$C = 210 + 35n.$$

If you know that the cost, C, is \$1890, you can solve the resulting equation to find n, the number of students who went on the trip.

To solve such an equation, use the addition property for equations first. Then use the multiplication property.

EXAMPLE 1   Solve and check: $3x + 8 = 23$

Solution:

$$3x + 8 = 23 \quad \longleftarrow \text{ Add } (-8) \text{ to each side.}$$
$$3x + 8 + (-8) = 23 + (-8)$$
$$3x = 15 \quad \longleftarrow \text{ Multiply each side by } \tfrac{1}{3}.$$
$$\frac{1}{3} \cdot 3x = \frac{1}{3} \cdot 15 \quad \longleftarrow \tfrac{1}{3} \cdot 3x = \left(\tfrac{1}{3} \cdot 3\right)x = 1 \cdot x$$
$$x = 5$$

Check:

$$3x + 8 = 23 \quad \longleftarrow \text{ Replace } x \text{ with 5.}$$
$$3 \cdot 5 + 8 \overset{?}{=} 23$$
$$15 + 8 \overset{?}{=} 23$$
$$23 \overset{?}{=} 23 \quad \text{Yes } \swarrow \quad \text{Solution set: } \{5\}$$

Always check your answer in the original equation.

EXAMPLE 2   Solve and check: $-7 + \dfrac{3n}{5} = 14$

Solution:

$$-7 + \frac{3n}{5} = 14 \quad \longleftarrow \text{ Add 7 to each side.}$$
$$7 + (-7) + \frac{3n}{5} = 7 + 14$$
$$\frac{3n}{5} = 21 \quad \longleftarrow \begin{array}{l} \text{Since } \frac{3n}{5} = \frac{3}{5}n, \text{ multiply} \\ \text{each side by } \frac{5}{3}. \end{array}$$
$$\frac{5}{3} \cdot \frac{3}{5}n = \frac{5}{3} \cdot 21$$
$$n = 35$$

Check:

$$-7 + \frac{3n}{5} = 14 \quad \longleftarrow \text{ Replace } n \text{ with 35.}$$
$$-7 + \frac{3(35)}{5} \overset{?}{=} 14$$
$$-7 + 21 \overset{?}{=} 14$$
$$14 \overset{?}{=} 14 \quad \text{Yes } \swarrow \quad \text{Solution set: } \{35\}$$

Quick Quiz
Solve and check
1. $8x = 32$
   Ans: {4} or x = 4
2. $-25x = -125$
   Ans: {5} or x = 5
3. $\frac{3}{4}r = -36$
   Ans: {48} or r = 48
4. $\frac{8}{5}y = 12$
   Ans: $\{7\frac{1}{2}\}$ or $y = 7\frac{1}{2}$
5. $\frac{a}{7} = -9$
   Ans: {−63} or a = −63
6. $-18 = -\frac{c}{8}$
   Ans: {144} or c = 144

Additional Examples
Example 1
Solve and check
1. $5x + 7 = 22$
   Ans: {3} or x = 3
2. $7n - 8 = 27$
   Ans: {5} or n = 5

Example 2
Solve and check
1. $\frac{4}{3}t + 8 = 16$
   Ans: {6} or t = 6
2. $-16 + \frac{3n}{8} = 14$
   Ans: {80} or n = 80

Solving Equations   **89**

CLASSROOM EXERCISES

What number would you add to each side of the equation to get the term with the variable alone on one side?

1. $4n + 7 = 19$ -7 **2.** $20 + 1.2x = 0$ -20 **3.** $8x - 5 = 11$ 5 **4.** $3t - 7 = 8$ 7

5. $-12 + r = 10$ 12 **6.** $13 = 6x - 17$ 17 **7.** $10 - 7x = 3$ -10 **8.** $6\frac{1}{2} - 5x = 11\frac{1}{2}$
$-6\frac{1}{2}$

Solve and check each equation.

9. $2x + 4 = 8$ $x = 2$ **10.** $3x - 1 = 8$ $x = 3$ **11.** $5 + 6t = 17$ $t = 2$ **12.** $10 = -3x - 5$
-5

WRITTEN EXERCISES

Assignment Guide
Minimal
Day 1 p. 90: 1–20
Day 2 p. 90: 21–47 odd
Average p. 90: 1–51 odd
Above Average p. 90: 3, 6, 9, . . . 48, 49–57

Additional Answers
Written Exercises
4. $x = -2$
8. $n = -4\frac{1}{3}$
12. $a = 6$
16. $v = -6$
20. $t = -5$
22. $b = 12\frac{1}{3}$
23. $x = -4$
24. $t = 27$
27. $y = -12$
30. $n = -10$
33. $n = 6$
36. $n = 96$
39. $x = 28$
42. $t = 144$
45. $n = 100$
48. $x = -55$
51. $z = -0.09$
52. 1. Assoc. post. for add.
    2. Add. inv. post.
    3. Ident. post. for add.
53. 1. Add. inv. post.
    2. Comm. post. for add.
    3. Add. inv. post.
    4. Add. inv. post.

A Solve and check each equation.

1. $5n + 3 = 33$ $n = 6$ **2.** $2n + 3 = 7$ $n = 2$ **3.** $5n - 3 = 17$ $n = 4$ **4.** $5x - 9 = -19$

5. $3t + 17 = 5$ $t = -4$ **6.** $4a + 17 = 53$ $a = 9$ **7.** $2n + 5 = 17$ $n = 6$ **8.** $3n + 17 = 4$

9. $3n - 4 = 17$ $n = 7$ **10.** $3n - 17 = 4$ $n = 7$ **11.** $2a + 15 = 3$ $a = -6$ **12.** $6a + 1 = 37$

13. $8a - 7 = 41$ $a = 6$ **14.** $9a - 1 = 80$ $a = 9$ **15.** $2b + 3 = 21$ $b = 9$ **16.** $4v + 27 = 3$

17. $5 - 3a = 32$ $a = -9$ **18.** $5 - 2y = 15$ $y = -5$ **19.** $7 = 6x + 19$ $x = -2$ **20.** $8 = 5t + 33$

21. $4 = 30 - 6t$ $t = 4\frac{1}{3}$ **22.** $-5 = 32 - 3b$ **23.** $5x + 37 = 17$ **24.** $\frac{2}{3}t + 5 = 23$

25. $9a - 8 = 73$ $a = 9$ **26.** $15 - \frac{5}{4}v = 23$ $v = -6\frac{2}{5}$ **27.** $\frac{1}{2}y + 11 = 5$

28. $8n + 22 = 70$ $n = 6$ **29.** $1.2t + 3.4 = -1.0$ $t = -3\frac{2}{3}$ **30.** $-0.6n + 11 = 17$

31. $2.1 = 4.3 - 1.1w$ $w = 2$ **32.** $7.0 = 2.2 - 0.8n$ $n = -6$ **33.** $0 = 0.6n - 3.6$

34. $0 = \frac{7}{10}n - 35$ $n = 50$ **35.** $\frac{5}{6}n + 34 = 9$ $n = -30$ **36.** $\frac{6}{8}n + 12 = 84$

37. $\frac{9}{10}x - 17 = 19$ $x = 40$ **38.** $\frac{16}{15}x + 78 = 14$ $x = -60$ **39.** $\frac{3}{4}x - 3 = 18$

40. $\frac{7}{8}t - 8 = 34$ $t = 48$ **41.** $\frac{2}{3}t - 13 = 57$ $t = 105$ **42.** $\frac{5}{12}t - 12 = 48$

43. $28 = \frac{17}{32}n - 23$ $n = 96$ **44.** $6 = 26 + \frac{2}{5}n$ $n = -50$ **45.** $15 = \frac{3}{10}n - 15$

46. $18 = -\frac{9}{32}n - 26$ $n = 192$ **50.** $53 + \frac{3}{5}x = 26$ $x = -45$ **48.** $49 + \frac{3}{5}x = 16$

B

49. $32,856 + 49x = 41,284$ $x = 172$ **50.** $-683 + 33t = -485$ $t = 6$ **51.** $0.6z + 0.06 = 0.006$

C In Exercises 52–55, give the reason for each step of the proof. In the proofs, all variables represent real numbers.

52. Prove: $(a + b) + (-b) = a$

Statements	Reasons
1. $(a + b) + (-b) =$ $a + [b + (-b)]$	1. ___?___
2. $(a + b) + (-b) = a + 0$	2. ___?___
3. $(a + b) + (-b) = a$	3. ___?___

53. Prove: $-(-a) = a$

Statements	Reasons
1. $a + (-a) = 0$	1. ___?___
2. $-a + a = 0$	2. ___?___
3. $-a + [-(-a)] = 0$	3. ___?___
4. $-(-a) = a$	4. ___?___

90 *Chapter 3*

54. Prove: $(-a) + (-b) = -(a + b)$

Statements	Reasons
1. $[-a + (-b)] + [a + b] = -a + (-b + a) + b$	**1.** __?__
2. $-a + (-b + a) + b = -a + [a + (-b)] + b$	**2.** __?__
3. $-a + [a + (-b)] + b = (-a + a) + (-b + b)$	**3.** __?__
4. $(-a + a) + (-b + b) = 0 + 0$	**4.** __?__
5. $0 + 0 = 0$	**5.** __?__
6. $[-a + (-b)]$ and $(a + b)$ are additive inverses.	**6.** __?__
7. $-a + (-b) = -(a + b)$	**7.** __?__

55. Prove: **If $a = b$, then $a + c = b + c$ and $c + a = c + b$.**

Statements	Reasons
1. $a + c = a + c$	**1.** __?__
2. $a = b$	**2.** Given
3. $a + c = b + c$	**3.** __?__
4. $a + c = c + a;$ $b + c = c + b$	**4.** __?__
5. $c + a = c + b$	**5.** __?__

Additional Answers
Written Exercises
54. 1. Assoc. post. for add.
   2. Comm. post. for add.
   3. Assoc. post. for add.
   4. Add. inv. post.
   5. Ident. post. for add.
   6. Add. inv. post.
   7. Add. inv. post.
55. 1. Refl. post. for equal.
   3. Subst. prin.
   4. Comm. post. for add.
   5. Subst. prin.

ᑕᗩᒪᑕᑌᒪᗩᎢOᖇ ᗩᑭᑭᒪIᑕᗩᎢIOᑎᔕ

Checking Equations

A calculator does not automatically follow the rules for the order of operations. Therefore, to check the answer to an equation, it may be necessary to rewrite the equation.

EXAMPLE **Equation:** $30 - 6t = 4$ **Answer:** $t = \frac{13}{3}$

SOLUTION Because multiplication is performed before addition or subtraction, rewrite the left side of the equation.

$$30 - 6t = -6t + 30$$
$$= -6\left(\frac{13}{3}\right) + 30$$

To enter -6, press the sign change key, $\boxed{+/-}$ (sometimes indicated as $\boxed{sc}$), *after* you enter the 6.

6 $\boxed{+/-}$ $\boxed{\times}$ 1 3 $\boxed{\div}$ 3 $\boxed{+}$ 3 0 $\boxed{=}$ | $\boxed{\quad\quad\quad 4.}$

Since the two sides of the equation have the same value, $\frac{13}{3}$ is the correct answer.

EXERCISES

Check the given "answer" to each equation. Correct any incorrect answers.

1. $16 + 4n = -4$; -5 **2.** $3p - 5 = -7$; 4 **3.** $8 - \frac{7}{8}y = 6$; -16 **4.** $-16 = 1.2c - 2.2$; 11.5
     correct $p = -\frac{2}{3}$ $y = \frac{16}{7}$ $c = -11.5$

Solving Equations **91**

This lesson is optional. It applies the skills of multiplication of decimals and positive and negative numbers to saving energy.

Consumer Applications

Saving Energy: Heating Costs

For many people, heating costs make up the largest part of their total energy costs. To save money, it is recommended that thermostats are set no higher than **65°F**. For each degree Fahrenheit that a thermostat is lowered, heating costs are lowered by **3%**.

EXAMPLE 1 Last year the Jenkins family spent $1500 to heat their home with the thermostat set at 69°F. How much could they save by setting the thermostat at 65°F?

Solution: $69° - 65° = 4°$ lower

$4 \times 3\% = 12\%$

$\$1500 \times 12\% = \$1500 \times 0.12 = \$180$

They would save **$180.**

To help explain why the above savings occur, energy conservationists use the following formula that relates to the concept of **heat transfer:** a hotter object will give up its heat to a cooler one.

A = area of surface in ft²
U = heat transfer factor
i = inside temperature in °F
o = outside temperature in °F

Heat Transfer $= A \cdot U(o - i)$ ⬅

The thermogram below records the heat transfer of the house shown above. The brighter portions of the thermogram (for example, around windows and the chimney) indicate the location of the greatest amount of heat loss.

The variable U represents a number that depends on the surface through which the heat must pass. Heat transfer is measured in **British thermal units (Btu's) per hour.**

The table below gives the value of U for several different surfaces.

Surface	Value of U
Brick, 8 inches thick	0.41
Wood, 2 inches thick	0.43
Glass, double paned	0.50
Concrete, 6 inches thick	0.58
Glass, single paned	1.13

EXAMPLE 2   The side wall of the Carlton home is 6-inch concrete and is 20 feet long and 10 feet high. The outside temperature is 20°F. Estimate the rate of heat transfer when **a.** $i = 65°F$ **b.** $i = 69°F$

Solution: Calculate A: $A = 20 \times 10 = 200$ square feet

a. $HT = 200 \cdot 0.58(20 - 65)$
$= 200 \cdot 0.58(-45)$
$= \mathbf{-5220}$ **Btu's per hour**

b. $HT = 200 \cdot 0.58(20 - 69)$
$= 200 \cdot 0.58(-49)$
$= \mathbf{-5684}$ **Btu's per hour**

The negative signs in the answers indicate that heat is being lost from the inside. Notice that at the lower temperature, less heat is lost. This is one reason why savings occur.

EXERCISES

In Exercises 1–8, find how much each family could save on last year's heating costs.

Yearly Heating Costs	Last Year's Thermostat Setting	This Year's Thermostat Setting		Yearly Heating Costs	Last Year's Thermostat Setting	This Year's Thermostat Setting
1. $900	68°	65°	**5.**	$750	67°	65°
2. $1200	72°	67°	**6.**	$940	69°	66°
3. $800	69°	64°	**7.**	$1260	70°	64°
4. $1100	68°	66°	**8.**	$1150	71°	68°

In Exercises 9–12, use the table on page 92 to estimate the amount of heat transfer with the given conditions.

9. 2-inch solid wood wall
$l = 12$ feet
$h = 10$ feet
$i = 65°F; o = 30°F$

10. 8-inch brick wall
$l = 15$ feet
$h = 9$ feet
$i = 65°F; o = 24°F$

11. Double-paned glass window
$l = 10$ feet
$h = 7$ feet
$i = 66°F; o = 10°F$

12. 6-inch concrete wall
$l = 20$ feet
$h = 10$ feet
$i = 68°F; o = 36°F$

Insulation is installed in houses to reduce heat transfer. Proper insulation can help keep heat inside in winter and outside in summer.

Saving Energy: Heating Costs   93

Problem Solving and Applications

OBJECTIVE: To use formulas to solve word problems

3–4 Using Formulas to Solve Word Problems

Teaching Suggestions p. M-16

Quick Quiz

Solve and check

1. $6s - 8 = 46$
   Ans: {9} or s = 9
2. $8y + 17 = 53$
   Ans: $\{4\frac{1}{2}\}$ or $y = 4\frac{1}{2}$
3. $-9 + \frac{2c}{3} = 15$
   Ans: {36} or c = 36
4. $\frac{8}{5}d + 17 = 27$
   Ans: $\{6\frac{1}{4}\}$ or $d = 6\frac{1}{4}$

Additional Examples
Example 1
Use the formula
$M = 3np$ to solve the problem.
How many $1\frac{1}{2}$-inch pleats
can be made from a piece
of material that is 54 inches
wide?   **Ans: 12**

In Chapter 1, you substituted for a variable in formulas. In this section, you will use formulas to solve word problems.

EXAMPLE 1   The Chic Tailoring Company uses this formula to find the width, M, of material needed to make n pleats where each pleat is p inches wide.

$$M = 3np$$

A worker is making $\frac{3}{4}$-inch pleats from material that is one yard wide. How many pleats can be made?

Solution: $M = 3np$ ⟵ **Replace M with 36 (36 inches = 1 yard) and p with $\frac{3}{4}$.**

$36 = 3n\left(\frac{3}{4}\right)$ ⟵ **Solve for n.**

$36 = \frac{9}{4}n$

$\frac{4}{9} \cdot 36 = \frac{4}{9} \cdot \frac{9}{4}n$ ⟵ **By the Multiplication Property for equations**

$16 = n$

Check: $M = 3np$ $36 \overset{?}{=} 3 \cdot 16 \cdot \frac{3}{4}$

$36 \overset{?}{=} 36$ Yes ✔   Thus, **16** pleats can be made.

The formula in Example 2 involves more than one operation.

Example 2
Use the formula
$R = 3.50\,A + 1.50\,C$
to solve the problem.
On Sunday, 250 children's
tickets were sold at the
Trylon Theatre and the
total receipts were $1075.
How many adult tickets
were sold?   **Ans: 200**

EXAMPLE 2   The Trylon Theater uses this formula to calculate the total ticket receipts, R, each day. In the formula, A represents the number of adult tickets sold and C represents the number of children's tickets sold.

$$R = 3.50A + 1.50C$$

On Monday, 230 adult tickets were sold and the total receipts were $962.50. How many children's tickets were sold?

Solution: $R = 3.50A + 1.50C$ ⟵ **Replace R with $962.50 and A with 230.**

$962.50 = 3.50(230) + 1.50C$ ⟵ **Solve for C.**

$962.50 = 805 + 1.50C$

$-805 + 962.50 = -805 + 805 + 1.50C$ ⟵ **By the Addition Property for equations**

$157.50 = 1.50C$

$\frac{1}{1.50}(157.50) = \frac{1}{1.50}(1.50C)$ ⟵ **By the Multiplication Property for equations**

$105 = C$

94   *Chapter 3*

Check:
$$R = 3.50A + 1.50C$$
$$962.50 \overset{?}{=} 3.50(230) + 1.50(105)$$
$$962.50 \overset{?}{=} 962.50 \quad \text{Yes} \quad \checkmark$$

Thus, **105** children's tickets were sold.

CLASSROOM EXERCISES

The yearly interest, i, in dollars on an investment, p, earning $14\frac{1}{2}\%$ interest is given by the formula $i = 0.145p$. Use this formula in Exercises 1–3.

1. What investment will earn $181.25 in interest in 1 year? $1250
2. What investment will earn $391.50 in interest in 1 year? $2700
3. What investment will earn $812.00 in interest in 1 year? $5600

The cost, C, in dollars of making n copies on a certain copying machine is given by the formula $C = 0.90 + 0.30n$. Use this formula in Exercises 4–6.

4. What is the cost of making 150 copies? $45.90
5. What is the cost of making 300 copies? $90.90
6. How many copies can be made for $16.00?   50 copies

WORD PROBLEMS

A   Use the formula from Example 1 in Exercises 1–4.

1. A worker is making $1\frac{1}{3}$-inch pleats from material that is one yard wide. How many pleats can be made?   9 pleats
2. A worker is making $\frac{5}{8}$-inch pleats from material that is 30 inches wide. How many pleats can be made?   16 pleats
3. A skirt having 24 pleats is to be made from material that is 24 inches wide. Find the width of each pleat. $\frac{1}{3}$ in.
4. A skirt having 8 pleats is to be made from material that is one yard wide. Find the width of each pleat. $1\frac{1}{2}$ in.

Use the formula from Example 2 in Exercises 5–8.

5. On Wednesday, total receipts at the Trylon Theater amounted to $623 and 151 adult tickets were sold. How many children's tickets were sold?   65
6. For the Saturday matinee, the Trylon Theater sold 472 children's tickets. Total receipts were $1646. How many adult tickets were sold?   268
7. On Saturday evening, 452 adults tickets and 178 children's tickets were sold at the Trylon Theater. What were the total receipts that evening? $1849
8. Total receipts at the Trylon Theater for one week in April were $8089.50. During that week, 976 children's tickets were sold. How many adult tickets were sold?   1893

Assignment Guide
Minimal
Day 1 p. 95: 1–4
Day 2 p. 95–96: 5–10
Average
Day 1 p. 95: 1–8
Day 2 p. 96: 9–16
Above Average
pp. 95–96: 2–16 even

Solving Equations   **95**

A salesperson earns a base salary of $265 per week plus a 3% commission on sales. The formula

$$W = \$265 + 0.03A,$$

where W represents total weekly wages, A represents the amount of weekly sales, and $0.03A$ represents the amount of commission, can be used to find the salesperson's weekly wages. Use this formula in Exercises 9–12.

9. Last week, the salesperson's wages were $505. Find the total sales. $8000

10. This week, the salesperson's wages were $460. Find the total sales.

11. What were the salesperson's total sales for a week in which the total weekly wages were $430? $5500

12. What were the salesperson's total sales for a week in which the total weekly wages were $403.30? $4610

B A bank uses the formula

$$M = (1 - P)C$$

to calculate the amount of mortgage on a house. In the formula, M represents the amount of the mortgage, C represents the cost of the house, and P represents the per cent (expressed as a decimal) of the down payment (the initial amount paid toward the cost of the house). Use this formula in Exercises 13–16.

13. The mortgage on a house is $60,000 and the per cent of down payment is 25%. Find the cost of the house. $80,000

14. The mortgage on a house is $45,000 and the per cent of down payment is 20%. Find the cost of the house.

15. The mortgage on a house is $140,000 and the per cent of down payment is 30%. Find the cost of the house. $200,000

16. The mortgage on a house is $85,000 and the per cent of down payment is 50%. Find the cost of the house.

Review

Solve and check each equation. *(Section 3–1)*

1. $x + 9 = 7$ $x = -2$
2. $-12 + n = 7$ $n = 19$
3. $0.4 + v = 1.3$
4. $\frac{1}{2} + a = 6\frac{1}{2}$

(Section 3–2)

5. $5x = 10$ $x = 2$
6. $-6b = 24$ $b = -4$
7. $-3.1n = 12.4$ $n = 4$
8. $\frac{y}{5} = -\frac{5}{2}$

(Section 3–3)

9. $3a + 4 = 13$ $a = 3$
10. $5n + 20 = 10$ $n = -2$
11. $9 = 6x - 3$ $x = 2$
12. $-2 = 4 - 3m$
13. $8.0 = 1.4 - 3.3x$ $x = -2$
14. $0 = 0.4a - 2.4$ $a = 6$
15. $23 + \frac{5}{6}y = 3$
16. $10 + 2r = 6$

In Exercises 17–18, use the formula $d = rt$ where d represents the distance, d, in kilometers, r represents the rate in kilometers per hour and t represents the time in hours. *(Section 3–4)*

17. A car is traveling at 80 kilometers per hour. How far will it travel in 3 hours?

18. Find the time required for a jet to travel 45 kilometers at a speed of 900 kilometers per hour.

96   *Solving Equations*

Combine like terms. *(Pages 60–63)*

1. $7x + 9x + 2$ $16x + 2$ 2. $8y + y - 9$ $9y - 9$ 3. $4a + 2a - a$ $5a$ 4. $8a + (-3a) - 9$ $5a - 9$

5. $6t - 5t + 1$ $t + 1$ 6. $-6y - y + 9y$ $2y$ 7. $-32 + 4r - 9r$ $-32 - 5r$ 8. $-7 - 10b + 15b$ $5b - 7$

OBJECTIVE: To solve equations involving like terms

3–5   Solving Equations: Like Terms

In solving equations, you sometimes have to combine like terms. Usually it is better to do this first. Then you apply the addition and multiplication properties for equations.

EXAMPLE 1   Solve and check: $9m - 2m + 6 = 27$

Solution:

$9m - 2m + 6 = 27$ ◄────── **Combine 9m and 2m.**

$7m + 6 = 27$ ◄────── $9m - 2m = (9 - 2)m = 7m$

$7m = 21$

$m = 3$

Check: $9m - 2m + 6 = 27$ ◄────── **Replace m with 3.**

$9(3) - 2(3) + 6 \stackrel{?}{=} 27$

$27 - 6 + 6 \stackrel{?}{=} 27$

$27 \stackrel{?}{=} 27$ Yes ✔   **Solution set: {3}**

Sometimes it is helpful to use parentheses to group the like terms.

EXAMPLE 2   Solve and check: $t + (3t - 9) + t + (3t - 9) = 62$

Solution:

$t + (3t - 9) + t + (3t - 9) = 62$ ◄────── **Group the like terms.**

$(t + 3t + t + 3t) + [(-9) + (-9)] = 62$ ◄────── **Combine like terms.**

$8t + (-18) = 62$ ◄────── $t + 3t + t + 3t = 8t$

$8t = 80$

$t = 10$

Check: $t + (3t - 9) + t + (3t - 9) = 62$ ◄────── **Replace t with 10.**

$10 + (3 \cdot 10 - 9) + 10 + (3 \cdot 10 - 9) \stackrel{?}{=} 62$

$10 + 21 + 10 + 21 \stackrel{?}{=} 62$

$62 \stackrel{?}{=} 62$ Yes ✔   **Solution set: {10}**

When parentheses within an equation indicate multiplication, use the distributive postulate to multiply. For example,

$$-2(x - 5) = -2(x) + (-2)(-5)$$
$$= -2x + 10$$

Then you combine like terms and solve for the variable.

Solving Equations   **97**

Teaching Suggestions p. M-16

Quick Quiz

Use the formula $M = 3np$ to solve the problems.

1. How many $1\frac{1}{2}$-inch pleats can be made from material that is 72 inches wide?
 Ans: 16

2. A skirt having 12 pleats is to be made from material that is 45 inches wide. Find the width of each pleat.
 Ans: $1\frac{1}{4}$ inches

Use the formula $R = 3.50A + 1.50C$ to solve the problems.

3. On Friday, the Trylon Theatre sold 325 adult tickets and the total receipts were $1625. How many children's tickets were sold?
 Ans: 325

4. On Monday, 185 adult tickets and 75 children's tickets were sold. What were the total receipts on Monday?
 Ans: $760

Additional Examples
Example 1
Solve and check
1. $8x - 3x + 7 = 52$
 Ans: {9} or x = 9
2. $7x + 4x - 9 = 24$
 Ans: {3} or x = 3

Example 2
Solve and check
1. $r + (2r - 3) + r + (2r - 3) = 66$
 Ans: {12} or r = 12
2. $y + (2y + 7) + -1 + (2y + 7) = 8$
 Ans: {-1} or y = -1

EXAMPLE 3   Solve and check: $4x - 3(x - 2) = 41$

Solution:
$$4x - 3(x - 2) = 41 \longleftarrow \text{ Write } -3(x - 2) \text{ as } + (-3)(x - 2).$$
$$4x + (-3)(x - 2) = 41$$
$$4x + (-3)(x) + (-3)(-2) = 41 \longleftarrow \text{ By the distributive postulate}$$
$$4x - 3x + 6 = 41$$
$$x + 6 = 41 \longleftarrow \text{ Solve for } x.$$
$$x + 6 + (-6) = 41 + (-6)$$
$$x = 35$$

Check:
$$4x - 3(x - 2) = 41 \longleftarrow \text{ Replace } x \text{ with 35.}$$
$$4(35) - 3(35 - 2) \stackrel{?}{=} 41$$
$$140 - 3(33) \stackrel{?}{=} 41$$
$$140 - 99 \stackrel{?}{=} 41$$
$$41 \stackrel{?}{=} 41 \quad \text{Yes } \checkmark \qquad \text{Solution set: } \{35\}$$

The following procedure summarizes the steps for solving equations.

Procedure

Steps for Solving Equations
$\boxed{1}$ Remove parentheses by using the distributive postulate.
$\boxed{2}$ Combine like terms.
$\boxed{3}$ Use the addition property for equations.
$\boxed{4}$ Use the multiplication property for equations.
$\boxed{5}$ Check the equation.

CLASSROOM EXERCISES

Use the distributive property to find each product.

1. $9(x - 1)$ $9x - 9$
2. $2(5x + 3)$ $10x + 6$
3. $7(-2x - 1)$ $-14x - 7$
4. $8(3x - 10)$
5. $-2(x + 1)$ $-2x = 2$
6. $-3(x - 7)$ $-3x + 21$
7. $-5(x - 1)$ $-5x + 5$
8. $-2(x - 5)$

Solve and check.

9. $3a + a = 8$ $a = 1$
10. $6a - a + 3 = 15$ $a = 2\frac{2}{5}$
11. $7b + 3b - b = 16$
12. $2(x + 3) = 9$ $x = 1\frac{1}{2}$
13. $3(x - 5) = 21$ $x = 12$
14. $-2(-3 - 4x) = -10$

WRITTEN EXERCISES

Ⓐ   Use the distributive postulate to find each product.

1. $2(x - 3)$ $2x - 6$
2. $4(x - 4)$ $4x - 16$
3. $3(2x + 1)$ $6x + 3$
4. $3(2x - 1)$ $6x - 3$
5. $4(5x - 7)$ $20x - 28$
6. $4(2b - 3)$ $8b - 12$
7. $4(b - 6)$ $4b - 24$
8. $2(9 - b)$ $18 - 2b$

98   *Chapter 3*

Use the distributive postulate to find each product.

9. $-4(x-9)$ $-4x+36$ **10.** $-2(y-3)$ $-2y+6$ **11.** $-4(5-n)$ $-20+4n$ **12.** $-5(y-6)$

13. $-4(3-x)$ $-12+4x$ **14.** $-1(5-m)$ $-5+m$ **15.** $-1(9-4m)$ $-9+4m$ **16.** $-2(m-4)$

Solve and check each equation.

17. $7x-3x=8$ $x=2$ **18.** $5n-2n=12$ $n=4$ **19.** $3y+2y-4y=6$

20. $8m-2m+7=19$ $m=2$ **21.** $15=7x-2x$ $x=3$ **22.** $16=8a+7a+a$

23. $2n-5n=12$ $n=-4$ **24.** $-3n-4n=-21$ $n=3$ **25.** $-5x-4x+3=12$

26. $7-x+2x=7$ $x=0$ **27.** $2(x-3)=-10$ $x=-2$ **28.** $2(x-5)=-8$

29. $2(x-5)=4$ $x=7$ **30.** $3(2x+1)=-15$ $x=-3$ **31.** $3(2x-1)=9$

32. $4(5x-7)=12$ $x=2$ **33.** $2(5-3n)=-14$ $n=4$ **34.** $4(7-2x)=4$

35. $-7b+4(2b-3)=16$ $b=28$ **36.** $2x+3(x+5)=0$ $x=-3$ **37.** $-3x+6(x-4)=9$

38. $2y+4(y-5)=4$ $y=4$ **39.** $2a-5(a-6)=3$ $a=9$ **40.** $2b+4(b-6)=12$

41. $-4(x-9)+5=1$ $x=10$ **42.** $2(9-b)-8=0$ $b=5$ **43.** $6m-15m=3$

44. $2b+6b=12$ $b=1\frac{1}{2}$ **45.** $2(x-6)=3$ $x=7\frac{1}{2}$ **46.** $-3(y+5)=10$

47. $b-2(4-b)=-5$ $b=1$ **48.** $x-4(3-x)=0$ $x=2\frac{2}{5}$ **49.** $5-2(m+2)=9$

B

50. $6-(m-4)=18$ $m=-8$ **51.** $-2-(5+3m)=20$ **52.** $-8-(9-4m)=15$

53. $\frac{1}{2}x+\frac{3}{4}x=2\frac{1}{2}$ $x=2$ **54.** $0.04x+0.96x=4.80$ **55.** $1.6a+2.4-7=3$

C   In Exercises 56–57, give the reason for each step of each proof. In these proofs, all variables represent real numbers.

56. If $ac=bc$ and $c \neq 0$, then $a=b$.

Statements	Reasons
1. $ac=bc$	1. Given
2. $(ac)\left(\frac{1}{c}\right)=bc\left(\frac{1}{c}\right)$	2. ___?___
3. $a\left[c\left(\frac{1}{c}\right)\right]=b\left[c\left(\frac{1}{c}\right)\right]$	3. ___?___
4. $a(1)=b(1)$	4. ___?___
5. $a=b$	5. ___?___

57. If $a+c=b+c$, then $a=b$.

Statements	Reasons
1. $a+b=b+c$	1. Given
2. $(a+c)+(-c)=$ $b+c+(-c)$	2. ___?___
3. $a+[c+(-c)]=$ $b+[c+(-c)]$	3. ___?___
4. $a+0=b+0$	4. ___?___
5. $a=b$	5. ___?___

A set, S, of numbers is **closed under division** if the quotient of any two numbers in set S is also in set S. (Remember that division by zero is excluded.)

Which of the following sets are closed under division?

58. $\{1\}$ Yes   **59.** $\{-1, 0, 1\}$ No   **60.** $\{-1\}$ No   **61.** I   No   **62.** Q   Yes

63. Is the set $\{-1, 1\}$ closed under division?   Yes

Solving Equations   **99**

Problem Solving and Applications

OBJECTIVE: To use equations to solve word problems involving geometric formulas

3–6 Formulas to Equations

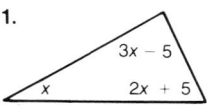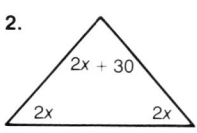
Many problems that relate to geometry can be solved by writing an equation for a formula. For example,

the sum of the measures of the angles of a triangle is 180°.

That is,

$$A + B + C = 180°$$

where A, B, and C, represent the measures of the angles of a triangle.

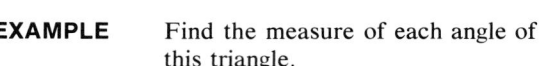

EXAMPLE   Find the measure of each angle of this triangle.

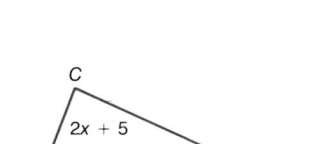

Solution: Use the formula. Replace A with $2x$, B with x, and C with $2x + 5$.

$$A + B + C = 180°$$
$$2x + x + 2x + 5 = 180 \quad\longleftarrow\quad \textbf{Combine like terms.}$$
$$5x + 5 = 180$$
$$5x = 175$$
$$x = 35 \quad\longleftarrow\quad \textbf{Find 2x and 2x + 5.}$$
$$2x = 2(35) = 70$$
$$2x + 5 = 2(35) + 5 = 75$$

Check: Does the sum of the measures of the angles equal 180?

$35 + 70 + 75 = 180$?   Yes ✔

Thus, the angle measures are **35°, 70°, and 75°.**

CLASSROOM EXERCISES

In Exercises 1–3, find the measure of each angle of the triangle.

1. $30°$; $60°$; $90°$

2. $45°$; $45°$; $90°$

3. $30°$; $30°$; $120°$

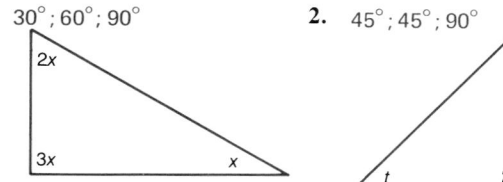

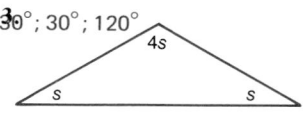

4. The measures of the angles of a triangle can be represented by a, $2a + 30$, and $a + 10$. Find the measure of each angle of the triangle. $35°; 55°; 90°$

5. The measures of the angles of a triangle can be represented by d, $d - 15$, and $d - 30$. Find the measure of each angle of the triangle. $45°; 60°; 75°$

WRITTEN EXERCISES

Ⓐ In Exercises 1–6, find the measure of each angle of the triangle.

1. Acute Triangle
$42.5°; 52.5°; 85°$

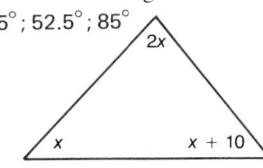

2. Obtuse Triangle
$15°; 45°; 120°$

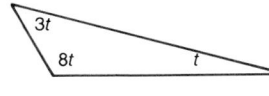

3. Right Triangle
$75°; 15°$

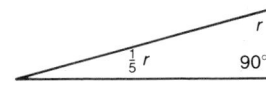

4. Isosceles Triangle
$50°; 65°; 65°$

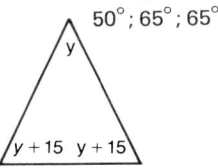

5. Equilateral Triangle
$60°; 60°; 60°$

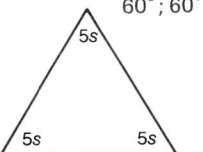

6. Isosceles Right Triangle
$45°; 45°$

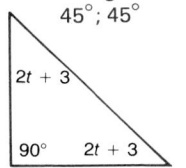

The sum of the measures of the angles of a quadrilateral (closed *polygon* having four sides) *is 360°.* That is,

$$A + B + C + D = 360°,$$

where A, B, C, and D represent the measures of the angles of the quadrilateral. In Exercises 7–12, refer to this formula to find the measure of each angle of the given quadrilateral.

7. Rectangle

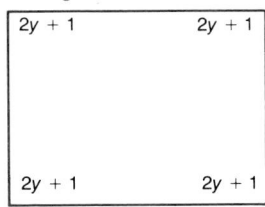

8. Square

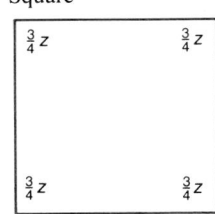

9. Parallelogram

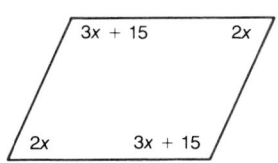

10. Rhombus

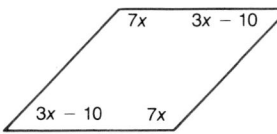

11. Trapezoid

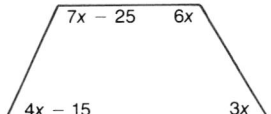

12. Quadrilateral

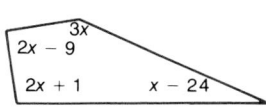

Solving Equations **101**

Assignment Guide
Minimal
Day 1 p. 101: 2–12 even
Day 2 p. 102: 13–17
Average
Day 1 pp. 101–102: 1–14
Day 2 p. 102: 15–20
Above Average pp. 101–102:
2–20 even, 21–24

Additional Answers
Written Exercises
 7. $90°; 90°; 90°; 90°$
 8. $90°; 90°; 90°; 90°$
 9. $66°; 66°; 114°; 114°$
10. $47°; 47°; 133°; 133°$
11. $60°; 120°; 115°; 65°$
12. $25°; 89°; 99°; 147°$

WORD PROBLEMS

13. The measures of the angles of a triangle can be represented by s, $\frac{1}{2}s$, and $3s$. Find the measure of each angle of the triangle.   20°; 40°; 120°

14. The measure of one angle of a triangle is 70°. The measure of each of the other angles can be represented by $5x$. Find the measures of the two angles.

15. The measure of one angle of a triangle can be represented by $10p$. The measure of each of the other two angles is 15 more than the first angle. Find the measure of each angle of the triangle.   50°; 65°; 65°

16. The sum of the measures of two angles is 90°. The measure of one of these angles is $2r$; the measure of the other angle is $2r - 18$. Find the measure of each of these angles.   36°; 54°

17. The sum of two angles is 90°. The measures of the angles can be represented by x and $(x + 28)$. Find the measure of each angle.   31°; 59°

18. The sum of two angles is 90°. The measures of the angles can be represented by t and $(t - 12)$. Find the measure of each angle.   39°; 51°

19. The sum of two angles is 180°. Their measures can be represented by y and $(y + 36)$. Find the measure of each angle.   72°; 108°

20. The sum of two angles is 180°. Their measures can be represented by w and $(3w + 18)$. Find the measure of each angle.   40.5°; 139.5°

21. The measures of the angles of a parallelogram can be represented by x, x, $3x$, and $3x$. Find the measure of each angle of the parallelogram.

22. The sum of the measures of two angles is 180°. The measure of one angle is $5x$. The measure of the other angle is twice the first. Find the measure of each angle.   60°; 120°

23. The sum of the measures of two angles is 90°. The measure of one angle is $4q$. The measure of the second angle is three times the first. Find the measure of each angle.   22.5°; 67.5°

24. The sum of the measures of two angles is 180°. The measure of one angle is $7t$. The measure of the second angle is 2 more than the first. Find the measure of each angle.   89°; 91°

Puzzle

Solve each equation. Match each solution with a letter or "!" mark below. Then unscramble the letters in each word to find the secret message.

A: $x + \frac{3}{4} = 1$ E: $-x = -4$ O: $4x = -16$ U: $x - 5 = -10$ L: $x - 3x = \frac{1}{2}$

P: $12x + 7 = 16$ R: $2(x - 3) = 4$!: $\frac{4}{5}x + 1 = \frac{2}{5}$ S: $4 = 2(5x + 1)$ Y: $10x = -2$

YOU ARE REALLY SUPER!

-4	$-\frac{1}{5}$	-5		4	$\frac{1}{4}$	5		$-\frac{1}{4}$	4	$-\frac{1}{5}$	$\frac{1}{4}$	5	$-\frac{1}{4}$
O	Y	U		E	A	R		L	E	Y	A	R	L
4	$\frac{3}{4}$	$\frac{1}{5}$	5	-5		$-\frac{3}{4}$							
E	P	S	R	U		!							

Write a two-place decimal for each fraction or mixed number.

Example: $\dfrac{9}{10}$ ⟶ **0.90** ⟵ **Answer**
$$10\overline{)9.00}$$

1. $\dfrac{7}{10}$ 0.70   **2.** $\dfrac{3}{5}$ 0.60   **3.** $\dfrac{3}{4}$ 0.75   **4.** $5\dfrac{1}{2}$ 5.50   **5.** $7\dfrac{1}{4}$ 7.25   **6.** $8\dfrac{3}{10}$
8.30

Write a fraction in lowest terms for each decimal.

Example: $0.32 = \dfrac{32}{100} = \dfrac{8}{25}$

7. 0.45 $\dfrac{9}{20}$ **8.** 0.64 $\dfrac{16}{25}$ **9.** 0.25 $\dfrac{1}{4}$ **10.** 0.50 $\dfrac{1}{2}$ **11.** 0.70 $\dfrac{7}{10}$ **12.** 0.125
$\dfrac{1}{8}$

OBJECTIVE: To solve percent problems

3–7 Equations and Per Cent

Per cent means **per hundred** or **hundredths.**

$$13\% = \frac{13}{100} = \mathbf{0.13} \qquad\qquad 6\% = \frac{6}{100} = \mathbf{0.06}$$

$$0.5\% = \frac{0.5}{100} = \frac{5}{1000} = \mathbf{0.005} \qquad 215\% = \frac{215}{100} = \mathbf{2.15}$$

There are three types of per cent problems. Each type involves three numbers. When you know two of the numbers, you can write an equation and solve it to find the third number.

Finding a Per Cent of a Number	**Finding What Per Cent a Number is of Another**	**Finding a Number Given its Per Cent**
What number is 75% of 900?	What per cent of 5 is 2?	72 is 9% of what number?
$n \quad = 0.75 \cdot 900$	$n \quad\cdot 5 = 2$	$72 = 0.09 \cdot \quad n$

EXAMPLE 1 **a.** What number is 75% of 900?   **b.** What per cent of 5 is 2?
　　　　　　　　　c. 72 is 9% of what number?

Solutions: **a.** Let $y =$ the number.

What number is 75% of 900?

$$y \quad = 0.75 \cdot 900$$
$$y \quad = 675$$

Thus, **675** is 75% of 900.

b. Let $a =$ the per cent.

What per cent of 5 is 2?

$$a \quad \cdot 5 = 2$$
$$5a = 2$$
$$a = \frac{2}{5} = 0.40$$
$$a = 40\%$$

Thus, 2 is **40%** of 5.

Teaching Suggestions p. M-16

Quick Quiz
1. The measures of the angles of a triangle can be represented by x, x, and $2x$. Find the measure of each angle of the triangle. **Ans: 45°; 45°; 90°**
2. The measures of the angles of a triangle can be represented by $(2x - 3)$, $(3x + 5)$, and $(x + 10)$. Find the measure of each angle of the triangle. **Ans: 38°; 53°; 89°**

Additional Examples
Example 1
1. **a.** What number is 70% of 800? **Ans: 560**
   b. What per cent of 8 is 6? **Ans: 75%**
   c. 27 is 4% of what number? **Ans: 675**
2. **a.** What per cent of 50 is 75? **Ans: 150%**
   b. 80 is 1% of what number? **Ans: 8000**
   c. What number is 85% of 2000? **Ans: 1700**

Solving Equations **103**

c. Let s = the number.

72 is 90% of what number?

$72 = 0.90 \qquad s$

$\dfrac{72}{0.90} = \dfrac{0.90s}{0.90}$

$\mathbf{80} = s$

Thus, 72 is 90% of **80**.

NOTE: When finding what per cent one number is of another as in Example 1b and in Example 2, you can express the unknown as a decimal or as a fraction. Then you write a per cent for the decimal or fraction.

To find the per cent of increase or decrease, first find the *amount* of increase or decrease. Then compare this with the *original amount* and write a per cent.

EXAMPLE 2   In 1978, the cost for the first 3 ounces of first-class mail was 15¢. In 1981, the cost rose to 20¢. Find the per cent of increase.

Solution: $\boxed{1}$ Let y = the per cent of increase.

$\boxed{2}$ Amount of increase: $20¢ - 15¢ = 5¢$

$\boxed{3}$ 5 is what per cent of 15? ◄——— **15 is the original amount.**

$5 = \qquad y \qquad \cdot \; 15, \quad$ or

$15y = 5$

$y = \dfrac{5}{15} = \dfrac{1}{3}$ ◄——— **Write a per cent for $\frac{1}{3}$.**

Check: The per cent of increase is $33\frac{1}{3}$%. Does $33\frac{1}{3}$% of 15 = 5?   Yes ✔

CLASSROOM EXERCISES

Complete.

1. $18 = 20\%$ of __?__   90
2. $6 = 15\%$ of __?__   40
3. __?__% of 20 = 15
4. __?__% of 96 = 72   75%
5. 35% of 246 = __?__   86.1
6. 1% of 81 = __?__
7. __?__% of 20 = 12   60%
8. 45% of 120 = __?__   54
9. 18% of 150 = __?__
10. $72 = 9\%$ of __?__   800
11. $28 = $ __?__% of 70   40%
12. $48.6 = 90\%$ of __?__

13. By raising the thermostat setting, the Arico family reduced their monthly costs for air conditioning from $170 to $100. Find the amount of decrease. $70

14. Last month, Carol earned $1250 selling vacuum cleaners for ABC Vac Corporation. This month she earned $1500. Find the amount of increase. $250

104   *Chapter 3*

15. By lowering the thermostat setting, the Gould family reduced their monthly heating costs from $90 to $85. Find the per cent of decrease. $5\frac{5}{9}\%$

16. One-way train fare from Chicago to New Orleans cost $45 in 1970. By 1980, the fare was $75. Find the per cent of increase. $66\frac{2}{3}\%$

WRITTEN EXERCISES

1. 35% of 28 is what number? 9.8

2. 40% of 25 is what number? 10

3. What per cent of 92 is 69? 75%

4. What per cent of 65 is 39? 60%

5. 15 is 20% of what number? 75%

6. 21 is 30% of what number? 70

7. 125% of what number is 45? 36

8. 3 is what per cent of 3000? 0.1%

9. $37\frac{1}{2}\%$ of 2400 is what number? 900

10. 3% of what number is 1.86? 62

11. What per cent of 35 is 28? 80%

12. 2.5% of 400 is what number? 10

APPLICATIONS: Using Per Cent

13. The price of a new car is $6500. Mrs. Gomez made a down payment of 15% of the price of the car when she bought it. How much was the down payment?

14. In a factory, 54,600 parts were made in one week. When they were tested, 3% were found to be defective. How many were defective? 1638

15. Mr. Garvey bought a suit for $180 and paid $10.80 as a sales tax. What per cent of the cost was the sales tax? 6%

16. A baseball team won 8 games. This was 40% of the games played. How many games did the team play? 20

17. An advertisement claims that each serving of a brand of oatmeal contains 4 grams of protein. This is 6% of a person's daily recommended need. How many grams of protein make up a person's daily recommended need? $66\frac{2}{3}$

18. Jeff earns $1050 a month as a key punch operator for a bank. He spends $84 per month on his automobile insurance. What per cent of his monthly income is spent on automobile insurance? 8%

19. Jennifer bought a coat at a "20% off" sale and saved $35. What was the original price of the coat? $175

20. How much silver is in 12.5 kilograms of an alloy (mixture) which is 8% silver? 1 kilogram

21. A worker who earns $6.50 per hour receives a raise of $0.52 per hour. What is the per cent of increase in the worker's wages? 8%

22. The list price (regular price) of a typewriter is $355. A discount (reduction in price) of $106.50 is given. What per cent of the list price is the discount?

23. The discount on a set of golf clubs is $69 and the rate of discount is 15%. What is the list price? $460

24. The list price on a camera is $60 but it is on sale for $44.40. What is the rate (per cent) of discount?

25. A sports car that originally cost $6000 is now valued at $8000. What is the per cent increase in value? $133\frac{1}{3}\%$

26. The monthly rent for an apartment rose from $425 to $476. What is the per cent of increase? 12%

Assignment Guide
Minimal
Day 1 p. 105: 1–12
Day 2 p. 105: 13–25 odd
Average
Day 1 p. 105: 2–18 even
Day 2 pp. 105–106: 19–31 odd
Above Average pp. 105–106:
3, 6, 9, . . . 30, 31–36

Additional Answers
Applications
13. $975
22. 30%
24. 74%

27. The price of pocket-size calculators decreased from $40 to $12 over a 9-year period. Find the per cent of decrease.

B

29. An art dealer bought an oil painting for $1200 and then sold it at an auction for a 40% profit. What was the selling price of the painting? $1680

31. A business executive received a salary increase of 15%. This brought his salary to $27,600. What was the executive's salary before the raise? $24,000

33. After Kenneth Sims lost 20% of his real estate investment, he had $12,500 left. How much did he invest originally?

C

35. A store owner is trying to sell a $450 stereo. First the owner raises the price by 20%. Then the owner advertises a "20% off" sale on the new price. What is the final price of the stereo? $432

28. The value of a certain four-door car decreased from $7000 to $4550 in two years. Find the per cent of decrease.

30. The population of a village decreased from 21,000 to 16,000. Find the per cent of decrease. Round your answer to the nearest whole per cent. 76%

32. After the price of a pound of meat was increased 12%, the new price was $1.68. What was the price per pound before the increase? $1.50

34. Shirley bought some stock valued at $62.50 per share and sold it for $67.50 per share. Find the per cent of profit.

36. On January 1, Tim's credit-card balance was $350. The interest rate is 1.5% per month and Tim pays $75 at the end of each month. How much will he owe on April 1? $134.17

CALCULATOR APPLICATIONS

Per Cent of Increase and Decrease

A calculator with a per cent key, ⧠%, allows you to find the per cent of increase and decrease.

EXAMPLE A coat with a regular price of $75 is selling for $63.75. Find the per cent of decrease.

SOLUTION ⧠1 Find the amount of decrease.

7 5 ⧠− 6 3 . 7 5 ⧠= $\boxed{11.25}$

⧠2 Find the per cent of decrease.

1 1 . 2 5 ⧠÷ 7 5 ⧠% $\boxed{15.}$

EXERCISES

1. A sedan that originally cost $10,500 is now valued at $8925. What is the per cent decrease in value? 15

2. A painting worth $750 ten years ago was auctioned for $4200. Find the per cent increase in value. 460

Problem Solving and Applications

OBJECTIVE: To solve integer problems

3–8 Integer Problems

Teaching Suggestions p. M-16

To solve integer problems, you have to represent consecutive integers, consecutive even integers, and consecutive odd integers.

Word Expression	Algebraic Expression	Example
Three **consecutive integers**	Let x = the first integer Then $x + 1$ = the second integer, and $x + 2$ = the third integer.	-5 -4 -3 x $x+1$ $x+2$
Three **consecutive even integers**	Let t = the first even integer. Then $t + 2$ = the second even integer, and $t + 4$ = the third even integer.	22 24 26 t $t+2$ $t+4$
Three **consecutive odd integers**	Let h = the first odd integer. Then $h + 2$ = the second odd integer, and $h + 4$ = the third odd integer	3 5 7 h $h+2$ $h+4$

To solve word problems involving integers, follow these steps.

Procedure

> To solve word problems involving integers:
> 1. Choose a variable. Use the variable to represent the integers.
> 2. Write an equation for the word sentence.
> 3. Solve the equation and find the integers.
> 4. Check in the statement of the problem.

EXAMPLE 1 Find two consecutive integers whose sum is 147.

Solution:
1. Let t = the first integer.
   Then $t + 1$ = the second integer. ◄──── **Represent the integers.**
2. $t + (t + 1) = 147$ ◄──── **Their sum is 147.**
3. $2t + 1 = 147$
   $2t = 146$
   $t = 73$ ◄──── **Find $t + 1$.**
   $t + 1 = 73 + 1 = 74$

Check:
4. Are the integers consecutive? Yes ✔
   Does $73 + 74 = 147$? Yes ✔ The integers are **73** and **74**.

Solving Equations   **107**

Always check your solution with the original statement of the problem.

NOTE: The steps in Example 2 correspond to the steps in the procedure.

EXAMPLE 2   Find three consecutive odd integers whose sum is −15.

Solution: $\boxed{1}$ Let r = the first odd integer.
Then $r + 2$ = the second odd integer,
and $r + 4$ = the third odd integer.

$\boxed{2}$ $r + (r + 2) + (r + 4) = -15$ ◄——— **Their sum is −15.**

$\boxed{3}$ $\qquad\qquad 3r + 6 = -15$

$\qquad\qquad\qquad 3r = -21$

$\qquad\qquad\qquad r = -7$ ◄——— **Don't forget to find $r + 2$ and $r + 4$.**

$\qquad\qquad r + 2 = -7 + 2 = -5$

$\qquad\qquad r + 4 = -7 + 4 = -3$

Check: $\boxed{4}$ Are the integers consecutive odd integers?   Yes ✔
Does $(-7) + (-5) + (-3) = -15$?   Yes ✔

The integers are **−7, −5,** and **−3.**

CLASSROOM EXERCISES

Beginning with the given integer, write the next four larger consecutive integers.

1. 18   2. 97   3. 0   4. −8   5. −1   6. r

Beginning with the given integer, write the next four larger consecutive even integers.

7. 12   8. 100   9. −12   10. −66   11. q 12. $b + 4$

Beginning with the given integer, write the next four larger consecutive odd integers.

13. 9   14. 1   15. −21   16. −101   17. k 18. $k + 10$

In each of Exercises 19–22, write an algebraic expression to represent each integer. Then write the equation you would use to solve the problem.

19. The sum of two consecutive integers is 43. n; $n + 1$; $n + (n + 1) = 43$
20. The sum of two consecutive even integers is 86. n; $n + 2$; $n + (n + 2) = 86$
21. The sum of two consecutive odd integers is 0. n; $n + 2$; $n + (n + 2) = 0$
22. The sum of two consecutive integers is −29. n; $n + 1$; $n + (n + 1) = -29$

108   *Chapter 3*

WORD PROBLEMS

A   Solve each problem.

1. The sum of two consecutive integers is −17. Find the integers. −9; −8

2. The sum of three consecutive integers is 279. Find the integers. 92; 93, 94

3. Find four consecutive integers whose sum is −130. −34; −33; −32; −31

4. Find two consecutive integers whose sum is −25. −13; −12

5. Find three consecutive integers whose sum is 48. 15; 16; 17

6. The sum of two consecutive odd integers is 112. Find the integers. 55; 57

7. The sum of three consecutive odd integers is −105. Find the integers.

8. The sum of four consecutive even integers is −420. Find the integers.

9. Find four consecutive odd integers whose sum is 0. −3; −1; 1; 3

10. Find three consecutive even integers whose sum is 0. −2; 0; 2

11. Are there three consecutive integers whose sum is 40? No

12. Are there three consecutive odd integers whose sum is 59? No

B

13. Find two consecutive integers such that four times the smaller minus three times the larger equals 0. 3; 4

14. Find three consecutive integers such that the sum of the first and third is 40. 19, 20, 21

15. Find four consecutive integers such that the sum of the second and fourth is 132. 64, 65, 66, 67

16. Find three consecutive integers such that the sum of the first two decreased by the third equals 68. 69; 70; 71

17. Find two consecutive odd integers such that twice the smaller decreased by the larger equals 53. 55; 57

18. Find three consecutive odd integers such that their sum decreased by the second equals 50. 23; 25; 27

19. If n is an integer, is $2n + 2$ even or odd?

20. If n is an integer, is $2n + 1$ even or odd?

21. If $2h + 1$ is an odd integer, what is the preceding even integer? $2h$

22. If $2h + 1$ is an odd integer, what is the preceding integer? $2h$

C   The French mathematician, Pierre de Fermat (1601–1665), proved this theorem about prime numbers.

If n is a natural number, prime numbers of the form 4n + 1 can be expressed as the sum of the squares of two integers.

Example: Prime number: **5**

Expressed as $4n + 1$: **4(1) + 1**

Expressed as the square of two integers: $2^2 + 1^2$

23. Express the numbers 13, 17, and 29 in the form $4n + 1$.

24. Express the numbers 13, 17, and 29 as the sum of the squares of two integers.

25. What other prime numbers less than 50 can be expressed as $4n + 1$? 37; 41

26. Express the primes you found in Exercise 25 as the sum of the squares of two integers.

Solving Equations **109**

Assignment Guide
Minimal
Day 1 p. 109: 1–5
Day 2 p. 109: 6–12
Average
Day 1 p. 109: 1–12
Day 2 p. 109: 13–22
Above Average
p. 109: 5–24

Additional Answers
7. −37; −35; −33
8. −108; −106; −104; −102
23. 4(3) + 1; 4(4) + 1; 4(7) + 1
24. $3^2 + 2^2$; $4^2 + 1^2$; $5^2 + 2^2$
26. $6^2 + 1^2$; $5^2 + 4^2$

BASIC: SOLVING AX + B = C

Problem: *Given a, b, and c, write a program which solves the equation $ax + b = c$. Include the possibilities that the solution set contains all real numbers or is the empty set.*

```
100 PRINT "FOR THE EQUATION AX + B = C, WHAT ARE"
110 PRINT "A, B, AND C";
120 INPUT A, B, C
130 IF A = 0 THEN 170
140 LET X = (C - B)/A
150 PRINT "X = ";X
160 GOTO 210
170 IF B = C THEN 200
180 PRINT "NO SOLUTION"
190 GOTO 210
200 PRINT "ALL REAL NUMBERS ARE SOLUTIONS."
210 PRINT
220 PRINT "ANY MORE EQUATIONS TO SOLVE (1=YES, 0=NO)";
230 INPUT Z
240 IF Z = 1 THEN 120
250 END
```

The following is the output from a sample run of the program above.

Output:
```
RUN
FOR THE EQUATION AX + B = C, WHAT ARE
A, B, AND C? 1,3,5
X =  2

ANY MORE EQUATIONS TO SOLVE (1=YES, 0=NO)? 1
? 4,8,6
X = -.5

ANY MORE EQUATIONS TO SOLVE (1=YES, 0=NO)? 1
? 0,5,-3
NO SOLUTION

ANY MORE EQUATIONS TO SOLVE (1=YES, 0=NO)? 1
? 0,6,6
ALL REAL NUMBERS ARE SOLUTIONS.

ANY MORE EQUATIONS TO SOLVE (1=YES, 0=NO)? 0
READY
```

This lesson is optional. Each computer applications lesson relates directly to a topic covered within the given chapter. (See Section 3-3, pages 89–91.)

Analysis: Before the program could be written, some preliminary algebra had to be done.

$$ax + b = c$$
$$ax = c - b \quad \longleftarrow \quad \textbf{Subtract } \boldsymbol{b} \textbf{ from both sides.}$$
$$x = \frac{c - b}{a} \quad \longleftarrow \quad \textbf{Divide both sides by } \boldsymbol{a}.$$

Statements 130, 170–200: The last step of the work above assumes that A $\neq$ 0. If A = 0, then the formula (C - B)/A cannot be used. Instead the solution set will either be empty (if B $\neq$ C) or all real numbers (if B = C). These two special cases are handled by statements 170–200.

Statements 140–160: If A $\neq$ 0, the computer ignores the "THEN 170" in statement 130 and instead moves in order to statement 140. Here the formula developed above is used to compute X. Then statement 150 prints the answer. Statement 160 sends the computer to the statements (210–240) that determine whether the user has any more equations to solve.

EXERCISES See the Solution Key for the Answers to Ex. 13-16.

A Write each equation in the form $ax + b = c$. Then use the program on page 110 to solve the equation.

1. $71 = 5x - 3$
2. $89 + 10x = 284$
3. $104 - 15x = 73$
4. $234 = 45 + 21x$
5. $804 = 66 - 34x$
6. $1245 - 125x = 1542$
7. $54 + 0x = 120$
8. $81 = 81 - 0x$
9. $99 = 12 + 0x$
10. $4x + 83 + 7x = 135$
11. $25x - 75 - 12x = 90$
12. $342 = 17x - 135 + 14x$

Write a BASIC program for each problem.

13. Given the measures of two angles of a triangle, compute and print the measure of the third angle. Use the following formula. (See page 100.)
$$A + B + C = 180$$

14. Given the perimeter of a square, compute and print the length of the side. Use the following formula. (See page 10.)
$$P = 4s$$

15. Given the average of three numbers and two of the numbers, compute and print the third number. Use the following formula.
$$A = \frac{x + y + z}{3}$$

16. Given the winning percentage of a sports team, p, and the number of games played, g, compute and print the number of games won, w. Use the following formula.
$$P = \frac{w}{g} \cdot 100$$

Quiz: Sections 3-5–3-8
After completing this Review you may want to administer a quiz covering the same sections. See page M-44 of the Teacher's Manual for the suggested quiz.

Review

Solve and check each equation. *(Section 3–5)*

1. $8x - 5x = 9$ $x = 3$

2. $4y + 5y - 2y = 14$ $y = 2$

3. $18 = 3(4a - 2)$ $a = 2$

4. $0.02m + 0.83m = 1.70$ $m = 2$

5. $\frac{1}{4}x + \frac{3}{8}x = 3\frac{1}{5}$ $x = 5\frac{3}{25}$

6. $-3 - 4(a - 3) = 17$ $a = -2$

In Exercises 7–8 use the formula $A + B + C = 180°$ where A, B, and C represent the measures of the angles of a triangle. *(Section 3–6)*

7. The measure of one angle of a triangle is 30°. The measure of a second angle is 55°. Find the measure of the remaining angle. 95°

8. The measure of one angle of a triangle is 120°. The measure of each of the other angles can be represented by $6x$. Find the measures of these angles. 30°; 30°

Solve. *(Section 3–7)*

9. 30% of 40 is what number? 12

10. What per cent of 16 is 9? $56\frac{1}{4}$

11. Jaime bought a suit at a "15% off" sale and saved $30. What was the original price of the suit? $200

12. A living room set that originally cost $800 is on sale for $720. What is the rate of discount? 10%

(Section 3–8)

13. Find three consecutive integers whose sum is 30. 9; 10; 11

14. The sum of two consecutive even integers is 46. Find the integers. 22; 24

15. Find four consecutive integers such that the sum of the first and third is 84. 41; 42; 43; 44

16. Find two consecutive odd integers whose sum is -28. -15; -13

Chapter Summary

IMPORTANT TERMS

Equivalent equations (p. 84)
Per cent (p. 103)

Solution set (p. 87)

IMPORTANT IDEAS

1. **Addition Property for Equations:** Adding the same number to each side of an equation results in an equivalent equation.

2. The replacement set for the variables in equations is the set of real numbers, unless it is otherwise stated.

3. **Multiplication Property for Equations:** Multiplying each side of an equation by the same nonzero number results in an equivalent equation.

4. You solve a formula for one of the variables in the same way as you solve an equation.

5. When parentheses within an equation indicate multiplication, use the distributive postulate to multiply.

112   *Chapter 3*

6. **Steps for Solving Equations**

    ☐1 Use the distributive postulate.

    ☐2 Combine like terms.

    ☐3 Use the addition property for equations.

    ☐4 Use the multiplication property for equations.

    ☐5 Check the equation.

7. To find the per cent of increase or decrease, first find the amount of increase or decrease. Then compare with the original amount and write a per cent.

8. **Steps for Solving Word Problems Involving Integers**

    ☐1 Choose a variable. Use the variable to represent the integers.

    ☐2 Write an equation for the word sentence.

    ☐3 Solve the equation and find the integers.

    ☐4 Check in the statement of the problem.

——— Chapter Objectives and Review ———

Objective: *To use the addition property for equations to solve equations (Section 3–1)*

Solve and check each equation.

1. $x + 9 = 15$ $x = 6$

2. $-8 + n = 0$ $n = 8$

3. $-14 + t = 7$

4. $k - (-10) = 5\frac{1}{2}$ $k = -4\frac{1}{2}$

5. $r - \frac{1}{5} = 4\frac{4}{5}$ $r = 5$

6. $-2.9 + z = 11.3$

Objective: *To use the multiplication property for equations to solve equations (Section 3–2)*

Solve and check each equation.

7. $4x = 12$ $x = 3$

8. $-3c = 18$ $c = -6$

9. $7.5x = 1.5$

10. $\frac{3}{5}t = 21$ $t = 35$

11. $-m = \frac{4}{9}$ $m = -\frac{4}{9}$

12. $-\frac{y}{8} = 1\frac{1}{16}$

Objective: *To use the addition and multiplication properties for equations to solve equations (Section 3–3)*

Solve and check each equation.

13. $3x + 7 = 19$ $x = 4$

14. $11 - \frac{4}{5}m = 3$ $m = 10$

15. $0.4t - 1.3 = 0.3$

Objective: *To use formulas to solve word problems (Section 3–4)*

16. The formula for the width of material, M, needed to make n pleats where each pleat is p inches wide is $M = 3np$. Find the number of $\frac{5}{8}$-inch pleats that can be made from material that is 45 inches wide.   24

17. The formula for a salesperson's weekly wages, W, is $W = \$315 + 0.05A$, where A represents the amount of total weekly sales. Find his total weekly sales if his wages for this week were $352.74.
$754.80

Solving Equations   **113**

Objective: *To solve equations involving like terms (Section 3–5)*

Use the distributive postulate to find each product.

18. $3(x - 7)$ $3x - 21$ **19.** $-1(m + 6)$ $-m - 6$ **20.** $11(3y - 2)$ $33y - 22$ **21.** $-5(5 - a)$

Solve and check each equation.

22. $14n - 3n = -44$ $n = -4$ **23.** $3b + 11 - 8b = -24$ **24.** $8(4 + y) = 16$

25. $-9(7 - k) - 27 = -90$ $k = 0$ **26.** $-4 - (6 - 2t) = -12$ **27.** $1.2r + 4 + 3.2 = 10.8$

Objective: *To use equations to solve word problems involving geometric formulas (Section 3–6)*

In Exercises 28–30, find the measure of each angle of the triangles. Use the formula $A + B + C = 180°$.

28. Right Triangle $\quad$ **29.** Acute Triangle $\quad$ **30.** Obtuse Triangle

$20°; 70°; 90°$ $\qquad$ $40°; 60°; 80°$

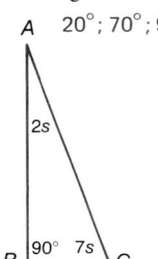
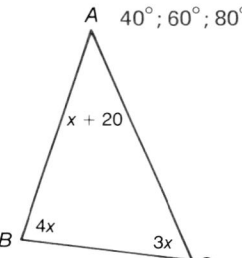
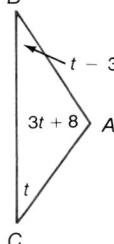

Objective: *To solve percent problems (Section 3–7)*

31. 25% of 68 is what number? 17

32. 3.5% of what number is 7? 200

33. What per cent of 38 is 57? 150%

34. 2% of 75 is what number? 1.5

35. The price of a home computer is $1800. Ronald made a down payment of 20% when he bought it. How much was the down payment? $360

36. A basketball team won 15 games. That was $62\frac{1}{2}\%$ of the games played. How many games did the team play? 24

37. A dealer bought an antique clock for $375 and sold it for $450. What was the per cent of profit? 20%

38. The enrollment at a college increased from 1850 to 2175. Find the per cent of increase, to the nearest whole per cent. 17%

Objective: *To solve integer problems (Section 3–8)*

Solve each problem.

39. Find three consecutive even integers whose sum is 126. 40; 42; 44

40. Find two consecutive integers such that three times the smaller increased by twice the larger equals -43. 2; 3

114 *Chapter 3*

Chapter Test

A formal Chapter Test is provided in the Teacher's Manual. See p. M-66.

Solve and check each equation.

1. $5 + z = 23$ $z = 18$

2. $9k = -72$ $k = -8$

3. $t - (-4.3) = 0$

4. $\frac{r}{7} = 6$ $r = 42$

5. $x - 3\frac{1}{4} = 11$ $x = 14\frac{1}{4}$

6. $-\frac{1}{9}y = 1\frac{2}{3}$

7. $\frac{1}{3}p - 4 = -2$ $p = 6$

8. $14w + 6 = 13$ $w = \frac{1}{2}$

9. $\frac{v}{15} - 9 = -16$

10. $7a + 11a = 9$ $a = \frac{1}{2}$

11. $6b - 4b + 3 = 11$ $b = 4$

12. $5(-3c - 8) = 35$

13. $12d - 3(d - 1) = 15$ $d = 1\frac{1}{3}$

14. $6 = 3 - (f + 7)$ $f = -10$

15. $\frac{3}{4}g + 7 + \frac{1}{4}g = 7$

16. A broker's weekly wage, W, amounted to \$390.52. Use the formula $W = \$370 + 0.02A$ to find A, the broker's total amount of weekly sales.   \$1026

17. The angles of a triangle measure b, $2b + 20$, and $b + 20$. Find the measure of each angle. Use the formula $A + B + C = 180°$, where A, B, and C represent the measures of the angles of the triangle. $35°; 55°; 90°$

18. Paul bought boots at a "30% off" sale. The original price was \$42. How much did he save?   \$12.60

19. Find two consecutive even integers whose sum is 70.   35; 36

20. Find three consecutive odd integers whose sum is 171.   55; 57; 59

Additional Practice
You may wish to use all or some of these exercises, depending on how well students performed on the formal chapter test.

Skills

Solve and check each equation. *(Sections 3–1, 3–2, 3–3)*

1. $x + 9 = 17$ $x = 8$

2. $16 = r - 7$ $r = 23$

3. $s + 3.1 = 0$

4. $t - (-7) = 21$ $t = 14$

5. $y + \frac{1}{2} = 3\frac{1}{4}$ $y = 2\frac{3}{4}$

6. $\frac{2}{5} = b - 4\frac{1}{5}$

7. $8n = 32$ $n = 4$

8. $2.2m = -8.8$ $m = -4$

9. $-v = \frac{7}{8}$

10. $\frac{c}{10} = 15$ $c = 150$

11. $\frac{d}{3} = -4.3$ $d = -12.9$

12. $-\frac{5}{9} = \frac{f}{6}$

13. $4g + 7 = 27$ $g = 5$

14. $3h - 3 = -15$ $h = -4$

15. $\frac{2}{3}j + 6 = 16$

16. $3 = -\frac{2}{11}u + 9$ $u = 33$

17. $1.7w - 0.44 = 5$ $w = 3.2$

18. $-0.9k + 8 = 3.5$

19. If $z + 7 = 13$, find the value of $4z$.   24

20. If $6p - 9 = -39$, find the value of $2p$. -10

Use the distributive postulate to find each product. *(Section 3–5)*

21. $6(x - 9)$

22. $-4(n + 7)$

23. $(12 - y)6$

24. $-1(7x - 8)$

25. $-4(-3 + 4y)$

26. $8(2a - 6)$

27. $-3(4 - 5a)$

28. $-2(-8 - 5b)$

Solving Equations   **115**

Solve and check each equation. *(Section 3-5)*

29. $3y + 5y = -40$ $y = -5$

30. $-19 = 4a - 3$ $a = -4$

31. $-36 = 7b - b$

32. $4(3x - 7) = 32$ $x = 5$

33. $2c - 1(c + 6) = 11$ $c = 17$

34. $-1.6r + 7(r - 1) = 3.8$

Solve. *(Section 3-7)*

35. 8% of 175 is what number?   14

36. What per cent of 120 is 45? $37\frac{1}{2}$%

37. 27% of 200 is what number?   54

38. 32% of what number is 32?   100

Applications

In Exercises 39 and 40, use the formula $M = 3np$, where M is the width of material needed to make n pleats that are p inches wide. *(Section 3-4)*

39. A skirt having 25 pleats is to be made from material that is 50 inches wide. Find the width of each pleat. $\frac{3}{5}$ inch

40. How many $\frac{1}{2}$-inch pleats can be made from material that is 45 inches wide?   30

In Exercises 41 and 42, use the formula $R = 3.50A + 1.50C$, where R represents the total ticket receipts collected at the Trylon Theater when A adult tickets and C children's tickets are sold. *(Section 3-4)*

41. On Friday, total receipts at the Trylon Theater were $920 and 100 children's tickets were sold. How many adult tickets were sold?   220

42. For the Sunday matinee, 58 adult tickets were sold and total receipts were $542. How many children's tickets were sold?   226

In Exercises 43-45, find the measure of each angle. Use the formula $A + B + C = 180°$. *(Section 3-6)*

43. Acute Triangle
$40°; 60°; 80°$

44. Isosceles Triangle
$45\frac{1}{2}°; 45\frac{1}{2}°; 89°$

45. Isosceles Right Triangle
$45°; 45°; 90°$

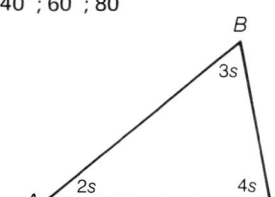

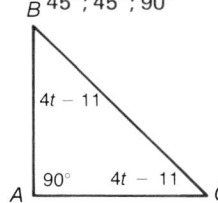

Solve each problem. *(Sections 3-7, 3-8)*

46. The value of an antique pewter pitcher increased 350% in the last ten years. If it was valued at $92 ten years ago, what is its value now? $322

47. Jill received a 6% increase in wages, bringing her earnings to $4.77 per hour. What did she earn per hour before she got the raise? $4.50

48. The sum of two consecutive integers is 49. Find the integers.   24; 25

49. The sum of two consecutive odd integers is -32. Find the integers.

CHAPTER **4 Equations and Inequalities**

Problem Solving and Applications

OBJECTIVE: To represent word expressions by algebraic symbols

Teaching Suggestions p. M-17

4–1   From Words to Symbols

Translating word expressions to algebraic expressions is an essential skill in solving word problems. This table shows that the *same* algebraic symbol of operation can be used to translate *more than one* word expression.

	Word Expression	Algebraic Expression
Addition Expressions	The **sum** of a number, t, and -3	$t + (-3)$
	$z°$ **plus** $1.9°$	$z + 1.9$
	Add $7\frac{1}{2}$ to k.	$k + 7\frac{1}{2}$
	\$50 **more than** d dollars	$d + 50$
	$-\frac{7}{8}$ **increased by** n	$-\frac{7}{8} + n$
	Increase t by 3.9.	$t + 3.9$
	The **total** of 16 and $-r$	$16 + (-r)$
Subtraction Expressions	x **minus** $2\frac{3}{8}$	$x - 2\frac{3}{8}$
	The **difference** of \$60 and \$$b$	$60 - b$
	The **difference between** \$60 and \$$b$	$60 - b$
	Subtract 7.8 **from** n.	$n - 7.8$
	t **decreased by** -8	$t - (-8)$
	a **diminished by** -1	$a - (-1)$
	$y°$ **less** $5°$	$y - 5$
	$y°$ **less than** $5°$	$5 - y$
Multiplication Expressions	1.7 **times** z	$1.7z$
	b **multiplied by** $\frac{2}{3}$	$\frac{2}{3}b$, or $\frac{2b}{3}$
	The **product** of 5 and g	$5g$
	Twice m centimeters	$2m$
	Triple the width, w	$3w$
Division Expressions	The **cost**, c, **divided by** 12	$c \div 12$, or $\frac{c}{12}$
	The **quotient of** y and 15	$y \div 15$, or $\frac{y}{15}$
	The **quotient** of 15 and y	$15 \div y$, or $\frac{15}{y}$

Note carefully how these two subtraction expressions differ.

$y°$ less $5°$ **is not the same as** $y°$ less than $5°$.

$y - 5$ **is not the same as** $5 - y$.

To translate a word expression to an algebraic expression, follow this procedure.

Procedure

> **To represent a word expression by algebraic symbols:**
> 1. Choose a variable. Tell what it represents.
> 2. Identify the key word or words that indicate which operation to use.
> 3. Represent the word expression by symbols.

EXAMPLE

Use algebraic symbols to represent each word expression.

a. 1.5 seconds more than Amy's record time.

b. The amount of the car loan divided by 36, the number of monthly payments.

Solutions:

a. 1. Let t = Amy's record time.

2. 1.5 seconds more than t 3. $t + 1.5$

b. 1. Let a = the amount of the car loan.

2. a divided by 36   3. $a \div 36$, or $\dfrac{a}{36}$

Additional Examples
Use algebraic symbols to represent each word expression.
1. **a.** 3.5 centimeters more than the perimeter of a rectangle
   Ans: $p + 3.5$
   b. 8 meters less than the height of a house
   Ans: $h - 8$
2. **a.** The amount of Muriel's pay check divided by 35, the number of hours worked
   Ans: $p \div 35$, or $\dfrac{p}{35}$
   b. The cost of a pencil multiplied by 12, the number of pencils Ray bought
   Ans: $12c$

CLASSROOM EXERCISES

In Exercises 1–18, choose from the box at the right the algebraic expression that represents each word expression. More than one answer may be possible in some cases.

1. The product of y and (-6) $-6y$

2. y minus 6 $y - 6$

3. 6 plus y $6 + y$ or $y + 6$

4. y increased by 6 $y + 6$ or $6 + y$

5. Subtract 6 from y. $y - 6$

6. The quotient of y and (-6) $\dfrac{y}{-6}$

7. Six times y $6y$

8. y more than 6 $6 + y$ or $y + 6$

9. Subtract y from 6. $6 - y$

10. 6 less y $6 - y$

11. 6 less than y $y - 6$

12. The product of (-6) and y $-6y$

13. The quotient of (-6) and y $\dfrac{-6}{y}$

14. -6 multiplied by y $-6y$

15. y divided by (-6) $\dfrac{y}{-6}$

16. The sum of 6 and y

17. 6 divided by twice y $\dfrac{6}{2y}$

18. 6 diminished by y $6 - y$

$y + 6$	$6 + y$
$y - 6$	$6 - y$
$-6y$	$6y$
$\dfrac{y}{-6}$	$\dfrac{-6}{y}$
$y \div 6$	$6 \div y$
$\dfrac{2y}{6}$	$\dfrac{6}{2y}$

16. $6 + y$ or $y + 6$

Equations and Inequalities   **119**

Assignment Guide
Minimal
pp. 120–121: 2–58 even
Average
pp. 120–121: 2–64 even
Above Average
pp. 120–121: 16–58 even,
59–64

WORD PROBLEMS

A   Represent each word expression by an algebraic expression.

1. The difference of 25 and n $25 - n$
2. 16 more than $(-r)$ $(-r) + 16$
3. The total of x and $(-6\frac{1}{4})$ $x + (-6\frac{1}{4})$
4. y decreased by 19.3 $y - 19.3$
5. Subtract b from (-9). $-9 - b$
6. 19.1 increased by x $19.1 + x$
7. $\frac{1}{2}$ plus $(-a)$ $\frac{1}{2} + (-a)$
8. $-18\frac{2}{3}$ minus $(-r)$ $-18\frac{2}{3} - (-r)$
9. t less (-100) $t - (-100)$
10. t less than (-100) $-100 - t$
11. n increased by $\frac{4}{5}$ $n + \frac{4}{5}$
12. The sum of x and $(-x)$ $x + (-x)$
13. 4 less than r $r - 4$
14. a increased by $\frac{5}{8}$ $a + \frac{5}{8}$
15. 5 less s $5 - s$
16. -2 subtracted from m $m - (-2)$
17. Subtract (-30) from m. $m - (-30)$
18. Subtract m from (-30). $-30 - m$
19. 12 decreased by $|y|$ $12 - |y|$
20. $|y|$ decreased by 12 $|y| - 12$
21. $9\frac{1}{2}$ more than q $q + 9\frac{1}{2}$
22. q more than $9\frac{1}{2}$ $9\frac{1}{2} + q$
23. -0.5 less than r $r - (-0.5)$
24. -0.5 less r $-0.5 - r$
25. r less than (-0.5) $-0.5 - r$
26. r less (-0.5) $r - (-0.5)$
27. The quotient of 9 and x $\frac{9}{x}$
28. The quotient of x and 9 $\frac{x}{9}$
29. q multiplied by 7 $7q$
30. The product of (-2) and q $-2q$
31. Twice p $2p$
32. Three times r $3r$
33. 212 divided by $(-t)$ $\frac{212}{-t}$
34. $(-t)$ divided by 212 $\frac{-t}{212}$
35. z multiplied by $\frac{1}{5}$ $\frac{1}{5}z$ or $\frac{z}{5}$
36. $\frac{1}{5}$ multiplied by z
37. z divided by 5
38. The quotient of z and 5 $\frac{z}{5}$ or $z \div 5$
39. -1 times p $-1p$ or $-p$
40. p times (-1) $p(-1)$ or $-p$
41. The product of r and $\frac{1}{12}$ $r(\frac{1}{12})$ or $\frac{r}{12}$
42. The quotient of t and (-3)
   $t \div (-3)$ or $\frac{t}{-3}$

In Exercises 43–58, first choose a variable and tell what it represents. Then write an algebraic expression for each word expression.

43. Five centimeters more than the width of a rectangle
44. The number of hours worked less $\frac{1}{2}$ hour
45. One-third the perimeter of the base of the Great Pyramid in Egypt
46. The quotient of the distance traveled and the rate, 50 miles per hour
47. The cost of the dinner plus a tip of $5.45
48. Four centimeters less than Bob's height
49. The cost of a new car less the depreciation, $1200
50. The distance traveled divided by the time, 3 hours
51. Twice the air distance from San Francisco to Chicago
52. Fifteen pounds more than the average weight
53. The cost of a tennis racquet minus the discount, $6.90
54. Nine degrees less than the average temperature

Additional Answers

36. $z(\frac{1}{5})$ or $\frac{z}{5}$

37. $\frac{z}{5}$ or $z \div 5$

43. w = width of rectangle; $w + 5$

44. h = number of hours worked; $h - \frac{1}{2}$

45. p = perimeter of a base; $\frac{1}{3}(p)$

46. d = distance travelled; $d \div 50$ or $\frac{d}{50}$

47. c = cost of dinner; $c + 5.45$

48. h = Bob's height; $h - 4$

49. c = cost of new car; $c - 1200$

50. d = distance travelled; $d \div 3$ or $\frac{d}{3}$

51. a = air distance; $2a$

52. w = average weight; $w + 15$

53. c = cost of tennis racquet; $c - 6.90$

54. t = average temperature; $t - 9$

55. The number of quarts of oil multiplied by $1.10

56. The quotient of the number of dimes Sally has and 10

57. $20 more than the amount of Jeff's checking account

58. The quotient of $969.50 and the number of tickets sold

B

59. A car travels 6 hours at an average rate of k kilometers per hour. Represent the distance traveled. $6k$

60. A plane travels t hours at an average rate of 320 miles per hour. Represent the distance traveled. $320t$

61. The Nolan family repays a debt of $1200 in equal monthly payments over m months. Represent the amount of each monthly payment.

62. The Martinez family spent a total of $1500 for a vacation that lasted d days. Represent the average cost per day.

63. Last year, Glenda paid $3500 in gasoline and maintenance costs for her car. She used the car to travel m miles. Represent the average cost per mile.

$\dfrac{3500}{m}$ or $3500 \div m$

64. Richard had a total of 23 hits in k times at bat. Represent his batting average. (HINT: Batting average = Times at bat ÷ Number of hits)

$k \div 23$ or $\dfrac{k}{23}$

CALCULATOR APPLICATIONS

A Paper Caper

You can use a calculator to find the thickness of a folded piece of paper. You may be surprised at how quickly the thickness can build up!

EXAMPLE A sheet of paper 0.0015 inch thick is folded in half 15 times. Find the thickness.

SOLUTION Each fold doubles the thickness of the paper. For example,

$$1 \text{ fold} = 2 \times 0.0015 \text{ inch.}$$
$$2 \text{ folds} = 2 \times 2 \times 0.0015 \text{ inch (or } 2^2 \times 0.0015)$$
$$\vdots$$
$$15 \text{ folds} = 2^{15} \times 0.0015 \text{ inch}$$

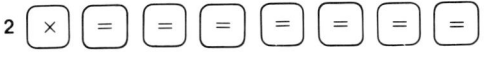 ← Press $=$ 14 times.

 $\boxed{49.152}$

The folded sheet will be **about 49 inches thick.**

EXERCISES

In Exercises 1–4, find the thickness of the sheet of paper. Round your answers to the nearest inch.

1. Folded 12 times
   6 in

2. Folded 16 times
   98 in

3. Folded 20 times
   1573 in

4. Folded 25 times
   50,332 in

Equations and Inequalities   **121**

Quick Quiz
Use algebraic symbols to
represent each word
expression.
1. The product of p and $\frac{5}{8}$
   Ans: $\frac{5}{8}p$
2. $50 less than the amount
   of money in Frank's bank
   account
   Ans: $a - 50$
3. The quotient of the number of records Janet has
   and 12
   Ans: $r \div 12$, or $\frac{r}{12}$
4. The cost of a car plus a
   sales tax of $700
   Ans: $c + 700$

Problem Solving and Applications

OBJECTIVE: To use equations to solve word problems with one unknown

4-2 One Unknown

Sometimes a word expression involves more than one arithmetic operation.

Word Expression	Algebraic Expression
Five **more** than 3 **times** a number, n	$3n + 5$
Twice the distance, d, **subtracted from** 1800	$1800 - 2d$
Four times the number of students, s, **divided by** 15	$\frac{4s}{15}$, or $\frac{4}{15}s$
Three more than **twice** the number of girls, g, on the tennis team	$2g + 3$
Twice the amount, a, Earl budgeted for a vacation **less** $125	$2a - 125$
The **quotient** of $3500 and n, the number of monthly payments	$\frac{3500}{n}$

You can use equations to solve word problems. The table below shows word sentences with their corresponding equations. Note that the word "is" is replaced by the "=" symbol.

Word Sentence	Equation
Eighteen more than some number x is 54.	$x + 18 = 54$
16 is 10 less than twice some number, n.	$2n - 10 = 16$
The product of some number q and 0.3 is 78.	$0.3q = 78$
The quotient of three times an unknown number, p, and 5 is 21.	$\frac{3p}{5} = 21$
When the sum of 12 and an unknown number, t, is divided by 3, the result is 8.	$\frac{12 + t}{3} = 8$

This procedure will help you to solve word problems having one unknown.

Procedure

> **To solve word problems having one unknown:**
> 1. Choose a variable to represent the unknown.
> 2. Write an equation for the problem.
> 3. Solve the equation.
> 4. Check your answer with the statements in the problem. Answer the question.

NOTE: The steps in the Example correspond to the steps in the procedure.

122 *Chapter 4*

EXAMPLE When $78 is subtracted from the amount in Fred's checking account, the balance (amount remaining) is $31. How much is in the account?

Solution: ① Let a = the amount in the account.

② $a - 78 = 31$ ◄——— **78 subtracted from a is 31.**

③ $a - 78 + 78 = 31 + 78$

$a = 109$

Check: ④ Does $109 - 78 = 31$? Yes ✔ There is **$109** in the account.

Additional Examples
1. When $87 is deposited in Florence's checking account, the balance is $120. How much was in the account? **Ans: $33**
2. The cost of a coat less a discount of $49.95 is $200. What is cost of the coat? **Ans: $249.95**

CLASSROOM EXERCISES

Use algebraic symbols to represent each word expression.

1. The quotient of twice an unknown number, p, and 7 $\frac{2p}{7}$

2. Three times some number, g, less 48.1 $3g - 48.1$

3. The sum of 150 and three times the number of pages, p $150 + 3p$

4. Ten less than three times John's score, s $3s - 10$

5. Twenty-five kilometers more than twice the distance, d, traveled by the Stealle family $2d + 25$

6. The difference between the number of coins in the piggy bank, c, and 412 $c - 412$

Write an equation to represent each word sentence.

7. An unknown number, z, increased by $1\frac{3}{4}$ equals 20. $z + 1\frac{3}{4} = 20$

8. The quotient of an unknown number, n, and 7 equals 6.9. $\frac{n}{7} = 6.9$

9. Two hundred decreased by an unknown number, t, is $71\frac{3}{4}$. $200 - t = 71\frac{3}{4}$

10. Two-thirds of a certain number, r, is 40. $\frac{2}{3}(r) = 40$ or $\frac{2r}{3} = 40$

11. The total of 9 and one-half of a certain number, n, is 29. $9 + \frac{n}{2} = 29$

12. The product of a number, q, and 15 is 255. $15q = 255$

WORD PROBLEMS

🅐 Use algebraic symbols to represent each word expression.

1. Three times Beth's age, a, minus 2 years $3a - 2$

2. Three dollars more than four times the amount, t, that Phil has $4t + 3$

3. Twenty less than twice the number of marathon runners, r $2r - 20$

4. Five degrees more than twice the present temperature, t $2t + 5°$

5. The quotient of four times the amount of the loan, l, and 5 $\frac{4l}{5}$ or $4l \div 5$

6. The product of the rate, r, and 3.5 divided by 4 $\frac{3.5r}{4}$ or $3.5r \div 4$

7. The product of 25 and the number of quarters, n, divided by 100 $\frac{25n}{100}$ or $25n \div 100$

8. Three times the amount budgeted for food, f, decreased by $25 $3f - 25$

9. The amount of the bill, b, increased by the product of 0.15 and b $b + 0.15b$

10. The quotient of $1200 and five times a round-trip fare, r $\frac{1200}{5r}$ or $1200 \div 5r$

Equations and Inequalities **123**

Assignment Guide
Minimal
pp. 123–124: 1–31 odd
Average
pp. 123–124: 1–40 odd
Above Average
pp. 123–124: 3, 6, 9, . . . 24, 27–40

Write an equation to represent each word sentence.

11. Nineteen more than an unknown number, t, is 42.6. $t + 19 = 42.6$

12. Ninety-seven is 17 less than a certain number, r. $97 = r - 17$

13. The quotient of a number, n, and 14 is 9. $\frac{n}{14} = 9$

14. The product of some number, q, and 24 equals 356. $24q = 356$

15. The difference between 4 times a number, z, and 3 is 35. $4z - 3 = 35$

16. Two-thirds of a number, z, equals 40. $\frac{2}{3}z = 40$

17. One-third of a number, t, increased by 7 equals 23. $\frac{t}{3} + 7 = 23$

18. The sum of 38 and $\frac{5}{9}$ of a certain number, p, is 128. $38 + \frac{5}{9}p = 128$

19. The quotient of 5 times a certain number, b, and 3 is 100. $\frac{5b}{3} = 100$

20. Eight less than 6 times some number, p, is 10. $6p - 8 = 10$

21. Twelve times a number, c, minus 6 equals 60. $12c - 6 = 60$

22. The total of 9 and one-half of a certain number, c, is 29. $9 + \frac{1}{2}c = 29$

23. When the quotient of a certain number, q, and 6 is decreased by 14, the result is 4. $\frac{q}{6} - 14 = 4$

24. When the quotient of 3 times a certain number, t, and 2 is increased by 12, the result is 39. $\frac{3t}{2} + 12 = 39$

25. When the product of 4 and a certain number, s, is diminished by 8, the result is -4. $4s - 8 = -4$

26. When the sum of an unknown number, c, and 9 is multiplied by 5, the result is 35. $(c + 9)5 = 35$

Solve each problem. Follow the steps of the procedure on page 122.

27. When $102 is added to the amount in Jill's checking account, the total is $461.70. How much is in Jill's account? $359.70

28. Thirty-nine kilometers more than the distance traveled by the Blair family is 721 kilometers. How far did they travel? 682 km

29. Last year's interest increased by $41.50 equals $72.80. Find the amount of last year's interest. $31.30

30. Seven and one-half times the number of voters in the election is 90,000. How many persons voted? 12,000 voters

31. Twice the cost of a pair of skis decreased by $60 equals $225. Find the cost of the skis. $142.50

32. Four times the perimeter of the parking lot less 16 is 2000 yards. What is the perimeter of the lot? 504 yd

33. The amount of the Ohira family's electric bill divided by 375 kilowatt-hours equals $0.22. Find the amount of the bill. $82.50

34. The amount of last month's telephone bill, decreased by the product of 3 and 0.30, equals $131.95. Find the amount of the bill. $132.85

35. Sixteen less than seven times the number of sandwiches is 264. How many sandwiches are there? 40

36. The quotient of four times the number of cars and 15 decreased by 7 is 105. Find the number of cars. 420

37. Three times the number of words Dot types per minute increased by 14 is 194. How many words does Dot type per minute? 60

38. The quotient of the number of pages in a telephone directory and 9 is increased by 500. The result is 2128. How many pages are in the directory? 14,652

39. The sum of three times a number and 33 is 51. Find the number. 6

40. One hundred less than 6 times a number is 26. Find the number. 21

Combine like terms. *(Pages 60–63)*

1. $7(5y + 4) + 8(1 + 3y)$
$59y + 36$

2. $5p - 2(4 + 3p) + 6p$
$5p - 8$

3. $-3(8 - 3z) + 9(4 - 3z)$
$-18z + 12$

Solve and check each equation. *(Pages 97–99)*

4. $15 + 9 = 8d - 3d + 1$

5. $7x - 8x + 2 = -9$ $x = 11$

6. $6 - 3x - x = 30$ $x = -6$

7. $9t + 7 - t = 35$ $t = \frac{7}{2}$ or $3\frac{1}{2}$

8. $29 = 3t - 1 - t$ $t = 15$

9. $4 - x - 3x = 0$ $x = 1$

4. $d = \frac{23}{5}$ or $4\frac{3}{5}$

Problem Solving and Applications

OBJECTIVE: To solve word problems by first identifying two conditions

4–3 Identifying Conditions

In some word problems, one condition tells how the unknown quantities are related. Call this Condition 1 and use this condition to represent the unknowns.

A second condition tells what quantities are equal. Call this Condition 2 and use this condition to write an equation. Then solve the equation.

EXAMPLE 1 Felipe is thinking of two numbers. The larger is 5 more than twice the smaller (Condition 1). Their sum is 47 (Condition 2). Find the numbers.

Solution: $\boxed{1}$ Use Condition 1 to represent the unknowns.

Let $x =$ the smaller number.
Then $2x + 5 =$ the larger number.

$\boxed{2}$ Use Condition 2 to write an equation.

$x + (2x + 5) = 47$ ◄——— **The sum of the numbers is 47.**

$\boxed{3}$ Solve the equation.

$x + 2x + 5 = 47$ ◄——— **Combine like terms.**

$3x + 5 = 47$ ◄——— **Add (−5) to each side.**

$3x = 42$ ◄——— **Multiply each side by $\frac{1}{3}$.**

$x = 14$ ◄——— **Don't forget to find 2x + 5.**

$2x + 5 = 2(14) + 5 = 33$

Check: $\boxed{4}$ **Condition 1**   Does $33 = 2(14) + 5$?   Yes ✔
Condition 2 $14 + 33 = 47$?   Yes ✔

The numbers are **14** and **33**.

The procedure on page 126 summarizes the steps shown in Example 1.

Equations and Inequalities   **125**

Review Capsule
This Review Capsule reviews the prior taught skills used in Section 4-3. The reference is to the pages where the skills were taught.

Teaching Suggestions p. M-17

Quick Quiz
1. The cost of a book plus a sales tax of $0.63 equals $9.58. Find the cost of the book.
Ans: $8.95
2. This year's interest decreased by $63.90 equals $102.10. Find the amount of this year's interest.
Ans: $166

Additional Examples
Example 1
1. Nancy is thinking of two numbers. The larger is 5 more than twice the smaller. Their sum is 56. Find the numbers.
Ans: 17 and 39
2. One number is 2 more than 4 times another. Their sum is 27. What are the numbers?
Ans: 5 and 22

Procedure

> **Steps for Solving Word Problems**
>
> 1. Identify Condition 1. Use this condition to represent the unknowns.
> 2. Identify Condition 2. Use this condition to write an equation for the problem.
> 3. Solve the equation.
> 4. Check the results with the two conditions. Answer the question(s).

NOTE: The steps in the Examples correspond to the steps in the procedure.

Additional Examples
Example 2

1. The total number of pages in two books is 1024. The science book has 128 less than twice the number of pages in the algebra book. Find the number of pages in the science book.
Ans: 640
2. The sum of two numbers is 32. The larger number is 8 less than four times the smaller number. What is the larger number?
Ans: 24

EXAMPLE 2   The total number of apartments in two buildings is 348 (Condition 2). The Fair View apartment building has 12 less than three times the number of apartments in the Tulip Vista apartment complex (Condition 1). Find the number of apartments in Fair View.

Solution:
1. Let a = the number of apartments in Tulip Vista.
   Then $3a - 12$ = the number in Fair View.
2. $a + (3a - 12) = 348$
3. $\quad 4a - 12 = 348$
   $\qquad 4a = 360$
   $\qquad a = 90$ ◄——— **Don't forget to find $3a - 12$.**
   $\quad 3a - 12 = 258$

Check:
4. **Condition 1**   Does $258 = 3(90) - 12$?   Yes ✔
   Condition 2 $90 + 258 = 348$?   Yes ✔

Fair View has **258** apartments.

CLASSROOM EXERCISES

With each sentence in Exercises 1–8, match the corresponding item in **a–h**.

1. The larger number is 1 more than twice the smaller. e

2. The smaller of two numbers is 1 less than the larger. b

3. The larger of two numbers is 8 times the smaller. h

4. The smaller of two numbers is 8 less than twice the larger. f

5. One number is twice another. a

a. Let h = first number.
   Then $2h$ = second number.

b. Let q = larger number.
   Then $q - 1$ = smaller number.

c. Let x = larger number.
   Then $x - 2$ = smaller number.

d. Let p = smaller number.
   Then $3p + 9$ = larger number.

e. Let t = smaller number.
   Then $2t + 1$ = larger number.

6. One number is two less than another. c

7. One number is 9 more than 3 times a second number. d

8. One number is 3 less than 9 times another. g

f. Let a = larger number.
   Then $2a - 8$ = smaller number.

g. Let w = first number.
   Then $9w - 3$ = second number.

h. Let r = smaller number.
   Then $8r$ = larger number.

WORD PROBLEMS

A Solve each problem.

In some problems, one condition is underscored once. Use this condition to represent the unknowns. A second condition is underscored twice. Use this condition to write an equation for the problem.

1. One number is 5 times another. The sum of the numbers is 72. Find the numbers. 12; 60

2. One number is 5 more than a second number. The sum of the numbers is 115. Find the numbers. 55; 60

3. One number is 4 less than another. The sum of the numbers is 20. Find the numbers. 12; 8

4. The sum of two numbers is 21. One number is 3 less than the other. Find the numbers. 12; 9

5. One number minus a smaller number is 18. The larger number is 3 times the smaller. Find the numbers. 9; 27

6. The sum of two numbers is 110. One of the numbers is 7 less than twice the second. Find the numbers. 39; 71

7. One number is $\frac{2}{3}$ of another. The sum of the numbers is 50. What are the numbers? 30; 20

8. The larger of two numbers is 12 more than the smaller. The sum of the numbers is 36. What are the numbers? 12; 24

9. The smaller of two numbers is 10 less than the larger. The sum of the numbers is 76. What are the numbers? 33; 43

10. A number is 7 more than five times another number. The sum of the numbers is 55. Find the numbers. 8; 47

11. The sum of three numbers is 72. The first is three times the second and the third is twice the result of subtracting 6 from the second. Find the numbers.

12. The sum of three numbers is 64. The second number is 3 more than the first. The third number is 11 less than twice the first. Find the numbers. 18; 21; 25

13. The second of three numbers is 4 times the first. The third number is 1 more than the second. Their sum is 73. Find the numbers. 8; 32; 33

14. The second of two numbers is 16 less than 3 times the first. The sum of the two numbers is 64. What are the numbers? 20; 44

15. Together, Bob and Dan earned $52. Bob earned 3 times as much as Dan. How much did each boy earn?

16. Louisa is $\frac{3}{4}$ as tall as Carla. The difference between their heights is 0.4 meters. How tall is each girl?

17. A coat costs $35.50 more than a dress. The total cost of both items is $161.30. How much does each cost?

18. A house and a lot are sold for $140,000. The house costs 1.5 times as much as the lot. How much does each cost?

Equations and Inequalities   **127**

Assignment Guide
Minimal
Day 1 p. 127: 1–15
Day 2 pp. 127–128: 16–22
Average
pp. 127–128: 2–28 even
Above Average
pp. 127–128: 2–28 even, 29–32

Additional Answers
11. 42; 14; 16
15. $13 = Dan's earnings;
    $39 = Bob's earnings
16. 1.6m = Carla's height;
    1.2m = Louisa's height
17. $62.90 = cost of dress;
    $98.40 = cost of coat
18. $56,000 = cost of lot;
    $84,000 = cost of house

19. The number of persons entering the A–Z Department Store at 10 A.M. one day was 235 more than at 10 A.M. the next day. The total for both days was 885. How many persons entered the store at 10 A.M. on each day?

20. Together, Carol and Dick own 152 shares of stock in Sierra Engineering Corporation. Carol owns 4 less than twice the number of shares that Dick owns. How many shares of stock does each person own?

21. The amount of the Yang family's electric bill for June was $14.81 less than the gas bill. The total bill for gas and electricity was $97.63. Find the amount of each bill.

22. The Harris family's telephone bill for October was $63.80. The cost of long distance calls was $41.96 more than the cost for local calls. Find the cost for long-distance calls.

B   The following terms are used in Exercises 23–28. Be sure that you know the meaning of each term.

> The price of merchandise before it is offered to consumers at a reduced price is called the **list price** or **regular price**.
>
> The amount that an item is reduced is called the **discount.**
>
> The reduced price is called the **sale price.**

23. The rate of discount at a sale is 20%. Jim bought a lamp on sale for $40. Find the list price and the discount. (HINT: Let p = the list price. Then $0.20p$ = the amount of discount and $p - 0.20p = \underline{\quad?\quad}$.)

24. At a kitchen appliance sale, the Gomez family bought a refrigerator that was on sale at a 10% discount. The sale price was $594. Find the list price and the amount of discount on the refrigerator.

25. A camera is on sale for $90.40. The rate of discount is 20%. Find the list price and the amount of discount.

26. An 8–track tape is on sale for $5.10. The rate of discount is 25%. Find the list price and the amount of discount.

27. A clock radio is on sale at a discount rate of 35%. The sale price is $45.50. Find the list price and the amount of discount.

28. The sale price of a television set is $360. The discount rate is 40%. Find the list price and the amount of discount.

C

29. Dick's bank contains an equal number of nickels, dimes and quarters. The total value is $10.00. How many of each kind of coin is there? 25 of each coin

30. Elaine has only dimes and quarters in her purse. The total value is $2.50. There are 3 more quarters than dimes. How many quarters are there? 8

31. A piece of string, 60 centimeters long, is cut into 3 pieces. One piece is 2 centimeters longer than the shortest piece and 2 centimeters shorter than the longest piece. How long is each piece?
18 cm; 20 cm; 22 cm

32. Gina has $2 more than three times the amount that Fred has. When Gina gave Fred $5, Fred than had one–half as much as Gina. How much did Gina have at first? $41

Problem Solving and Applications

OBJECTIVE: To solve measurement problems

4–4 Measurement Problems

The **perimeter**, P, of a geometric figure such as a triangle is the distance around it. To find this distance, add the lengths of the sides.

Triangle

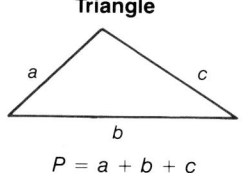

$P = a + b + c$

Rectangle

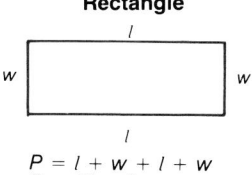

$P = l + w + l + w$
$P = 2l + 2w$

Square

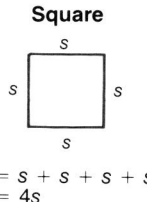

$P = s + s + s + s$
$P = 4s$

To solve problems that involve a geometric figure, follow the steps of this procedure.

Procedure

> **To solve problems involving a geometric figure:**
>
> ☐1 Draw and label the figure.
>
> ☐2–☐5 Follow Steps 1–4 of the Procedure in Section 4–3 on page 126.

The steps in the Example correspond to the steps in the procedure.

EXAMPLE The length of a tennis court for singles is 0.9 meter shorter than three times the width (Condition 1). The perimeter is 63.8 meters (Condition 2). Find the dimensions (length and width) of the court.

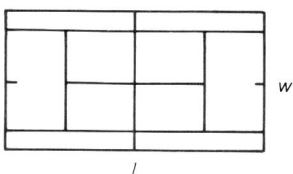

Solution:

☐1 Draw and label a figure.

☐2 Let w = the width.   ◄——— **Represent the unknowns.**
Then $3w - 0.9$ = the length.

☐3 $w + (3w - 0.9) + w + (3w - 0.9) = 63.8$ ◄——— **The perimeter is 63.8 meters.**

☐4 $\qquad\qquad\qquad 8w - 1.8 = 63.8$

$\qquad\qquad\qquad\qquad 8w = 65.6$

$\qquad\qquad\qquad\qquad\ w = 8.2$ ◄——— **Don't forget to find the length.**

$\qquad\quad 3w - 0.9 = 3(8.2) - 0.9 = 23.7$

Check:

☐5 **Condition 1** Does $23.7 = 3(8.2) - 0.9$? Yes ✔

Condition 2 $8.2 + 23.7 + 8.2 + 23.7 = 63.8$? Yes ✔

The width is **8.2 meters** and the length is **23.7 meters.**

Teaching Suggestions p. M-17

Quick Quiz

1. One number is 3 more than 5 times another. Their sum is 45. What are the numbers?
Ans: 7 and 38

2. The sum of two numbers is 29. The larger number is 7 less than three times the smaller number. What is the larger number?
Ans: 20

Additional Examples

1. The length of a picture frame is 0.4 meter shorter than twice the width. The perimeter is 4 meters. Find the dimensions of the frame.
Ans: width: 0.8 m; length: 1.2 m

2. The length of a rectangle is 9 centimeters longer than its width. The perimeter is 50 centimeters. Find the dimensions of the rectangle.
Ans: width: 4 cm; length: 21 cm

Since the figure in the Example is a rectangle, you could also use the formula $P = 2l + 2w$ to find the perimeter. That is,

$$63.8 = 2(3w - 0.9) + 2w \longleftarrow \text{Solve for } w.$$

CLASSROOM EXERCISES

Find the length of each side of each figure.

1. $s = 9$ m

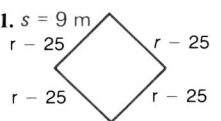

Perimeter: 36 meters

2.

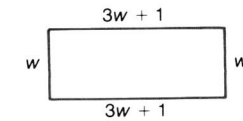

Perimeter: 374 feet

3.

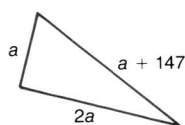

Perimeter: 623 meters

4. $x = 7$ m; $3x = 21$ m; $3x + 2 = 23$ m

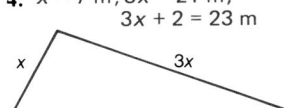

Perimeter: 51 meters

5. $2t = 6$ yd; $t - 1 = 2$ yd

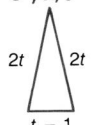

Perimeter: 14 yards

6. $s = 9$ in

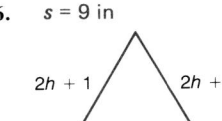

Perimeter: 27 inches

7. $l = 3$ cm; $w = 1.6$ cm

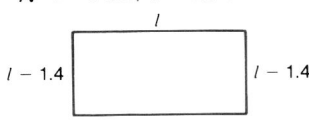

Perimeter: 9.2 centimeters

8. $s = 36$ ft

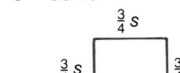

Perimeter: 144 feet

9.

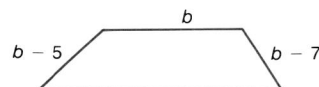

Perimeter: 56 meters

WORD PROBLEMS

A Solve each problem.

In some problems, one condition is <u>underscored once</u>. Use this condition to represent the unknowns. A second condition is <u>underscored twice</u>. Use this condition to write the equation.

1. The length of a rectangle is 7 times its width. The perimeter of the rectangle is 64 centimeters. Find the dimensions of the rectangle. $l = 28$ cm; $w = 4$ cm

2. The length of a rectangle is $2\frac{1}{2}$ times its width. The perimeter of the rectangle is 84 feet. Find the dimensions of the rectangle. $l = 30$ ft; $w = 12$ ft

3. The perimeter of a triangle is 52 inches. The second side is three times the first side and the third side is $2\frac{1}{2}$ times the first side. Find the length of each side of the triangle. 8 in; 24 in; 20 in

4. The lengths of the sides of a triangle can be represented by three consecutive even integers. The perimeter of the triangle is 96 meters. Find the lengths of the sides of the triangle. 30 m; 32 m; 34 m

5. The length of a rectangle is 8 inches more than twice its width. The perimeter is 112 inches. Find the length and width of the rectangle.

6. The width of a badminton court is 8 yards less than its length. The perimeter is $42\frac{2}{3}$ yards. Find the length and width of the court. $\;l = 14\frac{2}{3}$ yd; $w = 6\frac{2}{3}$ yd

7. An isosceles triangle has two equal sides. The third side of an isosceles triangle is 9 centimeters longer than each of the equal sides. The perimeter is 27 centimeters. Find the length of each side. 6 cm; 6 cm; 15 cm

8. Each of the equal sides of an isosceles triangle is 2 feet more than three times the third side. The perimeter is 32 feet. Find the length of each side of the triangle. 14 ft; 14 ft; 4 ft

9. A plane flies 1971 kilometers along a triangular route formed by three cities, Malone, Stockton, and Cooper. The distance from Malone to Stockton is 299 kilometers more than the distance from Stockton to Cooper and the distance from Malone to Cooper is 674 kilometers. Find the distance from Malone to Stockton. 798 km

10. A triangular, 764-kilometer course for a boat race is marked out by three buoys. The distance between the first and second buoys is 3 kilometers more than the distance between the second and third buoys. The distance between the first and third buoys is 281 kilometers. How far is it from the first to the second buoy? 243 km

11. The perimeter of a squash court (rectangular in shape) is 31.2 meters. The length of the court is 1.2 meters more than the width. Find the length and width of the court. 8.4 m; 7.2 m

12. An artist is making a rectangular wooden frame for a painting. The perimeter is 250 centimeters and the length is 1.5 times the width. Find the width and length of the frame.

13. Surveyors working on a freeway placed stakes at points A, B, and C such that the distance from A to C equals the distance from B to C. The distance from A to B is 1.6 times the distance from A to C. The perimeter of the triangle is 1929.6 meters. Find all three distances.

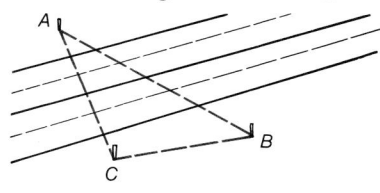

14. The frame of a garage roof forms a triangle having two sloping sides of equal length. The third side of the triangle is 4 feet longer than either of the equal sides and the perimeter of the triangle is 37 feet. Find the length of a sloping side. 11 ft

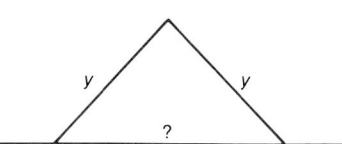

B In Exercises 15–18, recall the following.

The sum of the measures of the angles of a triangle is 180°.

15. In triangle ABC, the measure of angle B is twice the measure of angle A and the measure of angle C is three times the measure of angle A. Find the measure of each angle.
$m\angle A = 30°$; $m\angle B = 60°$; $m\angle C = 90°$

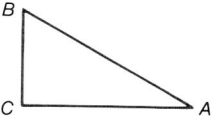

Equations and Inequalities   **131**

16. An isosceles triangle has two angles of equal measure. In isosceles triangle ABC, angles A and B are equal in measure and each of these angles is 20° more than three times the measure of angle C. Find the measure of each angle.

17. In triangle ABC, angle B is 8° more than twice the measure of angle A and angle C is 12° less than the measure of angle A. Find the measure of each angle.

18. In triangle ABC, the measure of angle A is twice the measure of angle B and the measure of angle B is 20° more than the measure of angle C. How many degrees are there in each angle?

19. In triangle DEF, the measure of angle F is three times the measure of angle D and the measure of angle D is 80° less than the measure of angle E. Find the measure of each angle.

C

20. The length of a rectangle is twice its width. When the length is increased by 4 inches and the width is decreased by 1 inch, a new rectangle is formed. The perimeter of the new rectangle is 198 inches. Find the length and width of the original rectangle.

21. A square has four equal sides. When one side of the square is increased by 4 meters and the adjacent side is multiplied by 4, a rectangle is formed. The perimeter of the rectangle is 3 times the perimeter of the original square. Find the length of one side of the square.   4 m

22. The length of a rectangle is 4 feet more than the width. When the width is doubled and the length is decreased by 2 feet, the new rectangle that is formed has a perimeter that is 48 feet more than the perimeter of the original rectangle. Find the width of the original rectangle.   26 ft

23. A hexagon has six sides. Each side of a certain hexagon is 4 centimeters less than the length of a side of a square. The perimeter of the hexagon equals the perimeter of the square. Find the length of a side of the hexagon.   8 cm

Puzzle   See the Solution Key.

Maria invested some money and doubled the amount. After spending $4000, she reinvested the remaining money and tripled the amount. She then spent $5000, and had $10,000 left. How much money did she originally invest?

────── **REVIEW CAPSULE FOR SECTION 4–5** ──────

Multiply. *(Pages 30–33)*

1. $-4(2t + 5)$ $-8t - 20$ **2.** $-3(4y - 5)$ $-12y + 15$ **3.** $-3(2 - 6r)$ $-6 + 18r$ **4.** $-1(4 - 6n)$ $-4 + 6n$

5. $-1(6 - m)$ $-6 + m$ **6.** $-1(x + 9)$ $-x - 9$ **7.** $-1(-1 + b)$ $1 - b$ **8.** $-1(-2x - 3)$ $2x + 3$

4–5 Solving Equations: Variable on Both Sides

Teaching Suggestions p. M-17

In the following equation, terms with the variable, x, appear on both sides of the equation.

$$4x - 6 = x + 9$$

Use the addition property for equations to get these terms on the same side of the equation. Then solve for the variable.

EXAMPLE 1 Solve and check: $4x - 6 = x + 9$

Solution:

$$4x - 6 = x + 9 \qquad \longleftarrow \text{ Add } (-x) \text{ to each side.}$$
$$4x - 6 + (-x) = x + 9 + (-x) \longleftarrow \begin{array}{l}\textbf{Group and combine}\\\textbf{like terms.}\end{array}$$
$$[4x + (-x)] - 6 = [x + (-x)] + 9$$
$$3x - 6 = 9$$
$$3x - 6 + 6 = 9 + 6 \qquad \longleftarrow \begin{array}{l}\textbf{By the addition property}\\\textbf{for equations}\end{array}$$
$$3x = 15$$
$$\tfrac{1}{3}(3x) = \tfrac{1}{3}(15) \qquad \longleftarrow \begin{array}{l}\textbf{By the multiplication property}\\\textbf{for equations}\end{array}$$
$$x = 5$$

Check:
$$4x - 6 = x + 9$$
$$4(5) - 6 \overset{?}{=} 5 + 9$$
$$14 \overset{?}{=} 14 \quad \text{Yes} \;\; \unicode{x2714} \qquad \textbf{Solution set: } \{5\}$$

When an equation has no solution for the given replacement set, the solution is the **empty set, or ϕ.**

EXAMPLE 2 Solve and check: $-4(3x - 20) = -1 - 12x$

Solution:

$$-4(3x - 20) = -1 - 12x$$
$$-4(3x) + (-4)(-20) = -1 - 12x \longleftarrow \textbf{ By the distributive postulate}$$
$$-12x + 80 = -1 - 12x \longleftarrow \textbf{ Add 12x to each side.}$$
$$-12x + 80 + \mathbf{12x} = -1 - 12x + \mathbf{12x}$$
$$80 \neq -1 \qquad \text{The solution is the } \textbf{empty set, or } \phi.$$

CLASSROOM EXERCISES

What would you add to each side of the equation in order to get the variable terms on the left side of the equation?

1. $2x + 8 = x + 9$ $-x$
2. $4z + 7 = z - 2$ $-z$
3. $-4y - 7 = -9y + 8$ $9y$
4. $2x + 5 = -3x + 25$ $3x$
5. $7a - 9 = 3a - 1$ $-3a$
6. $-3t + 5 = -4t - 7$ $4t$

Equations and Inequalities **133**

What would you add to each side of the equation in order to get the variable terms on the right side of the equation?

7. $5 - 2t = 3t$ $2t$ **8.** $-r + 6 = 2r$ r **9.** $100 - 9d = 41d$ $9d$

10. $1 - 9m = 6m - 14$ $9m$ **11.** $-5m + 6 = 7m - 6$ $5m$ **12.** $2y + 1 = 3y - 2$ $-2y$

Solve each equation.

13. $3x + 5 = 2x - 6$ $x = -11$ **14.** $m = 2m - 9$ $m = 9$ **15.** $4 - 7n = 1 - 6n$ $n = 3$

WRITTEN EXERCISES

Assignment Guide
Minimal
p. 134: 1–27 odd
Average
p. 134: 1–45 odd
Above Average
p. 134: 1–57 odd

Additional Answers
Written Exercises
9. ϕ
12. $b = -1$
15. $x = -26$
18. $b = 6$
21. $r = 4$
24. $b = 0$
27. $k = 10\frac{1}{2}$
30. $y = 5$
33. $p = 6$
39. All real numbers

A   Solve and check.

1. $5x = 2x + 12$ $x = 4$ **2.** $7x = 3x + 24$ $x = 6$ **3.** $4y + 12 = 7y$ $y = 4$

4. $7y + 8 = 11y$ $y = 2$ **5.** $5a - 9 = 2a$ $a = 3$ **6.** $9y - 42 = 3y$ $y = 7$

7. $12x + 15 = 7x$ $x = -3$ **8.** $6y + 32 = 2y$ $y = -8$ **9.** $7x + 4 = 9x + 24 - 2x$

10. $3y + 9 = 3y + 15$ ϕ **11.** $4a + 1 = 7a - 17$ $a = 6$ **12.** $2b - 5 = 8b + 1$

13. $-7m = 9m - 12$ $m = \frac{3}{4}$ **14.** $-4p = 9p - 26$ $p = 2$ **15.** $5x - 9 = 6x + 17$

16. $8y - 15 = 7y + 2$ $y = 17$ **17.** $4a - 5 = 7a - 7$ $a = \frac{2}{3}$ **18.** $-6b + 9 = -4b - 3$

19. $-3r - 8 = -5r + 12$ $r = 10$ **20.** $-6x - 7 = -5x + 3$ $x = -10$ **21.** $4 - 3r = -16 + 2r$

22. $t - 7 = 3\frac{1}{2} + 2t$ $t = -10\frac{1}{2}$ **23.** $\frac{1}{2}y + 6 = y - 4$ $y = 20$ **24.** $\frac{1}{4}b + \frac{3}{4}b = 0 - b$

25. $0.7a + 0.3a = 2a - 4$ $a = 4$ **26.** $q + 7q = -12q + 10$ $q = \frac{1}{2}$ **27.** $6k - k = 9k - 42$

B

28. $4(x + 2) = 3x$ $x = -8$ **29.** $7y = -2(y + 9)$ $y = -2$ **30.** $-3(y - 8) = 2y - 1$

31. $-4(x + 2) = -6x + 2$ $x = 5$ **32.** $5(m - 5) = 3(m + 1)$ $m = 14$ **33.** $5(p - 6) = 3(p - 6)$

34. $2x + 3(x - 9) = 2(x + 3)$ $x = 11$ **35.** $3y + 5(y + 3) = 5y$ $y = -5$

36. $-4(a - 5) = -7(a - 2) + 6$ $a = 0$ **37.** $3x - 5 = 2(x - 1) + 6$ $x = 9$

38. $-5(y - 9) = -(3 + 5y)$ ϕ **39.** $6 - (8 - 4n) = 2(2n - 1)$

40. $3(1 - 2c) - 4 = -2(3c - 1)$ ϕ **41.** $7x - (x - 4) = 25$ $x = \frac{7}{2}$

42. $36 - 2(c - 28) = -4(2c + 52)$ $c = -50$ **43.** $2(x - 3) + 3(x - 2) = 8$ $x = 4$

44. $2(2n + 1) - 3(n - 5) = 0$ $n = -17$ **45.** $1.3 + 9.4n - 0.03n = 3.52$ $n = 6$

List the members in these sets. Note that **set-builder notation** is used. That is, $\{x: x + 2 = 7\}$ means the set of all real numbers x such that $x + 2 = 7$. This set has one member, 5. Thus, $\{x: x + 2 = 7\} = \{5\}$.

46. $\{x: 8x - 13x = 2x + 56\}$ $\{-8\}$ **47.** $\{n: -6n + 13 = -5n + 12\}$ $\{1\}$

48. $\{n: 5n - 20 = -32 - 7n\}$ $\{-1\}$ **49.** $\{n: -16 - 3n = 5n + 16\}$ $\{-4\}$

50. $\{t: 11 - 2t - 16 = 8t\}$ $\{-\frac{1}{2}\}$ **51.** $\{n: 14n = 14n - 5n + 6\}$ $\{1\frac{1}{5}\}$

52. $\{n: 26n - 9n = 46 + 26n\}$ $\{-5\frac{1}{9}\}$ **53.** $\{c: 5c - 13 = 6c - 18\}$ $\{5\}$

54. $\{c: 4c + 12 = 7c + 3\}$ $\{3\}$ **55.** $\{x: 5 - 3x = 5x + 21\}$ $\{-2\}$

56. $\{r: -5r + 2 = -9r - 16\}$ $\{-4\frac{1}{2}\}$ **57.** $\{s: -6s = -7 + 2s - 13\}$ $\{2\frac{1}{2}\}$

Problem Solving and Applications

4–6 Age Problems OBJECTIVE: To solve age problems

To solve age problems, you often have to represent a person's present age, the person's age a number of years ago, and the person's age a number of years from now.

	Age Now	Age 4 Years Ago	Age 7 Years From Now
Kiyo	15	15 − 4, or 11	15 + 7, or 22
Gordon	a	$a - 4$	$a + 7$
Rosa	$3t$	$3t - 4$	$3t + 7$

Thus, to represent a past age, *subtract* from the present age. To represent a future age, *add* to the present age.

To solve age problems, follow the steps of the procedure in Section 4–3 on page 126. The steps in the following Example correspond to the steps of this procedure. In the Example, Condition 1 is <u>underscored once</u>. Condition 2 is <u>underscored twice</u>.

EXAMPLE Mrs. Garcia is now three times as old as her son, Tony. In 14 years, Mrs. Garcia's age will be twice Tony's age then. How old is each now?

Solution: Make a table. Use Condition 1.

1	Age Now	Age 14 Years From Now
Tony	y	$y + 14$
Mrs. Garcia	$3y$	$3y + 14$

2 Use the table and Condition 2 to write an equation.

<u>Mrs. Garcia's age in 14 years</u> <u>will be</u> <u>twice Tony's age in 14 years.</u>

$$3y + 14 \qquad = \qquad 2(y + 14)$$

3   $3y + 14 = 2(y + 14)$ ◄——— **Solve for y.**

$3y + 14 = 2y + 28$ ◄——— **By the distributive property**

$(-2y) + 3y + 14 = (-2y) + 2y + 28$

$y + 14 + (-14) = 28 + (-14)$

$y = 14$ ◄——— **Don't forget to find Mrs. Garcia's age.**

$3y = 42$

Check: 4 **Condition 1** Does $42 = 3(14)$? Yes ✔

Condition 2 $42 + 14 = 2(14 + 14)$? Yes ✔

Tony is now **14 years old** and Mrs. Garcia is **42.**

Equations and Inequalities **135**

CLASSROOM EXERCISES

1. Charles is x years old now. Represent his age 12 years from now. $x + 12$

2. Jill is y years old now. Represent her age 8 years ago. $y - 8$

3. Peter is $2z$ years old now. Represent his age 2 years from now. $2z + 2$

4. Eduardo is $5t$ years old now. Represent his age 4 years ago. $5t - 4$

5. Miyako is $(2r - 3)$ years old now. Represent her age 9 years from now. $2r + 6$

6. Gina is $(30 - q)$ years old now. Represent her age 7 years ago. $23 - q$

Meg is t years old. Ted is three times as old as Meg.

7. Represent Meg's age 6 years from now. $t + 6$

8. Represent Ted's age 6 years from now. $3t + 6$

9. Represent Meg's age 5 years ago. $t - 5$

10. Represent Ted's age 5 years ago. $3t - 5$

WORD PROBLEMS

A Solve each problem.

In some Exercises, Condition 1 is <u>underscored once</u>. Condition 2 is <u>underscored twice</u>.

1. <u>Anna is now four times as old as her brother Ramon.</u> <u><u>In 4 years, Anna's age will be twice Ramon's age then.</u></u> How old is each now? Anna: 8; Ramon: 2

2. <u>Tom's present age is twice Sue's present age.</u> <u><u>Two years ago, Tom was three times as old as Sue was then.</u></u> Find their present ages. Tom: 8; Sue: 4

3. <u>Skip is now three times as old as Paul.</u> <u><u>In 5 years, Skip will be twice as old as Paul will be then.</u></u> What will their ages be in five years? Skip: 20; Paul: 10

4. <u>Carla is now twice as old as Jennifer.</u> <u><u>Seven years ago, the sum of their ages was 16.</u></u> How old is each girl now? Carla: 20; Jennifer: 10

5. <u>Andy Anderson is now 25 years older than his brother, Bob.</u> <u><u>In 15 years, Andy's age will be twice Bob's age then.</u></u> How old are Andy and Bob Anderson now? Andy: 35; Bob: 10

6. Mrs. Montez is 20 years older than Mrs. Cooke. Sixteen years ago, Mrs. Montez was 3 times as old as Mrs. Cooke was then. How old are Mrs. Montez and Mrs. Cooke now?

7. The ages of two cousins can be represented as consecutive integers. Fifteen years from now, the sum of their ages will be 57. How old is each now? 13; 14

8. The ages of two sisters can be represented as consecutive odd integers. Twelve years ago, the sum of their ages was 8. How old is each now?

9. An electrician has 5 times as many years experience as her apprentice. Four years from now, the electrician will have 3 times as many years experience as the apprentice. How many years experience does each have now?

10. One teacher has 4 times as many years experience as a second. Six years from now, the first teacher will have twice as many years experience as the second. How many years experience does each teacher have now? 12 yr; 3 yr

Assignment Guide
Minimal
pp. 136–137: 2–12 even
Average
pp. 136–137: 2–18 even
Above Average
pp. 136–137: 2–12 even, 13–18

Additional Answers
Word Problems
6. Mrs. Montez: 46;
   Mrs. Cooke: 26
8. 15; 17
9. Electrician: 20 yr;
   Apprentice: 4 yr

11. Mr. Connors is 15 years younger than Mr. Saito. Five years from now, Mr. Saito will be $1\frac{1}{2}$ times as old as Mr. Connors will be then. Find their present ages.

B

13. Sandra Klee was 25 years old when her son was born. Her present age is 7 years less than three times her son's present age. How old is Sandra now?

15. A woman is now 40 years old and her daughter is 14 years old. In how many years will the mother be exactly twice as old as her daughter? 12 yr

17. A woman's age is 32 and her son's age is 2. In how many years will the mother be four times as old as her son? 8 yr

12. Linda is 10 years younger than Harold. In 6 years, Harold's age will be $1\frac{1}{2}$ times as old as Linda's will be then. Find their present ages.

14. A man is 40 years old and his son is 8. In how many years will the father's age be exactly three times the son's age? (HINT: Let n = the number of years.)

16. Mae Ying Chung is now 17 years old and her aunt is 50. In how many years will Mae be one half as old as her aunt? 16 yr

18. The sum of Louellen's age and Fred's age is 20. Louellen's age one year from now will be nine times Fred's age one year ago. How old is each now?

─── **Review** ───────────────

Represent each word expression by an algebraic expression. *(Section 4-1)*

1. The product of -6 and m $-6m$

3. The total of $2\frac{1}{4}$ and k $2\frac{1}{4} + k$

5. Fifteen dollars plus four times the daily rental charge for a boat is $79. What is the daily rental charge? *(Section 4-2)* $16

7. Together, Bob and Jane own 128 shares of Intek stock. Bob owns 4 more than three times the number of shares Jane owns. How many shares does each own? *(Section 4-3)*

2. The quotient of x and 12 $\frac{x}{12}$

4. n less than 4.6 $4.6 - n$

6. One number is $\frac{2}{3}$ of another number. The difference between the two numbers is 12. Find the numbers. *(Section 4-3)* 36; 24

8. The length of a rectangular park is three times the width. The perimeter of the park is 160 meters. Find the dimensions of the park. *(Section 4-4)*

Solve and check. *(Section 4-5)*

9. $9g + 7 = 2g$ $g = 1$

11. $6 - \frac{1}{2}b = 1\frac{1}{2}b + 18$ $b = -6$

13. $4(0.5x - 3) = 9 + 2x$ ϕ

10. $18 - n = 5n + 6$ $n = 2$

12. $4(2n + 1) = 2(3n - 1)$ $n = -3$

14. $3(4 - c) - 6(2c + 1) = -9$ $c = 1$

15. Maria is now 3 years younger than her sister, Ann. Four years ago Maria's age was one-half Ann's age. How old is each girl now? *(Section 4-6)*

Equations and Inequalities   **137**

Career Applications: **Statistics**

Statisticians are concerned with gathering data and analyzing the results. They sometimes research consumer topics on behalf of federal agencies and private companies.

For example, statisticians may study the effects a vehicle's speed, brakes, and the road conditions have on the ability of motorists to stop quickly in an emergency.

The **stopping distance**, s, of a vehicle is the sum of the reaction distance, D, and the braking distance, b.

$$s = D + b$$

Reaction distance is the distance a car travels during the time it takes a driver to begin braking. **Braking distance** is the distance a car travels when the brakes are applied and until the car stops completely.

A calculator is an important tool for a statistician.

Based on statistical research, it has been found that the formula

$$D = 1.1r$$

estimates the reaction distance in feet of a car traveling at r miles per hour.

EXAMPLE 1   Mary Sandoval was driving at 45 miles per hour when she saw a branch lying on the road. Estimate the reaction distance.

Solution: $D = 1.1r$ ⟵ $r = 45$

$D = 1.1(45)$

$D = 49.5$

The reaction distance is about $49\frac{1}{2}$ **feet.**

Statisticians have also found that such factors as road surface and condition, as well as the brakes of the car, will affect braking distance. A formula that has been developed to estimate braking distance is

$$b = \frac{r^2}{30F},$$

where F is the **coefficient of friction**, a number based on the condition and surface of the road. The table at the right gives several values for F.

Type of Surface	Coefficient of Friction	
	Dry Road	Wet Road
Asphalt	0.85	0.65
Concrete	0.90	0.60
Gravel	0.65	0.65
Packed Snow	0.45	0.45

138   **Career Applications**

EXAMPLE 2   **a.** Mary was driving on a dry concrete road. Estimate the braking distance.

b. Estimate the total stopping distance of Mary's car.

Solutions: **a.** $b = \dfrac{r^2}{30F}$ ⟵ **r = 45;**
F = 0.9 from the table

$b = \dfrac{(45)^2}{30(0.9)}$

4 5 $\boxed{\times}$ $\boxed{=}$ $\boxed{\div}$ 3 0 $\boxed{\div}$. 9 $\boxed{=}$ $\boxed{\quad 75. \quad}$

The braking distance is about **75 feet.**

b. $s = D + b$
$s = 49\frac{1}{2} + 75$
$s = 124\frac{1}{2}$
The stopping distance is about **$124\frac{1}{2}$ feet.**

NOTE: You can also express the formula for stopping distance as the sum of two formulas.

$$s = 1.1r + \frac{r^2}{30F}$$

EXERCISES

Estimate the reaction distance a car will travel at the following rates of speed.

1. 55 miles per hour   **2.** 30 miles per hour   **3.** 45 miles per hour
4. 42 miles per hour   **5.** 54 miles per hour   **6.** 28 miles per hour

Estimate the braking distance of a car traveling under the given conditions.

7. 54 mi/hr on wet concrete   **8.** 30 mi/hr on dry concrete
9. 42 mi/hr on wet concrete   **10.** 52 mi/hr on gravel

Complete the table below.

Rate	Road Conditions	Reaction Distance	Braking Distance	Stopping Distance
11. 39 mi/hr	wet asphalt	?	?	?
12. 54 mi/hr	dry concrete	?	?	?
13. 45 mi/hr	wet concrete	?	?	?
14. 27 mi/hr	packed snow	?	?	?

Statistics   139

Teaching Suggestions p. M-17

Quick Quiz
1. Rose is 37 years older than her granddaughter, Desirée. In 7 years, the sum of their ages will be 77 years. How old are Rose and Desirée now?
Ans: Rose: 50; Desirée: 13
2. Bill is 31 years younger than his father, Frank. Eight years ago, the sum of their ages was 61 years. How old are they now?
Ans: Bill: 23; Frank: 54

Additional Examples
Example 1
Solve and graph.
1. $x + 4 < 1$
    Ans: $x < -3$

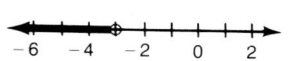

2. $x - 3 > -1$
    Ans: $x > 2$

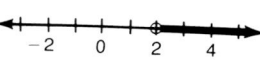

Solve each inequality. The replacement set is $\{-4, -3, -2, -1, 0, 1, 2, 3, 4\}$. *(Pages 17–19)*

1. $3z < 9$ 2. $2z > 4 \; \{3, 4\}$ 3. $z + 1 > 2 \; \{2, 3, 4\}$ 4. $\frac{1}{2}z < 6$

5. $z - 1 < 0$ 6. $1 - z > 0$ 7. $|z| > 1$ 8. $|z| \le 3$

OBJECTIVE: To solve inequalities using the addition property of inequality

4–7 Solving Inequalities: Addition Property

Compare the solution sets and graphs for each pair of inequalities in the table below. The replacement set is $\{-1, 0, 1, 2, 3, 4, 5, 6, 7, 8\}$.

Inequalities	Solution Set	Graph
$x < 4$ $x + 7 < 4 + 7$ or $x + 7 < 11$	$\{-1, 0, 1, 2, 3\}$	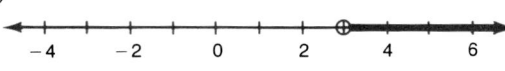
$x > 4$ $x + 7 > 4 + 7$ or $x + 7 > 11$	$\{5, 6, 7, 8\}$	

In the table, $x < 4$ is *equivalent* to $x + 7 < 11$, and
$x > 4$ is *equivalent* to $x + 7 > 11$,

because each pair has the *same solution set*. This suggests an addition property for inequalities similar to the addition property for equations.

Property

> **Addition Property for Inequalities**
> Adding the same number to each side of an inequality results in an **equivalent inequality**.

In solving inequalities, assume that the replacement set is the set of real numbers unless you are told otherwise.

EXAMPLE 1   Solve and graph: $x + 3 > 6$

Solution: $x + 3 > 6$ ◄───── **Add −3 to each side.**
$x + 3 + (-3) > 6 + (-3)$
$x > 3$

Solution set: {**all real numbers greater than 3**}

Note that the open circle around the point 3 on the number line indicates that 3 is *not* a solution.

The symbol $\le$ used in Example 2 is read: "is less than or equal to."

EXAMPLE 2 Solve and graph: $3x - 1 \le 2x + 3$

Solution: $3x - 1 \le 2x + 3$ ◄——— **Add (−2x) to each side.**

$$-2x + 3x - 1 \le -2x + 2x + 3$$

$$x - 1 \le 3 \text{ ◄——— \textbf{Add 1 to each side.}}$$

$$x - 1 + 1 \le 3 + 1$$

$$x \le 4$$

Solution set: {all real numbers less than or equal to 4}

You can check an inequality by substituting two or more of its solutions in the original inequality. Here is a check for Example 2, using the solutions $x = 0$ and $x = -5$.

Check:

$3x - 1 \overset{?}{<} 2x + 3$ ◄—— **Replace x with 0.**

$3(0) - 1 \overset{?}{<} 2(0) + 3$

$-1 < 3$ Yes ✔

$3x - 1 \overset{?}{<} 2x + 3$ ◄—— **Replace x with (−5).**

$3(-5) - 1 \overset{?}{<} 2(-5) + 3$

$-16 < -7$ Yes ✔

CLASSROOM EXERCISES

Complete each statement. Use $>$ or $<$.

1. Since $18 > 12$, $18 + (-5) \underline{\ ?\ } 12 + (-5)$. $>$
2. Since $21 < 30$, $21 + 15 \underline{\ ?\ } 30 + 15$. $<$
3. Since $-8 > -10$, $-8 + 2 \underline{\ ?\ } -10 + 2$. $>$
4. Since $-21 < -18$, $-21 + (-5) \underline{\ ?\ } -18 + (-5)$. $<$
5. If $z + 3 > 5$, then $z + 3 + (-3) \underline{\ ?\ } 5 + (-3)$, or $z \underline{\ ?\ } 2$. $>;>$
6. If $t - 8 < 2$, then $t - 8 + 8 \underline{\ ?\ } 2 + 8$, or $t \underline{\ ?\ } 10$. $<;<$
7. If $q - 21 > -106$, then $q - 21 + 21 \underline{\ ?\ } -106 + 21$, or $q \underline{\ ?\ } -85$. $>;>$
8. If $r + 9 < 0$, then $r + 9 + (-9) \underline{\ ?\ } 0 + (-9)$, or $r \underline{\ ?\ } -9$. $<;<$
9. If $w + 5 < -7$, then $w + 5 + (-5) \underline{\ ?\ } -7 + (-5)$, or $w \underline{\ ?\ } -12$. $<;<$
10. If $s + 2 < 2$, then $s + 2 + (-2) \underline{\ ?\ } 2 + (-2)$, or $s \underline{\ ?\ } 0$. $<;<$

WRITTEN EXERCISES See the Solution Key for the graphs.

A Solve and graph each inequality.

1. $t + 4 > 1$
2. $n + 3 < 4$
3. $y - 5 > 7$
4. $x + 7 > 16$
5. $r + 9 < 16$
6. $x - 15 > -22$
7. $r - 1.5 < 3.5$
8. $m + 0.1 < 2.1$
9. $-5\frac{1}{2} > c + 1\frac{1}{2}$

Equations and Inequalities **141**

Example 2
Solve and graph.
1. $2x - 3 \ge x - 8$
   Ans: $x \ge -5$

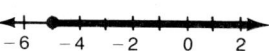

2. $6x + 5 \le 5 + 5x$
   Ans: $x \le 0$

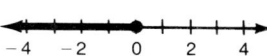

Assignment Guide
Minimal
pp. 141–142: 1–18 odd
Average
pp. 141–142: 1–32 odd
Above Average
pp. 141–142: 11–32 odd, 33–43

Additional Answers
Written Exercises
1. $t > -3$; all points to the right of, and not including, -3
2. $n < 1$; all points to the left of, and not including, 1
3. $y > 12$; all points to the right of, and not including, 12
4. $x > 9$; all points to the right of, and not including, 9
5. $r < 7$; all points to the left of, and not including, 7
6. $x > -7$; all points to the right of, and not including, -7
7. $r < 5$; all points to the left of, and not including, 5
8. $m < 2$; all points to the left of, and not including, 2
9. $c < -7$; all points to the left of, and not including, -7

Solve and graph each inequality. See the Solution Key for the graphs.

10. $q + \frac{1}{4} > 3$ **11.** $z - 8 > 8$ **12.** $19 < y + 14$

13. $x + 2 < 8$ **14.** $6d + 1 \leq 5d - 3$ **15.** $x - 3 \geq 5$

16. $6x + 2 \geq 14 + 5x$ **17.** $3.5r - 10 \geq 2.5r + 9$ **18.** $\frac{1}{3}t - 1 < 1\frac{1}{3}t - 1$

B

19. $3n - 2(n - 1) \geq 0$ **20.** $4t - 3(t + 6) > -5$

21. $3(2z - 1) + 8 < 5z$ **22.** $7 + 4(2y) \leq 7y - 5$

23. $1 + 2(y - 1) \geq 3y$ **24.** $6(r - \frac{1}{2}) \geq 5(r + \frac{3}{5})$

25. $5q + 2(9 - 2q) \leq 0$ **26.** $0 \leq 4(1 - 7n) + 29n$

27. $-2(4x - 8) > -3(3x + 5)$ **28.** $-5(1 - 5x) > -12(1 - 2x)$

29. $9x + 1 \leq 4(2x + \frac{1}{4})$ **30.** $3(7y - \frac{1}{3}) \geq 20y - 1$

Complete each statement. In each statement, the variables represent real numbers.

31. If $x > y$, then $x + z \underline{\quad ? \quad} y + z$. (Addition Property for Inequalities) $>$
32. If $x < y$, then $x + z \underline{\quad ? \quad} y + z$. (Addition Property for Inequalities) $<$

C

33. If $x < y$ and $y < z$, then $x < \underline{\quad ? \quad}$. (Transitive Property for Inequalities) z
34. If $z > y$ and $y > x$, then $z > \underline{\quad ? \quad}$. (Transitive Property for Inequalities) x
35. If $a > 2$, then $a - 2 > \underline{\quad ? \quad}$. 0
36. If $a - 3 < 0$, then $a < \underline{\quad ? \quad}$. 3
37. If $a + 5 > 0$, then $a > \underline{\quad ? \quad}$. -5
38. If $a - 3 < 0$, which is greater, a or 3? 3
39. If $a + 5 > 0$, which is greater, a or -5? a
40. If $b < 0$, which is greater, $b + 3$ or b? $b + 3$
41. If $b < 0$, which is greater, $b + 3$ or 3? 3
42. The reflexive property of equality states that $a = a$. Is there a similar reflexive property for $>$ and $<$? No
43. Show by using examples that if $a > b$ and $c > d$, then it is not always true that $a - c > b - d$.

─────── **REVIEW CAPSULE FOR SECTION 4-8** ───────

In Exercises 1–6, solve each inequality. Use the given replacement set. (Pages 17–19)

1. $2x > -1$; $\{-2, 0, 2\}$ $\{0, 2\}$ **2.** $2x + 3 > 9$; $\{-4, -3, -2, -1, 0\}$ $\{\phi\}$
3. $6 - 3x < 0$; $\{-2, -1, 0, 1, 2\}$ ϕ **4.** $7 - 4x \geq 0$; $\{-2, -1, 0, 1, 2\}$ $\{-2, -1, 0, 1\}$
5. $3(x + 1) \leq 3x + 3$; $\{-3, -1, 1, 3\}$ **6.** $-2(p + 1) > 2p - 2$; $\{-6, -3, 0, 3, 6\}$
  $\{-3, -1, 1, 3\}$ $\{-6, -3\}$

142 *Chapter 4*

OBJECTIVE: To solve inequalities using the multiplication property for inequalities

4–8 Solving Inequalities: Multiplication Property

The table below shows that *multiplying each* side of an inequality by the *same positive number* does not change the order of the inequality.

Multiplying each side by a negative number, however, reverses the order of the inequality.

Inequality	Multiply by 1.	Multiply by 3.	Multiply by −1.	Multiply by −3.
$3 < 7$	$3 < 7$	$9 < 21$	$-3 > -7$	$-9 > -21$
$-3 < 2$	$-3 < 2$	$-9 < 6$	$3 > -2$	$9 > -6$
$4 > -6$	$4 > -6$	$12 > -18$	$-4 < 6$	$-12 < 18$

The table suggests the following.

Properties

> **Multiplication Properties for Inequalities**
>
> 1. **For all real numbers a, b, and c, if $a > b$ and $c > 0$, then $ac > bc$.**
>
> 2. **For all real numbers a, b, and c, if $a > b$ and $c < 0$, then $ac < bc$.**

EXAMPLE 1 Solve and graph: $-\frac{1}{2}x > 1$

Solution:

$$-\frac{1}{2}x > 1 \longleftarrow \text{Multiply each side by } (-2). \text{ Change } > \text{ to } <.$$

$$(-2)\left(-\frac{1}{2}x\right) < (-2)(1)$$

$$x < -2$$

Solution set: {all real numbers less than −2}

In Example 2, both the addition and multiplication properties of inequalities are used. As when solving equations, it is usually easier to apply the addition property first.

EXAMPLE 2 Solve: $5 - 4x \le 17$

Solution:

$$5 - 4x \le 17 \longleftarrow \text{Add } (-5) \text{ to each side.}$$

$$-4x \le 12 \longleftarrow \text{Multiply each side by } \left(-\frac{1}{4}\right). \text{ Change } \le \text{ to } \ge.$$

$$-\frac{1}{4}(-4x) \ge -\frac{1}{4}(12)$$

$$x \ge -3$$

Solution set: {all real numbers greater than or equal to −3}

In Examples 1 and 2, the check is left for you.

Equations and Inequalities **143**

Teaching Suggestions p. M-17

Quick Quiz
Solve and graph.
1. $x + 5 < 2$ **Ans: x < −3**

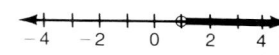

2. $x - 3 > -2$ **Ans: x > 1**

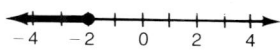

3. $7x + 1 \le 6x - 1$ **Ans: x ≤ −2**

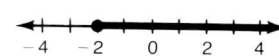

4. $8x + 3 \ge 7x + 1$ **Ans: x ≥ −2**

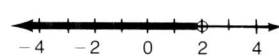

Additional Examples
Example 1
Solve and graph.
1. $-\frac{1}{2}x < 2$ **Ans: x > −4**

2. $-3x > -6$ **Ans: x < 2**

Example 2
1. Solve: $7 - 3x \le 25$
   Ans: x ≥ −6 or
   {all real numbers greater than or equal −6}
2. Solve: $9 - 7x \ge 58$
   Ans: x ≤ −7 or
   {all real numbers less than or equal to −7}

CLASSROOM EXERCISES

Complete each statement.

1. Since $12 > 3$, $\frac{1}{3}(12)$ ___?___ $\frac{1}{3}(3)$. $>$
2. Since $16 > 12$, $(-\frac{1}{4})(16)$ ___?___ $(-\frac{1}{4})(12)$. $<$
3. Since $-1 < 5$, $10(-1)$ ___?___ $10(5)$. $<$
4. Since $-8 < -4$, $(-\frac{1}{8})(-8)$ ___?___ $(-\frac{1}{8})(-4)$. $>$
5. Since $\frac{1}{5} < 10$, $(-5)(\frac{1}{5})$ ___?___ $(-5)(10)$. $>$
6. Since $-\frac{1}{4} > -\frac{3}{4}$, $(-4)(-\frac{1}{4})$ ___?___ $(-4)(-\frac{3}{4})$. $<$
7. If $2x > 9$, then $\frac{1}{2}(2x)$ ___?___ $\frac{1}{2}(9)$, or x ___?___ $\frac{9}{2}$. $>;>$
8. If $-\frac{1}{3}t < 27$, then $(-3)(-\frac{1}{3}t)$ ___?___ $(-3)(27)$, or t ___?___ -81. $>;>$
9. If $-6p < 1.5$, then $(-\frac{1}{6})(-6p)$ ___?___ $(-\frac{1}{6})(1.5)$, or p ___?___ -0.25. $>;>$

WRITTEN EXERCISES See the Solution Key for the graphs.

A   Solve and graph each inequality.

1. $2x < 8$
2. $5z > 45$
3. $7q > 14$
4. $-4z > 8$
5. $-4d < 8$
6. $-4n > 12$
7. $-6x \le 0$
8. $-9y \ge 0$
9. $-9t \le -36$
10. $-10w \ge -20$
11. $\frac{1}{3}z > 2$
12. $-\frac{2}{3}r > 6$
13. $2a + 2\frac{1}{2} > 10\frac{1}{2}$
14. $2c - 5 \ge 10$
15. $3h + 7 \le 16$
16. $16 < 3x + 4$
17. $7y < 20 - 3y$
18. $5 + 2p < 17$

Solve each inequality.

19. $2t + 3 > 4t - 7$ $t < 5$
20. $3y + 9 > -2$ $y > -\frac{11}{3}$
21. $-2x + 5 > 10$ $x < -\frac{5}{2}$
22. $-3a - 4a > -21$ $a < 3$
23. $8r - 3r + 1 \le 29$ $r \le 5\frac{3}{5}$
24. $5 - 6x \le 17$ $x \ge -2$
25. $4(5a + 7) \le 13$ $a \le -\frac{3}{4}$
26. $8t \le 5(2t + 4)$ $t \ge -10$
27. $-3m + 6(m - 4) > 9$

B

28. $8z - 2(2z + 3) > 0$ $z > \frac{3}{2}$
29. $-2y - 5 \ge 10$ $y \le -\frac{15}{2}$
30. $4 - 3p \ge 16 + p$
31. $-2x - 5 < -x + 10$ $x > -15$
32. $12x + 3 < 3x - 9$ $x < -\frac{4}{3}$
33. $-4x + 2 < x + 9$
34. $3(x + 2) < -x + 4$ $x < -\frac{1}{2}$
35. $-7(-3x + 4) < 0$ $x < \frac{4}{3}$
36. $3(x + 2) \ge -2(x + 1)$
37. $3(y + 2) + 8 < 10 - (2 - y)$ $y < -3$
38. $-3(2m - 8) < 2(m + 14)$
39. $15x - 2(x - 4) > 3$ $x > -\frac{5}{13}$
40. $-2(n - 3) < 6n - 7(n - 4)$
41. $3(k - 4) - 3 \ge 2k + 1$ $k \ge 16$
42. $5s \le 10 + 2(3s - 4)$
43. $4 - 5(r - 2) \le -2(-9 + 2r)$ $r \ge -4$
44. $-3(t + 1) - 5(t + 2) \ge 0$
45. $3z + 7 \ge 8z - 2(5z - 2)$ $z \ge -\frac{3}{5}$
46. $2(2r + 5) + 1 \le 5 - 2(3 - r)$
47. $1 - (4d - 1) > 2(d - 3)$ $d < \frac{4}{3}$
48. $k - 3(2k + 1) < 5(1 + k) + 2$

Assignment Guide
Minimal
p. 144: 1–25
Average
p. 144: 2–48 even
Above Average
pp. 144–145: 10–62 even

Additional Answers
Written Exercises

1. $x < 4$; all points to the left of, and not including, 4
2. $z > 9$; all points to the right of, and not including, 9
3. $q > 2$; all points to the right of, and not including, 2
4. $z < -2$; all points to the left of, and not including, -2
5. $d > -2$; all points to the right of, and not including, -2
6. $n < -3$; all points to the left of, and not including, -3
7. $x \ge 0$; all points to the right of, and including, 0
8. $y \le 0$; all points to the left of, and including, 0
9. $t \ge 4$; all points to the right of, and including, 4
10. $w \le 2$; all points to the left of, and including, 2
11. $z > 6$; all points to the right of, and not including, 6
12. $r < -9$; all points to the left of, and not including, -9
13. $a > 4$; all points to the right of, and not including, 4

See page 156 for the answers to Exercises 14–18, 27, 30, 33, 36, 38, 40, 42, 44, 46, and 48.

C Complete each statement. In each statement, x, y, and z represent real numbers. (Exercises 49–52 express the Multiplication Property for Inequalities in generalized form.)

49. If $x > y$ and z is positive ($z > 0$), then xz __?__ yz. $>$
50. If $x < y$ and z is positive ($z > 0$), then xz __?__ yz. $<$
51. If $x > y$ and z is negative ($z < 0$), then xz __?__ yz. $<$
52. If $x < y$ and z is negative ($z < 0$), then xz __?__ yz. $>$

In Exercises 53–62, classify each statement as true, T, or false, F. When a statement is false, give an example that shows why it is false. In these Exercises, x and y represent real numbers where $x > y$.

53. $y < x$ F 54. $x > 0$ F 55. $y^2 > 0$ T 56. $y^2 > y$ F 57. $xy > 0$ F

58. $x + y > y$ F 59. $y^2 > x$ F 60. $y^2 < xy$ F 61. $xy < x^2$ F 62. $x^3 < x^2$ F

CALCULATOR APPLICATIONS

Checking Inequalities

You can use a calculator to check whether a given number is in the solution set of an inequality.

EXAMPLE Is -9.5 a solution of $4p - 6 > -20$?

SOLUTION Substitute -9.5 in the left side of the inequality.

4 $\boxed{\times}$ 9 . 5 $\boxed{+/-}$ $\boxed{-}$ 6 $\boxed{=}$

$-44.$

Since $-44 > -20$ is *false*, -9.5 **is not** a solution.

EXERCISES

Check the given "answer" to each inequality.

1. $2b + 4 \geq -9$; -6.5 Correct
2. $-8 + 4d < 5$; 1 Correct
3. $5q + 7 > -5$; -2 Correct
4. $5(2 - 3n) \leq -8$; -4 Incorrect
5. $10 - 4k \geq 16$; 5.2 Incorrect
6. $6 - 3(4 + z) < -9$; 1 Incorrect

———— REVIEW CAPSULE FOR SECTION 4–9 ————

Choose a variable to represent one unknown and tell what it represents. Represent the second unknown in terms of the variable. *(Pages 118–121)*

1. The sum of two consecutive integers.
2. Nadia bought 7 more pencils than pens.
3. One number is 36 more than three times a second number.
4. Room 203 has 5 more than twice the number of students that Room 201 has.
5. The entertainment part of a TV program lasted 10 minutes less than four times the length of the advertising part.
6. Each side of a triangle is 4 meters shorter than twice the length of each side of a square.

Equations and Inequalities **145**

Problem Solving and Applications

OBJECTIVE: To solve word problems using inequalities

4–9 Using Inequalities

Many word problems can be solved by using inequalities.

EXAMPLE 1 Ellen plans to spend less than $120 for a dress and a pair of shoes (Condition 2). The cost of the dress Ellen would like to buy is $30 more than twice the cost of a pair of shoes (Condition 1). What is the greatest amount she can spend for the shoes?

Solution: Let p = the cost of the shoes.
Then $2p + 30$ = the cost of the dress. ← **Condition 1**

$p + 2p + 30 < 120$ ← **Condition 2**

$3p + 30 < 120$ ← **Add (−30) to each side.**

$3p < 90$ ← **Multiply each side by $\frac{1}{3}$.**

$p < 30$

Since $p < 30$, the greatest amount Ellen can spend for shoes is **$29.99**.

Check: Amount for shoes: $29.99 Amount for dress: 2($29.99) + $30 = $89.98
Is $29.99 + $89.98 < $120? Yes ✔

Recall that the *average* of two or more scores is the sum of the scores divided by the number of scores.

EXAMPLE 2 Tom's scores on four tests were 87, 92, 88, and 86. What is the lowest score Tom needs to achieve on the next test in order to have an average score greater than 90?

Solution: Let x = Tom's score on the next test.

$\dfrac{87 + 92 + 88 + 86 + x}{5} > 90$ ← **Multiply each side by 5.**

$5\left(\dfrac{87 + 92 + 88 + 86 + x}{5}\right) > 5(90)$

$87 + 92 + 88 + 86 + x > 450$

$353 + x > 450$

$x > 97$ Tom's next score must be **greater than 97.**

Check: Will a score of 98 give Tom an average greater than 90?

Is $\dfrac{87 + 92 + 88 + 86 + 98}{5} > 90$? $\dfrac{451}{5} > 90$? Yes ✔

Will a score of 97 give Tom an average greater than 90?

Is $\dfrac{87 + 92 + 88 + 86 + 97}{5} > 90$? $\dfrac{450}{5} > 90$? No

146   *Chapter 4*

The check for Example 2 shows another way to check the solution set of an inequality. First replace the variable with a number in the solution set. This number *should satisfy* the inequality. Then replace the variable with a number *not* in the solution set. This number *should not satisfy* the inequality.

CLASSROOM EXERCISES

In Exercises 1–5, choose a variable to represent the unknown(s). Then write the inequality you would use to represent the given situation.

1. Several pipe sections, each 8 meters long, are to be joined to form a pipe greater than 110 meters long.

2. Claude is 5 years older than Tom. The sum of their ages is less than 53, Tom's mother's age.

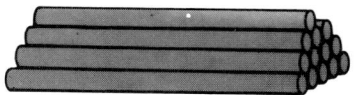

3. George has two test scores of 82 and 91. What must be his score on the next test in order to have an average of 90 or greater?

4. A trailer can safely carry 1000 kilograms. A number of 40-kilogram bags are being loaded onto the trailer. How many bags can be loaded?

WORD PROBLEMS

A Solve each problem. For some problems, Condition 1 is <u>underscored once</u>. Condition 2 is <u>underscored twice</u>.

1. <u>Larry plans to spend no more than $140 for a jacket and a sweater.</u> Suppose that <u>the cost of a jacket is $10 less than twice the cost of a sweater.</u> What is the greatest amount that Larry can spend for the sweater? $50

2. Beth and Sara estimate that <u>they should spend less than $600 each month for rent and food</u> and that <u>the amount budgeted for rent should be $30 more than twice the amount budgeted for food.</u> What is the greatest amount budgeted for food?

3. Rosa's scores on three quizzes were 78, 81 and 93. What must be her lowest score on the next quiz in order to have an average greater than 85? 89

4. Peter's grades on four tests were 68, 82, 78 and 80. What must be his lowest grade on the next test in order to have an average greater than 80? 93

5. Bob's scores for three games in bowling were 76, 103, and 121. What must be his lowest score in the next game in order to have an average greater than 100 for the four games? 101

6. Roseanne's scores for three games she bowled were 147, 137, and 130. What must be her lowest score in the next game in order to have an average greater than 140 for the four games? 147

7. <u>Ada had a sum of money in a savings account.</u> <u>After she deposited an additional $130, there was more than $750 in the account.</u> What is the smallest amount that could have been in the account originally? $620.01

8. <u>A drama club agreed to buy more than 250 tickets for a theater party.</u> <u>The number of orchestra seats they bought was 80 fewer than the number of balcony tickets.</u> What was the least number of balcony tickets bought? 166

Equations and Inequalities **147**

Additional Answers
Classroom Exercises
1. x = number of pipe sections; $8x > 110$
2. x = Tom's age; $x + 5$ = Claudia's age; $x + x + 5 < 53$
3. x = score on third test; $\frac{82 + 91 + x}{3} \geq 90$
4. x = no. of bags; $40x \leq 1000$

Assignment Guide
Minimal Omit
Average
pp. 147–148: 1–15 odd
Above Average
pp. 147–148: 1–15 odd, 16–18

Additional Answers
Word Problems
2. $189.99

9. The sum of two consecutive positive integers is less than or equal to 10. Find the integers.

10. The sum of two consecutive positive integers is less than 50. Find the pair with the greatest sum. 24 and 25

11. The sum of two consecutive odd integers is greater than 55. Find the pair with the smallest sum. 27 and 29

12. The sum of two consecutive even integers is less than 100. Find the pair with the greatest sum. 48 and 50

13. Philip is paid $225 a week plus a $15 commission on each piece of photographic equipment that he sells. How many pieces of equipment must he sell in order to make at least $400 per week? 12

14. A gain of 2 pounds would put a certain amateur boxer in the welterweight class. What is the least amount the boxer must weigh now if the minimum welterweight class weight is 140 pounds? 138 lb

B

15. The product of 3 and any number from a set of numbers is greater than 12. Find the set of numbers. $\{x: x > 4\}$

16. The product of 4 and any number from a set of numbers is increased by 7. The result is less than 19. Find the set of numbers. $\{x: x < 3\}$

C

17. The sum of two consecutive even integers is greater than 98 decreased by twice the larger integer. Find the smallest possible values for the integers. 24 and 26

18. Find the largest possible values for three consecutive integers if the sum of the two smaller integers is less than 32 decreased by half the largest integer. 11, 12, and 13

Review

See the Solution Key for the graphs.
Solve and graph each inequality. *(Section 4–7)*

1. $n + 8 < 11$

2. $-4.8 > x - 2.3$

3. $3g + 4 \leq 2g - 1$

Solve each inequality. *(Section 4–7)*

4. $6(a - 1) > 5a - 9$ $\quad a > -3$

5. $2(2 - a) + 3a \geq 0$ $\quad a \geq -4$

6. $2(1\frac{1}{2} - 4p) < 3(1 - 3p)$ $\quad p < 0$

Solve and graph each inequality. *(Section 4–8)* See the Solution Key for the graphs.

7. $4h > 12$

8. $6y - 4 \geq -10$

9. $3 + 7s < 2(4s + 1)$

Solve each inequality. *(Section 4–8)*

10. $2(b + 3) + 8 > 7 - (b - 4)$ $\quad b > -1$

11. $t - 2(3t + 1) \leq 5(4 + t) + 8$ $\quad t \geq -3$

12. Paula's grades on three tests were 85, 92, and 75. What is the lowest grade she can get on the next test in order to have an average greater than 85? *(Section 4–9)* 89

13. One integer is five times as great as a second integer. Their sum is less than 78. What are the greatest possible values of the two integers? *(Section 4–9)* 12 and 60

BASIC: SOLVING INEQUALITIES

One use of the computer is the solution of inequalities.

Problem: *Write a program to solve any inequality of the following form.*

$$ax + b < c$$

Include the possibilities that the solution set may be all real numbers or the empty set.

This lesson is optional. Each computer applications lesson relates directly to a topic covered within the chapter. (See Section 4-8, page 143)

```
100 PRINT "ENTER VALUES FOR A, B, C"
110 PRINT "(IN THAT ORDER, SEPARATED BY COMMAS)";
120 INPUT A, B, C
130 IF A = 0 THEN 200
140 LET X = (C - B)/A
150 IF A < 0 THEN 180
160 PRINT "X < ";X
170 GOTO 240
180 PRINT "X > ";X
190 GOTO 240
200 IF B < C THEN 230
210 PRINT "NO SOLUTION"
220 GOTO 240
230 PRINT "ALL REAL NUMBERS ARE SOLUTIONS."
240 PRINT "ANY MORE INEQUALITIES TO SOLVE (1=YES, 0=NO)";
250 INPUT Z
260 IF Z = 1 THEN 120
270 END
```

Analysis

Statement 130: If A = 0, the solution set will be either the null set or all real numbers. So when A = 0, the computer is told to jump to statement 200, where it will compare B and C to decide between these two possibilities.

Statement 140: The computer reaches this statement when A $\neq$ 0. The programmer must solve the inequality for the computer and give it the correct formula. The following steps justify the formula in statement 140.

$$ax + b < c \quad \longleftarrow \text{ Subtract } b \text{ from both sides.}$$
$$ax < c - b \quad \longleftarrow \text{ Divide both sides by } a.$$
$$x < \frac{c - b}{a} \quad \text{if } a > 0,$$

or

$$x > \frac{c - b}{a} \quad \text{if } a < 0$$

Solving Inequalities   **149**

Statements 150–190: In the work just shown, the inequality sign must be reversed if A < 0. In this case, statement 150 sends the computer to statement 180, which prints the answer with a ">" sign. If A > 0, the computer moves to statement 160, which prints the answer with a "<" sign. In either case, the computer is told (statements 170 and 190) to jump to statement 240, which asks the user if there are more inequalities to be solved.

Statements 200–230: The computer can get to statement 200 only from statement 130, when A = 0. In this case, the inequality becomes B < C, which will be true either all the time or never. So, in statement 200, if B < C, the computer goes to statement 230 and prints ALL REAL NUMBERS ARE SOLUTIONS. But if B is not less than C, statement 210 is executed, printing NO SOLUTION. In either event the computer moves to statement 240 to see if the user has any more data to enter.

In IF...THEN statements in BASIC, the IF part contains an equation or inequality in which the following symbols are used.

Algebraic symbol	=	<	>	≤	≥	≠
BASIC Symbol	=	<	>	<=	>=	<>

Either or both sides of the equation or inequality in the IF part may include operation symbols. For example, 130 IF C/D <= 2*(A + B) THEN 20 is a valid statement.

EXERCISES

A Run the program on page 149 for the following values of *a*, *b*, and *c*.

1. $a = 2; b = 5; c = 9$ $x < 2$ **2.** $a = 3; b = 4; c = 10$ $x < 2$ **3.** $a = 2; b = -6; c = 0$ $x < 3$

4. $a = -2; b = 5; c = 9$ **5.** $a = 0; b = 7; c = 8$ **6.** $a = 0; b = 8; c = 7$

$x > -2$ ALL REAL NUMBERS   NO SOLUTION

Write each of the following inequalities in the form $ax + b < c$.
Then use the program on page 149 to solve the inequality.

7. $6 + 4x < 12$ **8.** $18 > 3x - 2$ **9.** $25 > 7 + 11x$

10. $112 < 16x - 123$ **11.** $254 < 24x + 123$ **12.** $82 - 9x < 233$

See the Solution Key for the answers to Exercises 7–16.

13. Write REM statements that can be added to the sample program on page 149 to explain what the program is doing. For example,

145 REM LINES 150-190 DECIDE WHETHER TO REVERSE THE < SIGN.

14. Change the problem in the example on page 149 to solve $ax + b \leq c$. What statements in the program must be changed and how?

B Write a BASIC program for each problem.

15. Solve equations of the form $ax + b = cx + d$. Include the possibilities that the solution set may be all real numbers or the null set.

16. Given a real number, print its absolute value. Do not use any "built-in" absolute value function that your computer may have.

_____ Chapter Summary _____

IMPORTANT TERMS
Average (p. 146)
Discount (p. 128)
Empty set, ϕ (p. 133)
List price (p. 128)
Perimeter (p. 129)
Regular price (p. 128)
Sale price (p. 128)

IMPORTANT IDEAS

1. **Steps in Representing a Word Expression by Algebraic Symbols**
   1. Choose a variable. Tell what it represents.
   2. Identify the key word or words that indicate which operation to use.
   3. Represent the word expressions by symbols.

2. **Steps in Solving a Word Problem with One Unknown**
   1. Choose a variable to represent the unknown.
   2. Write an equation for the problem.
   3. Solve the equation.
   4. Check your answer with the statements in the problem.
   5. Answer the question.

3. **Steps in Solving a Word Problem with Two Conditions**
   1. Identify Condition 1. Use this condition to represent the unknowns.
   2. Identify Condition 2. Use this condition to write an equation for the problem.
   3. Solve the equation.
   4. Check the results with the two conditions. Answer the question(s).

4. When terms with the variable occur on both sides of an equation, use the addition property for equations to get the terms on the same side. Then combine like terms.

5. **Addition Property for Inequalities:** Adding the same number to each side of an inequality results in an equivalent inequality.

6. **Multiplication Property for Inequalities:** Multiplying each side of an inequality by the same positive number gives an equivalent inequality. Multiplying each side of an inequality by the same negative number gives an equivalent inequality *when the inequality sign is reversed.*

_____ Chapter Objectives and Review _____

Objective: *To represent word expressions by algebraic symbols (Section 4–1)*

Represent each word expression by an algebraic expression.

1. 4.5 less w $4.5 - w$
2. p divided by -7 $\dfrac{p}{-7}$
3. 5 increased by x $5 + x$
4. c multiplied by $\frac{1}{4}$ $\frac{1}{4}c$

Equations and Inequalities   **151**

Objective: *To use equations to solve word problems with one unknown (Section 4-2)*

5. The cost of a battery, plus $2.49 sales tax, is $43.99. What is the price of the battery? $41.50

6. The quotient of a certain number and 9, decreased by 4, is 6. Find the number. 90

7. Twenty-four more than twice the number of people at a movie is 850. How many people were at the movie? 413

8. Three times the perimeter of the garden plus 12 yards is 57 yards. What is the perimeter of the garden? 15 yd

Objective: *To solve word problems by first identifying two conditions (Section 4-3)*

9. One number plus another number is 75. The smaller number is 13 less than the larger number. Find the numbers.

10. Together, Bill and Jim earned $95. Jim earned $4 less than twice what Bill did. How much did each earn?

11. Profits for the Solatech Company this month were $500 less than twice the profits last month. The total profits for the two months were $4300. What were the profits for each of the two months?

12. The larger of two hospitals has 1.8 times as many beds as the smaller hospital. The larger hospital has 116 more beds than the smaller one. Find the number of beds in each hospital.

Objective: *To solve measurement problems (Section 4-4)*

13. The width of a swimming pool is 20 meters less than its length. The perimeter is 160 meters. Find the length and width of the pool.

14. In triangle XYZ, angles X and Y have the same measure. The sum of the measures of angles Y and Z is 100°. How many degrees are there in each of the three angles?

15. The lengths of the sides of a triangle can be represented by three consecutive odd integers. The perimeter of the triangle is 87 feet. Find the lengths of the sides of the triangle. 27; 29; 31

16. A mason is building a wall around a rectangular patio. The perimeter of the patio is 70 feet and the length is 2.5 times the width. Find the length and width of the patio.

Objective: *To solve equations in which the variable occurs on both sides (Section 4-5)*

Solve and check.

17. $8x = 3x + 15$ $x = 3$

18. $2y + 5 = 2(y - 1)$ ϕ

19. $3(n + 2) - 16 = 8n$ $n = -2$

20. $4 - (6 - 5n) = 2(n + 5)$ $n = 4$

Objective: *To solve age problems (Section 4-6)*

21. Jim's present age is three times Tony's present age. Five years ago, the sum of their ages was 14. What is each boy's present age? Tony: 6; Jim: 18

22. John Lukas was 50 years old when his granddaughter was born. Now he is 2 years more than four times his granddaughter's age. How old is his granddaughter now? 16 years old

23. The ages of two friends can be represented as consecutive even integers. Twelve years from now, the sum of their ages will be 46. How old is each now? 10; 12

24. A man is now 38 years old and his son is 14 years old. In how many years will the father be exactly twice as old as his son? 10

Objective: *To solve inequalities using the addition property of inequality (Section 4–7)*

Solve and graph each inequality.

25. $y - 4 > 2$

26. $6 \leq 9 + t$

27. $-2 + 3b < 2b + 3$

Solve each inequality.

28. $3(2 - n) < 9$ $n > -1$

29. $6(f + \frac{1}{2}) - 5(1 + f) \geq 0$ $f \geq 2$

30. $-3(4 - p) \leq 2(p + 1)$ $p \leq 14$

31. $3(2n + 4) - 12 < 5n$ $n < 0$

Objective: *To solve inequalities using the multiplication property of inequality (Section 4–8)*

Solve and graph each inequality.

32. $8d < -16$

33. $3 - 2r > 7$

34. $-\frac{3}{4}x \leq -3$

Solve each inequality.

35. $2(y - 4) \geq 7 - y$ $y \geq 5$

36. $3m - 4 < 2(5m + 6) - 3m$ $m > -4$

Objective: *To solve word problems using inequalities (Section 4–9)*

37. The charge to rent a car for a day is $25. There is an additional charge of $0.06 per mile. What is the greatest number of miles that a rented car can be driven in a day if the total bill is to be less than $40? 249 mi

38. Andrea scored 18 points in one basketball game and 13 points in another. What is the least number of points she must score in the next game if her average for the 3 games is to be more than 14 points? 12

A formal Chapter Test is provided in the Teacher's Manual. See p. M-67.

_____ **Chapter Test** _____

Represent each word expression by an algebraic expression.

1. 9 more than t $t + 9$

2. y decreased by 1.5 $y - 1.5$

3. The quotient of -6 and w $\dfrac{-6}{w}$

4. Twice n, less 58 $2n - 58$

Solve and check.

5. $6d = 20 - 4d$ $d = 2$

6. $8 - x = 3x + 12$ $x = -1$

7. $2(3y + 1) = -2(y - 5)$ $y = 1$

8. $3(3 - a) - 1 = a + 8$ $a = 0$

Solve and graph each inequality. See the Solution Key for the graphs.

9. $x + 9 < 8$

10. $-5c > 10$

11. $4r - 7 \leq -3$

12. $3t + 2 \geq 11$

Equations and Inequalities **153**

Additional Answers
Chapter Objectives and Review

25. $y > 6$; all points to the right of, and not including, 6

26. $t \geq -3$; all points to right of, and including, -3

27. $b < 5$; all points to the left of, and not including, 5

32. $d < -2$; all points to the left of, and not including, -2

33. $r < -2$; all points to the left of, and not including, -2

34. $x \geq 4$; all points to the right of, and including, 4

Chapter Test

9. $x < -1$; all points to the left of, and not including, -1

10. $c < -2$; all points to the left of, and not including, -2

11. $r \leq 1$; all points to the left of, and including, 1

12. $t \geq 3$; all points to the right of, and including, 3

Solve each inequality.

13. $3(x + 4) - 4 > 2$ $x > -2$

14. $5(n - 1) < 2(2n + 1)$ $n < 7$

15. $6 + 2y - (5y - 3) < 0$ $y > 3$

16. $2(2z + 6) \geq 3(4 - z)$ $z \geq 0$

17. The number of tickets printed, less 76, is 424. Find the number of tickets printed.   500

18. Last week Jean earned $24 more than Laura. Together, they earned $96. How much did each girl earn?

19. The length of a table top is 26 centimeters longer than its width. Its perimeter is 612 centimeters. Find the length and width.

20. Keith is 10 years older than Mark. Five years ago, Keith was twice as old as Mark was then. How old are Keith and Mark now?

——— More Challenging Problems ———

1. Simplify: $\dfrac{(-12)\left(\frac{1}{4}\right)}{(-18)\left(-\frac{1}{3}\right)} \div \dfrac{(16)\left(-\frac{1}{2}\right)}{\left(-\frac{1}{5}\right)(-25)}$ $\frac{5}{16}$

2. Solve for x and graph the solution set: $7 - [4 - (3 + x)] > 3 - (9 + x)$. The replacement set is the set of real numbers.

3. Solve for x: $7(b + 5d) = 5(x - 3b)$ $x = \dfrac{22b + 35d}{5}$

4. Simplify: $6 + 7[4(3a + 2b - 6) - 3(-4b + 6a - 7) + 2]$ $-42a + 140b - 1$

5. How many feet are there in y yards, f feet, and i inches? $3y + f + \frac{i}{12}$

6. Show that these are equivalent formulas.
   $$\frac{9}{5}C + 32 = F \quad \text{and} \quad C = \frac{5}{9}(F - 32)$$

7. Simplify: $5x - y + 3 \cdot 5z - 1\frac{1}{6}z + 2\frac{1}{2}x + 3\frac{1}{2}y$ $7\frac{1}{2}x + 2\frac{1}{2}y + 13\frac{5}{6}z$

8. After selling $\frac{1}{4}$ of his crop, a farmer sold the remainder for $900 at the same price per bushel. What was the value of the crop? $1200

9. The three digit number $2a3$ is added to the number 326 to give the three digit number $5b9$. If $5b9$ is divisible by 9, find $a + b$.   6

10. A positive number is mistakenly divided by 6 instead of being multiplied by 6. Based on the correct answer, what is the per cent of error? $97\frac{2}{9}\%$

11. Find the sum of the solutions of $|x + 2| = 2|x - 2|$. $6\frac{2}{3}$

12. A rectangular field is half as wide as it is long. Its perimeter is x yards. Find its area in terms of x. $\frac{x^2}{18}$ square yards

13. A house and store were sold for $12,000 each. The house was sold at a loss of 20% of the cost, and the store was sold at a gain of 20% of the cost. Find the result of the entire transaction and state whether it was a loss or a gain.

14. In a group of cows and chickens, the number of legs was 14 more than twice the number of heads. Find the number of cows.   7

Additional Practice

You may wish to use all or some of these exercises, depending on how well students performed on the formal chapter test.

Skills

Represent each word expression by an algebraic expression. *(Section 4-1)*

1. 6.5 less x $6.5 - x$
2. The product of -5 and n $-5n$
3. 28 divided by c $\frac{28}{c}$
4. p increased by $3\frac{1}{2}$ $p + 3\frac{1}{2}$

Solve and check. *(Section 4-5)*

5. $9a - 4 = 5a$ $a = 1$
6. $5 - 3n = 2n + 15$ $n = -2$
7. $2x - 3 = 3(x - 2)$ $x = 3$
8. $4(a + 2) = 6(a - 3)$ $a = 13$
9. $2(\frac{1}{2}y + 7) = 8y$ $y = 2$
10. $2(x + 1) - 3(2x - 2) = 4$ $x = 1$

Solve each inequality. *(Section 4-7)*

11. $2(x - 3) > 4 + x$ $x > 10$
12. $-2(4 - n) < 3n$ $n > -8$
13. $5(a + 1) - 2(2a - 1) \leq 0$ $a \leq -7$
14. $3(2n + 1) - 5n \geq 2n - 1$ $n \leq 4$

Solve each inequality. *(Section 4-8)*

15. $3x \leq 5x - 8$ $x \geq 4$
16. $6(2 - n) < 12 + 5n$ $n > 0$
17. $1 + n > 3(1 - n)$ $n > \frac{1}{2}$
18. $5(3 - n) \geq 2(n + \frac{1}{2})$ $n \leq 2$

Applications

19. Five dollars, plus three times the daily rental charge for a rug cleaning machine, is $47. What is the daily rental charge? *(Section 4-2)* $14

20. The sale price of a book is $9.72. The rate of discount is 25%. Find the list price and the amount of discount. *(Section 4-3)*

21. Jean and Emily have 110 old coins in their combined collections. Jean has 25 less than twice the number of coins that Emily has. How many coins does each girl have? *(Section 4-3)*

22. The width of a rug is 2 meters less than the length. The perimeter of the rug is 28 meters. Find the length and width of the rug. *(Section 4-4)*

23. In triangle ABC, the measure of angle B is three times the measure of angle A, and the measure of angle C is five times the measure of angle A. Find the measure of each angle. *(Section 4-4)*

24. Mr. Sanchez is 25 years older than his son. In 15 years he will be twice as old as his son. Find their present ages. *(Section 4-6)*

25. Jim threw the javelin four times for distances of 165, 170, 158, and 178 feet. What is the least distance he must get on his fifth throw in order to average at least 170 feet for the five throws? *(Section 4-9)*   179 ft

26. Sally is paid $245 per week plus an $8 commission on each major appliance she sells. How many major appliances must she sell in order to make at least $325 per week? *(Section 4-9)*   10

Equations and Inequalities   **155**

In this "cumulative review" of word problems, note that each problem

Review of Word Problems: Chapters 1–4

is referenced to the related section.

1. A 946–milliliter bottle of lemon juice costs $1.29. A 315–milliliter bottle of the same brand of lemon juice costs $0.49. Which size is the better buy? *(Section 1–4)*   946 ml

2. At sunrise, the temperature was $-5°C$. At noon, the temperature had risen 8 degrees, and by sunset it had fallen 6 degrees. What was the temperature at sunset? *(Section 2–3)* $-3°C$

3. The average temperature on Monday was 4°C. The average temperature on Tuesday was $-3°C$. Find the difference between the two temperatures. *(Section 2–4)* $7°C$

4. In five consecutive days, the following gains and losses in the price of a stock were reported: $+1\frac{1}{2}, -\frac{3}{4}, -\frac{1}{4}, +\frac{1}{2}, -\frac{3}{8}$ Find the average change over the five days. *(Section 2–7)* $+\frac{1}{8}$

5. John Hammond earns $1450 per month plus a 5% commission on the sales he makes. Last month he earned a total of $1720. What were his sales that month? *(Section 3–4)* $5400

6. The sum of the measures of two angles is 180°. Their measures can be represented by x and $(2x + 15)$. Find the measure of each angle. *(Section 3–6)*   55°; 125°

7. Maria earns $1120 a month as a computer programmer. She spends $56 per month on entertainment. What per cent of her monthly income is spent on entertainment? *(Section 3–7)*   5%

8. A basketball team won 24 games. This was 60% of all the games they played. How many games did the team play? *(Section 3–7)*   40 games

9. The sum of three consecutive odd integers is 93. Find the integers. *(Section 3–8)*   29, 31, 33

10. Five times the cost of a ticket, decreased by $2, equals $16.75. Find the cost of a ticket. *(Section 4–2)* $3.75

11. Janet bought skis and ski boots for $175. The boots cost $23 more than the skis. What was the price of the skis? *(Section 4–3)* $76

12. The sale price of a typewriter is $230. The discount rate is 20%. Find the list price and the amount of discount. *(Section 4–3)* $287.50; $57.50

13. The length of a rectangular court is 10 meters less than twice its width. The perimeter of the court is 106 meters. Find the length and width of the court. *(Section 4–4)*   length: 32 m; width: 21 m

14. Keith is 8 years younger than Sean. In 4 years, Keith will be $\frac{2}{3}$ as old as Sean is then. Find their present ages. *(Section 4–6)*   Sean: 20; Keith: 12

15. In the last three weeks, Carla earned $38, $45, and $52. How much must she earn this week in order to have average earnings of $48 per week for the four weeks? *(Section 4–9)* $57

The Test Booklet contains another form of the cumulative review.

Cumulative Review: Chapters 1–4

Choose the best answer. Choose *a, b, c,* or *d.*

1. What is the cost in dollars of *r* stamps at 30¢ each? **b**

   a. 30*r*   **b.** 0.30*r*   **c.** $\dfrac{r}{30}$ **d.** $\dfrac{r}{0.30}$

2. Find the value of $m - 3n$ when $m = 18$ and $n = 5$. **c**

   a. 75   **b.** -3 **c.** 3   **d.** -49

3. What is the value of *A* in the formula $A = P(1 + 0.06t)$ when $P = \$700$ and $t = 2.5$ years? **a**

   a. $805   **b.** $8050   **c.** $1750   **d.** $743.75

4. What is the solution set of $3(4 + x) = 12 + 3x$, where the replacement set is $\{0, -4, 8, -12\}$? **d**

   a. $\{0\}$ **b.** $\{-4\}$ **c.** ϕ **d.** $\{0, -4, 8, -12\}$

5. Which statement is false? **c**

   a. N ⊂ Q   **b.** Ir ⊂ R   **c.** I ⊂ N   **d.** N ⊂ W

6. Which number is a rational number? **b**

   a. π **b.** $\sqrt{49}$ **c.** $\sqrt{7}$ **d.** $\sqrt{9 \cdot 2}$

7. What is the name of the postulate illustrated by $-2(x + 3) = -2x + (-2 \cdot 3)$? **d**

   a. Commutative for Multiplication   **b.** Multiplicative Inverse
   c. Additive Inverse   **d.** Distributive

8. What is the solution set of $-y = 13$? **b**

   a. $\{13\}$ **b.** $\{-13\}$ **c.** $\{12\}$ **d.** $\{14\}$

9. Which can replace ___?___ in $|-7\frac{1}{2}|$ ___?___ -8 and make a true sentence? **a**

   a. $>$ **b.** $<$ **c.** $=$ **d.** $\leq$

10. Which expression does not equal -8? **c**

    a. $2 \cdot -4$ **b.** $-16 - (-8)$ **c.** $0 - (-8)$ **d.** $0 - 8$

11. Simplify: $7 - [4 + (2 \cdot -6)]$ **d**

    a. -9 **b.** -15 **c.** -1 **d.** 15

12. Evaluate $2r - 7s - 9$ when $r = -1.5$ and $s = -3$. **a**

    a. 9   **b.** -9 **c.** -19 **d.** 9.5

13. For which of the numbers -5, 0, and 5 is $|x|$ positive? **c**

    a. -5, 0, and 5   **b.** 5   **c.** -5 and 5   **d.** 0

14. Solve $8 + 7a - 5a = 2a + 8$, where the replacement set is $\{-10, 0, 10\}$. **a**

    a. All three   **b.** Only 0   **c.** Only -10 and 10   **d.** Only 10

Cumulative Review: Chapters 1–4   **157**

15. Simplify: $1.8m - 6n + 3m + 2.4n$ **c**

    a. $4.8m^2 - 3.6n^2$ **b.** $1.2mn$ **c.** $4.8m - 3.6n$ **d.** $4.8m - 4.6n$

16. Which expression is equal to y?   **d**

    a. $\frac{4}{3}(-\frac{3}{4}y)$ **b.** $-\frac{3}{4}y + \frac{3}{4}$ **c.** $-\frac{3}{4}y - \frac{3}{4}$ **d.** $-\frac{4}{3}(-\frac{3}{4}y)$

17. If t is an integer, which of the following represents three consecutive integers?   **c**

    a. $t, 2t, 3t$ **b.** $t, t + 2, t + 4$ **c.** $t, t + 1, t + 2$ **d.** $t, t + 1, t + 4$

18. Which equation does not have $\{-7\}$ as its solution set?   **a**

    a. $\frac{1}{2}x = -14$ **b.** $x + (-7) = -14$ **c.** $2x = -14$ **d.** $-x + 7 = 14$

19. What is the solution set of $5a - 2 = 17$?   **b**

    a. $\{3\}$ **b.** $\{3\frac{4}{5}\}$ **c.** $\{-3\}$ **d.** $\{-3\frac{4}{5}\}$

20. Which of the following has the same solution set as $8 - 3(2x - 5) = 6$?   **c**

    a. $8 - 6x - 15 = 6$ **b.** $8 - 6x + 5 = 6$ **c.** $8 - 6x + 15 = 6$ **d.** $10x - 25 = 6$

21. The equation $5m + 7m - 8 = 4.7$ is equivalent to which of the following equations?   **b**

    a. $12m^2 - 8 = 4.7$ **b.** $12m = 12.7$ **c.** $12m = -3.3$ **d.** $4m = 4.7$

22. The measures of the angles of a triangle are represented by x, $2x$, and $3x - 60$. Find the measure of the smallest angle.   **b**

    a. $20°$ **b.** $40°$ **c.** $60°$ **d.** $80°$

23. At an average speed of 70 kilometers per hour, how many hours will it take to travel 455 kilometers?   **c**

    a. 6   **b.** 7   **c.** 6.5   **d.** $\frac{455}{140}$

24. A number is 0.86 less than r. Represent the number by an algebraic expression.   **d**

    a. $0.86 - r$ **b.** $r + 0.86$ **c.** $n - r - 0.86$ **d.** $r - 0.86$

25. Twice Mary's allowance decreased by $6.82 is $3.18. How much is Mary's allowance?   **a**

    a. $5.00   **b.** $10.00   **c.** $3.64   **d.** $1.82

26. The length of a rectangle is three times its width. If the perimeter is 240 centimeters, what is the length of the rectangle?   **c**

    a. 30 cm   **b.** 60 cm   **c.** 90 cm   **d.** 180 cm

27. What is the solution set of $-3(2x - 8) = -5x + 2$?   **c**

    a. $\{-10\}$ **b.** $\{-22\}$ **c.** $\{22\}$ **d.** $\{-26\}$

28. Solve: $n + 7 < -15$ **a**

    a. $n < -22$ **b.** $n < -8$ **c.** $n < 8$ **d.** $n > -22$

29. Solve: $-4n + 6 > -n - 30$ **c**

    a. $n < -12$ **b.** $n > 12$ **c.** $n < 12$ **d.** $n > -12$

Preparing for College Entrance Tests

Accuracy and **speed** are important in College Entrance tests. If you can recognize situations in which the basic postulates for the real numbers can be applied, it is often possible to reduce the amount of time needed to determine a correct answer.

REMEMBER: The fewer the computations, the less possibility there is for error!

EXAMPLE: $\dfrac{12(16-8)-8(16-8)}{4} = \underline{\quad?\quad}$ (a) 2   (b) 4   (c) 8   (d) 16

Solution: By the distributive postulate, $12x - 8x = (12 - 8)x = 4x$.

Thus, $\dfrac{12(16-8)-8(16-8)}{4} = \dfrac{\overset{1}{4}(16-8)}{\underset{1}{4}}$

$$= 16 - 8, \text{ or } \mathbf{8} \qquad \textbf{Answer: c}$$

Choose the best answer. Choose *a*, *b*, *c*, or *d*.

1. $\dfrac{6(15-3)-3(15-3)}{3} = \underline{\quad?\quad}$ a

   (a) 12   (b) 24   (c) 45   (d) 72

2. $\dfrac{2(21+3)-4(21+3)}{2} = \underline{\quad?\quad}$ c

   (a) -72 (b) -48 (c) -24 (d) 24

3. $\dfrac{3(38-14)+5(38-14)}{24} = \underline{\quad?\quad}$ a

   (a) 8   (b) 15   (c) 18   (d) 24

4. $\dfrac{6(31-29)-2(31-29)}{2} = \underline{\quad?\quad}$ b

   (a) 2   (b) 4   (c) 6   (d) 8

5. $3(20-5) - 4(20-5) + (20-5) = \underline{\quad?\quad}$ c

   (a) -30 (b) -15 (c) 0   (d) 15

6. $\dfrac{42+42+42+42}{4} = \underline{\quad?\quad}$ $\left(\text{Think: } \dfrac{4(42)}{4} = \underline{\quad?\quad}\right)$ c

   (a) 4   (b) $40\frac{1}{2}$ (c) 42   (d) 84

7. $\dfrac{36+36+36+36+36}{36} = \underline{\quad?\quad}$ a

   (a) 5   (b) 18   (c) 36   (d) 72

8. $(25-38) - (20-38) = \underline{\quad?\quad}$ d

   (a) -91 (b) -71 (c) 0   (d) 5

This feature is optional. Each focuses on a specific type of problem that appears in many college entrance tests. The example is intended to illustrate how the student might best approach the solution of that type of problem. Each also relates to the algebra content that has been studied up to this point. Additional practice of each type is provided in the Teacher's Manual portion of the Teacher's Edition.

See the comments on page 159.

Preparing for College Entrance Tests

It is not always necessary to solve an equation for the variable in order to answer a question about the variable.

REMEMBER: It is important to watch for ways to save yourself time and work on College Entrance tests!

EXAMPLE: If $2n - 6 = 1$, what is the value of $n - 3$?

(a) $3\frac{1}{2}$ (b) 2 (c) $\frac{1}{2}$ (d) -1

Think: By the distributive postulate, $2(n - 3) = 2n - 6$.
Thus, $2n - 6 = 2(n - 3)$. Solve for $n - 3$.

Solution: $2(n - 3) = 1$
$n - 3 = \frac{1}{2}$ **Answer: c**

Choose the best answer. Choose *a, b, c,* or *d.*

1. If $2x + 4 = 6$, what is the value of $x + 2$?   b
   (a) 1 (b) 3 (c) 6 (d) 12

2. If $3y - 3 = 2$, what is the value of $y - 1$?   b
   (a) -1 (b) $\frac{2}{3}$ (c) $1\frac{2}{3}$ (d) 2

3. If $4n - 12 = -8$, what is the value of $n - 3$?   c
   (a) 2 (b) 1 (c) -2 (d) -8

4. If $4 - 8a = 5$, what is the value of $1 - 2a$?   d
   (a) $-\frac{1}{8}$ (b) $\frac{1}{8}$ (c) $\frac{3}{4}$ (d) $1\frac{1}{4}$

5. If $6c + 8 = 3$, what is the value of $3c + 4$?   c
   (a) -1 (b) $-\frac{5}{6}$ (c) $1\frac{1}{2}$ (d) 3

6. If $9p - 6 = -1$, what is the value of $3p - 2$?   c
   (a) 1 (b) $\frac{1}{3}$ (c) $-\frac{1}{3}$ (d) -4

7. If $4p - 4 = \frac{1}{2}$, what is the value of $p - 1$?   a
   (a) $\frac{1}{8}$ (b) $\frac{1}{4}$ (c) $1\frac{1}{8}$ (d) 2

8. If $\frac{1}{3}x + \frac{1}{3} = 1$, what is the value of $x + 1$?   d
   (a) $\frac{1}{3}$ (b) $\frac{2}{3}$ (c) 2 (d) 3

9. If $\frac{n}{4} = 3$, what is the value of $\frac{n}{3}$?   c
   (a) $\frac{1}{4}$ (b) $\frac{3}{4}$ (c) 4 (d) 12

10. If $\frac{y}{6} = 4$, what is the value of $\frac{y}{4}$?   d
    (a) $\frac{1}{6}$ (b) $\frac{2}{3}$ (c) $\frac{3}{2}$ (d) 6

160   *Preparing for College Entrance Tests*

CHAPTER **5** **Graphing Relations and Functions**

Teaching Suggestions p. M-18

5–1 Solving Equations for a Variable

Problems in science and business often involve solving an equation for one variable in terms of the others. The procedures for solving are illustrated in the table below. To solve for x in the equation

$$x + a = b,$$

you find x in terms of a and b. Compare the solutions of the given equations in the table with those of the general equations.

Quick Quiz

State what you would do to each side of the equation to get x alone on one side of the equation.

1. $x + 8 = 15$
   Ans: Add −8 to each side.
2. $x - 9 = 3$
   Ans: Add 9 to each side.
3. $3x + 5 = 10$
   Ans: Add −5 to each side. Then multiply each side by $\frac{1}{3}$.
4. $-\frac{1}{4}x - 8 = 3$
   Ans: Add 8 to each side. Then multiply each side by −4.

Additional Examples

1. **a.** Solve for x: $x - 9 = 6$
   Ans: $x = 15$
   b. Solve for x: $x - c = d$
   Ans: $x = c + d$
2. **a.** Solve for x: $6x + 7 = 49$
   Ans: $x = 7$
   b. Solve for x: $6x + p = q$
   Ans: $x = \dfrac{q - p}{6}$
3. **a.** Solve for x: $-8 = -4x$
   Ans: $x = 2$
   b. Solve for x: $y = mx$
   Ans: $x = \dfrac{y}{m}$

Given Equation	General Equation
Solve for x.	Solve for x.
$x + 7 = 12$	$x + a = b$
$x + 7 + (-7) = 12 + (-7)$	$x + a + (-a) = b + (-a)$
$x = 5$	$x = b + (-a)$
Check: $x + 7 = 12$	**Check:** $x + a = b$
$5 + 7 \overset{?}{=} 12$	$b + (-a) + a \overset{?}{=} b$
$12 \overset{?}{=} 12$ Yes ✔	$b \overset{?}{=} b$ Yes ✔
The solution is **5**.	The solution is $b + (-a)$, or **$b - a$**.
Solve for w.	Solve for w.
$38 = 16 + 2w$	$p = 2 + 2w$
$-16 + 38 = -16 + 16 + 2w$	$p - 2 = 2w$
$22 = 2w$	$\frac{1}{2}(p - 2) = \frac{1}{2}(2w)$
$\frac{1}{2}(22) = \frac{1}{2}(2w)$	$\dfrac{p - 2}{2} = w$
$w = 11$	
Check: $38 = 16 + 2w$	**Check:** $p = 2 + 2w$
$38 \overset{?}{=} 16 + 2(11)$	$p \overset{?}{=} 2 + 2\left(\dfrac{p - 2}{2}\right)$
$38 \overset{?}{=} 38$ Yes ✔	$p \overset{?}{=} 2 + p - 2$
The solution is **11**.	$p \overset{?}{=} p$ Yes ✔
	The solution is $\dfrac{p - 2}{2}$.
Solve for t.	Solve for t.
$-12 = -3t$	$d = rt$
$4 = t$ The solution is **4**.	$\dfrac{d}{r} = t$ The solution is $\dfrac{d}{r}$.
The check is left for you.	The check is left for you.

162   *Chapter 5*

CLASSROOM EXERCISES

Solve each equation for x. Check.

1. $x + b = 7$ $x = 7 - b$
2. $x + a = c$ $x = c - a$
3. $x - t = 2$ $x = t + 2$
4. $x - a = b$ $x = b + a$
5. $3x = a$ $x = \dfrac{a}{3}$
6. $ax = b$ $x = \dfrac{b}{a}$

WRITTEN EXERCISES

A   Solve the first equation in each pair. Then use the same procedure to solve the second equation for x. Check each solution.

1. $\dfrac{x}{6} = 24$; $\dfrac{x}{a} = b$ $x = 144$; $x = ab$
2. $5x + 4 = 10$; $ax + b = c$
3. $\dfrac{3x}{5} = 2$; $\dfrac{ax}{b} = c$ $x = \dfrac{10}{3}$; $x = \dfrac{bc}{a}$
4. $x + 6 = 8 + \dfrac{1}{4}$; $x + a = b + c$
5. $5x + 4 = 10$; $5x + a = b$ $x = \dfrac{6}{5}$; $x = \dfrac{b - a}{5}$
6. $-2x = 16$; $-ax = b$
7. $3(x + 4) = 8$; $3(x + a) = b$
8. $-x + 4 = -5$; $-x + a = b$
9. $-2x + 6 = 0$; $-2x + a = b$
10. $3x + 5 = -7$; $3x + a = -b$

Solve each formula for the variable indicated.

11. Formula for the circumference of a circle: $C = \pi d$ Solve for d. $d = \dfrac{C}{\pi}$
12. Formula for the area of a parallelogram: $A = bh$ Solve for b. $b = \dfrac{A}{h}$
13. Formula for the area of a triangle: $A = \frac{1}{2}bh$ Solve for h. $h = \dfrac{2A}{b}$
14. Formula for the perimeter of a rectangle: $p = 2l + 2w$ Solve for w.
15. Distance/rate/time formula: $d = rt$ Solve for r. $r = \dfrac{d}{t}$
16. Simple interest formula: $i = prt$ Solve for t. $t = \dfrac{i}{pr}$
17. Simple interest formula: $i = prt$ Solve for r. $r = \dfrac{i}{pt}$
18. Formula for the volume of a rectangular box: $V = lwh$ Solve for h.
19. Formula for calculating a Celsius temperature from a Fahrenheit temperature: $C = \frac{5}{9}(F - 32)$ Solve for F.
20. Formula for the sum of the measures of the angles of a triangle: $a + b + c = 180°$ Solve for b. $b = 180 - a - c$

Solve each formula for the unknown variable. Then substitute the given values to find the required length.

21. $C = \pi d$

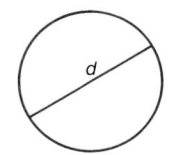

$C = 22.6\pi$; $d = \underline{\quad ? \quad}$

22. $P = a + b + c$

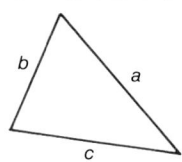

$P = 29.9$; $a = 11.4$;
$b = 7.9$; $c = \underline{\quad ? \quad}$

23. $P = 2l + 2w$

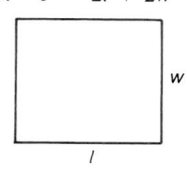

$P = 84$; $w = 20$;
$l = \underline{\quad ? \quad}$

Assignment Guide
Minimal p. 163: 1–23
Average pp. 163–164: 2–38 even
Above Average pp. 163–164: 6–38 even, 39–44

Additional Answers
Written Exercises

2. $x = \dfrac{6}{5}$; $x = \dfrac{c - b}{a}$
4. $x = 2\dfrac{1}{4}$; $x = b + c - a$
6. $x = -8$; $x = -\dfrac{b}{a}$
7. $x = -\dfrac{4}{3}$ or $-1\dfrac{1}{3}$; $x = \dfrac{b}{3} - a$
8. $x = 9$; $x = a - b$
9. $x = 3$; $x = \dfrac{b - a}{-2}$
10. $x = -4$; $x = \dfrac{-b - a}{3}$
14. $w = \dfrac{p - 2l}{2}$
18. $h = \dfrac{V}{lw}$
19. $F = \dfrac{9}{5}C + 32$
21. $d = \dfrac{C}{\pi}$; $d = 22.6$
22. $c = P - a - b$; $c = 10.6$
23. $l = \dfrac{P - 2w}{2}$; $l = 22$

24. $b = \dfrac{A}{h}$; $b = 7.9$

25. $w = \dfrac{A}{l}$; $w = 2.8$

26. $h = \dfrac{2A}{b}$; $h = 16$

27. $n = \dfrac{b - a}{2}$

28. $n = \dfrac{3a}{2}$

29. $n = 3a + b$

30. $n = \dfrac{a + b}{2}$

31. $n = 5b - 3a$

32. $n = \dfrac{5a + b}{2}$

33. $n = b + c - a$

34. $n = \dfrac{b + c - 2a}{2}$

35. $n = 4b$

36. $n = a - b$

37. $n = \dfrac{b + c}{a}$

38. $n = \dfrac{b - ac}{a}$ or $n = \dfrac{b}{a} - c$

39. $b = \dfrac{c}{a} - n$

40. $a = \dfrac{n}{b + n}$

41. $a = \dfrac{c}{n} - b$

42. $n = \dfrac{c}{b} + a$

43. $b = \dfrac{2A}{h} - b'$

44. $r = \dfrac{A - p}{pt}$

Solve each formula for the unknown variable. Then find the required length.

24. $A = bh$

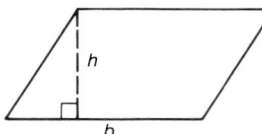

$A = 36.34$ square units;
$h = 4.6$; $b = $ ___?___

25. $A = lw$

$A = 36.4$ square units;
$l = 13$; $w = $ ___?___

26. $A = \frac{1}{2}bh$

$A = 72$ square units;
$b = 9$; $h = $ ___?___

B Solve each equation for n. Check each solution.

27. $2n + a = b$

28. $2n + 5a = 8a$

29. $6a + 2b = 2n$

30. $2n - a = b$

31. $3a + n = 5b$

32. $2n - b = 5a$

33. $n + a = b + c$

34. $2a + 2n = b + c$

35. $-n = -4b$

36. $-n + a = b$

37. $an = b + c$

38. $an + ac = b$

C Solve each equation for the variable indicated. Check each solution.

39. $a(b + n) = c$ for b

40. $\dfrac{n}{a} = b + n$ for a

41. $(a + b)n = c$ for a

42. $b(n - a) = c$ for n

43. $A = \frac{1}{2}h(b + b')$ for b

44. $A = p(1 + rt)$ for r

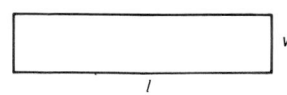

See the Solution Key.

Unscramble the letters below to form 10 words introduced in Chapters 1–4. Then use the circled letters to find someone whose name lives on after 2400 years.

1. □ □ □ □ ⊙ □ □
   T E N G I R E

2. □ □ □ □ ⊙
   M Y P T E

3. □ ⊙ □ □ □ □ □ □
   B A R A L I V E

4. □ □ □ □ ⊙ □ □ □
   T A R A L I O N

5. □ □ □ □ □ □ ⊙
   P E N T E X O N

6. ⊙ □ □ □ □ □ □ □
   M E R E T R I P E

7. □ ⊙ □ □ □
   H E L O W

8. ⊙ □ □ □ □ □ □ □
   L I O N O U S T

9. □ □ □ □ ⊙ □ □
   H O M E T E R

10. □ □ □ □ □ □ ⊙
    R O A M F U L

Answer: □ □ □ □ □ □ □ □ □ □

Problem Solving and Applications

OBJECTIVE: To solve distance/rate/time problems

5–2 Distance/Rate/Time

To solve distance/rate/time problems, you use the following formula.

Distance = Rate · Time   or $d = rt$

In solving distance/rate/time problems, it is helpful to organize the given information in a table. This will help you to represent the unknowns (Condition 1). Drawing a figure will help you to write the equation (Condition 2).

EXAMPLE 1 Two cars 635 kilometers apart start at the same time and travel toward each other (Condition 2). One car travels at a rate of 75 kilometers per hour (abbreviated: 75 km/h); the other travels at a rate of 52 kilometers per hour. In how many hours will the cars meet (Condition 1)?

Solution: 1⃣ Organize the information in a table. Represent the unknowns.

Let t = the number of hours each car travels.

	Rate r	Time t	Distance $d = rt$
Car A	75	t	$75t$
Car B	52	t	$52t$

2⃣ Draw a figure. Use the figure and the table to write an equation.

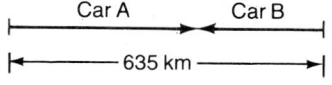

$$\underset{\substack{\downarrow \\ 75t}}{\text{Distance for Car A}} + \underset{\substack{\downarrow \\ 52t}}{\text{Distance for Car B}} = \underset{\substack{\downarrow \\ 635}}{\text{Total Distance}}$$

3⃣ Solve the equation.

$$75t + 52t = 635$$
$$127t = 635$$
$$t = 5$$

Check: 4⃣ Does the total distance covered equal 635 kilometers?

$75(5) + 52(5) = 635$?   Yes ✓   The cars will meet in **5 hours**.

The following procedure summarizes the steps shown in Example 1.

Procedure

To solve distance/rate/time problems:

1⃣ Organize the given information in a table. Use this information to represent the unknowns (Condition 1).

2⃣ Draw a figure to represent the information. Use this figure and the table to write an equation for the problem (Condition 2).

3⃣ Solve the equation.

4⃣ Check your answer with the conditions of the problem. Answer the question.

Graphing Relations and Functions   **165**

Teaching Suggestions p. M-18

Quick Quiz
1. Solve for x: $3x - a = b$
   Ans: $x = \dfrac{a + b}{3}$
2. Solve for x: $x - a = b - c$
   Ans: $x = a + b - c$
3. Solve $A = \frac{1}{2}bh$ for b.
   Ans: $b = \dfrac{2A}{h}$
4. Solve $i = prt$ for p.
   Ans: $p = \dfrac{i}{pr}$

Additional Examples
Example 1
1. Two hikers 35 kilometers apart start at the same time and travel toward each other (Condition 2). One hiker travels at the rate of 6 kilometers per hour, the other travels at the rate of 8 kilometers per hour. In how many hours will the hikers meet (Condition 1)?
   Ans: $2\frac{1}{2}$ hours
2. A freight train and a passenger train start at the same time from stations 630 kilometers apart and travel toward each other (Condition 2). The freight train travels at the rate of 70 kilometers per hour; the passenger train travels at the rate of 140 kilometers per hour. In how many hours will they pass each other (Condition 1)?
   Ans: 3 hours

1. Meg and her brother Tom left home by car at the same time traveling in opposite directions. Tom's rate was 8 kilometers per hour greater than Meg's rate. After 4 hours, they were 480 kilometers apart. Find the rate of travel for each person.
   Ans: Meg: 56 km/h;
   Tom: 64 km/h
2. Two jets leave from the same airport at the same time, one traveling north and one traveling south. The rate of the northbound jet is 50 miles per hour slower than the rate of the southbound jet. In 5 hours, they are 6250 miles apart. How fast is each jet flying?
   Ans: northbound: 600 mph;
   southbound: 650 mph

Additional Answers
1. Hiker A: r, 6, $6r$;
   Hiker B: $2r$, 6, $12r$
2. Susan: 45, t, $45t$;
   Joann: 50, $t - 3$, $50(t - 3)$
3. Passenger: $2r$, 3, $6r$;
   Freight: r, 3, $3r$

EXAMPLE 2 Marsha and her brother Don left home by car at the same time, traveling in opposite directions. Don's rate was 6 miles per hour (abbreviated mph) less than Marsha's rate. After 10 hours, they were 940 miles apart. Find the rate of travel for each person.

Solution: 1 Let r = Marsha's rate.
Then $r - 6$ = Don's rate.

	Rate r	Time t	Distance $d = rt$
Marsha	r	10	$10r$
Don	$r - 6$	10	$10(r - 6)$

2 Draw a figure.

Marsha   Don

|← —— d = 940 miles —— →|

3 $10r + 10(r - 6) = 940$ ← Marsha's Distance + Don's Distance = Total Distance

$10r + 10r - 60 = 940$

$20r - 60 = 940$

$20r = 1000$

$r = 50$ ← Don't forget to find Don's rate.

$r - 6 = 44$

Check: 4 Is Don's rate 6 mph less than Marsha's?
$44 = 50 - 6$?   Yes ✔

After 10 hours, were they 940 miles apart?
$50(10) + 44(10) = 940$?   Yes ✔

Marsha's rate is **50 mph** and Don's rate is **44 mph**.

CLASSROOM EXERCISES

In Exercises 1–4, use the given information to complete the table.

1. Two hikers start toward each other at the same time from different towns. They meet in 6 hours. The rate of one hiker is twice the rate of the other.

	r	t	$d = rt$
Hiker A	?	?	?
Hiker B	?	?	?

2. Susan and Joann leave from the same place driving in opposite directions, but Joann leaves 3 hours later than Susan. Susan's average rate of speed is 45 kilometers per hour and Joann's average rate is 50 kilometers per hour.

	r	t	$d = rt$
Susan	?	?	?
Joann	?	?	?

3. A passenger train and a freight train start at the same time from stations which are 648 kilometers apart. The rate of the passenger train is twice the rate of the freight train. They pass each other in 3 hours.

	r	t	$d = rt$
Passenger	?	?	?
Freight	?	?	?

4. Jack and Harry started on bicycles at the same time from two different places and rode toward each other. Jack traveled at 12 kilometers per hour and Harry traveled at 16 kilometers per hour. They met in 5 hours. Jack: 12, 5, 60; Harry: 16, 5, 80

	r	t	d = rt
Jack	?	?	?
Harry	?	?	?

Assignment Guide
Minimal
Day 1 p. 167: 1–5
Day 2 pp. 167–168: 6–11
Average
Day 1 p. 167: 1–8
Day 2 pp. 167–168: 9–15
Above Average
Day 1 pp. 167–168: 3–11
Day 2 p. 168: 12–16

WORD PROBLEMS

A   Solve each problem.

1. Two automobiles start at the same time at the same place and travel in opposite directions. One travels at the rate of 45 kilometers per hour and the other at the rate of 40 kilometers per hour. In how many hours will they be 225 kilometers apart? 3 hours

2. Two boys on bicycles start from the same place at the same time. One rides at the rate of 12 kilometers per hour and the other at 8 kilometers per hour. They travel in opposite directions. In how many hours will they be 24 kilometers apart? $1\frac{1}{5}$ hour

3. One car traveling 40 kilometers an hour left a certain place 4 hours later than another car traveling in the same direction at the rate of 30 kilometers an hour. In how many hours will the faster car overtake the other? 12 hours

4. Frank and Bob start from home in their cars and travel in opposite directions. Frank's rate of speed is twice Bob's. In 4 hours they are 480 kilometers apart. Find the rate at which each travels. Bob: 40 km/h; Frank: 80 km/h

5. A freight train traveling at an average rate of 30 kilometers per hour is followed two hours later from the same station by a passenger train traveling at an average rate of 50 kilometers per hour. How many hours after the passenger train leaves will it pass the freight train? 3 hours

6. Two jets leave Chicago at the same time, one flying east and one flying west. The rate of the second jet is 100 kilometers per hour faster than the first. In 3 hours, they are 4800 kilometers apart. Find the rate at which each is traveling. 750 km/h; 850 km/h

7. A plane leaves an airport at ten o'clock, flying due north. Another plane starts from the same airport at twelve o'clock, flying due south at twice the speed of the other plane. At two o'clock they are 1920 kilometers apart. Find the rate of speed of each. 240 km/h; 480 km/h

8. Mildred left camp 4 hours after Margaret did. They traveled in opposite directions. Mildred drove at 48 kilometers per hour and Margaret at 72 kilometers per hour. How many hours after Mildred left were the two girls 1008 kilometers apart? 6 hours

9. Ann starts from a certain place, traveling at 4 kilometers per hour. Five hours later, Fred starts from the same place and travels in the same direction at 6 kilometers per hour. In how many hours will Fred overtake Ann? 10 hours

10. A freight train leaves a station and travels at a rate of 30 miles per hour. Two hours later, an express train leaves the same station traveling in the same direction at a rate of 50 miles per hour. In how many hours will the express train overtake the freight train? 3 hours

11. Meg left home on her bicycle traveling at the rate of 6 miles per hour. One hour later, her twin sister, Mary, set out on the same route traveling at the rate of 8 miles per hour. In how many hours will Mary overtake Meg? 3 hours

B

12. How far can a person drive out into the country at an average rate of 64 kilometers per hour and return over the same road at an average rate of 48 kilometers per hour if the total trip takes 7 hours? (HINT: Use the table at the right. Remember that the distance going is the same as the distance returning.) 192 km

	r	t	d = rt
Going	64	t	64t
Returning	48	7 − t	48(7 − t)

13. A round trip in a helicopter lasted $4\frac{1}{2}$ hours. The average rate going was 160 km/h; the average rate returning was 80 km/h. What was the helicopter's greatest distance from the heliport? 240 km

14. A pilot plans to make a round-trip flight lasting 2.5 hours. How far can the pilot plan to go if the rate going is 480 kilometers per hour and the rate returning is 320 kilometers per hour? 480 km

15. Lisa left home in a car that was traveling at the rate of 48 kilometers per hour. She walked home at the rate of 6 kilometers per hour. The round trip took 1.5 hours. How far did Lisa ride? 8 km

16. A cyclist had been traveling 24 km/h for 8 hours when he was overtaken by a motorist who left the same starting point 5 hours after the cyclist. Find the motorist's speed. 64 km/h

17. Dick jogs from his house to school at a rate of 9 kilometers per hour. On the return trip from school, he jogs at a rate of 6 kilometers per hour. The round trip takes 1 hour 15 minutes. How far is the school from Dick's house? 4.5 km

18. A train traveling at 80 kilometers per hour started from Westville toward Easton. An hour later, a train traveling at 64 kilometers per hour started from Easton toward Westville. Westville and Easton are 656 kilometers apart. How long will it take the engines of the two trains to pass each other? (The trains are on parallel tracks.) 4 hours

OBJECTIVE: To graph ordered pairs on the coordinate plane

5–3 Graphing Ordered Pairs

Teaching Suggestions p. M-18

A flat surface, such as a chalkboard, can be thought of as representing a **plane**. A plane extends on and on in all directions. To locate, or **graph**, points on a plane, you use two number lines that are **perpendicular** to each other. (That is, they meet at a 90° angle.) The horizontal number line is called the **x axis**; the vertical number line is called the **y axis**.

To graph a point P in a plane, you use an **ordered pair** of numbers

$$(x, y).$$

The first number, x, shows distance to the right or left of the vertical axis. The second number, y, shows distance above or below the horizontal axis. Thus, in the figure at the right, $P(2, 3)$ is 2 units to the right of the y axis and 3 units above the x axis.

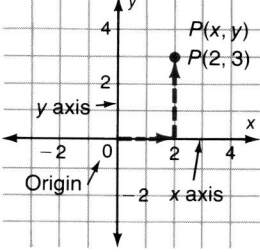

The axes cross at the **origin**. The origin is represented by the ordered pair $(0, 0)$.

EXAMPLE 1 Graph each point on the same set of axes.

    a. $Q(3, 4)$ **b.** $R(-6, -2)$ **c.** $S(6, -1)$ **d.** $T(-5, 5)$

Solutions:

a. For $Q(3, 4)$: Start at the origin. Move 3 units to the right, then 4 units up.

b. For $R(-6, -2)$: Start at the origin. Move 6 units to the left, then 2 units down.

c. For $S(6, -1)$: Start at the origin. Move 6 units to the right, then 1 unit down.

d. For $T(-5, 5)$: Start at the origin. Move 5 units to the left, then 5 units up.

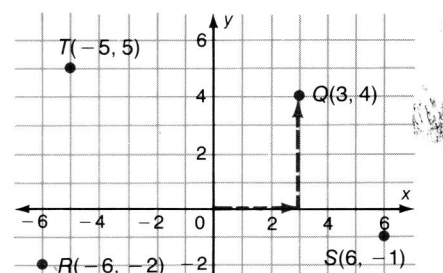

The numbers of an ordered pair are the **coordinates** of a point. The first number, or **x coordinate**, is the **abscissa**; the second number, or **y coordinate**, is the **ordinate**. Because the plane associates number pairs or coordinates with points, it is called the **coordinate plane**. The axes separate the coordinate plane into four regions or **quadrants**. *The axes are not in any quadrant.*

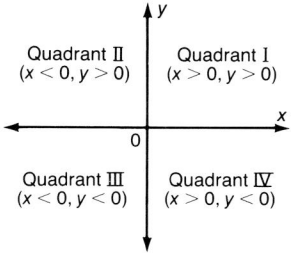

Quick Quiz

1. Bonnie and Lynn started on bicycles at the same time from towns which are 66 kilometers apart and rode toward each other. Bonnie traveled at 20 kilometers per hour and Lynn traveled at 24 kilometers per hour. In how many hours will they meet?
   Ans: 1 hours

2. Pete and Tony start from their clubhouse in their cars and travel in opposite directions. Pete drives 10 miles per hour faster than Tony. In 5 hours, they are 400 miles apart. Find each person's rate of travel.
   Ans: Tony: 35 mph; Pete: 45 mph

Additional Examples
Example 1

1. Graph each point on the same set of axes.
   a. $F(2, -3)$ **b.** $G(4, 3)$
   c. $H(-1, -4)$ **d.** $I(-3, 3)$
   Ans:

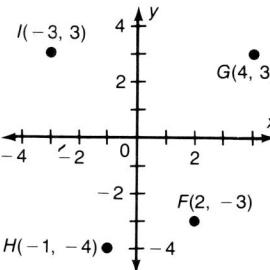

Graphing Relations and Functions   **169**

Additional Examples
Example 2
Name the quadrant or axis
on which each point lies.
1. $E(0, 3)$ **Ans: y axis**
2. $T(-9, 5)$ **Ans: Quadrant II**
3. $C(-7, 0)$ **Ans: x axis**
4. $H(-9, -8)$
   Ans: Quadrant III

Assignment Guide
Minimal pp. 170–171: 1–25 odd
Average pp. 170–172:
1–41 odd
Above Average pp. 170–172:
3, 6, 9, . . . 39, 42–48

Additional Answers
Written Exercises

1.

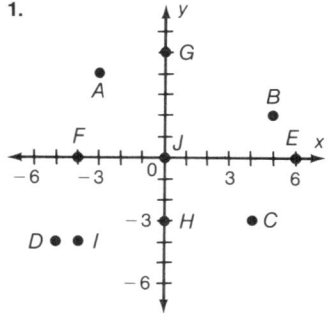

2. A: II; B: I; C: IV; D: III;
   E: x axis; F: x axis;
   G: y axis; H: y axis; I: III;
   J: x axis and y axis
3. abscissa: −3; ordinate: 4
4. abscissa: −5; ordinate: −4
5. abscissa: 0; ordinate: 5
6. abscissa: −4; ordinate: −4
7. abscissa: 0; ordinate: 0
8. $A(5, 0)$, $B(4, 5)$
   $C(-3, 3)$, $D(-6, 5)$,
   $E(-4, -3)$, $F(-6, -5)$,
   $G(4, -4)$, $H(7, -3)$, $I(1, 3)$,
   $J(0, -3)$, $K(0, 0)$

EXAMPLE 2   Name the quadrant or axis on which each point lies.

      a. $S(-1, -2)$ **b.** $P(6, -5)$ **c.** $V(0, -4)$ **d.** $T(5, 0)$

Solutions: Graph the points.

      a. S is in **Quadrant III.**

      b. P is in **Quadrant IV.**

      c. V is on the **y axis.**

      d. T is on the **x axis.**

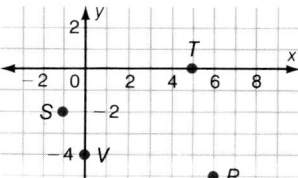

CLASSROOM EXERCISES

One coordinate of each point shown on the diagram is given. What is the other coordinate?

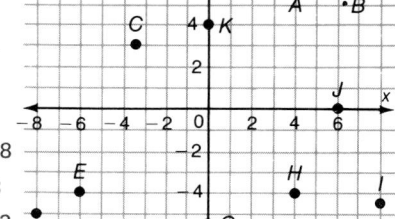

1. $A(4, ?)$ 6   2. $B(?, 6)$ 7   3. $C(-3.5, ?)$ 3
4. $D(?, 6)$ −8   5. $E(-6, ?)$ −4   6. $F(?, -5)$ −8
7. $G(?, -5.5)$ 0   8. $H(4, ?)$ −4   9. $I(?, -4.5)$ 8
10. $J(?, 0)$ 6   11. $K(?, 4)$ 0   12. $L(?, -6)$ −2

Name the quadrant or axis on which each point lies.

13. $R(0, 4)$ y axis   14. $S(-8, -1)$ III   15. $T(3, 3)$ I   16. $U(-2, 0)$ x axis   17. $V(-4, 5)$ II
18. $W(5, -6)$ IV   19. $A(0, -2)$ y axis   20. $B(-3, 7)$ II   21. $D(-6, 5)$ II   22. $E(5, -4)$ IV

WRITTEN EXERCISES

A

1. Graph these points on the same pair of coordinate axes.

    a. $A(-3, 4)$ **b.** $B(5, 2)$ **c.** $C(4, -3)$ **d.** $D(-5, -4)$ **e.** $E(6, 0)$
    f. $F(-4, 0)$ **g.** $G(0, 5)$ **h.** $H(0, -3)$ **i.** $I(-4, -4)$ **j.** $J(0, 0)$

2. Name the quadrant or axis on which each point in Exercise 1 lies.

Give the abscissa and the ordinate for these points in Exercise 1.

3. A 4. D 5. G 6. I 7. J

8. Name the coordinates for each point graphed at the right.

9. Name the ordinate of every point on the x axis.   0

10. Name the abscissa of every point on the y axis.   0

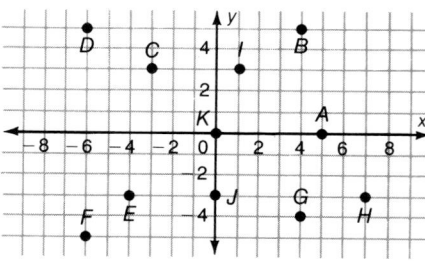

Name the quadrant or axis on which each point lies.

11. $(-3, -2)$ III 12. $(4, -1)$ IV 13. $(-5, 6)$ II 14. $(2, 5)$ I 15. $(5, -4)$

16. $(3, 0)$ x axis 17. $(0, -\pi)$ y axis 18. $(0, 0)$ 19. $(-1, 4)$ II 20. $(\pi, -\pi)$

21. $P(x, y)$ when $x > 0$ and $y > 0$ I 22. $Q(x, y)$ when $x < 0$ and $y < 0$ III

23. $R(x, y)$ when $x > 9$ and $y < 0$ IV 24. $T(x, y)$ when $x < 0$ and $y > 0$ II

25. Plot each set of points A–E. Connect the points of each set in order. The result should be a familiar picture. The picture is an elephant. See the Solution Key.

A: $\{(-2, 6), (1, 6), (4, 5), (6, 4), (7, 2), (7, 0), (6, -2\frac{1}{4}), (5, -4), (5, -9),$
$(2, -9), (3, -4), (3, -3), (1, -3), (-2, -2\frac{1}{4}), (-3, -2), (-4, -4),$
$(-5, -9), (-8, -9), (-6, -3), (-6, 1), (-9, 1), (-8\frac{1}{2}, 2\frac{1}{4}), (-11, 3),$
$(-12, 4), (-13, 6), (-12, 8), (-10, 10), (-9, 9), (-11, 7), (-11, 5),$
$(-10, 5), (-8, 7), (-5, 7), (-4, 8), (-3, 8), (-2, 7), (-2, 6), (-2, 5),$
$(-3, 3), (-4, 1), (-5, 0), (-6, 2), (-6, 3\frac{1}{2})\}$

B: $\{(7, 2), (8, 0), (9, -2), (10, -3), (11, -3)\}$

C: $\{(6, -2\frac{1}{4}), (6, -9), (5, -9)\}$

D: $\{(-2, -2\frac{1}{4}), (-3, -4), (-4, -9), (-5, -9)\}$ E: $\{(-7, 5)\}$

B

A fly walks along a certain path in the coordinate plane. List the coordinates, $P(x, y)$, of three points in its path. Draw a graph of the path and describe the graph.

Example: The fly walks along points with an ordinate of 2.
  Solution: $(5, 2)$; $(0, 2)$; $(-7\frac{1}{2}, 2)$ ←——— **Choose some points on the path.**

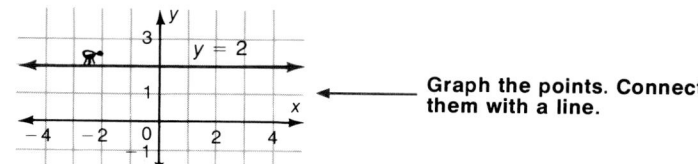

Graph the points. Connect them with a line.

A horizontal line 2 units above the x axis.

26. The fly walks along points with an abscissa of 3.

27. The fly walks along points with an ordinate of -4.

28. The fly walks along points with an ordinate of 0.

29. The fly walks along points with an abscissa of 0.

30. The fly walks along points whose x coordinates are positive and whose y coordinates are 5.

31. The fly walks along points whose x and y coordinates are opposites. (HINT: See the figure at the right.)

32. The fly walks along points whose distance from the origin is 6.

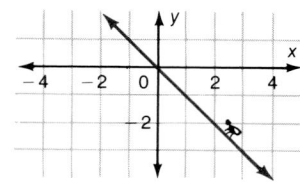

Graphing Relations and Functions **171**

Additional Answers

15. IV
18. x axis and y axis
20. IV
26. The graph is a vertical line 3 units to the right of the y axis.
27. The graph is a horizontal line 4 units below the x axis.
28. The graph is a horizontal line coinciding with the x axis.
29. The graph is a vertical line coinciding with the y axis.
30. The graph is a horizontal line 5 units above the x axis and to the right of the y axis.
31. The graph is a diagonal line passing through the origin at a 45° angle. The line is in Quadrants II and IV.
32. The graph is a circle centered at the origin and with a radius of 6 units.

33. Describe the graph of the set of all points that have the same ordinate.

34. Describe the graph of the set of all points that have the same abscissa.

35. What is the graph of the set of all points that have negative abscissas?

See the Solution Key for the graphs of Ex. 36-47.

Each of Exercises 36–41 lists three vertices of a rectangle. Graph the vertices. Then sketch the rectangle and give the coordinate of the fourth vertex.

36. (−3, −3), (−7, −5), (−7, −3) (−3, −5)   **37.** (−7, 3), (−4, 3), (−7, 5) (−4, 5)

38. (6, 8), (7, 2), (7, 8) (6, 2)   **39.** $(0, 3\frac{1}{2})$, (6, −4), $(6, 3\frac{1}{2})$ (0, −4)

40. (−6, 1), (−1, 5), (−6, 5) (−1, 1)   **41.** (−5, −1), (−8, −4), (−6, −6) (−3, −3)

C Each of Exercises 42–47 lists three vertices of a parallelogram. Graph the vertices. Then locate three points, each of which could be the fourth vertex. Give the coordinates of all three points.

42. (−3, −3), (−7, −5), (−7, −3)   **43.** (−7, 3), (−4, 3), (−7, 5)

44. (6, 8), (7, 2), (7, 8)   **45.** (3, 4), (2, 7), (3, 7)

46. (−6, 1), (−1, 5), (−6, 5)   **47.** (−6, 8), (−8, 5), (−1, 6)

Points in a plane can also be located by using an ordered pair of numbers to show distance along a ray and to show angle measure.

Example: Begin with a horizontal ray to represent 0°. Choose a unit of length and mark off distances along the way.

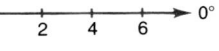

To locate A(3, 30°) draw a second ray that makes an angle of 30° with the first. Mark the second ray, 30°. Mark off three units on the 30° ray.

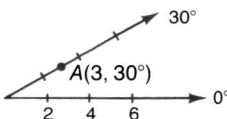

Coordinates such as (3, 30°) are called **polar coordinates.** Note that distance is given first in the ordered pair, and the angle measure is second.

48. Use polar coordinates to locate each point in the figure at the right.

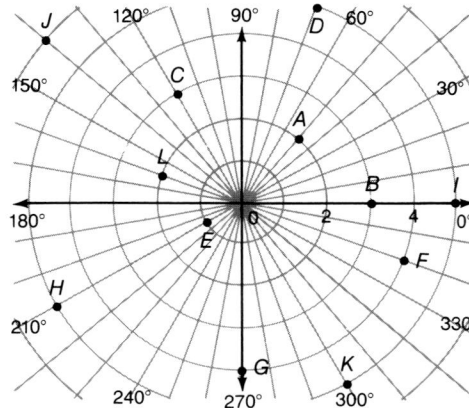

Review

Solve each equation for *x*. Check each solution. *(Section 5-1)*

1. $\frac{x}{4} = 9$ *x* = 36   2. $x + 7 = 24$ *x* = 17   3. $-3x + 1 = 10$ *x* = −3   4. $4x - 6 = 16$ *x* = 5½

Solve each problem. *(Section 5-2)*

5. Jackie and Joel started out from the same place at the same time. Jackie jogged at 6 miles per hour, and Joel bicycled at 20 miles per hour in the opposite direction. In how many hours will they be 65 miles apart?   2½ hours

6. A local bus traveling at a rate of 50 kilometers per hour was passed by an express bus traveling at a rate of 75 kilometers per hour. The express bus left the terminal one hour later than the local bus. How far had the buses traveled?   150 km

7. Graph these points on the same coordinate axes. *(Section 5-3)*

   a. $A(10, 0)$ **b.** $B(12, -5)$ **c.** $C(4, -9)$ **d.** $D(-4, -9)$ **e.** $E(-9, 0)$
   f. $F(-9, 4)$ **g.** $G(4, 9)$ **h.** $H(0, 9)$ **i.** $I(10, 0)$ **j.** $J(12, 5)$

8. Name the quadrant or axis on which each point in Exercise 1 lies. *(Section 5-3)*

9. Name the abscissa and the ordinate for each point in Exercise 1. *(Section 5-3)*

Puzzle

See the Solution Key.

Copy the coordinate axes shown at the right. Graph the ordered pairs in set **A** in the order listed and join each point to the next.

A: $\{(0, 6), (\frac{1}{2}, 5\frac{1}{2}), (\frac{1}{2}, 4), (1\frac{1}{2}, 4\frac{1}{2}), (2, 4),$
$(\frac{1}{2}, 3), (\frac{1}{2}, 2), (1\frac{1}{2}, 1\frac{1}{2}), (2\frac{1}{2}, 2), (2\frac{1}{2}, 3\frac{1}{2}),$
$(3\frac{1}{4}, 4), (3\frac{1}{4}, 2\frac{1}{2}), (4\frac{1}{4}, 3\frac{1}{4}), (5, 3), (5, 2\frac{1}{4}),$
$(4, 1\frac{1}{2}), (5, 1), (4, \frac{1}{2}), (3, 1), (2, \frac{1}{2}), (2, 0)\}$

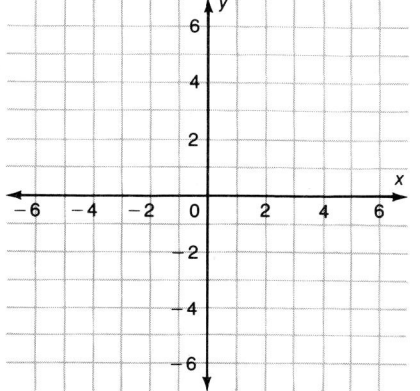

Now graph the points in sets **B**, **C**, and **D** to obtain a reflection of the first graph. Use the same axes.

B: $\{(0, 6), (-\frac{1}{2}, 5\frac{1}{2}), (-\frac{1}{2}, 4), \cdots, (-2, 0)\}$

C: $\{(0, -6), (\frac{1}{2}, -5\frac{1}{2}), (\frac{1}{2}, -4), \cdots, (2, 0)\}$

D: $\{(0, -6), (-\frac{1}{2}, -5\frac{1}{2}), (-\frac{1}{2}, -4), \cdots, (-2, 0)\}$

Graphing Relations and Functions   **173**

Quiz Sections 5-1–5-3
After completing this Review, you may want to administer a quiz covering the same sections. See page M-**46** of the Teacher's Manual for the suggested quiz.

Additional Answers
Review

7.
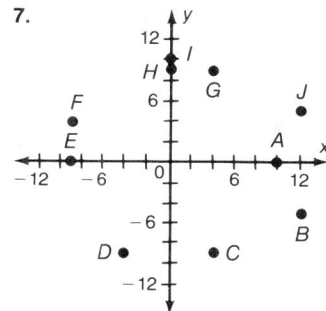

8. *A*: x axis; *B*: IV; *C*: IV; *D*: III; *E*: x axis; *F*: II; *G*: I; *H*: y axis; *I*: y axis; *J*: I

9. Abscissa: *A*: 10; *B*: 12; *C*: 4; *D*: −4; *E*: −9; *F*: −9; *G*: 4; *H*: 0; *I*: 0; *J*: 12
   Ordinate: *A*: 0; *B*: −5; *C*: −9; *D*: −9; *E*: 0; *F*: 4; *G*: 9; *H*: 9; *I*: 10; *J*: 5

This lesson is optional. It combines the skills of reading tables and operations with integers with concepts of ordered pairs, and applies these to the career area of navigation.

Career Applications: **Navigation**

Airplane pilots, ship captains, and others use a special coordinate system to describe the location of points on the surface of the earth. The system uses degrees of <u>latitude</u> and <u>longitude</u> to locate points.

Latitudes measure distance in degrees north (°N) or south (°S) of the **equator** (Latitude 0°). **Longitudes** measure distance in degrees east (°E) or west (°W) of the **prime meridian** (Longitude 0°). Points on the globe are described by the ordered pair (latitude, longitude). You can see from the globe at the right that the origin (Lat. 0°, Long. 0°) is the point where the equator and the prime meridian meet.

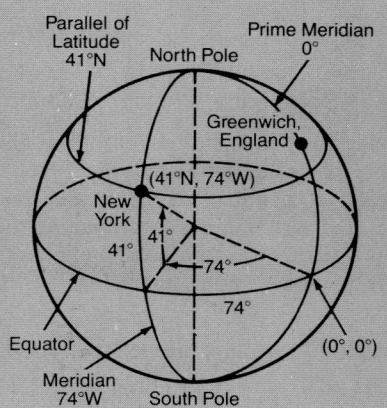

The table below gives the ordered pairs for several cities.

City	Location (Latitude, Longitude)	City	Location (Latitude, Longitude)
Cairo	(30°N, 31°E)	Paris	(49°N, 2°E)
Calcutta	(23°N, 88°E)	Rio de Janeiro	(23°S, 43°W)
Chicago	(42°N, 88°W)	Rome	(42°N, 13°E)
London	(52°N, 0°)	Sydney	(34°S, 151°E)
Los Angeles	(34°N, 118°W)	Tokyo	(36°N, 140°E)
New York	(41°N, 74°W)	Vancouver	(49°N, 123°W)

You can use the ordered pairs to compare the location of the cities in the table.

EXAMPLE 1 Use the table to find each of the following.

　　　　　a. The city directly east of Chicago

　　　　　b. The two cities that are the same distance from the equator

Solutions:　**a.** **Rome** (same latitude as Chicago, 42°N)

　　　　　b. **Los Angeles** (34°N) and **Sydney** (34°S)

You can also use the measure of longitude of the cities to compare the time in each place. The diagram at the right shows how the longitude of a place affects its time zone. Note that each zone spans 15° of longitude.

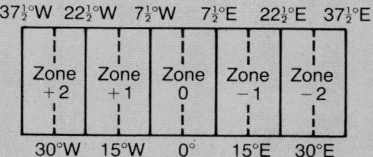

The **zone description (ZD)** of a point is an integer between 12 and −12. The ZD is positive for points west of the prime meridian, and negative for points east. Comparing the ZD of two points allows you to find the difference in local times. (A point in Zone +1 is one hour earlier than a point in Zone 0.)

EXAMPLE 2 Use the table on page 174 to find the ZD of Chicago and Rome. Then find the difference in local times.

Solution:
$\boxed{1}$ Chicago's longitude is 88°W, and Rome's longitude is 13°E.

$\boxed{2}$ Divide the longitude of each city by 15. Find the quotient to the nearest whole number.

Chicago: $\frac{88}{15} \approx 5.87 \approx 6$ Rome: $\frac{13}{15} \approx 0.87 \approx 1$

$\boxed{3}$ Assign a positive or negative number to each ZD.

ZD for Chicago: +6   ZD for Rome: −1

$\boxed{4}$ Find the difference between the zone factors.

$6 - (-1) = 7$

Chicago and Rome are **7 hours** apart.

EXERCISES

In Exercises 1–22, use the table on page 174.

1. Find the city that is farthest from the equator.

2. Find the city that is farthest from the prime meridian.

3. Find the city that is located on the prime meridian

4. Find the city that is farthest from London.

5. Find the two cities that are the same distance from the prime meridian.

6. Find the city that is the same distance from the equator as Calcutta.

7. Find the city that is directly east of Vancouver.

8. Find the city that is directly north of Bogotá (5°N, 74°W).

Find the ZD of each of the following cities.

9. London   10. Chicago   11. Calcutta   12. Tokyo

13. Sydney   14. Los Angeles   15. Rio de Janeiro   16. Rome

Find the difference in local times between each pair of cities.

17. Chicago and London

18. Sydney and Tokyo

19. Los Angeles and Calcutta

20. Rio de Janeiro and London

21. Find the local time in New York when it is 10:30 A.M. in Vancouver.

22. Find the local time in Cairo when it is 7:15 P.M. in Tokyo.

Navigation   175

Additional Answers
1. London
2. Sydney
3. London
4. Sydney
5. Calcutta and Chicago
6. Rio de Janeiro
7. Paris
8. New York
9. 0
10. +6
11. −6
12. −9
13. −10
14. +8
15. +3
16. −1
17. 6 hours
18. 1 hour
19. 14 hours
20. 3 hours
21. 1:30 PM
22. 12:15 PM

5-4 Relations and Functions

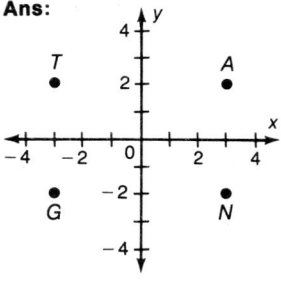
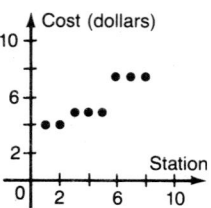

At his part time job, Jim Noble is paid at the rate of $6.00 per hour. The equation

$$e = 6h$$

shows the relation between Jim's earnings, e, and the number of hours worked, h.

TIME CARD	*Jim Noble*
Monday	3 hours
Tuesday	
Wednesday	2 hours
Thursday	
Friday	
Saturday	4 hours
TOTAL	9 hours

This relation can be shown in several ways.

Kind of Description	Description
1. Words	1. Multiply 6 and the number of hours worked
2. Equation	2. $e = 6h$
3. Table of ordered pairs	3. (see table below)
4. Graph	4. (see graph below)

h	0	1	2	3	4	5	6	7	8	9
e	0	6	12	18	24	30	36	42	48	54

Some relations cannot be described by an equation. For this reason, we use ordered pairs to define a *relation*.

Definition | **A relation is a set of ordered pairs.**

EXAMPLE 1 A railroad divided its line into zones and charged one fare to any station in the zone.

Station	1, 2, or 3	4 or 5	6, 7, or 8
Fare	$3.50	$5.00	$7.10

Solution: List the ordered pairs of the relation and graph the relation.

{(1, 3.50), (2, 3.50), (3, 3.50), (4, 5.00), (5, 5.00), (6, 7.10), (7, 7.10), (8, 7.10)} ← **Associate each station with a fare.**

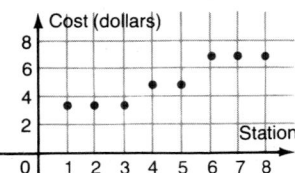

← **Graph the relation.**

For the ordered pairs of a relation, the set of all first coordinates is the **domain** of the relation. The set of all second coordinates the ordered pairs is the **range** of the relation. The letter, D, is often used to represent the domain of a relation; the letter, R, is used to represent the range.

EXAMPLE 2 Give the domain and range of the relation described in Example 1.

Solution: {(1, 3.50), (2, 3.50), (3, 3.50), (4, 5.00)   ◄——— Relation
            (5, 5.00), (6, 7.10), (7, 7.10), (8, 7.10)}

   D = {1, 2, 3, 4, 5, 6, 7, 8} ◄——— Domain: Set of all first coordinates of each ordered pair

   R = {3.50, 5.00, 7.10} ◄——— Range: Set of all second coordinates of each ordered pair

You can find the domain and range of a relation from its graph.

EXAMPLE 3 The graph at the right defines a relation.

Express the relation as a set of ordered pairs. Then give the domain and range of the relation.

Solution: Read the set of ordered pairs from the graph.

   {(−3, 3), (−2, 2), (−1, 1), (0, 0),
   (1, −1), (2, −2), (3, −3)}

   D = {−3, −2, −1, 0, 1, 2, 3} ◄——— Domain: Set of all first coordinates of each ordered pair

   R = {3, 2, 1, 0, −1, −2, −3} ◄——— Range: Set of all second coordinates of each ordered pair

A *function* is a special kind of relation.

Definition
> A **function** is a relation for which no two ordered pairs have the same first element.

Relation	Ordered Pairs with the Same First Elements	Is the Relation a Function?
{(0, 0, (1, 11), (2, 22), (3, 33), (4, 44)}	None	**Yes**
{(1, 7), (1, 14), (1, 21)}	(1, 7), (1, 14), (1, 21)	**No**
{(0, 0), (1, 1), (2, 4), (3, 9), (4, 16)}	None	**Yes**
{(1, 1.50), (2, 1.50), (3, 1.50), (4, 1.75)}	None	**Yes**
{(10, 20), (11, 30), (12, 40), (10, 50)}	(10, 20), (10, 50)	**No**
{(−2, −2), (−1, −2), (0, −2), (3, −2)}	None	**Yes**

Graphing Relations and Functions   **177**

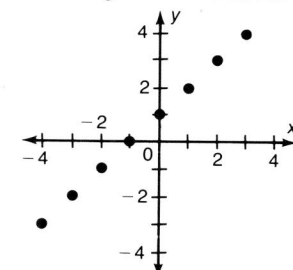

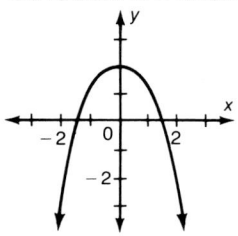
The graph of a relation shows whether it is a function. If a vertical line can be drawn through two or more points of the graph, the points have the same x coordinate, so the relation is *not* a function. This is called the **Vertical Line Test**.

EXAMPLE 4   Use the graphs to tell whether each relation is a function.

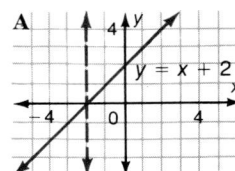   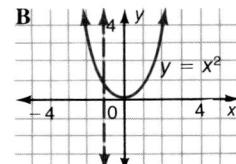   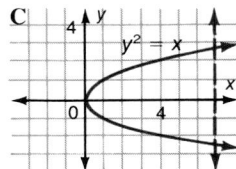

Solutions: **A** and **B** are functions.
C is not a function because a vertical line will intersect its graph in more than one point.

CLASSROOM EXERCISES

Give the domain and range for each relation.

1. {(0, 1), (2, 3), (4, 5), (6, 7)}   2. {(−1, 1), (−2, 2), (−3, 3), (−4, 4)}
3. {(0, −2), (1, −2), (2, −2), (3, −2)}   4. {($\frac{1}{2}$, $\frac{1}{4}$), ($\frac{3}{2}$, $\frac{1}{8}$), (2, $\frac{7}{2}$)}

State whether the given set of ordered pairs is a function. When a relation is not a function, tell why it is not.

5. {(1, 2), (0, 1), (1, 3), (2, 1)}   6. {(0, 0), (−1, −1), (2, 2), (3, 3)} Yes
7. {(−3, 5), (−1, 5), (3, 5), (7, 5)} Yes   8. {(−6, −5), (−6, −2), (−6, 0), (−6, 3)}

WRITTEN EXERCISES

A   Give the domain and range for each relation.

1. {(1, 50), (2, 100), (3, 150), (4, 200), (5, 250)}
2. {(−1, 1), (−2, 4), (−3, 9), (−4, 16), (−5, 25)}
3. {(1, π), (2, 4π), (3, 9π), (4, 16π), (5, 25π)}
4. {(1, π), (2, 2π), (3, 3π), (4, 4π), (5, 5π)}
5. The graph at the right defines a relation. Define this relation by listing the ordered pairs that are the coordinates of the points.
6. The relation in Exercise 5 cannot be defined easily by a simple sentence, but it can be defined easily by a table. Construct such a table for this relation.
7. Give the domain and range of the relation in Exercise 5.
   D = {−4, −2, −1, 1, 2, 4}; R = {−2, −3, 1, 3, 2}

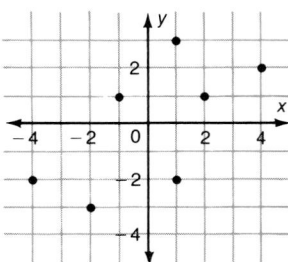

In Exercises 8–10, write the set of ordered pairs for each relation. Then give the domain and range for each relation.

8.
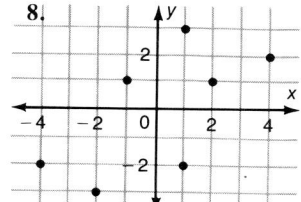

9.
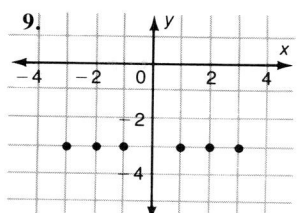

10.
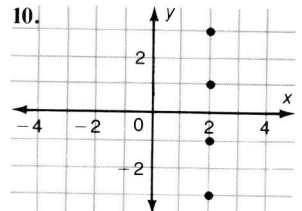

Give the domain and range for each relation.

11. $\{(1, 50), (2, 100), (3, 150), (4, 200), (5, 250)\}$
12. $\{(-1, 1), (-2, 4), (-3, 9), (-4, 16), (-5, 25)\}$
13. $\{(1, \pi), (2, 4\pi), (3, 9\pi), (4, 16\pi), (5, 25\pi)\}$
14. $\{(1, \pi), (2, 2\pi), (3, 3\pi), (4, 4\pi), (5, 5\pi)\}$

Write *Yes* or *No* to tell whether the relation is also a function.

15. Yes
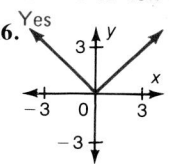

16. Yes
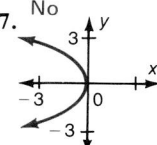

17. No
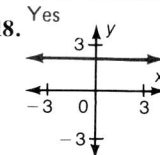

18. Yes

19. No
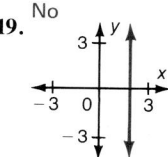

Determine whether each relation in Exercises 20–27 is also a function. When a relation is not a function, state why it is not.

20. $\{(-1, 1), (-2, 4), (-3, 9), (-4, 16), (-5, 25)\}$ Yes
21. $\{(-3, -3), (0, 0), (3, 3), (5, 5)\}$ Yes
22. $\{(1, 5¢), (2, 10¢), (3, 10¢), (4, 15¢), (5, 20¢), (6, 20¢)\}$ Yes
23. $\{(-5, 5), (-1, 1), (2, -2), (4, -4)\}$ Yes
24. $\{(5, 8), (5, 9), (6, 10), (6, 11), (7, 12), (7, 13)\}$
25. $\{(3, -2), (3, -1), (3, 0), (3, 1), (3, 2)\}$
26. $\{(-2, 4), (-1, 4), (0, 4), (1, 4), (2, 4)\}$ Yes
27. $\{(-7, 7), (-5, 5), (0, 0), (5, 5), (7, 7)\}$ Yes

APPLICATIONS: Using Functions and Relations

In Exercises 28–33, write the ordered pairs for each relation. Then give the domain and range of the relation.

28.

Time (*t*)	8 A.M.	9 A.M.	10 A.M.	11 A.M.	12 noon
Temperature (*T*)	4°	8°	8°	10°	11°

Graphing Relations and Functions **179**

29. {(1976, 11,000),
(1978, 12,000),
(1980, 13,000),
(1982, 15,000),
(1984, 16,000)};
D = {1976, 1978, 1980,
1982, 1984};
R = {11,000, 12,000,
13,000, 15,000, 16,000}
30. {(150, 5), (180, 6), (210, 7)};
D = {150, 180, 210};
R = {5, 6, 7}
31. {(4, 256), (6, 576),
(8, 1024), (10, 1600)};
D = {4, 6, 8, 10};
R = {256, 576, 1024, 1600}
32. {(5, 150), (10, 600),
(15, 1350), (20, 2400)};
D = {5, 10, 15, 20};
R = {150, 600, 1350, 2400}
33. {(1, 4), (2, 33),
(3, 113), (5, 523)};
D = {1, 2, 3, 5};
R = {4, 33, 113, 523}
34. a. 35, 45, 50, 60, 70, 75, 85
b. D = {0, 1, 2, 3, 4, 5,
6, 7, 8, 9, 10};
R = {0, 10, 20, 25, 35,
45, 50, 60, 70, 75, 85}
36. a.

Cans	0	1	2	3	4	5	6
Cost	0	30	60	89	119	149	178

Cans	7	8	9	10
Cost	208	238	267	297

b. D = {0, 1, 2, 3, 4, 5,
6, 7, 8, 9, 10};
R = {0, 30, 60, 89,
119, 149, 178, 208,
238, 267, 297}
37. c.

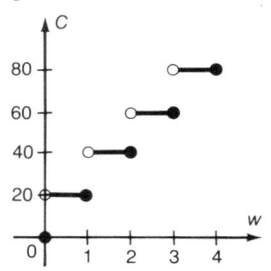

29.

Year (y)	1976	1978	1980	1982	1984 (est.)
Population (P)	11,000	12,000	13,000	15,000	16,000

B

30. $N = \dfrac{A}{30}$, a formula for finding the number of rolls of wallpaper needed to cover a rectangular wall, where A is the area of the wall and $A \in \{150, 180, 210\}$

31. $s = 16t^2$, the formula for the distance, s, a freely falling object falls in t seconds, where $t \in \{4, 6, 8, 10\}$

32. $A = 6s^2$, the formula for the surface area, A, of a cube, where $s \in \{5, 10, 15, 20\}$

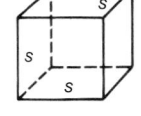

33. $V = \dfrac{4}{3}\pi r^3$, the formula for the volume, V, of a sphere, where r is the length of the radius and $r \in \{1, 2, 3, 5\}$. Use 3.14 for π and round each value for V to the nearest whole number

34. Pencils are selling at 3 for 25¢ or at 10¢ each.

a. Complete the table below showing the cost in cents of x pencils if x is 10 or less.

When x is	0	1	2	3	4	5	6	7	8	9	10
Cost is	0	10	20	25	?	?	?	?	?	?	?

b. Give the domain and range of this relation.

All are functions.

35. Which of the relations in Exercises 28–34 are also functions?

36. A brand of soup sells at 3 cans for 89¢ or at 30¢ per can.

a. Make a table that shows the cost of n cans if n is 10 or less.

b. Give the domain and range of this relation.

37. Suppose that the cost of mailing a package is 20¢ per ounce or fraction of an ounce. Thus, the cost for $2\frac{1}{4}$ ounces is 3×20¢, or 60¢.

a. Complete this table that shows the cost, C, in cents for a package weighing w ounces.   40, 40, 40, 60, 60, 80, 80, 100

w	0	$\frac{1}{2}$	$\frac{3}{4}$	1	$1\frac{1}{2}$	$1\frac{7}{8}$	2	$2\frac{1}{8}$	3	$3\frac{1}{2}$	4	5
C	0	20	20	20	?	?	?	?	?	?	?	?

b. Complete this sentence: If the amount is 5 ounces or less, then the cost of mail will be any one of the numbers _?_.   0, 20, 40, 60, 80, 100

c. Part of the graph is shown at the right. Complete the graph for values of w from $w = 0$ through $w = 4$.

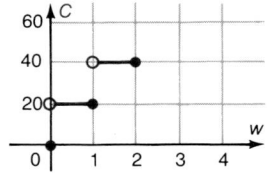

OBJECTIVE: To graph linear equations

5-5 Graphing Linear Equations

Teaching Suggestions p. M-18

An equation such as

$$5x - 9 = 11$$

is an equation in one variable, x. It has *one solution*, 4, because $5 \cdot 4 - 9 = 11$ and this is the only value of x for which $5x - 9 = 11$. An equation such as

$$y - 2x = 3$$

has two variables, x and y. The solution of this equation is the *set of ordered pairs (x, y)* for which $y - 2x = 3$. For example, the ordered pairs $(0, 3)$, $\left(-\frac{3}{2}, 0\right)$, and $(2, 7)$ are some of the solutions of $y - 2x = 3$.

Check:

$y - 2x = 3$	$y - 2x = 3$	$y - 2x = 3$
$3 - 2(0) \stackrel{?}{=} 3$	$0 - 2(-\frac{3}{2}) \stackrel{?}{=} 3$	$7 - 2(2) \stackrel{?}{=} 3$
$3 \stackrel{?}{=} 3$ Yes ✔	$3 \stackrel{?}{=} 3$ Yes ✔	$3 \stackrel{?}{=} 3$ Yes ✔

To solve an equation such as $y - 2x = 3$, you find *all* its solutions for the given replacement set. When the replacement set for x is {real numbers}, there is an infinite number of ordered pairs that are solutions. In such cases, you usually show the solution set as a graph.

EXAMPLE 1   Graph the equation $y - 2x = 3$.

Solution: ☐1 Solve the equation for y.   ⟶ $y - 2x = 3$

$$y = 2x + 3$$

☐2 Make a table. First, choose values for x. To find y, substitute these values in $y = 2x + 3$.

Replace x with -3.   Replace x with 0.   Replace x with 1.

Replace x with -3.	Replace x with 0.	Replace x with 1.
$y = 2x + 3$	$y = 2x + 3$	$y = 2x + 3$
$y = 2(-3) + 3$	$y = 2(0) + 3$	$y = 2(1) + 3$
$y = -6 + 3$	$y = 0 + 3$	$y = 2 + 3$
$y = -3$	$y = 3$	$y = 5$

x	-3	0	1
y	-3	3	5

☐3 Graph the points.

Since x can be any real number, draw a line containing the points.

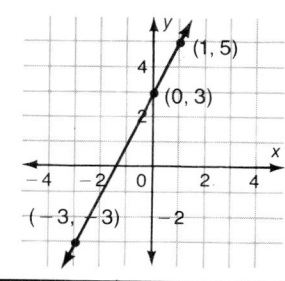

Quick Quiz

Give the domain and range for each relation.

1. $\{(1, 30), (2, 60), (3, 90), (4, 120), (5, 150)\}$
   Ans: D = {1, 2, 3, 4, 5}
   R = {30, 60, 90, 120, 150}
2. $\{(-1, 2\pi), (-2, 4\pi), (-3, 6\pi), (-4, 8\pi)\}$
   Ans: D = {−1, −2, −3, −4}
   R = {2π, 4π, 6π, 8π}

Determine whether each relation is also a function.

3. $\{(-2, 2), (-3, 3), (-4, 4), (-5, 5), (-6, 6)\}$
   Ans: Yes
4. $\{(4, 6), (4, 7), (5, 8), (6, 9), (7, 10)\}$
   Ans: No

Additional Example
Example 1
Graph the equation.
$y - 2x = -3$
Ans:

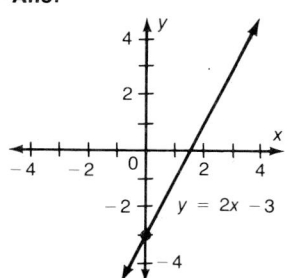

Graphing Relations and Functions   **181**

Additional Examples
Example 2
Graph each of the following in the coordinate plane.
1. $x = -4$
 Ans:

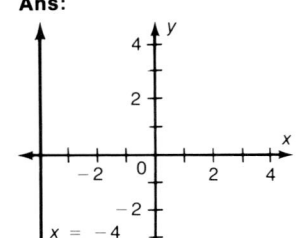

2. $y = 2$
 Ans:

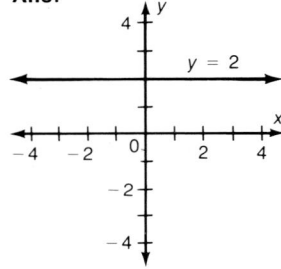

EXAMPLE 2   Graph each of the following in the coordinate plane.

a. $x = 2$ **b.** $y = -3$

Solutions: **a.** All ordered pairs with an x coordinate of 2 are solutions of the equation. Thus, the graph is a vertical line.

b. All ordered pairs with a y coordinate of -3 are solutions of the equation. Thus, the graph is a horizontal line.

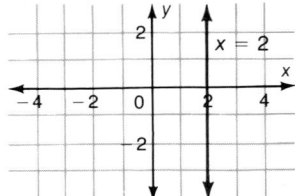

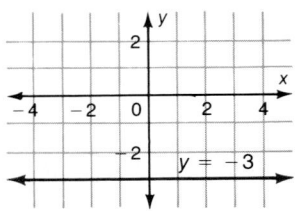

Unless stated otherwise, assume that the replacement set for each variable in a linear equation is {real numbers}.

Here is another way to describe a linear equation.

Definition

> An equation that can be written in the form
>
> $$Ax + By = C$$
>
> where A, B, and C are real numbers and A and B are not both zero, is a **linear equation in two variables.**

Thus, by definition, equations such as $3x - 2y = -6$ and $y - 5 = 0$ are linear equations; equations such as $x^2 + y = 9$ and $xy = 4$ are not.

A function whose ordered pairs satisfy a linear equation is a **linear function.** Thus, the equation $y - 2x = 3$ defines a linear function.

CLASSROOM EXERCISES

Complete the tables.

1. $y = 2x$

x	0	2	4	6
y	0	4	?	?

8, 12

2. $y = 4x$

	0	4	8	12	16
x	0	1	2	3	4
y	?	?	?	?	?

3. $y = 3x$

x	0	-1	-2	-3
y	0	-3	?	?

−6 −9

4. $y = -2x + 3$

x	-3	-1	0	1	3
y	9	?	?	?	?

5   3   1 −3

Complete the tables. 4   6   10

5. $y = 2x + 4$

x	−3	−1	0	1	3
y	−2	2	?	?	?

6   4   2   −2

6. $y = -2x + 4$

x	−3	−1	0	1	3
y	10	?	?	?	?

7. $y = -3x + 5$

x	−3	−2	−1	0	1
y	?	?	?	?	?

8. $y = 3x + 5$

x	−3	−2	−1	0	1
y	?	?	?	?	?

14   11   8   5   2   −4   −1   2   5   8

Determine whether the given ordered pair of numbers is a solution of the given sentence. Answer *Yes* or *No*.

9. $x + y = 5$; $(0, 3)$ No
10. $x - 3y = 16$; $(16, 0)$ Yes
11. $y - x = 10$; $(-\frac{1}{2}, 9\frac{1}{2})$ Yes

12. $y - x = 0$; $(2.6, 2.6)$ Yes
13. $4x + 3y = -12$; $(3, 0)$ No
14. $2x + y = 10$; $(-5, 0)$ No

15. $y = 7x$; $(0, 0)$ Yes
16. $y - 7x = 0$; $(\frac{1}{7}, -1)$ No
17. $y - 8 = 0$; $(3, 8)$ Yes

State whether each equation is linear. Answer *Yes* or *No*.

18. $3x + 7y = 19$ Yes
19. $y = 4x^2 - 7$ No
20. $7x^2 - 5xy + 9y^2 = 15$ No

21. $y = 3x$ Yes
22. $y - 8x = 0$ Yes
23. $\frac{y}{3} = 2x + 1$ Yes

State whether the graph of each equation is a straight line. Answer *Yes* or *No*.

24. $y + 1 = 5$ Yes
25. $2x - y = 8$ Yes
26. $y = \frac{4}{3}x - 1$ Yes

27. $y = 2x^2 - 1$ No
28. $xy = 1$ No
29. $x - y = 0$ Yes

WRITTEN EXERCISES

See the Solution Key for the graphs.

Ⓐ Graph each linear equation in the coordinate plane.

1. $y = 4x - 3$
2. $y = -3x$
3. $y = -2x - 4$
4. $y = -2x + 3$

5. $y = x - 5$
6. $y = 5 - x$
7. $x + y = 10$
8. $x + y = 4$

9. $y = \frac{1}{2}x$
10. $y = \frac{1}{3}x$
11. $y = -\frac{1}{4}x$
12. $y = -\frac{1}{2}x$

13. $2x + y = 4$
14. $3x + y = 6$
15. $2x + 3y = 6$
16. $3x + 4y = 12$

17. $2x - y = 4$
18. $3x - 2y = 0$
19. $y = -4$
20. $y = 7$

21. $y = -9$
22. $x = 3$
23. $x = 6\frac{1}{2}$
24. $x = -8$

Ⓑ Equations of the form $By = C$ where $B \neq 0$ define constant functions.

In Exercises 25–28, complete the table of values for each constant function. Then graph each function.

25. $y = 3$

x	−2	0	2
y	?	?	?

$(-2, 3), (0, 3), (2, 3)$

26. $y + 5 = 0$

x	−1	0	3
y	?	?	?

$(-1, -5),$ $(0, -5),$ $(3, -5)$

Graphing Relations and Functions   **183**

Assignment Guide
Minimal p. 183: 1–20
Average pp. 183–184:
1–39 odd
Above Average pp. 183–184:
1–49 odd

Additional Answers
Written Exercises
For Exercises 1–24, each graph is a straight line containing the given points.
1. $(0, -3), (1, 1)$
2. $(1, -3), (0, 0)$
3. $(-2, 0), (0, -4)$
4. $(0, 3), (2, -1)$
5. $(0, -5), (5, 0)$
6. $(0, 5), (5, 0)$
7. $(0, 10), (10, 0)$
8. $(0, 4), (4, 0)$
9. $(0, 0), (2, 1)$
10. $(0, 0), (3, 1)$
11. $(0, 0), (4, -1)$
12. $(0, 0), (2, -1)$
13. $(0, 4), (2, 0)$
14. $(0, 6), (2, 0)$
15. $(0, 2), (3, 0)$
16. $(0, 3), (4, 0)$
17. $(0, -4), (2, 0)$
18. $(0, 0), (2, 3)$
19. $(0, -4), (4, -4)$
20. $(0, 7), (7, 7)$
21. $(0, -9), (9, -9)$
22. $(3, 0), (3, 3)$
23. $(6\frac{1}{2}, 0), (6\frac{1}{2}, 6)$
24. $(-8, 0), (-8, 8)$

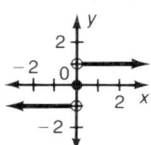
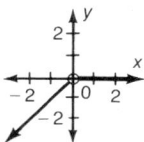
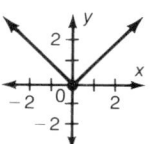
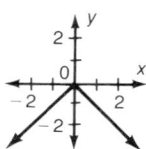
27. $y = 0$

x	−4	0	4
y	?	?	?

(−4, 0), (0, 0), (4, 0)

28. $2y − 3 = 0$

$(-3, \frac{3}{2})$, $(0, \frac{3}{2})$, $(6, \frac{3}{2})$

x	−3	0	6
y	?	?	?

Refer to the graphs in Exercises 25–28 to complete the statements in Exercises 29–31.

29. The graph of a constant function is the __?__ axis or a line parallel to the __?__ axis. x x

30. The domain of the constant function is __?__.   the set of real numbers

31. The range of the constant function is __?__.   one real number

Complete the table for each relation in Exercises 32–35. Then graph the relation.   See the Solution Key for the graphs.

32. $x = 3$

x	?	?	?
y	−3	0	4

33. $x − 8 = 0$

x	?	?	?
y	−3	0	4

34. $x = 0$

x	?	?	?
y	−5	0	5

35. $\frac{2}{3}x = -6$

x	?	?	?
y	−2	0	2

Refer to the tables and graphs in Exercises 32–35 to complete the statements in Exercises 36–39.

36. The graph of each relation in Exercises 32–35 is the __?__ axis, or a line parallel to the __?__ axis. y y

37. The range of each relation in Exercises 32–35 is __?__.   the set of real numbers

38. An equation of the form $Ax = C$, $A \neq 0$ defines a __?__ (relation or function).   relation

39. A relation of the form $Ax = C$, $A \neq 0$ does *not* define a function because __?__.   each ordered pair has the same first element.

C   For each equation, write the coordinates of the points $(0, y)$ and $(x, 0)$.   (0, 2), (3, 0)

40. $y = 2x − 6$ (0, −6), (3, 0)   **41.** $9y − 26 = 2x$ (0, $2\frac{8}{9}$), (−13, 0)   **42.** $2x + 3y = 6$

43. $3x + y = 4$ (0, 4), ($1\frac{1}{3}$, 0)   **44.** $y = −2x$ (0, 0), (0, 0)   **45.** $3(2x − 4) = 2(y − 5)$

In Exercises 46–50, graph each function. Tell whether each function is a linear function. Give the domain and range of each function.

46. The function pairs each positive real number with the number 1, the number 0 with 0, and each negative real number with the number −1.

47. The function pairs each positive real number with the number 0, and each negative real number x with itself.

48. The function pairs each nonnegative real number x, with itself, and each negative real number x with the opposite of x.

49. The function pairs each real number x with its absolute value, $|x|$.

50. The function pairs each real number with $−|x|$.

Problem Solving and Applications

OBJECTIVE: To estimate answers to problems using the graphs of a linear equation

5–6 Graphs and Estimation

Graphs of functions can be useful in estimating answers. For example, to determine the distance to an approaching thunderstorm.

1. Count the number of seconds between a flash of lightning and the resulting sound of thunder.

2. Use this number to read the distance from a graph that shows the distance sound travels in air as a function of time.

EXAMPLE For every 3 seconds, sound travels about 1 kilometer. That is, $s = \frac{1}{3}t$ where s is the distance in kilometers and t is the time in seconds.

Questions

a. Write three ordered pairs for this function. Note that t cannot be negative.

b. Use the ordered pairs to graph the function. (Note the scale on each axis.)

Solutions

a.

t	0	2	4
s	0	$\frac{2}{3}$	$1\frac{1}{3}$

b.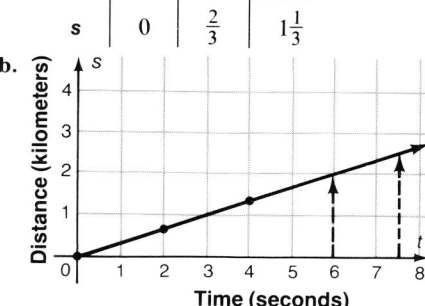

c. Use the graph to estimate the distance to an approaching thunderstorm when a person counts 6 seconds between the lightning and the thunder.

c. Read from the graph. For $t = 6$, s is about **2 kilometers.**

d. Use the graph to estimate the distance when $t = 7.5$ seconds.

d. For $t = 7.5$, s is about **2.5 kilometers.**

CLASSROOM EXERCISES

Suppose that a new oil filter for a car costs $6.00 and that oil costs $1.00 per quart. That is, $C = 6 + q$, where C is the total cost of a new filter and an oil change, and q is the number of quarts of oil used.

1. Write three ordered pairs for the function. Let $q = 0$, 2, and 3. (0, 6), (2, 8), (3, 9)

2. Use the ordered pairs in Exercise 1 to graph the function. See page 186.

3. Use the graph to estimate C when $q = 2\frac{1}{2}$. $8\frac{1}{2}$

4. Use the graph to estimate C when $q = 3\frac{3}{4}$. $9\frac{3}{4}$

Graphing Relations and Functions **185**

Teaching Suggestions p. M-18

Quick Quiz
Graph each of the following on the same set of coordinate axes.
  $y + 2x = 1$; $y = 3$; $x = -2$
  Ans:

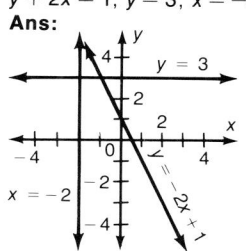

Additional Examples
For every 3 seconds, sound travels about 0.6 mile. That is, $s = 0.6t$ where s is the distance in miles and t is the time in seconds.

1. Write three ordered pairs for this function. Let $t = 0$, 2, and 4.
   Ans: (0, 0), (2, 1.2), (4, 2.4)

2. Use the ordered pairs to graph the function.
   Ans:

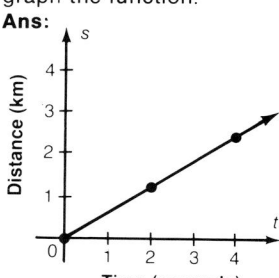

3. Use the graph to estimate the distance to an approaching thunderstorm when a person counts 7 seconds between the lightning and the thunder.
   Ans: About 4.2 mi

Additional Answers
2.

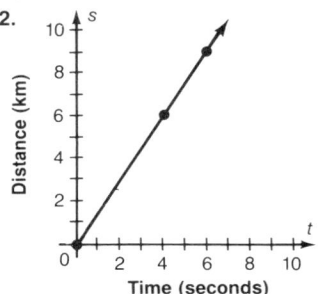

7.

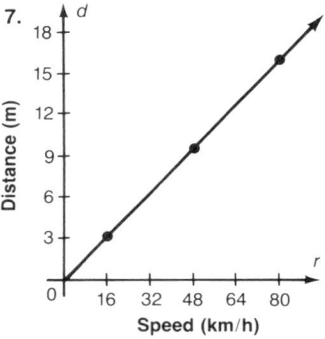

Additional Answers
Classroom Exercises p. 185
2.

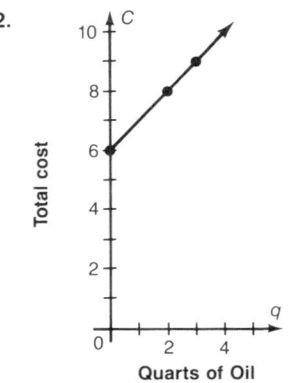

WORD PROBLEMS

A Sound travels in water at a rate of about 1.5 kilometers per second. That is, $s = 1.5t$, where t is the time in seconds and s is the distance in kilometers. Use this function in Exercises 1–5.

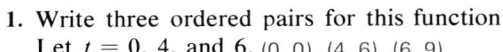

1. Write three ordered pairs for this function. Let $t = 0$, 4, and 6. (0, 0), (4, 6), (6, 9)

2. Use the ordered pairs in Exercise 1 to graph the function.

3. A ship using sonar finds that it takes sound waves 0.5 second to reach the bottom of a lake. Use the graph in Exercise 2 to estimate the depth of the lake at this point. 0.75 km

4. A ship using sonar finds that it takes sound waves 7 seconds to reach a point at the bottom of a body of water. Use the graph in Exercise 2 to estimate the depth at this point. 10.5 km

5. Use the graph in Exercise 2 to estimate how long it would take sound waves to reach a point 4 kilometers below the surface of the ocean. $2\frac{2}{3}$ seconds

The function $d = 0.2r$ represents the distance, d, in meters covered by a car traveling at a rate of r kilometers per hour during the average driver's reaction time of $\frac{3}{4}$ second. **Reaction time** is the length of time between the moment a driver decides to stop the car and the moment the brakes are applied.

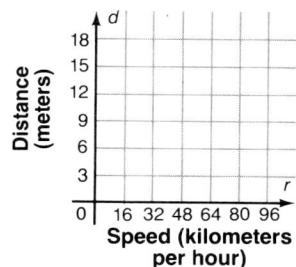

6. Write three ordered pairs for this function. Let $r = 16$, 48, and 80. (16, 3.2), (48, 9.6), (80, 16)

7. Use the ordered pairs in Exercise 6 to graph the function.

Use the graph in Exercise 7 to estimate how many meters a car traveling at each rate will cover during a reaction time of $\frac{3}{4}$ second.

8. 32 kilometers per hour
6.4 m

9. 64 kilometers per hour
12.8 m

10. 88 kilometers per hour
17.6 m

The rate of sales tax for a certain state is 5%. Use this information in Exercises 11–19.

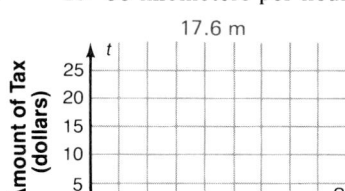

11. Complete the table.

Amount of Sales, S	$100	$200	$300
Amount of Tax, t	? 5	? 10	? 15

12. Use the ordered pairs in Exercise 11 to graph the function. Assume that the graph is linear.

Use the graph in Exercise 12 to estimate the tax on each amount.

13. $50 $2.50 **14.** $150 $7.50 **15.** $400 $20 **16.** $375 $18.75 **17.** $225 $11.25 **18.** $75 $3.75

19. Write an equation that describes the amount of sales, S, as a function of the amount of tax, t. $S = 20t$

The basic fee for renting a floor polisher is $5 plus an additional $2.50 for each hour of rental. Use this information for Exercises 20–25.

20. Complete the table. 10, 15, 20

Number of Hours (h)	2	4	6
Cost (C)	?	?	?

21. Use the ordered pairs in Exercise 20 to graph the function. Assume that the graph is linear.

Use the graph in Exercise 21 to estimate the rental cost for each number of hours.

22. 3 hours $12.50 **23.** 5 hours $17.50 **24.** $4\frac{1}{2}$ hours $16.25 **25.** $5\frac{1}{4}$ hours $18

26. Write an equation that describes the cost of rental, C, as a function of the number of hours, h. $C = 2.50h + 5$

B A plane at an altitude of 22,000 feet begins to climb at the rate of 50 feet per second. Use this information for Exercises 27–32.

27. Complete the table. 100, 200, 300

Time, t, in seconds	2	4	6
Altitude, A, in feet	?	?	?

28. Use the ordered pairs in the table for Exercise 27 to graph the function. Assume that the graph is linear.

Use the graph in Exercise 28 to estimate the altitude of the plane for each time, t.

29. $t = 3$ seconds **30.** $t = 5$ seconds **31.** $t = 2.5$ seconds **32.** $t = 8$ seconds

33. Write an equation that describes the altitude, A, of the plane as a function of the time, t, in seconds. $A = 50t$

C The cost of first class mail is a function of weight. In 1981, the cost for any weight up to, and including, 1 ounce rose to 20¢. Each additional ounce or fraction thereof cost 17¢. For example, 1.6 ounces cost 37¢ and 3.2 ounces cost 71¢.

Use this information and the graph at the right for Exercises 34–36.

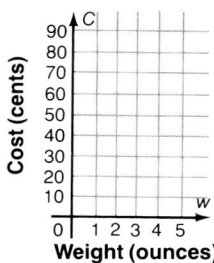

Graphing Relations and Functions **187**

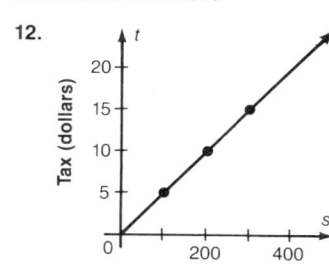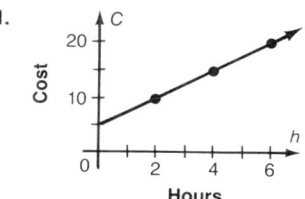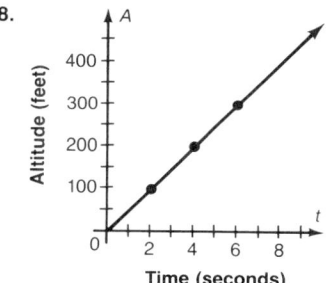

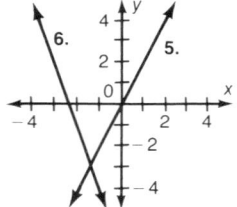
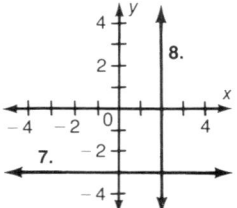
34. Complete the table. 37¢, 54¢, $1.05

Weight	1.4 oz	2.7 oz	5.8 oz
Costs	?	?	?

35. This rate holds for 12 ounces and less. Thus, the domain of this function is all possible weights of mail less than or equal to 12 ounces. List the 12 numbers in the range of this function.

36. Graph this function for weights up to, and including, 5 ounces.

Review   See p. 566 for Ex. 1-3.

Give the domain and range for each relation. *(Section 5–4)*

1. $\{(1, 12°), (2, 14°), (3, 8°), (4, 4°), (5, 6°), (6, -2°)\}$

2. $\{(1, \$10), (2, \$15), (3, \$25), (4, \$40), (5, \$60), (6, \$85)\}$

3. $\{(1, \pi), (2, \frac{3\pi}{2}), (2, 2\pi), (3, \frac{5\pi}{2}), (4, 3\pi)\}$

4. Write *Yes* or *No* to indicate whether each relation in Exercises 1–3 is also a function. *(Section 5–4)*   1: Yes; 2: Yes; 3: No

Graph each linear equation in the coordinate plane. *(Section 5–5)*

5. $y = 2x$ **6.** $y = -3x - 7$ **7.** $y = -3$ **8.** $x = 2$

In a movie theater, the projector is placed so that the picture is the same size as the screen. In a certain theater, the function $w = \frac{4}{9}d$ represents the relationship between the distance, d, from the projector to the screen and the width, w, of the picture.

Use this information for Exercises 9–11. *(Section 5–6)*

9. Write three ordered pairs for this function. Let $d = 9$, 18, and 36. (9, 4), (18, 8), (36, 16)

10. Use the ordered pairs to graph the function. (0, 0) is the endpoint The graph contains (9, 4), (18, 8) and (36, 16).

11. Estimate the width of the picture when the distance from the projector is 15 units. 7 units

See the Solution Key for the graph.

REVIEW CAPSULE FOR SECTION 5-7

Simplify. *(Pages 56–58, 68–71)*

1. $-9 - (-4)$ -5 **2.** $2 - 5$ -3 **3.** $3 - (-2)$ 5   **4.** $-6 - 3$ -9

5. $0 - 10$ -10 **6.** $0 - (-2)$ 2   **7.** $9 - (-1)$ 10   **8.** $-8 - (-11)$ 3

9. $\frac{2-4}{4+2}$ $-\frac{1}{3}$ **10.** $\frac{-6-2}{3-2}$ -8 **11.** $\frac{-8-(-2)}{7-5}$ -3 **12.** $\frac{2-2}{8-4}$ 0

13. $\frac{-1-(-1)}{-2-6}$ 0   **14.** $\frac{3-3}{2-(-1)}$ 0   **15.** $\frac{3-(-1)}{2-3}$ -4 **16.** $\frac{3-(-2)}{0-(-4)}$ $\frac{5}{4}$

188   *Chapter 5*

OBJECTIVE: To find the slope of a line

5–7 Slope of a Line

When you talk about the grade, or steepness, of a certain road you can say that it rises a vertical distance of 100 feet over a horizontal distance of 400 feet. That is,

rise: 100
run: 400

$$\text{steepness} = \frac{\text{rise}}{\text{run}} = \frac{\text{vertical change}}{\text{horizontal change}} = \frac{100}{400} = \frac{1}{4}.$$

The measure of steepness is a ratio called *slope*. A **ratio** is the quotient of two numbers, such as $\frac{2}{5}$.

Definition

> The **slope** of a line is the ratio of the vertical change to the horizontal change between any two points on the line. That is,
>
> $$\text{slope} = \frac{\text{vertical change}}{\text{horizontal change}}, \ (\text{horizontal change} \neq 0).$$

EXAMPLE 1 Find the slope of each line graphed at the right below.

Solutions:

Line	Vertical Change	Horizontal Change	Slope = $\dfrac{\text{Vertical Change}}{\text{Horizontal Change}}$
A	5	2	$\frac{5}{2}$
B	4	4	$\frac{4}{4}$, or **1**
C	9	−3	$\frac{9}{-3}$, or **−3**
D	2	7	$\frac{2}{7}$

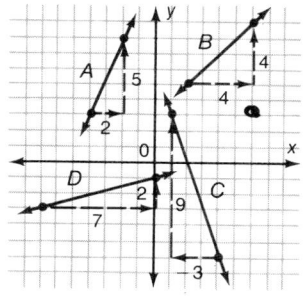

When you know the coordinates of any two points on a line, you can determine the slope of a line. First, you find the difference between the y coordinates, or the vertical change, and the difference between the x coordinates, or the horizontal change. Then you write the ratio of these differences.

EXAMPLE 2 Find the slope of the line containing the points $(1, 3)$ and $(6, 7)$.

Solution: Subtract the y coordinates first. Then subtract the x coordinates.

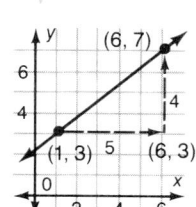

Graphing Relations and Functions   **189**

Teaching Suggestions p. M-18

Quick Quiz

A certain company gives a cost of living increase of 8% of the current annual salary. That is $i = 0.08s$ where i is the increase in dollars and cents and s is the current salary in dollars.

1. Write three ordered pairs for this function. Let $s =$ $14,000, $15,000, and $16,000.
   Ans: (14,000, 1120), (15,000, 1200), (16,000, 1280)
2. Graph the function.
   Ans:

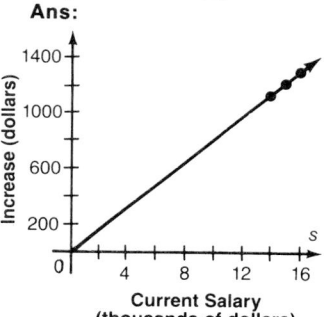

Current Salary (thousands of dollars)

3. Use the graph to estimate the increase on a salary of $20,000.
   Ans: $1600

Additional Example
Example 1
Find the slope of each line.

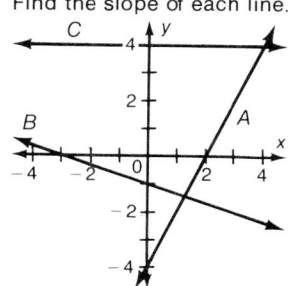

Ans: A: 2; B: $-\frac{1}{3}$; C: 0

189

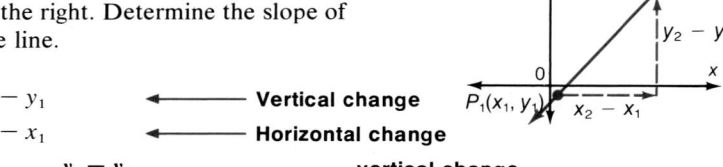

$$7 - 3 = 4 \longleftarrow \text{Vertical change: difference of } y \text{ coordinates}$$

$$6 - 1 = 5 \longleftarrow \text{Horizontal change: difference of } x \text{ coordinates}$$

$$\text{slope} = \frac{4}{5} \longleftarrow \text{Slope} = \frac{\text{vertical change}}{\text{horizontal change}}$$

The ratio of the vertical change to the horizontal change is the same everywhere, no matter which two points are chosen. Thus, the slope of a given line is a constant.

Let $P_1(x_1, y_1)$ and $P_2(x_2, y_2)$ be any two points on the line graphed at the right. Determine the slope of the line.

$$y_2 - y_1 \longleftarrow \text{Vertical change}$$

$$x_2 - x_1 \longleftarrow \text{Horizontal change}$$

$$\text{slope} = \frac{y_2 - y_1}{x_2 - x_1} \longleftarrow \text{Slope} = \frac{\text{vertical change}}{\text{horizontal change}}$$

The letter m is customarily used to denote slope.

Definition

For any two points in a line, $P_1(x_1, y_1)$ and $P_2(x_2, y_2)$,

$$\text{slope} = m = \frac{\text{vertical change}}{\text{horizontal change}} = \frac{y_2 - y_1}{x_2 - x_1}, \; (x_2 - x_1 \neq 0).$$

EXAMPLE 3 Find the slope of the line containing the points $P_1(-4, 3)$ and $P_2(6, -9)$.

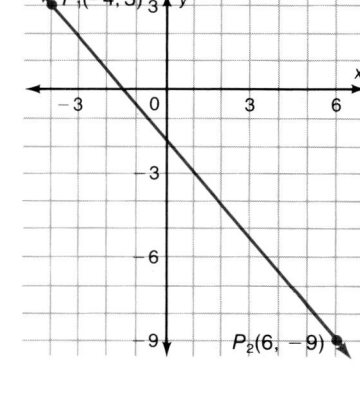

Solution: $m = \dfrac{y_2 - y_1}{x_2 - x_1}$

$$m = \frac{\overset{y_2 \quad y_1}{\downarrow \quad \downarrow}}{\underset{x_2 \quad x_1}{\uparrow \quad \uparrow}} \frac{-9 - (3)}{6 - (-4)}$$

$$= \frac{-9 + (-3)}{6 + 4}$$

$$= \frac{-12}{10}, \text{ or } -\frac{6}{5}$$

Lines with positive slope rise from left to right.
Lines with negative slope fall from left to right.

Thus, the line in Example 3 falls from left to right.

EXAMPLE 4 Find the slope of the lines containing each pair of points.

    a. $S(-1, -3)$ and $T(2, -3)$ **b.** $P(4, 5)$ and $N(4, 9)$

Solutions: **a.** $m = \dfrac{y_2 - y_1}{x_2 - x_1}$ **b.** $m = \dfrac{y_2 - y_1}{x_2 - x_1}$

          $m = \dfrac{-3 - (-3)}{2 - (-1)}$ $m = \dfrac{9 - 5}{4 - 4}$ ⟵ **Cannot divide by 0**

          $m = \dfrac{0}{2 + 1} = \mathbf{0}$ The slope of the line is **undefined**.

Example 4 suggests the following.

> The slope of any horizontal line is **0**.
>
> The slope of a vertical line is **undefined**.

CLASSROOM EXERCISES

Classify the slope of each line as *positive, negative,* or *equal to zero.* If the slope of a line is undefined, write *ND*.

1. 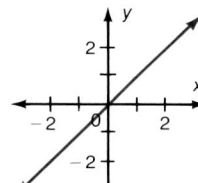   **2.** 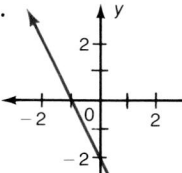   **3.** 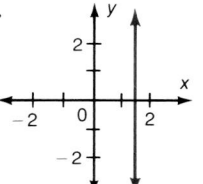   **4.**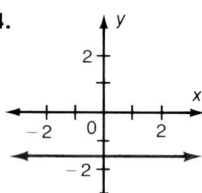

Find the slope of the line containing the given points.

5. $P(1, 2)$; $Q(-3, 5)$ $-\frac{3}{4}$ **6.** $R(-5, -1)$; $S(-2, -4)$ -1 **7.** $T(-3, -11)$; $V(2, -7)$ $\frac{4}{5}$

8. $M(4, -2)$; $R(3, 2)$ -4 **9.** $W(6, -9)$; $N(-1, -1)$ $-\frac{8}{7}$ **10.** $A(8, -2)$; $P(12, 1)$ $\frac{3}{4}$

11. $C(0, 0)$; $D(-4, 2)$ $-\frac{1}{2}$ **12.** $F(3, -2)$; $H(0, 0)$ $-\frac{2}{3}$ **13.** $E(7, 3)$; $G(9, 1)$ -1

WRITTEN EXERCISES

A   Find the slope of each line from its graph.

1. 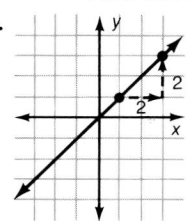   **2.** 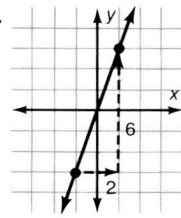   **3.** 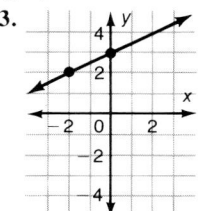   **4.**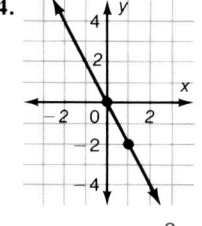

           1   3 $\frac{1}{2}$ -2

Graphing Relations and Functions   **191**

Additional Examples
Example 4
Find the slope of the line containing the given points.
1. a. $A(-2, -5)$ and $B(4, -5)$
    Ans: 0
  b. $C(-3, 6)$ and $D(-3, 8)$
    Ans: undefined
2. a. $X(4, 8)$ and $Y(8, 8)$
    Ans: 0
  b. $P(8, 4)$ and $Q(8, -2)$
    Ans: undefined

Additional Answers
Classroom Exercises
1. Positive
2. Negative
3. ND
4. Equal to zero

Assignment Guide
Minimal pp. 191–192: 1–25 odd
Average pp. 191–193:
1–39 odd
Above Average pp. 191–193:
1–33 odd, 35–39

5.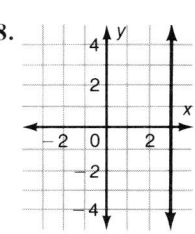

$-\frac{1}{3}$

6. $-\frac{5}{4}$

7. 0

8. 0

Find the slope of the line containing the given points.

9. $R(3, 2)$; $N(6, 8)$ 2
10. $S(7, 1)$; $T(5, 9)$ -4
11. $A(-4, 3)$; $B(-8, 6)$

12. $Q(5, -2)$; $S(-7, 4)$ $-\frac{1}{2}$
13. $G(-5, -1)$; $W(-11, -4)$ $\frac{1}{2}$
14. $T(-6, 3)$; $Q(-2, -9)$

15. $H(2, 6)$; $T(-2, -3)$ $\frac{9}{4}$
16. $J(3, -5)$; $K(-4, 9)$ -2
17. $B(-8, 2)$; $C(10, -4)$

18. $P(0, 4)$; $S(-6, 4)$ 0
19. $D(2, -8)$; $G(-1, -8)$ 0
20. $E(-6, -2)$; $F(-6, 9)$

Find the slope, if it exists, of each side of the given figure.

21. Triangle

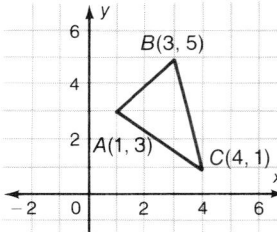

22. Rectangle

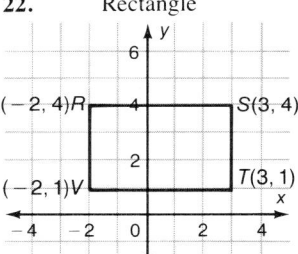

23. Parallelogram

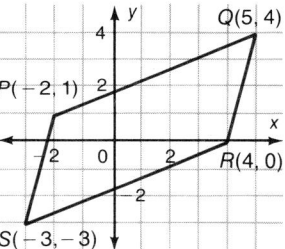

24. Square

25. Rhombus

26. Trapezoid

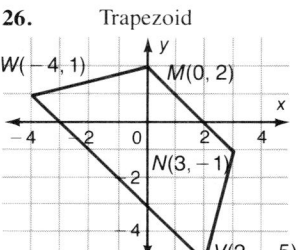

B   Determine whether the given points lie on the same line. (HINT: The slope is the same for all pairs of points on a line.)

27. $(-5, 11)$, $(0, 8)$, $(5, 5)$ Yes
28. $(0, 1)$, $(4, -2)$, $(6, -4)$ No

29. $(6, 3)$, $(3, 2)$, $(0, 0)$ No
30. $(4, 1)$, $(-1, 7)$, $(3, 3)$ No

31. Find y so that the line containing $(2, y)$ and $(-3, 4)$ has a slope of 2. 14
32. Find y so that the line containing $(5, 1)$ and $(6, y)$ has a slope of -3. -2

33. Find the slope of a line passing through $(a, 0)$ and $(0, a)$. -1
34. Find the slope of a line containing the origin and the point $P(40,000, -20,000)$. $-\frac{1}{2}$

35. Let $P_1(x_1, y_1)$ and $P_2(x_2, y_2)$ be any two points on the line graphed at the right. Write a formula for m, the slope of the line.

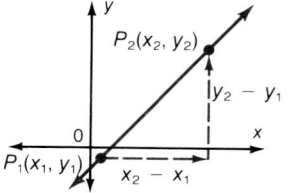

36. Suppose that the line in Exercise 35 is horizontal. How will y_1 and y_2 be related? $y_1 = y_2$

37. Suppose that the line in Exercise 35 is vertical. How will x_1 and x_2 be related? $x_1 = x_2$

38. What is the slope of all lines defined by equations of the form $By = C$, $B \neq 0$? zero

39. What is the slope of all lines defined by equations of the form $Ax = C$, $A \neq 0$? undefined

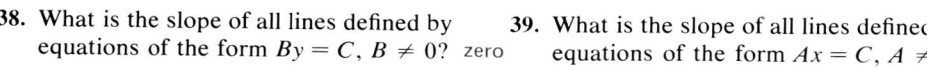 **CALCULATOR APPLICATIONS** _____

Computing y Values for Functions

You can use a calculator to compute y values for a function, given the function's formula and domain.

EXAMPLE Complete the table of values. $y = -5x - 15$

x	−6	−4	0	3
y	?	?	?	?

SOLUTION Substitute x values from the table in the formula.

$$y = -5x - 15 \longrightarrow y = -5(-6) - 15$$

Repeat the procedure above for $x = -4$, $x = 0$, and $x = 3$.
The range is $\{15, 5, -15, -30\}$.

EXERCISES

Complete the tables.

1. $y = \frac{1}{2}x - 17$

x	−3	0	1	4
y	?	?	?	?

2. $y = -6x - 11$

x	−2	−1	2	5
y	?	?	?	?

3. $y = 2\frac{1}{4}x - 6$

x	−6	−4	5	8
y	?	?	?	?

4. $y = 9x + 21$

x	−4	−1	0	3
y	?	?	?	?

_____ **REVIEW CAPSULE FOR SECTION 5–8** _____

Solve each equation for y. *(Pages 162–164)*

1. $3x - y = 4$ **2.** $2y = 5(x + 1)$ **3.** $4x - 3y = 0$ **4.** $2x + 3y = 7$

For each equation, find y when $x = 0$. *(Pages 9–11)*

5. $2y - 4x = 9$ **6.** $y - 4x = 3$ **7.** $y - 3x = 2$ **8.** $2x - 3y - 6 = 0$

Graphing Relations and Functions   **193**

5–8 Slope-Intercept Form of a Line

The graphs of each of these linear functions show that when the x coordinates differ by 1, the y coordinates differ by 3.

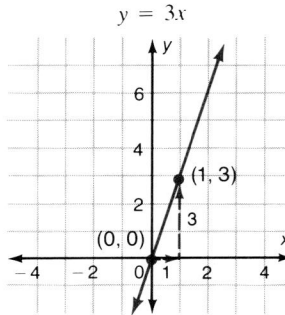
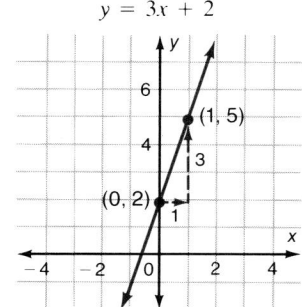

Since, for each linear function,

$$\text{slope} = \frac{\text{vertical change}}{\text{horizontal change}} = \frac{3}{1} = 3,$$

it appears that in the equations

$$y = 3x \qquad \text{and} \qquad y = 3x + 2$$

the "3" represents the slope of the line.

More generally, if a line l is the graph of an equation of the form

$$y = mx + b,$$

m represents the slope of the line. In the equation $y = mx + b$, note that the coefficient of y is 1.

EXAMPLE 1 Find the slope of the line defined by the equation $2x + y = 18$.

Solution: Solve for y in order to write the equation in the form $y = mx + b$.

$2x + y = 18$

$\quad y = -2x + 18$ ◄——— **Compare with y = mx + b.**

$\quad y = \ \ mx + \ b$

$\quad m = -2$

The y coordinate at which a line crosses the y axis is called the **y intercept.** Since $x = 0$ for any point on the y axis, you can find the y intercept of a linear function by replacing x with 0 in its equation.

$$y = mx + b \quad ◄——— \textbf{Replace x with 0.}$$

$$y = m(0) + b$$

$$y = b \quad ◄——— \textbf{y intercept}$$

194 *Chapter 5*

Slope-Intercept Form	The equation $y = mx + b$ is called the **slope-intercept form** of the linear equation. Its graph is a straight line with **slope m** and **y intercept b**.

EXAMPLE 2 Find the slope and y intercept of the graph of $5x + y = 6$.

Solution: Rewrite the equation in the form $y = mx + b$.

$y = -5x + 6$ ⟵——— $m = -5; b = 6$ Slope: -5 y intercept: 6

You can use the slope and y intercept of a line to draw its graph.

EXAMPLE 3 Graph the line with slope -2 and y intercept 3.

Solution:
$\boxed{1}$ The y intercept is 3. Therefore, graph the point $P(0, 3)$.

$\boxed{2}$ Since the slope is -2,

$$\frac{\text{vertical change}}{\text{horizontal change}} = -2 = \frac{-2}{1}.$$

Start at P. Move 1 unit to the right and 2 units down. Label the point Q.

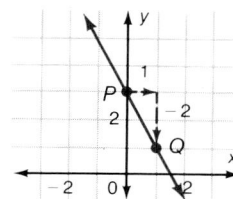

$\boxed{3}$ Connect points P and Q with a straight line.

NOTE: In Example 3, you could also start at point P, move 2 units down and then 1 unit to the right. You would arrive at the same point, Q.

You can also write the slope as $-2 = \frac{2}{-1}$. The graph would be the same.

EXAMPLE 4 Use the slope and y intercept of $2x - 3y = 9$ to draw its graph.

Solution:
$\boxed{1}$ $2x - 3y = 9$ ⟵——— **Solve for y.**
$-3y = -2x + 9$

$y = \frac{2}{3}x - 3$ ⟵——— **Compare with y = mx + b.**

Slope: $\frac{2}{3}$ y intercept: -3

$\boxed{2}$ The y intercept is -3. Therefore, graph the point $P(0, -3)$.

Since $m = \frac{2}{3}$, start at P. Move 3 units to the right and 2 units up. Label point Q.

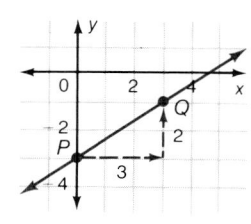

$\boxed{3}$ Connect points P and Q with a straight line.

Additional Examples
Example 2
Find the slope and y intercept of the graph of the given equation.
1. $3x + y = 9$
    Ans: $m = -3; b = 9$
2. $y - 6x = -7$
    Ans: $m = 6; b = -7$

Example 3
Graph the line with slope 2 and y intercept -2.
Ans:

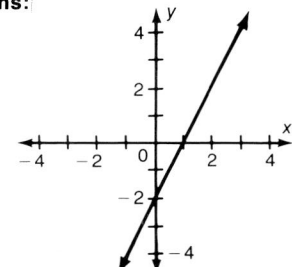

Example 4
Use the slope and y intercept of $3x + 2y = 6$ to draw its graph.
Ans:

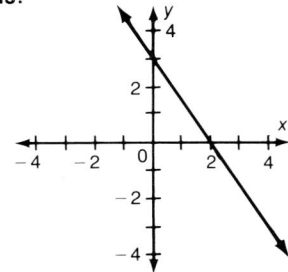

CLASSROOM EXERCISES

Give the slope and y intercept of the graph of each equation.

4; 0

1. $y = 2x + 5$ 2; 5
2. $y = 6x - 7$ 6; −7
3. $y = 3x + 2$ 3; 2
4. $y = 4x$
5. $y = \frac{2}{3}x + \frac{1}{2}$ $\frac{2}{3}; \frac{1}{2}$
6. $y = -\frac{1}{2}x - 5$ $-\frac{1}{2}; -5$
7. $y = 3$ 0; 3
8. $y + 8 = 0$ 0; −8

WRITTEN EXERCISES

Assignment Guide
Minimal p. 196: 1–30 even
Average p. 196: 1–40 even
Above Average p. 196:
1–36 even, 37–42

Additional Answers
Written Exercises
1. $y = -2x + 4$; −2; 4
2. $y = -3x + 8$; −3; 8
3. $y = -5x - 3$; −5; −3
4. $y = 4x + 1$; 4; 1
5. $y = 2x - 4$; 2; −4
6. $y = 3x - 1$; 3; −1
7. $y = -2x - \frac{5}{2}$; −2; $-\frac{5}{2}$
8. $y = 4x - 3$; 4; −3
9. $y = -x + 3$; −1; 3
10. $y = 2x - 6$; 2; −6
11. $y = -4$; 0; −4
12. $y = 2x - 3$; 2; −3
For Exercises 13–30, each
graph is a straight line
containing the given points.
13. $(-1, -3)$, $(0, 6)$
14. $(-1, 6)$, $(0, -2)$
15. $(0, 1)$, $(1, 4)$
16. $(0, 1)$, $(2, 2)$
17. $(0, 0)$, $(3, -2)$
18. $(0, -2)$, $(4, -1)$
19. $(0, -2)$, $(1, -2)$
20. $(0, 5)$, $(1, 5)$
21. $(-5, 1)$, $(0, -1)$
27. $(0, -6)$, $(1, -3)$
30. $(0, -3)$, $(1, -1)$
38. $y = -2x$
39. $y = -\frac{1}{3}x + 5$
40. $y = -\frac{5}{6}x - 3$

A First write each equation in the form $y = mx + b$. Then give the slope and y intercept of its graph.

1. $2x + y = 4$
2. $3x + y = 8$
3. $5x + y = -3$
4. $y - 4x = 1$
5. $y - 2x = -4$
6. $2y = 6x - 2$
7. $-2y = 4x + 5$
8. $6 + 2y = 8x$
9. $9 - 3y = 3x$
10. $4x - 2y = 12$
11. $2y + 8 = 0$
12. $2y - 4x + 6 = 0$

See the Solution Key for the Graphs of Ex. 13-30.

Graph the line whose slope and y intercept are given.

13. $m = 9$, $b = 6$
14. $m = -8$, $b = -2$
15. $m = 3$, $b = 1$
16. $m = \frac{1}{2}$, $b = 1$
17. $m = -\frac{2}{3}$, $b = 0$
18. $m = \frac{1}{4}$, $b = -2$
19. $m = 0$, $b = -2$
20. $m = 0$, $b = 5$
21. $m = -\frac{2}{5}$, $b = -1$

Use the slope and y intercept to graph each line. (0, −6), (1, −1)

22. $y = 3x - 2$ (0, −2)(1, 1)
23. $y = -6x$ (−1, 6), (0, 0)
24. $y = 5x - 6$
25. $-2x + y = 4$ (0, 4), (1, 6)
26. $y = -\frac{2}{3}x - 6$ (−3, −4), (0, −6)
27. $3x = y + 6$
28. $y - 3x = 1$ (0, 1), (1, 4)
29. $4y = 5x + 12$ (0, 3), (4, 8)
30. $2x - y = 3$

B Use this theorem from geometry to tell whether each pair of lines in Exercises 31–36 is parallel.

Theorem | **Parallel lines have the same slope.**

31. $2x + y = 1$ Yes
$6x + 3y = 4$
32. $x - 3y = 4$ No
$6y + 2x = 8$
33. $3x - 2y = 2$ Yes
$6x = 4y - 9$
34. $2y = 4x - 5$ Yes
$3y - 6x = 7$
35. $3y + 10 = 2x$ No
$2y - 3x = 0$
36. $y + 6 = 0$ Yes
$y - 2 = 0$

37. What is the slope of all lines parallel to $y = -\frac{3}{4}x$? $-\frac{3}{4}$

38. What is the equation of a line whose slope is −2 and whose y intercept is 0?

39. What is the equation of a line whose slope is $-\frac{1}{3}$ and whose y intercept is 5?

40. What is the equation of a line whose slope is $-\frac{5}{6}$ and whose y intercept is −3?

C

41. Write the general form of the linear equation $Ax + By = C$ in the form $y = mx + b$. $y = -\frac{A}{B}x + \frac{C}{B}$

42. Use your answer to Exercise 41 to represent the slope m of the line $Ax + By = C$ in terms of A and B. $-\frac{A}{B}$

5-9 Direct Variation

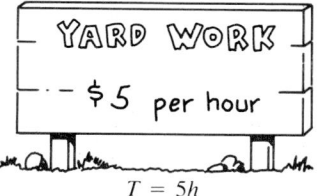

$T = 5h$ $T = 10h + 12$

For one of the examples above, doubling the number of hours, h, doubles the total cost, T. Do you recognize $T = 5h$ as the equation that defines this relationship?

The equation $T = 5h$ expresses *direct variation*. It is called **direct variation** because only multiplication by a constant is involved.

	Direct Variation $T = 5h$	**Not Direct Variation** $T = 10h + 12$
Let $h = 3$.	$T = 15$	$T = 42$
Let $h = 6$.	$T = 30$	$T = 72$
Let $h = 12$.	$T = 60$	$T = 132$
Let $h = 24$.	$T = 120$	$T = 252$
	T is doubled when h is doubled.	T is not doubled when h is doubled.

Direct variation is a special case of the linear function $y = mx + b$, with $b = 0$. Thus, the graph of a linear function expressing direct variation will always pass through the origin.

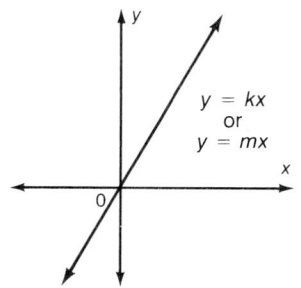

The equation $y = kx$ expresses **direct variation between x and y**. That is, y is said to vary directly as x, and k is called the **constant of variation**. Note that k is the slope of the graph of $y = kx$.

EXAMPLE 1 **a.** If y varies directly as x, and $y = 8$ when $x = 3$, find k.
b. Write the equation that expresses the variation.

Solution: **a.** $y = kx$ ⟵ **y varies directly as x.**

$8 = k(3)$ ⟵ **When $y = 8$, $x = 3$.**

$\dfrac{8}{3} = k$ ⟵ **Constant of variation**

b. $y = \dfrac{8}{3}x$ ⟵ **Write the equation with $k = \dfrac{8}{3}$.**

Graphing Relations and Functions   **197**

Teaching Suggestions p. M-18

Quick Quiz
Find the slope and y intercept of the graph of the given equation. Then graph the line.
1. $5x + 2y = 8$
   Ans: $m = -\dfrac{5}{2}$; $b = 4$

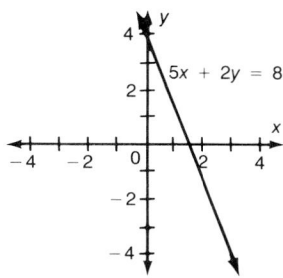

2. $3y - 2x = -9$
   Ans: $m = \dfrac{2}{3}$; $b = -3$

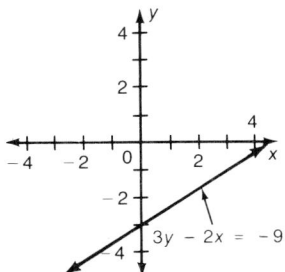

Additional Examples
Example 1
In Exercises 1–2, y varies directly as x. Find k. Then write the equation that expresses the variation.
1. $y = 7$ when $x = 2$
   Ans: $k = \dfrac{7}{2}$; $y = \dfrac{7}{2}x$
2. $y = 12$ when $x = 4$
   Ans: $k = 3$; $y = 3x$

After you have found the equation that expresses the direct variation, you can find ordered pairs (x, y) that satisfy the equation.

EXAMPLE 2   If y varies directly as x, and $y = 21$ when $x = 1\frac{1}{2}$, find y when $x = 9$.

Solution:

$$y = kx \longleftarrow \text{ \bf Linear direct variation}$$

$$21 = k\left(\frac{3}{2}\right) \longleftarrow \text{ \bf Multiply each side by } \frac{2}{3}.$$

$$21\left(\frac{2}{3}\right) = k\left(\frac{3}{2}\right)\left(\frac{2}{3}\right)$$

$$14 = k \longleftarrow \text{ \bf Constant of variation}$$

Thus, $y = 14x$. $\longleftarrow$ **Find y when x = 9.**

$$y = 14(9)$$

$$y = \mathbf{126}$$

Additional Examples
Example 2
1. If y varies directly as x, and $y = 24$ when $x = 2\frac{1}{4}$, find y when $x = 8$.
Ans: y = 96
2. If y varies directly as x, and $y = 15$ when $x = \frac{2}{3}$, find y when $x = 16$.
Ans: y = 360

CLASSROOM EXERCISES

Determine whether each set of ordered pairs (x, y) is an example of direct variation. Answer *Yes* or *No*.

1.

x	1	2	3	4
y	3	6	9	12

Yes

2.

x	0	1	2	3
y	5	6	7	8

No

3.

x	-1	-2	-3	-4
y	-7	-14	-21	-28

Yes

Determine whether each equation is an example of direct variation. Answer *Yes* or *No*.

4. $x = 4y$ Yes   5. $x + y = 6$ No   6. $y = 6x$ Yes   7. $x - y = 4$ No

8. $\frac{x}{4} = y$ Yes   9. $x + 5y = 10$ No   10. $x - 8y = 0$ Yes   11. $xy = 10$ No

If y varies directly as x, find the constant of variation, k, for the given values of x and y.

12. $x = 3, y = 2$ $\frac{2}{3}$ 13. $x = -1, y = 4$ -4 14. $x = 5, y = -2$ $-\frac{2}{5}$ 15. $x = -\frac{1}{2}, y = -1$ 2

WRITTEN EXERCISES

A   In Exercises 1–2, determine whether the relation between the variables is that of direct variation. Explain your answer.

1. P is the perimeter of a square and s is the length of one side.

2. John earns $3.25 an hour mowing lawns. The amount that he earns in cents is A. The number of hours that he works is n.

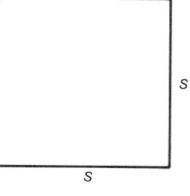

Assignment Guide
Minimal
Day 1 pp. 198–199: 1–14
Day 2 p. 199: 15–30
Average
Day 1 pp. 198–199: 1–24
Day 2 pp. 199–200: 25–35
Above Average pp. 198–200: 2–30 even, 31–39

Additional Answers
Written Exercises
1. Yes; P is always 4 times s.
2. Yes; A is always 325 times n.

198   *Chapter 5*

In Exercises 3–6, refer to the table at the right.

x	0	1	2	3	4	5	6
y	0	$2\frac{1}{2}$	5	$7\frac{1}{2}$	10	$12\frac{1}{2}$	15

3. Does each number for y equal a constant times the corresponding number for x? Does y vary directly as x? Explain.   Yes; Yes; y is always $\frac{5}{2}$ times x.

4. Write an equation that shows the relation between x and y. ($y = \underline{\quad?\quad}$) $y = \frac{5}{2}x$

5. When x is 4, y is 10. When x is 8, y is $\underline{\quad?\quad}$. If you double the value of x, is the corresponding value of y doubled? If you choose any value of x and double it, the corresponding value of y is $\underline{\quad?\quad}$. 20; Yes; doubled

6. When x is 2, y is $\underline{\quad?\quad}$. When x is 6, y is $\underline{\quad?\quad}$. If you triple any value of x, the corresponding value of y is $\underline{\quad?\quad}$. 5; 15; tripled

Determine whether each equation is an example of direct variation. Answer *Yes* or *No*.

7. $x = 12y$ Yes

8. $5x = y$ Yes

9. $y = \frac{1}{8}x$ Yes

10. $y + 3x = 0$ Yes

11. $xy + 4 = y$ No

12. $y = \frac{x}{4}$ Yes

13. $\frac{x}{y} = 7$ Yes

14. $y = \frac{18}{x}$ No

Express each relationship as an equation. Use k as the constant of variation.

15. y varies directly as x. $y = kx$

16. p varies directly as q. $p = kq$

17. r varies directly as s. $r = ks$

18. s varies directly as t. $s = kt$

In Exercises 19–30, assume that y varies directly as x.

19. If $x = 2$ when $y = 3$, find k. $\frac{3}{2}$

20. If $x = 5$ when $y = 2$, find k. $\frac{2}{5}$

21. If $x = -3$ when $y = 6$, find k. -2

22. If $x = 1$ when $y = -4$, find k. -4

23. If $x = \frac{1}{2}$ when $y = \frac{2}{3}$, find k. $\frac{4}{3}$

24. If $x = -2$ when $y = -8$, find k. 4

25. If $y = 9$ when $x = 3$, find k. Then find y when x is 1. 3, 3

26. If $y = 10$ when $x = 2$, find k. Then find y when x is -2. 5, -10

27. If $y = 6$ when $x = 4$, find y when x is 10. 15

28. If $y = -2$ when $x = -1$, find y when x is 5. 10

29. If $x = -3$ when $y = -2$, find x when y is -4. -6

30. If $x = 4$ when $y = -3$, find x when y is 0. 0

B In Exercises 31–33, refer to the figure at the right. The figure shows the graph of $y = kx$ for various values of k.

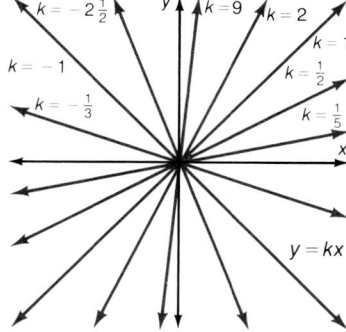

31. As k increases from $\frac{1}{5}$ to 9, what happens to the graph of $y = kx$? The slope of the line increases.

32. As k decreases from $-2\frac{1}{2}$ to $-\frac{1}{3}$, what happens to the graph of $y = kx$? The slope of the line increases

33. Why does the graph of an equation expressing direct variation always pass through the origin?

Graphing Relations and Functions   **199**

Note: In Exercise 32 the word "decreases" should read "increases."

Additional Answers
33. The y intercept of an equation expressing direct variation is 0, and if $y = 0$, then $x = 0$.

In Exercises 34–35, use the fact that $C = \pi d$ expresses the relation between the circumference of a circle and the length of a diameter.

34. Does C vary directly as d? Explain.   Yes; C is always π times d.

35. When d is 10, C is 10π. When d is 20, C is __?__ . If you take one circle and draw another circle that has a diameter twice that of the first, its circumference is __?__ the circumference of the first circle. 20π; twice

C　　　In Exercises 36–39, assume that y equals a negative number times x.

36. As x increases, does y increase or decrease? decreases

37. As x decreases, does y increase or decrease? increases

38. Complete: When any number for x is doubled, the corresponding number for y is __?__ . doubled

39. Complete: When any number for x is multiplied by n, the corresponding number for y is __?__ . multiplied by n

 *CALCULATOR APPLICATIONS* _____

Direct Variation

You can use the memory keys on a calculator, [M+] and [MR] , to check whether a relation is an example of direct variation.

EXAMPLE Determine whether each set of ordered pairs at the right is an example of direct variation. If so, write an equation that expresses the variation.

x	−3	0	2.5	7.5
y	−16.5	0	13.75	41.25

SOLUTION First find the quotient, $\frac{y}{x}$, in the first ordered pair, and store in memory. Then test the value of k for each ordered pair in the relation.

1 6 . 5 [+/−] [÷] 3 [+/−] [=] [M+]　　　5.5　←—— Value of $\frac{y}{x}$.

0 [×] [MR] [=] 2 . 5 [×] [MR] [=] 7 . 5 [×] [MR] [=]　　　41.25

Since each ordered pair checks, the relation is an example of direct variation. The equation is **$y = 5.5x$**.

EXERCISES

Determine whether each relation is an example of direct variation. If so, write an equation that expresses the variation.

1.

x	−5	−1	4	9
y	$-2\frac{1}{2}$	$-\frac{1}{2}$	2	$4\frac{1}{2}$

2.

x	−2	−1	0	1
y	12	6	0	6

3.

x	−2	0	1	8
y	−13.5	0	6.75	54

Problem Solving and Applications

OBJECTIVE: To solve problems involving direct variation

5–10 Using Direct Variation

You can use direct variation to solve word problems.

EXAMPLE The length of an official flag of the United States varies directly with its width, and the constant of variation is fixed by Federal law. If an official flag is 3 meters wide and 5.7 meters long, what should be the length of an official flag that is 1.5 meters wide?

Solution: Let l = the length of the flag and let w = the width.
Then $l = kw$. ◄——— **Replace l with 5.7 and w with 3.**

$$5.7 = k(3)$$
$$1.9 = k$$ ◄——— **Use k to write the direct linear variation.**

Thus, $l = 1.9w$.
$$l = 1.9(1.5)$$
$$l = 2.85$$ The length should be **2.85 meters.**

In the Exercises that follow, assume that all variations are linear.

CLASSROOM EXERCISES

1. David paid an import tax of $160 on a $25,000 car. The tax varies directly as the cost of the car. At that rate, how much import tax would be owed on a car that cost $17,000? $108.80

2. The labor costs for an automobile repair job vary directly as the number of hours a mechanic works on the car. If labor costs for 3 hours amount to $87, what will be the labor costs for 7 hours? $203

3. The estimated cost of building a house varies directly as the number of square feet of floor space. If 1200 square feet cost $60,000, how many square feet could you expect to get for $100,000? 2000

4. A real estate dealer makes a commission of $6720 on a sale of $112,000. At the same rate, how much could the dealer expect to make on a sale of $85,000? $5100

5. Operating costs for driving a car 20,000 kilometers per year total $4800. At the same rate, how much will it cost to drive the car 36,804 kilometers? $8832.96

Graphing Relations and Functions **201**

Assignment Guide
Minimal p. 202: 1–6
Average
pp. 202–203: 2–14 even
Above Average
pp. 202–203: 5–14

WORD PROBLEMS

Ⓐ   Solve each problem.

1. The amount of pay, A, that Sue earns varies directly with the number of hours, h, that she works. Last week, she earned $108.75 for 25 hours of work. How much pay will she earn for 120 hours of work? Assume that the pay rate remains the same. $522

2. The mass of an object on the moon varies directly as its mass on earth. Thus, an object with a mass of 14.4 kilograms on the moon will have a mass of 90 kilograms on earth. If an object has a mass of 120 kilograms on earth, find its mass on the moon. 19.2 kg

3. On a scale drawing, 2 centimeters represent 50 meters. How many meters will 5 centimeters represent? 125 m

4. The cost of gold varies directly as its mass. If 3 grams of gold cost $235, how much will 5 grams cost? $391.67

5. The gas consumption of a car varies directly as the distance traveled. If a certain car uses 20 liters of gas to travel 200 kilometers, how many liters of gasoline will be used on a trip of 700 kilometers? 70

6. The amount of stretch, S, in a spring varies directly as the weight attached, w. A certain spring stretches 5 inches when a weight of 15 pounds is attached. Find the weight needed for a stretch of $7\frac{1}{2}$ inches. $22\frac{1}{2}$ lb

7. The distance between two towns on a map varies directly with the actual distance between the towns. If $2\frac{1}{2}$ inches on the map represent 150 miles, what is the actual distance represented by 7 inches on the map? 420 mi

8. The number of calories in a container of milk varies directly with the amount of milk in the container. If a 10-ounce glass of milk contains 180 calories, how many calories are there in a 14-ounce glass? 252 calories

9. The toll, T, on a bridge varies directly with the number of axles on a vehicle. On a certain bridge, the toll for a 4-axle truck is $3.00. What will be the toll for a 6-axle truck? $4.50

10. The speed of the blade tips of a windmill varies directly with the speed of the wind. In a 20 mile-per-hour wind, the speed of the blade tips of a windmill near Sandusky, Ohio is 180 miles per hour. Find the speed of the blade tips in a 5 mile-per-hour wind. 45 mph

11. The amount of time, T, that it takes to read an article varies directly with the length of the article. Ted takes 3 minutes to read an article of 315 words. How many minutes will it take him to read an article of 945 words if he reads at the same rate? 9 minutes

12. The cost, c, of cleaning a carpet varies directly with the area, A, of the carpet. The cost of cleaning a 9-foot by 12-foot carpet is $21.60. At the same rate per square foot, how much will it cost to clean a carpet 18 feet long by 10 feet wide? $36.00

202   *Chapter 5*

13. The weight, w, of a steer being raised for food varies directly with the number of pounds of feed, f consumed. It takes 96 pounds of fodder to produce a 6-pound roast of beef. How many pounds of fodder does it take to produce 15 pounds of beef?   240 lb

14. The amount of antifreeze required to prevent freezing at $-25°C$ varies directly with the capacity of the cooling system. A 20-liter cooling system requires 6.2 liters of antifreeze. How much antifreeze is needed in a 25-liter system?   7.75 liters

_____ Review _____

Find the slope of the line containing the given points. *(Section 5–7)*

1. $(5, -1)$; $(8, 2)$ 1
2. $(0, 0)$; $(-1, 1)$ -1
3. $(-8, 6)$; $(3, -9)$ $-\frac{15}{11}$
4. $(-5, 9)$; $(3, 9)$ 0

Write each equation in the form $y = mx + b$. Then give the slope and y intercept of its graph. *(Section 5–8)*

5. $3x + y = 5$
6. $3x - 2y = 8$
7. $y + 8 = 0$
8. $-5y = 3x$

9. Use the slope and y intercept of $2x + y = 8$ to draw its graph. *(Section 5–8)*

Determine whether each equation is an example of direct variation. Answer *Yes* or *No. (Section 5–9)*

10. $y = 4x$ Yes
11. $2y = x$ Yes
12. $y = -\frac{x}{5}$ Yes
13. $y = 3x - 1$ No

14. If y varies directly as x, and $y = 40$ when $x = 5$, find y when $x = 20$.   160
(Section 5–9)

Solve. *(Section 5–10)*

15. The cost, C, of keeping a lamp lit for 24 hours varies directly with the number of watts, w, of the lamp bulb. It costs 10 cents a day to keep a 100-watt bulb burning for 24 hours. How much would you save each day if the bulb were changed to 60 watts?   4¢

 See the Solution Key.

Without actually graphing, tell whether each line would intersect the graph of the house shown in 1 point, 0 points, or infinitely many points.

1. $y = 1$
2. $y = 2$
3. $y = 3$
4. $x = 1$
5. $x = 2$
6. $y = x + 3$
7. $y = x + 2$
8. $y = x - 2$
9. $y = x + 8$
10. $y + x = 8$
11. $y + x = 3$
12. $y = 4x$

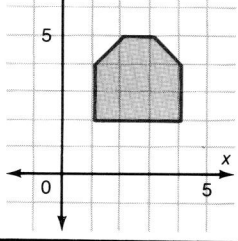

Graphing Relations and Functions   **203**

Quiz Sections 5-7–5-10
After completing this Review, you may want to administer a quiz covering the same sections. See page M-**47** of the Teacher's Manual for the suggested quiz.

Additional Answers
Review
5. $y = -3x + 5$; -3; 5
6. $y = \frac{3}{2}x - 4$; $\frac{3}{2}$; -4
7. $y = -8$; 0; -8
8. $y = -\frac{3}{5}x$; $-\frac{3}{5}$; 0
9.

BASIC: DIRECT VARIATION

Problem: *y varies directly as x. Given the constant of variation and the smallest and largest x values, write a program which prints a table of ordered pairs.*

Program:
```
100 PRINT "Y VARIES DIRECTLY AS X. WHAT ARE"
110 PRINT "THE CONSTANT OF VARIATION AND THE"
120 PRINT "SMALLEST AND LARGEST X VALUES";
130 INPUT K, X1, X2
140 PRINT
150 PRINT " X", " Y"
160 PRINT
170 FOR X = X1 TO X2
180 LET Y = K * X
190 PRINT X, Y
200 NEXT X
210 PRINT
220 END
```

The following is the output from a sample run of the program above.

Output:
```
RUN
Y VARIES DIRECTLY AS X.  WHAT ARE
THE CONSTANT OF VARIATION AND THE
SMALLEST AND LARGEST X VALUES? 5,0,10

 X              Y

 0              0
 1              5
 2             10
 3             15
 4             20
 5             25
 6             30
 7             35
 8             40
 9             45
10             50

READY
```

Analysis

Statements 140–160: These print the heading for the table. Statement 140 skips a line. Then statement 150 puts the titles on the columns before statement 160 skips another line.

This section is optional. Each computer applications lesson relates directly to a topic covered within the chapter. (See Section 5-10, pages 201–203)

Statements 170–200: These form a FOR–NEXT loop. This section of the program is executed over and over, one time for each X value. The first time the computer reaches statement 170, X is set to its starting value (X1, which is 0 for the sample run on page 204). Statements 180 and 190 are done. Then statement 200 sends the computer back to statement 170, where X is increased by 1. Statements 180 and 190 are executed again. The loop continues like this until X reaches X2, its final value. Statements 180–190 are done one last time before the computer moves to statement 210, which skips a line at the end of the printout.

If statement 170 were changed to 170 FOR X = X1 TO X2 STEP .5, the difference between successive X values would be 0.5 instead of 1. Thus, for the data in the sample run, X would take on the values 0, 0.5, 1, 1.5, · · · , 9.5, 10.

Examples of valid FOR statements are shown below.

```
110 FOR J = I+1 TO N          235 FOR K = A-B TO C*C STEP 2
340 FOR D = 100 TO 1 STEP -1   432 FOR R = 2*X TO X+10 STEP J/2
```

EXERCISES

A Run the program on page 204 for the following values of k, x_1, and x_2.

1. $k = 4$; $x_1 = 1$; $x_2 = 5$ **2.** $k = 2.5$; $x_1 = 0$; $x_2 = 4$ **3.** $k = 10$; $x_1 = -3$; $x_2 = 3$

4. $k = -4$; $x_1 = 10$; $x_2 = 15$ **5.** $k = -1.5$; $x_1 = -5$; $x_2 = 0$ **6.** $k = -6$; $x_1 = -2$; $x_2 = 2$

See the Solution Key for the answers to Ex. 7-12.
Write a BASIC program for each problem.

7. y varies directly as x. The input is an x value and its corresponding y value, along with another x value. Print the y value that corresponds to the second x value.

8. Given two ordered pairs, print whether the set of ordered pairs is an example of direct variation.

9. For the equation $y = mx + b$, print a table of values that can be used to draw the graph of the equation. Let the user specify the smallest and largest x values.

10. Given the x and y coordinates of a point, print the quadrant in which the point lies or the axis on which the point lies. (See page 170.)

B

11. For the equation $Ax + By = C$, input A, B, and C. Print the slope and the y intercept of the line with that equation. Include the possibility that the slope may be undefined.

12. Given the slope and y intercept of a line, print the equation of the line in the form $y = mx + b$. Print the equation as "neatly" as possible. For example, print Y = 3 X - 2 and not Y = 3 X + -2; print Y = -2 X and not Y = -2 X + 0; print Y = -4 and not Y = 0 X - 4.

Direct Variation **205**

Chapter Summary

IMPORTANT IDEAS

1. **Distance Formula:** distance = rate · time, or $d = rt$
2. **Steps in Solving Distance/Rate/Time Problems**

   1. Organize the given information in a table. Use this information to represent the unknowns (Condition 1).

   2. Draw a figure to represent the information. Use this figure and the table to write an equation for the problem (Condition 2).

   3. Solve the equation.

   4. Check your answer with the conditions of the problem. Answer the question.

3. In an ordered pair, the first number, x, shows distance to the right or left of the vertical axis. The second number, y, shows distance above or below the horizontal axis.

4. It is necessary to plot only two points to graph a linear equation. However, a third point should be plotted as a check.

5. For any two points on a line, $P_1(x_1, y_1)$ and $P_2(x_2, y_2)$,

$$\text{slope} = m = \frac{\text{vertical change}}{\text{horizontal change}} = \frac{y_2 - y_1}{x_2 - x_1}, \ (x_2 - x_1 \neq 0)$$

6. Lines with positive slope rise from left to right.

   Lines with negative slope fall from left to right.

   The slope of a horizontal line is 0.

   A vertical line has no slope.

7. The graph of an equation of the form $y = mx + b$ is a straight line with slope m and y intercept b.

8. Parallel lines have the same slope.

Chapter Objectives and Review

Objective: *To solve an equation for one variable in terms of the other variables (Section 5–1)*

Solve each equation for *n*. Check each solution.

1. $s = \dfrac{n}{t}$ $n = st$

2. $4n - c = d$ $n = \dfrac{c + d}{4}$

3. $a - n = 2b$ $n = a - 2b$

4. $-n = a - b$ $n = -a + b$

5. $3h = 2n + g$ $n = \dfrac{3h - g}{2}$

6. $cn - d = 1 - e$ $n = \dfrac{d - e + 1}{c}$

Solve the formula for the variable indicated.

7. Formula for the area of a parallelogram: $A = bh$ Solve for h. $h = \dfrac{A}{b}$

8. Formula for the perimeter of a rectangle: $P = 2l + 2w$ Solve for l. $l = \dfrac{P - 2w}{2}$

Objective: *To solve distance/rate/time problems (Section 5–2)*

9. Two runners going in opposite directions pass each other along a straight trail. The speed of the faster runner is $1\frac{1}{4}$ times that of the slower runner. In one hour they are 18 kilometers apart. Find the rate of each runner.

10. Two buses leave Atlanta at the same time, headed in the same direction. One bus averages 80 kilometers per hour, and the other averages 85 kilometers per hour. In how many hours will the buses be 15 kilometers apart? 3 hr

Objective: *To graph ordered pairs on the coordinate plane (Section 5–3)*

See the Solution Key for the graphs of Ex. 11-13.

11. Graph these points on the same pair of coordinate axes.

   a. $Q(3, -7)$ **b.** $R(-3, 7)$ **c.** $S(0, -2)$ **d.** $T(6, -5)$ **e.** $U(-6, -6)$
   f. $V(7, 5)$ **g.** $W(6\frac{1}{2}, 0)$ **h.** $X(-2, -5)$ **i.** $Y(-1, 4)$ **j.** $Z(3\frac{1}{2}, -5)$

12. Describe the graph of the set of all points with an abscissa of -2.

13. The coordinates of three vertices of a square are $(2, 3)$, $(-5, -4)$, and $(2, -4)$. Graph the vertices, sketch the square, and give the coordinates of the fourth vertex. $(-5, 3)$

Objective: *To identify the domain and range of a relation and to identify functions (Section 5–4)*

Give the domain and range for each relation.

14. $\{(1, 2), (1, 4), (2, 6), (2, 8), (3, 10), (3, 12)\}$ D: $\{1, 2, 3\}$; R: $\{2, 4, 6, 8, 10, 12\}$

15. $\{(-2, 1), (-1, \frac{1}{2}), (0, 0), (1, -\frac{1}{2}), (2, -1)\}$ D: $\{-2, -1, 0, 1, 2\}$; R: $\{-1, -\frac{1}{2}, 0, \frac{1}{2}, 1\}$

16. $\{(-2, 4), (-1, 1), (0, 0), (1, 1), (2, 4)\}$ D: $\{-2, -1, 0, 1, 2\}$; R: $\{0, 1, 4\}$

17. Write *Yes* or *No* to indicate whether each relation in Exercises 14–16 is also a function.   14. No; 15. Yes; 16. Yes

Objective: *To graph linear equations (Section 5–5)* See the Solution Key for the graphs.

Graph each linear equation in the coordinate plane.

18. $y = 3x - 1$ 19. $y = -4x$ 20. $4x + 2y = -4$ 21. $3x + 9 = 0$

Graphing Relations and Functions   **207**

Objective: *To estimate answers to problems using the graph of a linear equation (Section 5-6)*

The yearly property taxes on private homes in one city are set at 2% of the value of the property. The relationship between the amount of the tax, t, and the property value, p, is expressed by the function $t = 0.02p$. Use this information to complete the table in Exercise 22 and to complete Exercises 23–24.

22.

Property Value (p)	$40,000	$60,000	$80,000
Amount of Tax (t)	?	?	?

23. Use the ordered pairs in the table in Exercise 22 to graph the function.

24. Use the graph from Exercise 23 to estimate the amount of tax when the property value is $50,000. $1000

Objective: *To find the slope of a line (Section 5-7)*

Find the slope of the line containing the given points.

25. $(-7, 16)$; $(1, 0)$ -2

26. $(8, 2)$; $(4, -1)$ $\frac{3}{4}$

27. $(-3, 2)$; $(0, 2)$ 0

Objective: *To graph a line using the slope–intercept form of its equation (Section 5-8)*

Write each equation in the form $y = mx + b$. Then give the slope and y intercept of its graph.

28. $3y = 2x - 9$

29. $x + y = 0$

30. $4x - 2y = 8$

See the Solution Key for the graphs of Ex. 31-36.

Use the slope and y intercept to graph each line.

31. $y = x + 2$

32. $y = 2x + 1$

33. $x + 2y = -4$

34. $3y - 9 = x$

35. $4x + 6 = y$

36. $x - 2y = 11$

Objective: *To write an equation expressing direct variation and find ordered pairs that satisfy the equation. (Section 5-9)*

Determine whether each equation is an example of direct variation. Answer *Yes* or *No*.

37. $x = 4y$ Yes

38. $x = 2y + 7$ No

39. $y = x$ Yes

40. $xy = -8$ No

41. If y varies directly as x, and $y = 4\frac{1}{2}$ when $x = -2$, find y when $x = 8$. $y = -18$

Objective: *To solve problems involving direct variation (Section 5-10)*

42. On a scale drawing, 3 centimeters represent 90 meters. How many meters will 5 centimeters represent? 150 m

43. The cost of silver varies directly as its weight. If 4 ounces of silver cost $56, how much will 7 ounces cost? $98

208   *Chapter 5*

Additional Answers

22. $800; $1200; $1600

23. To draw the graph, use multiples of $400 for the t axis and multiples of $10,000 for the p axis.

28. $y = \frac{2}{3}x - 3$; $\frac{2}{3}$; -3

29. $y = -x$; -1; 0

30. $y = 2x - 4$; 2; -4

For Exercises 31–36, the graph is a straight line through the given points.

31. $(0, 2)$, $(-2, 0)$

32. $(0, 1)$, $(1, 3)$

33. $(0, -2)$, $(-4, 0)$

34. $(0, 3)$, $(-9, 0)$

35. $(0, 6)$, $(-1, 2)$

36. $(0, -5\frac{1}{2})$, $(11, 0)$

44. The distance traveled in a given time varies directly as the rate of travel, r. Mr. Anders drove 260 miles at an average rate of 50 miles per hour. How far could he drive in the same amount of time at an average rate of 55 miles per hour? 286 miles

45. The length of a steel beam shown on a blueprint varies directly with its actual length. On the blueprint, 5 centimeters represent 1 meter. If the length of the beam on the blueprint is 21.5 centimeters, what is the actual length of the steel beam? 4.3 m

_____ Chapter Test _____

A formal Chapter Test is provided in the Teacher's Manual. See p. M-68.

Solve each equation for x. Check each solution.

1. $\dfrac{x}{p} = k$ $x = kp$

2. $2x - a = b$ $x = \dfrac{a + b}{2}$

3. $y - x = z$ $x = y - z$

4. Graph these points on the same coordinate axes. See the Solution Key.

   a. $A(4, -3)$ **b.** $B(-3, 4)$ **c.** $C(0, -2)$ **d.** $D(-5, -5)$

Give the domain and range of each relation. Then state whether each relation is a function.

5. $\{(0, 0), (1, 1), (2, 2), (3, 2), (4, 3), (5, 3)\}$

6. $\{(5, 0), (0, -5), (-3, 4), (-3, -4), (-5, 0), (0, 5)\}$

Find the slope of the line containing the given points.

7. $(7, -4); (-5, -4)$ 0   **8.** $(0, -4); (-2, -5)$ $\frac{1}{2}$ **9.** $(3, -2); (-4, 7)$ $-\frac{9}{7}$

Write each equation in the form $y = mx + b$. Then give the slope and y intercept of its graph.

10. $x - y = 2$ $y = x - 2; 1; -2$

11. $3x + 4y = 4$ $y = -\frac{3}{4}x + 1; -\frac{3}{4}; 1$

12. $2y = 4x - 6$ $y = 2x - 3; 2; -3$

Graph each linear equation in the coordinate plane. See the Solution Key.

13. $y = x + 4$

14. $y = -2x - 1$

Determine whether each equation is an example of direct variation. Answer *Yes* or *No*.

15. $3y = x$ Yes   **16.** $x - y = 8$ No   **17.** $xy = 7$ No

18. If y varies directly as x, and $y = 12$ when $x = 3$, find y when $x = 5$. $y = 20$

19. Two automobiles leave the same place at the same time, one headed north and one south. One travels at an average rate of 60 kilometers per hour and the other at an average rate of 70 kilometers per hour. In how many hours will they be 325 kilometers apart? $2\frac{1}{2}$ hours

20. The weight of a steel cable varies directly with its length. How heavy is a 150–meter roll of cable, if the weight of a 2–meter section is 0.8 kilogram? 60 km

Graphing Relations and Functions   **209**

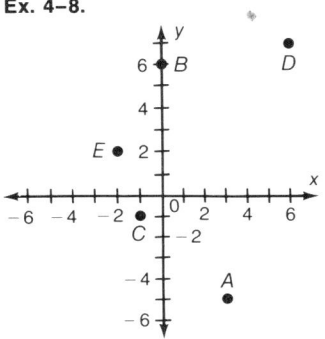

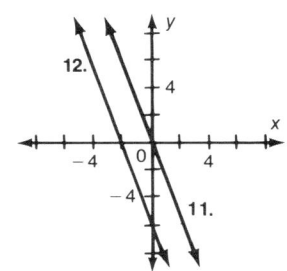

12.

11.

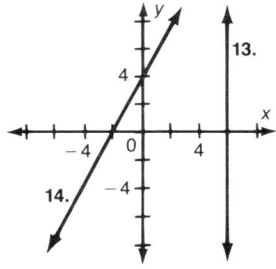

13.

14.

18. $y = -4x - 3; -4; -3$
19. $y = -2x + 5; -2; 5$
22.

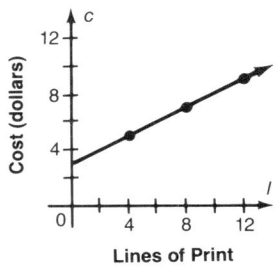

Cost (dollars)

Lines of Print

Additional Practice

You may wish to use all or some of these exercises, depending on how well students performed on the formal chapter test.

Skills

Solve each equation for n. *(Section 5–1)*

$n = \dfrac{d - c}{3}$

1. $a = nb$ $\quad n = \dfrac{a}{b}$

2. $y - n = 4h$ $\quad n = y - 4h$

3. $3n + c = d$

Graph these points on the same pair of coordinate axes. *(Section 5–3)*

4. $A(3, -5)$
5. $B(0, 6)$
6. $C(-1, -1)$
7. $D(6, 7)$
8. $E(-2, 2)$

Give the domain and range for each relation. Then tell if each relation is a function. *(Section 5–4)* D: $\{-13, -12, 0, 5, 12\}$; R: $\{-13, 0, 5, 12, 13\}$;

9. $\{(-13, 0), (-12, 5), (0, 13), (0, -13), (5, 12), (12, 5)\}$ not a function

10. $\{(-2, 2), (-1, 3), (0, 0), (1, -3), (2, -2)\}$
   D: $\{-2, -1, 0, 1, 2\}$; R: $\{-3, -2, 0, 2, 3\}$; function

Graph each linear equation in the coordinate plane. *(Section 5–5)*

11. $y = -3x$
12. $y + 3x = -6$
13. $x = 6$
14. $y - 2x = 4$

Find the slope of the line containing the given points. *(Section 5–7)* $-\dfrac{1}{2}$

15. $(2, 6); (-4, -6)$ $\quad 2$
16. $(3, -4); (5, -4)$ $\quad 0$
17. $(0, -4); (4, -6)$

Write each equation in the $y = mx + b$ form. Then give the slope and y intercept of its graph. *(Section 5–8)* $\quad y = \dfrac{2}{3}x + 2; \dfrac{2}{3}; 2$

18. $4x + y + 3 = 0$
19. $5 - y = 2x$
20. $3y - 6 = 2x$

21. If y varies directly as x and $y = -3$ when $x = 1$, find y when $x = 4$. *(Section 5–9)* $y = -12$

Applications

The cost, c, of running a classified ad in a newspaper is $3 plus 50 cents for each line of print, l, required.

Use this information for Exercises 22–23. *(Section 5–6)*

22. Write three ordered pairs for this function. Let l equal 4, 8, and 12. Graph the function.

23. Use the graph in Exercise 22 to estimate the cost for a fourteen-line ad. $10

24. Frank leaves home at 8 A.M. and drives at a speed of 40 miles per hour. His sister leaves home at 9:30 A.M. driving in the same direction at a speed of 46 miles per hour. At what time will Frank's sister overtake him? *(Section 5–2)* 7:30 P.M.

25. The actual distance between cities varies directly with the distance shown on a map. On the map, 2 centimeters represent 5 kilometers. If the distance between two cities on the map is 14 centimeters, what is the actual distance between the cities? *(Section 5–10)* 35 km

6 Systems of Sentences

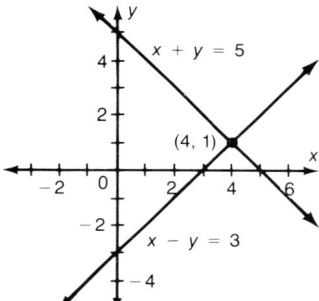

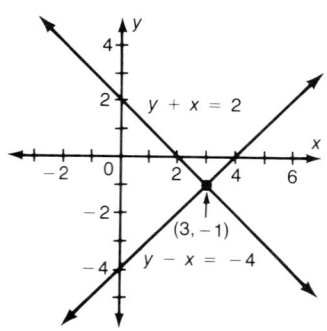

Objective: To solve systems of equations by graphing

6-1 Graphing Systems of Equations

Two or more equations such as

$$\begin{cases} x + y = 10 \\ x - y = 2 \end{cases}$$

form a **system of linear equations** or a system of **simultaneous linear equations.** To solve such a system, you find the ordered pair that makes both equations true. To solve a system of linear equations graphically, graph each equation on the same set of coordinate axes. For two lines that intersect at a point, the coordinates of that point are the **solution** of the system.

EXAMPLE 1 Solve by graphing: $\begin{cases} x + y = 10 \\ x - y = 2 \end{cases}$

Solution: $x + y = 10$ $x - y = 2$

x	y
3	7
5	5
10	0

x	y
0	−2
5	3
2	0

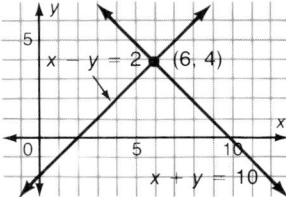

The point of intersection is $(6, 4)$. ◄———— **Read directly from the graph.**

Check: $x + y = 10$ $x - y = 2$ ◄———— **Check in both equations.**
$6 + 4 \overset{?}{=} 10$ $6 - 4 \overset{?}{=} 2$
$10 \overset{?}{=} 10$ Yes ✔ $2 \overset{?}{=} 2$ Yes ✔   **Solution set:** $\{(6, 4)\}$

The figures below show how the graphs of two linear equations can be related.

Two Intersecting Lines

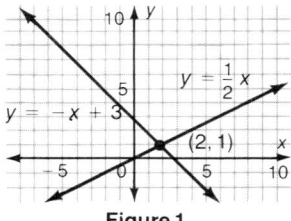

Figure 1

The graphs are *intersecting lines.* Thus, the system has **one solution,** the ordered pair $(2, 1)$.

Two Parallel Lines

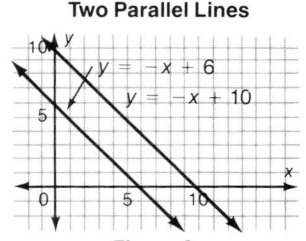

Figure 2

The graphs are *parallel lines.* (**Parallel lines** are lines that lie in the same plane but have no points in common.) Thus, the system has **no solutions.**

Same Line

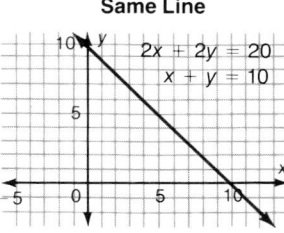

Figure 3

The graphs are the *same line.* (The lines **coincide** or are **coincident.**) **Every point on the line is a solution;** there are an **infinite number of solutions.**

212 *Chapter 6*

Intersecting lines have *different slopes* <u>and</u> the *same, or different, y intercepts*. (See Figure 1.) Parallel lines have the *same slope* and *different y intercepts*. (See Figure 2.) Coincident lines have the *same slope* and the *same y intercept*. (See Figure 3.) Thus, to determine whether a system of linear equations has one, none, or an infinite number of solutions, examine the slope and y intercept of each line.

EXAMPLE 2   Determine the number of solutions for each system.

a. $\begin{cases} y = \frac{1}{3}x + 7 \\ y = 2x - 5 \end{cases}$ b. $\begin{cases} y + x = 5 \\ 3x = 15 - 3y \end{cases}$ c. $\begin{cases} y = 2x - 5 \\ y = 2x + 10 \end{cases}$

Solutions: a. The slopes, $\frac{1}{3}$ and 2, are different. The y intercepts, 7 and -5, are different. Thus, the graphs are intersecting lines and there is **one solution.**

b. Write each equation in the form $y = mx + b$.

$\begin{cases} y = -x + 5 \\ y = -x + 5 \end{cases}$ ⟵——— **Same equation**

Since the slopes are the same and the y intercepts are the same, the graphs coincide. Every point on the graph is a solution and there are an **infinite number of solutions.**

c. The slopes, 2 and 2, are the same. The y intercepts, -5 and 10, are different. Thus, the graphs are parallel lines, and there are **no solutions.**

This table summarizes how to determine the number of solutions for a system of two linear equations.

Graphs of the Equations		Number of Solutions	Graph of the System
Slopes	y intercepts		
Different	Same or different	One	Two intersecting lines
Same	Different	None	Two parallel lines
Same	Same	Infinitely many	Same line

A system of equations having no solutions is called an **inconsistent system.** Systems that have solutions are called **consistent systems.**

CLASSROOM EXERCISES

Complete the tables for each exercise. Give the point of intersection of each pair of equations.

1. $x + y = 5$ $x - y = 3$

x	0	1	2	3	4
y	?	?	?	?	?

x	0	1	2	3	4
y	?	?	?	?	?

2. $2x - y = 7$ $x + 2y = 6$

x	-1	0	1	2	3	4
y	?	?	?	?	?	?

x	-1	0	1	2	3	4
y	?	?	?	?	?	?

Systems of Sentences   **213**

Additional Examples
Example 2
Determine the number of solutions for each system.
1. **a.** $\begin{cases} y = \frac{2}{3}x + 8 \\ y = 4x - 3 \end{cases}$
   Ans: one
   b. $\begin{cases} y + x = 6 \\ 4x = 24 - 4y \end{cases}$
   Ans: infinitely many
   c. $\begin{cases} y = 3x - 9 \\ y = 3x + 12 \end{cases}$
   Ans: none
2. **a.** $\begin{cases} x + 3y = 15 \\ x = 9 - 3y \end{cases}$
   Ans: none
   b. $\begin{cases} y = 3x + 8 \\ y = 5x - 10 \end{cases}$
   Ans: one
   c. $\begin{cases} y + x = 1 \\ 5y = 5 - 5x \end{cases}$
   Ans: infinitely many

Additional Answers
1. $x + y = 5$: 5, 4, 3, 2, 1; $x - y = 3$: -3, -2, -1, 0, 1; (4, 1)
2. $2x - y = 7$: -9, -7, -5, -3, -1, 1; $x + 2y = 6$: $3\frac{1}{2}$, 3, $2\frac{1}{2}$, 2, $1\frac{1}{2}$, 1; (4, 1)

Determine whether the ordered pair (3, 7) is a solution of each system.

3. $\begin{cases} x + y = 4 \\ x - y = 10 \end{cases}$ No

4. $\begin{cases} y - x = 4 \\ y + x = 10 \end{cases}$ Yes

5. $\begin{cases} x + y = -4 \\ x - y = -10 \end{cases}$ No

Determine whether each system graphed below has one solution, an infinite number of solutions, or no solution.

6.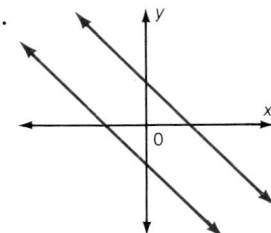

7.

8.

Determine the number of solutions for each system.

9. $\begin{cases} y = 3x + 7 \\ y = 2x - 5 \end{cases}$
one solution

10. $\begin{cases} y = 2x - 5 \\ y = 2x + 10 \end{cases}$
no solution

11. $\begin{cases} 2y = 8 - 7x \\ 4y = 16 - 14x \end{cases}$
an infinite number
of solutions

WRITTEN EXERCISES

A Read the solution set of each system of equations from its graph. Check by substituting in both equations.

1. $\begin{cases} x + y = 10 \\ x - y = 4 \end{cases}$ (7,3)

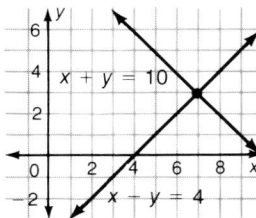

2. $\begin{cases} 2x - y = 3 \\ 3x + y = 7 \end{cases}$ (2, 1)

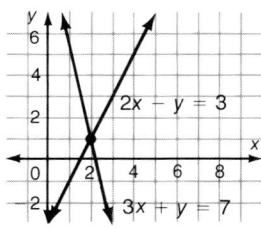

3. $\begin{cases} x + 2y = 4 \\ 2x - y = 8 \end{cases}$ (4, 0)

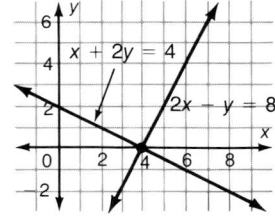

4. $\begin{cases} 2x + y = 3 \\ x - 3y = 5 \end{cases}$ (2, −1)

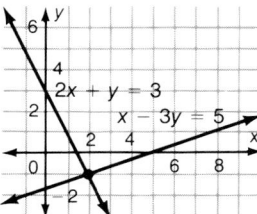

5. $\begin{cases} x + y = 6 \\ x = 5 \end{cases}$ (5, 1)

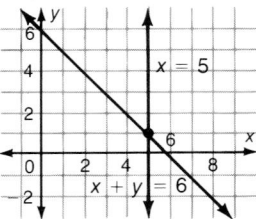

6. $\begin{cases} x = -3 \\ y = 2 \end{cases}$ (−3, 2)

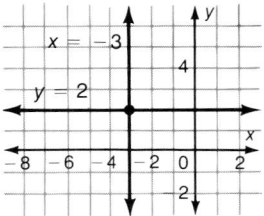

214 *Chapter 6*

214

See the Solution Key for the Graphs.
Solve each system by graphing. Check your solutions.

7. $\begin{cases} x + y = 6 \\ x - y = 4 \end{cases}$ (5, 1)

8. $\begin{cases} x - y = 5 \\ x + y = 7 \end{cases}$ (6, 1)

9. $\begin{cases} x + y = 4 \\ y - x = 2 \end{cases}$

10. $\begin{cases} x - y = 9 \\ 2x + y = 6 \end{cases}$ (5, −4)

11. $\begin{cases} x + y = 2 \\ 2y - x = 10 \end{cases}$ (−2, 4,

12. $\begin{cases} 3x + y = 6 \\ x - 2y = 2 \end{cases}$

13. $\begin{cases} 2x - y = 10 \\ x + 2y = -5 \end{cases}$ (3, −4)

14. $\begin{cases} 3x + y = 3 \\ x - 4y = 1 \end{cases}$ (1, 0)

15. $\begin{cases} x - 5y = -14 \\ 3x + y = 6 \end{cases}$

16. $\begin{cases} 3x + 2y = 4 \\ 2x - 3y = 7 \end{cases}$ (2, −1)

17. $\begin{cases} y = -x + 5 \\ y = \frac{1}{3}x + 1 \end{cases}$ (3, 2)

18. $\begin{cases} x + 4y = -5 \\ 3x + y = -4 \end{cases}$

19. $\begin{cases} x + y = 1 \\ y = x + 1 \end{cases}$ (0, 1)

20. $\begin{cases} y = 2x - 3 \\ x - y = -6 \end{cases}$ (9, 15)

21. $\begin{cases} y = x - 6 \\ y = -2 \end{cases}$

Write *one*, *none*, or *infinitely many* to describe the number of solutions for each system.

22. $\begin{cases} y = -3x + 7 \\ y = -3x + 5 \end{cases}$ none

23. $\begin{cases} y = 3x + 7 \\ y = -3x + 5 \end{cases}$ one

24. $\begin{cases} y = 7 - 3x \\ 2y + 6x = 14 \end{cases}$

25. $\begin{cases} y = -x + 10 \\ y = -x + 4 \end{cases}$ none

26. $\begin{cases} y = x + 10 \\ y = x - 1 \end{cases}$ none

27. $\begin{cases} y = -x \\ y = -x + 1 \end{cases}$

28. $\begin{cases} 4x + 4y = 7 \\ x + y = \frac{7}{4} \end{cases}$ infinitely many

29. $\begin{cases} y = -2x + 2 \\ y = -2x \end{cases}$ none

30. $\begin{cases} y = 2x - 8 \\ y = 2x + 10 \end{cases}$

31. $\begin{cases} y = 5 \\ y = -1 \end{cases}$ none

32. $\begin{cases} y - 9 = 0 \\ y + 1 = 0 \end{cases}$ none

33. $\begin{cases} y - 3x = 0 \\ 5y - 15x = 0 \end{cases}$

B

34. $\begin{cases} x + y = 9 \\ x - y = 9 \end{cases}$ one

35. $\begin{cases} y = 2x - 8 \\ 2x - y = 10 \end{cases}$ none

36. $\begin{cases} y = -4x + 5 \\ 8x + 2y = 10 \end{cases}$

37. $\begin{cases} x = y + 5 \\ 2x - 2y = 7 \end{cases}$ none

38. $\begin{cases} y = 4x - 2 \\ x - 4y = 2 \end{cases}$ one

39. $\begin{cases} 2\frac{1}{2}x - 4 = 3y \\ 6y + 8 = 5x \end{cases}$

APPLICATIONS: Using Systems of Equations

The Q Street Flea Market charges $1 per hour to rent a display area. Residents of Q Street pay no base fee. Town residents, not from Q Street, pay a base fee of $2.00. Out-of-town residents pay a base fee of $5.00.

Use this information and the figure at the right in Exercises 40–42.

40. On the same set of coordinate axes, draw graphs showing the rental fees for residents of Q Street, town residents, and out-of-town residents for 1 to 12 hours.

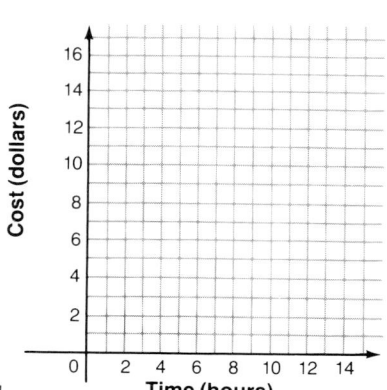

41. How are the slopes of the graphs related? All equal

42. Use the graphs to determine how much more it costs an out-of-town person than a Q Street resident to rent a display area for 8 hours. $5 more

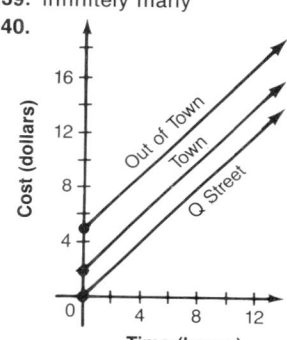
Systems of Sentences   **215**

Suppose that the cost of using solar energy to heat a home involves an initial cost of $10,000 with an average yearly cost of $200 for every year after the first. Suppose also that heating with oil involves an initial cost of $4000 with an average yearly cost of $800 for every year after the first.

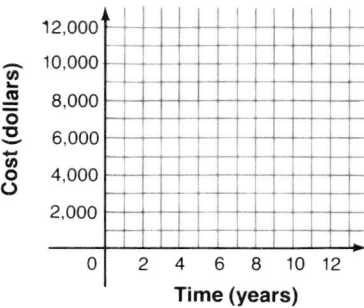

Use this information and the figure at the right in Exercises 43–47.

43. On the same coordinate axes, draw graphs showing yearly costs for heating with solar energy and with oil for 12 years.

44. Which graph has the greater slope? heating with oil

45. For how many years does it cost less to heat with oil than with solar energy? (Include the initial costs.) 10 years

46. How many years does it take for the costs to be equal? (Include the initial costs.)
C   11 years

47. About how much more does it cost to heat with oil than with solar energy during the twelfth year? $600

A supermarket offers two plans for renting a floor polisher. Under Plan A, the charge is $5 per hour. Under Plan B, there is a basic fee of $6 and an additional charge of $2 per hour.

Use this information in Exercises 48–52.

48. On the same set of coordinate axes, draw a graph showing rental costs under each plan for 0 to 6 hours.

49. When will the costs for both plans be the same?

50. When will it cost less to use Plan A?   **51.** When will it cost less to use Plan B?

52. For which plan do costs increase the fastest for $t > 2$?

Write *one, none,* or *infinitely many* to describe the number of solutions for each system.

53. $\begin{cases} Ax + By = C \\ Ax + By = D, \ C \neq D \end{cases}$ **54.** $\begin{cases} Ax + By = C \\ NAx + NBy = NC, \ N \neq 0 \end{cases}$ **55.** $\begin{cases} Ax + By = C \\ Ax - By = C, \ B \neq 0 \end{cases}$

REVIEW CAPSULE FOR SECTION 6-2

Combine like terms. *(Pages 60–63)*

1. $3x + y - (2x - y)$ $x + y$

2. $4x + y + (-4x + 3y)$ $4y$

3. $2x + y - (x - y)$ $x + 2y$

4. $-4a + 2b + (a - 2b)$ $-3a$

5. $9r - 3t - (-9r + 8t)$
$18r - 11t$

6. $-3.5v + s - (-v - 1.2s)$
$-2.5v + 2.2s$

43.

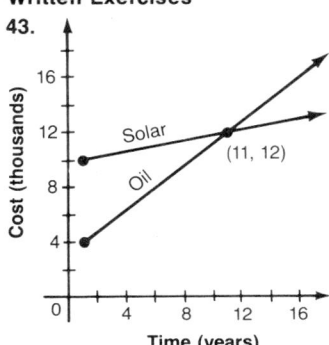

48.

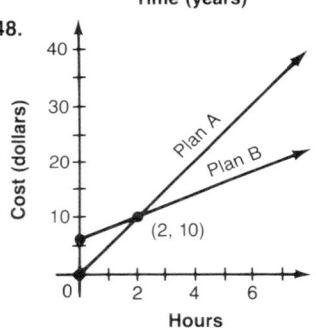

49. 2 hours
50. less than 2 hours
51. more than 2 hours
52. Plan A
53. none
54. infinitely many
55. one

Review Capsule
This Review Capsule reviews the prior-taught skills used in Section 6-2. The reference is to the pages where the skills were taught.

Objective: To solve systems of equation by the addition method

6–2 Addition Method

When you add the left sides of the two equations of a system and then add the right sides, the resulting **sum equation** will have the same solution set as the original system. For example, for

$$\begin{cases} x = 5 \\ y = 2 \end{cases}$$

the sum equation is $x + y = 7$.

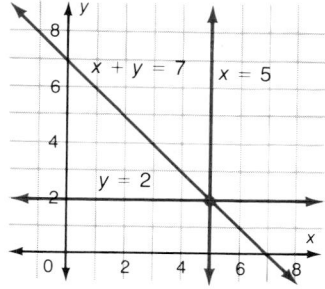

The graph shows that the ordered pair $(5, 2)$ is a solution of each equation. Thus, a system consisting of any two of the equations is *equivalent* to the original system. **Equivalent systems have the same solution set.**

$$\begin{cases} x = 5 \\ y = 2 \end{cases} \qquad \begin{cases} x = 5 \\ x + y = 7 \end{cases} \qquad \begin{cases} y = 2 \\ x + y = 7 \end{cases} \longleftarrow \textbf{Equivalent systems}$$

To solve a system of equations algebraically, you find an equivalent system from which you can read the solution directly.

Example 1 shows how to use the **addition method** to do this. The addition method is useful when the coefficients of either the x terms or of the y terms are additive inverses of each other.

EXAMPLE 1 Solve by the addition method: $\begin{cases} 3x + y = 10 & \quad 1 \\ 2x - y = 5 & \quad 2 \end{cases}$

Solution: Since the coefficients of the y terms are additive inverses, adding the corresponding sides of the equations will **eliminate** the y terms.

$$\begin{array}{ll} 3x + y = 10 & \quad 1 \\ \underline{2x - y = 5} & \quad 2 \\ 5x = 15 & \\ x = 3 & \quad 3 \longleftarrow \textbf{Substitute } x = 3 \textbf{ in Equation 1} \\ & \qquad \textbf{or in Equation 2.} \\ 3x + y = 10 & \quad 1 \\ 3(3) + y = 10 & \\ y = 1 & \quad 4 \end{array}$$

Thus, $\begin{cases} x = 3 \\ y = 1 \end{cases}$ is an equivalent system. Check in the original equations.

Check:

$$\begin{array}{ll} 3x + y = 10 & \qquad 2x - y = 5 \\ 3(3) + 1 \overset{?}{=} 10 & \qquad 2(3) - 1 \overset{?}{=} 5 \\ 9 + 1 \overset{?}{=} 10 & \qquad 6 - 1 \overset{?}{=} 5 \\ 10 \overset{?}{=} 10 \quad \text{Yes} \ \checkmark & \qquad 5 \overset{?}{=} 5 \quad \text{Yes} \ \checkmark \qquad \textbf{Solution set: } \{(3, 1)\} \end{array}$$

Teaching Suggestions p. M-19

Quick Quiz

1. Solve by graphing:
$$\begin{cases} x + y = 1 \\ x - y = 3 \end{cases}$$
   Ans: $(2, -1)$

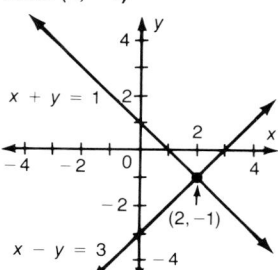

Determine the number of solutions for each system.

2. $\begin{cases} 3x + 5y = 15 \\ 2x - 5x = 10 \end{cases}$
   Ans: one

3. $\begin{cases} 2x + 2y = 12 \\ 3y = 18 - 3x \end{cases}$
   Ans: infinitely many

4. $\begin{cases} y = 3x + 7 \\ y = 3x - 5 \end{cases}$
   Ans: none

Additional Examples
Example 1
Solve by the addition method.

1. $\begin{cases} 4x + y = 13 \\ 3x - y = 8 \end{cases}$
   Ans: $\{(3, 1)\}$

2. $\begin{cases} 2y - 3x = 19 \\ 3y + 3x = -9 \end{cases}$
   Ans: $\{(-5, 2)\}$

When a and b in the solution (a, b) of a system of linear equations are not integers, it is sometimes difficult to read the solutions accurately from a graph. In such cases, the addition method gives more accurate results.

EXAMPLE 2   Solve by the addition method: $\begin{cases} p + q = 4 & \quad 1 \\ -p + q = 7 & \quad 2 \end{cases}$

Solution:

$$\begin{array}{ll} p + q = 4 & \quad 1 \\ \underline{-p + q = 7} & \quad 2 \end{array}$$ ⟵ **Add to eliminate p.**
$$2q = 11$$

$$q = 5\frac{1}{2} \qquad 3$$ ⟵ **Substitute in Equation 1 or Equation 2**
$$p + q = 4 \qquad 1$$
$$p + 5\frac{1}{2} = 4$$
$$p = -1\frac{1}{2} \qquad 4$$ ⟵ **Check the values for p and q in the original system.**

Check:

$$\begin{array}{c} p + q = 4 \\ -1\frac{1}{2} + 5\frac{1}{2} \overset{?}{=} 4 \\ 4 \overset{?}{=} 4 \quad \text{Yes} \; ✔ \end{array} \qquad \begin{array}{c} -p + q = 7 \\ -(-1\frac{1}{2}) + 5\frac{1}{2} \overset{?}{=} 7 \\ 7 \overset{?}{=} 7 \quad \text{Yes} \; ✔ \end{array}$$

Solution set: $\{(-1\frac{1}{2}, 5\frac{1}{2})\}$

NOTE: It is customary to give the solution(s) of the system in the alphabetical order of the variables involved. In Example 2, the variables used were p and q. Thus, the solution is given as $(-1\frac{1}{2}, 5\frac{1}{2})$.

Procedure

> To solve a system of two linear equations by the addition method:
> 1. Add to eliminate one of the variables. Solve the resulting equation.
> 2. Substitute the known value of one variable in one of the original equations of the system. Solve for the other variable.
> 3. Check the solution in both equations of the system.

CLASSROOM EXERCISES

Write the sum equation for each system.

1. $\begin{cases} x = -2 \\ y = 3 \end{cases}$ $x + y = 1$

2. $\begin{cases} x + y = 7 \\ x - y = 2 \end{cases}$ $2x = 9$

3. $\begin{cases} p + q = \frac{1}{2} \\ -p + q = -\frac{3}{2} \end{cases}$ $2q = -1$

4. $\begin{cases} -r + s = 6 \\ r + s = 2 \end{cases}$ $2s = 8$

WRITTEN EXERCISES

A   Use the addition method to solve each system.

1. $\begin{cases} x - y = 4 \\ x + y = 2 \end{cases}$ $(3, -1)$

2. $\begin{cases} 2x + y = 7 \\ 3x - y = 3 \end{cases}$ $(2, 3)$

3. $\begin{cases} y - 4x = 8 \\ y + 4x = 0 \end{cases}$ $(-1, 4)$

4. $\begin{cases} a + 5b = 10 \\ -a + 4b = 8 \end{cases}$ (0, 2)

5. $\begin{cases} y = 3x + 6 \\ 2y = -3x + 3 \end{cases}$ (−1, 3)

6. $\begin{cases} 3y = -7x + 7 \\ 2y = 7x - 7 \end{cases}$

7. $\begin{cases} 2t + 3n = 9 \\ 5t - 3n = 5 \end{cases}$ (2, $1\frac{2}{3}$)

8. $\begin{cases} -7c - 8d = 8 \\ 7c - 8d = 8 \end{cases}$ (0, −1)

9. $\begin{cases} y = 2x - 4 \\ y = -2x + 3 \end{cases}$

10. $\begin{cases} c + d = 12 \\ -d = 8 \end{cases}$ (20, −8)

11. $\begin{cases} x - y = 8 \\ y = 7 \end{cases}$ (15, 7)

12. $\begin{cases} x - y = 2\frac{1}{2} \\ y = 4 \end{cases}$

13. $\begin{cases} x - 2y = 2\frac{1}{2} \\ x + 2y = 3 \end{cases}$ ($2\frac{3}{4}$, $\frac{1}{8}$)

14. $\begin{cases} x + 3y = 9 \\ -x + 2y = 6 \end{cases}$ (0, 3)

15. $\begin{cases} 2x - 3y = 8 \\ 2x + 3y = 4 \end{cases}$

16. $\begin{cases} 7x + 3y = 19 \\ 4x - 3y = 3 \end{cases}$ (2, $1\frac{2}{3}$)

17. $\begin{cases} -6x + 3y = 5 \\ 6x - 5y = 7 \end{cases}$ ($-3\frac{5}{6}$, −6)

18. $\begin{cases} 7a + 6b = 0 \\ 15a - 6b = 0 \end{cases}$

B

19. $\begin{cases} \frac{1}{2}x + y = 9 \\ \frac{3}{4}x - y = 0 \end{cases}$ ($7\frac{1}{5}$, $5\frac{2}{5}$)

20. $\begin{cases} 0.4x + y = 1.2 \\ 0.6x - y = 3.9 \end{cases}$ (5.1, −0.84)

21. $\begin{cases} \frac{3}{4}x - \frac{1}{2}y = 4 \\ \frac{1}{4}x + \frac{1}{2}y = 2\frac{1}{2} \end{cases}$

22. $\begin{cases} 0.1x - 0.01y = 0.1 \\ 0.3x + 0.01y = 0.3 \end{cases}$ (1, 0)

23. $\begin{cases} 5\frac{1}{2}x - y = 8 \\ 3\frac{1}{2}x + y = 1 \end{cases}$ (1, $-2\frac{1}{2}$)

24. $\begin{cases} a - b = -1 \\ -a - b = 1 \end{cases}$

Puzzle

Solve each system in 1–3 below by the addition method and graph its solution set. Connect the points associated with each solution set in order. The answers form a secret message.

1. $\begin{cases} x + y = -7 \\ x - y = -5 \end{cases}$ $\begin{cases} -x + 2y = 10 \\ x - 3y = -13 \end{cases}$ $\begin{cases} 6x = 4y - 8 \\ -x = -4y - 2 \end{cases}$

$\begin{cases} x + 2y = -1 \\ -x + 3y = 6 \end{cases}$ $\begin{cases} y = x + 6 \\ -y = x + 4 \end{cases}$

2. $\begin{cases} x = y - 2 \\ x = -y \end{cases}$ $\begin{cases} 2y - x = 1 \\ -2y + 3x = 1 \end{cases}$

3. $\begin{cases} 2x - 3y = 0 \\ -2x + 2y = -2 \end{cases}$ $\begin{cases} 9x + 15y = 81 \\ -9x - 2y = -42 \end{cases}$ $\begin{cases} 8x - 10y = 42 \\ -8x - 3y = -29 \end{cases}$

$\begin{cases} 3y = -4x + 5 \\ -2y = 4x - 6 \end{cases}$ $\begin{cases} 6x + 21y = 15 \\ -6x + 10y = -46 \end{cases}$ See the Solution Key.

REVIEW CAPSULE FOR SECTION 6-3

Write the additive inverse of each number. *(Pages 47–50)*

1. 21 _−21_   **2.** −9 _9_   **3.** 0 _0_   **4.** −11 _11_   **5.** 18.3 _−18.3_   **6.** $\frac{1}{3}$ _$-\frac{1}{3}$_

Multiply. *(Pages 97–99)*

7. $2(3x - 2y)$ **8.** $-3(6a + b)$ **9.** $-1(2w - 3s)$ **10.** $-1(r + 3t)$

11. $-1(-v + 7q)$ **12.** $-1(7q - 9)$ **13.** $-\frac{1}{2}(4r - 6p)$ **14.** $-9(\frac{1}{9}s - t)$

Systems of Sentences   **219**

6-3 Using Multiplication with the Addition Method

Adding the corresponding sides of the two equations in a linear system *does not always eliminate* one of the variables. To obtain a sum equation having a single variable in such cases, multiply each side of one or both equations of the system by a number or numbers, so that, after multiplying, the coefficients of one of the variables will be additive inverses.

EXAMPLE 1 Solve: $\begin{cases} 3x + y = 10 & 1 \\ 2x + y = 15 & 2 \end{cases}$

Solution: Multiply each side of Equation 1 by -1.

$\begin{array}{ll} -3x - y = -10 & 1 \\ \underline{2x + y = 15} & 2 \\ -x = 5 \end{array}$ ← Now the coefficients of the y terms are additive inverses.

$x = -5$ 3 ← Substitute $x = -5$ in Equation 1 or in Equation 2.

$2x + y = 15$ 2

$2(-5) + y = 15$

$y = 25$ 4 ← The check is left for you.

Solution set: $\{(-5, 25)\}$

Sometimes it is necessary to multiply Equation 1 by one number and to multiply Equation 2 by another number.

EXAMPLE 2 Solve: $\begin{cases} 2x + 3y = -1 & 1 \\ 5x - 2y = -12 & 2 \end{cases}$

Solution: Multiply each side of Equation 1 by 2 and multiply each side of Equation 2 by 3. Then *the y terms will be additive inverses* of each other.

$\begin{array}{ll} 4x + 6y = -2 & \text{← } 2(2x + 3y) = 2(-1) \\ \underline{15x - 6y = -36} & \text{← } 3(5x - 2y) = 3(-12) \\ 19x = -38 \end{array}$

$x = -2$ 3 ← Substitute $x = -2$ in Equation 1.

$2x + 3y = -1$ 1

$2(-2) + 3y = -1$

$3y = 3$

$y = 1$ 4 ← The check is left for you.

Solution set: $\{(-2, 1)\}$

The following procedure summarizes the steps for solving a system of two linear equations by this method.

220 *Chapter 6*

Procedure

To solve a system of two linear equations using multiplication with addition:

$\boxed{1}$ Multiply each side of one of the equations by a number, and, if necessary, multiply each side of the second equation by another number. Choose the two numbers so that, after multiplying, the coefficients of one of the variables will be additive inverses of each other.

$\boxed{2}$ Use the addition method to solve the new system.

CLASSROOM EXERCISES

Determine the number by which you could multiply *one* equation in each pair in order to eliminate one of the variables.

1. $\begin{cases} 5x + 2y = 14 & \quad 1 \\ 4x - y = 6 & \quad 2 \end{cases}$

2. $\begin{cases} 2p + 3q = 1 & \quad 1 \\ 3p - q = 18 & \quad 2 \end{cases}$

3. $\begin{cases} 9a - 3b = 3 & \quad 1 \\ a + 5b = 11 & \quad 2 \end{cases}$

Determine the number by which each of the equations in **a** has been multiplied in order to obtain the corresponding equation in **b**.

	a		**b**	

4. $\begin{cases} 3x - 2y = -4 & 1 \\ -5x + 3y = -1 & 2 \end{cases}$ $\begin{cases} 15x - 10y = -20 & 1 \\ -15x + 9y = -3 & 2 \end{cases}$

5. $\begin{cases} 3x - 2y = -9 & 1 \\ 3x - 5y = -10 & 2 \end{cases}$ $\begin{cases} 15x - 10y = -45 & 1 \\ -6x + 10y = 20 & 2 \end{cases}$

6. $\begin{cases} 3r + 7t = 22 & 1 \\ 2r - 8t = 2 & 2 \end{cases}$ $\begin{cases} 6r + 14t = 44 & 1 \\ -6r + 24t = -6 & 2 \end{cases}$

7. $\begin{cases} 5p + 3q = 17 & 1 \\ 4p - 5q = 21 & 2 \end{cases}$ $\begin{cases} 25p + 15q = 85 & 1 \\ 12p - 15q = 63 & 2 \end{cases}$

WRITTEN EXERCISES

A   Solve each system.

1. $\begin{cases} 3x + y = 9 \\ 2x + y = 1 \end{cases}$ $(8, -15)$

2. $\begin{cases} 3x + y = 10 \\ 2x + y = 7 \end{cases}$ $(3, 1)$

3. $\begin{cases} 5r - s = -23 \\ 3r - s = -15 \end{cases}$

4. $\begin{cases} 2a + 3b = -5 \\ 5a + 3b = 1 \end{cases}$ $(2, -3)$

5. $\begin{cases} 3x + 2y = -7 \\ 5x - 2y = -1 \end{cases}$ $(-1, -2)$

6. $\begin{cases} x + 3y = 14 \\ x - 2y = -1 \end{cases}$

7. $\begin{cases} 2t + 3v = 6 \\ 2t - 5v = 22 \end{cases}$ $(6, -2)$

8. $\begin{cases} 2x + 3y = 8 \\ 3x + y = 5 \end{cases}$ $(1, 2)$

9. $\begin{cases} 2x + y = 3 \\ 7x - 4y = 18 \end{cases}$

10. $\begin{cases} 5x + y = 15 \\ 3x + 2y = 9 \end{cases}$ $(3, 0)$

11. $\begin{cases} 7r - 5t = -2 \\ -8r - t = 9 \end{cases}$ $(-1, -1)$

12. $\begin{cases} 4p - 2q = 20 \\ p + 5q = -17 \end{cases}$

13. $\begin{cases} 2a + 5b = 18 \\ -5a + b = -18 \end{cases}$ $(4, 2)$

14. $\begin{cases} 2u + 2z = 8 \\ 5u - 3z = 4 \end{cases}$ $(2, 2)$

15. $\begin{cases} 4a + 3b = -2 \\ 8a - 2b = 12 \end{cases}$

16. $\begin{cases} 2x - 5y = 7 \\ 3x - 2y = -17 \end{cases}$ $(-9, -5)$

17. $\begin{cases} 9c + 7d = 14 \\ -6c - d = -2 \end{cases}$ $(0, 2)$

18. $\begin{cases} 4r + 3s = 7 \\ 4r + 4s = 12 \end{cases}$

19. $\begin{cases} 4x - 3y - 5 = 0 \\ -2x + 9y + 1 = 0 \end{cases}$ $(1\frac{2}{5}, \frac{1}{5})$

20. $\begin{cases} 5a - 2b - 11 = 0 \\ 3a + 5b - 19 = 0 \end{cases}$ $(3, 2)$

21. $\begin{cases} 6n - 2k + 3 = 0 \\ 2n + 4k - 5 = 0 \end{cases}$

Systems of Sentences   **221**

Additional Answers
Classroom Exercises
1. Equation 2: 2
2. Equation 2: 3
3. Equation 2: 9
4. Equation 1: 5
   Equation 2: 3
5. Equation 1: 5
   Equation 2: −2
6. Equation 1: 2
   Equation 2: −3
7. Equation 1: 5
   Equation 2: 3

Assignment Guide
Minimal p. 221: 1–21 odd
Average pp. 221–222:
1–34 odd
Above Average pp. 221–222:
3, 6, 9, . . . 21, 23–43 odd

Additional Answers
Written Exercises
3. $(-4, 3)$
6. $(5, 3)$
9. $(2, -1)$
12. $(3, -4)$
15. $(1, -2)$
18. $(-2, 5)$
21. $\left(-\frac{1}{14}, 1\frac{2}{7}\right)$

B

22. $\begin{cases} 9x - 2y = 2\frac{1}{2} \\ 5x - 6y = -3\frac{1}{2} \end{cases}$ $(\frac{1}{2}, 1)$

23. $\begin{cases} 3x + 5y = 4\frac{1}{2} \\ -9x - 2y = -7 \end{cases}$ $(\frac{2}{3}, \frac{1}{2})$

24. $\begin{cases} 8x + 6y = 10 \\ -4x + 3y = -1 \end{cases}$

25. $\begin{cases} 5x + 4y = -\frac{1}{3} \\ 7x + 2y = \frac{4}{3} \end{cases}$ $(\frac{1}{3}, -\frac{1}{2})$

26. $\begin{cases} 2x - 3y = 9.4 \\ -5x + 9y = -12.4 \end{cases}$ $(15.8, 7.4)$

27. $\begin{cases} x + 3y = 17.3 \\ 2x - 7y = -36.9 \end{cases}$

28. $\begin{cases} 2r - 7t = 8 \\ 4r - 9t = 19 \end{cases}$ $(6\frac{1}{10}, \frac{3}{5})$

29. $\begin{cases} 4c - 6d = 8 \\ -9c - 6d = -96 \end{cases}$ $(8, 4)$

30. $\begin{cases} 2w - 3q = 8 \\ 3w - 7q = 7 \end{cases}$

What values of r and s will eliminate the y term? Answers will vary.

31. $r(-2x + y - 5) + s(x + 3y - 1) = 0$

32. $r(2x + 3y - 3) + s(3x - 5y + 2) = 0$

33. $r(3x + 4y - 10) + s(2x - y + 8) = 0$

34. $r(3x + 2y - 2) + s(2x + 3y + 2) = 0$

C Solve each system.

$(2, -4)$

35. $\begin{cases} 2x + 1.5y = -1 \\ 0.5x + 2y = 3 \end{cases}$ $(-2, 2)$

36. $\begin{cases} x - 2.3 = -5y \\ 2x - 2 = 3y \end{cases}$ $(1.3, 0.2)$

37. $\begin{cases} 2a - 1.5b = 10 \\ 0.3a - 0.05b = 0.8 \end{cases}$

38. $\begin{cases} 2x - 3y = 0.1 \\ 3x - 3 = -5y \end{cases}$ $(\frac{1}{2}, \frac{3}{10})$

39. $\begin{cases} 1.25s + 8.25t = 107.5 \\ 2.5s - t = 0.8 \end{cases}$ $(5.216, 12.24)$

40. $\begin{cases} 10x + 5y = 3.5 \\ 3y - 0.6 = 3x \end{cases}$
$(\frac{1}{6}, \frac{11}{30})$

41. Solve the system: $\begin{cases} -3x - y + 10\frac{1}{2} = 0 \\ 6x - 2y - 7 = 0 \end{cases}$ $(2\frac{1}{3}, 3\frac{1}{2})$

42. Show that for all real numbers f and g, the solution of the system in Exercise 41 is also a solution of

$$f(-3x - y + 10\frac{1}{2}) + g(6x - 2y - 7) = 0.$$

43. Prove this statement.

For all real numbers A, B, C, and D where $A \neq 0$, $B \neq 0$, and $C \neq D$, the following system has no solutions.

$$\begin{cases} Ax + By = C \\ Ax + By = D \end{cases}$$

————— **REVIEW CAPSULE FOR SECTION 6-4** —————

Choose a variable to represent one unknown and tell what it represents. Then represent the second unknown in terms of the variable. *(Pages 122–124)*

1. Nancy invested $2,100 more than Hal.

2. Emily is one-half as old as Roger.

3. Jim has three times as many shirts as he has pants.

4. Suzanne had four more dollars than Joe had.

5. The bookcase is twice as high as it is wide.

6. Cindy owns three fewer pairs of shoes than her mother does.

7. The Owens have one more than twice as many children as the Bakers.

8. The swimming pool is two-thirds as wide as it is long.

222 *Chapter 6*

Problem Solving and Applications

Objective: To solve word problems using systems of equations

6-4 Using Two Variables

You can use systems of equations to solve word problems. First, you use Condition 1 to represent the unknowns by two variables. You also use this condition to write one equation of the system.

Condition 1	Represent the unknowns	Equation for Condition 1
The sum of two numbers is 12.	Let x = the first number. Let y = the second number.	$x + y = 12$
The length of a rectangle is 3 meters less than twice its width.	Let l = the length. Let w = the width.	$l = 2w - 3$
Jaime's age exceeds his sister's age by 8 years.	Let a = Jaime's age. Let b = his sister's age.	$a = b + 8$, or $a - b = 8$
The total number of balcony and orchestra seats sold was 685.	Let a = the number of balcony seats. Let c = the number of orchestra seats.	$a + b = 685$
A trucker buys 200 fewer crates of apples than pears.	Let c = the number of crates of apples. Let p = the number of crates of pears.	$c = p - 200$

You use Condition 2 to write the second equation for the system. The Example shows you how to do this.

EXAMPLE Joe has 6 fewer EE bonds than Art (Condition 1). Twice the number Art has is 5 more than three times the number Joe has (Condition 2). How many EE bonds does each have?

Solution: Let x = the number Art has. ← Represent the unknowns.
Let y = the number Joe has.

$\begin{cases} x - y = 6 & \quad 1 \\ 2x = 3y + 5 & \quad 2 \end{cases}$ ← Equation for Condition 1
← Equation for Condition 2

To solve the system, multiply Equation 1 by -3.

$$\begin{array}{rl} -3x + 3y = -18 & \quad 1 \\ \underline{2x - 3y = 5} & \quad 2 \\ -x = -13 & \end{array}$$

$x = 13$ ← Don't forget to find y.

$x - y = 6$ ← Replace x with 13.

$13 - y = 6$

$-y = -7$

$y = 7$

Systems of Sentences   **223**

Quick Quiz
Solve.
1. $\begin{cases} x + 4y = 6 \\ x + 3y = 8 \end{cases}$
   Ans: $\{(14, -2)\}$
2. $\begin{cases} 2x + 5y = 14 \\ 3x - 10y = -84 \end{cases}$
   Ans: $\{(-8, 6)\}$
3. $\begin{cases} 3x + 4y = 33 \\ 2x - 3y = 5 \end{cases}$
   Ans: $\{(7, 3)\}$
4. $\begin{cases} 5y - 3x = 0 \\ 2y + 7x = -41 \end{cases}$
   Ans: $\{(-5, -3)\}$

Additional Examples
1. Jay's Supermarket has 200 fewer crates of pears than apples (Condition 1). Twice the number of crates of apples is 100 more than three times the number of crates of apples (Condition 2). How many crates of each does Jay's have?
   Ans: apples: 500 crates;
   pears: 300 crates
2. At a sale, a wallet and a belt cost $30. Mrs. Lobel bought 4 wallets and 3 belts for $106. How much did each cost?
   Ans: wallet: $16; belt: $14

Check: **Condition 1**   Does Joe have 6 fewer bonds than Art?

$6 = 13 - 7$?   Yes ✔

                 Condition 2   Does twice the number Art has equal 5 more than three times the number Joe has? $2 \cdot 13 = 3 \cdot 7 + 5$?   Yes ✔

Art has **13 EE bonds** and Joe has **7**.

The procedure that follows summarizes the steps for using a system of equations in two variables to solve word problems.

Procedure

> To solve word problems using a system of equations in two variables:
>
> 1. Use Condition 1 and two variables to represent the unknowns. Write an equation in two variables that expresses Condition 1.
> 2. Write a second equation in two variables that expresses Condition 2.
> 3. Solve the system of equations.
> 4. Check your solution in the original conditions of the problem. Answer the question.

CLASSROOM EXERCISES

Choose two variables to represent the unknowns. Then write an equation to express Condition 1.

1. The sum of two numbers is 16.

2. Two angles have a sum of 90°.

3. The difference between the heights of two boys is 4 centimeters.

4. A service station operator sells twice as much regular as premium gas.

5. A cup of cooked macaroni contains 105 calories more than an ounce of cheese.

6. Amy sold a total of 870 adult and student tickets for the senior class play.

7. The length of a rectangle is twice the width.

8. The perimeter of a rectangular picture frame is 246 centimeters.

9. A truck is loaded to capacity with apples and peaches. The capacity of the truck is 5000 pounds.

10. A health store has a mixture of 40 kilograms of walnuts and pecans on hand.

WORD PROBLEMS

A   Solve each problem. In some problems, Condition 1 is <u>underscored once</u>. Condition 2 is <u>underscored twice</u>.

1. <u>The sum of two numbers is 52.</u> <u><u>The difference of the same two numbers is 20.</u></u> Find the numbers. 16, 36

2. <u>One number is 5 more than a second number.</u> <u><u>The sum of the numbers is 115.</u></u> What are the numbers? 55, 60

3. One number is 3 times a second number. The larger number decreased by the smaller is 18. Find the numbers. 9, 27

4. The sum of two numbers is 21. One number is 3 less than the other. Find the numbers. 9, 12

5. The difference between two numbers is 4. Three times the larger is 2 more than five times the smaller. Find the numbers. 5, 9

6. The sum of two unknown numbers is 20. Twice the larger number is three times the smaller number. Find each of the numbers. 8, 12

7. The width of a rectangle is 6 inches less than the length. The perimeter is 72 inches. Find the length and the width.

8. The length of a rectangle is 4 feet more than the width. The perimeter is 40 feet. Find the length and width.

9. The distance from St. Louis to Chicago is 111 miles more than the distance from Chicago to Minneapolis. The sum of the two distances is 697 miles. Find the distance from St. Louis to Chicago.
404 miles

10. The distance by air from New York to London is 545 kilometers more than twice the distance from London to Moscow. The sum of the two distances is 8105 kilometers. Find the distance from New York to London. 5585 km

11. Two sides of a triangle are equal. Each of the two equal sides is 5 inches more than the third side. The perimeter is 35 inches. Find the length of each side. $13\frac{1}{3}$ in; $13\frac{1}{3}$ in; $8\frac{1}{3}$ in

12. Each of the two equal sides of a triangle is 1.2 centimeters longer than the third side. The perimeter is 17.4 centimeters. Find the length of each side.
6.2 cm; 6.2 cm; 5 cm

B

13. Two angles are supplementary; that is, the sum of their measures is 180°. The measure of one angle is 30° more than twice the other. What is the measure of each angle? 50°, 130°

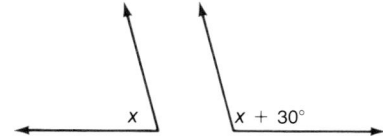

14. Two angles are **complementary;** that is, the sum of their measures is 90°. The measure of one angle is twice the measure of the other. What is the measure of each angle? 30°, 60°

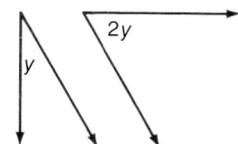

15. Seven times the sum of two numbers is 28. When the second number is multiplied by 3 and added to the first number, the sum equals the second number. Find each number.

16. An oak tree is 20 years older than a pine tree. In eight years, the oak tree will be 3 times as old as the pine tree will be then. Find the present age of each tree.

17. Enrico's father is now twice his age. In 20 years, Enrico will be two–thirds his father's age then. How old is each now? Enrico: 20 yr; Father: 40 yr

18. Find two numbers such that one is as much more than 30 as the other is less than 30, and 8 times their difference is equal to the larger.

Systems of Sentences   **225**

Additional Answers
7. length: 21 in; width: 15 in
8. width: 8 ft length: 12 ft
15. first: 8 second: −4
16. oak tree: 22 yr pine tree: 2 yr
18. larger: 32 smaller: 28

Objective: To solve digit problems using systems of equations

6–5 Digit Problems

Teaching Suggestions p. M-19

Systems of equations in two variables are particularly useful in solving problems related to numbers and their digits. Suppose that you are asked to represent a two-digit number.

Two–Digit Number

Example: 85	**In General:** $10t + u$
Tens digit: 8	Tens digit: t
Units digit: 5	Units digit: u
Number: $10 \cdot 8 + 5$, or 85	Number: $10t + u$
Sum of digits: $8 + 5$	Sum of digits: $t + u$

When solving digit problems, be careful to distinguish between representing the *sum of the digits* and representing *the number*.

EXAMPLE The sum of the digits of a two-digit number is 6 (Condition 1). The number is six times the units digit (Condition 2). Find the number.

Solution: Follow the steps of the procedure in Section 6–4 on page 224.

$\boxed{1}$ Let $t =$ the tens digit.
Let $u =$ the units digit. ◀——— **Represent the unknowns.**
Then $10t + u =$ the number.

$\boxed{2}$ $\begin{cases} t + u = 6 & \text{1} \\ 10t + u = 6u & \text{2} \end{cases}$ ◀——— **The sum of the digits is 6.**
◀——— **The number is 6 times the units digit.**

$\boxed{3}$ Combine like terms in Equation 2.

$10t - 5u = 0$ 2

To eliminate the variable u, multiply Equation 1 by 5.

$$\begin{array}{ll} 5t + 5u = 30 & 1 \\ \underline{10t - 5u = 0} & 2 \\ 15t = 30 \end{array}$$

$t = 2$ ◀——— **Don't forget to find u.**

$t + u = 6$ 1 ◀——— **Replace t with 2 in Equation 1.**

$2 + u = 6$

$u = 4$ ◀——— **Don't forget to find the number.**

Number: $10t + u = 10 \cdot 2 + 4 = 24$

Check: $\boxed{4}$ **Condition 1** Is the sum of the digits equal to 6? $2 + 4 = 6$? Yes ✔

Condition 2 Is the number six times the units digit?

$24 = 6 \cdot 4$? Yes ✔ The number is **24**.

To represent a three-digit number, let h represent the hundreds digit, t represent the tens digit and u represent the units digit. Then the number is

$$100h + 10t + u. \longleftarrow \textbf{Three-digit number}$$

CLASSROOM EXERCISES

For each problem in Exercises 1–6, let t represent the tens digit and let u represent the units digit. Write the system of equations you would use to solve the problem.

1. The sum of the digits of a two-digit number is 12. The number is 12 times the tens digit.

2. The sum of the digits of a two-digit number is 9. The number is 6 times the units digit.

3. The sum of the digits of a two-digit number is 10. The tens digit is 4 more than the units digit.

4. The sum of the digits of a two-digit number is 9. The units digit is 7 more than the tens digit.

5. The units digit of a two-digit number is twice the tens digit. The number is 6 more than 5 times the units digit.

6. The tens digit of a two-digit number is 2 more than the units digit. The number is 5 more than 7 times the tens digit.

WORD PROBLEMS

A Write a system of equations in two variables for each problem. Then solve the problem. For some problems, Condition 1 is underscored once, Condition 2 is underscored twice.

1. The sum of the digits of a two-digit number is 12. The number is 12 times the tens digit. Find the number.

2. The sum of the digits of a two-digit number is 10. The tens digit is 4 more than the units digit. Find the number.

3. The units digit of a two-digit number is twice the tens digit. The difference between the digits is 4. Find the number.

4. The units digit of a two-digit number is 2 less than the tens digit. The number is 2 more than 6 times the sum of the digits. Find the number.

5. The units digit of a two-digit number is 11 less than twice the tens digit. The number is 6 less than 7 times the sum of the digits of the number. Find the number.

6. The tens digit of a two-digit number is 14 less than twice the units digit. The number is 3 less than 4 times the sum of the digits of the number. Find the number.

7. The sum of the digits of a two-digit number is 9. The number is 27 more than the original number with its digits reversed. Find the number. (HINT: The number with its digits reversed is $10u + t$.)

8. A two-digit number is 5 times the sum of its digits. When 9 is added to the number, the result is the original number with its digits reversed. Find the number.

Additional Answers
Classroom Exercises

1. $\begin{cases} t + u = 12 \\ 10t + u = 12t \end{cases}$

2. $\begin{cases} t + u = 9 \\ 10t + u = 6u \end{cases}$

3. $\begin{cases} t + u = 10 \\ t = u + 4 \end{cases}$

4. $\begin{cases} t + u = 9 \\ u = t + 7 \end{cases}$

5. $\begin{cases} u = 2t \\ 10t + u = 5u + 6 \end{cases}$

6. $\begin{cases} t = u + 2 \\ 10t + u = 7t + 5 \end{cases}$

Assignment Guide
Minimal p. 227: 1–8
Average pp. 227–228: 2–14 even
Above Average pp. 227–228: 5–14 odd, 15–20

Word Problems

1. $\begin{cases} t + u = 12 \\ 10t + u = 12t; \ 48 \end{cases}$

2. $\begin{cases} t + u = 10 \\ t = u + 4; \ 73 \end{cases}$

3. $\begin{cases} u = 2t \\ u - t = 4; \ 48 \end{cases}$

4. $\begin{cases} u = t - 2 \\ 10t + u = 6(t + u) + 2; \ 86 \end{cases}$

5. $\begin{cases} u = 2t - 11 \\ 10t + u = 7(t + u) - 6; \ 85 \end{cases}$

6. $\begin{cases} t = 2u - 14 \\ 10t + u = 4(t + u) - 3; \ 49 \end{cases}$

7. $\begin{cases} t + u = 9 \\ 10t + u = 10u + t + 27; \ 63 \end{cases}$

8. $\begin{cases} 10t + u = 5(t + u) \\ 10t + u + 9 = 10u + t; \ 45 \end{cases}$

Systems of Sentences **227**

9. The sum of the digits of a two-digit number is 11. When 45 is added to the number, the result is the original number with its digits reversed. Find the number.

10. When 63 is subtracted from a two-digit number, the result is the original number with its digits reversed. The tens digit of the original number exceeds 4 times the units digit by 1. Find the number.

B

11. A two-digit number is 5 times the sum of its digits. The digits from left to right name consecutive integers. Find the number.

12. A two-digit number is 6 more than 4 times the sum of its digits. The digits from left to right are consecutive even integers. Find the number.

13. The sum of the digits of a certain three-digit number is 8. The tens digit is two less than the hundreds digit, and the units digit is three times the hundreds digit. Find the number.

14. The sum of the digits of a three-digit number is 14. The tens digit is one more than twice the hundreds digit and the units digit is one less than 4 times the hundreds digit. Find the number.

C

15. Represent the difference between any two-digit number and the number with its digits reversed.

16. Represent the sum of any two-digit number and the number with its digits reversed.

17. Use your answer to Exercise 15 to show that the difference between any two-digit number and the number with the digits reversed is divisible by 9.

18. Use your answer to Exercise 16 to show that the sum of a two-digit number and the number with its digits reversed is divisible by 11.

19. Show that the difference between a three-digit number and the number with its digits reversed is divisible by 99.

20. Show that the difference between a four-digit number and the number with its digits reversed is divisible by 9.

_____ **Review** _____

Solve each system by graphing. *(Section 6–1)*

1. $\begin{cases} 2x - y = 8 \\ x + y = 4 \end{cases}$ (4, 0)

2. $\begin{cases} x + y = 9 \\ x - y = 5 \end{cases}$ (7, 2)

3. $\begin{cases} 3x = 9 \\ x + y = -1 \end{cases}$ (3, −4)

Write *one*, *none*, or *infinitely many* to describe the number of solutions for each system. *(Section 6–1)*

4. $\begin{cases} y = 3x - 1 \\ y = 5x \end{cases}$ one

5. $\begin{cases} y = 4x - 1 \\ 8x = 2y + 2 \end{cases}$ infinitely many

6. $\begin{cases} x = 2y - 4 \\ y = x + 7 \end{cases}$ one

Use the addition method to solve each system. *(Section 6–2)*

7. $\begin{cases} x + 2y = -4 \\ -x + y = 1 \end{cases}$ (−2, −1)

8. $\begin{cases} 2a - 7b = 41 \\ a + 7b = -32 \end{cases}$ (3, −5)

9. $\begin{cases} 0.6x + 0.5y = 0 \\ 0.2x - 0.5y = 0.4 \end{cases}$ (0.5, −0.6)

In Exercises 10–12, use multiplication with the addition method to solve each system. *(Section 6–3)*

10. $\begin{cases} 2x + y = 7 \\ -x + y = 4 \end{cases}$ (1, 5)

11. $\begin{cases} 4r - 7s = 18 \\ r + 3s = -5 \end{cases}$ (1, −2)

12. $\begin{cases} 4x + 3y = -2 \\ 3x + 2y = 1 \end{cases}$ (7, −10)

13. The length of a rectangular desk is 11 inches less than twice the width. The perimeter of the desk is 206 centimeters. Find the length and the width. *(Section 6–4)* length: 65 cm; width 38 cm

14. Karl's age is now 2 years more than twice his brother's. In 5 years, Karl's age will equal three times his brother's age now. How old is each now? *(Section 6–4)* Karl: 16 yr; brother: 7 yr

15. The sum of the digits of a two-digit number is 12. The ones digit is one-half as large as the tens digit. Find the number. *(Section 6–5)* 84

16. The sum of the digits of a two–digit number is 15. The number is 9 less than the number obtained by reversing the digits. Find the number. *(Section 6–5)* 78

CALCULATOR APPLICATIONS

Checking Systems of Equations

You can use a calculator to check whether a given ordered pair is a solution of a system of equations.

EXAMPLE Check the solution set, $\{(-2, 1)\}$, of Example 2 on page 220.

SOLUTION 1. $2x + 3y = -1$

2 [×] 2 [+/−] [=] [M+] 3 [×] 1 [+] [MR] [=] ⟶ `-1.`

2. $5x - 2y = -12$

5 [×] 2 [+/−] [=] [M+] 2 [+/−] [×] 1 [+] [MR] [=] ⟶ `-12.`

EXERCISES

Check each given solution set. Correct any incorrect solutions.

1. $\begin{cases} x + y = 5 \\ 2x - y = -2 \end{cases}$; $\{(1, 4)\}$ Checks

2. $\begin{cases} 2x + y = 1 \\ 2x - y = 7 \end{cases}$; $\{(-2, 3)\}$ Does not check; (2, −3)

3. $\begin{cases} -2x + y = 1 \\ 4x + 3y = 23 \end{cases}$; $\{(2, -5)\}$ Does not check; (2, 5)

4. $\begin{cases} -x - 5y = -6 \\ 2y - 3x = 16 \end{cases}$; $\{(-4, 2)\}$ Checks

───── REVIEW CAPSULE FOR SECTION 6-6 ─────

Solve each equation for x in terms of y. *(Pages 162–164)*

1. $2x + 4y = 6$

2. $-x + 3y = 7$

3. $3x + 5y = 9$

4. $2y - x = 1$

5. $y = 3 - x$

6. $y = \frac{1}{3}x$

7. $y - x = -3$

8. $-12x = 7y$

Systems of Sentences **229**

Consumer Applications

Saving Energy: Cooling Costs

To save energy in warm weather, power companies recommend a setting of **78° Fahrenheit** on your air conditioner. The table at the right shows the per cent of savings and loss with respect to 78°F for settings from 72°F to 80°F. A loss is indicated by a negative per cent.

Setting	Savings Loss (−)
80°F	16%
79	8%
78	0
77	−8%
76	−18%
75	−28%
74	−39%
73	−50%
72	−63%

EXAMPLE 1   Last year the Carlton family spent $800 to operate their air conditioner with the thermostat set at 75°F. How much would they save by setting the thermostat at 79°F?

Solution: Subtract to find the per cent of change.

$8\% - (-28\%) = 36\%$ savings   ←—— **From the table**

$800 \times 36\% = 800 \times 0.36 = \$288$

They would save **$288**.

Example 1 assumes that the Carlton family has an air conditioner with the correct cooling capacity. The **cooling capacity** is the amount of heat (measured in Btu's) that an air conditioning unit can remove from the air in an hour. If the air conditioner is too small, it will run constantly and still not cool the room. If it is too large, the air conditioner will stop and start, lower the temperature quickly, but not remove the humidity from the room. So you will still be uncomfortable.

The graph at the right can be used to estimate the cooling capacity needed for a given room of a house or apartment. (The graph can be used for any room that is about 8 feet high, provided that it is not directly below an attic floor.) The exposure of the room's exterior wall determines which part of the shaded band you should use.

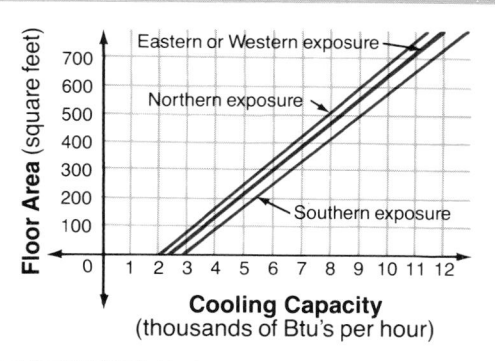

230   **Consumer Applications**

EXAMPLE 2 A room of a house has a northern exposure. Its floor area is 300 square feet. What must be the size (cooling capacity) of the air conditioner for this room?

Solution:

1. On the vertical scale, find the room's floor area, 300 square feet.

2. Since the room has a northern exposure, find the point on the <u>left</u> portion of the band directly to the right of the 300 reading.

3. From this point on the band read directly <u>down</u> on the horizontal scale to find the correct cooling capacity. **5500 Btu's per hour.**

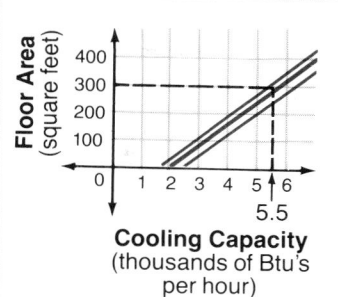

Cooling Capacity
(thousands of Btu's per hour)

Additional Answers
1. $329
2. $115.20
3. $467.50
4. $166.40
5. $450
6. $57
7. $167.40
8. $359.60
9. 6000 Btu's
10. 3000 Btu's
11. 5500 Btu's
12. 4000 Btu's
13. 5500 Btu's
14. 6000 Btu's
15. 6500 Btu's
16. 10,500 Btu's
17. 7000 Btu's

EXERCISES

In Exercises 1–8, use the table on page 230 to find how much each family would save over last year's air conditioning costs.

	Yearly Cooling Costs	Last Year's Thermostat Setting	This Year's Thermostat Setting
1.	$700	74°F	79°F
2.	$480	77°F	80°F
3.	$850	72°F	77°F
4.	$640	76°F	79°F
5.	$900	73°F	78°F
6.	$570	75°F	76°F
7.	$540	74°F	77°F
8.	$620	73°F	79°F

Monitoring a Large Air Conditioning Unit

In Exercises 9–17, estimate the size of an air conditioner needed to cool each room described. Round each answer to the nearest 500 Btu's.

9. Western exposure
300 square feet

10. Northern exposure
100 square feet

11. Southern exposure
200 square feet

12. Eastern exposure
150 square feet

13. Western exposure
250 square feet

14. Northern exposure
350 square feet

15. Southern exposure
300 square feet

16. Western exposure
700 square feet

17. Eastern exposure
400 square feet

6-6 Substitution Method

The **substitution method** is another way to solve a system of two linear equations. First you solve one of the equations for one of the variables. Then you substitute the value of this variable in the other equation.

EXAMPLE Solve by the substitution method: $\begin{cases} -x + 2y = 4 & \quad 1 \\ 5x - 3y = 1 & \quad 2 \end{cases}$

Solution: Since the x term in Equation 1 has a coefficient of -1, it will probably be simpler to solve this equation for x.

$$-x + 2y = 4 \qquad\qquad 1$$
$$-x = 4 - 2y \qquad \longleftarrow \text{ Multiply each side by } (-1).$$
$$x = 2y - 4$$
$$5x - 3y = 1 \qquad 2 \longleftarrow \text{ Replace } x \text{ with } (2y - 4).$$
$$5(2y - 4) - 3y = 1 \qquad \longleftarrow \text{ Solve for } y.$$
$$10y - 20 - 3y = 1$$
$$7y = 21$$
$$y = 3 \qquad 3 \longleftarrow \text{ Replace } y \text{ with 3 in Equation 1}$$
$$-x + 2y = 4 \qquad 1$$
$$-x + 2(3) = 4$$
$$x = 2 \qquad 4 \longleftarrow \text{ The check is left for you.}$$

Solution set: $\{(2, 3)\}$

The following procedure summarizes the steps for solving a system of two linear equations by the substitution method.

Procedure

> **To solve a system of two linear equations by the substitution method:**
> 1 Solve one equation for one of the variables.
> 2 Substitute the resulting expression in the other equation.
> 3 Solve the resulting equation.
> 4 Find the values of the variables.

CLASSROOM EXERCISES

Determine the solution set of each system.

1. $\begin{cases} 3x + y = 5 \\ x = 1 \end{cases}$ (1, 2)

2. $\begin{cases} b = 4 \\ a - b = 7 \end{cases}$ (11, 4)

3. $\begin{cases} 2p - q = 2 \\ p = -1 \end{cases}$ $(-1, -4)$

4. $\begin{cases} 3x - 2y = 7 \\ -y = 1 \end{cases}$ $(\frac{5}{3}, -1)$

5. $\begin{cases} p + 2r = -1 \\ p = 5 \end{cases}$ (5, -3)

6. $\begin{cases} s - t = -5 \\ -t = 3 \end{cases}$ $(-8, -3)$

WRITTEN EXERCISES

A   Use the substitution method to solve each system.

1. $\begin{cases} x = y + 4 \\ 2x - 5y = 2 \end{cases}$ (6, 2)

2. $\begin{cases} y = 3 - x \\ 5x + 3y = -1 \end{cases}$ (−5, 8)

3. $\begin{cases} x = 8y \\ x - 4y = 12 \end{cases}$ (24, 3)

4. $\begin{cases} 5x - y = 1 \\ 3x + 2y = 13 \end{cases}$ $(1\frac{2}{13}, 4\frac{10}{13})$

5. $\begin{cases} 5a = b \\ a = 10b + 5 \end{cases}$ $(-\frac{5}{49}, -\frac{25}{49})$

6. $\begin{cases} r = 5 - s \\ 2r + 7s = 0 \end{cases}$ (7, −2)

7. $\begin{cases} c = d + 4 \\ 2c + 3d = -2 \end{cases}$ (2, −2)

8. $\begin{cases} x + 3y = 5 \\ -3x + 2y = 18 \end{cases}$ (−4, 3)

9. $\begin{cases} c = d - 4 \\ 3c + d = 4 \end{cases}$ (0, 4)

10. $\begin{cases} 3x + y = 7 \\ x - y = 1 \end{cases}$ (2, 1)

11. $\begin{cases} 4x - y = 7 \\ 5x - 8y = 2 \end{cases}$ (2, 1)

12. $\begin{cases} r + s = 3 \\ r - s = 1 \end{cases}$ (2, 1)

13. $\begin{cases} 2a + b = 5 \\ 8a - b = 45 \end{cases}$ (5, −5)

14. $\begin{cases} p - 3q = 0 \\ 2p - 5q = 4 \end{cases}$ (12, 4)

15. $\begin{cases} 5c - 3d + 1 = 0 \\ -c + 3d + 7 = 0 \end{cases}$ (−2, −3)

B

16. $\begin{cases} y + 2x = 0 \\ x + 2y - 9 = 0 \end{cases}$ (−3, 6)

17. $\begin{cases} r + t = 0 \\ 3r + 2t - 5 = 0 \end{cases}$ (5, −5)

18. $\begin{cases} 3t - u = 0 \\ t + u = 12 \end{cases}$

19. $\begin{cases} y = 8 - x \\ 4x - 3y = -3 \end{cases}$ (3, 5)

20. $\begin{cases} 3x + 2y = 16 \\ 7x + y = 19 \end{cases}$ (2, 5)

21. $\begin{cases} c + 2d = 4 \\ 3c - 4d = 7 \end{cases}$

22. $\begin{cases} 2r + s = 11 \\ r - s = 2 \end{cases}$ $(4\frac{1}{3}, 2\frac{1}{3})$

23. $\begin{cases} 4x - 2y = 3 \\ 3x - y = 4 \end{cases}$ $(2\frac{1}{2}, 3\frac{1}{2})$

24. $\begin{cases} 5a - b = -9 \\ 4a + 3b = -11 \end{cases}$

25. $\begin{cases} 4a + b - 8 = 0 \\ 5a + 3b - 3 = 0 \end{cases}$ (3, −4)

26. $\begin{cases} 2u - r + 2 = 0 \\ 6u + 12r - 1 = 0 \end{cases}$ $(\frac{7}{15}, -\frac{23}{30})$

27. $\begin{cases} 4s + 3t - 1 = 0 \\ 8s + 6t - 2 = 0 \end{cases}$

C   Use the substitution method to solve each system. Solve for x and y in terms of the other variables.

28. $\begin{cases} 6x - 4y = 2d \\ x - y + d = 0 \end{cases}$ (3d, 4d)

29. $\begin{cases} 3x = y + h \\ 5x = 3y + 7h \end{cases}$ (−h, −4h)

30. $\begin{cases} 5x - 3y = -2a \\ 2x + 5y = 24a \end{cases}$ (2a, 4a)

─────── **REVIEW CAPSULE FOR SECTION 6–7** ───────

Write an algebraic expression to represent the value of each word expression.

Example: The number of cents in *n* dimes   **Solution: 10 · *n***   or   **10*n***

1. The number of cents in *k* nickels. 5*k*

2. The number of cents in *t* quarters 25*t*

3. The number of dollars in *b* half-dollars $\frac{1}{2}b$

4. The number of dollars in *k* $5.00-raffle tickets 5*k*

5. The number of cents in *m* 20¢ stamps 20*m*

6. The number of dollars in *p* $1,000-bonds 1000*p*

7. The number of cents in *q* quarters and *d* dimes 25*q* + 10*d*

8. The number of cents in *d* dimes and *n* nickels 10*d* + 5*n*

9. The number of dollars in *r* raffle tickets at $2.50 each and *t* tickets at $5.00 each 2.5*r* + 5*t*

10. The number of dollars in *b* $100-bonds and *q* $1000-bonds 100*b* + 1000*q*

Systems of Sentences   **233**

Assignment Guide
Minimal
Day 1 p. 233: 1–8
Day 2 p. 233: 9–15
Average
Day 1 p. 233: 1–12
Day 2 p. 233: 14–25
Above Average
Day 1 p. 233: 1–19 odd
Day 2 p. 233: 20–30

Additional Answers
Written Exercises
18. (3, 9)
21. $(3, \frac{1}{2})$
24. (−2, −1)
27. infinite number of solutions

Quick Quiz
Solve by the substution
method.
1. $\begin{cases} 3y - x = 6 \\ 5y - 2x = 11 \end{cases}$
   Ans: {(−3, 1)}
2. $\begin{cases} y = x + 5 \\ y - 3x = 9 \end{cases}$
   Ans: {(−2, 3)}

Additional Examples
Example 1
1. A concert is being held in
   an auditorium that seats
   8500. How many tickets for
   $7.50 each and how many
   tickets for $8.50 each must
   be sold in order to receive
   total receipts of $68,700
   when the auditorium is
   full?
   Ans: $7.50-tickets: 4950
   ** $8.50-tickets: 3550**
2. Rita Gomez owns a total of
   500 stocks and bonds. The
   stocks are worth $59.50
   each and the bonds are
   worth $50 each. The total
   value of the stocks and
   bonds is $26,425. How
   many shares of stock and
   how many bonds does she
   own?
   Ans: stock: 150 shares;
   **   bonds: 350**

Problem Solving and Applications

Objective: To solve money problems using systems of equations

6-7   Money Problems

Problems that involve the cost of two items can often be solved by using a system of equations in two variables. In solving such problems, it is helpful to make a table showing the number of items (Condition 1) and the value of the items (Condition 2).

EXAMPLE 1   An auditorium seats 2500 persons. How many balcony tickets must be sold for $4.50 each and how many orchestra tickets must be sold for $5.25 each in order to receive total receipts of $12,675 each time the auditorium is full?

Solution: $\boxed{1}$ Follow the steps of the procedure on page 224.

	Number (Condition 1)	Price per Ticket	Total Sales (Condition 2)
Balcony tickets	x	$4.50	$4.50x$
Orchestra tickets	y	$5.25	$5.25y$
TOTAL	2500		$12,675

Use Conditions 1 and 2 to write a system of equations.

$\boxed{2}$ $\begin{cases} x + y = 2500 \\ 4.50x + 5.25y = 12,675 \end{cases}$ 1 ◄——— **Number of tickets sold**
  2 ◄——— **Total sales**

$\boxed{3}$ Solve the system. The substitution method is used below.

$\quad x + y = 2500$ 1 ◄——— **Solve for x in terms of y.**

$\quad\quad x = 2500 - y$

$\quad\quad\quad 4.50x + 5.25y = 12,675$ 2 ◄——— **Replace x with $(2500 - y)$.**

$\quad 4.50(2500 - y) + 5.25y = 12,675$

$\quad 11,250 - 4.50y + 5.25y = 12,675$

$\quad\quad 11,250 + 0.75y = 12,675$

$\quad\quad\quad\quad 0.75y = 1425$

$\quad\quad\quad\quad\quad y = 1900$ ◄——— **Don't forget to find x.**

$\quad\quad\quad x + y = 2500$ ◄——— **Replace y with 1900.**

$\quad\quad\quad x + 1900 = 2500$

$\quad\quad\quad\quad\quad x = 600$

Check: $\boxed{4}$ **Condition 1**   Were 2500 tickets sold? 600 + 1900 = 2500?   Yes ✔

Condition 2   Do total receipts equal $12,675?

$\quad 600(\$4.50) + 1900(\$5.25) = \$12,675?$ Yes ✔

Thus, **600 balcony seats** and **1900 orchestra seats** must be sold.

Investment problems are based on the simple interest formula,

$$i = prt.$$

Since the time, t, in these problems is usually one year, multiply the principle or amount invested, p, and the rate, r, (expressed as a decimal) to find the interest. That is,

$$i = pr.$$

As in Example 1, making a table will help you to organize the given information and to write the equations for the system. Use the method you prefer to solve the system.

EXAMPLE 2   Cora invested $5000, part at a yearly interest rate of 8.5% and part at a yearly interest rate of 9% (Condition 1). The total interest earned in one year was $442.50 (Condition 2). Find the amount invested at each rate.

Solution: 1

	Amount Invested (Condition 1)	Interest Rate	Interest (Condition 2)
Lower rate	x	8.5% or 0.085	$0.085x$
Higher rate	y	9% or 0.09	$0.09y$
TOTAL	$5000		$442.50

2   $\begin{cases} x + y = 5000 \\ 0.085x + 0.09y = 442.50 \end{cases}$ 1 ◄——— **Amount invested**
   2 ◄——— **Total interest**

3   Solve the system. The substitution method is used below.

$$x + y = 5000$$ 1 ◄——— **Solve for x in terms of y.**
$$x = 5000 - y$$
$$0.085x + 0.09y = 442.50$$ 2 ◄——— **Replace x with $(5000 - y)$.**
$$0.085(5000 - y) + 0.09y = 442.50$$
$$425 - 0.085y + 0.09y = 442.50$$
$$425 + 0.005y = 442.50$$
$$0.005y = 17.50$$
$$y = 3500$$ ◄——— **Don't forget to find x.**
$$x + y = 5000$$
$$x + 3500 = 5000$$
$$x = 1500$$

Check: 4   **Condition 1**   Does $1500 + $3500 = $5000?   Yes ✔

Condition 2   Does 0.085($1500) + 0.09($3500) = $442.50?

$1500 + 0.09($3500) = $442.50?
$127.50   + $315.00   = $442.50?   Yes ✔

Thus, **$1500** was invested at 8.5% and **$3500** was invested at 9%.

1. George invested $10,000, part at a yearly interest rate of 11.8% and part at a yearly interest rate of 13% (Condition 1). The total interest earned in one year was $1223.20 (Condition 2). Find the amount invested at each rate.
Ans: 11.8%: $6400; 13%: $3600
2. Stabile's Motor Repairs borrowed $50,000, part at a yearly interest rate of 15% and part at a yearly interest rate of 16%. For one year, Stabile's paid a total of $7730 in interest on the loans. How much borrowed at each rate?
Ans: 15%: $27,000; 16%: $23,000

An equation such as

$$0.005y = 17.50$$

in Example 2 is sometimes easier to solve by multiplying each side by 10, by 100, by 1000, and so on, in order to eliminate the decimal coefficient of y. Thus,

$$0.005y = 17.50 \longleftarrow \text{Multiply each side by 1000.}$$
$$5y = 17{,}500$$
$$y = 3500$$

CLASSROOM EXERCISES

In Exercises 1–4, first complete the table. Then write a system of equations that could be used to solve for x and y.

1. Eugene has 12 coins in dimes and quarters. The total value of the coins is $1.95.

	Number of Coins	Value of Each	Total Value
Dimes	x	$0.10	?
Quarters	y	?	?
TOTAL	?		?

2. Martha bought 13 stamps having a total value of $2.85. She bought 15¢ stamps and 25¢ stamps.

	Number of Stamps	Value of Each	Total Value
15¢ stamps	x	$0.15	?
25¢ stamps	y	?	?
TOTAL	?		?

3. Gina worked a total of 37 hours on two jobs. One job paid $4.50 an hour and the other paid $4.75 an hour. Her total pay for the 37 hours amounted to $260.75.

	Number of Hours	Wages per Hour	Total Wages
First job	x	$4.50	?
Second job	y	?	?
TOTAL	?		?

4. The Ciara family invested a sum of money, part at a yearly interest rate of 7.5% and part at a yearly interest rate of 9.6%. The total investment of $15,500 earned $1425 in one year.

	Amount Invested	Interest Rate	Interest
Lower rate	x	7.5%, or ___?___	___?___
Higher rate	y	9.6%, or ___?___	___?___
TOTAL	___?___		___?___

WORD PROBLEMS

A Solve each problem.

1. Melissa has 45 coins in dimes and quarters. The total value of the coins is $7.65. How many coins of each kind does she have? 21 quarters; 24 dimes

2. José puts quarters and nickels aside for paying tolls. He has a total of 18 coins with a total value of $2.90. How many quarters does he have? 10 quarters

3. Dick Arico invested $5000, part at a yearly rate of 7% and part at a yearly rate of 9%. The total interest earned for one year was $368. How much did he invest at each rate?

4. Partners in a business agreed to take out two loans totaling $35,000. The yearly interest rates were 12% and 15% and the total yearly interest was $4650. Find the amount of each loan.

5. A total of 7500 tickets were sold for a concert. Total receipts amounted to $45,000. Tickets sold for $6.50 and $7.00. How many of each type of ticket were sold?

6. Five full-fare bus tickets and one half-fare ticket cost $90.75. Four full-fare tickets and two half-fare tickets cost $82.50. How much does a full-fare ticket cost?

7. Rachel makes a bank deposit of $595 with 96 five- and ten-dollar bills. How many of each kind of bill did she deposit?

8. Maria paid $6.60 for some 15¢ stamps and some 20¢ stamps. She bought 37 stamps in all. How many of each kind did she buy?

9. A store had a special sale on two models of calculators. One model sold for $22.75 and another model for $15.95. In all, thirty-one calculators were sold. The total amount of sales, not including tax, was $576.05. How many of each model were sold?

10. A door-to-door salesperson sells dictionaries at $15 each and almanacs at $6.50 each. Sales over three days amounted to 36 books sold with total sales amounting to $361.50. How many of each kind of book were sold? 15 dictionaries; 21 almanacs

B

11. A lending library charges a fixed amount for the first day that a book is overdue and an additional charge for each day thereafter. Raoul paid $0.75 for one book that was 7 days overdue and $1.95 for a book that was 19 days overdue. Find the fixed charge and the charge for each additional day. first day: $0.15; thereafter $0.10

12. Bob West loaned $7800 to a bank customer for one year, part at 10% and the rest at 12%. If the rates of interest were interchanged, the interest for one year would have been $24 more. Find the amount he loaned at each rate. 12%: $3300; 10%: $4500

Assignment Guide
Minimal
Day 1 p. 237: 1–5
Day 2 p. 237: 6–10
Average
Day 1 p. 237: 1–8
Day 2 p. 237: 9–12
Above Average
p. 237: 2–10 even, 11, 12

Additional Answers
Word Problems
3. $900 invested at 9%; $4100 invested at 7%
4. $15,000 at 15%; $20,000 at 12%
5. 5000 tickets at $5.50; 2500 tickets at $7.00
6. $16.50 full-fare;
7. 23 ten-dollar bills; 73 five-dollar bills
8. 21 20¢ stamps; 16 15¢ stamps
9. 19 calculators at $15.95; 12 calculators at $22.75

Systems of Sentences **237**

Problem Solving and Applications

Objective: To solve mixture problems using systems of equations

6–8 Mixture Problems

Mixture problems involve two or more ingredients that are combined to produce a given mixture with a given value. Making a table to show the *amount* of each ingredient (Condition 1) and the *total value* of each ingredient (Condition 2) will help you to organize the information and to write a system of equations for the problem.

EXAMPLE 1 The owner of Corner Health Foods wishes to mix raisins that sell at $5.75 per kilogram with nuts that sell at $4.00 per kilogram to make a 100-kilogram mixture that sells at $4.70 per kilogram. How many kilograms of raisins and how many kilograms of nuts must be used?

Solution: $\boxed{1}$ Follow the steps of the procedure given on page 224.

	Number of Kilograms (Condition 1)	Value per Kilogram	Total Value (Condition 2)
Raisins	x	$5.75	$5.75x$
Nuts	y	$4.00	$4.00y$
Mixture	100	$4.70	$4.70(100)$

$\boxed{2}$ $\begin{cases} x + y = 100 \\ 5.75x + 4.00y = 4.70(100) \end{cases}$　1 ◄——— **Amount**
　　　　　　　　　　　　　　　　　　　　 2 ◄——— **Value**

$\boxed{3}$ Solve the system. The substitution method is used below.

$\qquad x + y = 100$　　　　　　　　　　　　1 ◄——— **Solve for x in terms of y.**
$\qquad\quad x = 100 - y$
$\qquad\qquad\quad 5.75x + 4.00y = 470$　　　 2 ◄——— **Replace x with (100 − y).**
$\qquad 5.75(100 - y) + 4.00y = 470$
$\qquad 575 - 5.75y + 4.00y = 470$
$\qquad\qquad 575 - 1.75y = 470$
$\qquad\qquad\qquad -1.75y = -105$
$\qquad\qquad\qquad\qquad y = 60$　　　 ◄——— **Don't forget to find x.**
$\qquad\qquad x + y = 100$　　　1
$\qquad\qquad x + 60 = 100$
$\qquad\qquad\qquad x = 40$

Check: $\boxed{4}$ **Condition 1**　Are there 100 kilograms in all?　$40 + 60 = 100$?　Yes ✔

Condition 2　Does the total value equal $4.70(100)$ or 470?
$\qquad\qquad 40(\$5.75) + 60(\$4.00) = \$470$?　Yes ✔

The owner should mix **40 kg** of raisins with **60 kg** of nuts.

Per cents are often used to express the strength of a solution or the amount of a specific ingredient in a solution or mixture. In such problems, one condition expresses the amounts of the two ingredients in the solution or mixture. The other condition expresses the strength of the solution or the per cent of a substance in the mixture.

EXAMPLE 2 A soil analysis of a lawn determines that 50 pounds of fertilizer containing 20% nitrogen is needed. How can this mixture be made from two different fertilizers, one containing 15% nitrogen and the other containing 24% nitrogen?

Solution: $\boxed{1}$

	Number of Pounds (Condition 1)	Per Cent of Nitrogen	Amount of Nitrogen (Condition 2)
Fertilizer A		15%	$0.15x$
Fertilizer B		24%	$0.24y$
Mixture		20%	$0.20(50)$

$\boxed{2}$ $\begin{cases} x + y = 50 & \text{1} \longleftarrow \text{— Condition 1} \\ 0.15x + 0.24y = 10 & \text{2} \longleftarrow \text{— Condition 2} \end{cases}$

$\boxed{3}$ The addition method is used below to solve the system. To eliminate the decimals, multiply each side of Equation 2 by 100.

$$\begin{array}{rl} 15x + 24y = & 1000 \qquad \text{2} \\ -15x - 15y & \underline{-750} \qquad \text{1} \longleftarrow \text{—} -15(x + y) = -15(50) \\ 9y = & 250 \end{array}$$

$$y = 27.7 \text{ or } 28 \quad \longleftarrow \text{ Rounded to the nearest pound}$$

$$x + y = 50$$
$$x + 28 = 50$$
$$x = 22$$

$\boxed{4}$ The check is left for you.

About **22 pounds** of Fertilizer A and **28 pounds** of Fertilizer B are needed.

Additional Examples
Example 2

1. A pharmacist determines that 50 liters of an antiseptic containing 20% peroxide is needed. How can this mixture be made from two different antiseptics, one containing 25% peroxide and the other containing 15% peroxide?
   Ans: 25 L of each
2. A chemist needs 20 liters of a 15% iodine solution. How can this mixture be made from two different solutions, one containing 12% iodine and the other containing 17% iodine?
   Ans: 12%: 8 L; 17%: 12 L

CLASSROOM EXERCISES

Read the problem and complete the table. Then write the system of equations you would use to solve each problem.

1. Cashews that sell for $6.50 per kilogram are mixed with almonds that sell for $8.00 per kilogram to make a 100-kilogram mixture. The mixture will sell for $7.40 per kilogram. How many kilograms of cashews and how many kilograms of almonds must be used? (See the table on page 240.)

Systems of Sentences **239**

240

1. Total value of cashews: $6.50x; total value of almonds: $8.00y; weight of mixture: 100 kg; total value of mixture: $7.40 (100);
$$\begin{cases} x + y = 100 \\ 6.50x + 8.00y = 7.40 \end{cases}$$

2. Value per kg of A: $5.50; total value of A: $5.50x; value per kg of B: $6.50; total value of B: $6.50y; weight of mixture: 20 kg; value per kg of mixture: $6.10; total value of mixture: $6.10 (20);
$$\begin{cases} x + y = 20 \\ 5.50x + 6.50y = 122 \end{cases}$$

1. 18 lb of $1.70 cookies
   27 lb of $0.95 cookies
2. $16\frac{2}{3}$ kg of cashews
3. $\frac{1}{2}$ oz of each type of seed
4. 200 g of Solution B;
   120 g of Solution A
5. 100 g of the 8% solution;
   300 g of the 4% solution
6. 7 g of 55% silver alloy;
   23 g of 25% silver alloy
7. 4 kg of alloy that is 65%;
   16 kg of alloy that is 35% copper
8. 60 qt of 24% butterfat cream; 30 qt of 18% butterfat cream

	Number of Kilograms	Value per Kilogram	Total Value
Cashews	x	$6.50	?
Almonds	y	$8.00	?
Mixture	?	$7.40	?

2. A 20-kilogram mixture of coffee is made from two brands. Brand A sells at $5.50 per kilogram and Brand B at $6.50 per kilogram. The mixture will sell at $6.10 per kilogram. How many kilograms of Brand A and of Brand B must be used?

	Number of Kilograms	Value per Kilogram	Total Value
Brand A	x	?	?
Brand B	y	?	?
Mixture	?	?	?

WORD PROBLEMS

A   Solve each problem.

1. A baker mixes cookies worth $0.95 per pound with cookies worth $1.70 per pound. How many of each kind must be used to produce a 45-pound mixture that sells for $1.25 per pound?

3. A seed company sells one-ounce packets of a mixture of marigold seeds. Pretty Face marigolds sell at 50¢ per ounce and Golden Face marigolds sell at 40¢ per ounce. The mixture will sell at 45¢ per packet. How many ounces of each kind of seed must be used?

5. A 4% salt solution is mixed with an 8% salt solution. How many grams of each solution are needed to obtain 400 grams of a 5% solution?

7. An alloy that is 35% copper is melted with a second alloy that is 65% copper. How many kilograms of each alloy must be melted to obtain 20 kilograms of an alloy that is 41% copper?

2. How many kilograms of cashews selling at $6.00 per kilogram must be mixed with 20 kilograms of peanuts selling at $3.25 per kilogram to produce a mixture worth $4.50 per kilogram?

4. Solution A, which is 10% iodine, is mixed with Solution B, which is 18% iodine, to obtain 320 grams of a solution that is 15% iodine. How many grams of Solution A and how many grams of Solution B are needed for the 15%–solution?

6. A 25% silver alloy is to be melted with a 55% silver alloy. How many grams of each must be used to obtain 30 grams of a 32% silver alloy?

8. A milk distributor has cream that is 24% butterfat and cream that is 18% butterfat. How many quarts of each must be used to obtain 90 quarts of cream that is 22% butterfat?

9. A chemist has one solution that is 40% acid and a second solution that is 15% acid. How many grams of each should be used to obtain 40 grams of a solution that is 25% acid?
16 g of 40% acid; 24 g of 15% acid

10. Pecans priced at $5.85 per kilogram are mixed with almonds priced at $4.93 per kilogram to make a 40-kilogram mixture that is to sell at $5.62 per kilogram. How many kilograms of each kind of nut must be used?
30 kg pecans; 10 kg almonds

B

11. A solution contains 8 grams of acid and 32 grams of water. How many grams of water must be evaporated to obtain a solution that is 40% acid? 20g

12. A tank contains 100 liters of a solution of acid and water. The solution is 20% acid. How much water must be evaporated to obtain a solution that is 50% acid? 60 L

Review

Use the substitution method to solve each system. *(Section 6–6)*

1. $\begin{cases} x + y = 10 \\ 3x - 2y = 5 \end{cases}$ (5, 5)

2. $\begin{cases} 2r + t = 0 \\ 4r - 3t = -10 \end{cases}$ (−1, 2)

3. $\begin{cases} p - 2q = 1 \\ 2p + q = 12 \end{cases}$ (5, 2)

4. $\begin{cases} p - 2n = 3 \\ 2p + n = 1 \end{cases}$ (1, −1)

5. $\begin{cases} 3c + 2d = 0 \\ 2c - d = 7 \end{cases}$ (2, −3)

6. $\begin{cases} 3a + b - 1 = 0 \\ 2a - 6b - 4 = 0 \end{cases}$ $(\frac{1}{2}, -\frac{1}{2})$

Solve.

7. Timothy has $5.00 in dimes and nickels. He has exactly 66 coins. How many coins of each kind does he have? *(Section 6–7)*

8. Rosita made a bank deposit of $250 with 17 ten– and twenty–dollar bills. How many bills of each type did she deposit? *(Section 6–7)*

9. Bob invested $1500, part at a yearly interest rate of 10% and the rest at a yearly interest rate of 9.5%. The total interest earned in one year was $145. How much did he invest at each rate? *(Section 6–7)*

10. Wild rice worth $9.50 per pound is mixed with brown rice worth $2.25 per pound. How many pounds of each kind of rice must be used to produce a 50-pound mixture selling for $3.70 per pound? *(Section 6–8)*

11. A 12% tin alloy is to be melted with an 18% tin alloy. How many kilograms of each alloy must be used to obtain 15 kilograms of an alloy that is 14% tin? *(Section 6–8)*

12. An 8% plant food solution is mixed with a 12% solution. How many liters of each solution are needed to obtain 10 liters of a 9% solution? *(Section 6–8)*

— **Puzzle** — See the Solution Key.

Cristina can buy a bracelet and a watch band for $55, or the watch band and a locket for $46, or the locket and the bracelet for $37. What does the bracelet cost?

Systems of Sentences **241**

Quiz Sections 6-6–6-8
After completing this Review you may want to administer a quiz covering the same sections. See page M-**48** of the Teacher's Manual for the suggested quiz.

Additional Answers
Review
7. nickels: 32; dimes: 34
8. ten-dollar bills: 9; twenty-dollar bills: 8
9. 10%: $500; 9.5%: $1000
10. $9.50 per pound: 10 lb; $2.25 per pound: 40 lb
11. 12% alloy: 10 kg; 18% alloy: 5
12. 8% solution: $7\frac{1}{2}$ liters; 12% solution: $2\frac{1}{2}$ liters

BASIC: SOLVING SYSTEMS OF EQUATIONS

One of the most common uses of computers is in solving systems of equations. For a system of the form

$$\begin{cases} A_1x + B_1y = C_1 \\ A_2x + B_2y = C_2 \end{cases}$$

the general solution is the following.

$$x = \frac{B_2C_1 - B_1C_2}{A_1B_2 - A_2B_1} \qquad\qquad y = \frac{A_1C_2 - A_2C_1}{A_1B_2 - A_2B_1}$$

Problem: *Write a program which solves systems of two linear equation in two variables.*

```
100 REM SOLVE A1*X + B1*Y = C1
110 REM        A2*X + B2*Y = C2
120 REM
130 PRINT "ENTER THE COEFFICIENTS OF THE FIRST EQUATION";
140 INPUT A1, B1, C1
150 PRINT "ENTER THE COEFFICIENTS OF THE SECOND EQUATION";
160 INPUT A2, B2, C2
170 LET D = A1*B2 - A2*B1
180 IF D = 0 THEN 230
190 LET X = (B2*C1 - B1*C2)/D
200 LET Y = (A1*C2 - A2*C1)/D
210 PRINT "SOLUTION IS (";X;",";Y;")"
220 GOTO 240
230 PRINT "NO UNIQUE SOLUTION"
240 PRINT "ANY MORE SYSTEMS TO SOLVE (1=YES, 0=NO)";
250 INPUT Z
260 IF Z = 1 THEN 130
270 END
```

The following is the output from a sample run of the program above.

```
RUN
ENTER THE COEFFICIENTS OF THE FIRST EQUATION? 1,1,1
ENTER THE COEFFICIENTS OF THE SECOND EQUATION? 2,2,2
NO UNIQUE SOLUTION

ANY MORE SYSTEMS TO SOLVE (1=YES, 0=NO)? 1
ENTER THE COEFFICIENTS OF THE FIRST EQUATION? 1,1,1
ENTER THE COEFFICIENTS OF THE SECOND EQUATION? 2,2,-7
NO UNIQUE SOLUTION
```

242 *Computer Applications*

This lesson is optional. The following is a derivation of the formulas shown for the solution of a system of two linear equations. This derivation uses multiplication with the addition method.
(See Section 6-3, pp. 220–222)

$$\begin{cases} A_1x + B_1y = C_1 \\ A_2x + B_2y = C_2 \end{cases}$$

$$A_1B_2x + B_1B_2y = C_1B_2$$
$$\underline{-A_2B_1x - B_1B_2y = -C_2B_1}$$
$$A_1B_2x - A_2B_1x = C_1B_2 - C_2B_1$$
$$(A_1B_2 - A_2B_1)x = C_1B_2 - C_2B_1$$
$$x = \frac{C_1B_2 - C_2B_1}{A_1B_2 - A_2B_1}$$

Similarly, by eliminating x you can find the solution for y.

$$y = \frac{A_1C_2 - A_2C_1}{A_1B_2 - A_2B_1}$$

```
ANY MORE SYSTEMS TO SOLVE (1=YES, 0=NO)? 1
ENTER THE COEFFICIENTS OF THE FIRST EQUATION? 1,1,1
ENTER THE COEFFICIENTS OF THE SECOND EQUATION? 2,-1,2
SOLUTION IS ( 1 , 0 )

ANY MORE SYSTEMS TO SOLVE (1=YES, 0=NO)? 0
READY
```

Analysis

Statement 170: D is the denominator of the fraction used in statements 190 and 200.

Statements 180 and 230: If $D = 0$, the computer prints NO UNIQUE SOLUTION. The program does not decide whether the system has no solution or infinitely many solutions. (See Exercise 16 below.)

Statements 190–210: If $D \neq 0$, then X and Y are computed. In statement 210, because the parentheses and the comma are inside quotation marks, the solution is printed as an ordered pair. (Notice the output for the last set of data in the sample run.)

EXERCISES

A   In Exercises 1–15, write each system in the following form.

$$\begin{cases} A_1x + B_1y = C_1 \\ A_2x + B_2y = C_2 \end{cases}$$

Then use the program on page 242 to solve each system.

1. $\begin{cases} 3x = 2y + 8 \\ 5y = 4x - 6 \end{cases}$

2. $\begin{cases} y = 5x + 1 \\ x - 2y + 6 = 0 \end{cases}$

3. $\begin{cases} x = y + 6 \\ 4y + 4x = 15 \end{cases}$

4. $\begin{cases} y = 2x + 4 \\ 2x = 4 - y \end{cases}$

5. $\begin{cases} 2x + y = -2 \\ 2y = 4x - 1 \end{cases}$

6. $\begin{cases} 3y + 4x = 0 \\ 5 + 6y = 2x \end{cases}$

7. $\begin{cases} 4x - 17 = -3y \\ 3y + 2x - 13 = 0 \end{cases}$

8. $\begin{cases} y = 9 - x \\ y = 5x - 3 \end{cases}$

9. $\begin{cases} 8x + 13 = -5y \\ 3x = 2y - 1 \end{cases}$

10. $\begin{cases} 4x = 3y - 2 \\ 6 + 12x = 9y \end{cases}$

11. $\begin{cases} x = -2 \\ y = 2x + 4 \end{cases}$

12. $\begin{cases} x = 4y \\ \frac{1}{4}x = 20 - y \end{cases}$

13. $\begin{cases} x + y = 12 \\ -y = 8 \end{cases}$

14. $\begin{cases} 0.4x = 1.2 - y \\ 0.6x = y + 3.9 \end{cases}$

15. $\begin{cases} 0.5y = 0.75x - 4 \\ 0.25x + 0.5y = 2.5 \end{cases}$

B

16. Expand the program on page 242 so that, when $D = 0$, it prints whether the system has no solution or infinitely many solutions. For the first set of data in the sample run of the program on page 242, the revised program should print DEPENDENT SYSTEM--INFINITELY MANY SOLUTIONS. For the second set of data in the sample run, the revised program should print INCONSISTENT SYSTEM--NO SOLUTION. See the Solution Key.

Solving Systems of Equations   **243**

Additional Answers

1. $3x - 2y = 8$
   $-4x + 5y = -6$
   $(4, 2)$

4. $-2x + y = 4$
   $2x + y = 4$
   $(0, 4)$

7. $4x + 3y = 17$
   $2x + 3y = 13$
   $(2, 3)$

10. $4x - 3y = -2$
    $12x - 9y = -6$
    NO UNIQUE SOLUTION

13. $x + y = 12$
    $0x - y = 8$
    $(20, -8)$

2. $-5x + y = 1$
   $x - 2y = -6$
   $(.444445, 3.22222)$

5. $2x + y = -2$
   $-4x + 2y = -1$
   $(-.375, -1.25)$

8. $x + y = 9$
   $-5x + y = -3$
   $(2, 7)$

11. $x + 0y = -2$
    $-2x + y = 4$
    $(-2, 0)$

14. $0.4x + y = 1.2$
    $0.6x - y = 3.9$
    $(5.1, -.84)$

3. $x - y = 6$
   $4x + 4y = 15$
   $(4.875, -1.125)$

6. $4x + 3y = 0$
   $-2x + 6y = -5$
   $(.5, -.666667)$

9. $8x + 5y = -13$
   $3x - 2y = -1$
   $(-1, -1)$

12. $x - 4y = 0$
    $\frac{1}{4}x + y = 20$
    $(40, 10)$

15. $-0.75x + 0.5y = -4$
    $0.25x + 0.5y = 2.5$
    $(6.5, 1.75)$

243

Chapter Summary

IMPORTANT TERMS

Consistent system (p. 213)
Equivalent systems (p. 217)
Inconsistent system (p. 213)

Simultaneous linear equations (p. 212)
System of linear equations (p. 212)

IMPORTANT IDEAS

1. In a system of two linear equations:

If the slopes of the lines for the two equations are different, the system has one solution.

If the slopes are the same and the y intercepts are different, the system has no solutions.

If the slopes are the same and the y intercepts are the same, the system has an infinite number of solutions.

2. Steps in Solving a System of Two Linear Equations by the Addition Method

[1] Add to eliminate one of the variables. Solve the resulting equation.

[2] Substitute the known value of one variable in one of the original equations of the system. Solve for the other variable.

[3] Check the solution in both equations of the system.

3. Steps in Solving a System of Two Linear Equations Using Multiplication with the Addition Method

[1] Multiply each side of one of the equations by a number, and, if necessary, multiply each side of the second equation by another number. Choose the two numbers so that, after multiplying, the coefficients of one of the variables will be additive inverses of each other.

[2] Use the addition method to solve the new system.

4. Steps in Solving Word Problems Using Systems of Equations in Two Variables

[1] Use Condition 1 and two variables to represent the unknowns.

[2] Write an equation in two variables that expresses Condition 1.

[3] Write a second equation in two variables that expresses Condition 2.

[4] Solve the system of equations.

[5] Check your solution in the original conditions of the problem.

[6] Answer the question.

5. A two-digit number may be expressed as $10t + u$, where t represents the tens digit and u the units digit.

A three-digit number may be expressed as $100h + 10t + u$, where h represents the hundreds digit.

6. **Steps in Solving a System of Two Linear Equations by the Substitution Method**

$\boxed{1}$ Solve one equation for one of the variables.

$\boxed{2}$ Substitute the resulting expression in the other equation.

$\boxed{3}$ Solve the resulting equation.

$\boxed{4}$ Find the values of the variables.

7. **Simple Interest Formula:** interest = principal · rate · time, or $i = prt$.

_____ Chapter Objectives and Review _____

Additional Answers

Objective: *To solve systems of equations by graphing (Section 6–1)*

Solve each system by graphing.

1. $\begin{cases} x - y = 2 \\ 2x + y = 4 \end{cases}$

2. $\begin{cases} y = 3x - 4 \\ y = -2x + 1 \end{cases}$

3. $\begin{cases} 2x + y = -3 \\ 3x + 4y = 3 \end{cases}$

Write *one*, *none*, or *infinitely many* to describe the number of solutions for each system.

infinitely many

4. $\begin{cases} y = 2x - 5 \\ y = -x - 5 \end{cases}$ one

5. $\begin{cases} 2y - x = 6 \\ 2x + 6 = 4y \end{cases}$ none

6. $\begin{cases} 2x + y = 1 \\ 3y = 3 - 6x \end{cases}$

Objective: *To solve systems of equations by the addition method (Section 6–2)*

Use the addition method to solve each system.

$\left(6, -\tfrac{1}{2}\right)$

7. $\begin{cases} x + y = 4 \\ 3x - y = -6 \end{cases}$ $\left(-\tfrac{1}{2}, 4\tfrac{1}{2}\right)$

8. $\begin{cases} 2x - 3y = -2 \\ -2x + 5y = 2 \end{cases}$ $(-1, 0)$

9. $\begin{cases} \tfrac{2}{3}x - 2y = 5 \\ \tfrac{1}{3}x + 2y = 1 \end{cases}$

Objective: *To solve systems of equations using multiplication with the addition method (Section 6–3)*

Use multiplication with the addition method to solve each system. $(2, -5)$

10. $\begin{cases} 2x + 3y = 8 \\ 7x + 3y = -2 \end{cases}$ $(-2, 4)$

11. $\begin{cases} 2p - 3q = 2 \\ -6p + 4q = 9 \end{cases}$ $\left(-3\tfrac{1}{2}, -3\right)$

12. $\begin{cases} 3a + 5b = -19 \\ 5a - 7b = 45 \end{cases}$

Objective: *To solve word problems using systems of equations (Section 6–4)*

13. The sum of two numbers is 22. Four times the greater number is equal to seven times the smaller number. Find the two numbers. 14, 8

14. Eighty-five more student tickets than adult tickets were sold for a concert. The total number sold was 343. How many tickets of each type were sold?

Objective: *To solve digit problems using systems of equations (Section 6–5)*

15. The tens digit of a two-digit number is 3 less than the units digit. The sum of the digits is 13. Find the number. 58

16. A two-digit number is 4 times the sum of its digits. The number is 18 less than the number obtained when the digits are reversed. Find the number. 24

1.

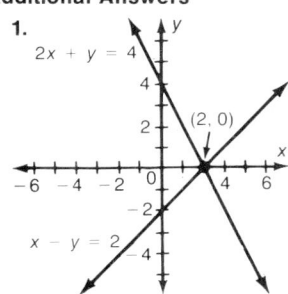

2.

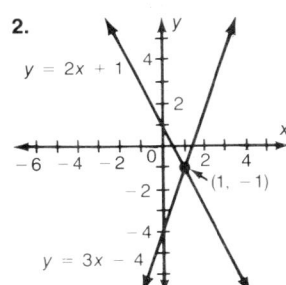

3.

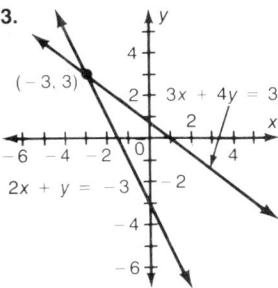

14. adult: 129; student: 214

Objective: *To solve systems of equations using the substitution method (Section 6–6)*

Use the substitution method to solve each system. $(1, \frac{1}{3})$

17. $\begin{cases} y - 2x = 3 \\ y + 3x = 8 \end{cases}$ $(1, 5)$
18. $\begin{cases} c + 2d = 0 \\ 4c - 7d = 15 \end{cases}$ $(2, -1)$
19. $\begin{cases} 2r - 3s - 1 = 0 \\ r + 6s - 3 = 0 \end{cases}$

Objective: *To solve money problems using systems of equations (Section 6–7)*

20. The Lawn and Garden Shop sold 40 bags of lawn seed one week for a total of $263. Large bags of lawn seed sell for $8.50 each and smaller bags for $5.75 each. How many bags of each size were sold that week?
large: 12; small: 28

21. Ralph Minton borrowed $4000 for one year, part at 12% interest and the rest at 15% interest. If he had borrowed the entire amount at 12% interest, Ralph would owe $30 less interest for the year. Find the amount borrowed at each rate. 12%: $3,000; 15%: $1,000

Objective: *To solve mixture problems using systems of equations (Section 6–8)*

22. A 25-kilogram mixture of tea is made from one brand that sells for $4.50 per kilogram and another brand that sells for $5.75 per kilogram. How many kilograms of each must be used to make a mixture that sells at $4.90 per kilogram? $4.50: 17 kg; $5.75: 8 kg

23. Solution A, which is 5% sugar, is mixed with Solution B which is 10% sugar to obtain 10 liters of a solution that is 8% sugar. How many liters of Solution A and how many liters of Solution B are needed for the 8% solution? Solution A: 4 liters; Solution B: 6 liters

Chapter Test

A formal Chapter Test is provided in the Teacher's Manual. See p. M-69.

1. Solve this system by graphing: $\begin{cases} 2x - y = 8 \\ x + y = 1 \end{cases}$

Use the addition method to solve.

2. $\begin{cases} -2x + y = -4 \\ 5x - y = -1 \end{cases}$ $(-1\frac{2}{3}, -7\frac{1}{3})$
3. $\begin{cases} -3x + 2y = -3 \\ 5x - 3y = 5 \end{cases}$ $(1, 0)$

4. Use the substitution method to solve: $\begin{cases} 3a - b = -6 \\ 6a + 2b = 0 \end{cases}$ $(-1, 3)$

Use any method to solve each system.

5. $\begin{cases} 4x + y = 10 \\ y = -x + 1 \end{cases}$ $(3, -2)$
6. $\begin{cases} 3m + 2n = -8 \\ 5m - 8 = 2n \end{cases}$ $(0, -4)$

Solve each problem.

7. Tony worked 6 hours more than Carl last week. Together, the two boys worked a total of 58 hours. How many hours did each of them work?
Carl: 26 hours; Tony: 32 hours

8. The sum of the digits of a two-digit number is 9. The value of the number is 6 times the value of its units digit. Find the number. 36

246   *Chapter 6*

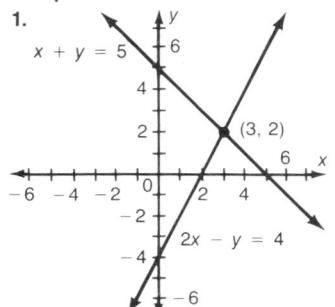

9. A restaurant owner bought 24 new tables, some large and some smaller. The large tables cost $145 each, while the smaller ones cost $120 each. The total cost of the tables was $3080. How many tables of each size did he buy?
small: 16; large: 8

10. A mixture of birdseed contains sunflower seeds worth $1.30 per kilogram and other seeds worth $0.90 per kilogram. How many kilograms of each kind must be used to produce 100 kilograms of a mixture that sells for $1.00 per kilogram?
sunflower: 25 kg; other: 75 kg

More Challenging Problems

Solve each system.

1. $\begin{cases} x - 5y = 27 \\ 2x + 3y = 2 \\ 5x + 8y = 3 \end{cases}$ $(7, -4)$

2. $\begin{cases} 9x + 4y = 0 \\ 5x - 2y = 19 \\ 3x + 4y = -12 \end{cases}$ $(2, -4\frac{1}{2})$

3. $\begin{cases} 6x - 5y = 3 \\ 2y + 10 = 2x \\ 12 - 4y = 12x \end{cases}$ ϕ

Solve each system for x and y in terms of a, b, and c.

4. $\begin{cases} ax + by = c \\ bx - ay = 7c \end{cases}$

5. $\begin{cases} ax + by + a^2 + b^2 = 0 \\ bx + ay + 2ab = 0 \end{cases}$

6. $\begin{cases} cy + (b + c)x = 2bc \\ by + (b - c)x = 2^2 - b^2 \end{cases}$

7. At what two times between 7:00 P.M. and 8:00 P.M. will the minute hand and the hour hand of a clock be exactly 15 minute spaces apart?

8. Mr. Teal has a 99-year lease on his farm. When asked how much of the lease had expired, he said: "Two thirds of the time past is equal to four fifths of the time to come." How much of the lease had expired? 54 years

Additional Practice
You may wish to use all or some of these exercises depending on how well students performed on the formal chapter test.

Skills

Solve each system by graphing. *(Section 6–1)*

1. $\begin{cases} x + y = 5 \\ 2x - y = 4 \end{cases}$

2. $\begin{cases} y = -2 \\ 4x - y = 6 \end{cases}$

3. $\begin{cases} x - 2y = 8 \\ 2x + y = 6 \end{cases}$

Write *one*, *none*, or *infinitely many* to describe the number of solutions for each system. *(Section 6–1)*

4. $\begin{cases} x + y = 5 \\ 2y = -2x + 10 \end{cases}$ infinitely many

5. $\begin{cases} 2y = x - 8 \\ y - 3 = \frac{1}{2}x \end{cases}$ none

6. $\begin{cases} y - 3x = 2 \\ y + \frac{1}{3}x + 1 = 0 \end{cases}$ one

Use the addition method to solve each system. *(Section 6–2)*

7. $\begin{cases} x - y = 14 \\ 3x + y = 6 \end{cases}$ $(5, -9)$

8. $\begin{cases} 2x - y = -2 \\ -2x + 3y = 0 \end{cases}$ $(-1\frac{1}{2}, -1)$

9. $\begin{cases} 5x - 4y = 0 \\ -x + 4y = 2 \end{cases}$ $(\frac{1}{2}, \frac{5}{8})$

10. $\begin{cases} 3x - 2y = 12 \\ 4x + 2y = 2 \end{cases}$ $(2, -3)$

11. $\begin{cases} -5x + 3y = 20 \\ 5x + 9y = 4 \end{cases}$ $(-2\frac{4}{5}, 2)$

12. $\begin{cases} 4x - 2y = 25 \\ x + 2y = 10 \end{cases}$ $(7, 1\frac{1}{2})$

Systems of Sentences **247**

1.
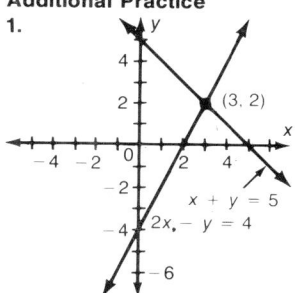

2.
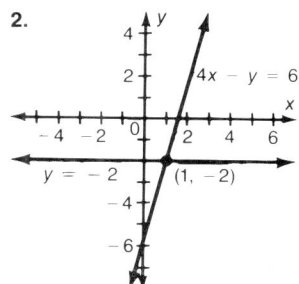

3.
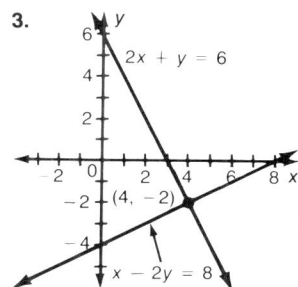

Use multiplication with the addition method to solve each system.
(Section 6–3)

$(-5, 5)$

13. $\begin{cases} 4x - y = 3 \\ 3x + 2y = 5 \end{cases}$ $(1, 1)$

14. $\begin{cases} 3x + 5y = 7 \\ -x + 3y = 0 \end{cases}$ $(1\frac{1}{2}, \frac{1}{2})$

15. $\begin{cases} 3x + 4y = 5 \\ 2x + 3y = 5 \end{cases}$

16. $\begin{cases} 2x + y = 6 \\ x + 3y = -2 \end{cases}$ $(4, -2)$

17. $\begin{cases} 4x - 5y = 2 \\ 7x - 11y = -1 \end{cases}$ $(3, 2)$

18. $\begin{cases} 3x - 2y = 22 \\ 2x - 5y = 0 \end{cases}$ $(10, 4)$

Use the substitution method to solve each system. *(Section 6–6)* $(1\frac{5}{8}, -\frac{1}{4})$

19. $\begin{cases} 3x + 2y = 5 \\ 2x - y = 8 \end{cases}$ $(3, -2)$

20. $\begin{cases} x + 2y = 0 \\ 5x - 6y = -4 \end{cases}$ $(-\frac{1}{2}, \frac{1}{4})$

21. $\begin{cases} 6x - y = 10 \\ -4x - 6y = -5 \end{cases}$

22. $\begin{cases} x - 5y = 20 \\ 3x + 7y = -6 \end{cases}$ $(5, -3)$

23. $\begin{cases} 7x - y = 14 \\ 2x + 5y = 41 \end{cases}$ $(3, 7)$

24. $\begin{cases} 3x - 4y = 43 \\ x + y = -9 \end{cases}$ $(1, -10)$

Applications

A $550 refrigerator costs $85 per year to operate. A $650 refrigerator costs $60 per year to operate. Use this information for Exercises 25 and 26.

25. On the same set of coordinate axes, draw graphs showing the total cost after each of the first 10 years for each refrigerator. (Include the initial cost of each.) *(Section 6–1)*

26. Use the graph to determine after which year the total costs for each refrigerator are the same. *(Section 6–1)* 4 years

27. Voting District A has 146 more registered voters than District B. In all, the two districts have 6432 registered voters. How many are there in each district? *(Section 6–4)*
District A: 3289; District B: 3143

28. The length of a rectangle is 8 centimeters more than its width. The perimeter is 68 centimeters. Find the length and width of the rectangle. *(Section 6–4)*

29. The units digit of a two-digit number is 5 more than the tens digit. The sum of the two digits is 13. Find the number. *(Section 6–5)* 49

30. A two-digit number is 7 times the sum of its digits. The number is 36 more than the number obtained when its digits are reversed. Find the number. *(Section 6–5)* 84

31. Sandra borrowed $10,000, part at a 12% yearly interest rate and the rest at 14%. She paid $1270 in interest for a year. Find the amount of each loan. *(Section 6–7)* 12%: $6500; 14%: $3500

32. Thomas has 56 coins in dimes and quarters. The total value of the coins is $8.00. How many coins of each kind does he have? *(Section 6–7)*

33. A 10% salt solution and a 5% salt solution are available. How many liters of each must be used in order to make 25 liters of an 8% salt solution? *(Section 6–8)*
10%: 15 liters; 5%: 10 liters

34. A 7% iodine solution is to be mixed with a 12% iodine solution. How many liters of each must be used to obtain 5 liters of a 10% solution? *(Section 6–8)*
7%: 2 liters; 12%: 3 liters

248 *Chapter 6*

CHAPTER **7** **Inequalities**

Quick Quiz
Solve and graph.
1. $3x + 6 > 12$
  Ans: $x > 2$

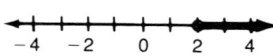

2. $10 - 5x > 5$
  Ans: $x < 1$

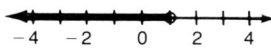

OBJECTIVE: To solve linear inequalities and graph them on a number line

7-1 Combined Inequalities

A sentence such as

$$x \geq 5 \longleftarrow \text{ Read: "x is greater than or equal to 5."}$$

combines an inequality with an equation. Because $x \geq 5$ can be written as two simple sentences with the connective <u>or</u>, it is called a **compound sentence**. A compound sentence with <u>or</u> is a **disjunction**.

$$x \geq 5 \text{ means } x = 5 \quad \underline{\text{or}} \quad x > 5.$$

The solution set of $x \geq 5$ is the set that makes $x = 5$ true <u>or</u> the set that makes $x > 5$ true. This means that the solution set of $x \geq 5$ is the *union* of the solution sets of $x = 5$ and $x > 5$.

In general, the **union of two sets A and B** (in symbols: $A \cup B$) is the set that contains all the elements in set A <u>or</u> in set B.

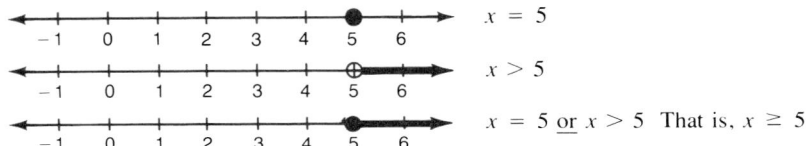

In the graph for $x \geq 5$, the solid dot indicates that the graph includes $x = 5$.

Additional Examples
Example 1
Solve and graph.
1. $3x \geq -15$
  Ans: {**all real numbers greater than or equal to -5**}

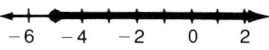

2. $4x \leq 8$
  Ans: {**all real numbers less than or equal to 2**}

EXAMPLE 1 Solve and graph: $2x \geq -6$

Solution: Write the inequality with <u>or</u>. Then solve for x.

$$2x \geq -6 \quad \text{means} \quad 2x = -6 \quad \underline{\text{or}} \quad 2x > -6$$
$$x = -3 \quad \underline{\text{or}} \quad x > -3$$

Solution set: {**all real numbers greater than or equal to -3**}

A sentence such as

$$-6 < x < 2$$

combines two inequalities. Because the sentence can be written as two simple sentences with the connective <u>and</u>, it is also a compound sentence. A compound sentence with <u>and</u> is a **conjunction**.

$$-6 < x < 2 \quad \text{means} \quad -6 < x \quad \underline{\text{and}} \quad x < 2.$$

The solution set of $-6 < x < 2$ is the set that makes both $-6 < x$ true <u>and</u> $x < 2$ true. Thus, the solution of a compound <u>and</u> sentence is the *intersection of two sets*.

In general, the **intersection of two sets A and B** (in symbols: $A \cap B$) is the set that contains the elements belonging to <u>both</u> set A <u>and</u> set B.

250   *Chapter 7*

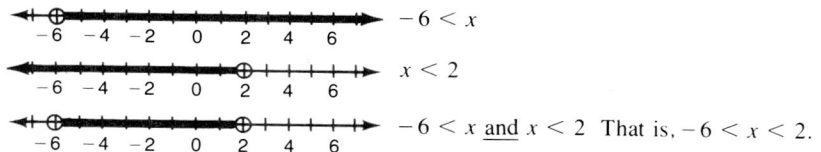

$-6 < x$

$x < 2$

$-6 < x$ and $x < 2$ That is, $-6 < x < 2$.

EXAMPLE 2 Solve and graph: $-9 < 2x - 1 < 5$

Solution: Write the inequality with <u>and</u>. Then solve for x.

$-9 < 2x - 1 < 5$ means $-9 < 2x - 1$ <u>and</u> $2x - 1 < 5$

$$\begin{array}{ccc} -8 < 2x & & 2x < 6 \\ -4 < x & \text{and} & x < 3 \end{array}$$

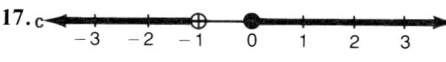

Solution set: {all real numbers greater than -4 and less than 3}

CLASSROOM EXERCISES

Write each compound sentence as two simple sentences joined by <u>or</u> or <u>and</u>.

1. $x \le 3$ **2.** $1 < x < 5$ **3.** $x \ge -1$ **4.** $-3 < x < 0$

5. $3y \le 12$ **6.** $5 \ge p - 2$ **7.** $x + 2 \le 8$ **8.** $-a \le 5$

Write each compound sentence without <u>or</u>.

9. $x < 5$ <u>or</u> $= 5$ **10.** $x < 0$ <u>or</u> $x = 0$

11. $x < -3$ <u>or</u> $x = -3$ **12.** $x < 2$ <u>or</u> $x = 2$

Write each compound sentence without <u>and</u>.

13. $x < 4$ <u>and</u> $x > 1$ **14.** $a > -1$ <u>and</u> $a < 0$

15. $t > -1$ <u>and</u> $t < 3$ **16.** $-3 < x$ <u>and</u> $x < 0$

Match each graph in Exercises 17–22 with one of the compound sentences given in a–f.

17. c **a.** $-2 \le x$ <u>and</u> $x < 1$

18. e **b.** $x < -3$ <u>or</u> $x > 3$

19. d **c.** $x < -1$ <u>or</u> $x \ge 0$

20. a **d.** $0 \le x$ <u>and</u> $x \le 2$

21. b **e.** $0 \le x$ <u>and</u> $x < 3$

22. f **f.** $x < -2$ <u>or</u> $x > 0$

Inequalities **251**

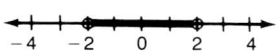
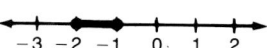

Additional Answers
1. $3x - 1 = 11$ or $3x - 1 < 11$
2. $\frac{1}{3}m = 4$ or $\frac{1}{3}m > 4$
3. $3 < y$ and $y < 8$
4. $-1 < a$ and $a < 0$
5. $t - \frac{1}{2} = 3\frac{1}{2}$ or $t - \frac{1}{2} > 3\frac{1}{2}$
6. $-5 < 2x$ and $2x < 10$

10.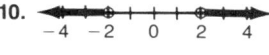
  $\begin{array}{ccccc} -4 & -2 & 0 & 2 & 4 \end{array}$
11.
  $\begin{array}{ccccc} -4 & -2 & 0 & 2 & 4 \end{array}$
12.
  $\begin{array}{ccccc} -4 & -2 & 0 & 2 & 4 \end{array}$
13.
  $\begin{array}{ccccc} -2 & 0 & 2 & 4 & 6 \end{array}$
14.
  $\begin{array}{ccccc} -4 & -2 & 0 & 2 & 4 \end{array}$
15.
  $\begin{array}{ccccc} -4 & -2 & 0 & 2 & 4 \end{array}$
16.
  $\begin{array}{ccccc} -4 & -2 & 0 & 2 & 4 \end{array}$
17.
  $\begin{array}{ccccc} -4 & -2 & 0 & 2 & 4 \end{array}$
18.
  $\begin{array}{ccccc} -4 & -2 & 0 & 2 & 4 \end{array}$

22. $-1 < x < 3$
23. $2 \le x < 4$
32. $-3 \le x \le -1$
33. $-3 \le m < 0$

WRITTEN EXERCISES

A　　Write each compound sentence as two simple sentences joined by <u>or</u> or <u>and</u>.

1. $3x - 1 \le 11$
2. $\frac{1}{3}m \ge 4$
3. $3 < y < 8$
4. $-1 < a < 0$
5. $t - \frac{1}{2} \ge 3\frac{1}{2}$
6. $-5 < 2x < 10$
7. $-3 < x + 2 < 1$
   $-3 < x + 2$ <u>and</u> $x + 2 < 1$
8. $-2 < -\frac{1}{2}x < -1$
   $-2 < -\frac{1}{2}x$ <u>and</u> $-\frac{1}{2}x < -1$
9. $-9 < 3k < 15$
   $-9 < 3k$ <u>and</u> $3k < 15$

Graph the solution set of each compound sentence.

10. $x > 2$ <u>or</u> $x < -2$
11. $-2 < x$ <u>and</u> $x < 2$
12. $w > -3$ <u>and</u> $w < 4$
13. $a > 3$ <u>and</u> $a < 5$
14. $y < 4$ <u>or</u> $-y < 4$
15. $y \ge 1$ <u>or</u> $y > 0$
16. $t < -1$ <u>or</u> $t < -3$
17. $t \le -1$ <u>or</u> $t \le -3$
18. $3a - 4 = 2$ <u>or</u> $5a + 1 < -4$

Solve and graph each inequality. See the Solution Key for the graphs.

19. $3x \ge 21$　$x \ge 7$
20. $-5x < 20$　$x \ge -4$
21. $-5 < 2x < 10$　$-2\frac{1}{2} < x < 5$
22. $-9 < -2x - 3 < -1$
23. $-2 < -\frac{1}{2}x \le -1$
24. $\frac{1}{3}m \le -4$　$m \le -12$
25. $-3 < t \le 6$　$-3 < t \le 6$
26. $-2 \le x \le 8$　$-2 \le x \le 8$
27. $2y + 1 \le 7$　$y \le 3$
28. $-\frac{1}{2} \le w < \frac{3}{2}$　$-\frac{1}{2} \le w < \frac{3}{2}$
29. $2c + 1 \ge 6$　$c \ge 2\frac{1}{2}$
30. $3(p + 2) \le 6$　$p \le 0$
31. $-(x - 2) \ge 3$　$x \le -1$
32. $-14 \le 4x - 2 \le -6$
33. $-19 \le 5m - 4 < -4$
34. $9 \le 2a + 5 < 15$
    $2 \le a < 5$
35. $1 \le 3m - 2 \le 16$
    $1 \le m \le 6$
36. $3 < 2x - 1 < 8$
    $2 < x < 4\frac{1}{2}$

APPLICATIONS: Using Combined Inequalities

37. The weight of each boy on a football team is more than 130 pounds and less than 205 pounds. If x represents the weight of any player, then
    <u>　?　</u> $< x <$ <u>　?　</u> is true.　130,205

38. In one high school wrestling weight class, wrestlers may weigh more than 167 pounds but no more than 185 pounds. Represent this weight class as an inequality, where w is the weight of any wrestler.　$167 < w \le 185$

Olympic boxers compete in classes based on mass (weight) expressed in kilograms. In a particular class, a boxer's mass must be greater than the maximum of the next lighter class and no more than the maximum limit for the particular class.

Use this information in Exercises 39–42 to express each class as an inequality where y represents the mass of a boxer in kilograms.

39. Light heavyweight: 76–81　$76 < y \le 81$
40. Welterweight: 64–67　$64 < y \le 67$
41. Lightweight: 58–60　$58 < y \le 60$
42. Bantamweight: 52–54　$52 < y \le 54$

B
43. Stocks are sold only in integral numbers of dollars and eighths of a dollar. The inequality $51\frac{1}{8} < x < 52\frac{3}{4}$ indicates that a stock sold on a particular day above $51\frac{1}{8}$ and below $52\frac{3}{4}$. What is the solution set for the inequality?

$\{51\frac{1}{4}, 51\frac{3}{8}, 51\frac{1}{2}, 51\frac{5}{8}, 51\frac{3}{4}, 51\frac{7}{8}, 52, 52\frac{1}{8}, 52\frac{1}{4}, 52\frac{3}{8}, 52\frac{1}{2}, 52\frac{5}{8}\}$

Solve each inequality. Graph the solution set. See the Solution Key for the graphs.

44. $3x - 7 < 28$ <u>and</u> $9x - 4 > x + 4$ $1 < x < 11\frac{2}{3}$ 45. $5 + 2y < -1$ <u>or</u> $-3 + 2y \geq 3$

46. $3 - 4a \leq 5$ <u>or</u> $2a - 3 \leq 7$ all real numbers   47. $3n - 9 > -3$ <u>and</u> $-9n > -27$

48. $-4 \geq 2y + 8$ <u>and</u> $3y + 10 \geq 7$ ϕ 49. $3 + 4x < 3x - 2$ <u>and</u> $2 + x \geq -6$

50. $6y - 9 \leq 17y + 13$ <u>and</u> $3(y - 4) \leq 2(3y - 9)$ 51. $3 - 2n > n$ <u>or</u> $2n < 6 + 8$

Puzzle   See the Solution Key.

Some numbers have very interesting properties, as you can see in 1–3 below.

1. **a.** Think of a three-digit number. (For example, 293.)
   b. Make a six-digit number by writing the number twice. (293293)
   c. Divide the new number by 7.
   d. Divide by 11.
   e. Divide by 13. What number do you get?

2. Look at the pattern below.

   $2^2 = 4 = 1^2 + 1 + 2$ $4^2 = 16 = 3^2 + 3 + 4$

   $3^2 = 9 = 2^2 + 2 + 3$ $5^2 = 25 = 4^2 + 4 + 5$

   Use the pattern to find 25^2 without multiplying. (HINT: $24^2 = 576$)

3. Look at the pattern below.

   $999 \times 2 = 1998$ $999 \times 4 = 3996$

   $999 \times 3 = 2997$ $999 \times 5 = 4995$

   Use the pattern to evaluate each expression below without using pencil and paper.

   a. 999×6 **b.** 999×8 **c.** $8991 \div 2997$ **d.** $3996 \div 7992$

REVIEW CAPSULE FOR SECTION 7-2

Tell whether the given ordered pair is a solution of the given equation. *(Pages 181–184)*

1. $y = x$; $(-4, 4)$ No   2. $y = -x$; $(-1, 1)$ Yes   3. $y - x = 5$; $(0, 5)$ Yes

4. $x = 5$; $(5, 0)$ Yes   5. $y = -2$; $(8, -2)$ Yes   6. $3y + 2x = 7$; $(\frac{1}{2}, 2)$ Yes

In Exercises 7–10, solve for y in terms of x. *(Pages 162–164)*

7. $y - 5x = 0$ 8. $x + 2y = 6$ 9. $-y + 2x - 1 = 0$ 10. $5x - y + 3 = 0$
   $y = 5x$ $y = -\frac{1}{2}x + 3$ $y = 2x - 1$ $y = 5x + 3$

In Exercises 11–15, give the slope and y intercept of each line. *(Pages 194–196)*

11. $y - 5 = 0$ $0; 5$ 12. $3x - 4y = 12$ $\frac{3}{4}; -3$ 13. $2y + x - 1 = 0$ $-\frac{1}{2}; \frac{1}{2}$ 14. $2x - 3y + 6 = 0$ $\frac{2}{3}; 2$

Inequalities   **253**

Additional Answers
Written Exercises
45. $y < -3$ <u>or</u> $y \geq 3$
47. $2 < n < 3$
49. $-5 > x \geq -8$
50. $y \geq 2$
51. $n < 7$

Review Capsule
This Review Capsule reviews the prior-taught skills used in Section 7-2. The reference is to the pages where the skills were taught.

7-2 Graphing Linear Inequalities

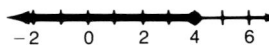
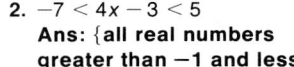
The graph of a linear equation separates the coordinate plane into three sets of points: the points in the two **half-planes** and the points on the line. Thus, every point on the coordinate plane is either in one of the half-planes or on the line.

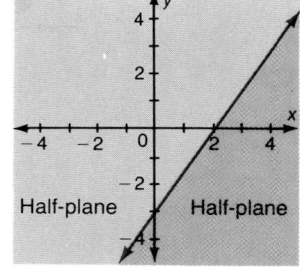

Half-plane   Half-plane

The equation of the line graphed at the right is $y = \frac{3}{2}x - 3$. Thus, the coordinates of every point in the plane make one of these sentences true.

$$y = \frac{3}{2}x - 3 \qquad y > \frac{3}{2}x - 3 \qquad y < \frac{3}{2}x - 3$$

The graph of an inequality that uses > or < *does not include* the graph of the related equation. To show this, the graph of the related equation is dashed.

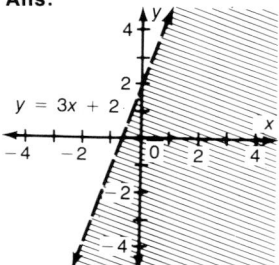
EXAMPLE 1   Graph $y > 2x - 1$.

Solution:

1. Draw the graph of $y = 2x - 1$ as a dashed line.
2. To identify the half-plane for which $y > 2x - 1$, test a point in each half-plane.

   Try $(0, 1)$.   Try $(3, 0)$.

   $1 > 2(0) - 1$? $0 > 2(3) - 1$?

   $1 > -1$? Yes ✔ $0 > 5$? No

3. Shade the half-plane containing $(0, 1)$.

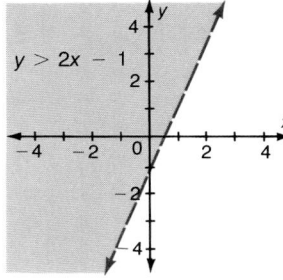

$y > 2x - 1$

Since the graph of $y > 2x - 1$ *does not include* the graph of the related equation, the graph is an **open half-plane.**

The graph of an inequality that uses ≥ or ≤ *includes* the graph of the related equation. To show this, the graph of the related equation is a solid line. This line is the **edge** or **boundary** of the half-plane.

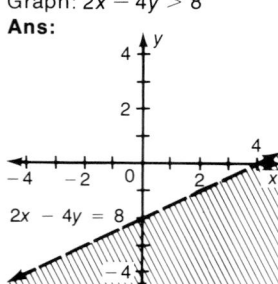
EXAMPLE 2   Graph $3x - 4y \leq 12$.

Solution:

1. Draw the graph of $3x - 4y = 12$ as a **solid** line.
2. To identify the half-plane for which $3x - 4y < 12$, test a point in each half-plane.

   Try $(0, 0)$.   Try $(3, -2)$.

   $3(0) - 4(0) < 12$? $3(3) - 4(-2) < 12$?

   $0 < 12$? Yes ✔ $9 + 8 < 12$? No

3. Shade the half-plane containing $(0, 0)$.

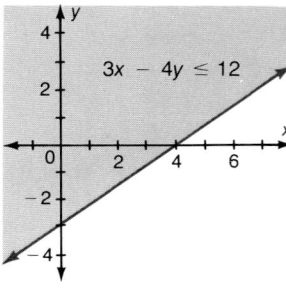

$3x - 4y \leq 12$

254   *Chapter 7*

Since the graph of $3x - 4y \le 12$ includes the edge or boundary of the half-plane, the graph is a **closed half-plane**.

CLASSROOM EXERCISES

Determine whether the given point belongs to the graph of the given inequality.

1. $y > x - 3$; $(0, 0)$ Yes

2. $y > 3x - 4$; $(2, 3)$ Yes

3. $x \ge 6$; $(-1, 5)$ No

4. $y \le 5$; $(0, -7)$ Yes

5. $y \le -\frac{1}{2}x + 1$; $(-4, 3)$ Yes

6. $3x - y \le 5$; $(0, -5)$ Yes

WRITTEN EXERCISES

A   Determine which of the given points, if any, belong to the graph of the given inequality.

1. $y < 3x - 2$; $(0, 0)$; $(-5, -7)$ none

2. $y \ge 3x - 2$; $(-1, -1)$; $(9, 0)$ $(-1, -1)$

3. $y > -2x + 1$; $(1, -6)$; $(-2, 1)$ none

4. $y \le -2x + 1$; $(2, -2)$; $(-2, 2)$ $(-2, 2)$

5. $x - y \le 2$; $(1, 0)$; $(0, 1)$ $(1, 0)$, $(0, 1)$

6. $x + y \ge 1$; $(1, 0)$; $(0, -1)$ $(1, 0)$

7. $y - x \le 0$; $(1, -1)$; $(0, 0)$ $(1, -1)$, $(0, 0)$

8. $y - x > 0$; $(0, 0)$; $(-4, -3)$ $(-4, -3)$

9. $2x - 3y \ge 6$; $(9, 2)$; $(-1, -7)$ $(9, 2)$, $(-1, -7)$

10. $2x + y - 4 < 0$; $(-8, 1)$; $(8, -1)$ $(-8, 1)$

See the Solution Key for the graphs of Ex. 11-38.

Graph each inequality in the coordinate plane.

11. $y > x - 3$ **12.** $y < x + 3$ **13.** $y > 3x - 4$ **14.** $y < 2x + 4$

15. $y > -3x$ **16.** $y < -4x$ **17.** $y < -2x - 4$ **18.** $y > -4x + 5$

19. $x + y > 4$ **20.** $x - y > 2$ **21.** $2x + 3y > 6$ **22.** $4x - y < 5$

23. $y > 0 \cdot x + 4$ **24.** $y < 0 \cdot x - 5$ **25.** $y < -4$ **26.** $y > -5$

27. $x < 8$ **28.** $x > -6$ **29.** $x < -4$ **30.** $x > 6$

31. $y \ge -4$ **32.** $y \ge 2x - 5$ **33.** $y \le 3x - 9$ **34.** $y \ge 2$

35. $y \le -5$ **36.** $x + y \ge 4$ **37.** $2x - y \le -6$ **38.** $3x + y < 5$

B   Write the inequality that defines the shaded portion of each plane.

39.
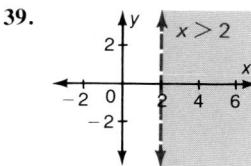

40.
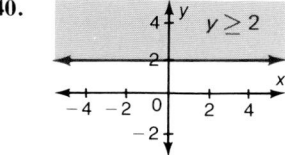

41.
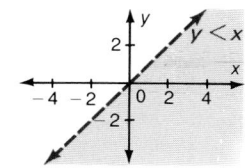

C   In Exercises 42–50, describe the graph of each inequality. Use one of the word descriptions below. In these exercises, $A \ne 0$, $B \ne 0$.

A straight line   *An open half-plane*   *A closed half-plane*

42. $Ax + By = C$ straight line   **43.** $Ax + By \le C$ **44.** $Ax + By < C$

45. $Ax + By \ge C$ **46.** $Ax + By > C$ open half-plane   **47.** $Ax = C$

48. $By = C$ straight line   **49.** $Ax \le C$ closed half-plane   **50.** $By > C$ open half-plane

Inequalities   **255**

Solve each system by graphing. Check your solutions. *(Pages 212–216)*

1. $\begin{cases} x = 4 \\ y = -1 \end{cases}$ $(4, -1)$ **2.** $\begin{cases} y = 2x \\ y = 3x - 3 \end{cases}$ $(3, 6)$ **3.** $\begin{cases} x + y = -4 \\ x - y = 6 \end{cases}$ $(1, -5)$ **4.** $\begin{cases} y + 2x + 6 = 0 \\ y - 2x = 0 \end{cases}$

$\left(-1\tfrac{1}{2}, -3\right)$

Determine whether the given point is a solution of the given system. Answer *Yes* or *No*. *(Pages 212–216)*

5. $\begin{cases} a + 2b = 1 \\ 3a + b = 8 \end{cases}$; $(3, -1)$
Yes

6. $\begin{cases} 3p + 5q = 9 \\ 9p + 2q = -12 \end{cases}$; $(-2, 3)$
Yes

7. $\begin{cases} -5s + 3v = 25 \\ 4s + 2v = 2 \end{cases}$; $(-2, -5)$
No

OBJECTIVE: To solve systems of linear inequalities by graphing

7–3 Systems of Inequalities

A system of linear inequalities in two variables is usually solved by graphing.

EXAMPLE 1 Solve by graphing: $\begin{cases} x + y > 10 \\ x - y > -4 \end{cases}$

Solution:

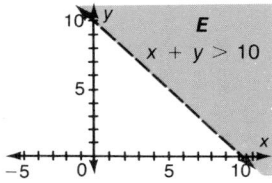

$\boxed{1}$ Graph $x + y > 10$. Any point in half-plane E is a solution of $x + y > 10$. Note that the graph of $x + y = 10$ is dashed to show that it is not included in the half-plane.

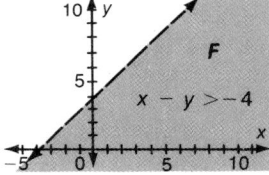

$\boxed{2}$ Graph $x - y > -4$. Any point in half-plane F is a solution of $x - y > -4$. Note that the points on the graph of $x - y = -4$ are not included in the half-plane.

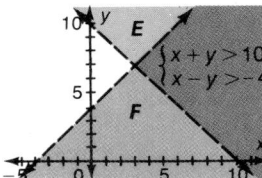

$\boxed{3}$ Any point in the intersection of the half-planes E and F (double shading) is a solution of $x + y > 10$ <u>and</u> $x - y > -4$.

Thus, **all points in the darkest region** (but no points on the lines) are solutions of the system.

Sometimes points on a line are included in the solutions of a system of linear inequalities. You indicate these points by showing all or part of the graph of the line as a solid line (see Example 2).

Teaching Suggestions p. M-20

Quick Quiz
Graph: $x + y \geq 2$
Ans:

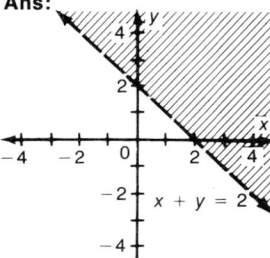

Additional Example
Example 1
Solve by graphing.
$\begin{cases} x + y < 4 \\ x - y < -2 \end{cases}$
Ans:

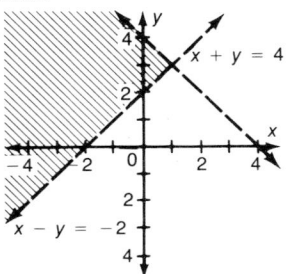

EXAMPLE 2 Solve by graphing: $\begin{cases} y \ge 2x - 4 \\ x + y \le 5 \end{cases}$

Solution:

[1] Graph $y \ge 2x - 4$.

Any point in half-plane E <u>or</u> on the line $y = 2x - 4$ (edge of half-plane E) is a solution of $y \ge 2x - 4$.

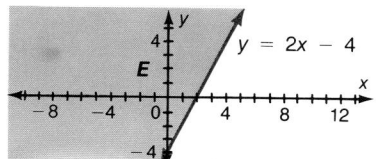

[2] Graph $x + y \le 5$.

Any point in half-plane F <u>or</u> on the line $x + y = 5$ (edge of half-plane F) is a solution of $x + y \le 5$.

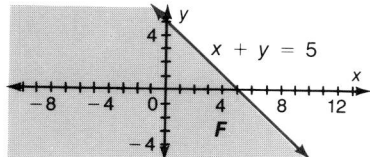

[3] Any point **in the intersection of half-planes E and F** (double-shading) and **any point on the lines that border the intersection** is a solution of $y \ge 2x - 4$ <u>and</u> $x + y \le 5$.

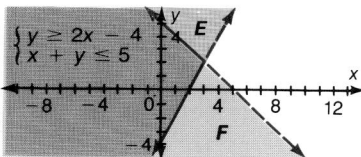

Additional Example
Example 2
Solve by graphing.
$\begin{cases} y \le 3x + 2 \\ x - y \ge 3 \end{cases}$
Ans:

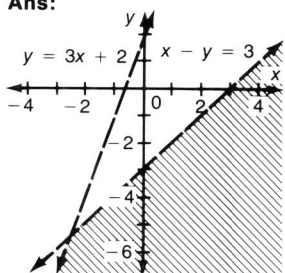

CLASSROOM EXERCISES

Match each graph in Exercises 1–4 with one of the systems given in a–d.

1.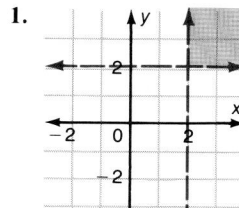

2.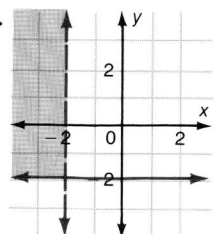

3.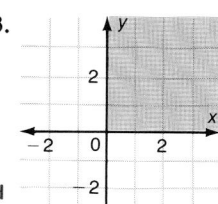

4.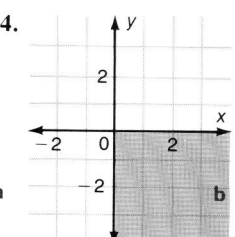

d   a   b

a. $\begin{cases} x \ge 0 \\ y \ge 0 \end{cases}$ **b.** $\begin{cases} x \ge 0 \\ y \le 0 \end{cases}$ **c.** $\begin{cases} x > 2 \\ y > 2 \end{cases}$ **d.** $\begin{cases} x < -2 \\ y \ge -2 \end{cases}$

WRITTEN EXERCISES See page 571 for Exercises 1 and 3.

A Solve each system by graphing.

ϕ

1. $\begin{cases} x + y \le 2 \\ x - y \le 4 \end{cases}$ **2.** $\begin{cases} y > 3x \\ y \le -3x \end{cases}$ **3.** $\begin{cases} x - y < 8 \\ x + y > 3 \end{cases}$ **4.** $\begin{cases} x + y > 10 \\ x + y < 4 \end{cases}$

Assignment Guide
Minimal Omit
Average
Day 1 pp. 257–258: 1–12
Day 2 p. 258: 13–20
Above Average
Day 1 pp. 257–258: 2–12 even, 13–16
Day 2 p. 258: 17–24

Additional Answers
Written Exercises

2.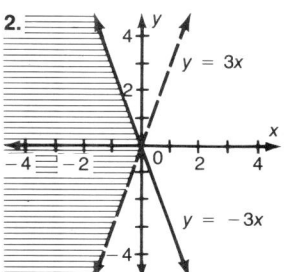

Inequalities   **257**

6.

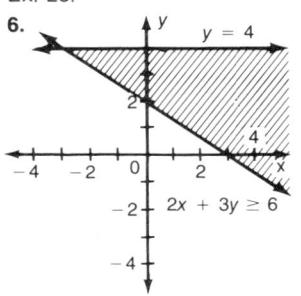

8.

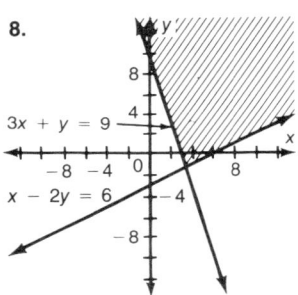

10.

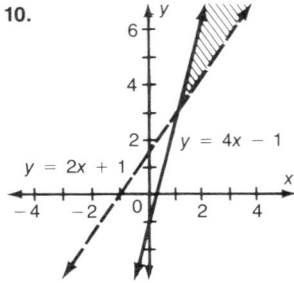

12.

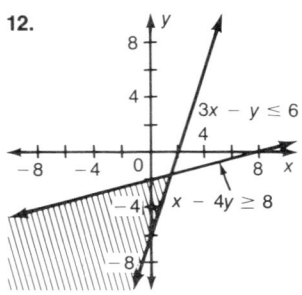

Solve by graphing.

5. $\begin{cases} y > 3x \\ y > 3x + 2 \end{cases}$

6. $\begin{cases} 2x + 3y \geq 6 \\ y \leq 4 \end{cases}$

7. $\begin{cases} x + 2y \geq 4 \\ 2x - y \leq -2 \end{cases}$

8. $\begin{cases} x - 2y \leq 6 \\ 3x + y \geq 9 \end{cases}$

9. $\begin{cases} 2x + y > -8 \\ y < -2 \end{cases}$

10. $\begin{cases} y \leq 4x - 1 \\ y > 2x + 1 \end{cases}$

11. $\begin{cases} y < x \\ y \geq 3 - x \end{cases}$

12. $\begin{cases} 3x - y \leq 6 \\ x - 4y \geq 8 \end{cases}$

B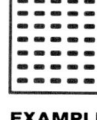

13. $y > -x$ <u>and</u> $y > \frac{1}{2}x - 4$

14. $\frac{1}{3}y - x \leq -9$ <u>and</u> $3x - 2y - 6 \geq 0$

15. $-2 < x < 2$ <u>and</u> $-2 < y < 2$

16. $0 \leq x \leq 6$ <u>and</u> $0 \leq y \leq 4$

17. $\begin{cases} y \geq x \\ y < 3 \\ x > 0 \end{cases}$

18. $\begin{cases} y < x + 1 \\ y - 2x > 1 \\ y \leq 1 \end{cases}$

19. $\begin{cases} x + y < 3 \\ x - y > 1 \\ 2x + y > -4 \end{cases}$

20. $\begin{cases} 2y > x + 2 \\ 2y + x < 6 \\ y > 0 \end{cases}$

C

21. $\begin{aligned} x &\geq 0 \\ x &\leq 2 \\ y &\geq 0 \\ y &\leq 2 \end{aligned}$

22. $\begin{aligned} x &\leq -2 \\ x &\geq -5 \\ y &\leq 6 \\ y &\geq 4 \end{aligned}$

23. $\begin{cases} y = x \\ x \leq 4 \\ y \geq 0 \end{cases}$

24. $\begin{cases} y - x > 0 \\ x > -1 \\ y < 5 \end{cases}$

CALCULATOR APPLICATIONS

Graphing Systems of Inequalities

A calculator can help you to find the region containing the points that are solutions of a system of inequalities.

EXAMPLE The graph at the right shows the linear equations $y = 4x + 2$ and $y = \frac{1}{3}x$. Find the region that contains the solution of the following system.

$$\begin{cases} y > 4x + 2 & \quad 1 \\ y < \frac{1}{3}x & \quad 2 \end{cases}$$

SOLUTION Choose a point in each region. Substitute in each inequality to test whether the point satisfies both inequalities.

Region **A**: $(-2, 2)$ 1 4 [×] 2 [+/−] [+] 2 [=]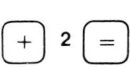

Test: Is $y > 4x + 2$? $2 > -6$?   Yes ✔

2 1 [÷] 3 [×] 2 [+/−] [=]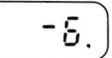

Test: Is $y < \frac{1}{3}x$? $2 < -0.\overline{6}$?   No

Thus, the point in region **A** does not satisfy the system.

Repeat the procedure for points in regions **B, C,** and **D. Region C** contains the solution of the system.

EXERCISES   See the answers to the Classroom Exercises on page 255.

Use a calculator to check your answers to the Classroom Exercises on page 255.

258   *Chapter 7*

Problem Solving and Applications

OBJECTIVE: To solve problems containing constraints, using linear programming methods

7-4 Linear Programming

Linear programming is a method of solving problems that contain restrictions, called **constraints**, which are often expressed as linear inequalities.

EXAMPLE

A small company has five 3-ton trucks and four 5-ton trucks for hauling gravel. Only 7 crews are available at any one time to operate the trucks. How many of each kind of truck should be used to haul the maximum amount of gravel per trip?

Solution:

$\boxed{1}$ Use two variables to represent the unknowns.

Let $x =$ the number of 3-ton trucks used.
Let $y =$ the number of 5-ton trucks used.
Then the number of tons of gravel hauled per trip is $3x + 5y$.

$\boxed{2}$ Write a system of inequalities to represent the constraints.

$$\begin{cases} x \leq 5 \\ y \leq 4 \\ x + y \leq 7 \\ x \geq 0 \\ y \geq 0 \end{cases}$$

- ⟵ **Only five 3-ton trucks are available.**
- ⟵ **Only four 5-ton trucks are available.**
- ⟵ **Only 7 crews are available.**
- ⟵ **A negative number of trucks is not possible.**

$\boxed{3}$ Graph these inequalities on the same coordinate axes. The intersection of the solution sets forms the shaded region (called a **polygonal region**) shown in the graph. *Any point in the region satisfies the system of inequalities.*

$\boxed{4}$ To find how many of each kind of truck are needed to haul the maximum amount of gravel per load means to find the ordered pair (x, y) for which $3x + 5y$ is a *maximum*.

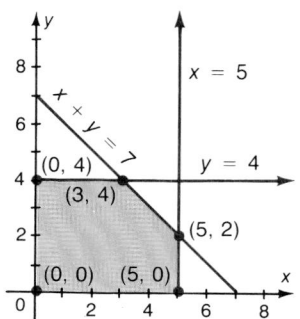

It has been proved that a maximum or minimum always occurs at one of the vertices or corners of the polygon. In this case, there are 5 vertices.

Check the ordered pair for each vertex in $k = 3x + 5y$.

Vertex	$k = 3x + 5y$	Value of k
$(0, 0)$	$k = 3 \cdot 0 + 5 \cdot 0$	0
$(5, 0)$	$k = 3 \cdot 5 + 5 \cdot 0$	15
$(5, 2)$	$k = 3 \cdot 5 + 5 \cdot 2$	25
$(3, 4)$	$k = 3 \cdot 3 + 5 \cdot 4$	29 ⟵ **Maximum value**
$(0, 4)$	$k = 3 \cdot 0 + 5 \cdot 4$	20

Thus, **three 3-ton trucks** and **four 5-ton trucks** are needed.

Inequalities   **259**

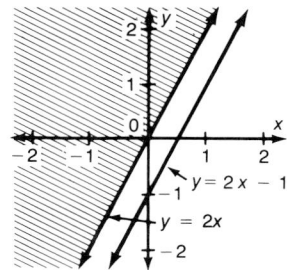

Of course, common sense would give you the answer to the Example without the use of linear programming techniques. The techniques are shown when the answer is obvious to help you understand how to apply them when the answer is not so obvious.

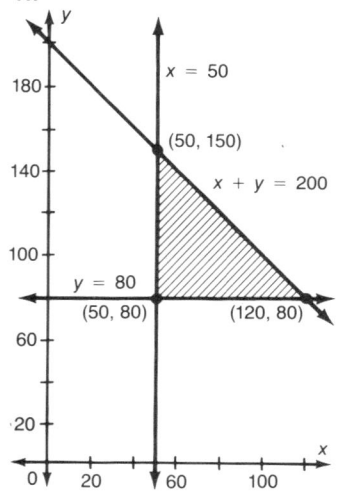
CLASSROOM EXERCISES

In Exercises 1–4, the vertices of a polygonal region are given. For each exercise, find the maximum and minimum values of k over the given region.

1. (0, 0); (0, 5); (6, 0); $k = 4x + y$
2. (0, 0); (0, 6); (4, 8); (2, 0); $k = 4x + y$
3. (1, −1); (0, 2); (3, 0); $y = 2x + 3k$
4. (1, 1); (0, 4); (4, 5); (3, 0); $y = -x + k$

WRITTEN EXERCISES

A In Exercises 1–4, find the maximum and minimum values for k, given the constraints shown in the graph.

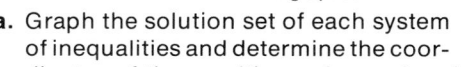

1. $k = x + 2y$ 40; 0
2. $k = 3x + 5y$ 100; 0
3. $k = 2x + 3y$ 60; 0
4. $k = 50x + 10y$ 800; 0

In Exercises 5–8:   See the Solution Key for the graphs.

a. Graph the solution set of each system of inequalities and determine the coordinates of the resulting polygonal region.

b. Find the minimum value of $k = 2x + y$ over the region graphed.

5. $\begin{cases} x \ge 0 \\ y \ge 0 \\ x + y \le 4 \end{cases}$

6. $\begin{cases} y \le 5 - \frac{1}{2}x \\ x \ge 0 \\ x \le 7 \\ y \ge 0 \end{cases}$

7. $\begin{cases} y \le 5 - x \\ x \le 4 \\ x \ge 0 \\ y \ge 0 \end{cases}$

8. $\begin{cases} y \ge 2 - \frac{1}{2}x \\ y \ge 1 \\ x \ge 0 \end{cases}$

WORD PROBLEMS

A manufacturer makes two models of a bicycle. The profit on Model A is $15 per bicycle and the profit on Model B is $18 per bicycle. Because of a labor shortage, the manufacturer can produce no more than 200 bicycles per week. To meet the market demand, at least 50 Model A bicycles and 80 Model B bicycles must be available each week.

Use this information in Exercises 9–13.

9. Let x represent the number of Model A bicycles and let y represent the number of Model B bicycles produced per week. Write an expression to represent the total weekly profit. $15x + 18y$

10. Write a system of inequalities that shows the constraints on x and y.

11. Graph the system of inequalities you wrote in Exercise 10.

260   *Chapter 7*

(50, 80)(50, 150), (120, 80)

12. State the coordinates of vertices of the polygonal region graphed in Exercise 11.

13. What is the maximum profit possible? $3450

> The manager of a small toy shop decides to make up two types of variety packages in order to sell off 12 whistles and 32 small cars left in the shop. Each type A package contains 2 whistles and 8 small cars and sells for $6.50. Each type B package contains 3 whistles and 5 small cars and sells for $5.75.
>
> Use this information in Exercises 14–18.

14. Let x represent the number of type A packages and let y represent the number of type B packages. Write an expression to represent the store's income from the sale of these packages. $6.50x + 5.75y$

15. Write a system of linear equations to show the constraints on x and y. $\begin{cases} x + y \leq 4 \\ x \geq 0 \\ y \geq 0 \end{cases}$

16. Graph the system of inequalities from Exercise 15.

17. State the coordinates of the vertices (corners) of the region graphed in Exercise 16.

18. What is the store's maximum possible income from the sale of the packages? $26

——— Review ———————————

See the Solution Key for the graphs of Exercises 1-11.

Solve and graph each inequality on a number line. *(Section 7–1)*

1. $2n \geq 6$ $n \geq 3$
2. $-9 < 3x < 6$ $-3 < x < 2$
3. $2(y - 3) \geq -10$ $y \geq -2$

Graph each inequality on the coordinate plane. *(Section 7–2)*

4. $3x \geq 6$
5. $x - y > 4$
6. $y > 2x + 5$
7. $4x - 2y < 6$

Solve each system by graphing. *(Section 7–3)*

8. $\begin{cases} x + y > 3 \\ x - y > -5 \end{cases}$
9. $\begin{cases} y \leq 2x \\ y \geq -x + 2 \end{cases}$
10. $\begin{cases} 2x - y < 1 \\ 3x + y > 4 \end{cases}$
11. $\begin{cases} y - 3x > 1 \\ y < -1 \\ x > -4 \end{cases}$

> Pamela makes and sells small woolen rugs. Plain rugs sell for $25 and take two hours to make. The fancier rugs take three hours to make and sell for $36 each. This week, Pamela plans to make a maximum of 10 rugs and to spend a maximum of 24 hours working on them. Use this information for Exercises 12–15. *(Section 7–4)*

12. Let x represent the number of plain rugs, and let y represent the number of fancier rugs. Write an expression to represent the total amount of money Pam will make on these rugs. $25x + 36y$

13. Write a system of inequalities that shows the constraints on x and y.

14. Graph the system of inequalities you wrote in Exercise 13. See the Solution Key.

15. How many of each type of rug should Pamela make in order to make the maximum amount of money?   6 plain, 4 fancy

Inequalities   **261**

Automobile Maintenance

This lesson is optional. It applies the algebraic skills of reading a table, finding a per cent of a number, and solving a linear equation to the consumer area of automobile maintenance.

The radiator of an automobile uses water, which has a **boiling point of 212°F**, or **100°C**, and a **freezing point of 32°F**, or **0°C**. Since this is not a wide enough temperature range, a solution is added to the water. This solution is referred to as **coolant** because it raises the boiling temperature of the water, or as **antifreeze** because it lowers the freezing temperature of the water.

The table below shows the changes in boiling point with different amounts of coolant.

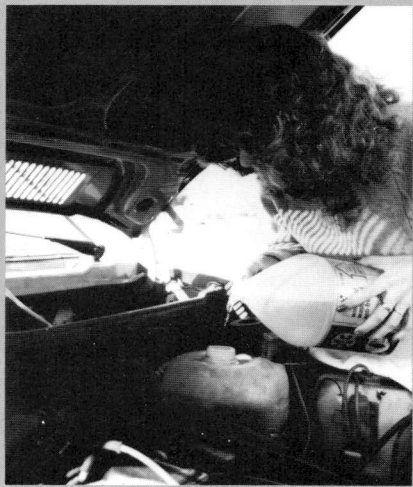

Per Cent of Coolant	Boiling Point
50%	265°F
60%	270°F
70%	275°F

EXAMPLE 1   A car radiator holds 15 quarts. How many quarts of coolant must be mixed with the water to raise the boiling point to 270°F?

Solution: Find 270°F in the table. Read the entry at the left: 60%

Find 60% of 15.   60% of $15 = 0.60 \times 15 = 9$

Amount of coolant needed: **9 quarts with 6 quarts of water.**

The opposite effect happens to the freezing temperatures when antifreeze is mixed with water in the radiator.

EXAMPLE 2   A solution of water and antifreeze (Solution A) has a freezing point of 17°C higher than the freezing point of a stronger solution (Solution B). The freezing point of Solution B is 22°C lower than one half the freezing point of Solution A. Find the freezing point of both solutions.

Solution: Let f equal the freezing point of Solution A. Then $\frac{1}{2}f - 22$ equals the freezing point of Solution B.

$f = (\frac{1}{2}f - 22) + 17$ ⟵ **A's freezing point is 17°C higher than B's.**

$f = \frac{1}{2}f - 5$

$\frac{1}{2}f = -5$

$f = -10$ $\frac{1}{2}f - 22 = -27$

Freezing point of Solution A: **−10°C**   Freezing point of Solution B: **−27°C**

EXERCISES

In Exercises 1–4, find the number of quarts of coolant needed to raise the boiling point of the water in a car radiator with the given capacity to 265°F.

1. 10 quarts   **2.** 18 quarts   **3.** 20 quarts   **4.** 14 quarts

In Exercises 5–8, find the number of quarts of coolant needed to raise the boiling point of the water in a car radiator with the given capacity to 270°F.

5. 19 quarts   **6.** 12 quarts   **7.** 13 quarts   **8.** 16 quarts

In Exercises 9–12, find the number of quarts of coolant needed to raise the boiling point of the water in a car radiator with the given capacity to 275°F.

9. 15 quarts   **10.** 14 quarts   **11.** 18 quarts   **12.** 20 quarts

13. A 15-quart radiator contains 10.5 quarts of coolant and 4.5 quarts of water. What is the boiling point?

14. A 20-quart radiator contains 12 quarts of coolant and 8 quarts of water. What is the boiling point?

15. A solution of water and antifreeze (Solution C) freezes at a point 10°F lower than a weaker solution (Solution D). The freezing point of Solution C is 4°F lower than four times Solution D's freezing point. Find the freezing points of both solutions.

16. A solution of water and antifreeze (Solution Y) freezes at a point 8°C higher than a stronger solution (Solution Z). The freezing point of Solution Z is 5°C higher than three times one half of Solution Y's freezing point. Find the two freezing points.

17. A solution of water and antifreeze (Solution A) freezes at a point 12°C lower than a weaker solution (Solution B). The freezing point of Solution B is 2°C higher than one half the freezing point of Solution A. Find the two freezing points.

18. A solution of water and antifreeze (Solution W) freezes at a point 8°F higher than a stronger solution (Solution X). The freezing point of Solution X is 12°F lower than twice the freezing point of Solution W. Find the two freezing points.

Automobile Maintenance   263

REVIEW CAPSULE FOR SECTION 7–5 ——

Evaluate. *(Pages 47–50)*

1. $|6|$ 6
2. $|-3|$ 3
3. $|0|$ 0
4. $-|7|$ −7
5. $-|-10|$ −10
6. $-|9 - (-2)|$ −11
7. $|5 - 6|$ 1
8. $|5| - |7|$ −2
9. $|-6| + |3|$ 9
10. $-|\frac{1}{2}| - |-\frac{1}{2}|$ −1

Solve and check. *(Pages 47–50)*

11. $|x| = 5$
12. $y = |-4|$
13. $n = -|-5.7|$
14. $|n| = |-2|$
15. $r + |-5| = 6$

7–5 Solving Absolute Value Equations

OBJECTIVE: To solve equations involving absolute value

Sentences involving absolute value can also be written as compound sentences. Consider an equation such as $|x| = 3$.

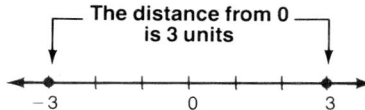

The distance from 0 is 3 units

$|x| = 3$ means $x = 3$ or $x = -3$.

Thus, to solve an equation involving absolute value, write it as two simpler equations with the connective or. Then solve these equations.

EXAMPLE 1 Solve: $|2x + 6| = 14$

Solution: $|2x + 6| = 14$ means $2x + 6 = 14$ or $2x + 6 = -14$

$2x = 8$ $2x = -20$

$x = 4$ or $x = -10$

Check: $|2x + 6| = 14$ ← Replace x with 4. $|2x + 6| = 14$ ← Replace x with −10.

$|2(4) + 6| \overset{?}{=} 14$ $|2(-10) + 6| \overset{?}{=} 14$

$14 \overset{?}{=} 14$ Yes ✔ $14 \overset{?}{=} 14$ Yes ✔

Solution set: {−10, 4}

Combine like terms *within* the absolute value symbols as a first step in solving equations involving absolute value.

EXAMPLE 2 Solve: $|2k + k| - 12 = 5$

Solution: $|2k + k| - 12 = 5$ ← **Combine like terms.**

$|3k| - 12 = 5$ ← **Add 12 to each side.**

$|3k| = 17$ ← **Write with "or."**

$|3k| = 17$ means $3k = 17$ or $3k = -17$

$k = \frac{17}{3}$ or $k = -\frac{17}{3}$ ← **The check is left for you.**

Solution set: $\left\{-\frac{17}{3}, \frac{17}{3}\right\}$

264 *Chapter 7*

CLASSROOM EXERCISES

Solve and check.

1. $|x + 5| = 10$ $x = -6 \text{ or } x = 16$
2. $|x - 5| = 11$
3. $|2t| = 4$ $t = -2 \text{ or } t = 2$
4. $|6r| = 18$ $r = -3 \text{ or } r = 3$
5. $|5n - n| + 1 = 9$
6. $|-3t + 7t| - 1 = 15$
7. $|5y - 10| = -0$
8. $|1 + h| = 0$
9. $|1 - 4q| = 12$
10. $|7 - r| = 3$
11. $|2k - 9| = 1$
12. $|2p - 10| = 6$

$q = -2\frac{3}{4} \text{ or } q = 3\frac{1}{4}$ $r = 4 \text{ or } r = 10$ $k = 4 \text{ or } k = 5$ $p = 2 \text{ or } p = 8$

WRITTEN EXERCISES

A   Solve and check each equation.

1. $|a + 3| = 2$
2. $\frac{1}{2}|k| = 6$ $k = -12 \text{ or } k = 12$
3. $|5y| = 10$ $y = -2 \text{ or } y = 2$
4. $|-2v| = 2$ $v = -1 \text{ or } v = 1$
5. $|3k - 6| = 2$
6. $|2y + 6| = 0$ $y = -3$
7. $12 = |3 - x|$
8. $|\frac{5}{6} + y| = \frac{2}{3}$
9. $|\frac{1}{5}(2 - k)| = 3$
10. $|y + y + y| = \frac{1}{3}$
11. $|t + 1| = 9$
12. $|7x - 5| = \frac{1}{2}$
13. $|\frac{1}{4}(5t - 2)| = 6$
14. $|3d - 2| = \frac{1}{2}$ $d = \frac{1}{2} \text{ or } d = \frac{5}{6}$
15. $|4k + 6 + 2k| = 5$
16. $|15| = |w + 2|$
17. $|\frac{2}{3}y| = \frac{1}{12}$ $y = -\frac{1}{8} \text{ or } y = \frac{1}{8}$
18. $|n| + 6 = 2$ ϕ
19. $|3m + 6| = 4$
20. $|-3m| = 14$
21. $6 - 2 = |x| + 3$
22. $|\frac{1}{2}w + \frac{1}{2}w| = 1$ $w = -1 \text{ or } w = 1$
23. $|2w + w| - 2 = 8$
24. $|6r + 2| + 6 = 9$

B $y = -\frac{2}{3} \text{ or } y = 2$ $w = -3\frac{1}{3} \text{ or } w = 3\frac{1}{3}$

25. $|3y - 2| - 4 = 0$
26. $|\frac{1}{4}x + 6| - 2 = 3$
27. $\left|\frac{k - 1}{3}\right| = 7$

28. $\left|\frac{3 - n}{5}\right| = 9$ $h = -42 \text{ or } h = 48$
29. $|3(t - 1) - 4| = 5$ $x = -44 \text{ or } x = -4$ $t = \frac{2}{3} \text{ or } t = 4$
30. $|8 - 2(y - 1)| = 6$ $y = 2 \text{ or } y = 8$

C   Solve and graph each inequality. See the Solution Key for the graphs of Ex. 31–38.

31. $|x| \geq 5$
32. $|x| \leq 5$
33. $|n - 2| < 3$
34. $|y + 4| > 6$
35. $|2x - 1| \leq 9$
36. $|3y - 2| \geq 8$
37. $|2(n - 3)| \leq 4$
38. $|3(2 - k)| < 2$

REVIEW CAPSULE FOR SECTION 7-6

In Exercises 1–5, write the equation of the line described in words. (Pages 181–184, 194–196)

1. A line parallel to the y axis and 5 units to its left $x = -5$
2. The y axis $x = 0$
3. A line with slope equal to -3 and y intercept at the origin $y = -3x$
4. A line parallel to the x axis and 5 units above it $y = 5$
5. A line with slope equal to $\frac{1}{2}$ and y intercept of 2 $y = \frac{1}{2}x + 2$

Complete the table of ordered pairs for each equation. (Pages 181–184)

6. $y = -5x$

x	−3	−1	0	1	3
y	?	?	?	?	?

15   5   0   −5   −15

7. $x + y = 4$

x	−3	−1	0	1	3
y	?	?	?	?	?

7   5   4   3   1

Inequalities   **265**

7-6 Graphing Absolute Value Relations

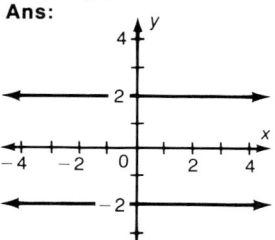
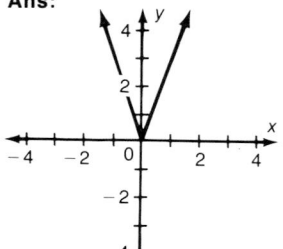
On a number line, the graph of $|x| = 3$ consists of two points whose coordinates are 3 and −3.

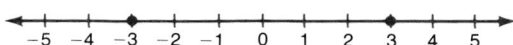

On the coordinate plane, however, the graph of $|x| = 3$ consists of two parallel lines.

EXAMPLE 1 Graph $|x| = 3$ on the coordinate plane.

Solution: ☐1 Write the equation with "or."
$|x| = 3$ means $x = 3$ or $x = -3$.

☐2 Draw the graphs of $x = 3$ and $x = -3$ on the coordinate plane.

The graph consists of two parallel lines, one three units to the right of the y axis, and the other three units to its left.

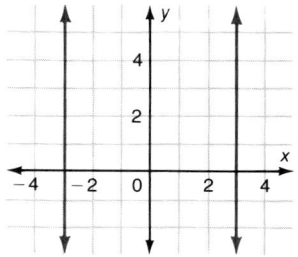

To graph absolute value relations on the coordinate plane, make a table using both positive and negative values of x.

EXAMPLE 2 Graph $y = |x|$.

Solution: ☐1 Make a table.

x	−5	−3	−1	0	1	3	5
y	5	3	1	0	1	3	5

☐2 Graph the points in the coordinate plane. Join the points.

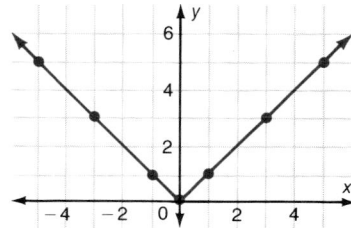

The graph consists of two rays with their initial point at the origin.

266   *Chapter 7*

CLASSROOM EXERCISES

Complete each table.

1. $y = |2x|$

x	-2	-1	0	1	2
y	?	?	?	?	?
	4	2	0	2	4

2. $y = -|x|$

x	-2	-1	0	1	2
y	?	?	?	?	?
	-2	-1	0	-1	-2

3. $y = |x| - 2$

x	-3	-2	-1	0	1	2
y	?	?	?	?	?	?
	1	0	-1	-2	-1	0

WRITTEN EXERCISES   See the Solution Key for the graphs of Ex. 1-28, 30, 32, 34.

 Graph each equation on the coordinate plane.

1. $|x| = 2$ **2.** $|x| = 5$ **3.** $|y| = 3$ **4.** $|y| = 1$

5. $y = |2x|$ **6.** $y = |5x|$ **7.** $y = -|x|$ **8.** $y = -|2x|$

9. $y = |x| - 4$ **10.** $y = |2x| - 5$ **11.** $y = |-3x| + 7$ **12.** $x = |2y| - 4$

13. $x = |y|$ **14.** $x = |-2y|$ **15.** $x = -|2y| - 6$ **16.** $x = |-4y| + 3$

17. $x = -|3y|$ **18.** $x + |y| = 4$ **19.** $x - |y| = 6$ **20.** $y + |x| = 10$

B

Example: Graph $|x| + |y| = 5$.

Solution: Solve for $|y|$. ⟶ $|y| = 5 - |x|$

x	-5	-4	-3	-2	-1	0	1	2
y	0	± 1	± 2	?	?	?	?	?

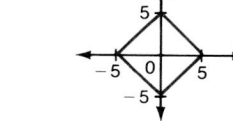

21. $|x| - |y| = 5$ **22.** $|y| = |x| + 5$ **23.** $|x| = |y|$ **24.** $|x + 2| = 5$

25. $|y - 4| = 1$ **26.** $|x| = -|y|$ **27.** $|y| = -|x|$ **28.** $|y - 1| = 4$

C Graph each inequality in the coordinate plane.   See page 573 for the graphs of Ex. 29, 31, 33, 35.

29. $|x| \leq 1$ **30.** $|x| \geq 4$ **31.** $|y| \geq 4$ **32.** $y \geq |x|$

33. $y \leq |x|$ **34.** $y \geq |x - 3|$ **35.** $y \leq |x + 3|$ **36.** $|y| \leq |x| + 3$

——— Review ———

Solve and check each equation. *(Section 7-5)* $m = -\frac{1}{3}$ or $m = \frac{1}{3}$

1. $|x + 2| = 5$ $x = -7$ or $x = 3$ **2.** $|\frac{1}{4}y| = 3$ $y = -12$ or $y = 12$ **3.** $|-3m| = 1$

4. $|q + 3q| = 8$ $q = -2$ or $q = 2$ **5.** $|2s - 3 + s| = 0$ $s = 1$ **6.** $|2n - 4\frac{1}{2}| = \frac{1}{2}$

7. $|3z| - 6 = -3$ $z = -1$ or $z = 1$ **8.** $|4(w + 1) - 3| = 5$ **9.** $|3(t - 1) + t| = 4$

$w = -1\frac{1}{2}$ or $w = 1$ $t = -\frac{1}{4}$ or $t = 1\frac{3}{4}$

Graph each equation on the coordinate plane. *(Section 7-6)*

10. $|x| = 4$ **11.** $y = |-3x|$ **12.** $y = -|3x|$

13. $y = |-x| + 5$ **14.** $|y| = 2|x|$ **15.** $|y - 3| = 1$

Inequalities   **267**

Assignment Guide
Minimal Omit
Average Omit
Above Average p. 267:
1–19 odd, 21, 25, 29, 33, 35

Quiz Sections 7-5–7-6
After completing this Review you may want to administer a quiz covering the same sections. See page M-49 of the Teacher's Manual for the suggested quiz.

Additional Answers
Review
6. $n = 2$ or $n = 2\frac{1}{2}$
See the Solution Key for the graphs of Ex. 10–15.

BASIC: SOLVING ABSOLUTE VALUE EQUATIONS

Problem: *Write a program which solves equations of the form $|Ax + B| = C$. Include the possibilities that the solution set may be all real numbers or may be the empty set.*

```
100 PRINT "FOR THE EQUATION !AX + B! = C,"
110 PRINT "WHAT ARE A, B, AND C";
120 INPUT A, B, C
130 IF C < 0 THEN 250
140 IF C = 0 THEN 200
150 IF A = 0 THEN 230
160 LET X1 = (C - B)/A
170 LET X2 = (-C - B)/A
180 PRINT "SOLUTIONS ARE ";X1;" AND ";X2
190 GOTO 280
200 LET X = -B/A
210 PRINT "SOLUTION IS ";X
220 GOTO 280
230 IF B = C THEN 270
240 IF B = -C THEN 270
250 PRINT "NO SOLUTION"
260 GOTO 280
270 PRINT "ALL REAL NUMBERS ARE SOLUTIONS."
280 PRINT
290 PRINT "ANY MORE EQUATIONS TO SOLVE (1=YES, 0=NO)";
300 INPUT Z
310 IF Z = 1 THEN 120
320 END
```

The following is the output from a sample run of the program above.

Output:
```
RUN
FOR THE EQUATION !AX + B! = C,
WHAT ARE A, B, AND C? -3,9,15
SOLUTIONS ARE -2   AND   8

ANY MORE EQUATIONS TO SOLVE (1=YES, 0=NO)? 1
? 2,8,0
SOLUTION IS -4

ANY MORE EQUATIONS TO SOLVE (1=YES, 0=NO)? 1
?0,6,8
NO SOLUTION
```

268   *Computer Applications*

This lesson is optional. Each computer applications lesson relates directly to a topic covered within the given chapter. (See Section 7-5, pages 264–265)

```
ANY MORE EQUATIONS TO SOLVE (1=YES, 0=NO)? 1
? 0,-8,8
ALL REAL NUMBERS ARE SOLUTIONS.

ANY MORE EQUATIONS TO SOLVE (1=YES, 0=NO)? 0
READY
```

Analysis

Statements 130, 250: An absolute value expression cannot equal a negative number. Thus if $C < 0$, there is no solution.

Statements 140, 200–210: If $C = 0$, the equation has only one solution.

Statements 150, 230–250: If $A = 0$, the formulas in statements 160 and 170 cannot be used. Instead, if $|B| = C$, any real number is a solution. But if $|B| \neq C$, no real number is a solution.

Statements 160–180: If the computer reaches statement 160, then $C > 0$ and $A \neq 0$. The equation has two solutions, as the following steps show.

$$|Ax + B| = C$$

$Ax + B = C$ <u>or</u> $Ax + B = -C$

$Ax = C - B$ <u>or</u> $Ax = -C - B$ ◄— **Subtract *B* from both sides.**

$x = \dfrac{C - B}{A}$ <u>or</u> $x = \dfrac{-C - B}{A}$ ◄— **Divide both sides by *A*.**

EXERCISES

A

Write each equation in the form $|Ax + B| = C$. Then use the program on page 268 to solve the equation.

1. $|x - 1| = 5$
2. $|x + 3| - 7 = 0$
3. $|2x| = 24$
4. $35 = |4x - 1|$
5. $|4 - x| = 44$
6. $|15 + 5x| = 55$
7. $0 = |6 - 2x|$
8. $100 = |-5x|$
9. $|4x + 2| + 8 = 0$
10. $|10 + 8x| = 0$
11. $0 = |80 - 10x| - 8$
12. $9 = |3x - 1| + 9$

Write a BASIC program for each problem.

13. Given the coordinates of a point, decide whether the point is in the solution set of the following system of inequalities.

$$\begin{cases} x \leq 0 \\ 2x + y \geq 6 \\ 4x + y < 3 \end{cases}$$

B

14. Solve inequalities of the form $|Ax + B| < C$.
15. Solve inequalities of the form $|Ax + B| > C$.

Solving Absolute Value Equations   **269**

Chapter Summary

IMPORTANT TERMS

Boundary of a half-plane (p. 254)
Closed half-plane (p. 255)
Compound sentence (p. 250)
Conjunction (p. 250)
Constraints (p. 259)
Disjunction (p. 250)
Edge of a half-plane (p. 254)

Half-plane (p. 254)
Intersection of two sets (p. 250)
Linear programming (p. 259)
Open half-plane (p. 254)
Polygonal region (p. 259)
Union of two sets (p. 250)

IMPORTANT IDEAS

1. The compound sentence $x \leq a$ means $x = a$ <u>or</u> $x < a$. The solution set is the union of the solution sets of $x = a$ and $x < a$. Similarly, the compound sentence $x \geq b$ means $x = b$ <u>or</u> $x > b$. The solution set is the union of the solution sets of $x = b$ and $x > b$.

2. The compound sentence $a < x < b$ means $a < x$ <u>and</u> $x < b$. The solution set is the intersection of the solution sets of $a < x$ and $x < b$.

3. The graph of a linear equation separates the coordinate plane into three sets of points—the points in the two half-planes and the points on the line.

4. The maximum or minimum value, if any, of a linear expression evaluated over a polygonal region occurs at one of the vertices of the polygon.

5. A sentence involving absolute value can be written as a compound sentence. For example, $|y| = 8$ means $y = 8$ <u>or</u> $y = -8$.

Chapter Objectives and Review

Objective: *To solve linear inequalities and graph them on a number line (Section 7–1)*

Write each compound sentence as two simple sentences joined by <u>or</u> or <u>and</u>.

1. $5x \geq -10$
2. $b + 3 \leq 0$
3. $-5 < y < 0$
4. $-12 < 3z < -3$
5. $6s - 8 \geq 4$
6. $-1 < \frac{1}{4}f + 1 < 3$

Solve and graph each inequality.

7. $-2 < c < 5$
8. $-4h \geq 0$
9. $-3 < m - 2 \leq 3$
10. $x + 4 \leq -1$
11. $-7 \leq 2y + 3 \leq -5$
12. $3(2 - d) \leq 9$

Objective: *To graph linear inequalities on the coordinate plane (Section 7–2)*

Graph each inequality on the coordinate plane. See the Solution Key.

13. $y > -4x$
14. $y \leq x - 1$
15. $x + y < -2$
16. $-x + y \geq 5$
17. $y \leq 0$
18. $x < -1$
19. $y \geq -2x - 3$
20. $3x + 2y > 6$

270   *Chapter 7*

Objective: *To solve systems of linear inequalities by graphing (Section 7-3)*

Match each graph in Exercises 21-24 with one of the systems given in a-d.

21.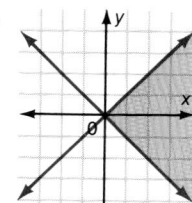
d

22.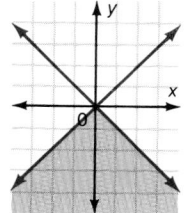
a

23.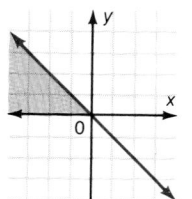
b

24.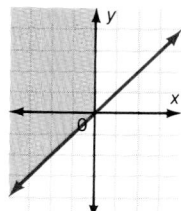
c

a. $\begin{cases} y \le x \\ y \le -x \end{cases}$

b. $\begin{cases} y \le -x \\ y \ge 0 \end{cases}$

c. $\begin{cases} x \le 0 \\ y \ge x \end{cases}$

d. $\begin{cases} y \le x \\ y \ge -x \end{cases}$

Solve each system by graphing.

25. $\begin{cases} y < x + 3 \\ y < -5x \end{cases}$
See page 573.

26. $\begin{cases} y \ge 2x \\ y \ge x - 1 \end{cases}$

27. $\begin{cases} 3x - y > -2 \\ x + 2y < 4 \end{cases}$
See page 573.

28. $\begin{cases} x + y \ge 2 \\ x - y \le 6 \\ y \le 0 \end{cases}$

Objective: *To solve problems containing constraints, using linear programming methods (Section 7-4)*

In Exercises 29-34, find the maximum and minimum values for k, given the constraints shown in the graph.

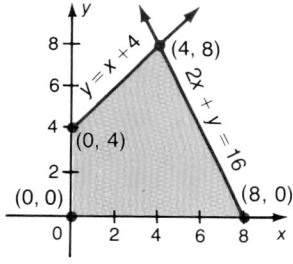

29. $k = x + y$

30. $k = 3x + y$

31. $k = x + 4y$

32. $k = 2x - y$

33. $k = 3x - 2y$

34. $k = x - 3y$

Each of three old machines can stamp out 4 parts per minute. Each of four newer machines can stamp out 6 parts per minute. Only 5 workers are available at any one time to operate the machines.

Use this information in Exercises 35-39.

35. Let x represent the number of old machines used and let y represent the number of newer machines used. Write an expression to represent the total number of parts made per minute. $4x + 6y$

36. Write a system of inequalities that shows the constraints on x and y.

37. Graph the system of inequalities you wrote in Exercise 36.

38. Write the coordinates of the vertices of the polygonal region graphed in Exercise 37.   (0,0), (3, 0), (3, 2), (1, 4), (0, 4)

39. What is the maximum number of parts that can be made per minute?   28

Inequalities **271**

 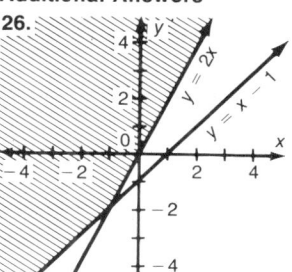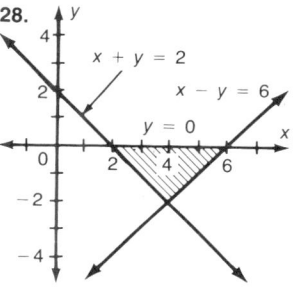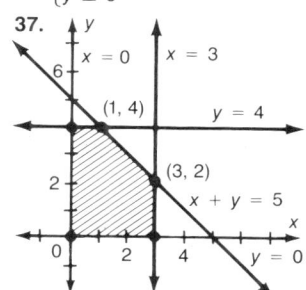

Objective: *To solve equations involving absolute value (Section 7-5)*

Solve and check each equation.

40. $|y - 1| = 7$ $y = -6$ or $y = 8$
41. $|4x| - 3 = 1$ $x = -1$ or $x = 1$
42. $\left|-\frac{1}{2}n\right| = 3$ $n = -6$ or $n = 6$
43. $12 = |p| + 4$ $p = -8$ or $p = 8$
44. $|6 - q| = 5$ $q = 1$ or $q = 11$
45. $|2(a + 3) - a| = 5$ $a = -11$ or $a = -1$

Objective: *To graph absolute value relations on the coordinate plane (Section 7-6)*

Graph each equation on the coordinate plane. See the Solution Key.

46. $|y| = 6$
47. $|x| = 1$
48. $y = -|4x|$
49. $y = |-x|$
50. $y = |-2x| + 2$
51. $x = |3y|$
52. $|x| - |y| = 2$
53. $|y + 1| = 3$

Chapter Test

A formal Chapter Test is provided in the Teacher's Manual. See p. M-70.

Write each compound sentence as two simple sentences joined by or or and.

1. $x - 3 \geq 9$
2. $3x + 2 \leq 10$
3. $-8 < 2n + 6 < -2$

Solve and graph each inequality on a number line.

4. $4x \leq 12$
5. $-3 < y + 1 < 5$

6. Graph the inequality $2x + y \leq 4$ on the coordinate plane.

7. Solve by graphing: $\begin{cases} y < x \\ y < 3x + 6 \end{cases}$ See p. 574.

A manufacturer makes two models of a watch. The profit on Model A is $5 per watch and the profit on Model B is $12 per watch. The manufacturer can produce no more than 300 watches per week. To meet the market demand, at least 110 Model A watches and 60 Model B watches must be available each week. Use this information for Exercises 8–12.

8. Let x represent the number of Model A watches and let y represent the number of Model B watches produced per week. Write an expression to represent the total weekly profit. $5x + 12y$

9. Write a system of inequalities that shows the constraints on x and y. $\begin{cases} x \geq 110 \\ y \geq 60 \\ x + y \leq 300 \end{cases}$

10. Graph the system of inequalities you wrote in Exercise 9.

11. State the coordinates of the vertices of the polygonal region graphed in Exercise 10. (240, 60), (110, 60), (110, 90)

12. What is the maximum profit possible? $2830

Solve and check each equation.

13. $|4x| = 20$ $x = -5$ or $x = 5$
14. $|y - 2| = 4$ $y = -2$ or $y = 6$

15. Graph $y = |-3x|$ on the coordinate plane.

272 *Chapter 7*

Additional Answers
Chapter Test
1. $x - 3 = 9$ or $x - 3 > 9$
2. $3x + 2 = 10$ or $3x + 2 < 10$
3. $-8 < 2n + 6$ and $2n + 6 < -2$
4.
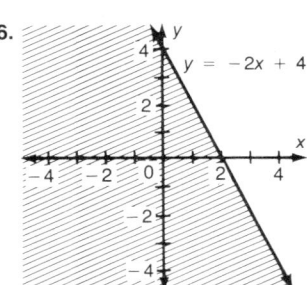

5.

6.

10.
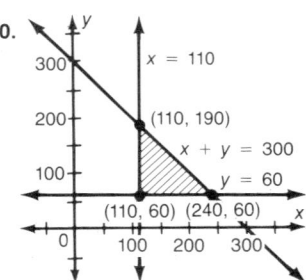

15.
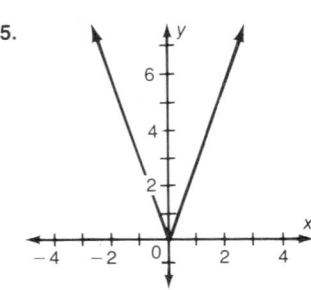

Additional Practice

You may wish to use all or some of these exercises, depending on how well students performed on the formal chapter test.

Skills

Write each compound sentence as two simple sentences joined by or or and. (Section 7-1)

1. $2y \geq 5$ $2y = 5$ or $2y > 5$

2. $\frac{1}{3}n - 2 \geq 3$ $\frac{1}{3}n - 2 = 3$ or $\frac{1}{3}n - 2 > 3$

3. $-6 < 4a + 6 < -2$ $-6 < 4a + 6$ and $4a + 6 < -2$

Solve and graph each inequality on a number line. (Section 7-1)

4. $3n \leq 12$

5. $-5 < 2p + 3 \leq 3$

6. $3(n + 1) \leq -6$

Graph each inequality on the coordinate plane. (Section 7-2)

7. $y > x - 1$

8. $y \leq -2x$

9. $x + y < -4$

10. $2x - y \geq 1$

Solve each system by graphing. (Section 7-3)

11. $\begin{cases} x - y < 4 \\ x + y > 0 \end{cases}$ See page 574.

12. $\begin{cases} y \geq 3x \\ y \geq -x + 1 \end{cases}$ See the Solution Key.

13. $\begin{cases} 3x - y > 2 \\ 2x + y < -3 \end{cases}$ See page 574.

14. $\begin{cases} y > -x + 4 \\ y > x \end{cases}$ See the Solution Key.

Solve and check each equation. (Section 7-5)

15. $|x - 1| = 3$ $x = -2$ or $x = 4$

16. $|3a - 4| - 6 = 0$ $a = -\frac{2}{3}$ or $a = 3\frac{1}{3}$

17. $|2(x - 2) + x| = 8$ $x = -1\frac{1}{3}$ or $x = 4$

Graph each equation on the coordinate plane. (Section 7-6)

18. $y = |-4x|$

19. $|2y + 1| = 3$

20. $|x| + |y| = 4$

See the Solution Key for the graphs of Exercises 18-20.

Applications

21. A garden supply company had a sale on seedlings. Each customer had to buy at least 15, but no more than 100, seedlings. Represent this as an inequality, where s is the number of seedlings per customer. (Section 7-1) $15 \leq s \leq 100$

22. Members of the swim team at the town pool must be at least 7 years old and younger than 18. Represent the permissible ages of the swim team members as an inequality, where a is the age in years. (Section 7-1) $7 \leq a < 18$

A group of 360 people is to be bused to the state fair. The bus company has four 60-passenger buses and six 40-passenger buses available. The cost of renting a 60-passenger bus is $200; the cost of renting a 40-passenger bus is $140. Use this information in Exercises 23-25. (Section 7-4)

23. Let x represent the number of 60-passenger buses rented and let y represent the number of 40-passenger buses. Write an expression to represent the total cost. $200x + 140y$

24. Write and graph a system of inequalities showing the constraints on x and y. See the Solution Key.

25. Write the coordinates of the vertices of the polygonal region graphed in Exercise 24 and find the minimum cost possible. $(2, 6), (4, 3), (4, 6)$; $1220

Additional Answers

4.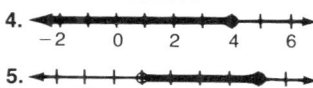

5.

6.

7.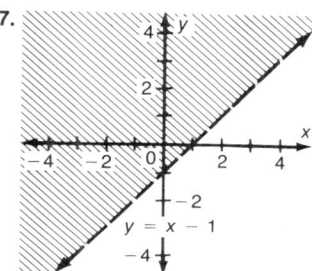

8.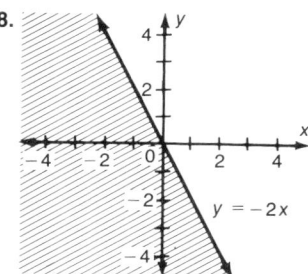

9.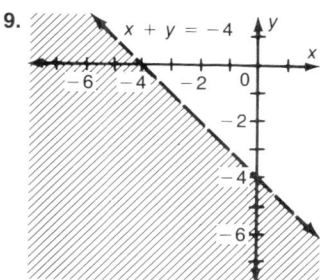

10.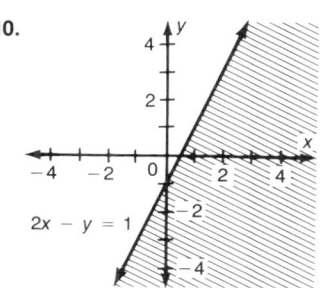

In this cumulative review of word problems, note that each problem is referenced to the related section.

Review of Word Problems: Chapters 1-7

1. A family's phone bill for December was $32.50 more than the phone bill for November. Phone service for the two months cost a total of $89.30. How much was the December bill? *(Section 4–3)* $60.90

2. Two trains 700 kilometers apart start at the same time and travel toward each other. One travels at a rate of 80 kilometers per hour and the other at a rate of 95 kilometers per hour. In how many hours will they meet? *(Section 5–2)*4

The sales tax rate for a certain state is 6%. Use this information in Exercises 3–5. *(Section 5–6)*

3. Make a table to show the amount of tax, *t*, for sales, *s*, of $100, $200 and $300.

4. Use the ordered pairs from the table in Exercise 3 to graph the function. Assume that the graph is linear.

5. Use the graph in Exercise 4 to determine the tax on $250. $15

6. The distance between two cities on a map varies directly with the actual distance between the cities. If 2.5 centimeters on the map represent 50 kilometers, what distance does 6 centimeters represent? *(Section 5–10)*   120 km

7. Robert drove from Dallas to Chicago and then from Chicago to Nashville. He drove 1387 miles in all. The distance from Dallas to Chicago is 34 miles greater than twice the distance from Chicago to Nashville. How far is it from Dallas to Chicago? *(Section 6–4)*   936 mi

8. The sum of the digits of a two-digit number is 10. When 54 is added to the number, the result is the original number with its digits reversed. Find the number. *(Section 6–5)*   28

9. The regular admission price at the movies is $4.50. Admission for senior citizens is $3.50. One evening, 284 tickets were sold for a total of $1226. How many tickets were sold to senior citizens? *(Section 6–7)*   52

10. A 3% salt solution is mixed with an 8% salt solution. How many milliliters of each are needed to obtain 800 milliliters of a 5% solution? *(Section 6–8)*
3% solution: 480 mL; 8% solution: 320 mL

A wholesale bakery makes large and small loaves of rye bread. The profit on a large loaf is 10 cents, and the profit on a small loaf is 8 cents. No more than 300 loaves of rye bread are baked daily. To meet the demand at the stores, at least 150 small loaves and at least 75 large loaves must be made each day. Use this information in Exercises 11–14. *(Section 7–4)*

11. Let *x* represent the number of small loaves and let *y* represent the number of large loaves of rye bread produced each day. Write an equation to represent the total daily profit. $0.08x + 0.10y$

12. Write a system of inequalities that shows the constraints on *x* and *y*.

13. Graph the system of inequalities you wrote in Exercise 12 and write the coordinates of the vertices of the polygonal region.

14. What is the maximum possible daily profit on rye bread? $27

274   *Review of Word Problems: Chapters 1–7*

Additional Answers

3.

s	100	200	300
t	6	12	18

4.

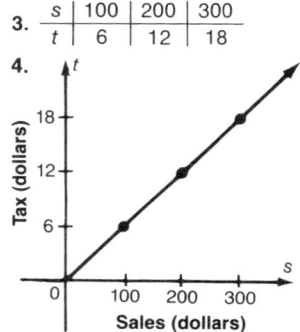

12. $\begin{cases} x + y \le 300 \\ x \ge 150 \\ y \ge 75 \end{cases}$

13.

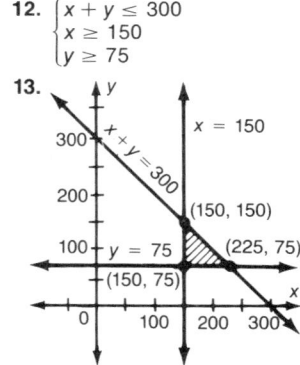

Cumulative Review: Chapters 5–7

The Test Booklet contains another form of the cumulative review.

Choose the best answer. Choose a, b, c, or d.

1. Solve for l: $P = 2l + 2w$ **b**

   a. $l = P - w$ **b.** $l = \dfrac{P}{2} - w$ **c.** $l = \dfrac{(2w - P)}{2}$ **d.** $l = P - 2w - 2$

2. Two cars leave the same place at the same time. One is traveling east at an average rate of 80 kilometers per hour and the other is traveling west at an average rate of 60 kilometers per hour. In how many hours will they be 1120 kilometers apart? **a**

   a. 8   **b.** 16   **c.** 4   **d.** 3

3. In which quadrant is the graph of $P(-6, 8)$ located? **b**

   a. I   **b.** II   **c.** III   **d.** IV

4. Which point is <u>not</u> on the line parallel to the x axis and 3 units below it? **a**

   a. $A(-3, 0)$ **b.** $B(0, -3)$ **c.** $C(-3, -3)$ **d.** $D(18, -3)$

5. Pencils cost 10¢ each or 3 for 25¢. Which number <u>cannot</u> be in the range of this function? **a**

   a. 30¢   **b.** 50¢   **c.** 60¢   **d.** $1.00

6. Which of the following is a correct description of this set of ordered pairs:
   $$\{(0, 7)(-8, 6)(9, -7)(0, -8)\} \quad \textbf{b}$$

   a. Function   **b.** Relation, not a function
   c. Function, not a relation   **d.** Neither a function nor a relation

7. What is the slope of the line containing the points $A(-2, 7)$ and $B(3, -8)$? **b**

   a. 3   **b.** -3 **c.** -1 **d.** 1

8. What is the slope of the graph of $2x + y = 7$? **a**

   a. -2 **b.** 2   **c.** 7   **d.** $\dfrac{7}{2}$

9. If y varies directly as x and $y = 8$ when x is 16, find y when $x = 2$. **c**

   a. -4 **b.** 4   **c.** 1   **d.** -1

10. Seventeen liters of gasoline cost $4.76. How much will 32 liters cost? **d**

    a. $28.00   **b.** $9.52   **c.** $13.72   **d.** $8.96

11. Which points are <u>not</u> on the graph of either line? **c** $\begin{cases} x + y = 10 \\ x - y = 5 \end{cases}$

    a. $A(17, -7)$ **b.** $B(12, 7)$ **c.** $C(12, -7)$ **d.** $D(-20, 30)$

12. Which point is a solution of this system? $\begin{cases} 2x + y = 17 \\ x - 3y = 5 \end{cases}$ **a**

    a. $A(8, 1)$ **b.** $B(-8, 1)$ **c.** $C(-8, -1)$ **d.** $D(8, -1)$

13. Which system has no solutions? **c**

    a. $\begin{cases} 3x + y = 7 \\ y - 3x = 9 \end{cases}$ **b.** $\begin{cases} 2x - 3y = 8 \\ 3y = 5x + 7 \end{cases}$ **c.** $\begin{cases} 8y - 5x = 7 \\ y = \dfrac{5}{8x} - 15 \end{cases}$ **d.** $\begin{cases} x - y = 15 \\ 2x + 7y = 92 \end{cases}$

14. Which of the following systems is equivalent to this system? $\begin{cases} y - 3x = 15 \\ 12y + x = 24 \end{cases}$ **a**

    a. $\begin{cases} y - 3x = 15 \\ 12y + x = 24 \end{cases}$ **b.** $\begin{cases} y - 3x = 15 \\ 12y + 3x = 24 \end{cases}$ **c.** $\begin{cases} 4y - 3x = 15 \\ 4y + x = 8 \end{cases}$ **d.** $\begin{cases} 4y - 3x = 15 \\ 4y + 3x = 24 \end{cases}$

15. The sum of two numbers is 40. Twice the smaller is 8 more than the larger. What are the numbers? **d**

    a. 14 and 26   **b.** 20 and 32   **c.** 48 and 88   **d.** 16 and 24

16. The hundreds, tens, and units digits of a number are h, t, and u, respectively. What is the value of the number if the digits are reversed? **b**

    a. $100h + 10t + u$ **b.** $h + 10t + 100u$ **c.** $h + t + u$ **d.** $100(h + t + u)$

17. Jim has $1.15 in nickels and dimes. He has one more dime than nickels. How many dimes does he have? **a**

    a. 8   **b.** 7   **c.** 11   **d.** 5

18. Cashews at $5.00 per pound are mixed with peanuts at $2.00 per pound to make a mixture worth $4.00 a pound. There are 15 pounds of the mixture. How many pounds of cashews are there? **a**

    a. 10   **b.** 5   **c.** 8   **d.** 12

19. Mr. Skidmore sold a adult tickets and c children's tickets to the school play. The cost of an adult's ticket is $5.75 and the cost of a child's ticket is $2.50. What expression shows the total cost of all the tickets? **c**

    a. $(a + c)8.25$ **b.** $5.75a + c$ **c.** $5.75a + 2.50c$ **d.** $2.50a + 5.75c$

20. Which of the following is equivalent to $8n \le 11$? **c**

    a. $11 > 8n$ **b.** $8n = 11$

    c. $8n < 11$ <u>or</u> $8n = 11$ **d.** $8n < 11$ <u>and</u> $8n = 11$

21. Which point is <u>not</u> on the graph of $y < 3x - 4$? **c**

    a. $A(10, 0)$ **b.** $B(0, -5)$ **c.** $C(-10, 10)$ **d.** $D(10, -10)$

22. Points on the graph of $y = 2x - 5$ are <u>not</u> included in the graph of which of the following? **a**

    a. $2x - y > 5$ **b.** $y \ge 2x - 5$ **c.** $y \le 2x - 5$ **d.** $2x - y \ge 5$

23. What is the solution set of $|2(x - 1) - 8| = 4$? **d**

    a. $\{7\}$ **b.** $\{3\}$ **c.** $\{-7, 3\}$ **d.** $\{7, 3\}$

24. Which point is <u>not</u> on the graph of $y = |x|$? **d**

    a. The origin   **b.** $B(-8, 8)$ **c.** $C(17, 17)$ **d.** $D(-9, -9)$

25. Which point lies on the graph of the system $\begin{cases} x \ge 3 \\ y \ge -2 \\ x + y \le 5 \end{cases}$? **d**

    a. $A(6, 0)$ **b.** $B(3, 7)$ **c.** $C(0, 0)$ **d.** $D(5, 0)$

26. Find the maximum value of $k = 3x - y$ given these constraints: $\begin{cases} x \ge 0 \\ y \ge 0 \\ x + y \le 4 \end{cases}$ **a**

    a. 12   **b.** 0   **c.** -4 **d.** 16

Preparing for College Entrance Tests

Additional practice can be found in the Teacher's Manual.

When comparing two quantities or expressions, it is sometimes helpful to choose real numbers that satisfy the conditions of the problem and substitute them in the given expressions.

REMEMBER: If you can find at least one number that makes a statement false, then you have shown that the statement is not always true.

EXAMPLE: If n is a real number and $n < 0$, which of the following statements must be true?

(a) $n > \dfrac{1}{n}$ (b) $(n^2 - 1) > (1 - n^2)$ (c) $(n - 1) > (1 - n)$ (d) $n^2 > n$

Think: Two choices involve n^2, and n^2 is always positive. Thus, check the choices involving n^2 first.

Solution: (b) $(n^2 - 1) > (1 - n^2)$ ←——— Not true when $n = -\frac{1}{2}$

(d) $n^2 > n$ ←——— Always true, since $n < 0$ and $n^2 > 0$

(a) $n > \dfrac{1}{n}$ ←——— Not true when $n = -2$

(c) $(n - 1) > (1 - n)$ ←——— Never true, since $(n - 1) < 0$ and $(1 - n) > 0$

Answer: **d**

Choose the best answer. Choose a, b, c, or d. (Assume that all variables represent real numbers.)

1. If $y > 0$, which of the following must be true? c

   (a) $y^2 > y$ (b) $y > \dfrac{1}{y}$ (c) $(y + 1) > (y - 1)$ (d) $\dfrac{1}{y} > \dfrac{1}{y^2}$

2. If $y < 0$, which of the following must be true? d

   (a) $y^4 > y^2$ (b) $y^3 > y$ (c) $y^3 > y^2$ (d) $y^4 > y$

3. If $p > 2$, which of the following must be true? b

   (a) $\dfrac{p - 2}{2} > \dfrac{p}{2}$ (b) $\dfrac{p + 2}{2} > \dfrac{p}{2}$ (c) $\dfrac{2}{p + 2} > \dfrac{2}{p}$ (d) $\dfrac{2}{p} > \dfrac{2}{p - 2}$

4. If $q \neq 0$, which of the following must be true? c

   (a) $\dfrac{q - (q + q)}{q} > 1$ (b) $\dfrac{q - (q - q)}{q} > 1$ (c) $\dfrac{q + (q + q)}{q} > 1$ (d) $\dfrac{q + (q - q)}{q} > 1$

5. If $w > 1$, which of the following must be true? a

   (a) $\dfrac{1}{w - 1} > \dfrac{1}{1 - w}$ (b) $\dfrac{1}{w - 1} > \dfrac{-1}{1 - w}$ (c) $\dfrac{1}{1 - w} > \dfrac{-1}{w - 1}$ (d) $\dfrac{1}{1 - w} > \dfrac{-1}{1 - w}$

6. If $n > 2$, which of the following must be true? d

    (a) $\dfrac{2n}{2} < \dfrac{2n}{n}$ **(b)** $\dfrac{2+n}{2} < \dfrac{2n}{n}$ **(c)** $\dfrac{2+n}{n} > \dfrac{2+n}{2}$ **(d)** $\dfrac{2n}{n} > \dfrac{2+n}{n}$

7. If $x > 0$, which of the following must be true? a

    (a) $-(2x - x) < -(x - 2x)$ **(b)** $-(2x - x) < (x - 2x)$

    (c) $x - 2x < -(x + 2x)$ **(d)** $2x - x < -(2x - x)$

8. If $x > 0$ and $y < 0$, which of the following must be true? b

    (a) $x + y > 0$ **(b)** $x - y > 0$ **(c)** $xy > 0$ **(d)** $\dfrac{x}{y} > 0$

9. If $a > 0$ and $b > 0$, which of the following must be true? b

    (a) $-(a - b) < 0$ **(b)** $-(a + b) < 0$ **(c)** $-(b - a) < 0$ **(d)** $-(-b - a) < 0$

10. If $p < 0$ and $r < 0$, which of the following must be true? c

    (a) $(p - r) > 0$ **(b)** $(p^2 - r^2) > 0$ **(c)** $pr > 0$ **(d)** $p(p - r) > 0$

11. If $c > 0$ and $d > c$, which of the following must be true? d

    (a) $(c + d) > 1$ **(b)** $(d - c) > 1$ **(c)** $cd > 1$ **(d)** $\dfrac{d}{c} > 1$

12. If $m < 0$ and $p < m$, which of the following must be true? a

    (a) $(p - m) < (m - p)$ **(b)** $\dfrac{p}{m} < 1$ **(c)** $\dfrac{m}{p} < 0$ **(d)** $p^2 < m^2$

13. If $ab > 0$, which of the following must be true? c

    (a) $a > 0$ **(b)** $b > 0$ **(c)** $\dfrac{a}{b} > 0$ **(d)** $(a - b) > 0$

14. If $s > t$ and $s + t > 0$, which of the following must be true? b

    (a) $t > 0$ **(b)** $s > 0$ **(c)** $-s > t$ **(d)** $(t - s) > 0$

15. If $a < 0$ and $ab > 0$, which of the following must be true? c

    (a) $0 < b$ **(b)** $b < a$ **(c)** $(a + b) < 0$ **(d)** $(a - b) < 0$

16. If $|k| > 1$, which of the following must be true? d

    (a) $k > 1$ **(b)** $|k| > k$ **(c)** $|k| > k^2$ **(d)** $k^2 > 1$

17. If $x < 0$, which of the following must be true? c

    (a) $|x - 2| < |x| - 2$ **(b)** $|2x| < 2|x|$

    (c) $|x + 2| < |x| + 2$ **(d)** $|2 - x| < 2 - |x|$

18. If $n > 0$ and $p < n$, which of the following must be true? a

    (a) $|p - n| > p - n$ **(b)** $|n| > |p|$

    (c) $|n| + |p| > |n + p|$ **(d)** $n + p > n - p$

19. If $c < d$ and $|c| > |d|$, which of the following must be true? c

    (a) $d > 0$ **(b)** $d < 0$ **(c)** $c < 0$ **(d)** $c > -d$

CHAPTER **8** # Exponents and Polynomials

Teaching Suggestions p. M-21

8-1 Exponents

Suppose that you were offered a position that paid 1¢ on the first day of work. Then, for each day after the first, you receive double the preceding day's wage. Here is a partial list of each day's wages.

Day	Wages in Cents	Powers of Two	
		Factor Form	**Exponent Form**
1	1		2^0
2	2	2	2^1
3	4	2×2	2^2
4	8	$2 \times 2 \times 2$	2^3
5	16	$2 \times 2 \times 2 \times 2$	2^4
6	32	$2 \times 2 \times 2 \times 2 \times 2$	2^5
⋮	⋮	⋮	⋮
29	268,435,456	$\underbrace{2 \times 2 \times 2 \cdots \times 2 \times 2}_{\text{28 factors}}$	2^{28}
30	536,870,912	$\underbrace{2 \times 2 \times \cdots \times 2 \times 2}_{\text{29 factors}}$	2^{29}

Each day's wages can be expressed as a power of 2. For example, the sixth day's wages can be written

$$2^5 = \underbrace{2 \cdot 2 \cdot 2 \cdot 2 \cdot 2}_{\textbf{5 factors of 2}} = 32$$

The wages on day 30 are 2^{29}¢, or over 5 million dollars!

Note how powers are read.

For 2^2, read "two squared" or "the second power of 2."

For 2^3, read "two cubed" or "the third power of 2."

For 2^4, read "two to the fourth" or "the fourth power of 2."

For 2^n, read "two to the nth" or "the nth power of 2."

Examples of exponents used with other bases are given below.

Expression	Base	Exponent	Meaning
3^2	3	2	$3 \cdot 3$
5^4	5	4	$5 \cdot 5 \cdot 5 \cdot 5$
15^1	15	1	15
$(-3)^2$	−3	2	$(-3)(-3)$
x^7	x	7	$x \cdot x \cdot x \cdot x \cdot x \cdot x \cdot x$
x^a	x	a	$\underbrace{x \cdot x \cdot x \cdots \cdot x}_{a \text{ factors}}$

280   *Chapter 8*

Definitions

> If x is a real number and a is an integer greater than 1, then
> $$x^a = \underbrace{x \cdot x \cdot x \cdot \,\cdots\, \cdot x}_{a \text{ factors}}.$$
> When $a = 1$, $x^a = x$. That is, $x^1 = x$.

Example 1 shows how the definition is used to write a number in exponential form.

EXAMPLE 1   Write 10,000 in exponential form.

  Solution: $10{,}000 = 10 \cdot 10 \cdot 10 \cdot 10$ ◄——— **Write as factors of 10.**

  $= 10^4$ ◄——— **By definition**

The definition can also be used to write certain products as a base with a single exponent.

EXAMPLE 2   Write $2^5 \cdot 2^3$ as a base with a single exponent.

  Solution: $2^5 \cdot 2^3 = \underbrace{\underbrace{2 \cdot 2 \cdot 2 \cdot 2 \cdot 2}_{\textbf{Five factors}} \cdot \underbrace{2 \cdot 2 \cdot 2}_{\textbf{Three factors}}}_{\textbf{Eight factors}}$

  $= 2^8$

Example 3 shows how the definition is applied when evaluating expressions.

EXAMPLE 3   Find the value of $x^3 y^2$ when $x = -2$ and $y = 3$.

  Solution: Replace x with -2 and y with 3.

  $x^3 y^2 = (-2)^3 (3)^2$

  $= \underbrace{(-2)(-2)(-2)}_{(-8)}\underbrace{(3)(3)}_{9}$ ◄——— **By definition**

  $= (-8) \quad 9 \quad = -72$

CLASSROOM EXERCISES

Complete.

	Expression	Base	Exponent	Meaning	
1.	10^6	?	?	?	$10; 6; 10 \cdot 10 \cdot 10 \cdot 10 \cdot 10 \cdot 10$
2.	7^4	?	?	?	$7; 4; 7 \cdot 7 \cdot 7 \cdot 7$
3.	?	3	4	?	$3^4; 3 \cdot 3 \cdot 3 \cdot 3$
4.	?	?	?	$2 \cdot 2 \cdot 2 \cdot 2 \cdot 2$	$2^5; 2; 5$
5.	?	?	?	$x \cdot x \cdot x \cdot x \cdot x \cdot x$	$x^6; x; 6$

Exponents and Polynomials   **281**

Assignment Guide
Minimal
Day 1 p. 282: 1–29
Day 2 p. 282: 30–59
Average
p. 282: 1–64 odd
Above Average
p. 282: 1–51 odd, 52–64

Additional Answers
13. 100,000
14. 10,000,000
15. 10,000,000,000

WRITTEN EXERCISES

A   Complete.

	Expression	Base	Exponent	Meaning
1.	5^6	?	?	? $5; 6; 5 \cdot 5 \cdot 5 \cdot 5 \cdot 5 \cdot 5$
2.	10^3	?	?	? $10; 3; 10 \cdot 10 \cdot 10$
3.	2^6	?	?	? $2; 6; 2 \cdot 2 \cdot 2 \cdot 2 \cdot 2 \cdot 2$
4.	a^5	?	?	? $a; 5; a \cdot a \cdot a \cdot a \cdot a$
5.	?	10	5	? $10^5; 10 \cdot 10 \cdot 10 \cdot 10 \cdot 10$
6.	?	2	3	? $2^3; 2 \cdot 2 \cdot 2$
7.	?	?	?	$10 \cdot 10 \cdot 10 \cdot 10$ $10^4; 10; 4$
8.	?	?	?	$x \cdot x \cdot x \cdot x \cdot x \cdot x \cdot x$ $x^7; x; 7$
9.	?	?	?	x $x^1; x; 1$

Evaluate.

10. 10^2 100   **11.** 10^4 10,000   **12.** 10^1 10   **13.** 10^5 **14.** 10^7 **15.** 10^{10}

16. How many zeros follow the "1" in the decimal numeral for 10^{13}? 13

17. How many zeros follow the "1" in the decimal numeral for 10^a? a

Evaluate.

18. $(-1)^3$ -1 **19.** $(-1)^7$ -1 **20.** $(-1)^9$ -1 **21.** $(-1)^5$ -1 **22.** $(-1)^{11}$ -1 **23.** $(-1)^{99}$ -1

24. $(-1)^2$ 1   **25.** $(-1)^6$ 1   **26.** $(-1)^4$ 1   **27.** $(-1)^{10}$ 1   **28.** $(-1)^{30}$ 1   **29.** $(-1)^{100}$ 1

Write in exponential form.

30. 1000 10^3 **31.** 100,000 10^5 **32.** 1,000,000 10^6 **33.** 1 million 10^6 **34.** 1 billion 10^9

35. 1 thousand 10^3 **36.** 10 billion 10^{10} **37.** 1,000,000,000 10^9 **38.** 10 10^1 **39.** 1 trillion 10^{12}

Write each product as a base with a single exponent.

40. $10^3 \cdot 10^2$ 10^5 **41.** $2^3 \cdot 2^4$ 2^7 **42.** $5^2 \cdot 5^3$ 5^5 **43.** $10 \cdot 10^4$ 10^5

44. $5^3 \cdot 5^2$ 5^5 **45.** $2^3 \cdot 2^3$ 2^6 **46.** $15^2 \cdot 15^4$ 15^6 **47.** $2^{15} \cdot 2^2$ 2^{17}

48. $x^2 \cdot x^3$ x^5 **49.** $a^4 \cdot a^2$ a^6 **50.** $y^5 \cdot y^4$ y^9 **51.** $m^6 \cdot m^2$ m^8

Find the value when $a = 1$, $b = 2$, and $c = -3$.

52. a^5 1   **53.** $(-b)^2$ 4   **54.** c^3 -27 **55.** a^2b 2

56. ab^2 4   **57.** a^2c^2 9   **58.** b^2c^2 36   **59.** abc -6

60. $a^2b^2c^2$ 36   **61.** abc^2 18   **62.** $a^{25}b^2c^0$ 4   **63.** $a^{100}b^3c$ -24

64. Evaluate $(a^2b^3c)^2$ for $a = 3$, $b = -2$, and $c = 5$. 129,600

282   *Chapter 8*

Multiply. *(Pages 64-67)*

1. $(-40)(-5)$ 200   **2.** $18(-21)-378$ **3.** $2(-3)(-3)(-3)-54$ **4.** $(-1)(-1)(-1)(-1)$ 1
5. $(-18)(-20)0$ 0   **6.** $(-6)(15)(20)(-2)$ **7.** $4(-1)(-7)(-10)$ **8.** $(-1)(-1)(-1)(-1)(-1)$
                                      3600 -280 -1

8-2 Multiplying Monomials

OBJECTIVE: To multiply monomials

When exponential expressions have the *same base*, their product can be expressed using the same base and a single exponent by applying the definition of exponent.

a. $4^3 \cdot 4^2 = 4 \cdot 4 \cdot 4 \cdot 4 \cdot 4$ **b.** $x^4 \cdot x^4 = x \cdot x \cdot x \cdot x \cdot x \cdot x \cdot x \cdot x$

          $= 4^5$ $= x^8$

Note in **a** and **b** that the *sum* of the exponents equals the *single exponent* in the answer. This suggests the following theorem.

Theorem 8-1

Multiplication Theorem for Exponents
If x is a real number and a and b are positive integers, then
$x^a \cdot x^b = x^{a+b}.$

Theorem 8-1 can be used to find products such as $(-3x^2)(2x)$.

EXAMPLE 1   Find each product.

        a. $(-3x^2)(2x)$ **b.** $(-3ab^2)(-2a^3b^5)$

Solutions:

a. $(-3x^2)(2x) = (-3 \cdot 2)(x^2 \cdot x)$ **b.** $(-3ab^2)(-2a^3b^5) = (-3 \cdot -2)(a \cdot a^3)(b^2 \cdot b^5)$
                 $= -6x^{2+1}$ $= 6a^{1+3}b^{2+5}$
                 $= -6x^3$ $= 6a^4b^7$

Expressions such as $-3x^2$ and $2x$ are *monomials*.

Definition

A **monomial** is a term that is the product of numbers and variables with nonnegative integral exponents.

Monomial	Not a Monomial	
$\sqrt{3}x^2$	$3x^{-2}$	⟵ **Negative exponent**
$\frac{1}{4}x^2y^2$	$3y^2 + 7y + 7$	⟵ **Sum of monomials**
8	$4x^{\frac{1}{2}}$	⟵ **Rational number exponent**

Exponents and Polynomials   **283**

Review Capsule
This Review Capsule reviews the prior-taught skills used in Section 8-2. The reference is to the pages where the skills were taught.

Teaching Suggestions p. M-21

Quick Quiz
Write in exponential form.
1. 100
   Ans: 10^2
2. 100,000,000
   Ans: 10^8
Write each product as a base with a single exponent.
3. $5^6 \cdot 5^{10}$
   Ans: 5^{16}
4. $m^3 \cdot m^5$
   Ans: m^8
Find the value when $m = 1$, $n = 2$, and $p = -3$.
5. $m^{30}n^3p^2$
   Ans: 72
6. $(-n)^3$
   Ans: -8
7. n^2p^3
   Ans: -108

Additional Examples
Example 1
Find each product.
1.a. $(6a^2)(-5a^4)$
     Ans: $-30a^6$
   b. $(-5cd^3)(-3c^4d^2)$
     Ans: $15\,c^5d^5$

EXAMPLE 2 Write in exponential form: $(4 \times 10^5)(2 \times 10^8)$

  Solution: $(4 \times 10^5)(2 \times 10^8) = (4 \times 2)(10^5 \times 10^8)$

  $= 8 \times 10^{5+8}$ ◄——— **By Theorem 8–1**

  $= 8 \times 10^{13}$

Additional Examples
Example 2
Write in exponential form.
  1. $(3 \times 10^4)(5 \times 10^8)$
    Ans: 15×10^{12}
  2. $(6 \times 10^7)(2 \times 10^3)$
    Ans: 12×10^{10}

CLASSROOM EXERCISES

Find each product.

$(-2)^{12} = 4096$

1. $x^8 \cdot x^2$ x^{10} **2.** $4^5 \cdot 4^3$ $4^8 = 65{,}536$ **3.** $-x^2 \cdot x^3$ $-x^5$ **4.** $(-2)^2(-2)^{10}$

5. $(-a)^6 \cdot a^3$ a^9 **6.** $(3x^2)(-4x^2y)$ $-12x^4y$ **7.** $(-2a^2b^3)(5ab)^0$ **8.** $x^2y^5 \cdot 3x^9y^4$

  $-2a^2b^3$ $3x^{11}y^9$

Assignment Guide
Minimal p. 284: 1–46 odd
Average
p. 284: 1–46 odd, 47–52
Above Average
p. 284: 3, 6, 9, . . . 51, 53–64

WRITTEN EXERCISES

A   Find each product.

$-m^4$

1. $(x \cdot x \cdot x \cdot x)(x \cdot x \cdot x)$ **2.** $(3 \cdot 3)(3 \cdot 3 \cdot 3 \cdot 3)$ **3.** $(-y)(y \cdot y)$ $-y^3$ **4.** $-1(m \cdot m \cdot m)(m)$

5. $x^4 \cdot x^5$ x^9 **6.** $x^2 \cdot x^4$ x^6 **7.** $m \cdot m^6$ m^7 **8.** $a^2 \cdot a^3$ a^5

9. $n^3 \cdot n^4$ n^7 **10.** $b \cdot b^2$ b^3 **11.** $a(a)$ a^2 **12.** $b^3 \cdot b$ b^4

13. $b^2 \cdot b^3$ b^5 **14.** $(-b)(-b)$ b^2 **15.** $b(-b)$ $-b^2$ **16.** $-a^5(a^2)$ $-a^7$

17. $x(-x^2)$ $-x^3$ **18.** $(-y^2)(y^2)$ $-y^4$ **19.** $-y^2(-y^2)$ y^4 **20.** $a(a^2)(a^3)$ a^6

21. $p^3 \cdot p^2$ p^5 **22.** $-x(-x^2)$ x^3 **23.** $3^6 \cdot 3^4$ **24.** $5(5^4)$ $5^5 = 3125$

25. $2(2^3)(2^4)$ **26.** $3(3^2)(3^4)$ **27.** $5^2(-5^2)(5^3)$ **28.** $(-2x^4)(-3x^2)$ $6x^6$

29. $(-4x^2y)(-5xy)$ **30.** $(-3a^2b)(ab)(-2ab)^0$ **31.** $(8mn^2)(-3m^2y^4)$ **32.** $(-x^5)(3x^2)(7x^4)$

33. $(2x)(3x^4)(-6x^3)$ **34.** $(4c^2d)(5cd)(cd^2)$ **35.** $-1(x^3)(-x)x^4$ **36.** $(-x^2y)(5xy)(9x^3y^2)$

37. $10^3 \cdot 10^2 \cdot 10^4$ **38.** $10^5 \cdot 10^8 \cdot 10$ 10^{14} **39.** $10 \cdot 10^5 \cdot 10^9$ 10^{15} **40.** $10^{10} \cdot 10^{15} \cdot 10^0$ 10^{25}

Write each product in exponential form.

41. $(2 \times 10^2)(3 \times 10^4)$ **42.** $(7 \times 10)(9 \times 10^5)$ **43.** $(1.5 \times 10^3)(2 \times 10^6)$

44. $(2.4 \times 10^7)(3.9 \times 10)$ **45.** $(2.8 \times 10^9)(a \times 10^2)$ **46.** $(a \times 10^x)(b \times 10^y)$

B   Identify the number named by each product as positive, *P*, or negative, *N*.

47. $(-1)^4(-1)^3$ *N*   **48.** $(-1)^{10}(-1)^8$ *P*   **49.** -10^4 **50.** -3^{15} *N*   **51.** $(-3)^{15}$ *N*   **52.** $(-4)^{25}$

  N

C   Write each product in exponential form. All exponents are positive integers.

53. $x^a \cdot x^2$ x^{a+2} **54.** $y^2 \cdot y^b$ y^{2+b} **55.** $x^a \cdot x^b$ x^{a+b}

56. $a^{x-2} \cdot a^5$ a^{x+3} **57.** $x^{3a} \cdot x^{2a}$ x^{5a} **58.** $(x^{2a+7})(x^{2a-8})^0$ x^{2a+7}

59. $3^x \cdot 3^2$ 3^{x+2} **60.** $2^{4a} \cdot 2^{3a}$ 2^{7a} **61.** $(2^{2a+7})(2^{7a-6})$ 2^{9a+1}

62. $(x+2)^2 \cdot (x+2)^4$ $(x+2)^6$ **63.** $(x+2)^a \cdot (x+2)^6$ **64.** $(x+2)^{2a} \cdot (x+2)^{b-a}$

  $(x+2)^{a+6}$ $(x+2)^{a+b}$

Additional Answers
Written Exercises
  1. x^7
  2. $3^6 = 729$
 23. $3^{10} = 59{,}049$
 25. $2^8 = 256$
 26. $3^7 = 2187$
 27. $(-5)^7 = -78{,}125$
 29. $20x^3y^2$
 30. $-3a^3b^2$
 31. $-24m^3n^2y^4$
 32. $-21x^{11}$
 33. $-36x^8$
 34. $20c^4d^4$
 36. $-45x^6y^5$
 37. $10^9 = 1{,}000{,}000{,}000$
 41. 6×10^6
 42. 63×10^6
 43. 3×10^9
 44. 9.36×10^8
 45. $2.8a \times 10^{11}$
 46. $ab \times 10^{x+y}$

284   *Chapter 8*

OBJECTIVE: To raise an expression to a power

8-3 Powers of Monomials

Teaching Suggestions p. M-21

The Multiplication Theorem for Exponents can be used to write expressions such as $(5^4)^2$ with a single exponent.

a. $(5^4)^2 = 5^4 \cdot 5^4$
  $= 5^{4+4}$
  $= 5^8$

b. $(t^3)^4 = t^3 \cdot t^3 \cdot t^3 \cdot t^3$
  $= t^{3+3+3+3}$
  $= t^{12}$

The examples suggest this theorem.

Theorem 8-2

> **Power Theorem for Exponents**
> If x is a real number and a and b are positive integers, then
> $$(x^a)^b = x^{ab}.$$

Example 1 shows you how to apply Theorem 8-2.

EXAMPLE 1 Simplify: **a.** $(6^3)^9$ **b.** $(z^5)^{10}$

Solutions: **a.** $(6^3)^9 = 6^{3 \cdot 9}$ ◄— **By Theorem 8-2** —► **b.** $(z^5)^{10} = z^{5 \cdot 10}$
  $= 6^{27}$
  $= z^{50}$

The following examples suggest a method for multiplying an exponential expression having a monomial base.

c. $(3r)^3 = (3r)(3r)(3r)$
  $= (3 \cdot 3 \cdot 3)(r \cdot r \cdot r)$
  $= 3^3 r^3$, or $27r^3$

d. $(xy)^5 = (xy)(xy)(xy)(xy)(xy)$
  $= (x \cdot x \cdot x \cdot x \cdot x)(y \cdot y \cdot y \cdot y \cdot y)$
  $= x^5 y^5$

Thus, a power of a product of two or more factors equals the product of the powers of each factor.

Theorem 8-3

> **Power of a Product Theorem for Exponents**
> If x and y are real numbers and a is a positive integer, then
> $$(xy)^a = x^a y^a.$$

Recall that $-a = -1 \cdot a$. Thus, two factors of $-a$ are -1 and a.

EXAMPLE 2 Simplify: **a.** $(-x)^6$ **b.** $\left(-\frac{2}{3}x^5y^2\right)^3$

Solutions: **a.** $(-x)^6 = (-1 \cdot x)^6$ **b.** $\left(-\frac{2}{3}x^5y^2\right)^3 = \left(-\frac{2}{3}\right)^3(x^5)^3(y^2)^3$
  $= (-1)^6(x)^6$
  $= x^6$
  $= -\frac{8}{27}x^{15}y^6$

Teaching Suggestions p. M-21

Quick Quiz
Find each product.
1. $-a^2(-a^3)$ **Ans: a^5**
2. $(-p^3)(-p^3)$ **Ans: p^6**
3. $7xy(-9x^2y^3)$ **Ans: $-63x^3y^4$**
4. $(-4b^2c)(-9bc^2)$
 Ans: $36b^3c^3$
Write each product in exponential form.
5. $(7 \times 10^8)(9 \times 10^2)$
 Ans: 63×10^{10}
6. $(2 \times 10^3)(6 \times 10^5)$
 Ans: 12×10^8

Additional Examples
Example 1
Simplify.
1. **a.** $(7^2)^{10}$ **Ans: 7^{20}**
 b. $(9^4)^{12}$ **Ans: 9^{48}**
2. **a.** $(a^3)^{20}$ **Ans: a^{60}**
 b. $(w^6)^9$ **Ans: w^{54}**

Example 2
Simplify.
1. **a.** $(-a)^{10}$ **Ans: a^{10}**
 b. $(-c)^{15}$ **Ans: $-c^{15}$**
2. **a.** $(-\frac{3}{2}x^5y^2)^3$ **Ans: $-\frac{27}{8}x^{15}y^6$**
 b. $(-2a^6b)^6$ **Ans: $64a^{36}b^6$**

NOTE: Raising a negative number to an *even-numbered* exponent gives a *positive* number. Raising a negative number to an *odd-numbered* exponent gives a *negative* number.

CLASSROOM EXERCISES

Simplify. No denominator equals zero. $-8x^6$

1. $(x^2)^3$ x^6 2. $(-y^3)^2$ y^6 3. $(3x^4)^2$ $9x^8$ 4. $(-2x^2)^3$

5. $(-a^3b^2)^3$ $-a^9b^6$ 6. $\left(\dfrac{2}{3}\right)^2$ $\dfrac{4}{9}$ 7. $\left(-\dfrac{3}{4}\right)^2$ $\dfrac{9}{16}$ 8. $\left(\dfrac{x}{y}\right)^3$ $\dfrac{x^3}{y^3}$

WRITTEN EXERCISES

A   Simplify. No denominator equals zero.

1. $(x^3)^2$ x^6 2. $(x^2)^6$ x^{12} 3. $(x^4)^2$ x^8 4. $(y^5)^3$ y^{15} 5. $(a^3)^4$ a^{12}

6. $(x^3)^5$ x^{15} 7. $(x^7)^3$ x^{21} 8. $(x^5)^2$ x^{10} 9. $(x^3)^{12}$ x^{36} 10. $(x^2)^5$ x^{10}

11. $(y^3)^3$ y^9 12. $(a^5)^6$ a^{30} 13. $(b^4)^6$ b^{24} 14. $(a^2)^7$ a^{14} 15. $(y^4)^8$ y^{32}

16. $(ab)^3$ a^3b^3 17. $(xy)^2$ x^2y^2 18. $(2x)^2$ $4x^2$ 19. $(5x)^2$ $25x^2$ 20. $(2xy)^2$

21. $(xyz)^4$ $x^4y^4z^4$ 22. $(-5)^2$ 25 23. $(-6)^2$ 36 24. $(-3)^3$ -27 25. $(-x)^4$ x^4

26. $(-x)^5$ $-x^5$ 27. $(-y)^2$ y^2 28. $(-4x)^2$ $16x^2$ 29. $(3b)^3$ $27b^3$ 30. $(-ab)^3$

31. $(3a^2b)^2$ $9a^4b^2$ 32. $(6a^2)^3$ $216a^6$ 33. $(-3b)^3$ $-27b^3$ 34. $(2x^5)^2$ $4x^{10}$ 35. $(2x^3y^2)^3$

36. $(3^2a^2b^4)^2$ 37. $(4x^3y^2)^3$ 38. $(2m^3n^2)^4$ 39. $(x^2y)^4$ 40. $(2a^2b)^3$

41. $(4a^4c^2d^3)^3$ $64a^{12}c^6d^9$ 42. $(16x^3y^2)^2$ $256x^6y^4$ 43. $(2x^3y^2)^6$ $64x^{18}y^{12}$ 44. $(a^2b)^3$ a^6b^3

45. $(-x^4y^3)^2$ x^8y^6 46. $(-x^4y^2)^3$ $-x^{12}y^6$ 47. $(2 \times 10^3)^2$ 4×10^6 48. $(3 \times 10^5)^4$

49. $(1.1 \times 10^6)^3$ 50. $(2.5 \times 10^{10})^2$ 51. $\left(\dfrac{x}{y}\right)^2$ 52. $\left(\dfrac{1}{2}\right)^2$

53. $\left(\dfrac{2}{3}\right)^3$ $\dfrac{8}{27}$ 54. $\left(\dfrac{1}{3}\right)^4$ $\dfrac{1}{81}$ 55. $\left(\dfrac{c}{d}\right)^7$ $\dfrac{c^7}{d^7}$ 56. $\left(\dfrac{ab}{c}\right)^5$ 57. $\left(\dfrac{x^2}{y^3}\right)^2$ $\dfrac{x^4}{y^6}$ 58. $\left(\dfrac{x^2}{y^2}\right)^4$

59. $\left(\dfrac{b^2}{a}\right)^2$ $\dfrac{b^4}{a^2}$ 60. $\left(\dfrac{c^2}{d}\right)^3$ $\dfrac{c^6}{d^3}$ 61. $\left(\dfrac{a^2}{b^3}\right)^3$ $\dfrac{a^6}{b^9}$ 62. $\left(\dfrac{a^3}{b}\right)^6$ $\dfrac{a^{18}}{b^6}$ 63. $\left(\dfrac{x^3}{y^2}\right)^2$ $\dfrac{x^6}{y^4}$ 64. $\left(\dfrac{c^3}{d^2}\right)^7$

B   Match each expression in Column I with an equivalent expression in Column II.

Column I

65. $(x^2)^n$ i   66. $(-3x^a)^3$ b

67. $(x^n)^n$ a   68. $(3x^a)^3$ e

69. $(xy^a)^b$ f   70. $\dfrac{3}{2}\left(\dfrac{m}{n}\right)^c$ c

71. $\left(\dfrac{x}{y^a}\right)^b$ d   72. $\left(\dfrac{3m}{2n}\right)^c$ g

Column II

a. x^{n^2} b. $-27x^{3a}$

c. $\dfrac{3m^c}{2n^c}$ d. $\dfrac{x^b}{y^{ab}}$

e. $27x^{3a}$ f. x^by^{ab}

g. $\dfrac{3^cm^c}{2^cn^c}$ h. $\dfrac{x^b}{y^a}$

i. x^{2n} j. xy^{ab}

Assignment Guide
Minimal
Day 1 p. 286: 1–27
Day 2 p. 286: 28–64 even
Average
Day 1 p. 286: 2–50 even
Day 2 p. 286: 51–71
Above Average
Day 1 p. 286: 2–64 even
Day 2 pp. 286–287: 65–88

Additional Answers
Written Exercises
20. $4x^2y^2$
30. $-a^3b^3$
35. $8x^9y^6$
36. $81a^4b^8$
37. $64x^9y^6$
38. $16m^{12}n^8$
39. x^8y^4
40. $8a^6b^3$
48. 81×10^{20}
49. 1.331×10^{18}
50. 6.25×10^{20}
51. $\dfrac{x^2}{y^2}$
52. $\dfrac{1}{4}$
56. $\dfrac{a^5b^5}{c^5}$
58. $\dfrac{x^8}{y^8}$
64. $\dfrac{c^{21}}{d^{14}}$

C Simplify. All variables represent positive integers.

73. $\left(\dfrac{a^2}{bc^3}\right)^4 \dfrac{a^8}{b^4c^{12}}$

74. $\left(\dfrac{r^3}{s^2t}\right)^5 \dfrac{r^{15}}{s^{10}t^5}$

75. $\left(\dfrac{a^3b^2}{c^4}\right)^3 \dfrac{a^9b^6}{c^{12}}$

76. $\left(\dfrac{xy^6}{z^2}\right)^2\dfrac{x^2y^{12}}{z^4}$

77. $(-2a^3b^2)(3a^4b^6)$

78. $x \cdot x^2(x^3)^2$

79. $\left(\dfrac{-3x^2}{4y^2}\right)^3$

80. $(a^n)^m \quad a^{mn}$

81. $(x^n)^n \quad x^{n^2}$

82. $(a^6)^m \ a^{6m}$

83. $\left(\dfrac{m}{n}\right)^k \dfrac{m^k}{n^k}$

84. $\left(\dfrac{x^2}{y}\right)^c \dfrac{x^{2c}}{y^c}$

85. $\left(\dfrac{3x^n}{5y^m}\right)^c \dfrac{3^cx^{cn}}{5^cy^{cm}}$

86. $\left(\dfrac{3x^3}{4y^2}\right)^m$

87. $\left(\dfrac{3a^mb^n}{2xy}\right)^k$

88. $\left(\dfrac{2ab}{4xy}\right)^d \dfrac{2^da^db^d}{4^dx^dy^d}$

CALCULATOR APPLICATIONS

Evaluating Expressions with Exponents

A calculator with a power key, $\boxed{x^y}$, allows you to evaluate expressions with exponents quickly. You can usually work from left to right.

EXAMPLE 1 Find the value of x^4y^3 when $x = -2$ and $y = 16$.

SOLUTION 2   4  1 6 3 $\boxed{=}$ $\boxed{65536.}$

EXAMPLE 2 Evaluate: $(4 \times 10^2)(3 \times 10^4)$

SOLUTION 4 1 0 2  3 1 0 $\boxed{x^y}$ 4 $\boxed{=}$ $\boxed{120000000.}$

EXAMPLE 3 Find the value of $(-2a^2b)^5$ when $a = 0.25$ and $b = 4$.

SOLUTION 2   . 2 5 2 4 $\boxed{=}$ 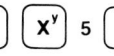 5 $\boxed{=}$ $\boxed{-0.03125}$

EXERCISES

Find the value of each expression when $x = 5$ and $y = -3$. $-16{,}875$

1. x^2y^2 225
2. x^3y^2 1125
3. x^2y^4 2025
4. x^3y^3 -3375
5. xy^6 3645
6. x^4y^3

Evaluate.

7. $(5 \times 10^3)(2 \times 10^2)$
  1,000,000
8. $(3 \times 10^2)(2 \times 10^5)$
  60,000,000
9. $(1.4 \times 10^3)(2.6 \times 10^4)$
  36,400,000

Find the value of each expression when $a = 8$ and $b = -0.4$.

10. $(a^2)^3$
11. $\left(\dfrac{a}{b}\right)^4$
12. $(2a^2b)^3$
13. $(10a^3b^3)^2$
14. $(a^5b^7)^3$
15. $(a^2b^2)^7$

REVIEW CAPSULE FOR SECTION 8-4

Find each quotient. *(Pages 68–71)*

1. $-8 \div (-8)$ 1
2. $0 \div 21$ 0
3. $-1 \div 1$ -1
4. $-1 \div \left(-\dfrac{1}{4}\right)$ 4

5. $\dfrac{1}{4} \div (-1)$ $-\dfrac{1}{4}$
6. $z \div (-1) -z$
7. $-8 \div \dfrac{1}{x}, x \neq 0 -8x$
8. $-r \div (-r), r \neq 0$ 1

Exponents and Polynomials   **287**

Additional Answers
Written Exercises
77. $-6a^7b^8$
78. x^9
79. $\dfrac{-27x^6}{64y^6}$
86. $\dfrac{3^mx^{3m}}{4^my^{2m}}$
87. $\dfrac{3^ka^{km}b^{kn}}{2^kx^ky^k}$

Calculator Exercises
10. 262,144
11. 160,000
12. $-134{,}217.73$
13. 107,374.18
14. $-154{,}742.5$
15. 11,805,916.2

Teaching Suggestions p. M-21

8-4 Dividing Monomials

Quick Quiz
Simplify.
1. $(y^6)^3$ **Ans:** y^{18}
2. $(a^7)^6$ **Ans:** a^{42}
3. $(5x)^3$ **Ans:** $125x^3$
4. $(-2)^5$ **Ans:** -32
5. $(-3)^4$ **Ans:** 81
6. $(-b)^8$ **Ans:** b^8
7. $(-c^2)^3$ **Ans:** $-c^6$
8. $(3x^2y^3)^3$ **Ans:** $27x^6y^9$
9. $(-\frac{3}{4}ab^2)^3$ **Ans:** $-\frac{27}{64}a^3b^6$
10. $(-2x^5y^4)^5$ **Ans:** $-32x^{25}y^{20}$

The quotient of two exponential expressions can be written with a single exponent *if the expressions have the same base.*

a. $\dfrac{2^5}{2^3} = \dfrac{2 \cdot 2 \cdot 2 \cdot 2 \cdot 2}{2 \cdot 2 \cdot 2}$ ← **By definition** → b. $\dfrac{x^6}{x^4} = \dfrac{x \cdot x \cdot x \cdot x \cdot x \cdot x}{x \cdot x \cdot x \cdot x}$

$= \left(\dfrac{2 \cdot 2 \cdot 2}{2 \cdot 2 \cdot 2}\right)(2 \cdot 2)$ ← **By the associative postulate** → $= \left(\dfrac{x \cdot x \cdot x \cdot x}{x \cdot x \cdot x \cdot x}\right)(x \cdot x)$

$= 1 \cdot 2^2$ $= 1 \cdot x^2$

$= 2^2$ ← $2^2 = 2^{5-3}$ $= x^2$ ← $x^2 = x^{6-4}$

NOTE: In **a** and **b**, subtracting the exponent of the denominator from the exponent of the numerator gives the single exponent in the answer. This suggests the following theorem.

Theorem 8-4

> **Division Theorem for Exponents**
> If x is a real number, $x \neq 0$, and a and b are positive integers such that $a \geq b$, then
> $$\frac{x^a}{x^b} = x^{a-b}.$$

Theorem 8-4 can be used to simplify quotients such as $\dfrac{x^4y^3}{x^2y}$.

Additional Examples
Simplify. No denominator equals zero.
1.a. $\dfrac{x^5y^3}{x^3y^2}$ **Ans:** x^2y
  b. $\dfrac{a^7b^5}{a^2b^3}$ **Ans:** a^5b^2
2.a. $\dfrac{-8a^5b^4c^3}{2ab^3c^2}$ **Ans:** $-4a^4bc$
  b. $\dfrac{9x^3y^2z^4}{-3xyz}$ **Ans:** $-3x^2yz^3$

EXAMPLE Simplify: **a.** $\dfrac{x^4y^3}{x^2y}$ **b.** $\dfrac{-6a^5b^3c^2}{2a^3b^2c}$

Solutions: **a.** $\dfrac{x^4y^3}{x^2y} = \left(\dfrac{x^4}{x^2}\right)\left(\dfrac{y^3}{y}\right)$

$= x^{(4-2)}y^{(3-1)}$

$= x^2y^2$

b. $\dfrac{-6a^5b^3c^2}{2a^3b^2c} = \left(\dfrac{-6}{2}\right)\left(\dfrac{a^5}{a^3}\right)\left(\dfrac{b^3}{b^2}\right)\left(\dfrac{c^2}{c}\right)$

$= -3a^{(5-3)}b^{(3-2)}c^{(2-1)}$

$= -3a^2bc$

NOTE: When $a = b$, it follows from Theorem 8-4 that
$$\frac{x^a}{x^b} = x^{a-b} = x^0 = 1.$$

Thus, $\dfrac{c}{c} = c^0 = 1,$ $\dfrac{a^2}{a^2} = a^0 = 1,$ and $\dfrac{x^3y^5}{x^3y^5} = x^0y^0 = 1.$

CLASSROOM EXERCISES

Simplify. No denominator equals zero.

1. $\dfrac{x^{12}}{x^6}$ x^6
2. $\dfrac{a^{10}}{a^{10}}$ 1
3. $\dfrac{-x^3y^5}{x^2y^3}$ $-xy^2$
4. $\dfrac{-56c^6}{-7c^2}$ $8c^4$
5. $\dfrac{8^{21}}{8^{19}}$
   $8^2 = 64$
6. $\dfrac{-42a^2b^5c^3}{3a^0b^3c^2}$ $-14a^2b^2c$

WRITTEN EXERCISES

A   Simplify. No denominator equals zero.

1. $\frac{2^3}{2}$ 2^2 or 4   2. $\frac{3^5}{3^2}$ 3^3 or 27   3. $\frac{5^6}{5^3}$ 5^3 or 125   4. $\frac{x^5}{x^5}$ 1   5. $\frac{a^6}{a}$ a^5 6. $\frac{a^9}{a^7}$ a^2

7. $\frac{x^8}{x^7}$ x 8. $\frac{x^3y^2}{xy}$ x^2y 9. $\frac{a^3y^3}{a^2y}$ ay^2 10. $\frac{y^3}{y^2}$ y 11. $\frac{a^3b^5}{ab^2}$ a^2b^3 12. $\frac{2x^7}{3x^7}$ $\frac{2}{3}$

13. $\frac{k^5m^3}{k^3m^2}$ k^2m 14. $\frac{18x^3y^4}{2xy^2}$ $9x^2y^2$ 15. $\frac{-15x^7y^5}{-3x^2y^4}$ $5x^5y$ 16. $\frac{-36a^2b^2c^4}{4abc^3}$ $-9abc$

17. $\frac{-27r^5s^8}{-3r^3s^6}$ $9r^2s^2$ 18. $\frac{-2k^4m^3}{4k^2}$ $-\frac{k^2m^3}{2}$ 19. $\frac{8 \times 10^2}{2 \times 10^2}$ 4   20. $\frac{8 \times 10^{11}}{4 \times 10}$ 2×10^{10}

Classify each quotient as positive, P, or negative, N.

21. $\frac{(-1)^8}{(-1)^2}$ P 22. $\frac{(-5)^{15}}{(-5)^5}$ P 23. $\left(\frac{-8}{-4}\right)^2$ P 24. $\frac{(-3)^{19}}{(-3)^9}$ P

Classify each quotient as positive, P, or negative, N, when $x = -1$ and $y = -3$.

25. $\frac{x^5}{x^2}$ N 26. $\frac{y^{10}}{y^3}$ N 27. $\frac{x^2y}{x^2y}$ P 28. $\frac{x^{95}}{x^3}$ P

B   Simplify. No denominator equals zero.

Example: $\dfrac{9xy(-4x^2y^3)}{-18x^2y^2} = \dfrac{-36x^3y^4}{-18x^2y^2} = \mathbf{2xy^2}$

29. $\frac{4ab(7a^2b^3)}{-14a^3b^3}$ $-2b$ 30. $\frac{4ab^2(-5ab^3)}{10a^2b^2}$ $-2b^3$ 31. $\frac{(-3ab^2)^2}{6ab}$ 32. $\frac{(3ab^2)^2(-6a^3b)}{(3a^2b^2)^2}$

33. $\frac{(5ab)^2(-20a^3b)}{4a^2b^3}$ 34. $\frac{(5a^2b)^2(-100b^3)}{(5^2b)^2}$ 35. $\frac{(5 \times 10^2)^3}{5 \times 10^2}$ 36. $\frac{(11 \times 10)^5}{(11 \times 10^2)^2}$

C   Simplify. All exponents are positive integers. No denominator equals zero.

37. $\frac{a^xb^2y}{a^xby}$ b 38. $\frac{a^xb^4}{a^y}$ $a^{x-y}b^4$ 39. $\frac{a^tb^w}{a^vb^{25}}$ 40. $\frac{x^{u-v}y^{w-z}}{x^{2v-u}y^w}$

41. $\frac{x^{3u-2v}y^3}{x^{2u+2v}y^2}$ $x^{u-4v}y$ 42. $\frac{a^{3x}}{a^{2x}}$ a^x 43. $\frac{a^{2x}b^{3y}c^k}{abc}$ 44. $\frac{ab^2c^4d^{2-k}}{ac^3d^k}$

45. $\frac{(x^{2a+1})^2}{x^{a-1}}$ x^{3a+3} 46. $\frac{(y^{3a-9})^6}{y^{2a-4}}$ y^{16a-50} 47. $\left(\frac{(x^{2a-4})^2}{x^{a+5}}\right)^3$ 48. $\frac{(1.69 \times 10^3)^a}{(1.3 \times 10^a)^2}$

———— REVIEW CAPSULE FOR SECTION 8–5 ————

Evaluate each expression. *(Pages 9–11, 280–282)*

1. 10^3 1000   2. 10^5 100,000   3. 10^6 1,000,000   4. 10^1 10   5. 10^4 10,000   6. 10^7

7. $\frac{1}{10^2}$ $\frac{1}{100}$ 8. $\frac{1}{10^3}$ $\frac{1}{1000}$ 9. $\left(\frac{1}{10}\right)^0$ 1   10. $\left(\frac{1}{10}\right)^3$ $\frac{1}{1000}$ 11. $\frac{1}{10^5}$ $\frac{1}{100,000}$ 12. $\frac{1}{10^4}$

Exponents and Polynomials   **289**

Assignment Guide
Minimal
Day 1 p. 289: 1–15
Day 2 p. 289: 16–28
Average
Day 1 p. 289: 1–20
Day 2 p. 289: 21–36
Above Average
Day 1 p. 289: 1–28
Day 2 p. 289: 29–36, 37–47 odd

Additional Answers
Written Exercises

31. $\frac{3ab^3}{2}$
32. $-6ab$
33. $-125a^3$
34. $-4a^4b^3$
35. 25×10^4
36. $11^3 \times 10$ or 13,310
39. $a^{t-v}b^{w-25}$
40. $x^{2u-3v}y^{-z}$
43. $a^{2x-1}b^{3y-1}c^{k-1}$
44. b^2cd^{2-2k}
47. x^{9a-39}
48. $1.69^{a-1} \times 10^a$

Review Capsule
6. 10,000,000
12. $\frac{1}{10,000}$

Teaching Suggestions p. M-21

8-5 Scientific Notation

Quick Quiz

Simplify. No denominator equals zero.

1. $\dfrac{k^6 m^4}{k^2 m^2}$ **Ans: $k^4 m^2$**

2. $\dfrac{mn^2 p^3}{mnp}$ **Ans: np^2**

3. $\dfrac{27 r^2 s^2 t^5}{-9 rs^2 t^4}$ **Ans: $-3rt$**

4. $\dfrac{-56 a^7 b^3 c^2}{-8 a^6 b^2 c}$ **Ans: $7abc$**

5. $\dfrac{-2 x^5 y^3}{8 x^2}$ **Ans: $\dfrac{-x^3 y^3}{4}$**

Suppose that the division theorem (Theorem 8–4) holds for positive integers a and b when $a < b$. That is, for any real number x, $x \neq 0$,

$$\frac{x^a}{x^b} = x^{a-b}, \text{ for } a < b.$$

Suppose the Division Theorem Holds	You Already Know	Reasonable Definition
$\dfrac{10^8}{10^{10}} = 10^{8-10} = 10^{-2}$	$\dfrac{10^8}{10^{10}} = \dfrac{10^8}{10^8} \cdot \dfrac{1}{10^2} = \dfrac{1}{10^2}$	$10^{-2} = \dfrac{1}{10^2}$
$\dfrac{10^7}{10^8} = 10^{7-8} = 10^{-1}$	$\dfrac{10^7}{10^8} = \dfrac{10^7}{10^7} \cdot \dfrac{1}{10^1} = \dfrac{1}{10}$	$10^{-1} = \dfrac{1}{10}$
$\dfrac{x^5}{x^8} = x^{5-8} = x^{-3}$	$\dfrac{x^5}{x^8} = \dfrac{x^5}{x^5} \cdot \dfrac{1}{x^3} = \dfrac{1}{x^3}$	$x^{-3} = \dfrac{1}{x^3}$
$\dfrac{y}{y^5} = y^{1-5} = y^{-4}$	$\dfrac{y}{y^5} = \dfrac{y}{y} \cdot \dfrac{1}{y^4} = \dfrac{1}{y^4}$	$y^{-4} = \dfrac{1}{y^4}$

The examples in the table suggest this definition.

Definition

> If x is any real number except zero and a is a positive integer, then
>
> $$x^{-a} = \frac{1}{x^a}.$$

You can use this definition to simplify expressions having negative exponents. To **simplify such an expression** means to rewrite it without exponents or with positive exponents only.

Additional Examples
Example 1

Simplify. No variable equals zero.

1. **a.** $(-3)^{-3}$ **Ans: $-\dfrac{1}{27}$**

   b. 6^{-2} **Ans: $\dfrac{1}{36}$**

2. **a.** $4y^{-4}$ **Ans: $\dfrac{4}{y^4}$**

   b. $-2a^{-3}$ **Ans: $-\dfrac{2}{a^3}$**

3. **a.** $\dfrac{x^3}{y^{-4}}$ **Ans: $x^3 y^4$**

   b. $\dfrac{a^5}{b^{-5}}$ **Ans: $a^5 b^5$**

EXAMPLE 1 Simplify: **a.** $(-5)^{-3}$ **b.** $3y^{-2}$ **c.** $\dfrac{x^2}{y^{-2}}$

Solutions: Write each expression with positive exponents. Simplify the result when possible.

a. $(-5)^{-3} = \dfrac{1}{(-5)^3}$

$= \dfrac{1}{-125}$

$= -\dfrac{1}{125}$

b. $3y^{-2} = 3 \cdot y^{-2}$

$= 3 \cdot \dfrac{1}{y^2}$

$= \dfrac{3}{y^2}$

c. $\dfrac{x^2}{y^{-2}} = x^2 \cdot \dfrac{1}{y^{-2}}$

$= x^2 \cdot \dfrac{1}{\frac{1}{y^2}}$

$= x^2 \cdot y^2 = x^2 y^2$

Very large and very small numbers are used in many scientific areas. For convenience, these numbers are expressed as the *product of some power of 10 and a number from 1 to 10*. This representation is called **scientific notation**.

Decimal Notation	Scientific Notation
Number	**$(1 \le x < 10) \times 10^a$**

<table>
<tr><td></td><td>95,672</td><td>9.5672×10^4</td><td></td></tr>
<tr><td></td><td>9567.2</td><td>9.5672×10^3</td><td></td></tr>
<tr><td>**Numbers greater than 1**</td><td>956.72</td><td>9.5672×10^2</td><td>**Numbers greater than 1**</td></tr>
<tr><td></td><td>95.672</td><td>9.5672×10^1</td><td></td></tr>
<tr><td></td><td>9.5672</td><td>9.5672×10^0</td><td></td></tr>
<tr><td></td><td>0.95672</td><td>9.5672×10^{-1}</td><td></td></tr>
<tr><td>**Numbers less than 1**</td><td>0.095672</td><td>9.5672×10^{-2}</td><td>**Numbers less than 1**</td></tr>
<tr><td></td><td>0.0095672</td><td>9.5672×10^{-3}</td><td></td></tr>
<tr><td></td><td>0.00095672</td><td>9.5672×10^{-4}</td><td></td></tr>
</table>

NOTE: When the given number *is greater than 10,* the power of 10 at the right in the table has a *positive exponent.*

When the given number *is less than 1,* the power of 10 at the right in the table has a *negative exponent.*

When the given number *is between 1 and 10,* the power of 10 has a *zero exponent.*

EXAMPLE 2 Write each number in scientific notation.

    a. 867,000,000,000   **b.** 0.00000305

Solutions: **a.** 867,000,000,000. ◄─────── **The number is greater than 1.**

      11 places ◄────── **Count the number of places the decimal point must be moved to get a number between 1 and 10.**

      8.67×10^{11} ◄────── **Write as a product.**

  b. 0.00000305 ◄────── **The number is less than 1.**

      6 places ◄────── **Count the number of places the decimal point must be moved to get a number between 1 and 10.**

      3.05×10^{-6} ◄────── **Write as a product.**

Additional Examples
Example 2
Write each number in scientific notation.
1. a. 58,000,000,000
    Ans: 5.8×10^{10}
  b. 1,230,000,000,000,000,000
    Ans: 1.23×10^{18}
2. a. 0.0000000789
    Ans: 7.89×10^{-8}
  b. 0.0000000000206
    Ans: 2.06×10^{-11}

CLASSROOM EXERCISES

Simplify.

1. $(4)^{-2}$ $\frac{1}{16}$ **2.** $5x^{-1}$ $\frac{5}{x}$ **3.** $(-4)^{-1}$ $\frac{1}{-4}$, or $-\frac{1}{4}$ **4.** $\left(-\frac{2}{3}\right)^{-3}$ $-\frac{27}{8}$ **5.** $(3b)^{-2}$ $\frac{1}{9b^2}$

Write in scientific notation.

6. 84,000,000 8.4×10^7 **7.** 7,000,000,000 7×10^9 **8.** 0.0003 3×10^{-4} **9.** 0.000063 6.3×10^{-5}

10. 1,556,000 1.556×10^6 **11.** 789 7.89×10^2 **12.** 0.159 1.59×10^{-1} **13.** 21.07 2.107×10^1

Exponents and Polynomials **291**

Assignment Guide
Minimal
Day 1 p. 292: 1–32
Day 2 p. 292: 36–65 odd
Average pp. 292–293: 1–69
odd
Above Average pp. 292–293
3, 6, 9, . . . 69, 70–77

Additional Answers
4. $\frac{1}{10}$
8. -8
12. 1
16. $\frac{1}{-64}$, or $-\frac{1}{64}$
20. -32
21. $\frac{1}{a^3}$
22. $\frac{1}{x^2}$
23. $\frac{3}{x^5}$
24. $\frac{2}{y^4}$
25. $\frac{1}{m}$
26. $\frac{3}{x^2}$
27. $\frac{1}{4y}$
28. $\frac{a}{c^4}$
29. $\frac{b^2}{a^3}$
30. $\frac{1}{4x^2}$
31. $\frac{1}{27y^3}$
32. $\frac{1}{c}$
35. 6.7×10^7
38. 4.3×10^{-3}
41. 2×10^{-5}
44. 5×10^{-3}
47. 6×10^6
50. 2.6×10^9
54. 4×10^{13} km
55. 2.976×10^5 km per second
60. 1.5×10^8 km
63. 1×10^{-8} gm

WRITTEN EXERCISES

A   Simplify. No variable equals zero.

1. 4^2 16
2. 3^{-2} $\frac{1}{9}$
3. 10^0 1
4. 10^{-1}

5. 10^3 1000
6. 10^{-4} $\frac{1}{10,000}$
7. 6^0 1
8. $(-2)^3$

9. $(-2)^{-3}$ $-\frac{1}{8}$
10. $(\frac{1}{2})^{-4}$ 16
11. $(\frac{3}{4})^{-3}$ $\frac{64}{27}$
12. 157^0

13. $(\frac{1}{4})^{-2}$ 16
14. $(-\frac{3}{4})^3$ $-\frac{27}{64}$
15. $(-\frac{3}{4})^{-3}$ $-\frac{64}{27}$
16. $(-4)^{-3}$

17. 10^{-3} $\frac{1}{1000}$
18. $(-\frac{1}{2})^{-2}$ 4
19. $(-\frac{2}{3})^{-2}$ $\frac{9}{4}$
20. $(-\frac{1}{2})^{-5}$

21. a^{-3}
22. x^{-2}
23. $3x^{-5}$
24. $2y^{-4}$

25. m^{-1}
26. $3x^{-2}$
27. $(4y)^{-1}$
28. ac^{-4}

29. $a^{-3}b^2$
30. $(2x)^{-2}$
31. $(3y)^{-3}$
32. $c^{-3} \cdot c^2$

Write each number in scientific notation.

33. 4600 4.6×10^3
34. 20,500,000 2.05×10^7
35. 67,000,000

36. 100,000 1×10^5
37. 24,000,000,000,000 2.4×10^{13}
38. 0.0043

39. 0.00057 5.7×10^{-4}
40. 0.0000008 8×10^{-7}
41. 0.00002

42. 0.07 7×10^{-2}
43. 0.0008 8×10^{-4}
44. 0.005

45. $\frac{2}{10,000}$ 2×10^{-4}
46. $\frac{7}{10,000,000}$ 7×10^{-7}
47. 6 million

48. 4 billion 4×10^9
49. 3 thousand 3×10^3
50. 2.6 billion

51. 40 million 4×10^7
52. 400 billion 4×10^{11}
53. 5 thousandths
5×10^{-3}

APPLICATIONS: Using Scientific Notation

Write each number in scientific notation.

54. The star Alpha Centauri is 40,000,000,-000,000 kilometers from the earth.

55. The speed of light is about 297,600 kilometers per second.

56. In one year, light travels about 10 trillion kilometers. 1×10^{13} km

57. The diameter of our galaxy is 100,000 light years. 1×10^5 light years

58. The center of our galaxy is 30,000 light years away. 3×10^4 light years

59. Our galaxy has about a hundred billion stars. 1×10^{11} stars

60. It is about 150,000,000 kilometers to our sun—a mere 8 light minutes away.

61. The sun is about 150,000,000 kilometers from the earth. 1.5×10^8 km

62. A teaspoon of neutron star material weighs 1 billion tons. 1×10^9 tons

63. Special balances can weigh something as small as 0.00000001 gram.

64. Astronomers have detected objects so far away that the light from these objects has taken 10 billion years to reach us. 1×10^{10} yr

65. When a neutron star collapses, the crust which has a thickness of one kilometer is 1,000,000,000,000,000 times stiffer than steel. 1×10^{15}

B   Write each number in decimal notation.

66. The sun has a mass of 2.2×10^{27} tons.

67. The temperature of the sun is 6×10^3 degrees Celsius.

68. If one foot of copper wire is heated $1°$ Celsius, it expands 1.6×10^{-5} feet.

69. A helium atom has a diameter of 2.2×10^{-8} centimeters.

C   Simplify. No variable equals zero.

70. $m^{-2} \cdot m^{-3}$ $\dfrac{1}{m^5}$

71. $(a^4)^{-2}$ $\dfrac{1}{a^8}$

72. $(x^{-3})^{-1}$ x^3

73. $\left(\dfrac{a}{b}\right)^{-2}$ $\dfrac{b^2}{a^2}$

74. $\left(\dfrac{d}{c}\right)^{-1}$ $\dfrac{c}{d}$

75. $\dfrac{x^3}{x^{-1}}$ x^4

76. $\dfrac{y^{-2}}{y^3}$ $\dfrac{1}{y^5}$

77. $(x^{-1})^{-1}$ x

_____ Review _____

Find the value when $a = -1$, $b = 3$, and $c = -4$. (Section 8-1)

1. ab^2 -9
2. a^2b 3
3. abc^2 -48
4. a^3c^3 64
5. a^3b^2c 36

Find each product. (Section 8-2)

6. $n \cdot n^3$ n^4
7. $x^2(-x^3)$ $-x^5$
8. $-(3a^3)(4a^4)$ $-12a^7$
9. $(2d)(3c^2d)(cd^2)$ $6c^3d^4$

Simplify. No denominator equals zero. (Section 8-3)

10. $(y^2)^4$ y^8
11. $(-a^2b)^4$ a^8b^4
12. $(2 \times 10^4)^2$ 4×10^8
13. $\left(\dfrac{r^2}{st}\right)^3$ $\dfrac{r^6}{s^3t^3}$

Simplify. No denominator equals zero. (Section 8-4)

14. $\dfrac{a^8}{a^6}$ a^2
15. $\dfrac{xy^4}{xy^3}$ y
16. $\dfrac{-12b^2c^2}{4b}$ $-3bc^2$
17. $\dfrac{4a(-2ab^2)}{2a^2}$ $-4b^2$

Simplify. No variable equals zero. (Section 8-5)

18. 3^{-4} $\dfrac{1}{3^4} = 81$
19. $(-4)^3$ -64
20. $\left(-\dfrac{2}{3}\right)^{-3}$
21. $3y^{-2}$ $\dfrac{3}{y^2}$
22. $(-3)^{-3}$

Write each number in scientific notation. (Section 8-5)

23. 6 million
24. 4 hundredths
25. 0.0007
26. 15,555

_____ REVIEW CAPSULE FOR SECTION 8-6 _____

Write the additive inverse of each polynomial. (Pages 47-50)

1. $2n$ $-2n$
2. $(-2n)$ $2n$
3. $2x - 5$ $-2x + 5$
4. $-3x^2 - 4x$
5. $-7a^2 - 3a + 4$

Write an addition problem for each subtraction problem. Do *not* subtract. (Pages 56-58)

6. $2x - (3x - 5)$
7. $3a - (2a - 3b)$
8. $-3y - (-6y - 3y + 4)$
9. $3a - (4a + 3b)$
10. $t - 4 - (2t - 1)$
11. $9 - r - (7r - 6)$

Exponents and Polynomials   **293**

Additional Answers
Written Exercise
66. 2,200,000,000,000,000,-000,000,000,000
67. 6000
68. 0.000016
69. 0.000000022

Quiz Sections 8-1–8-5
After completing this Review you may want to administer a quiz covering the same sections. See page M-50 of the Teacher's Manual for the suggested quiz.

Additional Answers
Review
20. $\dfrac{1}{\left(-\frac{2}{3}\right)^3} = -\dfrac{1}{\frac{8}{27}} = -\dfrac{27}{8} = -3\dfrac{3}{8}$
22. $\dfrac{1}{(-3)^3} = \dfrac{1}{-27} = -\dfrac{1}{27}$
23. 6×10^6
24. 4×10^{-2}
25. 7×10^{-4}
26. 1.5555×10^4

Review Capsule
4. $3x^2 + 4x$
5. $7a^2 + 3a - 4$
6. $2x + (-3x + 5)$
7. $3a + (-2a + 3b)$
8. $-3y + (6y + 3y - 4)$
9. $3a + (-4a - 3b)$
10. $t + (-4) + (-2t + 1)$
11. $9 + (-r) + (-7r + 6)$

This lesson is optional. It applies the algebraic skills of evaluating expressions with exponents, writing numbers in scientific notation, and rounding numbers to the career area of physics.

Career Applications: **Physics**

Astrophysicists study the structure of the universe. Speeds and distances are so great in space that astrophysicists use scientific notation to represent them and do computations with them.

Here are some approximate distances and speeds.

Minimum Distance from the Sun to:
Earth: 147,000,000 (1.47×10^8) kilometers
Mercury: 46,700,000 (4.67×10^7) kilometers
Mars: 206,000,000 (2.06×10^8) kilometers
Saturn: 1,350,000,000 (1.35×10^9) kilometers

Speed of Light or of a Radio Signal:
300,000 (3.0×10^5) kilometers per second.

The Earth as Seen From 400,000 Kilometers in Space

EXAMPLE 1 Find the approximate time in seconds needed for a radio signal to reach the sun from the earth.

Solution: Use $d = rt$.

$$1.47 \times 10^8 = (3.0 \times 10^5) \times t$$

$$t = \frac{1.47 \times 10^8}{3.0 \times 10^5}$$

$$= 0.49 \times 10^3 \text{ or } \textbf{490 seconds}$$

Physicists also study very small quantities and distances. They use scientific notation to represent and calculate with these numbers, also.

EXAMPLE 2 The ink used to print the word "Einstein" has a mass of 1×10^{-9} kilograms (1 **microgram**). In Einstein's formula, $E = mc^2$, the **joule** is the unit for measuring energy, E. Find how many joules of energy would be released if all the mass in kilograms, m, of the ink were converted to energy (c is the speed of light in meters per second).

Solution: $E = mc^2$
$E = (1 \times 10^{-9})(3 \times 10^8)^2$
$= (1 \times 10^{-9})(9 \times 10^{16})$
$= \textbf{9} \times \textbf{10}^7 \textbf{ joules}$

This is enough energy to lift a 6000-kilogram bus holding 44 students, each of mass 50 kilograms, 1.13 kilometers straight up in the air.

294   Career Applications

EXERCISES

In Exercises 1–4, refer to the speeds and distances given on page 294 to find each of the following. Round each answer to the nearest whole number.

1. The approximate time in seconds for light from the sun to reach Mercury.

2. The approximate time in seconds for light from the sun to reach Mars.

3. The approximate time in minutes for a radio signal to reach the sun from Saturn.

4. The approximate time in minutes for a radio signal to travel from the earth to the sun and back again.

Additional Answers
1. 156
2. 687
3. 75
4. 16
5. 3.36×10^{18}
6. 3.35×10^{18}
7. 3.31×10^{18}
8. 3.36×10^{18}
9. 3.37×10^{18}
10. 3.38×10^{18}
11. 81.99×10^{-15}
12. 45×10^{12}
13. 8.14×10^{-8}
14. 1.28×10^{19}

Kepler's Third Law of Planetary Motion says that for any planet in the solar system, the cube of its average distance from the sun, R^3, divided by the square of its time for one revolution, T^2, is a constant. Show that this is true in Exercises 5–10.

Planet	Average Radius of Orbit (m)	Time of One Revolution (sec)	$\dfrac{R^3}{T^2}\left(\dfrac{m^2}{sec^2}\right)$
5. Mercury	5.79×10^{10}	7.60×10^{6}	?
6. Venus	1.08×10^{11}	1.94×10^{7}	?
7. Earth	1.49×10^{11}	3.16×10^{7}	?
8. Mars	2.28×10^{11}	5.94×10^{7}	?
9. Jupiter	7.78×10^{11}	3.74×10^{8}	?
10. Saturn	1.43×10^{12}	9.30×10^{8}	?

In Exercises 11–12, use the formula $E = mc^2$ to find the number of joules of energy that would be released if the total mass given were converted to energy.

11. The mass of an electron: 9.11×10^{-31} kilograms.

12. A particle of mass 0.5 grams: 5×10^{-4} kilograms.

13. What is the volume of a droplet of water in a fog? The formula for the volume of a sphere is

$$V = \tfrac{4}{3}\pi r^3,$$

$r = 2.73 \times 10^{-3}$ centimeters (use $\pi \approx 3$).

14. An atom of gold has a diameter of about 2.5×10^{-10} meters. A thin square of gold foil, 1 centimeter on a side, is 1×10^{-6} meters thick. Find the approximate number of gold atoms in the foil.

Physicists use microscopes and electron microscopes in their work.

Physics 295

8-6 Addition and Subtraction of Polynomials

Quick Quiz
Simplify. No variable equals zero.

1. $(-4)^{-3}$ **Ans:** $-\frac{1}{64}$
2. $(-\frac{1}{2})^{-2}$ **Ans: 4**
3. 2^{-6} **Ans:** $\frac{1}{64}$
4. $-3a^{-2}$ **Ans:** $-\frac{3}{a^2}$
5. $6y^{-5}$ **Ans:** $\frac{6}{y^5}$
6. $\frac{a^2}{b^{-3}}$ **Ans:** a^2b^3
7. $\frac{3x^3}{y^{-5}}$ **Ans:** $3x^3y^5$

Write each number in scientific notation.
8. 98,700,000,000,000
   Ans: 9.87×10^{13}
9. 0.0000000861
   Ans: 8.61×10^{-8}
10. 0.0000000000000018
    Ans: 1.8×10^{-15}

To find the *perimeter of a polygon*, you add the lengths of its sides.

Polygon	Perimeter
	$5x^2 - 6$
	$5x^2 - 6$
	$2x^2$
	$2x^2$
	$14x^2 - 12$
	$3y^2$
	$4y^2$
	$6y^2 - 2$
	$13y^2 - 2$

The length of each side of each polygon is expressed as a *monomial* or as the sum of monomials. Recall from the definition on page 283 that expressions such as $13y^2$ and -2 are *monomials*.

A **polynomial** is a monomial or the sum of monomials. A polynomial with two terms is called a **binomial**; a polynomial with three terms is called a **trinomial**.

Polynomials

Monomial	Binomial	Trinomial
$7x^2y^2$	$4a + 3$	$3x^2 - 6x + 9$
-9	$9x^2 - 25z^2$	$6a - 7b - 3c$

To add polynomials, you add monomials that are *like terms*.

EXAMPLE 1 Add: $(4a + 6b) + (2a - 3b)$

Solution: First group the like terms. Then apply the distributive postulate.
$$(4a + 6b) + (2a - 3b) = (4a + 2a) + (6b - 3b)$$
$$= (4 + 2)a + (6 - 3)b \longleftarrow \text{By the distributive postulate}$$
$$= 6a + 3b$$

It is often convenient to arrange like polynomials in the same column before adding or subtracting.

EXAMPLE 2 Add: $(-3x^2 + 7xy - 6y^2) + (5xy + 3y^2 - 4x^2)$

Solution:
$$-3x^2 + 7xy - 6y^2$$
$$\underline{-4x^2 + 5xy + 3y^2} \longleftarrow \text{Arrange like terms in the same column.}$$
$$-7x^2 + 12xy - 3y^2 \longleftarrow \text{Add like terms.}$$

Additional Examples
Example 1
Add.
1. $(3x + 5y) + (5x - 2y)$
   Ans: $8x + 3y$
2. $(8a - 7b) + (9a + 3b)$
   Ans: $17a - 4b$

Example 2
Add.
1. $(-6a^2 + 9ab - 5b^2) + (6ab + 4b^2 - 3a^2)$
   Ans: $-9a^2 + 15ab - b^2$
2. $(x^2y^2 - y^3 + 2x^3) + (-y^3 + 3x^3 - 4x^2y^2)$
   Ans: $5x^3 - 3x^2y^2 - 2y^3$

296 *Chapter 8*

To subtract a polynomial, you add its additive inverse.

EXAMPLE 3   Subtract: $(x^3 + 2x^2 - 8x) - (-2x^2 + 7x - 5)$

Solution:
$$\begin{array}{l} x^3 + 2x^2 - 8x + 0 \quad\longleftarrow \textbf{Arrange like terms in the same column.} \\ \underline{ 2x^2 - 7x + 5} \quad\longleftarrow \textbf{Additive inverse of } -2x^2 + 7x - 5. \\ x^3 + 4x^2 - 15x + 5 \quad\longleftarrow \textbf{Add like terms.} \end{array}$$

CLASSROOM EXERCISES

Add or subtract as indicated.

1. $(4a - 3b) + (8a + 5b)$ $12a + 2b$
2. $(4a^2 - 5ab - 6b^2) + (10ab - 6a^2 - 6b^2)$ $-2a^2 + 5ab - 12b^2$
3. $(6r + 9s) - (4r + 3s)$ $2r + 6s$
4. $(h^2 + 6h + 9) - (25 - 10h + h^2)$ $16h - 16$
5. $(-3x^3 - 4) - (-6x^2 - 5x - 6)$ $-3x^3 + 6x^2 + 5x + 2$
6. $(8x^2 - 4x + 5) - (10x^2 - 9x - 8)$ $-2x^2 + 5x + 13$

WRITTEN EXERCISES

A   Add.

1. $\begin{array}{l}4a - 3b + 5c \\ \underline{8a + 5b - 9c}\end{array}$ $12a + 2b - 4c$
2. $\begin{array}{l}4r + 3s + t \\ \underline{6r + 9s + 5t}\end{array}$ $10r + 12s + 6t$
3. $\begin{array}{l}6p - 4t + x \\ \underline{-7p + 8t + 6x}\end{array}$ $-p + 4t + 7x$

4. $5b + 4c + 8d,\ 8b - 7c - 6d,\ 3b - 4c$ $16b - 7c + 2d$
5. $7x - 2y + 5z,\ 8y - 9z,\ 7x - 5y$ $14x + y - 4z$
6. $5x + 7y - 10,\ 8y - 2x + 3,\ 2x - 10y + 4$ $5x + 5y - 3$
7. $4a^2 - 5ab - 6b^2,\ 10ab - 6a^2 - 8b^2,\ 10b^2 - 3a^2 - 7ab$ $-5a^2 - 2ab - 4b^2$
8. $a - b + c,\ b - c - a,\ c - a + b,\ a - 2b - c$ $-b$
9. $4ab - 5bc + 6ac,\ 6bc - 7ab - 8ac,\ 10ab - bc - ac$ $7ab - 3ac$
10. $x^2 + y^2 - z^2,\ 3z^2 - 2x^2 - 4y^2,\ 4y^2 + x^2 + z^2$ $y^2 + 3z^2$
11. $x^2 - 6x + 7,\ 8x - 15 - x^2,\ 4x^2 + 6x - 9,\ 7x + 10$ $4x^2 + 15x - 7$
12. $a^2 - 2ab + b^2,\ 2ab + a^2 + b^2,\ 4a^2 - 4ab - b^2,\ a^2 - b^2$ $7a^2 - 4ab$
13. $a + 2b,\ 3b - 4c,\ 5a - 7c,\ 3b + 2d$ $6a + 8b - 11c + 2d$

APPLICATIONS: Using Addition of Polynomials

Find the perimeter of each polygon.

14.
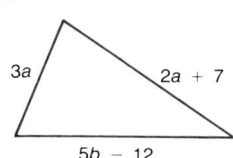

15.
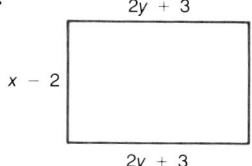

16.
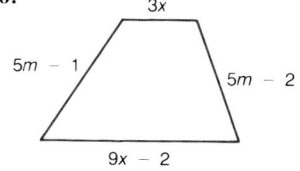

Additional Examples
Example 3
Subtract.
1. $(a^3 + 3a^2 - 9a) - (-2a^3 + 8a - 7)$
   Ans: $3a^3 + 3a^2 - 17a + 7$
2. $(c^2 - 2cd + d^2) - (3c^2 + d^2 - 7cd)$
   Ans: $-2c^2 + 5cd$

Assignment Guide
Minimal
Day 1 pp. 297–298, 1–13, 14–18 even
Day 2 p. 298: 20–41
Average
Day 1 pp. 297–298: 1–19
Day 2 p. 298: 20–40 even, 42–46
Above Average
pp. 297–298: 2–50 even

Additional Answers
Written Exercises
14. $5a + 5b - 5$
15. $2x + 4y + 2$
16. $10m + 12x - 5$

Find the perimeter of each polygon.

17.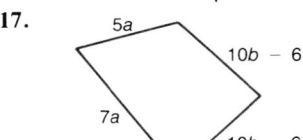

18.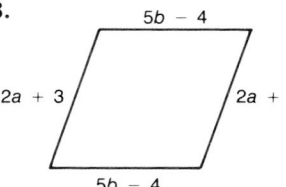

19.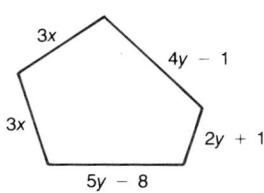

Subtract.

20.
$$\begin{array}{r} 3a + 4 \\ 2a + 9 \\ \hline \end{array}\quad a - 5$$

21.
$$\begin{array}{r} 7b - 5 \\ 10b - 8 \\ \hline \end{array}\quad -3b + 3$$

22.
$$\begin{array}{r} r + 8s \\ r - 5s \\ \hline \end{array}\quad 13s$$

23.
$$\begin{array}{r} 7x - 3 \\ -2x - 9 \\ \hline \end{array}\quad 9x + 6$$

24.
$$\begin{array}{r} 3x^2 + 8y^2 \\ x^2 - 8y^2 \\ \hline \end{array}\quad 2x^2 + 16y^2$$

25.
$$\begin{array}{r} 5m^2 - \ 9n \\ 8m^2 - 10n \\ \hline \end{array}$$

26.
$$\begin{array}{r} 8a - 9xy \\ -a + 9xy \\ \hline \end{array}\quad 9a - 18xy$$

27.
$$\begin{array}{r} a - b + c \\ a + b - c \\ \hline \end{array}\quad -2b + 2c$$

28.
$$\begin{array}{r} x^2 + 2x + 1 \\ x^2 - 2x + 1 \\ \hline \end{array}\quad 4x$$

29.
$$\begin{array}{r} 2a + 0 \\ a - b \\ \hline \end{array}\quad a + b$$

30.
$$\begin{array}{r} 2x^2 \quad\ - 4 \\ x + 2 \\ \hline \end{array}\quad 2x^2 - x - 6$$

31.
$$\begin{array}{r} x^3 + 0 \ + 0 \ + 8 \\ x^3 + x^2 - 2x + 0 \\ \hline \end{array}$$

32.
$$\begin{array}{r} x^2 + 6 \\ x^3 \qquad - 3 \\ \hline \end{array}\quad -x^3 + x^2 + 9$$

33.
$$\begin{array}{r} 3x^2 - 6x \\ 2x^2 \qquad + 7 \\ \hline \end{array}\quad x^2 - 6x - 7$$

34.
$$\begin{array}{r} -4x^2 - x + 9 \\ 3x^3 \qquad\ + x \\ \hline \end{array}$$

35. $(5x + y) - (2x - y)\ \ 3x + 2y$

36. $(a + 5b) - (4a - 3b)\ \ -3a + 8b$

37. $(3x^2 - 4y^2) - (2x^2 + 5y^2)\ \ x^2 - 9y^2$

38. $(4x^2 - 2x - 3) - (-5x - 4)\ \ 4x^2 + 3x + 1$

39. $(5x^2 - 10y^2) - (3x^2 + 2xy - 6y^2)\ \ 2x^2 - 2xy - 4y^2$

40. $(-4x^3 - 6x^2 + 3x - 1) - (8x^3 + 4x^2 - 2x + 3)\ \ -12x^3 - 10x^2 + 5x - 4$

41. $(-5a + 2b - 3c + 8d) - (4a - b + 3c + 5d)\ \ -9a + 3b - 6c + 3d$

B

42. From $3a - 2b + 5c$, take $-2a + 5b - c$. $5a - 7b + 6c$

43. Subtract $6x^2 - 3xy + y^2$ from $8x^2 + 5xy - y^2$. $2x^2 + 8xy - 2y^2$

44. From $6ab - 2ac + 5bc$, take $10ab - 2bc + 3ac$. $-4ab - 5ac + 7bc$

45. Subtract $x^2 - 2xy + y^2$ from $x^2 + 2xy + y^2$. $4xy$

46. From $x^2 - 2xy + y^2$, take $x^2 + 4xy + y^2$. $-6xy$

C

47. From the sum of $x + 3y$ and $-3x - y$, subtract $x - y$. $-3x + 3y$

48. Subtract $x^2 - y^2 - z^2$ from the sum of $2x^2 + 3y^2 - z^2$ and $4x^2 - 3y^2 + 5z^2$. $5x^2 + y^2 + 5z^2$

49. Take $a - b + 1$ from the sum of $a + c + 1$ and $a + b + 1$. $a + 2b + c + 1$

50. Subtract the sum of $(4x^3 + 2x^2 - 5)$ and $(15x - x^3 - x^2)$ from the difference of $(9 + 6x - 2x^2)$ and $(4x - 1 - 5x^3 + x^2)$. $2x^3 - 4x^2 - 13x + 15$

51. If x is 3 meters, which is greater: the perimeter of a square whose sides are each $(3x - 1)$ units long or the perimeter of a rectangle whose length is $x + 9$ and whose width is $2x - 3$? How much greater? The perimeter of the square is 2 meters larger.

Additional Answers
1. $6a + 15b - 12$
2. $-14x + 7y - 35$
3. $-2a + 6b - 1$
4. $20k - 15s + 10$
5. $-21 + 5t + 3r$
6. $6u - 10w + 11z$

Multiply. *(Pages 30-33, 283-284)*

1. $3(2a + 5b - 4)$ **2.** $-7(2x - y + 5)$ **3.** $(-1)(2a - 6b + 1)$

4. $-5(-4k + 3s - 2)$ **5.** $(-1)(21 - 5t - 3r)$ **6.** $(-1)(-6u + 10w - 11z)$

7. $a^4 \cdot a^5 \; a^9$ **8.** $q \cdot q^2 \; q^3$ **9.** $(-t^4)(t^3) \; -t^7$ **10.** $-a^5(-a^5) \; a^{10}$ **11.** $3x^2y(-9xy^5)$

$$-27x^3y^6$$

Simplify. *(Pages 61-64)*

12. $7a - (6a - 3 + b)$ **13.** $9b + (3c + 2) - b$ **14.** $5n - (-n + 2 - 3n)$

           $a - b + 3$ $8b + 3c + 2$ $9n - 2$

OBJECTIVE: To multiply polynomials

8-7 Products of Polynomials

To find the **area of a rectangle,** you multiply its length and its width.

Rectangle	Area
$3x$ [rectangle, width $7x - 9$]	$3x(7x - 9) = 3x[7x + (-9)]$ $= 3x(7x) + 3x(-9)$ $= 21x^2$ $= 21x^2 - 27x$
$4y + 2$ [square, side $4y + 2$]	$(4y + 2)(4y + 2) = (4y + 2)4y + (4y + 2)2$ $= 4y(4y) + 2(4y) + 4y(2) + 2(2)$ $= 16y^2 + 8y + 8y + 4$ $= 16y^2 + 16y + 4$

You can see from the table that you use the distributive postulate and the properties of exponents to multiply polynomials.

EXAMPLE 1   Multiply: $7y(-6y - 9)$

Solution: $7y(-6y - 9) = 7y[-6y + (-9)]$

                     $= 7y(-6y) + 7y(-9)$ ◄——— **By the distributive postulate**

                     $= (7)(-6)(y \cdot y) + (7)(-9)y$

                     $= -42y^2 - 63y$

Example 1 shows how to multiply a monomial and a binomial.

Examples 2 and 3 show how to multiply two binomials. To find the product of two binomials, you use the distributive postulate twice.

Exponents and Polynomials   **299**

Teaching Suggestions p. M-21

Quick Quiz
Add.
1. $(6r + 8s) + (9r - 7s)$
   Ans: 15r + s
2. $(8q - 9w) + (9q + 7w)$
   Ans: 17q − 2w
3. $(3x^2 - 5xy + 9y^2) +$
   $(-8x^2 - 10y^2 + 3xy)$
   Ans: −5x² − 2xy − y²
4. $(a^2 + b^2 - c^2) +$
   $(c^2 - a^2 + b^2)$
   Ans: 2b²
Subtract.
5. $(3x^3 + 2x^2 - 2x) -$
   $(-3x^3 + 8x - 9)$
   Ans: 6x³ + 2x² − 10x + 9
6. $(4a^2 + 8ab + b^2) -$
   $(5a^2 + b^2 - 6ab)$
   Ans: −a² + 14ab

Additional Examples
Example 1
Multiply.
1. $3a(-7a - 9)$
   Ans: −21a² − 27a
2. $-8b(9b - 7)$
   Ans: −72b² + 56b

EXAMPLE 2   Multiply: $(x + 2)(x - 5)$

Solution: $(x + 2)(x - 5) = [x + 2][x + (-5)]$

$= (x + 2)x + (x + 2)(-5)$ ◄───── **By the distributive post.**

$= (x)(x) + (x)(2) + (x)(-5) + (2)(-5)$ ◄ **By the distributive post.**

$= x^2 + 2x - 5x - 10$

$= x^2 - 3x - 10$

It is often easier to use a vertical format to multiply.

EXAMPLE 3   Multiply: $(5n + 2t)(7n + 2t)$

Solution: Arrange the polynomials vertically. Write like terms in the same column.

$$5n + 2t$$
$$7n + 3t$$
$$\overline{15nt + 6t^2}$$ ◄───── **$3t(5n + 2t)$**
$$35n^2 + 14nt$$ ◄───── **$7n(5n + 2t)$**
$$\overline{35n^2 + 29nt + 6t^2}$$ ◄───── **$35n^2 + (15nt + 14nt) + 6t^2$**

CLASSROOM EXERCISES

Multiply.

1. $3x(x + 9)$ $3x^2 + 27x$
2. $4x(-2x - 6)$ $-8x^2 - 24x$
3. $(x + 3)(7x + 4)$ $7x^2 + 25x + 12$
4. $(2y^2 - 5)(3y^2 + 6)$
5. $(-2n^3 - 5n)6n$
6. $-5y(3y^3 - 4y^2 + 6)$
7. $(a + 2)(a + 9)$ $a^2 + 11a + 18$
8. $(a^3 - 1)2a$ $2a^4 - 2a$
9. $-s(r^2 - 2r + 7)$
10. $a + 2(a + 9)$ $3a + 18$
11. $(x + y)(x - y)$ $x^2 - y^2$
12. $x + y(x - y)$ $x + xy - y^2$

WRITTEN EXERCISES

A   Multiply.

1. $a(2a + 3)$ $2a^2 + 3a$
2. $x^2(3x + 4)$ $3x^3 + 4x^2$
3. $3y(y - 8)$
4. $2y(3y - 4)$ $6y^2 - 8y$
5. $-2y(y + 6)$ $-2y^2 - 12y$
6. $-3x(x + 9)$
7. $m(5m - 2)$ $5m^2 - 2m$
8. $r(r^2 - 9)$ $r^3 - 9r$
9. $s(7s - 8)$ $7s^2 - 8s$
10. $3x^2(2x - 6)$ $6x^3 - 18x^2$
11. $-4a(3a - 5b)$ $-12a^2 + 20ab$
12. $5mn(7m - 2n)$
13. $2a(a^2 - 4a + 3)$
14. $-3x(x^2 + 5x + 2)$
15. $y^2(y^2 - 6y + 3)$
16. $-2ab(6a^2 - 4ab + 5b^2)$
17. $3xy(-x^4 - 4x^2y + 5xy^2)$
18. $(3a^2 - 2a - 9)(-a)$
19. $(a + 7)(a + 3)$ $a^2 + 10a + 21$
20. $(x + 9)(x + 5)$ $x^2 + 14x + 45$
21. $(2a + 4)(a + 5)$
22. $(7x + 3)(x + 1)$ $7x^2 + 10x + 3$
23. $(a + 3)(a - 4)$ $a^2 - a - 12$
24. $(2a + 3b)(a - b)$
25. $(2a - 5)(3a + 2)$
26. $(a + 3)(a + 2)$ $a^2 + 5a + 6$
27. $(2a + 3)(3a - 2)$ $6a^2 + 5a - 6$

$2a^2 - 3ab - 9b^2$

28. $(a - 3b)(2a + 3b)$

$ac + ad + bc + bd$

29. $(a + b)(c + d)$

$ac + ad - bc - bd$

30. $(a - b)(c + d)$

31. $(a - b)(c - d)$

32. $(a + b)(c - d)$

33. $(3b - 4c)(3b + 4c)$

34. $(3b - 4c)(2c + 3d)$

35. $(4x - 5)(4x + 5)$

36. $(7n - 3)(7n + 3)$

37. $(3x - 4)(3x - 4)$

38. $(2a - 3b)(a - 4b)$

39. $(5x - 3y)(3x + 4y)$

40. $(a + b)(a - b)$ $a^2 - b^2$

41. $(\frac{1}{2}x - y)(2x + y)$

42. $(\frac{1}{3}t - 5)(\frac{1}{3}t + 6)$

43. $(1.6n - 9)(0.2n - 5)$

44. $(a^2 + b)(a^2 - 2b)$

45. $(x^2 - y^2)(x^2 + y^2)$

46. $(m^2 - 2n^2)(m^2 - 2n^2)$

47. $(4s - 3)(2s^2 + 3)$

48. $(a^3 + b^3)(3a^3 - b^3)$

49. $(2x^2 + 3y^2)(3x^2 + 2y^2)$

50. $(x - 3)^2$ $x^2 - 6x + 9$

51. $(2x + 3y)^2$

52. $(x + 5)(x + 7)$ $x^2 + 12x + 35$

53. $x + 5(x + 7)$ $6x + 35$

54. $y - 6(2y + 8)$

55. $(y - 6)(2y + 8)$ $2y^2 - 4y - 48$

56. $2x + y(8x - 4y)$
$2x + 8xy - 4y^2$

57. $(2x + y)(8x - 4y)$
$16x^2 - 4y^2$

B

58. $(7x - 9)(3x - 4)$
$21x^2 - 55x + 36$

59. $4 - (5x + 2)$ $-5x + 2$

60. $5 - 2(8x + 3)$
$-16x - 1$

APPLICATIONS: Using Multiplication of Polynomials

Find the area of each region outlined in red.

61.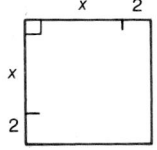

62.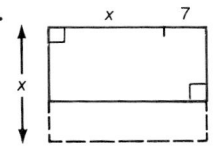

63.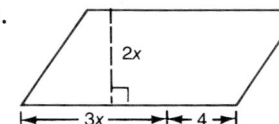

64.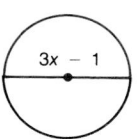

65.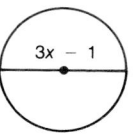

66.

67. Which has the greater area, a square with sides x units long or a rectangle with length $(x + 1)$ units and width $(x - 1)$ units. How much greater is it? *Square; 1 square unit larger*

68. Which has the greater area, a square with sides x units long, or a rectangle with length $(x + 2)$ units and width $(x - 2)$ units? How much greater is it? *Square; 4 square units larger*

69. Which has the greater area, a square with sides $(x + 1)$ units long or a rectangle with length $(x + 2)$ units and width x units? How much greater is it?
Square; 1 square unit larger

70. Which has the greater area, a square with sides $(x + 1)$ units long or a rectangle with length x units and width $(x - 2)$ units? How much greater is it?
Square; $4x + 1$ square units larger

C Multiply.

71. $(x^2 + 2x + 1)(x + 1)$

72. $(x^2 + 2x + 1)(x - 1)$

73. $(n^3 - 5n^2 + 2)(n^2 - 2n)$

74. $(x^2 - xy + y^2)(x + y)$

75. $(x^2 - 6xy + 9y)(x - 3y)$

76. $(2 - 3a^2 - a)(a - 1)$

77. $(c - 2c^2 + 3)(2 + c)$

78. $(x^3 + 3x^2 + 2x - 1)(x - 1)$

79. $(x^3 - 3x^2 + 3x - 1)(x - 1)$

Find each product. *(Pages 283–284)*

1. $(3c)(3c)$ $9c^2$
2. $(3x^4)(5x)$ $15x^5$
3. $(4ab)(3ab)$ $12a^2b^2$
4. $(2x^2)(3x^2)$ $6x^4$
5. $(2a^3)(4a^2)$ $8a^5$
6. $(4bc^2d)(9b^2c^2d^2)$ $36b^3c^4d^3$
7. $(xy^2z^3)(3x^3yz^4)$ $3x^4y^3z^7$
8. $(-x^2y^5)(x^4y^7z)$ $-x^6y^{12}z$

OBJECTIVE: To find the product of two binomials by inspection

8-8 Products of Binomials

Study the pattern in finding the product of two binomials. This is called the *FOIL method.*

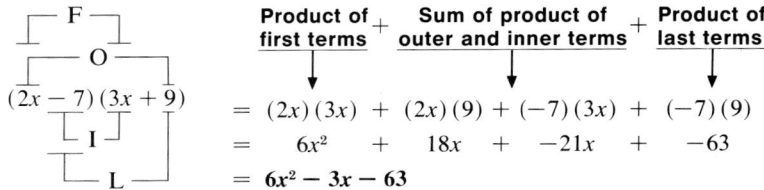

$$= (2x)(3x) + (2x)(9) + (-7)(3x) + (-7)(9)$$
$$= 6x^2 + 18x + -21x + -63$$
$$= 6x^2 - 3x - 63$$

You can use the FOIL method to multiply two binomials.

EXAMPLE Multiply by inspection: **a.** $(4x + 1)(2x - 3)$ **b.** $(5x - 4)(2x + 7)$

Solutions:
                         F   O   I   L

a. $(4x + 1)(2x - 3) = 8x^2 - 12x + 2x - 3 = 8x^2 - 10x - 3$

                         F   O   I   L

b. $(5x - 4)(2x + 7) = 10x^2 + 35x - 8x - 28 = 10x^2 + 27x - 28$

CLASSROOM EXERCISES

Match each pair of factors in Column 1 with its corresponding product in Column 2.

Column 1		Column 2
1. $(x + 5)(x - 3)$	h	a. $6a^2b^2 - 3ab - 9$
2. $(5a - 3)(2a - 2)$	d	b. $20a^2 - 29a + 5$
3. $(4a - 5)(5a - 1)$	b	c. $x^2 - 25$
4. $(8x - 3)(4x + 5)$	i	d. $10a^2 - 16a + 6$
5. $(2ab - 3)(3ab + 3)$	a	e. $10a^2 + 9ab - 9b^2$
6. $(5a - 3b)(2a + 3b)$	e	f. $6x^2 - 19xy + 10y^2$
7. $(6a + 2b)(9a - b)$	j	g. $a^2 - b^2$
8. $(3x - 2y)(2x - 5y)$	f	h. $x^2 + 2x - 15$
9. $(a - b)(a + b)$	g	i. $32x^2 + 28x - 15$
10. $(x - 5)(x + 5)$	c	j. $54a^2 + 12ab - 2b^2$

302 *Chapter 8*

Quick Quiz
Multiply.
1. $7x(-5x - 8)$
  Ans: $-35x^2 - 56x$
2. $-6c(8c^2 - 9c)$
  Ans: $-48c^3 + 54c^2$
3. $(r + 9)(r - 7)$
  Ans: $r^2 + 2r - 63$
4. $(x - 8)(x + 3)$
  Ans: $x^2 - 5x - 24$
5. $(4p - 3q)(5p + q)$
  Ans: $20p^2 - 11pq - 3q^2$
6. $(5a + 7b)(3a + 5b)$
  Ans: $15a^2 + 31ab + 35b^2$

Additional Examples
Multiply by inspection.
1. **a.** $(5x + 1)(3x - 4)$
  Ans: $15x^2 - 17x - 4$
  b. $(3x + 2)(2x - 3)$
  Ans: $6x^2 - 5x - 6$
2. **a.** $(3x - 4)(2x + 1)$
  Ans: $6x^2 - 5x - 4$
  b. $(4b - 7)(3b + 4)$
  Ans: $12b^2 - 5b - 28$

WRITTEN EXERCISES

See page 576 for the answers to Exercises 1-58 odd.

A   Find each product.

1. $(x+5)(x+3)$ 2. $(x-5)(x+7)$ 3. $(x+2)(x-2)$

4. $(x+3)(x+2)$ 5. $(a-2)(a+3)$ 6. $(y-5)(y+1)$

7. $(b-7)(b+3)$ 8. $(d+4)(d-5)$ 9. $(p+9)(p+11)$

10. $(2x+5)(5x+6)$ 11. $(d-4)(d+5)$ 12. $(m+n)(m-n)$

13. $(3y+2)(4y+3)$ 14. $(2x+5)(3x+1)$ 15. $(x+3)(2x+7)$

16. $(p-9)(p-11)$ 17. $(3x-4)(3x+4)$ 18. $(m-n)(p-q)$

19. $(b+4)(b+4)$ 20. $(n-2)(n+2)$ 21. $(m+7)(m-11)$

22. $(a+b)(2a-b)$ 23. $(a-2c)(a+2c)$ 24. $(3x-2y)(3x+2y)$

25. $(3x+2)(x-1)$ 26. $(x^2+2y)(x^2-2y)$ 27. $(y^2+3)(y^2+3)$

28. $(2b+3)(4b-7)$ 29. $(4y-3)(4y-3)$ 30. $(4y-3)(4y+3)$

31. $(2a+5)(2a+3)$ 32. $(4c-7)(5c+9)$ 33. $(5x+3)(x+1)$

34. $(2f+9)(3f+7)$ 35. $(7b+2)(5b-1)$ 36. $(10p+3)(6p-1)$

37. $(8x+3)(3x-4)$ 38. $(8r-5)(7r+5)$ 39. $(2c-9)(3c-8)$

40. $(4x+7)(5x-3)$ 41. $(x^2-4)(x^2+4)$ 42. $(y^2-2)(y^2+2)$

43. $(7a-2)(a+8)$ 44. $(a^2-3b)(a^2+2b)$ 45. $(3x-5y)(2x+3y)$

B

46. $(\frac{1}{2}x+5)(6x-10)$ 47. $(\frac{1}{2}x-3)(7x+8)$ 48. $(5a+1)(\frac{1}{2}a+4)$

49. $(\frac{1}{3}t+8)(\frac{1}{4}t+6)$ 50. $(5x+\frac{2}{3})(6x+\frac{3}{2})$ 51. $(\frac{1}{5}x-7)(\frac{1}{7}x-5)$

52. $(0.3u-0.4)(0.5u-0.1)$ 53. $(1.8w-2.4)(0.2w+0.5)$ 54. $(0.4m+0.3n)(1.1m+1.2n)$

APPLICATIONS: Using Products of Binomials

55. The sides of a square have length $(s+4)$. Write a polynomial for the area of the square.

56. A box has length $(5t-9)$, width $(t+7)$, and height, t. Write a polynomial for the volume of the box.

57. Which has the greater area, a rectangle with length $(a+2)$ units and width $(a+1)$ units, or a rectangle with length $(a+4)$ units and width $(a-1)$ units? How much greater is it?

58. Which has the greater area, a rectangle with length $(2a+1)$ units and width $(a-5)$ units, or a rectangle with length $(2a+3)$ units and width $(a-6)$ units? How much greater is it?

_____ **REVIEW CAPSULE FOR SECTION 8-9** _____

Raise to the indicated power. *(Pages 285–287)*

1. $(-2)^2$ 4   2. $(-x)^2$ x^2 3. $-(x)^2$ $-x^2$ 4. $(-xyz)^2$ $x^2y^2z^2$ 5. $(a^2)^2$ a^4

6. $(-a^2)^2$ a^4 7. $-(a^2)^2$ $-a^4$ 8. $(-2a)^2$ $4a^2$ 9. $-(-2a)^2$ $-4a^2$ 10. $-(-2a^4)^2$
$-4a^8$

Exponents and Polynomials   **303**

OBJECTIVE: To square binomials

8–9 Squaring Binomials

Study the table to find the pattern for squaring binomials.

Square of a Sum	Square of a Difference
$(x + 4)^2 = (x + 4)(x + 4)$	$(x - 4)^2 = (x - 4)(x - 4)$
$= x^2 + 4x + 4x + 16$	$= x^2 - 4x - 4x + 16$
$2(4x)$	$2(-4x)$
$= x^2 + 8x + 16$	$= x^2 - 8x + 16$
$(m + 3n)^2 = (m + 3n)(m + 3n)$	$(m - 3n)^2 = (m - 3n)(m - 3n)$
$= m^2 + 3mn + 3mn + 9n^2$	$= m^2 - 3mn - 3mn + 9n^2$
$2(3mn)$	$2(-3mn)$
$= m^2 + 6mn + 9n^2$	$= m^2 - 6mn + 9n^2$
$(a + b)^2 = (a + b)(a + b)$	$(a - b)^2 = (a - b)(a - b)$
$= a^2 + ab + ab + b^2$	$= a^2 - ab - ab + b^2$
$= a^2 + 2ab + b^2$	$= a^2 - 2ab + b^2$

The following procedure summarizes the steps for squaring a binomial.

Procedure

> **To square a binomial:**
> 1. Square the first term.
> 2. Add to this twice the product of the first and last terms when the binomial is of the form $(a + b)$.
>
>   Subtract twice the product of the first and last terms when the binomial is of the form $(a - b)$.
> 3. Add to this the square of the last term.

You can use this procedure to write the square of a binomial as a trinomial.

EXAMPLE 1 Write the square of each binomial as a trinomial.

    a. $(5x + 2y)^2$ **b.** $(2y - 3)^2$

Solutions: **a.** $(5x + 2y)^2 = (5x)^2 + 2(5x)(2y) + (2y)^2$
                           $= 25x^2 + 20x + 4y^2$

          b. $(2y - 3)^2 = (2y)^2 - 2(2y)(3) + 3^2$
                         $= 4y^2 - 12y + 9$

You can square a number by writing it as the sum or as the difference of the same two numbers.

EXAMPLE 2 Square each number: **a.** $(32)^2$ **b.** $(49)^2$

Solutions: **a.** $(32)^2 = (30 + 2)^2$ **b.** $(49)^2 = (50 - 1)^2$
$$= (30)^2 + 2(30)(2) + 2^2 \qquad = (50)^2 - 2(50)(1) + 1^2$$
$$= 900 + 120 + 4 \qquad\qquad = 2500 - 100 + 1$$
$$= \mathbf{1024} \qquad\qquad\qquad = \mathbf{2401}$$

You will find it useful to memorize these special binomial products.

Square of a Binomial Sum: $(a + b)^2 = a^2 + 2ab + b^2$

Square of a Binomial Difference: $(a - b)^2 = a^2 - 2ab + b^2$

CLASSROOM EXERCISES

Write the square of each binomial as a trinomial. $n^2 + 10nt + 25t^2$

1. $(x - 10)^2$ **2.** $(5x + 3)^2$ **3.** $(x - 2y)^2$ **4.** $(n + 5t)^2$

5. $(2p - q)^2$ **6.** $(2x + 3y)^2$ **7.** $(m^2 - 6)^2$ **8.** $(2x^2 + 1)^2$
$4p^2 - 4pq + q^2$ $4x^2 + 12xy + 9y^2$ $m^4 - 12m^2 + 36$ $4x^4 + 4x^2 + 1$

WRITTEN EXERCISES   See page 576 for Ex. 1-32 odd, 43, 45, 47

A   Write the square of each binomial as a trinomial.

1. $(a + 3)^2$ **2.** $(a - 2)^2$ **3.** $(a + 5)^2$ **4.** $(x - 3)^2$

5. $(a - 5)^2$ **6.** $(n - 6)^2$ **7.** $(x - y)^2$ **8.** $(2a + 3)^2$

9. $(2a + 1)^2$ **10.** $(4a - 1)^2$ **11.** $(5m - 1)^2$ **12.** $(7m - 4)^2$

13. $(n + 3)^2$ **14.** $(5m + 3)^2$ **15.** $(3x - y)^2$ **16.** $(x + 2)^2$

17. $(2x - 3)^2$ **18.** $(2x - 5)^2$ **19.** $(2x + y)^2$ **20.** $(y + 10)^2$

21. $(2x - 3y)^2$ **22.** $(3a - 2b)^2$ **23.** $(10a + 2)^2$ **24.** $(5c + 3d)^2$

25. $(2x^2 + 3y^2)^2$ **26.** $(5c^2 + 4y^3)^2$ **27.** $(a^2 - 3b^2)^2$ **28.** $(x^2y - 5)^2$

29. $(a^2 - 3)^2$ **30.** $(2a^2 + 3)^2$ **31.** $(11a^2 + c^2)^2$ **32.** $(8x^2 - 5d^2)^2$

Square each number.   11,025

33. $(20 - 1)^2$ 361   **34.** $(100 - 1)^2$ 9801   **35.** $(50 + 2)^2$ 2,704   **36.** $(100 + 5)^2$

37. $(21)^2$ 441 **38.** $(29)^2$ 841 **39.** $(999)^2$ **40.** $(98)^2$ **41.** $(101)^2$ **42.** $(19)^2$
                                              998,001   9,604   10,201   361

B   Write the square of each binomial as a trinomial.

43. $(x + \frac{1}{2})^2$ **44.** $(x + \frac{1}{3})^2$ **45.** $(x - \frac{1}{6})^2$ **46.** $(2y + \frac{1}{2})^2$ **47.** $(6b + \frac{1}{2})^2$

48. $\left(9a + \frac{1}{6}\right)^2$ **49.** $\left(x - \frac{a}{2}\right)^2$ **50.** $\left(y - \frac{1}{2}p\right)^2$ **51.** $\left(x + \frac{y}{2}\right)^2$ **52.** $\left(\frac{x}{2} + 4\right)^2$

$81a^2 + 3a + \frac{1}{36}$ $x^2 - ax + \frac{a^2}{4}$ $y^2 - py + \frac{1}{4}p^2$ $x^2 + xy + \frac{y^2}{4}$

Exponents and Polynomials   **305**

8-10 Product of $(a + b)$ and $(a - b)$ the same two numbers

Study the table to find the pattern for finding the product of the sum and difference of the same two numbers.

$(a + b)(a - b)$	Multiply by inspection.	Simplify.
$(x + 7)(x - 7)$	$x^2 + 7x - 7x - 49$	$x^2 - 49$
$(y + 10)(y - 10)$	$y^2 + 10y - 10y - 100$	$y^2 - 100$
$(2x + 5)(2x - 5)$	$4x^2 + 10x - 10x - 25$	$4x^2 - 25$

The following procedure summarizes the steps for finding the product.

Procedure

> To find the product of the sum and difference of the same two numbers:
> 1 Square the first term of either binomial.
> 2 Subtract the square of the second term of either binomial.

You can use this procedure to write the product of the sum and difference of the same two numbers as a binomial.

EXAMPLE 1   Write each product as a binomial.

a. $\left(\frac{1}{3} + y\right)\left(\frac{1}{3} - y\right)$ b. $(3r + 7t)(3r - 7t)$

Solutions: a. $\left(\frac{1}{3} + y\right)\left(\frac{1}{3} - y\right) = \left(\frac{1}{3}\right)^2 - y^2$ ◄—— **(First term)^2 − (Second term)^2**

$= \frac{1}{9} - y^2$

b. $(3r + 7t)(3r - 7t) = (3r)^2 - (7t)^2$ ◄—— **(First term)^2 − (Second term)^2**

$= 9r^2 - 49t^2$

This procedure is useful in finding certain products.

EXAMPLE 2   Find the product: 42×38

Solution: $42 \times 38 = (40 + 2)(40 - 2)$ ◄—— **Write 42 and 38 as the sum and difference of the same two numbers.**

$= (40^2) - (2)^2$

$= 1600 - 4 = 1596$

You will find it useful to memorize this special binomial product.

> **Product of a Sum and Difference**
> $$(a + b)(a - b) = a^2 - b^2$$

306   *Chapter 8*

CLASSROOM EXERCISES

Write each product as a binomial.

1. $(x + 1)(x - 1)$ $x^2 - 1$ **2.** $(a + 3)(a - 3)$ $a^2 - 9$ **3.** $(2r - 5)(2r + 5)$ $4r^2 - 25$

4. $(1 - 6q)(1 + 6q)$ $1 - 36q^2$ **5.** $(3h + 4s)(3h - 4s)$ **6.** $(0.2s - 0.1t)(0.2s + 0.1t)$
$9h^2 - 16s^2$ $0.04s^2 - 0.01t^2$

WRITTEN EXERCISES

Ⓐ   Write each product as a binomial.

1. $(p + 7)(p - 7)$ $p^2 - 49$ **2.** $(p - 5)(p + 5)$ $p^2 - 25$ **3.** $(p + 8)(p - 8)$ $p^2 - 64$

4. $(2p + 5)(2p - 5)$ $4p^2 - 25$ **5.** $(b + c)(b - c)$ $b^2 - c^2$ **6.** $(c - 2)(c + 2)$ $c^2 - 4$

7. $(2p + 3)(2p - 3)$ $4p^2 - 9$ **8.** $(3p + 5)(3p - 5)$ $9p^2 - 25$ **9.** $(R - r)(R + r)$ $R^2 - r^2$

10. $(2x + y)(2x - y)$ $4x^2 - y^2$ **11.** $(5x + 4y)(5x - 4y)$ **12.** $(7x - 6y)(7x + 6y)$

13. $(6x^2 - 7y)(6x^2 + 7y)$ **14.** $(a^2 + b^2)(a^2 - b^2)$ **15.** $(ab - c)(ab + c)$

16. $(y - x^2)(x^2 + y)$ $y^2 - x^4$ **17.** $(\frac{1}{2} - 2x)(\frac{1}{2} + 2x)$ $\frac{1}{4} - 4x^2$ **18.** $(y + 0.5)(y - 0.5)$

19. $(2c + d)(2c - d)$ $4c^2 - d^2$ **20.** $(3c + 2d)(3c - 2d)$ **21.** $(5y - 4)(4 + 5y)$

22. $(x^2 + y^2)(x^2 - y^2)$ $x^4 - y^4$ **23.** $(x^3 - y^3)(x^3 + y^3)$ $x^6 - y^6$ **24.** $(x^4 - y^4)(x^4 + y^4)$
$x^8 - y^8$

Find each product.

25. $(20 + 1)(20 - 1)$ 399 **26.** $(30 + 1)(30 - 1)$ 899 **27.** $(100 + 2)(100 - 2)$
9996

28. $(50 + 4)(50 - 4)$ 2484 **29.** $(10 + 5)(10 - 5)$ 75 **30.** $(1000 + 1)(1000 - 1)$

31. $18 \cdot 22$ 396 **32.** $101 \cdot 99$ 9999 **33.** $51 \cdot 49$ 2499

APPLICATIONS: Using Binomial Products

Ⓑ   Find the area of the region bounded by the red closed curve.

34.
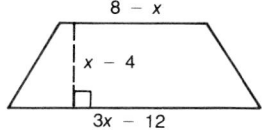

35.
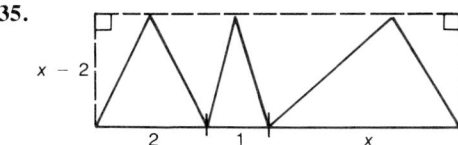

36. Which has the greater area, a square each of whose sides is x units long or a rectangle having the same perimeter but with width 5 units shorter than the width of the square?
Square is 25 square units greater

37. Which has the greater area, a square each of whose sides is y units long or a rectangle having the same perimeter but with length 4 units longer than the side of the square? How much greater is it?   Square is 16 square units greater

Ⓒ   Write each product as a binomial.

38. $(x^n + 1)(x^n - 1)$ **39.** $(1 - y^{2a})(1 + y^{2a})$ **40.** $(x^a - y^b)(x^a + y^b)$

41. $(a^2b^8 - 5)(a^2b^8 + 5)$ **42.** $(0.2 + x^3y^5)(0.2 - x^3y^5)$ **43.** $(b^n + c^{2n})(b^n - c^{2n})$

Exponents and Polynomials   **307**

Assignment Guide
Minimal p. 307: 1–33 odd
Average
p. 307: 1–33 odd, 34–37
Above Average
p. 305: 3, 6, 9, . . . 36, 38–43

Additional Answers
Written Exercises
11. $25x^2 - 16y^2$
12. $49x^2 - 36y^2$
13. $36x^4 - 49y^2$
14. $a^4 - b^4$
15. $a^2b^2 - c^2$
18. $y^2 - 0.25$
20. $9c^2 - 4d^2$
21. $25y^2 - 16$
30. $999,999$
34. $x^2 - 6x + 8$
35. $\frac{1}{2}x^2 + \frac{1}{2}x - 3$
38. $x^{2n} - 1$
39. $1 - y^{4a}$
40. $x^{2a} - y^{2b}$
41. $a^4b^{16} - 25$
42. $0.04 - x^6y^{10}$
43. $b^{2n} - c^{4n}$

BASIC: SQUARING BINOMIALS

This section is optional. Each computer applications lesson relates directly to a topic covered within the chapter. (See Section 8-9, pages 304–305.)

You can write a BASIC program to compute the square of a given binomial.

Problem: *Write a program which squares binomials of the form Ax + B.*

```
100 PRINT "FOR THE BINOMIAL TO BE SQUARED, AX + B,"
110 PRINT "WHAT ARE A AND B";
120 INPUT A, B
130 LET C = 2 * A * B
140 IF C < 0 THEN 170
150 PRINT A*A;"X↑2 +";C;"X +";B*B
160 GOTO 180
170 PRINT A*A;"X↑2 -";ABS(C);"X +";B*B
180 PRINT
190 PRINT "ANY MORE BINOMIALS TO SQUARE (1=YES, 0=NO)";
200 INPUT Z
210 IF Z = 1 THEN 120
220 END
```

The following is the output from a sample run of the program above.

Output:
```
RUN
FOR THE BINOMIAL TO BE SQUARED, AX + B,
WHAT ARE A AND B? 2,3
 4 X↑2 + 12 X + 9

ANY MORE BINOMIALS TO SQUARE (1=YES, 0=NO)? 1
? 1,-3
 1 X↑2 - 6 X + 9

ANY MORE BINOMIALS TO SQUARE (1=YES, 0=NO)? 1
? -6,4
 36 X↑2 - 48 X + 16

ANY MORE BINOMIALS TO SQUARE (1=YES, 0=NO)? 1
? -5,-7
 25 X↑2 + 70 X + 49

ANY MORE BINOMIALS TO SQUARE (1=YES, 0=NO)? 1
? 2,0
 4 X↑2 + 0 X + 0

ANY MORE BINOMIALS TO SQUARE (1=YES, 0=NO)? 0
READY
```

Analysis

Statement 130: When a binomial is squared, the result is a trinomial. The coefficient of the middle term of the square of the binomial is computed.

Statement 140: The first and last terms of the trinomial must have positive coefficients. For printing the trinomial, then, the only question is whether the middle term is positive or negative.

Statement 150: If C is positive, the trinomial is printed with a "+" in front of the middle term as well as a "+" in front of the last term (B^2).

Statement 170: If C is negative, the trinomial is printed with a "−" in front of the middle term and a "+" in front of the last term.

As the output from the second set of input data in the sample run shows, the program does not eliminate the printing of 1 or −1 coefficients. (See Exercise 14 below.) Also the program does not detect whether A or B = 0. (See Exercise 15 below.)

EXERCISES

Ⓐ Run the program on page 308 for the following values of *A* and *B*.

1. $A = 3$; $B = 4$ **2.** $A = 2$; $B = 9$ **3.** $A = 6$; $B = -3$

4. $A = -5$; $B = 2$ **5.** $A = -4$; $B = -4$ **6.** $A = -8$; $B = 0$

Write each binomial in the form $Ax + B$. Then use the program on page 308 to square each binomial.

7. $5 + x$ **8.** $10 + 3x$ **9.** $11 - 2x$

10. $21x$ **11.** $-32x$ **12.** $15 - 23x$

Rewrite the program on page 308 to do each of the following.

13. Square binomials of the form $Ax + By$. See the Solution Key for the answers to Ex. 13-18.

14. Eliminate the printing of coefficients equal to 1 or −1.

15. Test whether *A* or *B* (or both) equals 0 and change the printing of the trinomial accordingly. For example, for the binomial 5 X + 0, print the square simply as 2 5 X↑2 and not 2 5 X↑2 + 0 X + 0.

Ⓑ Write a BASIC program for each problem. As in the program on page 308 and in Exercises 14 and 15 above, print answers as "neatly" as possible. For example, print 5 X↑2 − 9 X − 2 and not 5 X↑2 + −9 X + −2; print X↑2 + 5 X + 6 and not 1 X↑2 + 5 X + 6; print −X↑2 + 3 X − 2 and not −1 X↑2 + 3 X + −2. Also, do not print terms with 0 coefficients.

16. Multiply $(Ax + B)$ and $(Cx + D)$.

17. Add $(Ax + B)$ and $(Cx + D)$.

18. Subtract $(Cx + D)$ from $(Ax + B)$.

Review

Add or subtract as indicated. *(Section 8–6)*

1. $(3a + 4b) + (2a - 6b)$ $5a - 2b$

2. $(5x^2y + 4xy^2) - (x^2y - 3xy^2)$ $4x^2y + 7xy^2$

3. $(4d^2 + 2d - 4) - (5d + d^2)$ $3d^2 - 3d - 4$

4. $(2x^3 + x^2 - 4x) - (x^3 + x^2)$ $x^3 - 4x$

Multiply. *(Section 8–7)*

5. $3(4x - 1)$ $12x - 3$

6. $2y^2(2y + 4)$ $4y^3 + 8y^2$

7. $(c - 4)(2c + 1)$ $2c^2 - 7c - 4$

8. $(2c + 3)(2c + 3)$ $4c^2 + 12c + 9$

9. $(4a^2 - 2c)(a^2 - c)$ $4a^4 - 6a^2c + 2c^2$

10. $4b - 3(b - 1)$ $b + 3$

Find each product by inspection. *(Section 8–8)*

11. $(y + 2)(y - 3)$ $y^2 - y - 6$

12. $(2b + 3)(3b + 1)$ $6b^2 + 11b + 3$

13. $(m^2 - 3n)(3m^2 + n)$ $3m^4 - 8m^2n - 3n^2$

14. $(x^2 + 5)(x^2 - 2)$ $x^4 + 3x^2 - 10$

15. $(a^2 - b)(a^2 + b)$ $a^4 - b^2$

16. $(3ab - 4)(ab - 1)$ $3a^2b^2 - 7ab + 4$

Write the square of each binomial as a trinomial. *(Section 8–9)*

17. $(a - 2)^2$ $a^2 - 4a + 4$

18. $(3y + 5)^2$ $9y^2 + 30y + 25$

19. $(2b - 6d)^2$ $4b^2 - 24bd + 36d^2$

20. $(r^2s + t)^2$ $r^4s^2 + 2r^2st + t^2$

Write each product as a binomial. *(Section 8–10)*

21. $(b + 2)(b - 2)$ $b^2 - 4$

22. $(r + s)(r - s)$ $r^2 - s^2$

23. $(1 - p)(1 + p)$ $1 - p^2$

24. $(3y + 2)(3y - 2)$ $9y^2 - 4$

25. $(3c + 2d)(3c - 2d)$ $9c^2 - 4d^2$

26. $(x^2 + 6)(x^2 - 6)$ $x^4 - 36$

Chapter Summary

IMPORTANT TERMS

Binomial (p. 296)
Monomial (p. 283)
Polynomial (p. 296)

Scientific notation (p. 290)
Trinomial (p. 296)

IMPORTANT IDEAS

1. If x is a real number and a is an integer greater than 1, then

$$x^a = \underbrace{x \cdot x \cdot x \cdot \cdots \cdot x}_{a \text{ factors}}.$$

When $a = 1$, $x^a = x$, that is, $x^1 = x$.

2. Multiplication Theorem for Exponents   If x is a real number and a and b are positive integers, then

$$x^a \cdot x^b = x^{a+b}.$$

3. Power Theorem for Exponents   If x is a real number and a and b are positive integers, then

$$(x^a)^b = x^{ab}.$$

4. Power of a Product Theorem for Exponents   If x and y are real numbers and a is a positive integer, then

$$(xy)^a = x^a y^a.$$

310   *Chapter 8*

5. Division Theorem for Exponents If x is a real number, $x \neq 0$, and a and b are positive integers such that $a \geq b$, then

$$\frac{x^a}{x^b} = x^{a-b}.$$

6. If x is any real number except zero and a is a positive integer, then

$$x^{-a} = \frac{1}{x^a}.$$

7. To add polynomials, add monomials that are like terms. To subtract a polynomial, add its additive inverse.

8. The FOIL Method for Finding the Product of Two Binomials
Add the product of the **first** terms, the product of the **outer** terms, the product of the **inner** terms, and the product of the **last** terms.

9. Steps in Squaring a Binomial
   1. Square the first term.
   2. Add to this twice the product of the first and last terms when the binomial is of the form $(a + b)$.
   3. Subtract twice the product of the first and last terms when the binomial is of the form $(a - b)$.
   4. Add to this the square of the last term.

$$(a + b)^2 = a^2 + 2ab + b^2$$
$$(a - b)^2 = a^2 - 2ab + b^2$$

10. Steps in Finding the Product of the Sum and Difference of the Same Two Numbers
   1. Square the first term of either binomial.
   2. Subtract the square of the second term of either binomial.

$$(a + b)(a - b) = a^2 - b^2$$

_____ Chapter Objectives and Review _____

Objective: *To evaluate expressions with exponents (Section 8–1)*

Evaluate.

1. $(-2)^3$ -8 **2.** $(-3)^2$ 9 **3.** 5^0 1 **4.** 10^8 100,000,000 **5.** $(-1)^{13}$ -1

Find the value when $a = 2$, $b = -4$, and $c = 5$.

6. a^2c 20 **7.** a^3b^2 128 **8.** abc^2 200 **9.** ab^3 -128 **10.** a^3b^2c 640

Objective: *To multiply monomials (Section 8–2)*

Find each product.

11. $a^2(a^6)$ a^8 **12.** $x^2 \cdot x^7$ x^9 **13.** $p^4 \times p$ p^5 **14.** $(-h)(-y)$ hy
15. $10^3 \cdot 10^3$ 10^6, or 1,000,000 **16.** $(3x^2)(-4x^3)$ $-12x^5$ **17.** $(-3mn)(-m^2)$ $3m^3n$ **18.** $(-st)(s^2t^3)$ $-s^3t^4$

Objective: *To raise an expression to a power (Section 8–3)*

Raise to the indicated power. No denominator equals zero.

19. $(x^3)^5$ x^{15}

20. $(x^5)^3$ x^{15}

21. $(3y)^3$ $27y^3$

$-a^3 b^6$

22. $(-ab^2)^3$

23. $(3cd^4)^3$ $27c^3 d^{12}$

24. $(-3 \times 10^3)^2$
  9×10^6, or 9,000,000

25. $\left(\dfrac{m^2}{pn^3}\right)^3$ $\dfrac{m^6}{p^3 n^6}$

26. $\left(\dfrac{q^2 r}{s^3}\right)^2$

Objective: *To divide monomials (Section 8–4)*

Simplify. All exponents are positive integers and no denominator equals zero.

27. $\dfrac{3c^3}{c^3}$ 3

28. $\dfrac{m^3 n^2}{m^2 n}$ mn

29. $\dfrac{-18a^2 b^4}{-6ab}$ $3ab^3$

30. $\dfrac{6p(3p^3)}{9p^2}$ $2p^2$

31. $\dfrac{(-6x^3 y)(-xy)^2}{-2x^2 y^2}$ $3x^3 y$

32. $\dfrac{q^{c+1}}{q^c}$ q

33. $\dfrac{s^{2x} t^{3y}}{st^2}$

34. $\dfrac{(y^{3k+4})^3}{y^{2k+12}}$

Objective: *To write numbers in scientific notation (Section 8–5)*

Simplify. No variable equals zero.

35. 3^{-4} $\dfrac{1}{3^4} = \dfrac{1}{81}$

36. $(-4)^3$ -64

37. y^{-6} $\dfrac{1}{y^6}$

38. $\left(-\dfrac{2}{3}\right)^{-3}$

39. $3n^{-2}$

Write each number in scientific notation.

40. $800,000,000$ 8×10^8

41. $29,000,000,000$ 2.9×10^{10}

42. 0.0000038 3.8×10^{-6}

Objective: *To add and subtract polynomials (Section 8–6)*

Add or subtract as indicated.

43. $(6x + 3y) - (2x + 5y)$ $4x - 2y$

44. $(2a^2 b - ab^2) + (ab^2 - 4a^2 b)$ $-2a^2 b$

45. $(m^2 + 6m) + (2m^2 - m)$ $3m^2 + 5m$

46. $(2cd + c + 5) - (d - cd - 6)$
  $3cd + c - d + 11$

Objective: *To multiply polynomials (Section 8–8)*

Multiply.

$2x^2 + 7xy - 4y^2$

47. $5(6y + 3)$ $30y + 15$

48. $-6a(3a^2 - 2)$ $-18a^3 + 12a$

49. $(2x - y)(x + 4y)$

50. $(\frac{1}{2}x - 1)(2x + 4)$ $x^2 - 4$

51. $(x - y)(y - x)$ $-x^2 + 2xy - y^2$

52. $(c^2 + 2d)(2c^2 + d)$
  $2c^4 + 5c^2 d + 2d^2$

Objective: *To find the product of two binomials by inspection (Section 8–8)*

Find each product by inspection.

$6a^2 + ab - 12b^2$

53. $(p - 4)(p + 1)$ $p^2 - 3p - 4$

54. $(3y - 4)(y - 2)$ $3y^2 - 10y + 8$

55. $(2a + 3b)(3a - 4b)$

56. $(2x^2 + 1)(x^2 + 4)$

57. $(2d - h)(d + 3h)$

58. $(0.5r + s)(1.4r - s)$

  $2x^4 + 9x^2 + 4$

  $2d^2 + 5dh - 3h^2$

  $0.7r^2 + 0.9rs - s^2$

Objective: *To square binomials (Section 8–9)*

Write the square of each binomial as a trinomial.

59. $(c + 6)^2$ $c^2 + 12c + 36$

60. $(6p - 1)^2$
  $36p^2 - 12p + 1$

61. $(x^2 + 3)^2$
  $x^4 + 6x^2 + 9$

62. $(4a - 3b)^2$
  $16a^2 - 24ab + 9b^2$

Objective: *To find the product of the sum and difference of the same two numbers (Section 8-10)*

Write each product as a binomial.

63. $(d-5)(d+5)$ $d^2 - 25$ 64. $(8+a)(8-a)$ $64 - a^2$ 65. $(f-g)(f+g)$ $f^2 - g^2$

66. $(4w-5)(4w+5)$ $16w^2 - 25$ 67. $(5m+2n)(5m-2n)$ $25m^2 - 4n^2$ 68. $(2b^2-7)(2b^2+7)$ $4b^4 - 49$

_____ Chapter Test _____

A formal Chapter Test is provided in the Teacher's Manual. See p. M-71.

Find the value when $a = -1$, $b = 2$, and $c = -4$.

1. $a^2 b$ 2   2. bc^3 -128 3. abc^2 -32

Simplify. No denominator equals zero.

4. $\dfrac{n^4}{n}$ n^3 5. $\dfrac{-15a^2bc^2}{3ab}$ $-5ac^2$ 6. $\dfrac{x^2(4xy)^2}{4x^2y}$ $4x^2y$

Write each number in scientific notation.

7. $650{,}000{,}000$ 6.5×10^8 8. 0.00003 3.0×10^{-5} 9. 7 million 7.0×10^6

Add or subtract as indicated.

10. $(3m - 4n) - (2n + m)$ $2m - 6n$ 11. $(x^2 + x - 4) + (3x - 1 - x^2)$ $4x - 5$

12. $(3a^2 + 4ab - 4b^2) - (ab - 6b^2)$ $3a^2 + 3ab + 2b^2$ 13. $(6m - n - 2p) + (p + 1 - 5m)$ $m - n - p + 1$

Raise to the indicated power.

14. $(-cd^2)^3$ $-c^3d^6$ 15. $(x-4)^2$ $x^2 - 8x + 16$ 16. $(3a + 4b^2)^2$ $9a^2 + 24ab^2 + 16b^4$

Multiply.

17. $w^3(-w^4)$ $-w^7$ 18. $(-4x^2)(-2x^5)$ $8x^7$ 19. $3b(2b-1)$ $6b^2 - 3b$

20. $3t(t^2 - 5t + 2)$ $3t^3 - 15t^2 + 6t$ 21. $(3y + 2x)(y - 3x)$ 22. $(4y^2 - 3)(y^2 + 1)$

23. $(3c - 2d)(c - d)$ 24. $(y + 4)(y - 4)$ $y^2 - 16$ 25. $(2a - b)(2a + b)$ $4a^2 - b^2$

Additional Practice

You may wish to use all or some of these exercises, depending on how well students did on the formal chapter test.

Skills

Find the value when $a = 1$, $b = -2$, and $c = 5$. *(Section 8-1)*

1. $a^2 b$ -2 2. $b^2 c$ 20 3. abc -10 4. $a^2 b^3 c$ -40 5. $a^3 b^4 c^2$ 400

Find each product. *(Section 8-2)*

6. $c^2(c^3)$ c^5 7. $(-3x)(4x)$ $-12x^2$ 8. $-(-4b^2)(-3)$ $-12b^2$ 9. $3n(2mn)(3n^2)$ $18mn^4$

Additional Answers
Chapter Test
21. $3y^2 - 7xy - 6x^2$
22. $4y^4 + y^2 - 3$
23. $3c^2 - 5cd + 2d^2$

Raise to the indicated power. No denominator equals zero. *(Section 8–3)*

10. $(x^3)^2$ x^6

11. $(ab^4)^3$ a^3b^{12}

12. $\left(\dfrac{n^2p}{2m^3}\right)^4$ $\dfrac{n^8p^4}{16m^{12}}$

13. $\left(\dfrac{ab^3}{c^4}\right)^5$

Simplify. All exponents are positive integers and no denominator equals zero. *(Section 8–4)*

14. $\dfrac{x^7}{x^4}$ x^3

15. $\dfrac{a^2b^4}{ab^2}$ ab^2

16. $\dfrac{(2mn^2)(5m^3n^2)}{(2mn^2)^2}$

17. $\dfrac{p^{5k-1}}{p^{3k-4}}$

Write in scientific notation. *(Section 8–5)*

6.52×10^{-5}

18. 0.0000024 2.4×10^{-6} **19.** $320,000,000$ 3.2×10^8 **20.** 2500 2.5×10^3 **21.** 0.0000652

Add or subtract as indicated. *(Section 8–6)*

$7m^2n^3 - 3mn$

22. $(3x + y^2) + (x + y - 2y^2)$ $4x + y - y^2$ **23.** $(5m^2n^3 - 2mn) - (-2m^2n^3 + mn)$

Multiply. *(Section 8–7)*

$15n^2 - 23n + 4$

24. $3x(2x - 1)$ $6x^2 - 3x$ **25.** $(a + 1)(a - 5)$ $a^2 - 4a - 5$ **26.** $(3n - 4)(5n - 1)$

Find each product by inspection. *(Section 8–8)*

$3n^4 - 14n^2 + 15$

27. $(y + 8)(y + 3)$ $y^2 + 11y + 24$ **28.** $(3x - 4)(x + 1)$ $3x^2 - x - 4$ **29.** $(n^2 - 3)(3n^2 - 5)$

Write the square of each binomial. *(Section 8–9)*

30. $(x + 7)^2$

31. $(2n - 3)^2$

32. $(2m + 5n)^2$

33. $(6y - \frac{2}{3})^2$

$x^2 + 14x + 49$ $4n^2 - 12n + 9$ $4m^2 + 20mn + 25n^2$ $36y^2 - 8y + \frac{4}{9}$

Write each product as a binomial. *(Section 8–10)*

34. $(2y - 9)(2y + 9)$ $4y^2 - 81$ **35.** $(xy + 1)(xy - 1)$ $x^2y^2 - 1$ **36.** $(6s - \frac{1}{2})(6s + \frac{1}{2})$

$36s^2 - \dfrac{1}{4}$

Applications

37. Find the perimeter of a square if the length of each of its four equal sides is $(2b + 3)$ units. *(Section 8–6)*

38. Find the perimeter of a rectangle if its length is $(4c - 8)$ units and its width is $(c + 3)$ units. *(Section 8–6)*

39. Which has the greater area, a square with sides each $(x + 2)$ units long or a rectangle with length $(x + 4)$ units and width x units? How much greater is it? *(Section 8–7)*

40. Which has the greater area, a rectangle with length $(a - 2)$ units and width $(a - 3)$ units or one with length $(a - 1)$ units and width $(a - 4)$ units? How much greater is it? *(Section 8–8)*

41. Which has the greater area, a rectangle with length $(2a + 1)$ units and width $(2a - 1)$ units or a rectangle with length $(4a + 4)$ units and width $(a - 1)$ units? How much greater is it? *(Section 8–10)*

42. Which has the greater area, a rectangle with length $(n + 1)$ units and width $(n - 1)$ units or a square with the same perimeter as the rectangle? How much greater is it? *(Section 8–10)*

CHAPTER **9** # Factoring Polynomials

OBJECTIVE: To write a number in prime factorization form and to write all of
its whole number factors

9–1   Factoring Integers

To *factor* a number or a polynomial means to write it as a product.

$$174 = 2 \cdot 3 \cdot 29$$ —————— **Factors of 174**

Each number below has only two whole-number factors, the number itself
and 1. These numbers are called *prime numbers*.

2, 3, 5, 7, 11, 13, 17, 19, 23, 29, 31

Definition

> A **prime number** is an integer greater than 1 that has exactly two
> positive integral factors, itself and 1.

Numbers such as 4, 9, 10, 16, 25, and so on, are *composite numbers*.

Definition

> A **composite number** is any integer greater than 1 that is not prime.

Every composite number can be expressed as a product of prime factors.

When a composite number is written as a product of prime-number factors
or of powers of prime-number factors, the number is in **prime-factorization
form**.

EXAMPLE   Write each number in prime-factorization form.

    a. 500   **b.** 756

Solutions: Divide by the prime numbers in order.

Divide by each prime number as many times as possible, before dividing
by the next prime number.

a. $500 = 2 \cdot 250$ ←—————— **Divide by 2 again.**

     $= 2 \cdot 2 \cdot 125$ ←—————— **125 is not divisible by 3 or 4. Try 5.**

     $= 2 \cdot 2 \cdot 5 \cdot 25$ ←—————— **Divide by 5 again.**

     $= 2 \cdot 2 \cdot 5 \cdot 5 \cdot 5$ ←—————— **Stop! All factors are prime factors.**

     $= 2^2 \cdot 5^3$ ←—————— **Prime factorization.**

b. $756 = 2 \cdot 378$ ←—————— **Divide by 2 again.**

     $= 2 \cdot 2 \cdot 189$ ←—————— **Divide by 3.**

     $= 2 \cdot 2 \cdot 3 \cdot 63$ ←—————— **Divide by 3 again.**

     $= 2 \cdot 2 \cdot 3 \cdot 3 \cdot 21$

     $= 2 \cdot 2 \cdot 3 \cdot 3 \cdot 3 \cdot 7$ ←—————— **Stop! All factors are prime factors.**

     $= 2^2 \cdot 3^3 \cdot 7$ ←—————— **Prime factorization**

The *Unique Factorization Theorem*, also called the *Fundamental Theorem of Arithmetic*, states that there is *one and only one way* to factor positive integers such as 500 and 756 into primes. The order in which the prime factors are written may vary.

Theorem 9-1

> **Unique Factorization Theorem**
> The factorization of any positive integer into primes is unique, disregarding the order of the factors.

When you are asked to find the factors of a number, you must know whether you are to find the whole-number, integral, rational, or real-number factors. For example,

$$\frac{1}{2} \text{ and } 36 \text{ are } \textit{rational-number factors of } 18.$$

Unless told otherwise in this text, assume that you are factoring over the set of integers.

CLASSROOM EXERCISES

Determine whether the second number is a factor of the number in parentheses. Answer *Yes* or *No*.

1. $(3^3 \cdot 5)$; $3 \cdot 5$ *Yes*   **2.** $(2 \cdot 5 \cdot 7)$; 3 *No*   **3.** $(8 + 2)$; 8 *No*

Identify each number as prime, *P*, or composite, *C*.

4. 15 *C*   **5.** 9 *C*   **6.** 13 *P*   **7.** 29 *P*   **8.** 31 *P*   **9.** 51 *C*

Write each number in prime-factorization form.

10. 24 $2^3 \cdot 3$ **11.** 20 $2^2 \cdot 5$ **12.** 70 $2 \cdot 5 \cdot 7$ **13.** 200 $2^3 \cdot 5^2$ **14.** 350 $2 \cdot 5^2 \cdot 7$ **15.** 41

15. 41 is prime.

WRITTEN EXERCISES

A   Determine whether the second number is a factor of the number in parentheses. Answer *Yes* or *No*.

1. $(5 \cdot 6^2 \cdot 8)$; 6 *Yes*   **2.** $(3 \cdot 4 \cdot 7)$; $3 \cdot 4$ *Yes*   **3.** $(8^2 \cdot 7 \cdot 4)$; $8 \cdot 7 \cdot 4$ *Yes*

4. $(5^2 \cdot 6^2 \cdot 8)$; $5^2 \cdot 8$ *Yes*   **5.** $(3^2 + 1)$; 3 *No*   **6.** $(9^2 + 1)$; 9 *No*

7. $(8^2 \cdot 9 \cdot 6)$; $8^3 \cdot 9$ *No*   **8.** $(5^2 \cdot 7^2)$; 12^2 *No*   **9.** $(8 \cdot 7 \cdot 6 \cdot 5 \cdot 4)$; $3 \cdot 8$ *Yes*

10. $(6 \cdot 5 \cdot 4)$; 8 *Yes*   **11.** $(8 \cdot 7 \cdot 6 \cdot 5)$; $3 \cdot 5$ *Yes*   **12.** $(8 \cdot 7 \cdot 6 \cdot 5 \cdot 4)$; $2 \cdot 4$ *Yes*

Identify each number as prime, *P*, or composite, *C*.

13. 29 *P*   **14.** 33 *C*   **15.** 18 *C*   **16.** 43 *P*   **17.** 49 *C*   **18.** 11 *P*

19. 13 *P*   **20.** 100 *C*   **21.** 23 *P*   **22.** 17 *P*   **23.** 48 *C*   **24.** 101 *P*

Assignment Guide
Minimal
pp. 317–318: 2–42 even
Average
pp. 317–318: 2–58 even
Above Average pp. 317–318: 3, 6, 9, . . . 42, 43–58

Factoring Polynomials   **317**

Write each number in prime-factorization form.

25. 18 $2 \cdot 3^2$ **26.** 36 $2^2 \cdot 3^2$ **27.** 21 $3 \cdot 7$ **28.** 15 $3 \cdot 5$ **29.** 42 $2 \cdot 3 \cdot 7$ **30.** 32

31. 45 $3^2 \cdot 5$ **32.** 49 7^2 **33.** 25 5^2 **34.** 28 $2^2 \cdot 7$ **35.** 33 $3 \cdot 11$ **36.** 44

37. 500 $2^2 \cdot 5^3$ **38.** 625 5^4 **39.** 300 $2^2 \cdot 3 \cdot 5^2$ **40.** 1000 $2^3 \cdot 5^3$ **41.** 960 $2^6 \cdot 3 \cdot 5$ **42.** 72

In Exercises 43-54, answers may vary.

B   Write each number as the product of two rational-number factors. $3 \cdot 3$

43. 4 $2 \cdot 2$ **44.** 6 $2 \cdot 3$ **45.** 3 $1 \cdot 3$ **46.** 10 $2 \cdot 5$ **47.** 7 $1 \cdot 7$ **48.** 9

49. 8 $2 \cdot 4$ **50.** 11 $1 \cdot 11$ **51.** $\frac{1}{8}$ $\frac{1}{2} \cdot \frac{1}{4}$ **52.** $\frac{1}{16}$ $\frac{1}{4} \cdot \frac{1}{4}$ **53.** $\frac{1}{10}$ $\frac{1}{2} \cdot \frac{1}{5}$ **54.** $\frac{1}{2}$

  $\frac{1}{2} \cdot 1$

APPLICATIONS: Using Factors

55. A marching band has 72 members. What rectangular formations are possible if each row and each column must have at least 6 players?

56. The Cobb City marching band has 100 members. What rectangular formations are possible if each row and each column must have at least 5 players?

57. Ann sets out 100 tomato plants in her garden. In what ways can she arrange them so that she has the same number in each row and there are at least 5 rows and 5 columns?

58. In how many ways could 150 apple trees be planted so that each row has the same number of trees and there are at least 5 rows and 5 columns?

CALCULATOR APPLICATIONS

Finding Prime Numbers

You can use a calculator to find certain prime numbers p by using the formula $p = 2^n - 1$ for some values of the variable n.

EXAMPLE   Use the formula $p = 2^n - 1$ to find p when $n = 7$.

SOLUTION   If your calculator does not have an exponent key, $\boxed{x^!}$, you may be able to use the method on page 121 or the method shown below.

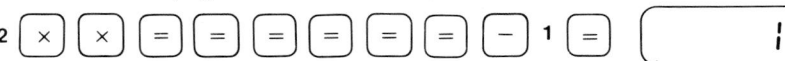

2   ×   ×   =   =   =   =   =   =   −   1   =   127.

EXERCISES

Use the formula $p = 2^n - 1$ to find a prime number p for each value of n.

1. 2   3   **2.** 3   7   **3.** 5   31   **4.** 13   8191   **5.** 17   131,071   **6.** 19

  524,287

REVIEW CAPSULE FOR SECTION 9-2

Multiply. (Pages 97-99)

1. $x(x + 3)$ **2.** $-2(a - 4)$ **3.** $ab(a - 2)$ **4.** $x^2y(xy + 7)$

5. $a(b + c - d)$ **6.** $-2x(y^2 - 6y + 3)$ **7.** $(x + y)4$ **8.** $-p(-qr + sq)$

9. $a(a - 2) + b(a - 2)$ **10.** $z(x + 2) + 3(x + 2)$ **11.** $t(y - 1) + 5(y - 1)$

OBJECTIVE: To factor polynomials by finding common monomial or binomial factors

9–2 Common Factors

Teaching Suggestions p. M-22

The distributive postulate is used to find products. It is also used to find factors of polynomials.

Multiplying	**Factoring**
$6(x + y) = 6x + 6y$	$6x + 6y = 6(x + y)$
$a(b + c) = ab + ac$	$ab + ac = a(b + c)$
$5x(3x^2 - 4x - 1) = 15x^3 - 20x^2 - 5x$	$15x^3 - 20x^2 - 5x = 5x(3x^2 - 4x - 1)$
$(x + 2)(x + 3) = x(x + 3) + 2(x + 3)$	$x(x + 3) + 2(x + 3) = (x + 2)(x + 3)$

Thus, since $6(x + y) = 6x + 6y$, then $6x + 6y = 6(x + y)$.

When you factor **over the integers,** you rewrite the polynomial as the product of factors that have integral coefficients only.

EXAMPLE 1   Factor over the integers.

   a. $3x + 3y$ **b.** $x^2 - x$ **c.** $7x^3 - 21x$ **d.** $2y^3 + 4y^2 + 6y$

Solutions: Look for common monomial factors in each term of the polynomial.

   a. $3x + 3y = 3(x + y)$ ⟵———— The common monomial factor is 3.
   b. $x^2 - x = x(x - 1)$ ⟵———— The common monomial factor is x.
   c. $7x^3 - 21x = 7x(x^2 - 3)$ ⟵———— The common monomial factor is 7x.
   d. $2y^3 + 4y^2 + 6y = 2y(y^2 + 2y + 3)$ ⟵——— The common monomial factor is 2y.

When a polynomial has no polynomial factors with integral coefficients except itself and 1, it is a **prime polynomial with respect to the integers.** For example, the polynomial

$$6x + 5y$$

is a prime polynomial over the integers because $6x$ and $5y$ have *no common factors with integral coefficients other than 1.*

Some polynomials have a common binomial factor.

EXAMPLE 2   Factor over the integers: $a(r + t) + b(r + t)$

Solution: Think of $(r + t)$ as a monomial.

   $a(r + t) + b(r + t) = ax + bx$ ⟵——— Let $x = (r + t)$.
                        $= x(a + b)$ ⟵——— The common factor is x.
                        $= (r + t)(a + b)$ ⟵——— Replace x with $(r + t)$.

Sometimes you have to group terms in order to find the common binomial factor.

Factoring Polynomials   **319**

Additional Examples
Example 3
Factor over the integers.
1. $by + bd + xy + dx$
   Ans: $(b + x)(y + d)$
2. $cx - cy - fx + fy$
   Ans: $(x - y)(c - f)$

EXAMPLE 3 Factor over the integers: $ax + cy + xy + ac$

Solution: The terms of the polynomial can be grouped in two ways.

Method I: $ax + cy + xy + ac = (ax + xy) + (cy + ac)$ ← Group terms with a common factor.

$\qquad\qquad\qquad = x(a + y) + c(y + a)$ ← Common monomial factors: x and c

$\qquad\qquad\qquad = x(a + y) + c(a + y)$ ← $y + a = a + y$

$\qquad\qquad\qquad = (a + y)(x + c)$ ← $(a + y)$ is the common factor.

Method II: $ax + cy + xy + ac = (ax + ac) + (cy + xy)$ ← Group terms with a common factor.

$\qquad\qquad\qquad = a(x + c) + y(c + x)$ ← Common monomial factors: a and y

$\qquad\qquad\qquad = a(x + c) + y(x + c)$ ← $c + x = x + c$

$\qquad\qquad\qquad = (x + c)(a + y)$ ← $(x + c)$ is the common factor.

CLASSROOM EXERCISES

Additional Answers
Classroom Exercises
7. $ab - 4bc + 2ac$
8. $p + r + q$
16. $5(2x^2y - 3xy + 1)$

One factor is given for each polynomial. Write the other factor.

1. $8a + 8b = \underline{\ ?\ }(a + b)$ 8
2. $xy + y^2 = \underline{\ ?\ }(x + y)$ y
3. $3x^3 + 3x = \underline{\ ?\ }(x^2 + 1)$ $3x$
4. $8x^3 - 4xy^2 = \underline{\ ?\ }(2x^2 - y^2)$ $4x$
5. $15a^2 + 15ab^2 = 15a(\underline{\ ?\ })$ $a + b^2$
6. $x^3y - y = y(\underline{\ ?\ })$ $x^3 - 1$
7. $-2ab + 8bc - 4ac = -2(\underline{\ ?\ })$
8. $pq + qr + q^2 = q(\underline{\ ?\ })$
9. $3(x - y) + a(x - y) = (\underline{\ ?\ })(3 + a)$ $x - y$
10. $t(x - 4) + w(x - 4) = (\underline{\ ?\ })(x - 4)$ $t + w$

Factor over the integers.

11. $14p + 14q$ $14(p + q)$
12. $12a - 12d$ $12(a - d)$
13. $xt + yt$ $t(x + y)$
14. $4s^2t + 4sw$ $4s(st + w)$
15. $13st - 26t$ $13t(s - 2)$
16. $10x^2y - 15xy + 5$
17. $a(t + w) + b(t + w)$ $(a + b)(t + w)$
18. $fg + f + 2g + 2$ $(f + 2)(g + 1)$
19. $4d + 4 + de + e$ $(4 + e)(d + 1)$

WRITTEN EXERCISES

Assignment Guide
Minimal
Day 1 pp. 320–321: 1–34
Day 2 p. 321: 35–55
Average pp. 320–321:
3, 6, 9, . . . 33, 35–75 odd
Above Average pp. 320–321:
4, 8, 12, . . . 56, 59–84 odd,
85–88

Additional Answers
Written Exercises
12. x^2, $2xy$, $3y$
14. 1, $6x$, 4
16. $4x$, $4y$, xy

A One factor is given for each polynomial. Write the other factor.

1. $3x + 6y = 3(\underline{\ ?\ } + 2y)$ x
2. $4n - 2 = 2(2n - \underline{\ ?\ })$ 1
3. $3b^2 - 24b = 3b(\underline{\ ?\ } - 8)$ b
4. $15ab^2 - 3b^2 = 3b^2(\underline{\ ?\ } - \underline{\ ?\ })$ $5a, 1$
5. $-3ax + 6ay = -3a(\underline{\ ?\ } - \underline{\ ?\ })$ $x, 2y$
6. $p^2 - p = p(\underline{\ ?\ } - \underline{\ ?\ })$ $p, 1$
7. $8y - 24 = 8(y - \underline{\ ?\ })$ 3
8. $8x^2y^2 - xy^2 = xy^2(\underline{\ ?\ } - \underline{\ ?\ })$ $8x, 1$
9. $x^2 - 3x^2y = x^2(\underline{\ ?\ } - \underline{\ ?\ })$ $1, 3y$
10. $6a^2b - 3ab^2 = 3ab(\underline{\ ?\ } - \underline{\ ?\ })$ $2a, b$
11. $5x + 20 = \underline{\ ?\ }(x + 4)$ 5
12. $3x^2 - 6xy + 9y = 3(\underline{\ ?\ } - \underline{\ ?\ } + \underline{\ ?\ })$
13. $16m - 4m^2 = \underline{\ ?\ }(4 - m)$ $4m$
14. $-xy + 6x^2y - 4xy = -xy(\underline{\ ?\ } - \underline{\ ?\ } + \underline{\ ?\ })$
15. $16x^2 - 2x = 2x(\underline{\ ?\ } - \underline{\ ?\ })$ $8x, 1$
16. $8x + 8y + 2xy = 2(\underline{\ ?\ } + \underline{\ ?\ } + \underline{\ ?\ })$

17. $4ab + b = b(\underline{\ ?\ } + \underline{\ ?\ })$ $4a, 1$

18. $-5x^2 - 10y^2 = -5(\underline{\ ?\ } + \underline{\ ?\ })$ $x^2, 2y^2$

19. $2mn - n = n(\underline{\ ?\ } - \underline{\ ?\ })$ $2m, 1$

20. $4xy - 2x - 3x^2y = x(\underline{\ ?\ } - \underline{\ ?\ } - \underline{\ ?\ })$

21. $12y - 4 = \underline{\ ?\ }(3y - 1)$ 4

22. $a^3 + 2a^2b = a^2(\underline{\ ?\ } + \underline{\ ?\ })$ $a^2, 2b$

23. $400x - x^2 = \underline{\ ?\ }(400 - x)$ x

24. $1000x^3 - x = x(\underline{\ ?\ } - \underline{\ ?\ })$ $1000x^2, 1$

25. $4ab - b = b(\underline{\ ?\ } - \underline{\ ?\ })$ $4a, 1$

26. $8x^2 - 28x - 4 = \underline{\ ?\ }(2x^2 - 7x - 1)$ 4

27. $25x^2 - 20y^2 = \underline{\ ?\ }(5x^2 - 4y^2)$ 5

28. $5m - 10mn - 15 = \underline{\ ?\ }(m - 2mn - 3)$ 5

29. $7x + 49xy = 7x(\underline{\ ?\ } + \underline{\ ?\ })$ $1, 7y$

30. $4x^3 + 6x^2 - 2x = 2x(\underline{\ ?\ } + \underline{\ ?\ } - \underline{\ ?\ })$

31. $a(x + y) + b(x + y) = (x + y)(\underline{\ ?\ } + \underline{\ ?\ })$ a, b

32. $t(a + 3) - y(a + 3) = (a + 3)(\underline{\ ?\ } - \underline{\ ?\ })$ t, y

33. $10 + 2t + 5s + st = (\underline{\ ?\ } + \underline{\ ?\ })(5 + t)$ $2, s$

34. $tx - wx + ty - wy = (\underline{\ ?\ } - \underline{\ ?\ })(x + y)$ t, w

Factor over the integers.

35. $7x + 7y$ $7(x + y)$

36. $3a + 9b$ $3(a + 3b)$

37. $8x - 4y$ $4(2x - y)$

38. $ax + bx$ $x(a + b)$

39. $3x - awx$ $x(3 - aw)$

40. $9x^2 - 6y^2$ $3(3x^2 - 2y^2)$

41. $4c + ac + bc$ $c(4 + a + b)$

42. $ay + by + 3y$ $y(a + b + 3)$

43. $d^2 + 2d + ad$

44. $ax - ay + a^2$ $a(x - y + a)$

45. $5x - 10y + 15z^2$

46. $5t + 10t^2 + t^3$

47. $2\pi r^2 + 2\pi rh$ $2\pi r(r + h)$

48. $a^2b + ab^2 + a^3b^3$

49. $cdh^3 + c^2dh + c^3d^2h^2$

50. $d(e + f) + g(e + f)$ $(d + g)(e + f)$

51. $a(b - c) + d(b - c)$ $(a + d)(b - c)$

52. $3(x + y) - g(x + y)$ $(3 - g)(x + y)$

53. $a(q - r) - s(q - r)$ $(a - s)(q - r)$

54. $(vx + xz) + sv + sz$ $(x + s)(v + z)$

55. $kp - kn + (pr - rn)$ $(k + r)(p - n)$

B

56. $6w - 15 - 14hw + 35h$

57. $2ax^2 + bx^2 - 2ay^2 - by^2$

Factor over the integers. If a polynomial cannot be factored over the integers, write *Prime*.

58. $3a + b$ prime

59. $7a^2b - 7ab$ $7ab(a - 1)$

60. $18r^2 - 6 + 24r$

61. $8x^2 - 3y^2$ prime

62. $64ab - 16b^2$ $16b(4a - b)$

63. $10a^2 + 33ab + 27b^2$

64. $12n^2 - 4 + 16n$ $4(3n^2 - 1 + 4n)$

65. $9p^2 - 5q^2$ prime

66. $36x^2 - 18xy$

67. $14x^2 + 7xy + 21y^2$

68. $7n^2 - 8mn + 3n^2$

69. $9ab + a^2 + 2b^2$

70. $39a^3 - 52ab^2 + 65ac^2$

71. $27x^4 + 3x^3 + 9ax$

72. $9s - 13s^2 + 5t$

73. $25xy - 50xz + 100x$

74. $4x^2 - 8x + 6$

75. $3x^2 + 6xy - 2x^3$

76. $a^3 + 3a^2b + 3ab^2$

77. $14 - 42p + 7$ $21(1 - 2p)$

78. $3ab^2 - ab + 2a^2$

79. $8x^2 - 12xy - 16xz$

80. $ay^2 + ab + 3a$ $a(y^2 + b + 3)$

81. $3x^3 - 15x^2 - 6x$

82. $8a^3 - 4ax^2 - 12a^2x^2$

83. $3a^2 + 4a^3 - 5a^4b$

84. $6x^3 - 2x^2y + z^3$

C   Find the missing factor.

85. $x^{n+3} + x^n = x^n(\underline{\ ?\ })$ $x^3 + 1$

86. $2y^{n+1} + 4y^n = 2y^n(\underline{\ ?\ })$ $y + 2$

87. $4w^{n-1} + 6w^{n+1} = (\underline{\ ?\ })(2w^{n-2} + 3w^n)$

$2w$

88. $9z^{2n} + 21z^{2n+2} = (\underline{\ ?\ })(3z^n + 7z^{n+1})$

$3z^n$

Factoring Polynomials   **321**

Multiply. *(Pages 302–303)*

$9x^2 - 4$

1. $(b + 5)(b - 5)$ $b^2 - 25$ **2.** $(2a + 1)(2a - 1)$ $4a^2 - 1$ **3.** $(3x - 2)(3x + 2)$

4. $(x^2 + y^2)(x^2 - y^2)$ $x^4 - y^4$ **5.** $(\frac{1}{2}x + y)(\frac{1}{2}x - y)$ $\frac{1}{4}x^2 - y^2$ **6.** $(9 - pq)(9 + pq)$

$81 - p^2 q^2$

OBJECTIVE: To factor the difference of two squares

Teaching Suggestions p. M-22

9-3 Factoring the Difference of Two Squares

A polynomial that represents the *difference of two squares* can be readily factored.

Finding Products	Finding Factors
$(x + 7)(x - 7) = x^2 - 49$	$x^2 - 49 = (x + 7)(x - 7)$
$(4x + y)(4x - y) = 16x^2 - y^2$	$16x^2 - y^2 = (4x + y)(4x - y)$

You will find it useful to memorize this formula for factoring the difference of two squares.

Factoring the Difference of Two Squares

$$a^2 - b^2 = (a + b)(a - b)$$

EXAMPLE 1 Factor over the integers: $25x^2 - 36y^2$

Solution: **Think!** $25x^2 = (5x)^2$ and $36y^2 = (6y)^2$.

$25x^2 - 36y^2 = (5x)^2 - (6y)^2$ ◄——— **Write as the difference of squares.**

$= (5x + 6y)(5x - 6y)$ ◄——— **Write as the product of a sum and difference.**

Some polynomials that *cannot be factored over the integers can be factored over the set of rational numbers.*

EXAMPLE 2 Factor over the rational numbers: $\frac{1}{4}p^2 - 9q^2$

Solution: $\frac{1}{4}p^2 - 9q^2 = (\frac{1}{2}p)^2 - (3q)^2$ ◄——— **Write as the difference of squares.**

$= (\frac{1}{2}p + 3q)(\frac{1}{2}p - 3q)$ ◄——— **Write as the product of a sum and difference.**

CLASSROOM EXERCISES

Factor over the integers.

$(3 + y)(3 - y)$

1. $m^2 - 1$ $(m + 1)(m - 1)$ **2.** $x^2 - 16$ $(x + 4)(x - 4)$ **3.** $4r^2 - 1$ $(2r + 1)(2r - 1)$ **4.** $9 - y^2$

5. $a^2 - 144$ **6.** $4t^2 - 121$ **7.** $-4 + y^2$ **8.** $-x^2 + 81$

$(a + 12)(a - 12)$ $(2t + 11)(2t - 11)$ $(y + 2)(y - 2)$ $(9 - x)(9 + x)$

322 *Chapter 9*

Factor over the rational numbers.

9. $b^2 - \dfrac{1}{25}$

$(b + \frac{1}{5})(b - \frac{1}{5})$

10. $\dfrac{1}{100} - r^2$

$(\frac{1}{10} + r)(\frac{1}{10} - r)$

11. $16t^2 - \dfrac{1}{49}$

$(4t + \frac{1}{7})(4t - \frac{1}{7})$

12. $\dfrac{n^2}{4} - \dfrac{1}{9}$

$(\frac{n}{2} + \frac{1}{3})(\frac{n}{2} - \frac{1}{3})$

WRITTEN EXERCISES

A Factor each polynomial over the integers. When a polynomial cannot be factored over the integers, write *Prime*.

$(y + 6)(y - 6)$

1. $y^2 - 9$ $(y + 3)(y - 3)$
2. $x^2 - 4$ $(x + 2)(x - 2)$
3. $x^2 - 25$ $(x + 5)(x - 5)$
4. $y^2 - 36$

5. $4x^2 - 9$
6. $9x^2 - 4$ $(3x + 2)(3x - 2)$
7. $16y^2 - 36$
8. $-64 + 4x^2$

9. $x^2y^2 - a^2$
10. $y^6 - 100$
11. $9x^4y^2 - b^2$
12. $1 - 81y^2$

13. $x^2y^2 - z^2$
14. $-25 + 4x^2y^2$
15. $x^2 + y^2$ prime
16. $x^2 - y^4$

17. $4x^2 + 16y^2$
$4(x^2 + 4y^2)$
18. $81x^2 - 64y^2$
$(9x + 8y)(9x - 8y)$
19. $25x^2 - 49$
$(5x + 7)(5x - 7)$
20. $49 - 25x^2$
$(7 + 5x)(7 - 5x)$

Factor each polynomial over the rational numbers.

21. $\dfrac{1}{9}x^2 - 16$
22. $\dfrac{25}{36}a^2 - b^2$
23. $\dfrac{4}{9}x^2 - \dfrac{25}{36}y^2$
24. $\dfrac{121}{9}r^2 - s^2$

25. $-\dfrac{1}{49} + x^2$
26. $-\dfrac{1}{16} + r^2$
27. $-25 + \dfrac{1}{64}b^2$
28. $\dfrac{a^2}{9} - \dfrac{b^4}{16}$

APPLICATIONS: Using Factoring

29. Within a large square whose side is a units is a small square whose side is b units. What is the area of the large square? What is the area of the small square? What is the area of the shaded surface between the two squares? Factor the expression for the shaded area.

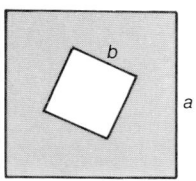

30. A small circle whose radius is r units is drawn within a large circle whose radius is R units. What is the area of the large circle? What is the area of the shaded part? Factor the expression for the shaded area.
(HINT: First, factor out the common monomial factor, π. Then factor the binomial.)

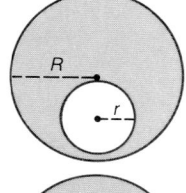

31. If four circular holes (radius r) are cut in a large circular plate of radius R, what is the area of the remaining surface in terms of R and r? Factor the expression for the shaded area. (See the hint for Exercise 30.)

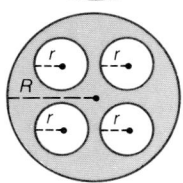

C Factor over the integers.

32. $(a + b)^2 - c^2$
33. $c^2 - (a + b)^2$

34. $(r + s)^2 - t^2$
35. $(r + s)^2 - (t + u)^2$

36. $(x - a)^2 - (y - b)^2$
37. $4(x - a)^2 - 9(y + b)^2$

38. $4(x - a)^2 - 9(y - b)^2$

Factoring Polynomials **323**

Review

Determine whether the second number is a factor of the number in parentheses. Answer *Yes* or *No*. *(Section 9-1)*
                                                                                        No

1. $(2 \cdot 5^2 \cdot 7)$; 5   *Yes*   2. $(2^2 \cdot 3^2 \cdot 4^3)$; 16   *Yes*   3. $(9 \cdot 7 \cdot 6 \cdot 5 \cdot 4)$; $2 \cdot 8$

Write each number in prime-factorization form. *(Section 9-1)*

4. 45 $3^2 \cdot 5$ 5. 48 $2^4 \cdot 3$ 6. 56 $2^3 \cdot 7$ 7. 78 $2 \cdot 3 \cdot 13$ 8. 250 $2 \cdot 5^3$ 9. 720

Factor over the integers. If a polynomial cannot be factored over the integers, write *Prime*. *(Section 9-2)*

10. $5a + 10b$ $5(a + 2b)$ 11. $3x + ax + dx$ $x(3 + a + d)$ 12. $pr^2 - p^2r$ $pr(r - p)$

13. $y^2 + 3y$ $y(y^2 + 3)$ 14. $3m^2 + 13n^2$ *Prime*   15. $s^3t^2 + s^2t^3 - s^2t$

16. $a(b + c) - 2(b + c)$ 17. $kx + wy + wx + ky$ 18. $2y + xy + 2x + 4$

Factor over the integers. If a polynomial cannot be factored over the integers, write *Prime*. *(Section 9-3)*

19. $1 - m^2$ $(1 + m)(1 - m)$ 20. $-9 + a^2$ $(a + 3)(a - 3)$ 21. $9b^2 - 16$ 22. $81x^2 - 1$

23. $5m^2 - p^2$ *Prime*   24. $4a^2 - b^4$ 25. $x^2y^2 - 9$ 26. $p^6 - q^8$

Factor each polynomial over the rational numbers. *(Section 9-3)*

27. $x^2 - \frac{1}{4}$ $(x + \frac{1}{2})(x - \frac{1}{2})$ 28. $4t^2 - \frac{1}{9}$ $(2t + \frac{1}{3})(2t - \frac{1}{3})$ 29. $\frac{4}{25}p^2 - 1$ 30. $\frac{n^2}{16} - \frac{m^2}{4}$

Puzzle — See the Solution Key.

Here are some brain teasers for you to solve.

1. Two riders race on a circular track. Rider A can circle the track in 6 minutes, and Rider B in 4 minutes. From the beginning of the race, how many minutes will it be before Rider B overtakes Rider A?

2. If a hen and a half lays an egg and a half in a day and a half, how many eggs will six hens lay in six days?

3. It takes a clock 2 seconds to strike 3 o'clock. How long will it take to strike 12 o'clock?

REVIEW CAPSULE FOR SECTION 9-4

Square each binomial. *(Pages 304–305)*
                                              $4x^2 - 20x + 25$ $81 + 18b + b^2$

1. $(a - 3)^2$ $a^2 - 6a + 9$ 2. $(x + 4)^2$ $x^2 + 8x + 16$ 3. $(2x - 5)^2$ 4. $(9 + b)^2$

5. $(2a + 5t)^2$ 6. $(3p^2 - 2)^2$ 7. $(0.1 + z)^2$ 8. $(\frac{1}{2} - bc)^2$

Consumer Applications: Nutrition

This lesson is optional. It applies the algebraic skill of evaluating a function with the use of a calculator to the consumer area of nutrition.

The average man or woman who is eating a balanced diet requires 16 or 19 calories per pound of body weight, per day, respectively, to maintain their current body weight.

The following function is used to predict the weight of an average adult after a given number of days of dieting.

$$W(t) = \frac{1}{a}\left[N + (aW_0 - N)\left(\frac{3500 - a}{3500}\right)^t\right]$$

where

a = calories per pound for constant weight

N = number of calories consumed daily

W_0 = initial weight

t = time in days

$W(t)$ = weight in t days.

A balanced diet consists of food from the four basic food groups: protein products (upper left), carbohydrates (upper right), dairy products (lower left), and fruits and vegetables (lower right).

EXAMPLE   Harry's doctor recommended that he go on a 2000-calorie diet. He weighs 200 pounds at present. Find his weight after 50 days.

Solution: $a = 16$; $N = 2000$; $W_0 = 200$; $t = 50$

$$W(50) = \frac{1}{16}\left[2000 + (16 \cdot 200 - 2000)\left(\frac{3500 - 16}{3500}\right)^{50}\right]$$

$$= \frac{1}{16}\left[2000 + 1200\left(\frac{3484}{3500}\right)^{50}\right] \longleftarrow \text{Use a calculator.}$$

$$= 184.64395$$

After 50 days, Harry will weigh about **185 pounds**.

EXERCISES

In Exercises 1–4, find the weight after the given number of days.

1. Janine's doctor told her to go on an 1800–calorie diet for 60 days. She now weighs 145 pounds.

2. Samuel's doctor told him to go on a 2100–calorie diet for 90 days. He now weighs 240 pounds.

3. Frank's doctor advised him to go on a 2000–calorie diet for 45 days. He now weighs 190 pounds.

4. Louise's doctor advised her to go on a 1600–calorie diet for 30 days. She now weighs 135 pounds.

Additional Answers
1. about 131 pounds
2. about 203 pounds
3. about 178 pounds
4. about 127 pounds

9–4 Factoring a Perfect Square Trinomial

A **perfect square trinomial** is the square of a binomial. That is, since

$$(x + 7)(x + 7) = (x + 7)^2 = x^2 + 14x + 49$$

and
$$(x - 7)(x - 7) = (x - 7)^2 = x^2 - 14x + 49,$$

both $x^2 + 14x + 49$ and $x^2 - 14x + 49$ are perfect square trinomials. To determine whether a trinomial is a perfect square, follow this procedure.

Procedure

> To determine whether a trinomial is a perfect square, check these two conditions:
>
> ☐1 The first and last terms must be squares of monomials.
>
> ☐2 The middle term must be twice the product of the monomials.

EXAMPLE 1 Determine whether each of the following is a perfect square trinomial.

  a. $x^2 - 14x + 49$ **b.** $4p^2 + 10pq + 9q^2$

Solutions:

a. $x^2 - 14x + 49$ ◄—— Check Condition 1. ——► **b.** $4p^2 + 10pq + 9q^2$

$x^2 = (x)^2; 49 = (7)^2$ ◄—— Check Condition 2. ——► $4p^2 = (2p)^2; 9q^2 = (3q)^2$

$14x = 2(x)(7)$ $10pq \neq 2(2p)(3q)$

The trinomial in **a** is a perfect square; the trinomial in **b** is not.

To factor a perfect square trinomial, you reverse the procedure for squaring a binomial. First, you find the first and last monomial terms. The sign between these terms is the *same as the sign of the middle term* of the trinomial.

EXAMPLE 2 Factor over the integers: **a.** $4x^2 + 12x + 9$ **b.** $25y^2 - 20y + 4$

Solutions:

a. $4x^2 = (2x)^2; 9 = (3)^2; 12x = 2(2x)(3)$ ◄—— Check for a perfect square trinomial.

  $4x^2 + 12x + 9 = (2x \quad 3)(2x \quad 3)$ ◄—— Write the monomial terms.

  $= (2x + 3)(2x + 3)$ ◄—— Write the same sign as the middle term of the trinomial.

  $= (2x + 3)^2$

b. $25y^2 = (5y)^2; 4 = (2)^2; 20y = 2(5y)(2)$ ◄—— Check for a perfect square trinomial.

  $25y^2 - 20y + 4 = (5y \quad 2)(5y \quad 2)$ ◄—— Write the monomial terms.

  $= (5y - 2)(5y - 2)$ ◄—— Write the same sign as the middle term of the trinomial.

  $= (5y - 2)^2$

Memorizing these formulas will help you to factor perfect square trinomials.

Factoring Perfect Square Trinomials

$a^2 + 2ab + b^2 = (a + b)(a + b) = (a + b)^2$

$a^2 - 2ab + b^2 = (a - b)(a - b) = (a - b)^2$

CLASSROOM EXERCISES

Determine whether each of the following is a perfect square trinomial. Answer *Yes* or *No*.

1. $x^2 - 2xy + y^2$ *Yes*
4. $b^2 - 20b + 20$ *No*

2. $x^2 - 5x + 16$ *No*
5. $4a^2 - 4ab + b^2$ *Yes*

3. $1 - 6x + 9x^2$ *Yes*
6. $y^2 + \frac{2}{5}y + \frac{1}{25}$ *Yes*

Write each perfect square trinomial as the square of a binomial. One term of the binomial is written for you.

7. $a^2 + 4ab + 4b^2 = (a + \underline{\ ?\ })^2$ $2b$
9. $4x^2 - 4x + 1 = (2x - \underline{\ ?\ })^2$ 1
11. $s^2 + 6st + 9t^2 = (s + \underline{\ ?\ })^2$ $3t$

8. $x^2 + 2xy + y^2 = (\underline{\ ?\ } + y)^2$ x
10. $b^2 - 8bc + 16c^2 = (b - \underline{\ ?\ })^2$ $4c$
12. $n^2 - 12n + 36 = (\underline{\ ?\ } - 6)^2$ n

WRITTEN EXERCISES

A Determine whether each of the following is a perfect square trinomial. Answer *Yes* or *No*.

1. $x^2 - 4x + 4$ *Yes*
4. $y^2 - 30y + 225$ *Yes*

2. $a^2 + 2a + 1$ *Yes*
5. $z^2 - 16z + 64$ *Yes*

3. $x^2 - 8x + 8$ *No*
6. $t^2 - 2t + 1$ *Yes*

Write each perfect square trinomial as the square of a binomial. One term of the binomial is written for you.

7. $4x^2 + 20x + 25 = (2x + \underline{\ ?\ })^2$ 5
9. $25 - 10y + y^2 = (\underline{\ ?\ } - y)^2$ 5
11. $1 + 8b + 16b^2 = (\underline{\ ?\ } + 4b)^2$ 1

8. $64x^2 - 16xy + y^2 = (\underline{\ ?\ } - y)^2$ $8x$
10. $9a^2 - 24a + 16 = (\underline{\ ?\ } - 4)^2$ $3a$
12. $a^2 - 6ab + 9b^2 = (\underline{\ ?\ } - 3b)^2$ a

Replace $\underline{\ ?\ }$ with $+$ or $-$ to make the square of the binomial equal the trinomial.

13. $x^2 - 16x + 64 = (x \underline{\ ?\ } 8)^2$ $-$
15. $n^2 - 12n + 36 = (n \underline{\ ?\ } 6)^2$ $-$

14. $p^2 - 10pq + 25q^2 = (p \underline{\ ?\ } 5q)^2$ $-$
16. $4x^2 - 12x + 9 = (2x \underline{\ ?\ } 3)^2$ $-$

Factor over the integers.

17. $x^2 + 6x + 9$ $(x + 3)^2$
20. $4x^2 - 12xy + 9y^2$ $(2x - 3y)^2$

18. $x^2 - 6x + 9$ $(x - 3)^2$
21. $4x^2 + 12xy + 9y^2$ $(2x + 3y)^2$

19. $n^2 + 14n + 49$ $(n + 7)^2$
22. $x^2 - 10x + 25$ $(x - 5)^2$

Factoring Polynomials **327**

Assignment Guide
Minimal
Day 1 p. 327: 1–16
Day 2 p. 327–328: 17–40
Average
pp. 327–328: 1–16, 18–40 even
Above Average
pp. 327–328: 2–30 even, 31–46

23. $1 + 8x + 16x^2$ $(1 + 4x)^2$ 24. $1 - 8x + 16x^2$ $(1 - 4x)^2$ 25. $a^2 + 8a + 16$ $(a + 4)^2$

26. $4x^2 - 4x + 1$ $(2x - 1)^2$ 27. $4x^2 + 4x + 1$ $(2x + 1)^2$ 28. $a^2 - 16a + 64$

29. $9y^2 + 12y + 4$ $(3y + 2)^2$ 30. $9y^2 - 12y + 4$ $(3y - 2)^2$ 31. $b^2 - 6b + 9$

32. $4a^2 - 4a + 1$ $(2a - 1)^2$ 33. $9a^2 - 12a + 4$ $(3a - 2)^2$ 34. $9 + 12x + 4x^2$

35. $49a^2 - 84a + 36$ $(7a - 6)^2$ 36. $4m^2 - 12m + 9$ $(2m - 3)^2$ 37. $x^2 - 18x + 81$

38. $a^2 + 14a + 49$ $(a + 7)^2$ 39. $1 - 6b + 9b^2$ $(1 - 3b)^2$ 40. $4 - 20b + 25b^2$ $(2 - 5b)^2$

B   Factor over the integers.

Example: $x^2 + 2xy + y^2 - z^2 = (x + y)^2 - z^2$
$$= (x + y + z)(x + y - z)$$

41. $(a^2 + 2ab + b^2) - c^2$ $(a + b + c)(a + b - c)$ 42. $c^2 - (a^2 + 2ab + b^2)$ $(c + a + b)(c - a - b)$

43. $(x^2 - 2xy + y^2) - 9$ $(x - y + 3)(x - y - 3)$ 44. $16 - (x^2 - 2xy + y^2)$ $(4 + x - y)(4 - x + y)$

45. $a^2 - 9 + 2ab + b^2$ $(a + b + 3)(a + b - 3)$ 46. $x^2 - 16 - 2xy + y^2$ $(x - y + 4)(x - y - 4)$

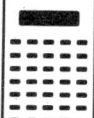

CALCULATOR APPLICATIONS

Finding A Sum

The formula for the sum of the first n natural numbers is $S = \dfrac{n^2 + n}{2}$. If $n = 4$, $S = \dfrac{4^2 + 4}{2} = 10$, which is the sum of the first four natural numbers, $1 + 2 + 3 + 4$.

EXAMPLE Find the sum of the first 478 natural numbers.

SOLUTION It may be easier to solve this problem with the calculator by factoring the formula,
$$S = \frac{n^2 + n}{2} = \frac{n(n + 1)}{2}.$$

When $n = 478$, $S = \dfrac{478(478 + 1)}{2} = \dfrac{478(479)}{2}$

$4\ 7\ 8$ $\boxed{\times}$ $4\ 7\ 9$ $\boxed{\div}$ 2 $\boxed{=}$ $\boxed{114481.}$

EXERCISES

Find the sum of the first n natural numbers for the given value of n.

1. 7 28   2. 13 91   3. 21 231   4. 35 630   5. 58 1711 6. 92 4278 7. 501   8. 1001

REVIEW CAPSULE FOR SECTION 9–5

Multiply. *(Pages 302–303)*

1. $(a + 1)(a + 2)$ $a^2 + 3a + 2$ 2. $(x - 3)(x - 2)$ $x^2 - 5x + 6$ 3. $(y + 4)(y - 3)$ $y^2 + y - 12$

4. $(2 - t)(5 + t)$ $10 - 3t - t^2$ 5. $(y - 5z)(y + 2z)$ 6. $(d - 8g)(d + 11g)$

7. $(r - 3s)(r + 7s)$ $r^2 + 4rs - 21s^2$ 8. $(x - 9y)(x + 2y)$ 9. $(w + 2z)(w - z)$ $w^2 + wz - 2z^2$

9–5 Factoring $x^2 + bx + c$

Teaching Suggestions p. M-22

Quick Quiz
Determine whether each of
the following is a perfect
square trinomial.
1. $x^2 - 2x + 1$ **Ans: yes**
2. $x^2 - 16x + 16$ **Ans: no**
3. $x^2 - 8x + 16$ **Ans: yes**
Factor over the integers.
4. $n^2 + 10n + 25$
  Ans: $(n + 5)^2$
5. $h^2 - 14h + 49$
  Ans: $(h - 7)^2$
6. $16c^2 - 26cd + 81d^2$
  Ans: $(4c - 9d)^2$

Since $(x + 2)(x + 3) = x^2 + 5x + 6$, it should be possible to factor $x^2 + 5x + 6$ as $(x + 2)(x + 3)$. The procedure lies in identifying two integers such that their product is 6 and their sum is 5.

EXAMPLE 1 Factor over the integers: $x^2 + 5x + 6$

Solution: $\boxed{1}$ $x^2 + 5x + 6 = (x \quad)(x \quad)$ ◄──────── **The factors of x^2 are x and x.**

$\boxed{2}$ Write the integral factors of 6.

$(1, 6); \quad (-1, -6); \quad (2, 3); \quad (-2, -3)$

$\boxed{3}$ Test the sum of the factors. Stop when you find two whose sum is 5.

$$\begin{array}{ccc} 1 & -1 & 2 \\ \dfrac{6}{7} \text{ No} & \dfrac{-6}{-7} \text{ No} & \dfrac{3}{5} \text{ Yes} \end{array}$$ ✔ Thus, $x^2 + 5x + 6 = (x + 2)(x + 3)$.

Example 1 illustrates that when the product of the two integral factors is positive *and* their sum is positive, the two factors will both be positive.

Additional Examples
Example 1
Factor over the integers.
1. $a^2 + 7a + 12$
  Ans: $(a + 4)(a + 3)$
2. $a^2 + 9a + 20$
  Ans: $(a + 4)(a + 5)$

EXAMPLE 2 Factor over the integers: $t^2 - 7t + 12$

Solution: $\boxed{1}$ $t^2 - 7t + 12 = (t \quad)(t \quad)$ ◄──────── **The factors of t^2 are t and t.**

$\boxed{2}$ Integral factors of 12:

$(1, 12); \quad (-1, -12); \quad (2, 6); \quad (-2, -6); \quad (3, 4); \quad (-3, -4)$

$\boxed{3}$ Test the sum of the factors to find two whose sum is -7.

$$-3 + (-4) = -7$$

Thus, $t^2 - 7t + 12 = (t - 3)(t - 4)$.

Example 2
Factor over the integers.
1. $p^2 - 6p + 8$
  Ans: $(p - 4)(p - 2)$
2. $m^2 - 11m + 24$
  Ans: $(m - 3)(m - 8)$

Example 2 illustrates that when the product of the two integral factors is positive *and* their sum is negative, the two factors will both be negative.

EXAMPLE 3 Factor over the integers: $x^2 - 5x - 14$

Solution: $\boxed{1}$ $x^2 - 5x - 14 = (x \quad)(x \quad)$

$\boxed{2}$ Integral factors of -14: $(1, -14); \quad (-1, 14); \quad (2, -7); \quad (-2, 7)$

$\boxed{3}$ Determine which two factors have a sum of -5.

$$2 + (-7) = -5$$

Thus, $x^2 - 5x - 14 = (x + 2)(x - 7)$.

Example 3
Factor over the integers.
1. $x^2 - 2x - 15$
  Ans: $(x + 3)(x - 5)$
2. $x^2 - x - 20$
  Ans: $(x + 4)(x - 5)$

Example 3 illustrates that when the product of two integral factors is negative *and* their sum is negative, one factor will be positive and one will be negative.

Factoring Polynomials **329**

With practice, you will be able to apply these procedures more quickly.

EXAMPLE 4 Factor over the integers.

a. $x^2 - 6x + 8$ **b.** $t^2 - 10t - 24$ **c.** $t^2 + 6rt - 27r^2$

Solutions:

a. $x^2 - 6x + 8 = (x - 4)(x - 2)$ ◄─── Since $-4(-2) = 8$ and $-4 + (-2) = -6$

b. $t^2 - 10t - 24 = (t - 12)(t + 2)$ ◄─── Since $-12(2) = -24$ and $-12 + 2 = -10$

c. $t^2 + 6rt - 27r^2 = (t - 3r)(t + 9r)$ ◄─── Since $-3(9) = -27$ and $-3 + 9 = 6$

CLASSROOM EXERCISES

For each of the following, identify two integers such that their sum equals the first number and their product equals the second number.

1. 7; 12 4, 3   **2.** −5; 6 −3,−2 **3.** 5; −24 8, −3   **4.** −6; 5 −5, −1   **5.** −6; 9 −3, −3 **6.** −2; −15 −5, 3

7. −9; 18 −6, −3 **8.** 4; −32 8, −4 **9.** −4; −32 −8, 4 **10.** −1; −72 −9, 8 **11.** 1; −72 9, −8 **12.** −13; 36 −9, −4

WRITTEN EXERCISES

A   Factor each trinomial over the integers.

1. $x^2 + 7x + 12$ $(x + 4)(x + 3)$ **2.** $x^2 + 6x + 8$ $(x + 4)(x + 2)$ **3.** $y^2 + 8y + 15$ $(y + 5)(y + 3)$

4. $m^2 + 10m + 21$ $(m + 7)(m + 3)$ **5.** $a^2 + 3a - 4$ $(a + 4)(a - 1)$ **6.** $x^2 + 3x - 10$

7. $y^2 + 7y - 8$ $(y + 8)(y - 1)$ **8.** $b^2 + 2b - 8$ $(b + 4)(b - 2)$ **9.** $x^2 - 5x + 6$

10. $x^2 - 6x + 5$ $(x - 5)(x - 1)$ **11.** $x^2 - 13x + 36$ $(x - 9)(x - 4)$ **12.** $x^2 - 9x + 18$

13. $x^2 - 2x - 15$ $(x - 5)(x + 3)$ **14.** $x^2 - 4x - 32$ $(x - 8)(x + 4)$ **15.** $x^2 - x - 72$

16. $x^2 - 5x - 14$ $(x - 7)(x + 2)$ **17.** $x^2 + 5x - 24$ $(x + 8)(x - 3)$ **18.** $x^2 + 6x + 5$

19. $x^2 + 4x - 32$ $(x + 8)(x - 4)$ **20.** $x^2 + x - 72$ $(x + 9)(x - 8)$ **21.** $x^2 - 10x + 21$

22. $x^2 - 6x + 8$ $(x - 4)(x - 2)$ **23.** $x^2 + 14x + 48$ $(x + 8)(x + 6)$ **24.** $x^2 - 8x + 15$

25. $x^2 + 6x + 8$ $(x + 4)(x + 2)$ **26.** $x^2 + 10x + 16$ $(x + 8)(x + 2)$ **27.** $x^2 + 2x - 8$

28. $y^2 + 9y + 18$ $(y + 6)(y + 3)$ **29.** $y^2 - 17y + 66$ $(y - 11)(y - 6)$ **30.** $x^2 + 2x - 15$

31. $y^2 - y - 156$ $(y - 13)(y + 12)$ **32.** $x^2 + x - 56$ $(x + 8)(x - 7)$ **33.** $y^2 + 6y - 72$

34. $3 - 4t + t^2$ $(3 - t)(1 - t)$ **35.** $20 + 12v + v^2$ $(10 + v)(2 + v)$ **36.** $-30 + 13w + w^2$

37. $51 - 20k + k^2$ $(17 - k)(3 - k)$ **38.** $x^2 + 5xy + 4y^2$ $(x + 4y)(x + y)$ **39.** $r^2 - 6rt + 8t^2$

40. $16p^2 - 8pq + q^2$ $(4p - q)^2$ **41.** $a^2 - 14ab + 24b^2$ **42.** $y^2 - 6yz - 16z^2$

43. $x^2 - 5xy - 6y^2$ $(x - 6y)(x + y)$ **44.** $48c^2 - 16cd + d^2$ **45.** $x^2 + 7xy - 18y^2$

46. $15r^2 + 2rs - s^2$ $(5r - s)(3r + s)$ **47.** $a^2 + 8ab + 12b^2$ $(a + 6b)(a + 2b)$ **48.** $66w^2 + 17wz + z^2$

49. $r^2 + 8rt + 15t^2$ $(r + 5t)(r + 3t)$ **50.** $y^2 - 7xy + 10x^2$ $(y - 5x)(y - 2x)$ **51.** $x^2 - 11xy - 60y^2$
                                                                                        $(x - 15y)(x + 4y)$

330   *Chapter 9*

B

APPLICATIONS: Using Factoring

52. Find the length of the rectangle. $x + 3$

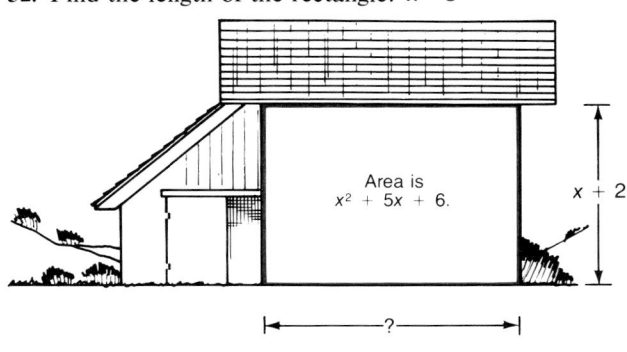

Area is
$x^2 + 5x + 6$.

$x + 2$

|←———?———→|

53. Find the missing factor.

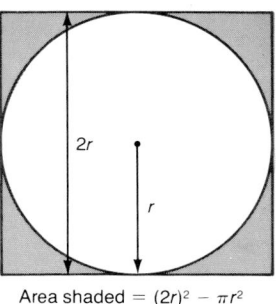

$2r$

r

Area shaded $= (2r)^2 - \pi r^2$
$= 4r^2 - \pi r^2$
$= (4 - \pi)(?)$

For Exercises 54–56, find the dimensions of each rectangle if the lengths of the sides are expressed as binomials with integral coefficients.

54.

Area $= x^2 - 169$

55.

Area $= x^2 + 13x + 12$

56.

Area $= x^2 - 4x + 4$

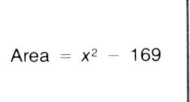**Puzzle** ——— See the Solution Key.

Complete the magic square below. The sum of each row, column, and diagonal is $3a^2 + 12a$. Each entry must be given in factored form.

$(a + 3)(a + 4)$	__?__	$(a + 4)(a + 1)$
__?__	__?__	__?__
__?__	$(a + 4)(a + 4)$	$(a - 3)(a + 4)$

———— **REVIEW CAPSULE FOR SECTION 9-6** ————

Multiply. *(Pages 302–303)*

1. $(2x + 3)(3x + 4)$ $6x^2 + 17x + 12$ **2.** $(b - 5)(3b + 7)$ $3b^2 - 8b - 35$ **3.** $(y - 2)(5y + 8)$ $5y^2 - 2y - 16$

4. $(5a + 7b)(5a + 3b)$ **5.** $(3a + b)(2a - 3b)$ **6.** $(7c - 2d)(c + 5d)$

7. $(5y - 4)(3y - 1)$ $15y^2 - 17y + 4$ **8.** $(4p + 3)(11p - 2)$ $44p^2 + 25p - 6$ **9.** $(3x - y)(4x - 3y)$

Factoring Polynomials   **331**

Quick Quiz
Factor over the integers.
1. $x^2 + 7x - 18$
   Ans: $(x + 9)(x - 2)$
2. $x^2 - 9x + 18$
   Ans: $(x - 3)(x - 6)$
3. $x^2 - 3xy - 18y^2$
   Ans: $(x - 6y)(x + 3y)$
4. $y^2 + 10y + 24$
   Ans: $(y + 6)(y + 4)$
5. $a^2 - a - 72$
   Ans: $(a - 9)(a + 8)$

Additional Examples
Example 1
Factor over the integers.
1. $2x^2 - 9x - 5$
   Ans: $(2x + 1)(x - 5)$
2. $2x^2 + x - 6$
   Ans: $(2x - 3)(x + 2)$

Example 2
Factor over the integers.
1. $6x^2 + 13x + 5$
   Ans: $(3x + 5)(2x + 1)$
2. $8x^2 - 14x + 5$
   Ans: $(4x - 5)(2x - 1)$

OBJECTIVE: To factor a polynomial of the form $ax^2 + bx + c$

9-6 Factoring $ax^2 + bx + c$

In the previous lesson, you factored trinomials such as $x^2 + 5x + 6$. The x^2-term of all these trinomials had a coefficient of 1. You can also factor some trinomials in which the x^2-term has a coefficient that is not 1.

EXAMPLE 1 Factor over the integers: $2x^2 - 5x - 3$

Solution: $\boxed{1}$ $2x^2 - 5x - 3 = (2x\quad)(x\quad)$ ◄── **Write the factors of $2x^2$. The only possibilities are $2x$ and x.**

$\boxed{2}$ Integral factors of -3: $(-1, 3)$; $(1, -3)$

$\boxed{3}$ Write all possible binomials. Test the sum of the outer and inner products to find those with a sum of $-5x$.

Binomials	Outer Product + Inner Product
$(2x - 1)(x + 3)$	$6x - x = 5x$ **No**
$(2x + 3)(x - 1)$	$-2x + 3x = x$ **No**
$(2x - 3)(x + 1)$	$2x - 3x = -x$ **No**
$(2x + 1)(x - 3)$	$-6x + x = -5x$ **Yes** ✔ Thus, $2x^2 - 5x - 3 = (2x + 1)(x - 3)$.

In Example 2, all three terms of the trinomial have positive coefficients. Thus, its binomial factors will also have positive coefficients. This reduces the number of possible binomial factors to be tested.

EXAMPLE 2 Factor over the integers: $6x^2 + 7x + 2$

Solution: $\boxed{1}$ $6x^2 + 7x + 2 = (6x\quad)(x\quad)$ ◄── **Write the factors of $6x^2$.**

$(3x\quad)(2x\quad)$

$\boxed{2}$ Integral factors of 2: $(2, 1)$

Binomials	Outer Product + Inner Product
$(6x + 1)(x + 2)$	$12x + x = 13x$ **No**
$(6x + 2)(x + 1)$	$6x + 2x = 8x$ **No**
$(3x + 1)(2x + 2)$	$6x + 2x = 8x$ **No**
$(3x + 2)(2x + 1)$	$3x + 4x = 7x$ **Yes** ✔ Thus, $6x^2 + 7x + 2 = (3x + 2)(2x + 1)$.

As the Examples show, you may have to write several pairs of binomial factors before you find the pair that works. As you gain experience, you will be able to find the pair that works after only a few trials.

EXAMPLE 3 Factor over the integers: $8x^2 - 35x + 12$

Solution: $\boxed{1}$ $8x^2 - 35x + 12 = (8x \quad)(x \quad)$ ◄——— **Write the factors of 8.**

$= (4x \quad)(2x \quad)$

Since the middle term of the trinomial is preceded by $-$ and the third term is preceded by $+$, both factors of 12 will be negative.

$\boxed{2}$ Integral factors of 12: $(-1, -12);\quad (-2, -6);\quad (-3, -4)$

$\boxed{3}$ Test the possible binomials.

Binomials	Outer Product + Inner Product
$(8x - 1)(x - 12)$	$-96x - x = -97x$ **No**
$(8x - 12)(x - 1)$	$-8x - 12x = -20x$ **No**
$(8x - 2)(x - 6)$	$-48x - 2x = -50x$ **No**
$(8x - 6)(x - 2)$	$-16x - 6x = -22x$ **No**
$(8x - 3)(x - 4)$	$-32x - 3x = -35x$ **Yes** ✔

Thus, $8x^2 - 35x + 12 = (8x - 3)(x - 4)$.

In Example 3, the correct binomial factors were found on the fifth trial. Thus, the five possibilities involving $4x$ and $2x$ did not have to be checked.

Additional Examples
Example 3
Factor over the integers.
1. $8x^2 - 51x + 18$
   Ans: (8x − 3)(x − 6)
2. $21a^2 + 19a - 12$
   Ans: (7x − 3)(3x + 4)

CLASSROOM EXERCISES

Match each trinomial in Column I with its corresponding factorization in Column II.

Column I

1. $2a^2 + 7ab - 15b^2$ d
2. $3a^2 + 10a - 8$ a
3. $12a^2 + 17a + 6$ e
4. $6a^2 - 43a + 72$ b
5. $4a^2 - 4ab - 15b^2$ c

Column II

a. $(3a - 2)(a + 4)$
b. $(2a - 9)(3a - 8)$
c. $(2a - 5b)(2a + 3b)$
d. $(2a - 3b)(a + 5b)$
e. $(3a + 2)(4a + 3)$

Factor over the integers. One factor is written for you.

6. $3a^2 + 5a + 2 = (3a + 2)(a + \underline{\ ?\ })$ 1
7. $2x^2 - 13x + 15 = (x - \underline{\ ?\ })(2x - 3)$ 5
8. $4y^2 - 23y - 35 = (y + 5)(4y - \underline{\ ?\ })$ 7
9. $9b^2 + 9b - 4 = (3b - 1)(3b + \underline{\ ?\ })$ 4
10. $8a^2 + 18a - 5 = (2a + 5)(\underline{\ ?\ } - 1)$ 4a
11. $7d^2 - 23d + 6 = (d - \underline{\ ?\ })(7d - 2)$ 3

Factoring Polynomials **333**

Assignment Guide
Minimal
Day 1 p. 334: 1–10
Day 2 p. 334: 11–34 odd
Average
Day 1 p. 334: 1–20
Day 2 p. 334: 21–46 odd
Above Average p. 334:
5, 10, 15, . . . 30, 35–46

Additional Answers
Written Exercises
13. $(3y + 2)(3y - 1)$
16. $(7x - 3)(3x + 2)$
19. $(5x - 1)(x - 3)$
22. $(x - 8)(x + 4)$
25. $(3x - 2)(x - 3)$
28. $(2n - 1)(n + 5)$
31. $(2x + 5)(x - 8)$
34. $(2d + 1)(d - 4)$
35. $(4x - 3y)(2x - y)$
36. $(7x + 3y)(2x - 9y)$
37. $(6 + 7y)(3 - 5y)$
38. $(-1)(21x^2 + 3x + 8)$
39. $(2x + 3)(x + 2)$
40. $(8c - 5d)(5c + 8d)$
41. $(4x - 7y)(3x - 2y)$
42. $(8x - 7)(7x + 8)$
43. $(4a + 7b)^2$
44. $(3x + y)(x - 3y)$
45. $(8a + 7b)^2$
46. $(6x - 5)(3x - 7)$

WRITTEN EXERCISES

A Factor over the integers. One factor is written for you.

1. $5x^2 + 9x - 18 = (5x - 6)(x + \underline{\ ?\ })$ 3
2. $2a^2 + 13a - 7 = (2a - \underline{\ ?\ })(a + 7)$ 1
3. $18n^2 + 21n - 4 = (6n - \underline{\ ?\ })(3n + 4)$ 1
4. $14x^2 - 13x - 12 = (7x + 4)(\underline{\ ?\ } - 3)$
 2x
5. $40n^2 + n - 6 = (\underline{\ ?\ } - 3)(\underline{\ ?\ } + 2)$ 8n, 5n
6. $2a^2 + 7ab - 15b^2 = (2a - \underline{\ ?\ })(a + \underline{\ ?\ })$ 3b, 5b
7. $5a^2 + 2a - 7 = (5a + \underline{\ ?\ })(a - \underline{\ ?\ })$ 7, 1
8. $x^2 + x - 72 = (x + \underline{\ ?\ })(x - \underline{\ ?\ })$ 9, 8
9. $5x^2 + 9x - 2 = (5x - \underline{\ ?\ })(x + \underline{\ ?\ })$ 1, 2
10. $6x^2 + x - 12 = (3x - \underline{\ ?\ })(2x + \underline{\ ?\ })$ 4, 3

Factor over the integers.

11. $2x^2 + 6x + 4$ $2(x + 2)(x + 1)$
12. $3x^2 + 11x + 10$ $(3x + 5)(x + 2)$
13. $9y^2 + 3y - 2$
14. $15y^2 - y - 2$ $(5y - 2)(3y + 1)$
15. $6y^2 - 17y + 12$ $(3y - 4)(2y - 3)$
16. $21x^2 + 5x - 6$
17. $6x^2 + 5x - 4$ $(3x + 4)(2x - 1)$
18. $9x^2 + 6x - 8$ $(3x + 4)(3x - 2)$
19. $5x^2 - 16x + 3$
20. $8y^2 - 2y - 1$ $(4y + 1)(2y - 1)$
21. $3y^2 + 4y - 7$ $(3y + 7)(y - 1)$
22. $x^2 - 4x - 32$
23. $2y^2 + 7y + 5$ $(2y + 5)(y + 1)$
24. $12y^2 + 7y + 1$ $(3y + 1)(4y + 1)$
25. $3x^2 - 11x + 6$
26. $2b^2 + 13b + 15$ $(2b + 3)(b + 5)$
27. $3a^2 - 10a - 25$ $(3a + 5)(a - 5)$
28. $2n^2 + 9n - 5$
29. $2t^2 + 5t - 3$ $(2t - 1)(t + 3)$
30. $3z^2 + 13z - 10$ $(3z - 2)(z + 5)$
31. $2x^2 - 11x - 40$
32. $2n^2 - 3n - 14$ $(2n - 7)(n + 2)$
33. $5q^2 - 42q - 27$ $(5q + 3)(q - 9)$
34. $2d^2 - 7d - 4$

B

35. $8x^2 - 10xy + 3y^2$
36. $14x^2 - 57xy - 27y^2$
37. $18 - 9y - 35y^2$
38. $-21x^2 - 3x - 8$
39. $2x^2 + 7x + 6$
40. $40c^2 + 39cd - 40d^2$
41. $12x^2 - 29xy + 14y^2$
42. $56x^2 + 15x - 56$
43. $16a^2 + 56ab + 49b^2$
44. $3x^2 - 8xy - 3y^2$
45. $64a^2 + 112ab + 49b^2$
46. $18x^2 - 57x + 35$

―――――― **REVIEW CAPSULE FOR SECTION 9–7** ――――――

State the greatest common monomial factor for each expression.
(Pages 319–321)

1. $sr - st$ s
2. $3x^2 - 6x - 30$ 3
3. $rs^2 - 2r$ r
4. $10x - 15x^3$ 5x
5. $18a - 27b$ 9
6. $21a^3b^2 - 14a^2b$ $7a^2b$
7. $2x^2 + 8x + 4$ 2
8. $t^3 - t^2 + t$ t

Classify each of the following as a difference of squares, *D*, a perfect square trinomial, *P*, or neither of these, *N*. *(Pages 306–307, 326–328)*

9. $a^2 + b^2$ N
10. $y^2 - 9$ D
11. $a^2 - 2a + 1$ P
12. $t^2 + t - 20$ N
13. $25 - r^2t^2$ D
14. $x^2 + xy + y^2$ N
15. $b^2 + 16b + 64$ P
16. $n^2 - 30n + 225$
 P

334 *Chapter 9*

9–7 Factoring Completely

A polynomial is **factored completely** when it is expressed as the product of prime polynomials. The following procedure will help you to factor polynomials completely.

Procedure

> To factor polynomials completely:
> 1. Look for common monomial factors.
> 2. Look for a difference of squares.
> 3. Look for a perfect square trinomial.
> 4. Look for a factorable trinomial of the form $x^2 + bx + c$ or $ax^2 + bx + c$.
> 5. When a polynomial has four or more terms, look for a way to group the terms in pairs to find a common binomial factor. Also, look for a group of three terms to find a perfect square trinomial.
> 6. Check each factor to be sure that it is prime. Check your work by multiplying the factors.

EXAMPLE 1 Factor completely over the integers.

a. $2x^2 - 10x + 12$ **b.** $5k^2 + 55kn + 90n^2$

Solutions: **a.** $2x^2 - 10x + 12 = 2(x^2 - 5x + 6)$ ◄── **Common monomial factor: 2**

$= 2(x - 3)(x - 2)$

b. $5k^2 + 55kn + 90n^2 = 5(k^2 + 11kn + 18n^2)$ ◄── **Common monomial factor: 5**

$= 5(k + 9n)(k + 2n)$

Remember to check whether the factors in your final answer are prime over the integers.

EXAMPLE 2 Factor over the integers.

a. $4x^2 - 4x^4$ **b.** $4x^3 + x^2 - x$ **c.** $8a^2 + 16a + 8$

Solutions: **a.** $4x^2 - 4x^4 = 4x^2(1 - x^2)$ ◄── **The common factor is $4x^2$.**

$= 4x^2(1 + x)(1 - x)$ ◄── $(1 - x^2) = (1 + x)(1 - x)$

b. $4x^3 + x^2 - x = x(4x^2 + x - 1)$ ◄── **The common factor is x.**

Since $4x^2 + x - 1$ is a prime polynomial over the integers,

$4x^3 + x^2 - x = x(4x^2 + x - 1)$.

c. $8a^2 + 16a + 8 = 8(a^2 + 2a + 1)$ ◄── **The common factor is 8.**

$= 8(a + 1)(a + 1)$ ◄── $a^2 + 2a + 1 = (a + 1)(a + 1)$

$= 8(a + 1)^2$

Factoring Polynomials **335**

Teaching Suggestions p. M-22

Quick Quiz
Factor over the integers.
1. $2x^2 - x - 6$
   Ans: $(2x + 3)(x - 2)$
2. $3x^2 + 14x - 5$
   Ans: $(3x - 1)(x + 5)$
3. $6x^2 + 17x + 5$
   Ans: $(3x + 1)(2x + 5)$
4. $10y^2 - 13y + 4$
   Ans: $(5y - 4)(2y - 1)$
5. $15a^2 + 19a - 56$
   Ans: $(5a - 7)(3a + 8)$
6. $6r^2 + 17r - 14$
   Ans: $(3r - 2)(2r + 7)$

Additional Examples
Example 1
Factor completely over the integers.
1. **a.** $3x^2 - 18x + 24$
      Ans: $3(x - 4)(x - 2)$
   b. $4a^2 + 24a + 20$
      Ans: $4(a + 5)(a + 1)$
2. **a.** $2m^2 + 20mn + 32n^2$
      Ans: $2(m + 8n)(m + 2n)$
   b. $3x^2 - 36xy + 81y^2$
      Ans: $3(x - 9y)(x - 3y)$

Example 2
Factor over the integers.
1. **a.** $8a^2 - 8a^4$
      Ans: $8a^2(1 + a)(1 - a)$
   b. $9x^4 - 9x^2$
      Ans: $9x^2(x + 1)(x - 1)$
2. **a.** $3a^3 - a^2 - a$
      Ans: $a(3a^2 - a - 1)$
   b. $2y^3 + 2y^2 + y$
      Ans: $y(2y^2 + 2y + 1)$
3. **a.** $5a^2 + 30a + 45$
      Ans: $5(a + 3)^2$
   b. $6a^2 - 48a + 96$
      Ans: $6(a - 4)^2$

335

CLASSROOM EXERCISES

Factor completely over the integers.

1. $2x^2 + 4x + 2$ $2(x + 1)^2$

2. $3y^2 + 9y + 6$ $3(y + 2)(y + 1)$

3. $6t^2 + 30t - 36$ $6(t + 6)(t - 1)$

4. $r^3 - rz^2$ $r(r + z)(r - z)$

5. $ax + bx + cx$ $x(a + b + c)$

6. $3b^2 - 12b + 12$ $3(b - 2)^2$

WRITTEN EXERCISES

A   Factor completely over the integers.

1. $5b^2 + 20b - 60$ $5(b + 6)(b - 2)$

2. $2x^2 + 10x - 28$ $2(x + 7)(x - 2)$

3. $6x^2 - 21x - 12$

4. $4b^2 + 26b - 14$ $2(2b - 1)(b + 7)$

5. $12x^2 - 10x - 12$ $2(3x + 2)(2x - 3)$

6. $18a^2 + 21a - 9$

7. $3x^2 - 3y^2$ $3(x + y)(x - y)$

8. $24a^2 - 54b^2$ $6(2a + 3b)(2a - 3b)$

9. $3b^2 - 3b$

10. $2y^3 - 4y^2 - 48y$ $2y(y - 6)(y + 4)$

11. $2m^3 - 20m^2 + 18m$

12. $6z^3 - 3z^2 - 30z$

13. $2a^3 - 2a$ $2a(a + 1)(a - 1)$

14. $4b^2 - 24b + 20$ $4(b - 5)(b - 1)$

15. $12m^2 + 33m - 9$

16. $3t^3 - 27t$ $3t(t + 3)(t - 3)$

17. $3x^2 + 6x - 24$ $3(x + 4)(x - 2)$

18. $4x^2 - 32x + 60$

19. $2x^2 + 12x - 80$ $2(x + 10)(x - 4)$

20. $5y^2 - 45y - 110$ $5(y - 11)(y + 2)$

21. $2t^2 - 28t + 98$

22. $3x^3 - 33x^2 + 84x$

23. $x^4 - 9x^2$ $x^2(x + 3)(x - 3)$

24. $5x^2 + 60x - 140$

25. $2a^2 + 14a + 24$ $2(a + 4)(a + 3)$

26. $5y^2 - 45$ $5(y + 3)(y - 3)$

27. $st^2 - st - 20s$

28. $7a^2 - 14a - 105$ $7(a - 5)(a + 3)$

29. $3x^2 + 12x + 45$ $3(x^2 + 4x + 15)$

30. $x^2 - 6x + 9$

31. $6t^2 - 15t^3$ $3t^2(2 - 5t)$

32. $2 - 128t^2$ $2(1 + 8t)(1 - 8t)$

33. $ab^2 - ab - 72a$

34. $n^2 + 5n + 7$ prime

35. $3a^2 + a - 2$ $(3a - 2)(a + 1)$

36. $2a^2 - 5a + 3$

37. $a^2 + 25$ prime

38. $q^2 - 12q - 28$ $(q - 14)(q + 2)$

39. $2x^2 - 14x + 24$

40. $y^4 - 6y^2 - 16$ $(y^2 - 8)(y^2 + 2)$

41. $49c^2 + 70c + 25$ $(7c + 5)^2$

42. $5a^2 - 80$

43. $x^3 - x$ $x(x + 1)(x - 1)$

44. $a^4 - 16$ $(a^2 + 4)(a + 2)(a - 2)$

45. $1 - 4y^2$

46. $x^2 + 4y^2$ prime

47. $2xy + 2yz + z^2 - y^2$ $2y(x + z) + (z + y)(z - y)$

48. $2 - 2y^2$

B

49. $x^2a + x^2b - 16a - 16b$ $(x + 4)(x - 4)(a + b)$

50. $y^2x + 2y^2 - 100x - 200$

51. $5r(r + 1)(r - 6) + 8(r - 6)$

52. $p(p - 5)(p + 1) + 9(p + 1)$

53. $x^2 - 2xy + y^2 - 3x + 3y$ $(x - y - 3)(x - y)$

54. $a^3 - 4a^2b + 2a^2 - 8b^2$

C

55. $z^4 - 81z^2q^2 - 4z^2 + 324q^2$

56. $y^3 - y^2 - 4y + 4$ $(y + 2)(y - 2)(y - 1)$

57. $(x^2 - 25)^2 - (5 - x)^2$

58. $16x^2y^2 - (x^2 + y^2 - g^2)^2$

59. $(x + y)^2 - (x - y)^2$ $4xy$

60. $(4x^2 - 12x + 9) - x^4$

61. $k^3 + k^2 - k - 1$ $(k + 1)(k + 1)(k - 1)$

62. $p^3 - p^2 - 8p + 8$ $(p^2 - 8)(p - 1)$

63. $t^4 + t^2 - 2$ $(t^2 + 2)(t + 1)(t - 1)$

64. $b^4 - 10b^2 + 9$ $(b + 3)(b - 3)(b + 1)(b - 1)$

65. $h^2 - (a^2 - 6a - 9)$ $(h + a - 3)(h - a + 3)$

66. $p^2 - 10p + 25 - q^2$ $(p - 5 + q)(p - 5 - q)$

67. $(2a + 3)^2 - (a - 1)^2$ $(3a + 2)(a + 4)$

68. $16d^8 - 8d^4 + 1$

69. $(x + y)^4 - 16(x + y)^2 + 63$

70. $(a + b)^2 - (x^2 - 2xy + y^2)$

OBJECTIVE: To solve equations by factoring

9–8 Using Factoring to Solve Equations

Some equations can be solved by factoring. The factoring method applies the Zero Product Theorem.

Theorem 9–2

> **Zero Product Theorem**
>
> **If the product of two real numbers a and b is zero, then**
>
> $a = 0$ or $b = 0$ or both a and b equal 0.

Thus, by the Zero Product Theorem, if

$$(x + 9)(x - 4) = 0, \text{ then } x + 9 = 0 \quad \text{or} \quad x - 4 = 0. \quad \text{That is,}$$
$$x = -9 \quad \text{or} \quad x = 4.$$

Example 1 shows how this theorem is applied in solving equations.

EXAMPLE 1   Solve by factoring: $x^2 - 7x + 12 = 0$

  Solution: $x^2 - 7x + 12 = 0$ ⟵ ——— **Factor $x^2 - 7x + 12$.**

  $(x - 3)(x - 4) = 0$

  $x - 3 = 0 \quad \text{or} \quad x - 4 = 0$ ⟵——— **By the Zero Product theorem**

  $x = 3 \quad \text{or} \quad x = 4$

  Check: $x^2 - 7x + 12 = 0$ ⟵ **Replace x with 3.** $x^2 - 7x + 12 = 0$ ⟵ **Replace x with 4.**

  $(3)^3 - 7(3) + 12 \overset{?}{=} 0$ $(4)^4 - 7(4) + 12 \overset{?}{=} 0$

  $9 - 21 + 12 \overset{?}{=} 0$ $16 - 28 + 12 \overset{?}{=} 0$

  $0 \overset{?}{=} 0 \ $ Yes ✔ $0 \overset{?}{=} 0 \ $ Yes ✔

  Solution set: $\{3, 4\}$

When an equation is not in the form $ax^2 + bx + c = 0$, rewrite it in that form before using the factoring method.

EXAMPLE 2   Solve by factoring: $2x^2 = -4x$

  Solution: $2x^2 = -4x$ ⟵——— **Add 4x to each side.**

  $2x^2 + 4x = 0$ ⟵——— **Factor $2x^2 + 4x$.**

  $2x(x + 4) = 0$

  $2x = 0 \quad \text{or} \quad x + 4 = 0$ ⟵——— **By the Zero Product Theorem**

  $x = 0 \quad \text{or} \quad x = -4$ The check is left for you.

  Solution set: $\{-4, 0\}$

Factoring Polynomials   **337**

CLASSROOM EXERCISES

Solve for the variable.

1. $b(b-1)=0$ $b = 0$ or $b = 1$
2. $z(z+6)=0$ $z = 0$ or $z = -6$
3. $(q-3)(q-7)=0$ $q = 3$ or $q = 7$

Solve by factoring.

4. $x^2-4=0$ $x = -2$ or $x = 2$
5. $t^2+2x+3=0$ $t = -3$ or $t = 1$
6. $z^2-2z-24=0$ $z = -4$ or $z = 6$
7. $4x^2=36$ $x = -3$ or $x = 3$
8. $y^2=8y$ $y = 0$ or $y = 8$
9. $2y^2=9y-9$ $y = 1\frac{1}{2}$ or $y = 3$

WRITTEN EXERCISES

A   Solve by factoring.

1. $x^2-5x-6=0$ $x = 2$ or $x = 3$
2. $x^2-5x+6=0$
3. $x^2-3x-10=0$ $x = -2$ or $x = 5$
4. $x^2=100$ $x = -10$ or $x = 10$
5. $n^2+n=0$
6. $y^2+7y=0$
7. $y^2-8y-9=0$
8. $a^2-36=0$
9. $c^2-49=0$
10. $3x^2=75$
11. $y^2=4y+12$
12. $y^2=-7y-10$
13. $5a^2+3a-2=0$
14. $3a^2-10a-8=0$
15. $6a^2+a-2=0$
16. $9x^2-36x=0$ $x = 0$ or $x = 4$
17. $n^2=7n$ $n = 0$ or $n = 7$
18. $y^2=8y$
19. $3n^2+7n=0$
20. $15a^2=13a+20$
21. $4a^2-9a=0$
22. $3x^2-2=x^2+6$
23. $24a^2+26a-63=0$
24. $5x^2-2x=3$
25. $0=9w^2+6w-27w^3$
26. $23p-6=-4p^2$
27. $4y^2+4y=-1$

B $w = -\frac{1}{3}$ or $w = 0$ or $w = \frac{2}{3}$ $p = -6$ or $p = \frac{1}{4}$ $y = -\frac{1}{2}$

28. $p^3-13p^2+36p=0$
29. $y^3-16y^2=0$
30. $3z^3+2z^2=z$
31. $3r^3-3r^2-3r+3=0$
32. $a^3+a^2=4a+4$
33. $w^3-2w^2=15w$
34. $(b-2)(b+3)=6$
35. $(b+2)(b-3)=6$
36. $(x-2)(x-1)=6$
37. $(z+1)(z+8)=-12$
38. $(t-5)(t-2)=4$
39. $3x^5=27x^3$
40. $(x-5)^2=16$
41. $(a+9)^2=25$
42. $(2a-4)^2=81$

C $x = 1$ or $x = 9$ $a = -14$ or $a = -4$ $a = -2\frac{1}{2}$ or $a = 6\frac{1}{2}$

43. $(a-1)^2-5(a-1)+6=0$ $a = 3$ or $a = 4$
44. $(t+3)^2-(t+3)-12=0$
45. $16(z-1)^2-16(z-1)=0$ $z = 1$ or $z = 2$
46. $6(r+2)^2-5(r+2)=6$
47. $(2a-1)(3a+4)-3(a-1)(a+2)=18$ $a = -2\frac{2}{3}$ or $a = 2$
48. $(3r-1)(3r+1)-(2r-1)(2r+1)=45$ $r = -3$ or $r = 3$

Puzzle

See the Solution Key.

What follows next in the sequence a–f below? (HINT: Factor each numerator.)

a. $\dfrac{x^2-16x+60}{x-6}$
    b. $\dfrac{2x^2+17x+30}{x+6}$
    c. $\dfrac{3x^2-22x+40}{x-4}$

d. $\dfrac{4x^2+21x+20}{x+4}$
    e. $\dfrac{25x^2-100}{5x+10}$
    f.   ?

Assignment Guide
Minimal p. 338: 1–27 odd
Average p. 338: 1–42 odd
Above Average
p. 38: 3, 6, 9, . . . 42, 43–48

Additional Answers
Written Exercises

1. $x = -1$ or $x = 6$
5. $n = -1$ or $n = 0$
6. $y = -7$ or $y = 0$
7. $y = -1$ or $y = 9$
8. $a = -6$ or $a = 6$
9. $c = -7$ or $c = 7$
10. $x = -5$ or $x = 5$
11. $y = -2$ or $y = 6$
12. $y = -5$ or $y = -2$
13. $a = -1$ or $a = \frac{2}{5}$
14. $a = -\frac{2}{3}$ or $a = 4$
15. $a = -\frac{2}{3}$ or $a = \frac{1}{2}$
18. $y = 0$ or $y = 8$
19. $n = -2\frac{1}{3}$ or $n = 0$
20. $a = -\frac{4}{5}$ or $a = 1\frac{2}{3}$
21. $a = 0$ or $a = 2\frac{1}{4}$
22. $x = -2$ or $x = 2$
23. $a = -2\frac{1}{4}$ or $a = 1\frac{1}{6}$
24. $x = -\frac{3}{5}$ or $x = 1$
28. $p = 0$ or $p = 4$ or $p = 9$
29. $y = 0$ or $y = 16$
30. $z = -1$ or $z = 0$ or $z = \frac{1}{3}$
31. $r = -1$ or $r = 1$
32. $a = -2$ or $a = -1$ or $a = 2$
33. $w = -3$ or $w = 0$ or $w = 5$
34. $b = -4$ or $b = 3$
35. $b = -3$ or $b = 4$
36. $x = -1$ or $x = 4$
37. $z = -5$ or $z = -4$
38. $t = 1$ or $t = 6$
39. $x = -3$ or $x = 0$ or $x = 3$
44. $t = 1$ or $t = -6$
46. $r = -2\frac{2}{3}$ or $r = -\frac{1}{2}$

338

Problem Solving and Applications

OBJECTIVE: To solve word problems using equations that can be solved by factoring

9–9 Using Factoring to Solve Problems

Some problems can be represented by equations that can be solved by factoring. However, some solutions of an equation may not satisfy the conditions of the problem. For example, the length of a rectangle cannot be a negative number. In such cases, you disregard these solutions.

EXAMPLE 1 The Calhoun Marching Band uses a rectangular formation with 8 rows and 10 columns as shown at the right. When 40 new members joined the band, an equal number of rows and columns were added to the formation. How many rows and how many columns were added?

Columns

x x x x x x x x x x
x x x x x x x x x x
x x x x x x x x x x
Rows x x x x x x x x x x
x x x x x x x x x x
x x x x x x x x x x
x x x x x x x x x x
x x x x x x x x x x

Solution: $\boxed{1}$ Represent the unknowns.

Let x = the number of rows added.
Then x = the number of columns added.

$\boxed{2}$ Write an equation for the problem.

$(8 + x)(10 + x) = 120$ ◄──── $\left(\begin{array}{c}\textbf{Number of}\\\textbf{Rows}\end{array}\right)\left(\begin{array}{c}\textbf{Number of}\\\textbf{Columns}\end{array}\right) = \textbf{Total}$

$\boxed{3}$ Solve the equation.

$(8 + x)(10 + x) = 120$
$80 + 18x + x^2 = 120$
$x^2 + 18x - 40 = 0$ ◄──── **Factor.**
$(x - 2)(x + 20) = 0$
$x - 2 = 0 \quad$ or $\quad x + 20 = 0$
$x = 2 \quad$ or $\quad x = -20$ ◄──── **The number of rows cannot be negative.**

Check: Does $10(12) = 120$? Yes ✔ **Two rows** and **two columns** were added.

Remember that equations with an x^2–term must be written in the form $x^2 + bx + c = 0$ or $ax^2 + bx + c = 0$ before factoring.

EXAMPLE 2 A photograph is 14 centimeters long and 11 centimeters wide. A white border of uniform width is placed around the photo. The area of the border is 116 square centimeters. What is the width of the border?

Solution: $\boxed{1}$ Let w = the width of the border.
Then the new length is $14 + 2w$.
The new width is $11 + 2w$.

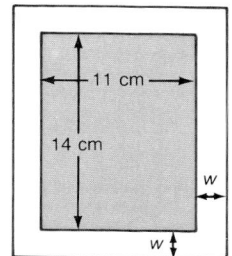

Factoring Polynomials **339**

Teaching Suggestions p. M-22

Quick Quiz
Solve by factoring.
1. $x^2 - 7x + 10 = 0$
   Ans: $\{2, 5\}$
2. $x^2 + 11x + 24 = 0$
   Ans: $\{-8, -3\}$
3. $6x^2 = -24x$ **Ans:** $\{-4, 0\}$
4. $8x^2 = 16x$ **Ans:** $\{0, 2\}$

Additional Examples
Example 1
1. The seats in a lecture hall were arranged in a rectangular formation with 10 rows and 10 columns. When 96 more students signed up for the lecture, an equal number of rows and columns were added to the formation. How many rows and how many columns were added?
   Ans: 4
2. An orange grove contained 500 trees. The number of trees per row was 5 more than the number of rows. How many rows were there? **Ans: 20**

Example 2
1. A painting is 46 centimeters long and 30 centimeters wide. A burlap border of uniform width is placed around the painting. The area of the border is 1536 square centimeters. How wide is the border?
   Ans: 1 cm
2. The area of a rectangle is 88 square meters. The length of the rectangle is 3 meters more than its width. Find the length and width.
   Ans: length: 11 m; width: 8 m

339

$$\boxed{2} \quad (14 + 2w)(11 + 2w) = 270 \quad \longleftarrow \quad \text{Area of Photo} + \text{Area of Border} = 11(14) + 116 = 270$$
$$\boxed{3} \quad 154 + 50w + 4w^2 \quad = 270$$
$$4w^2 + 50w - 116 \quad = 0$$
$$2(2w^2 + 25w - 58) \quad = 0 \quad \longleftarrow \quad \text{Factor.}$$
$$2(2w + 29)(w - 2) \quad = 0 \quad \longleftarrow \quad 2 \neq 0$$
$$2w + 29 = 0 \qquad \text{or} \quad w - 2 = 0$$
$$w = -14.5 \quad \text{or} \qquad w = 2 \quad \longleftarrow \quad \text{The width cannot equal } -14.5.$$

Check: Total area: $(11 + 4)(14 + 4) = 14(11) + 116?$ Yes ✔

The width of the border is **2 centimeters.**

CLASSROOM EXERCISES

In Exercises 1–4:
a. Represent the unknowns.
b. Write the equation you would use to solve the problem.

1. The length of a hallway is four times its width. The area is 144 square meters. Find the length and the width.

2. A living room is 3 feet longer than it is wide. Its area is 180 square feet. Find its length and width.

3. Find two consecutive integers whose product is 182.

4. The sum of an integer and its square is 156. Find the integer.

WORD PROBLEMS

A   Solve each problem.

1. The sum of two numbers is 12. The sum of their squares is 74. What are the numbers? 7, 5

2. The difference of two numbers is 3. The sum of their squares is 117. What are the numbers? 9, 6 or -6, -9

3. Find two consecutive integers whose product is 210. 15, 14 or -14, -15

4. Find two consecutive even integers whose product is 80. 8, 10 or -10, -8

5. Find two consecutive negative integers such that the sum of their squares is 113. -8, -7

6. The square of a certain positive integer is 30 more than the integer. Find the integer. 6

7. Twice the square of a certain number equals 144 more than twice the number. What is the number? 9 or -8

8. The square of a certain number is 4 more than three times the number. What is the number? 4 or -1

9. A rectangular parking lot is 20 meters longer than it is wide. The area of the lot is 1056 square meters. Find the dimensions (length and width).
   width: 24 m; length: 44 m

10. The area of a rectangular flower garden is 192 square meters. The length of the garden is 4 meters more than its width. Find the length and width.
    width: 12 m; length: 16 m

340   *Chapter 9*

11. Find two consecutive odd integers such that the square of the second decreased by the first is 14. −5, −3

12. Find two consecutive odd integers such that the square of the first decreased by the second is 28. −5, −3

13. A farmer planted 360 apple trees so that there were 9 more trees in a row than the number of rows. How many rows were there? 15

14. 55 band members are arranged in a formation so that there are 6 more rows than the number of persons per row. How many rows are there? 11

15. A fife-and-drum band has 120 members. When they are arranged in a rectangular formation, the number of players in each row is 7 less than the number of rows. How many players are there in each row? 8

16. A brass band uses a marching formation of 10 rows and 10 columns. When 54 new members joined the band, the new marching formation had 3 more rows than columns. How many rows were added to the old formation? 4

17. The length of a rectangle is 3 times its width. Increasing the width by 2 centimeters and the length by 4 centimeters doubles the area of the original rectangle. What are the dimensions of the original rectangle?

width: 4 cm; length: 12 cm

18. The length of a square lot is increased by 10 meters and the width is increased by 5 meters. The area of the resulting rectangular lot is 3 times the area of the square. What was the area of the square? 100 square meters

B

19. A real estate agency wishes to double the size (area) of its ad in a telephone directory by adding the same amount to the length and width of its present ad. The present ad is 4 centimeters wide and 6 centimeters long. What will be the new dimensions of the ad?

20. A billboard is 7 meters long and 5 meters high. An advertiser wishes to increase its size by adding the same amount to its length and width. The new area will be 63 square meters. How much must be added to the length and width of the billboard to do this?

21. The perimeter of a picture frame is 80 centimeters. The area is 396 square centimeters. Find the dimensions of the frame. width: 18 cm; length: 22 cm

22. The area of a rectangular heating panel is 192 square centimeters. Its perimeter is 56 centimeters. Find the length and width of the panel.

23. A city lot is 12 meters wide and 42 meters long. How wide a strip must be cut off one end and one side to make the area of the lot 400 square meters?

24. A creek runs along one side of a rectangular lot with an area of 4800 square feet. A fence on three sides requires 200 feet of fencing. What are the length and width of the lot?

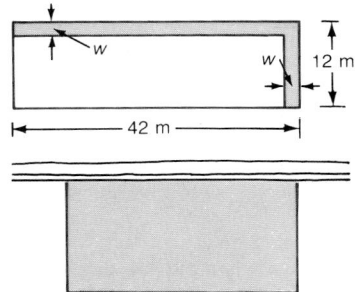

Factoring Polynomials **341**

C

25. A courtyard is designed so that the central rectangle with an area of 1000 square feet is surrounded by a walk which is 4 feet wide. The area of the walk is 624 square feet. Find the dimensions of the central rectangle. width: 20 ft; length: 50 ft

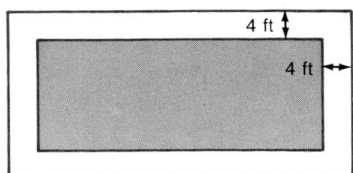

26. Squares 4 inches wide are cut out of a square sheet of metal at each corner. The sides are then turned up to form an open box. If the volume of the box is 1024 cubic inches, what was the original length of each side? 24 inches

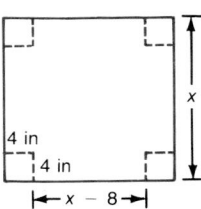

Quiz Sections 9-4–9-9
After completing this Review, you may want to administer a quiz covering the same sections. See page M-51 of the Teacher's Manual for the suggested quiz.

Additional Answers
Review
1. $(x + 4)(x + 4)$, or $(x + 4)^2$
2. $(8 - a)(8 - a)$, or $(8 - a)^2$
3. $(3x+1)(3x+1)$, or $(3x+1)^2$
14. $3(d+4)(d+4)$, or $3(d+4)^2$
15. $4(n-1)(n-1)$, or $4(n-1)^2$

Review

Factor over the integers. *(Section 9–4)*

1. $x^2 + 8x + 16$
2. $64 - 16a + a^2$
3. $9x^2 + 6x + 1$

(Section 9–5)

4. $x^2 + 4x + 3$ $(x + 3)(x + 1)$
5. $b^2 - 6b + 8$ $(b - 2)(b - 4)$
6. $r^2 - 4r - 12$ $(r - 6)(r + 2)$

(Section 9–6)

7. $5x^2 - 9x - 2$ $(5x + 1)(x - 2)$
8. $7y^2 - 8y + 1$ $(7y - 1)(y - 1)$
9. $6y^2 + 13y + 6$ $(3y + 2)(2y + 3)$
10. $3b^2 - 5b + 2$ $(3b - 2)(b - 1)$
11. $2a^2 - 5a - 12$ $(a - 4)(2a + 3)$
12. $30t^2 + 41t - 6$ $(15t - 2)(2t + 3)$

Factor completely over the integers. *(Section 9–7)*

13. $4a^2 - 4$ $4(a - 1)(a + 1)$
14. $3d^2 + 24d + 48$
15. $4n^2 - 8n + 4$
16. $x^3 - 7x^2 - 8x$ $x(x - 8)(x + 1)$
17. $4y^3 + 10y^2 - 6y$ $2y(2y - 1)(y + 3)$
18. $6b^4 - 10b^3 - 4b^2$ $2b^2(3b + 1)(b - 2)$

Solve by factoring. *(Section 9–8)*

19. $x^2 + 4x = 0$ $x = -4$ or $x = 0$
20. $2y^2 = 14y$ $y = 0$ or $y = 7$
21. $n^2 - n - 6 = 0$ $n = -2$ or $n = 3$
22. $a^2 = 16$ $a = -4$ or $a = 4$
23. $p^2 + 6p + 9 = 0$ $p = -3$
24. $6r^2 + r = 12$ $r = -1\frac{1}{2}$ or $r = 1\frac{1}{3}$

Solve each problem. *(Section 9–9)*

25. Six times a negative integer is 16 less than the square of the integer. Find the integer. -2

26. A store has 360 square meters of floor space. The length of the store is 9 meters greater than its width. Find the length and the width.
width: 15 m; length: 24 m

342   *Chapter 9*

BASIC: FACTORING THE DIFFERENCE OF TWO SQUARES

This lesson is optional. Each computer applications lesson relates directly to a topic covered within the given chapter. (See Section 9-3, pages 322–323)

The radical sign $(\sqrt{})$ does not usually appear on computer keyboards. Therefore, in BASIC the SQR function is used to obtain a square root. LET Y = SQR(X) means that Y will equal the square root of X (provided $X \geq 0$). Another BASIC function needed in the following program is the INT ("integer") function. INT(X) gives the largest integer less than or equal to X. Thus, INT(3.5) = 3; INT(2.9) = 2; INT(-1.8) = -2; INT(81) = 81.

Problem: *Write a program which factors, if possible, the difference of two squares.*

```
100 PRINT "FOR AX↑2 - B, WHAT ARE A AND B";
110 INPUT A, B
120 IF A <= 0 THEN 140
130 IF B > 0 THEN 160
140 PRINT "A AND B MUST BE POSITIVE. TRY AGAIN."
150 GOTO 110
160 LET S = INT(SQR(A) + .5)
170 IF ABS(SQR(A)-S) >= .001 THEN 200
180 LET S = INT(SQR(B) + .5)
190 IF ABS(SQR(B)-S) < .001 THEN 220
200 PRINT "CANNOT BE FACTORED"
210 GOTO 240
220 PRINT "FACTORS ARE (";SQR(A);"X +";SQR(B);")";
230 PRINT "(";SQR(A);"X -";SQR(B);")"
240 PRINT "ANY MORE BINOMIALS TO BE FACTORED (1=YES, 0=NO)";
250 INPUT Z
260 IF Z = 1 THEN 110
270 END
```

The following is the output from a sample run of the program above.

```
RUN
FOR AX↑2 - B, WHAT ARE A AND B? 16,1
FACTORS ARE ( 4 X + 1 )( 4 X - 1 )

ANY MORE BINOMIALS TO BE FACTORED (1=YES, 0=NO)? 1
? 25, 4
FACTORS ARE ( 5 X + 2 )( 5 X - 2 )

ANY MORE BINOMIALS TO BE FACTORED (1=YES, 0=NO)? 1
? 1,288
CANNOT BE FACTORED

ANY MORE BINOMIALS TO BE FACTORED (1=YES, 0=NO)? 0
READY
```

Factoring the Difference of Two Squares   **343**

Analysis

Statements 120–150: This section of the program is known as a "bad data trap." If either A or B is not positive, the binomial is not in the right form and cannot be factored.

Statements 160–190: The key questions the program must answer are whether A and B are perfect squares. One way to decide this is to test whether SQR(A) = INT(SQR(A)) and SQR(B) = INT(SQR(B)). For example, if A = 16 (a perfect square), SQR(A) = 4 and INT(SQR(A)) = 4. However, if A = 17 (not a perfect square), SQR(A) = 4.12311 but INT(SQR(A)) = 4. The problem with this approach is that computers can only *approximate* most square roots. Thus, SQR(225) might equal 14.999 instead of 15. In this case INT(SQR(225)) = 14 and not 15. To avoid this problem, 0.5 is added to the square root before the INT function is applied. This is the purpose of S in statements 160 and 180. Then 14.999 becomes 15.499 and INT(SQR(225)) does equal 15. But SQR(225) would still not exactly equal INT(SQR(225) + .5) since 14.999 ≠ 15. Hence a **tolerance** (allowance) of 0.001 is used. Thus, if SQR(A) is within 0.001 of S, the square root is considered an integer, and the small difference is due to the inaccuracy of the computer's calculation. Notice that the square roots in the sample output are correctly rounded to the nearest integer before being printed. On most computers, however, this does not necessarily mean that the square roots exactly equalled integers inside the machine.

EXERCISES   See the Solution Key.

A

1. As the last set of data in the sample output on page 343 shows, the program prints "1 X" instead of just "X". Add statements to the program to eliminate printing "1" as a coefficient.

B   Write a BASIC program for each problem.

2. The INT function can be used to decide whether one integer is a factor of another integer. For example, if A/B = INT(A/B), then B is a divisor of A. Given a positive integer A, print all the factors of A. For example, for A = 36, print 1 2 3 4 6 9 12 18 36.

3. Given two positive integers a and b, print all common factors of a and b.

4. For binomials of the form $Ax + B$, given integers A and B, decide whether A and B have a common factor other than 1 or −1. If they do, factor out the largest common factor of A and B. For example, for 3 X + 12, print 3 (X + 4).

5. Given nonzero integers b and c, factor trinomials of the form $x^2 + bx + c$ over the integers, if possible.

6. Given integers a, b, and c, factor $ax^2 + bx + c$ over the integers, if possible.

7. Given a positive integer x, determine whether x is prime. NOTE: 1 is not prime.

344   *Computer Applications*

Chapter Summary

IMPORTANT TERMS

Composite number (p. 316)
Factor (p. 316)
Factor completely (p. 335)
Perfect square trinomial (p. 326)

Prime-factorization form (p. 316)
Prime number (p. 316)
Prime polynomial with respect
to the integers (p. 319)

IMPORTANT IDEAS

1. **Unique Factorization Theorem (Fundamental Theorem of Arithmetic)** The factorization of any positive integer into primes is unique, disregarding the order of the factors.

2. **Formula for Factoring the Difference of Two Squares**
$$a^2 - b^2 = (a + b)(a - b)$$

3. **Conditions Under Which a Trinomial Is a Perfect Square**
   a. The first and last terms must be squares of monomials.
   b. The middle term must be twice the product of the monomials.

4. **Formulas for Factoring Perfect Square Trinomials**
$$a^2 + 2ab + b^2 = (a + b)(a + b) = (a + b)^2$$
$$a^2 - 2ab + b^2 = (a - b)(a - b) = (a - b)^2$$

5. **Steps for Factoring Polynomials Completely**
   1. Look for common monomial factors.
   2. Look for a difference of squares.
   3. Look for a perfect square trinomial.
   4. Look for a factorable trinomial of the form $x^2 + bx + c$ or $ax^2 + bx + c$.
   5. When a polynomial has four or more terms, look for a way to group the terms in pairs, or to find a common binomial factor. Also, look for a group of three terms to find a perfect binomial square.
   6. Check each factor to be sure that it is prime. Check your work by multiplying the factors.

6. **Zero Product Theorem** If the product of two real numbers a and b is zero, then $a = 0$, or $b = 0$, or both a and b equal 0.

Chapter Objectives and Review

Objective: *To write a number in prime factorization form and to write all of its whole number factors. (Section 9-1)*

Write each number in prime factorization form.

NOTE: In the first printing, the integers in Ex. 2 and 4 should have been positive.

1. 27 3^3 2. -75 $3 \cdot 5^2$ 3. 94 $2 \cdot 47$ 4. -180 5. 360   6. 630

Write all the whole–number factors of each expression. Do not include 1.

7. $3^2 \cdot 5$ 3, 5, 9, 15, 45   8. $2 \cdot 3 \cdot 11$ 9. $2 \cdot 7^2$ 2, 7, 14, 49, 98   10. $2 \cdot 3^2 \cdot 5$

Factoring Polynomials   **345**

Objective: *To factor polynomials by finding common monomial or binomial factors (Section 9–2)*

Factor over the integers. If a polynomial cannot be factored over the integers, write *Prime*.

11. $3a - 6b$ $3(a - 2b)$ **12.** $2c^3 - 4c$ $2c(c^2 - 2)$ **13.** $5p^3 - 8p^3$ Prime

14. $x^2y^3 + x^3y$ $x^2y(y^2 + x)$ **15.** $4n + mn - n^2$ $n(4 + m - n)$ **16.** $xy^3 - x^2y^4 + x^3y^3$
$xy^3(1 - xy + x^2)$

Objective: *To factor the difference of two squares (Section 9–3)*

Factor over the integers. If a polynomial cannot be factored over the integers, write *Prime*.

17. $9 - x^2$ $(3 + x)(3 - x)$ **18.** $4a^2 - 36$ $4(a - 3)(a + 3)$ **19.** $-1 + n^2$ $(n - 1)(n + 1)$ **20.** $4c^2 + d^2$ prime

21. $100 - 16x^2$ $4(5 - 2x)(5 + 2x)$ **22.** $9x^4 - y^2$ **23.** $m^2n^2 - c^2$ **24.** $d^6 - 1$

Factor each polynomial over the rational numbers.

25. $\dfrac{9}{16} - y^2$ $\left(\dfrac{3}{4} - y\right)\left(\dfrac{3}{4} + y\right)$ **26.** $9s^2 - \dfrac{4}{9}$ **27.** $25 - \dfrac{1}{25}r^2$ **28.** $\dfrac{x^2}{36} - \dfrac{4y^2}{9}$

Objective: *To factor a perfect square trinomial (Section 9–4)*

Factor over the integers.

29. $y^2 - 10y + 25$ **30.** $100 + 20b + b^2$ **31.** $16x^2 - 24x + 9$

32. $9c^2 + 24cd + 16d^2$ **33.** $4m^2 - 4mn + n^2$ **34.** $144 - 48a + 4a^2$

Objective: *To factor a polynomial of the form $x^2 + bx + c$ (Section 9–5)*

Factor over the integers.

35. $a^2 + 6a + 8$ $(a + 2)(a + 4)$ **36.** $c^2 - 9c + 8$ $(c - 8)(c - 1)$ **37.** $s^2 - 3s - 10$ $(s - 5)(s + 2)$

38. $t^2 + 4t - 45$ $(t + 9)(t - 5)$ **39.** $-16 + 6y + y^2$ $(y - 2)(y + 8)$ **40.** $w^2 - w - 2$

41. $-36 + 5n + n^2$ $(n + 9)(n - 4)$ **42.** $6a^2 - 5ab + b^2$ $(3a - b)(2a - b)$ **43.** $t^2 + 2st - 15s^2$
$(t + 5s)(t - 3s)$

Objective: *To factor a polynomial of the form $ax^2 + bx + c$ (Section 9-6)*

Factor over the integers.

44. $3x^2 - x - 2$ $(3x + 2)(x - 1)$ **45.** $5y^2 - 13y + 6$ $(y - 2)(5y - 3)$ **46.** $12y^2 + 16y + 5$
$(6y + 5)(2y + 1)$

47. $8x^2 - 25x + 3$ $(8x - 1)(x - 3)$ **48.** $8c^2 - 43c - 30$ $(8c + 5)(c - 6)$ **49.** $16n^2 - 2n - 3$

50. $4d^2 + d - 5$ $(4d + 5)(d - 1)$ **51.** $-10 + t + 24t^2$ $(8t - 5)(3t + 2)$ **52.** $-12h^2 + 11h - 2$
$(-4h + 1)(3h - 2)$

Objective: *To factor a polynomial completely over the integers (Section 9–7)*

Factor completely over the integers.

53. $2h^2 + 4h + 2$ **54.** $3b^2 - 27$ $3(b - 3)(b + 3)$ **55.** $4p^2 - 16p + 16$

56. $6r^2 + 18r + 12$ $6(r + 2)(r + 1)$ **57.** $5c^2 - 125$ $5(c - 5)(c + 5)$ **58.** $8r^2 - 56r - 64$

59. $y^3 + 2y^2 - 8y$ $y(y + 4)(y - 2)$ **60.** $6a^3 - 30a^2 + 24a$ **61.** $8n^4 + 6n^3 - 9n^2$
$6a(a - 4)(a - 1)$ $n^2(4n - 3)(2n + 3)$

346 *Chapter 9*

Objective: *To solve equations by factoring (Section 9–8)*

Solve by factoring.

62. $x^2 = x$ $x = 0$ or $x = 1$

63. $3y^2 + 12y = 0$ $y = -4$ or $y = 0$

64. $m^2 + 2m - 8 = 0$ $m = -4$ or $m = 2$

65. $b^2 = 9$ $b = -3$ or $b = 3$

66. $9q^2 + 4 = 12q$ $q = \frac{2}{3}$

67. $t^2 + 10t = 24$

68. $3d^2 + 5d - 2 = 0$ $d = -2$ or $d = \frac{1}{3}$

69. $y^3 = 36y$

70. $2a^3 - 2a^2 - 12a = 0$

Objective: *To solve word problems using equations that can be solved by factoring*
(Section 9–9)

71. Find three consecutive positive integers such that the square of the greatest of the three is equal to the sum of the squares of the other two. 3, 4, 5

72. Find three consecutive even integers such that the square of the greatest of the three is 148 more than the product of the other two. 22, 24, 26

73. There are 396 seats in a theater. The number of seats in each row is 4 more than the number of rows. How many seats are there in the theater? 22

74. A patio is twice as long as it is wide. Its area can be doubled by adding 3 meters to its length and 1 meter to its width. Find the patio's dimensions.

75. A marching band has 154 members. When they are arranged in a rectangular formation, the number of players in each row is 3 more than the number of rows. How many players are there in each row? 14

76. A rectangular lot is 6 meters wide and 10 meters long. When the length and width are increased by the same amount, the area of the lot is increased by 80 square meters. How much must be added to the length and width to do this? 4 m

Chapter Test

A formal Chapter Test is provided in the Teacher's Manual. See p. M-72.

Write each number in prime-factorization form. NOTE: The integer in Ex. 1 should be positive.

1. -96 $2^5 \cdot 3$

2. 300 $2^2 \cdot 3 \cdot 5^2$

3. 13 13

4. 55 $5 \cdot 11$

5. 220

Factor completely over the integers.

6. $2x^2 + 6xy$ $2x(x + 3y)$

7. $9b^2 - 1$ $(3b - 1)(3b + 1)$

8. $a^2 + 12a + 36$ $(a + 6)(a + 6)$, or $(a + 6)^2$

9. $y^2 + 11y + 24$ $(y + 3)(y + 8)$

10. $2x^2 - 4x + 2$

11. $a^2b^3 - a^3b$

12. $4 - 4n + n^2$

13. $n^2 + n - 56$ $(n + 8)(n - 7)$

14. $x^4 - 4$ $(x^2 - 2)(x^2 + 2)$

15. $6b^2 + 4b - 2$ $2(3b - 1)(b + 1)$

16. $4x^2 - 20xy + 25y^2$

17. $a^2b^2 - 16c^2$

18. $2m^2 + 20m + 50$

19. $a^3 - a^2 - 6a$ $a(a - 3)(a + 2)$

20. $m^3 - m$ $m(m + 1)(m - 1)$

Solve by factoring.

21. $x^2 + 2x - 15 = 0$

22. $2a^2 = 72$

23. $4p^2 + 8p - 12 = 0$

24. Four times the square of an integer is 6 more than twice the integer. What is the integer? -1

25. A rectangle is three times as long as it is wide. Its area is 48 square centimeters. Find its length and width. width: 4 cm; length: 12 cm

Factoring Polynomials **347**

348

NOTE: In the first printing, the integers in Ex. 3 and 5 should have been positive.

Additional Answers
6. $2^2 \cdot 3 \cdot 17$
13. $(x^5 - y)(x^5 + y)$
14. $(x - 9)(x - 9)$, or $(x - 9)^2$
15. $(2x + 3)(2x + 3)$, or $(2x + 3)^2$
16. $(3a - 4b)(3a - 4b)$, or $(3a - 4b)^2$

29. 10 rows, 24 chairs; 12 rows, 20 chairs; 15 rows, 16 chairs, 16 rows, 15 chairs, 20 rows, 12 chairs; 24 rows, 10 chairs
30. $9n^2 - 4m^2$; $(3n - 2m)(3n + 2m)$
31. width: $(x - 9)$ units; length: $(x + 4)$ units
32. width: 10 ft; length: 17 ft

Additional Practice
You may wish to use all or some of these exercises, depending on how well students performed on the formal chapter test.

Skills

Write each number in prime factorization form. *(Section 9–1)*

1. 63 $3^2 \cdot 7$ 2. 44 $2^2 \cdot 11$ 3. -60 $2^2 \cdot 3 \cdot 5$ 4. 273 $3 \cdot 7 \cdot 13$ 5. -375 $3 \cdot 5^3$ 6. 612

Factor over the integers. *(Section 9–2)*

7. $15a - 12a^2$ $3a(5 - 4a)$ 8. $x^2 y - x^2 y^3 + 2x^3 y$ $x^2 y(1 - y^2 + 2x)$ 9. $9a^2 - 18a^3$ $9a^2(1 - 2a)$

(Section 9–3)

10. $a^2 - 1$ $(a - 1)(a + 1)$ 11. $16m^2 - 49n^2$ $(4m - 7n)(4m + 7n)$ 12. $a^2 b^2 - 100$ $(ab - 10)(ab + 10)$ 13. $x^{10} - y^2$

(Section 9–4)

14. $x^2 - 18x + 81$ 15. $4x^2 + 12x + 9$ 16. $9a^2 - 24ab + 16b^2$

(Section 9–5)

17. $x^2 - 5x - 14$ $(x - 7)(x + 2)$ 18. $x^2 - 10x + 9$ $(x - 9)(x - 1)$ 19. $a^2 + ab - 12b^2$ $(a + 4b)(a - 3b)$

(Section 9–6)

20. $3n^2 - 11n - 4$ $(3n + 1)(n - 4)$ 21. $4x^2 + 6x - 10$ $2(2x + 5)(x - 1)$ 22. $8x^2 - 19x + 6$ $(8x - 3)(x - 2)$

Factor completely over the integers. *(Section 9–7)*

23. $5x^2 - 45$ $5(x - 3)(x + 3)$ 24. $3x^2 - 3x - 18$ $3(x - 3)(x + 2)$ 25. $18n^3 - 6n^2 - 4n$ $2n(3n - 2)(3n + 1)$

Solve by factoring. *(Section 9–8)*

26. $y^2 - 9y = 0$ $y = 0$ or $y = 9$ 27. $n^2 - 2n - 24 = 0$ $n = -4$ or $n = 6$ 28. $2y^2 - y - 36 = 0$ $y = -4$ or $y = 4\frac{1}{2}$

Applications

29. Two hundred forty folding chairs are arranged in a rectangular array for an outdoor concert. What formations are possible, if there must be at least 10 rows and at least 10 chairs in each row? *(Section 9–1)*

30. Each side of a square picture is $2m$ units long. The picture is centered over a square mat with each side $3n$ units long. Express the uncovered area of the mat in terms of m and n. Factor the expression. *(Section 9–3)*

31. The area of a rectangle is $(x^2 - 5x - 36)$ square units. Express the length and width of the rectangle as binomials. *(Section 9–5)*

32. It takes 170 one-foot square tiles to cover a floor. The length of the floor is 3 feet less than twice the width. What are its dimensions? *(Section 9–9)*

33. The names of 108 donors to the library fund are to be displayed in a rectangular array. There are to be 12 fewer columns than there are names in each column. How many columns will there be? *(Section 9–9)* 6

34. The length of a rectangle is twice its width. Increasing the width by 2 centimeters and the length by 6 centimeters doubles the area of the original rectangle. What are the dimensions of the original rectangle? *(Section 9–9)*
width: 6 cm; length: 12 cm

348   *Chapter 9*

CHAPTER **10** Rational Expressions

Problem Solving and Applications

OBJECTIVE: To solve proportions

10–1 Ratio and Proportion

Quick Quiz
Solve for the variable.
1. $7 \cdot 40 = 8 \cdot x$
   Ans: x = 35
2. $4 \cdot a = 5 \cdot 3$
   Ans: $a = 3\frac{3}{4}$
3. $3.8(5) = 1.9f$
   Ans: f = 10
4. $3(g - 5) = 8g$
   Ans: g = −3

A **ratio** is a comparison of two numbers by division. Ratios can be expressed in several ways.

	Ratio			
Example	**Using a Colon**	**As a Fraction**	**As a Decimal**	**As a Per Cent**
Batting Average: 30 hits out of 100 times at bat	30:100 (Read: "30 is to 100.")	$\frac{30}{100}$, or $\frac{3}{10}$	0.3, or 0.30	30%
Chances of rain: 3 out of 4	3:4	$\frac{3}{4}$	0.75	75%

A statement such as $\frac{40}{100} = \frac{2}{5}$ is a *proportion*.

Definition	A **proportion** is a statement that two ratios are equal.

Proportions can be used to solve many kinds of problems.

Additional Examples
Example 1
1. Noel has a recipe for filled oatmeal-date bars. The recipe calls for 3 cups of raw oats and makes 64 bars. Noel needs 160 bars for a social at her clubhouse. How many cups of oats should Noel use? **Ans: $7\frac{1}{2}$ cups**
2. Stan's recipe for potato pancakes uses 2 pounds of potatoes for 12 pancakes. How many pounds of potatoes will Stan need to make 40 pancakes?
Ans: $6\frac{2}{3}$ lb

EXAMPLE 1   A recipe for 60 cookies uses 3 cups of flour. How many cups of flour will be needed to make 135 cookies?

Solution: [1] Let $x =$ the number of cups needed. ◄——— **Represent the unknown.**

Known Ratio	**Unknown Ratio**
$\frac{3}{60}$ ◄——— Cups ◄——— Cookies	$\frac{x}{135}$ ◄——— Cups ◄——— Cookies

[2] $\dfrac{3}{60} = \dfrac{x}{135}$ ◄——— **Use the table to write a proportion.**

[3] $135\left(\dfrac{3}{60}\right) = 135\left(\dfrac{x}{135}\right)$ ◄——— **Solve for x.**

$\dfrac{405}{60} = x$

$6\dfrac{3}{4} = x$ Thus, **$6\frac{3}{4}$ cups** of flour will be needed.

Proportions are so useful in problem solving that a special property is often used to solve them.

First term ──────┐   ┌────── Third term

$$\frac{3}{60} = \frac{x}{135}$$

Second term ──────┘   └────── Fourth term

The first and fourth terms are called the **extremes.**

The second and third terms are called the **means.**

Property of Proportions

In a proportion, the product of the means equals the product of the extremes. That is,

if $\dfrac{a}{b} = \dfrac{c}{d}$ ($b \neq 0$, $d \neq 0$), then $ad = bc$.

Also,   if $ad = bc$, then $\dfrac{a}{b} = \dfrac{c}{d}$ ($b \neq 0$, $d \neq 0$).

EXAMPLE 2   A car travels 490 kilometers on 70 liters of gas. How far can it travel on a full tank of 100 liters?

Solution: $\boxed{1}$ Let $x =$ the number of kilometers.

Known Ratio	Unknown Ratio
$\dfrac{490}{70}$ ◄──── Kilometers ◄──── Liters	$\dfrac{x}{100}$ ◄──── Kilometers ◄──── Liters

$\boxed{2}$ $\dfrac{490}{70} \diagdown \dfrac{x}{100}$ ◄────── **Write a proportion.**

$\boxed{3}$ $(490)(100) = 70x$ ◄────── **Solve for x.**

$\dfrac{49,000}{70} = x$

$700 = x$ The car can travel **700 kilometers.**

In Examples 1 and 2, the check is left for you.

CLASSROOM EXERCISES

1. The directions on a can of orange juice concentrate call for adding three cans of water to one can of concentrate. Write the ratio of concentrate to water as a per cent. $33\frac{1}{3}$ %

A fabric is made up of 15% rayon, 45% polyester and 40% wool.

2. Write the ratio of rayon to polyester as a fraction in lowest terms. $\frac{1}{3}$
3. Write the ratio of rayon to wool as a fraction in lowest terms. $\frac{3}{8}$
4. Write the ratio of polyester to wool as a decimal.   1.125
5. Write the ratio of polyester to rayon as a fraction in lowest terms. $\frac{3}{1}$, or 3
6. Write the ratio of wool to rayon as a decimal. $2.6\overline{6}$

Rational Expressions   **351**

Additional Examples
Example 2
1. A truck traveled 450 kilometers on 60 liters of fuel. How far can it travel on 100 liters of fuel?
Ans: 750 km
2. A jumbo jet travels 1915 kilometers in 2 hours. How far can it travel in 6 hours?
Ans: 5745 km

One gallon of white paint, one quart of yellow paint, and one pint of red paint are mixed to make orange paint.

7. Write the ratio of yellow paint to white paint as a per cent. 25%

8. Write the ratio of red paint to yellow paint as a decimal. 0.5

9. Write the ratio of red paint to white paint as a fraction. $\frac{1}{8}$

WRITTEN EXERCISES

A   Solve each proportion.

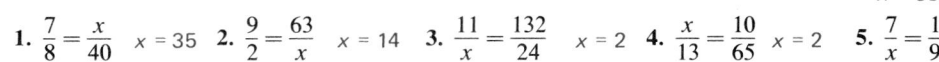

1. $\frac{7}{8} = \frac{x}{40}$ $x = 35$ 2. $\frac{9}{2} = \frac{63}{x}$ $x = 14$ 3. $\frac{11}{x} = \frac{132}{24}$ $x = 2$ 4. $\frac{x}{13} = \frac{10}{65}$ $x = 2$ 5. $\frac{7}{x} = \frac{1}{9}$ $x = 63$

6. $\frac{5}{13} = \frac{x}{65}$ $x = 25$ 7. $\frac{21}{5} = \frac{x}{2.5}$ $x = 10.5$ 8. $\frac{29}{7} = \frac{x}{1.75}$ $x = 7.25$ 9. $\frac{17}{2} = \frac{8.5}{x}$ $x = 1$ 10. $\frac{12}{3.1} = \frac{18}{x}$

11. $\frac{b+3}{5} = \frac{14}{20}$ $b = \frac{1}{2}$ 12. $\frac{3}{z} = \frac{8}{z+5}$ $z = 3$ 13. $\frac{r+4}{2} = \frac{r-3}{1}$ $r = 10$ 14. $\frac{t-4}{1} = \frac{t+3}{2}$

15. $s = \frac{s+5}{-9}$ $s = -\frac{1}{2}$ 16. $\frac{44-r}{r} = 21$ $r = 2$ 17. $\frac{a-2}{3} = \frac{2a+7}{5}$ $a = -31$ 18. $\frac{1}{x} = \frac{-6}{5-x}$

                                                                        $x = -1$

WORD PROBLEMS

In Exercises 19–22:
a. Represent the unknown.
b. Write a proportion that can be used to solve the problem.

19. A train traveled 90 miles in $1\frac{1}{2}$ hours. How many miles will it travel in 6 hours going at the same rate?

20. Fifty feet of copper wire weigh 2 pounds. How much will 325 feet of the same wire weigh?

21. The distance between two cities is 1500 kilometers. Find how far apart they are on a map with a scale that reads: "1 cm represents 500 km."

22. In a mixture of concrete, the ratio of sand to cement is 1:4. How many bags of cement are needed to mix with 100 bags of sand?

Solve each problem.

23. A recipe for a two-pound cake calls for $1\frac{1}{2}$ cups of butter. How many cups of butter will be needed for a five-pound cake? $3\frac{3}{4}$ cups

24. A nurse, checking the heartbeat of a patient, counted 19 beats in 15 seconds. What would be the patient's heartbeat for 60 seconds? 76 beats

25. On a map, 1.5 centimeters represents 60 kilometers. What distance does 6 centimeters represent?   240 km

26. A car travels 110 kilometers in 3 hours. How far will it travel in 5 hours at the same rate? $183\frac{1}{3}$ km

27. In a certain city, 0.7 centimeters of rain fell in 3 hours. How many centimeters of rain would fall in 9 hours at the same rate?   2.1 cm

28. A chef uses 5 pounds of meat to make 22 meat patties. How many patties of the same size can be made from $17\frac{1}{2}$ pounds of meat?   77 patties

352   *Chapter 10*

29. A pitcher allowed 10 earned runs in 15 innings. At this rate, how many runs would the pitcher allow in 9 innings? (The answer to Exercise 29 is called **earned run average**, or ERA.) 6 runs

30. What is the ERA of a pitcher who allows 21 earned runs in 58 innings? (See Exercise 29.) Round the answer to the nearest hundredth. 3.26

31. A 747-jumbo jet has a cruising speed of 595 miles per hour. How long will it take to travel at this rate from the east to the west coast, a distance of about 3300 miles? about 5.5 hr

32. The space shuttle Enterprise has an orbiting speed of 16,540 miles per hour. How long will it take to travel at this rate from the east to the west coast? (See Exercise 31.) about 0.2 hr

33. A printing press runs 500 copies of a brochure in 8 minutes. How long will it take to run 200,000 copies at the same rate? 3200 min

34. A 2-meter stick casts a shadow 1.3 meters long at the same time as a tree casts a 21–meter shadow. How tall is the tree? 32 m

35. Wallpaper to cover 55 square feet costs $16. How much will it cost to buy wallpaper to cover a wall with an area of 330 square feet? $96

36. A rate of 30 miles per hour is equivalent to 44 feet per second. How many feet per second are equivalent to a rate of 55 miles per hour? $80\frac{2}{3}$ ft/sec

B

37. Sally and Tom will do a job for $120. They agree to share the money in the ratio 3:2. How much will each receive? (HINT: Let $3y$ = Sally's share and $2y$ = Tom's share. Thus, $3y + 2y = 120$.)

38. Henry and Alice decide to divide a profit of $400 in the ratio 5:3. If Alice receives the larger amount, how much does each receive? Alice: $250; Henry: $150

39. The perimeter of a rectangle is 360 meters and the ratio of the length to the width is 11:4. Find the length and width of the rectangle.

40. The measures of two angles of a triangle are in the ratio 2:3. The sum of the measures of the angles is 90°. How many degrees are there in each angle?

**Additional Answers
Written Exercises**
37. Sally: $72;
   Tom: $48
39. length: 132 m;
   width: 48 m
40. 36° and 54°
46. $x = 6$

C Solve each proportion.

41. $\dfrac{x-3}{x+3} = \dfrac{x+5}{x-7}$ $x = \frac{1}{3}$

42. $\dfrac{x+1}{x-2} = \dfrac{x+3}{x-1}$ $x = 5$

43. $\dfrac{x}{x+4} = \dfrac{x+1}{x+6}$ $x = 4$

44. $\dfrac{3x+1}{5x-7} = \dfrac{3x+6}{5x-3}$ $x = 3$

45. $\dfrac{x-2}{3} = \dfrac{4}{x+2}$ $x = -4$ or $x = 4$

46. $\dfrac{-2}{x-2} = \dfrac{x-8}{4}$

47. If $7a - 4b = 0$, find $a:b$. $a:b = 4:7$

48. If $6a - 5b = 0$, find $b:a$. $b:a = 6:5$

49. If $5p = q$, find $(p + q):q$. $(p+q):q = 6:5$

50. If $6(r + s) = 11s$, find $r:s$. $r:s = 5:6$

REVIEW CAPSULE FOR SECTION 10-2

Complete. *(Pages 103–106)*

1. 22% of 600 = __?__ 132

2. 16.4% of 900 = __?__ 147.6

3. $33\frac{1}{3}$% of 192 = __?__ 64

4. 40% of 95 = __?__ 38

5. $12\frac{1}{2}$% of 104 = __?__ 13

6. 12% of 500 = __?__ 60

Rational Expressions   **353**

Review Capsule
This Review Capsule reviews the prior-taught skills used in Section 10-2. The reference is to the pages where the skills were taught.

Quick Quiz
1. A recipe for 5 servings of a baked custard uses 2 cups of milk. How many cups of milk are needed for 15 servings?   **Ans: 6 cups**
2. A car travels 500 kilometers on 50 liters of gas. On a vacation trip, the car used 450 liters of gas. How far did it travel?   **Ans: 4500 km**

Additional Examples
Example 1
1. José has $15,000 invested, part at a yearly interest rate of 9% and part at a yearly interest rate of 12% (Condition 1). How much is invested at each rate if the total yearly interest from both investments equals $1590 (Condition 2)?
Ans: 9%: $7000; 12%: $8000
2. Gladys has $16,000 invested, part at a yearly rate of 12% and part at a yearly interest rate of 14%. How much is invested at each rate if the total yearly interest from both investments equals $2090?
Ans: 12%: $7500; 14%: $8500

Problem Solving and Applications

OBJECTIVE: To solve investment problems and mixture problems

10–2   Investment Problems/Mixture Problems

In Chapter 6, you used a system of equations in two variables to solve investment (money) problems and mixture problems. These can also be solved by writing equations in one variable to represent the problem.

When money is invested, the rate of interest is expressed as a per cent.

The simple interest, i, on p dollars invested at r per cent per year for t years is given by this formula.

$$i = prt$$

EXAMPLE 1   Sandra has $12,000 invested, part at a yearly interest rate of 8% and part at a yearly interest rate of 13% (Condition 1). How much is invested at each rate if the total yearly interest from both investments equals $1310 (Condition 2)?

Solution: $\boxed{1}$ Use Condition 1 to express the amount invested at each rate.

Let a = the amount invested at 8%.
Then $12,000 - a$ = the amount invested at 13%.

Organize the information in a table.

Principal	Yearly Rate	Yearly Interest $i = prt$ $(t = 1)$
a	8%	$0.08a$
$(12,000 - a)$	13%	$0.13(12,000 - a)$

$\boxed{2}$ Use the table and Condition 2 to write an equation.

$0.08a + 0.13(12,000 - a) = 1310$ ◄——— **Interest at 8%** + **Interest at 13%** = **Total Interest**

$\boxed{3}$ Solve the equation.

$$0.08a + 1560 - 0.13a = 1310$$
$$-0.05a + 1560 = 1310$$
$$-0.05a = -250$$
$$a = 5000 \quad \longleftarrow \textbf{Don't forget to find } (12,000 - a).$$
$$12,000 - a = 12,000 - 5000 = 7000$$

Check: $\boxed{4}$ **Condition 1**   Does $5000 + $7000 = $12,000?   Yes ✔

Condition 2   Does $0.08($5000) + 0.13($7000) = $1310?   Yes ✔

Thus, **$5000** was invested at 8%; **$7000** was invested at 13%.

Many mixture problems use per cent to give the amount of each ingredient. For example, the amount of salt in 25 grams of a 20% solution of salt and water is

$$20\% \text{ of } 25 = 0.20(25), \text{ or 5 grams.}$$

EXAMPLE 2 How many grams of salt must a chemist add to 40 grams of a 15% salt solution to obtain a 20% salt solution?

Solution: $\boxed{1}$ Let $x = $ the number of grams of salt to be added.

	Number of Grams	Per Cent of Salt	Number of Grams of Salt
Original solution	40	15%	0.15(40)
Salt to be added	x	100%	1.00x
New solution	40 + x	20%	0.20(40 + x)

$\boxed{2}$ Write an equation. Refer to the table.

Amount of Salt in Original Solution	+	Amount of Salt Added	=	Amount of Salt in New Solution
0.15(40)	+	x	=	0.20(40 + x)

$\boxed{3}$ Solve the equation.
$$0.15(40) + x = 0.20(40 + x)$$
$$6 + x = 8 + 0.20x$$
$$0.80x = 2$$
$$x = 2.5$$

Check: $\boxed{4}$ Does $0.15(40) + 2.5 = 0.20(42.5)$? Yes ✔

The chemist must add **2.5 grams** of salt.

CLASSROOM EXERCISES

In Exercises 1–4, represent the total annual income from each investment.

1. $8000 invested at 12% per year

2. $$y$ invested at 13% per year

3. $($y$ + 8000) invested at $11\frac{1}{2}$% per year

4. $(12,000 − y) invested at 9% per year

5. Represent the amount of butterfat in 20 pounds of milk testing 4% butterfat.

6. Represent the amount of salt in $(15 + n)$ grams of a salt solution that is 10% salt.

7. Represent the amount of iodine in $(30 − d)$ grams of a solution of alcohol and iodine that is 60% iodine.

8. Represent the amount of alcohol in 32 grams of a solution of alcohol and water that is 20% alcohol.

Rational Expressions   **355**

Assignment Guide
Minimal
Day 1 p. 356: 1–5
Day 2 p. 356: 6–10
Average p. 356: 2–14 even
Above Average
p. 356: 3, 6, 9, 11–16

Additional Answers
  4. 40 ounces
  6. $3000 at 6%;
      $6000 at 15%
 11. 20 milliliters
 12. 30% alloy: 7 grams
      5% alloy: 18 grams
 13. 10%: $950;
      12%: $1900; 8%: $1400
 14. profitable business:
      $18,000; losing business:
      $12,000

WORD PROBLEMS

A   Solve each problem.

1. Tom Billings invested $8000, part at 6% per year and the rest at 9% per year. The total yearly interest was $660. How much did he invest at each rate? $2,000 at 6%; $6,000 at 9%

2. Laurie invested an amount of money at 8% per year and twice as much at 9% per year. The total yearly interest was $260. How much did she invest at each rate? $1,000 at 8%; $2,000 at 9%

3. How many grams of salt must be added to 600 grams of a 20% salt solution to obtain a 25% salt solution?   40 grams

4. How many ounces of salt must be added to 60 ounces of a 10% salt solution to obtain a 46% salt solution?

5. An investment club plans to invest in two types of bonds which yield 10% per year and 12% per year. The club has $12,500 to invest and wishes to earn at least $1450 on the investments. How much should be invested at each rate? $2,500 at 10%; $10,000 at 12%

6. Claude borrowed money from his parents and twice as much from a bank. The yearly rate of interest on his parents' loan was 6%; the rate of interest on the bank loan was 15%. The total interest for one year was $1080. How much did he borrow from the bank?

7. How many liters of sulfuric acid must be added to 63 liters of a 25% sulfuric acid solution (acid and water) to obtain a 60% sulfuric acid solution?   55.125 liters

8. A pharmacist has 10 liters of a 20% peroxide solution. How much peroxide must be added to obtain a 50% peroxide solution?   6 liters

9. How many quarts of antifreeze must be added to 30 quarts of a 10% antifreeze solution to obtain a 30% antifreeze solution?   about 8.57 quarts

10. A 100-gram solution is 4% salt and 96% water. How much water must be evaporated to obtain a solution that is 12% salt? $66\frac{2}{3}$ grams

B

11. Mary has 30 milliliters of a 10% alcohol solution. How many milliliters of a 15% alcohol solution must be added to make a 12% alcohol solution?

12. How many grams of a 30% gold alloy must be mixed with how many grams of a 5% gold alloy to obtain 25 grams of a 12% gold alloy?

13. Jack invested a sum of money at 10% yearly interest, twice this amount at 12% yearly interest, and $500 less at 8% than at 12%. The total yearly income from these investments is $435. How much did he invest at each rate?

14. Carla James invested $30,000 in two business enterprises. In one business, she made a 15% profit; in the other, she had an 8% loss. Her net profit for the year was $1740. How much did she invest in each business?

C

15. Claire has twice as much money invested at 9% as at 12%. Her annual interest on the money at 9% is $1140 more than her annual interest on the money at 12%. How much is invested at each rate?   9%: $38,000; 12%: $19,000

16. A car radiator is filled with 18 quarts of a 20% antifreeze solution. How much of this solution must be drained and replaced by pure antifreeze to obtain a 50% antifreeze solution?
      6.75 quarts

OBJECTIVE: To simplify rational expressions

10–3 Simplifying Rational Expressions

A rational expression is a ratio having polynomials as its terms. The following are rational expressions.

$$\frac{5}{9} \qquad \frac{3}{x} \qquad \frac{x^2 + y^2}{a^2} \qquad \frac{a^2 - b^2}{a + 5b}$$

Definition

A **rational expression** is an expression of the form $\frac{P}{Q}$, where P and Q are polynomials and $Q \neq 0$.

A rational expression is in **simplest form** when the numerator and denominator of the expression have no common factors other than 1 and -1. Thus, to simplify a rational expression, first factor the numerator and denominator. Then identify any common factors.

EXAMPLE 1 Simplify: $\dfrac{x^2 + xy}{x^2 - xy}$

Solution: Factor the numerator and denominator.

$$\frac{x^2 + xy}{x^2 - xy} = \frac{x(x + y)}{x(x - y)} \longleftarrow \text{ The common factor is } x.$$

$$= \frac{x}{x} \cdot \frac{x + y}{x - y} \longleftarrow \quad \frac{x}{x} = 1$$

$$= \frac{x + y}{x - y} \longleftarrow \text{ Simplest form}$$

Recall that *division by zero is not defined*. Thus, the values of the variables in a rational expression must be restricted so that the denominator cannot equal zero. In Example 1, x cannot equal zero or y.

EXAMPLE 2 Simplify: $\dfrac{a^2 - 9}{a^2 + 5a + 6}$

Solution: $\dfrac{a^2 - 9}{a^2 + 5a + 6} = \dfrac{(a + 3)(a - 3)}{(a + 3)(a + 2)} \longleftarrow \text{ The common factor is } (a + 3).$

$$= \frac{a + 3}{a + 3} \cdot \frac{a - 3}{a + 2} \longleftarrow \quad \frac{\cancel{a + 3}}{\cancel{a + 3}} = 1$$

$$= \frac{a - 3}{a + 2} \longleftarrow \text{ Simplest form}$$

NOTE: In Example 2, a cannot equal -2 or -3.

Rational Expressions   **357**

Teaching Suggestions p. M-23

Quick Quiz
1. The Kanes have $10,000 invested, part at 8% per year and the rest at 11% per year. The total yearly interest was $989. How much is invested at each rate?
   Ans: 8%: $3700; 11%: $6300
2. How many liters of peroxide must a pharmacist add to 20 liters of a 20% peroxide solution to obtain a 50% peroxide solution?
   Ans: 12L

Additional Examples
Example 1
Simplify. No denominator equals zero.
1. $\dfrac{a^3 + a^2 b}{a^3 - a^2 b}$ **Ans:** $\dfrac{a + b}{a - b}$
2. $\dfrac{3p^2 - 3pq}{3p^2 + 3pq}$ **Ans:** $\dfrac{p - q}{p + q}$

Example 2
Simplify. No denominator equals zero.
1. $\dfrac{r^2 - 16}{r^2 + 6r + 8}$ **Ans:** $\dfrac{r - 4}{r + 2}$
2. $\dfrac{a^2 - 25}{a^2 - 7a + 10}$ **Ans:** $\dfrac{a + 5}{a - 2}$

When simplifying rational expressions, watch for factors that are opposites of each other. Recall that

$$-(5y - x) = (-1)(5y - x) = x - 5y.$$

EXAMPLE 3   Simplify: $\dfrac{3x^2 - 15xy + 18y^2}{9y^2 - x^2}$

Solution: $\dfrac{3x^2 - 15xy + 18y^2}{9y^2 - x^2} = \dfrac{3(x^2 - 5xy + 6y^2)}{9y^2 - x^2}$

$= \dfrac{3(x - 3y)(x - 2y)}{(3y - x)(3y + x)}$ ← $(x - 3y)$ and $(3y - x)$ are opposites.

$= \dfrac{3(x - 3y)(x - 2y)}{-(x - 3y)(x + 3y)}$ ← $(3y - x) = -(x - 3y)$

$= \dfrac{\overset{1}{\cancel{x - 3y}}}{\underset{1}{\cancel{x - 3y}}} \cdot \dfrac{3(x - 2y)}{-(x + 3y)}$ ← The common factor is $(x - 3y)$.

$= \dfrac{3(x - 2y)}{-(x + 3y)}$, or $-\dfrac{3(x - 2y)}{(x + 3y)}$ ← Simplest form

NOTE: In Example 3, x cannot equal $3y$ or $-3y$.

CLASSROOM EXERCISES

Simplify.

1. $\dfrac{24}{44}$ $\dfrac{6}{11}$

2. $\dfrac{6ab}{6}$ ab

3. $\dfrac{6xy}{18x^2}$ $\dfrac{y}{3x}$

4. $\dfrac{x^2 - y^2}{(x + y)(x + y)}$ $\dfrac{x - y}{x + y}$

5. $\dfrac{a^2 + b^2}{a^2 + b^2}$ 1

6. $\dfrac{5 - w}{w - 5}$ -1

7. $\dfrac{4d - 14}{7 - 2d}$ -2

8. $\dfrac{y^2 - y - 2}{y^2 - 4}$ $\dfrac{y + 1}{y + 2}$

WRITTEN EXERCISES

A   Simplify. No denominator equals zero.

1. $\dfrac{3 \cdot 5}{3 \cdot 4}$ $\dfrac{5}{4}$

2. $\dfrac{3 \cdot 4 \cdot 5}{3 \cdot 4}$ 5

3. $\dfrac{6xy}{6}$ xy

4. $\dfrac{6xy}{6x}$ y

5. $\dfrac{12}{18}$ $\dfrac{2}{3}$

6. $\dfrac{9}{12}$ $\dfrac{3}{4}$

7. $\dfrac{a^2}{ab}$ $\dfrac{a}{b}$

8. $\dfrac{24a}{36b}$ $\dfrac{2a}{3b}$

9. $\dfrac{12x}{15xy}$ $\dfrac{4}{5y}$

10. $\dfrac{25x^2}{30x}$ $\dfrac{5x}{6}$

11. $\dfrac{18x^2y}{24xy}$ $\dfrac{3x}{4}$

12. $\dfrac{3xy}{24y}$ $\dfrac{x}{8}$

13. $\dfrac{4(x + y)}{7(x + y)}$ $\dfrac{4}{7}$

14. $\dfrac{5(x - y)}{2(x - y)}$ $\dfrac{5}{2}$

15. $\dfrac{4(a + b)}{8(a + b)}$ $\dfrac{1}{2}$

16. $\dfrac{a(x + y)}{b(x + y)}$ $\dfrac{a}{b}$

17. $\dfrac{24}{15(x + y)}$ $\dfrac{8}{5(x + y)}$

18. $\dfrac{m(x - y)^2}{e(x - y)}$ $\dfrac{m(x - y)}{e}$

19. $\dfrac{3(x - y)^2}{x - y}$ $3(x - y)$

20. $\dfrac{4(a + 2b)^2}{4(a + 2b)}$ $a + 2b$

358   *Chapter 10*

21. $\dfrac{7(x-6y)^2}{7x}$ $\dfrac{(x-6y)^2}{x}$ **22.** $\dfrac{36x}{15(x+2)}$ **23.** $\dfrac{15(a+b)}{6(2a+b)}$ **24.** $\dfrac{8(x-2y)}{18(2x-y)}$

25. $\dfrac{3x-6y}{9x+12y}$ $\dfrac{x-2y}{3x+4y}$ **26.** $\dfrac{a^2b-ab^2}{a^2b^2+ab^2}$ **27.** $\dfrac{2ab+b^2}{a^2-b^2}$ **28.** $\dfrac{4x-4y}{x+y}$

29. $\dfrac{3a+3b}{3(a+b)}$ 1 **30.** $\dfrac{x^2-y^2}{x^2-2xy+y^2}$ **31.** $\dfrac{a+b}{a^2+2ab+b^2}$ **32.** $\dfrac{x-1}{x^2-2x+1}$

33. $\dfrac{x+1}{x^2+2x+1}$ $\dfrac{1}{x+1}$ **34.** $\dfrac{5a+5}{a^2+7a+6}$ **35.** $\dfrac{a^2+a}{a}$ $a+1$ **36.** $\dfrac{3a^2-3}{a-1}$ $3(a+1)$

37. $\dfrac{5-v}{v-5}$ -1 **38.** $\dfrac{2(a-1)(a+7)}{(1-a)(a+7)}$ **39.** $\dfrac{b+9}{81-b^2}$ $\dfrac{1}{9-b}$ **40.** $\dfrac{c-d}{(d-c)^2}$ $\dfrac{1}{c-d}$

41. $\dfrac{(t-1)^2}{1-t^2}$ $-\dfrac{t-1}{t+1}$ **42.** $\dfrac{(x-y)^2}{(y-x)}$ $y-x$ **43.** $\dfrac{k-n}{(n-k)^3}$ **44.** $\dfrac{(5a-c)^5}{(c-5a)^5}$ -1

45. $\dfrac{2x^3-12x^2+2x}{x^2-6x+1}$ $2x$ **46.** $\dfrac{3a+3b}{a^2+2ab+b^2}$ **47.** $\dfrac{2x^2+6x+4}{4x^2-12x-16}$ **48.** $\dfrac{2x^3-2x^2-4x}{3x^3+3x^2+18x}$

49. $\dfrac{6x+12}{x^2-x-6}$ $\dfrac{6}{x-3}$ **50.** $\dfrac{x^2y-y}{x+1}$ $y(x-1)$ **51.** $\dfrac{3a^2-3}{1-a}$ $-3(a+1)$ **52.** $\dfrac{a^2+1}{a+1}$ prime

B

53. $\dfrac{R^2-r^2}{3r+3R}$ $\dfrac{R-r}{3}$ **54.** $\dfrac{6a^2+a-15}{6a^2-13a+6}$ $\dfrac{3a+5}{3a-2}$ **55.** $\dfrac{2a^2-ab-b^2}{2a^2+ab-b^2}$

56. $\dfrac{6a^2+42a+72}{18-2a^2}$ $-\dfrac{3(a+4)}{a-3}$ **57.** $\dfrac{3x^2-27}{24-11x+x^2}$ $\dfrac{3(x+3)}{x-8}$ **58.** $\dfrac{(a+b)^2(a-b)}{a^2-b^2}$

C

59. $\dfrac{(x+y)^2+(x+y)-2}{x+y+2}$ $x+y-1$ **60.** $\dfrac{(x+y)^2-(r+t)^2}{x+y-r-t}$ **61.** $\dfrac{2+a+2a^2+a^3}{a^3-5a^2+a-5}$

_____ Review _____

Solve each proportion. *(Section 10–1)* $t=6$

1. $\dfrac{30}{45}=\dfrac{x}{12}$ $x=8$ **2.** $\dfrac{5}{x}=\dfrac{20}{48}$ $x=12$ **3.** $\dfrac{9}{13}=\dfrac{2.25}{y}$ $y=3.25$ **4.** $\dfrac{3}{t-4}=\dfrac{6}{10-t}$

5. Out of every 10 columns in one newspaper, 4 columns are advertisements. At this rate, how many columns of advertisements are there in a 16-page newspaper having 6 columns per page? *(Section 10–1)* 38.4 columns

6. Bill has $6000 invested, part at a yearly interest rate of 12% and part at a yearly interest rate of 10%. Total yearly interest amounts to $640. How much is invested at each rate? *(Section 10–2)* 12%: $2000; 10%: $4000

7. How many ounces of salt must be added to 50 ounces of an 8% salt solution in order to obtain a 20% salt solution? *(Section 10–2)* 7.5 ounces

Simplify. No denominator equals zero. *(Section 10–3)* $\dfrac{3x-2y}{x-2y}$

8. $\dfrac{16c}{28cd}$ $\dfrac{4}{7d}$ **9.** $\dfrac{2a+b}{4a^2-b^2}$ $\dfrac{1}{2a-b}$ **10.** $\dfrac{3x+3y}{x^2+2xy+y^2}$ $\dfrac{3}{x+y}$ **11.** $\dfrac{6x^2-13xy+6y^2}{6y^2-7xy+2x^2}$

Rational Expressions   **359**

**Additional Answers
Written Exercises**

22. $\dfrac{12x}{5(x+2)}$

23. $\dfrac{5(a+b)}{2(2a+b)}$

24. $\dfrac{4(x-2y)}{9(2x-y)}$

26. $\dfrac{a-b}{b(a+1)}$

27. $\dfrac{b(2a+b)}{(a+b)(a-b)}$

28. $\dfrac{4(x-y)}{x+y}$

30. $\dfrac{x+y}{x-y}$

31. $\dfrac{1}{a+b}$

32. $\dfrac{1}{x-1}$

34. $\dfrac{5}{a+6}$

38. -2

43. $-\dfrac{1}{(n-k)^2}$

46. $\dfrac{3}{a+b}$

47. $\dfrac{x+2}{2(x-4)}$

48. $\dfrac{2(x-2)(x+1)}{3(x^2+x+6)}$

55. prime
58. $a+b$
60. $x+y+r+t$
61. $\dfrac{a+2}{a-5}$

Quiz Sections 10-1–10-3
After completing this Review, you may want to administer a quiz covering the same sections. See page M-52 of the Teacher's Manual for the suggested quiz.

Consumer Applications: Chemistry

Chemists perform experiments in a laboratory to explore the atomic and molecular nature of the world around them. Many times, in these experiments they prepare solutions of various chemicals. The table below shows the weight of one molecule, **molecular weight**, of some of these chemicals.

Chemical	Molecular Weight
Barium oxide	153.34
Glycerine	92.03
Silver nitrate	169.86
Sodium chloride	58.44
Zinc sulfide	97.44

A **mole** in chemistry is the mass of a substance that equals its molecular weight. A **one molar solution** of glycerine and water would contain 92.03 grams of glycerine in 1 liter of solution.

EXAMPLE 1 Find the number of grams of glycerine needed to make 1500 milliliters of a solution with 5% molarity.

Solution: $\boxed{1}$ Find the number of grams of glycerine to make 1 liter (1000 milliliters) of a 5% molarity solution.

5% of 92.03 = (0.05)(92.03) or **4.6 grams**

$\boxed{2}$ Find the number of grams of glycerine for 1500 milliliters. Solve the following proportion.

$$\frac{4.6}{1000} = \frac{n}{1500} \longleftarrow \quad n = \frac{(4.6)(1500)}{1000}$$

n = **6.9 grams of glycerine**

Sometimes chemists need to work with chemicals in solutions that are already mixed.

EXAMPLE 2 A chemist wants to do an experiment using 75 milligrams of a certain chemical. A solution is available that has 500 milligrams of the chemical in 10 milliliters of solution. How many milliliters of the solution will contain 75 milligrams of the chemical?

Solution: Solve the following proportion for m, the number of milliliters.

$$\frac{75}{m} = \frac{500}{10} \quad\longleftarrow\quad m = \frac{(75)(10)}{500}$$

$$m = 1.5$$

The chemist measures **1.5 milliliters** of solution.

EXERCISES

In Exercises 1–8 use the table on page 360 to help find, to the nearest tenth, the number of grams needed to make a solution of the given number of milliliters and molarity (%).

	Chemical	Milliliters	Molarity
1.	Barium oxide	1200	70%
2.	Silver nitrate	450	20%
3.	Glycerine	600	5%
4.	Zinc sulfide	840	3%

	Chemical	Milliliters	Molarity
5.	Sodium Chloride	1500	1.4%
6.	Glycerine	2000	3.5%
7.	Zinc sulfide	1850	0.3%
8.	Barium oxide	2320	2.8%

9. A chemist needs 30 milligrams of a certain chemical for an experiment. She has a solution of 150 milligrams of the chemical in 40 milliliters of solution. How many milliliters of the solution will contain 30 milligrams of the chemical?

10. Juan Rivera, a chemist, needs 24 milligrams of a certain chemical to complete an experiment. He has a 45-milliliter solution that contains 500 milligrams of the chemical. How much of the solution should Juan use for the experiment?

11. Rosemary Lyons needs to use 25 milligrams of a certain chemical. She has 200 milliliters of a solution that contains 150 milligrams of the chemical. How much solution should she use?

12. Jim Sachs needs 35 milligrams of a certain chemical. He has a solution of 210 milliliters that contains 50 milligrams of the chemical. How much of the solution should he use?

Simplify. *(Pages 283–284, 288–289)*

$12x^3y^3z^8$

1. $(4n)(3n)$ $12n^2$ **2.** $(2a^2b)(a^2b^3)$ $2a^4b^4$ **3.** $(\frac{1}{2}c^3)(-4c^7)$ $-2c^{10}$ **4.** $(-4x^2yz^3)(-3xy^2z^5)$

5. $\dfrac{x^{12}}{x^2}$ x^{10} **6.** $\dfrac{-8ab}{-32ab^3}$ $\dfrac{1}{4b^2}$ **7.** $\dfrac{14r^2st^3}{35rs^2t}$ $\dfrac{2rt^2}{5s}$ **8.** $\dfrac{(3x^5)(2x^4)}{(6x^2)^3}$ $\dfrac{x^3}{36}$

9. $\dfrac{36a^2b^3}{8a^5b}$ $\dfrac{9b^2}{2a^3}$ **10.** $\dfrac{36a^2b^3}{7ab^9}$ $\dfrac{36a}{7b^6}$ **11.** $\dfrac{36x^2y^3}{6x^2y^2}$ $6y$ **12.** $\dfrac{63x^2y^3}{28a^6b^6}$ $\dfrac{9x^2y^3}{4a^6b^6}$

Factor over the integers. *(Pages 319–323, 326–336)*

$4x(2x+1)(2x-1)$

13. $3x^3y^2 - 2x^2y^3$ $x^2y^2(3x-2y)$ **14.** $100z^2 - 1$ $(10z+1)(10z-1)$ **15.** $16x^3 - 4x$

16. $9t^2 + 18t + 9$ $9(t+1)^2$ **17.** $z^2 - 7z + 18$ $(z-9)(z+2)$ **18.** $8q^2 + 11q - 3$ $(4q-1)(q+3)$

OBJECTIVE: To multiply rational expressions

10-4 Multiplying Rational Expressions

Multiplying two rational expressions is similar to multiplying two rational numbers. To multiply rational expressions, you apply this theorem.

Theorem 10–1

Product of Rational Expressions
If $\dfrac{P}{Q}$ and $\dfrac{R}{S}$ are rational expressions, then $$\dfrac{P}{Q} \cdot \dfrac{R}{S} = \dfrac{P \cdot R}{Q \cdot S}.$$

EXAMPLE 1 Multiply: $\dfrac{3a^2b}{2ab^2} \cdot \dfrac{4abx}{9a^2by}$. Express the product in simplest form.

Solution: $\dfrac{3a^2b}{2ab^2} \cdot \dfrac{4abx}{9a^2by} = \dfrac{(3a^2b)(4abx)}{(2ab^2)(9a^2by)}$ ◄——— **By Theorem 10–1**

$= \dfrac{12a^3b^2x}{18a^3b^3y}$ ◄——— **Simplify the product.**

$= \dfrac{\cancel{12}a^3\cancel{b^2}x}{\cancel{18}a^3\cancel{b^3}y}$ ◄——— $\dfrac{2 \cdot 1 \cdot 1 \cdot x}{3 \cdot 1 \cdot b \cdot y} = \dfrac{2x}{3by}$

$= \dfrac{2x}{3by}$ ◄——— **Simplest form**

When multiplying rational expressions whose numerators and denominators are not monomials, it is usually easier to simplify first.

Example 2 shows how to do this.

Teaching Suggestions p. M-23

Quick Quiz
Simplify. No denominator equals zero.

1. $\dfrac{4x + 4y}{4x - 4y}$ **Ans:** $\dfrac{x+y}{x-y}$

2. $\dfrac{x^3 - x^2y}{x^3 + x^2y}$ **Ans:** $\dfrac{x-y}{x+y}$

3. $\dfrac{a^2 - 64}{a^2 - 6a - 16}$ **Ans:** $\dfrac{a+8}{a+2}$

4. $\dfrac{b^2 - 36}{b^2 - 12b + 36}$ **Ans:** $\dfrac{b+6}{b-6}$

5. $\dfrac{3d^2 + 12d - 15}{1 - d^2}$

Ans: $-\dfrac{3(d+5)}{(d+1)}$

6. $\dfrac{4x^2 - 20x - 24}{30 + x - x^2}$

Ans: $-\dfrac{4(x+1)}{(x+5)}$

Additional Examples
Example 1
Multiply. Express each product in simplest form.

1. $\dfrac{5a^3b^2}{2ab^3} \cdot \dfrac{4abc}{3a^2bd}$

Ans: $\dfrac{10ac}{3bd}$

2. $\dfrac{5x^2y}{3xy^2} \cdot \dfrac{2x^2y^3z}{6x^2yz^2}$

Ans: $\dfrac{5xy}{9z}$

EXAMPLE 2 Multiply: $\dfrac{3a + 3b}{a - b} \cdot \dfrac{a + 2b}{a^2 + 2ab + b^2}$. Express the product in simplest form.

Solution: Factor any polynomials that are not prime over the integers.

$$\frac{3a + 3b}{a - b} \cdot \frac{a + 2b}{a^2 + 2ab + b^2} = \frac{3(a + b)}{a - b} \cdot \frac{(a + 2b)}{(a + b)(a + b)}$$

$$= \frac{3\cancel{(a + b)}^{1}}{a - b} \cdot \frac{a + 2b}{\cancel{(a + b)}_{1}(a + b)} \qquad \longleftarrow \textbf{Simplify.}$$

$$= \frac{3(a + 2b)}{(a - b)(a + b)} \qquad \longleftarrow \textbf{Multiply.}$$

$$= \frac{\mathbf{3a + 6b}}{\mathbf{a^2 - b^2}}$$

Unless otherwise indicated, assume throughout the remainder of this text that no denominator equals zero.

CLASSROOM EXERCISES

Multiply. Express each product in simplest form.

1. $\dfrac{a^2}{b^2c} \cdot \dfrac{ab^2}{a}$ $\dfrac{a^2}{c}$

2. $\dfrac{5ab}{3x} \cdot \dfrac{12x^2}{10a^2b}$ $\dfrac{2x}{a}$

3. $\dfrac{a + b}{a} \cdot \dfrac{a^2}{b}$ $\dfrac{a^2 + ab}{b}$

4. $\dfrac{m^2 - n^2}{m + n} \cdot \dfrac{m + n}{m - n}$ $m + n$

5. $\dfrac{x^2 - xy}{x - y} \cdot \dfrac{1}{x}$ 1

6. $\dfrac{x - 2}{x^2 - 5x + 6} \cdot \dfrac{x^2 - 9}{x^2 - 3x}$ $\dfrac{x + 3}{x^2 - 3x}$

WRITTEN EXERCISES

A Multiply. Express each product in simplest form.

1. $\dfrac{x}{y} \cdot \dfrac{my}{nx}$ $\dfrac{m}{n}$

2. $\dfrac{3}{x} \cdot \dfrac{x^2}{3}$ x

3. $\dfrac{3x}{d} \cdot \dfrac{c}{3x}$ $\dfrac{c}{d}$

4. $\dfrac{ab^2}{2} \cdot \dfrac{c}{abd}$ $\dfrac{bc}{2d}$

5. $\dfrac{ab}{xy} \cdot \dfrac{x}{a^3b^2}$ $\dfrac{1}{a^2by}$

6. $\dfrac{xy^2}{m^3n} \cdot \dfrac{m^2}{y^3}$ $\dfrac{x}{mny}$

7. $\dfrac{7xy^2}{8x^2y} \cdot \dfrac{16xz^2}{49y^2z}$ $\dfrac{2z}{7y}$

8. $\dfrac{a}{b} \cdot \dfrac{c}{d} \cdot \dfrac{ax}{by} \cdot \dfrac{y^2}{x^2}$ $\dfrac{a^2cy}{b^2dx}$

9. $\dfrac{4 \cdot 6}{2 \cdot 3^2} \cdot \dfrac{27}{2^2 \cdot 3}$ 3

10. $(x + 2) \cdot \dfrac{x + 3}{x + 1}$ $\dfrac{x^2 + 5x + 6}{x + 1}$

11. $(2x + 5) \cdot \dfrac{2x + 3}{2x - 5}$

12. $\dfrac{(x - 5)^2}{3(x - 5)} \cdot \dfrac{x - 5}{3}$

13. $\dfrac{a + 1}{a + 2} \cdot \dfrac{a + 2}{a + 1}$ 1

14. $\dfrac{a + 3}{a - 3} \cdot \dfrac{1}{a + 3}$ $\dfrac{1}{a - 3}$

15. $(n + 3) \cdot \dfrac{n + 3}{n + 5}$

16. $(2x - 5) \cdot \dfrac{x + 7}{2x - 5}$ $x + 7$

17. $x^2y \cdot \dfrac{8}{2x + 2xy}$ $\dfrac{4xy}{1 + y}$

18. $\dfrac{3a - 3b}{10ab} \cdot \dfrac{50a^2b^2}{a^2 - b^2}$

19. $n(a + b) \cdot \dfrac{1}{m(a + b)}$ $\dfrac{n}{m}$

20. $\dfrac{a^2 - 4b^2}{a^2 - b^2} \cdot \dfrac{3a^2b^2}{a + b}$

21. $\dfrac{a^2 + 5a}{a^2 - 16} \cdot \dfrac{a^2 - 4a}{a^2 - 25}$

Rational Expressions **363**

Multiply. Express each product in simplest form.

22. $\dfrac{3x - 48y^2}{2x^2 - 8y^2} \cdot \dfrac{3x + 6y}{3x + 12y}$

23. $\dfrac{x^2 + 8x + 16}{x^2 - 9} \cdot \dfrac{x - 3}{x + 4} \quad \dfrac{x+4}{x+3}$

24. $\dfrac{a^2 - 3a - 10}{(a - 2)^2} \cdot \dfrac{a - 2}{a - 5}$

25. $\dfrac{9 - x^2}{x + 3} \cdot \dfrac{x}{3 - x} \quad x$

26. $\dfrac{24x^2}{3(x^2 - 4x + 4)} \cdot \dfrac{3x - 6}{2x} \quad \dfrac{12x}{x-2}$

27. $\dfrac{x^2 - 6x + 5}{x - 1} \cdot \dfrac{x - 1}{x - 5} \quad x - 1$

28. $\dfrac{c^2 - 6c}{c - 6} \cdot \dfrac{c + 3}{c} \quad c + 3$

29. $\dfrac{x^2 - 24 - 2x}{x^2 - 30 - x} \cdot \dfrac{x + 5}{x^2 - 16} \quad \dfrac{1}{x-4}$

30. $\dfrac{9 - y^2}{r^3 - r} \cdot \dfrac{r - 1}{y + 3} \quad \dfrac{3-y}{r^2+r}$

B

31. $\dfrac{a^2 + 7ab + 10b^2}{a^2 + 6ab + 5b^2} \cdot \dfrac{a + b}{a^2 + 4ab + 4b^2} \cdot \dfrac{a + 2b}{1} \quad 1$

32. $\dfrac{x^2 - y^2}{x^2 - 3xy + 2y^2} \cdot \dfrac{xy - 2y}{y^2 + xy} \cdot \dfrac{x(x - y)}{(x - y)^2} \quad \dfrac{x^2 - 2x}{x^2 - 3xy + 2y^2}$

33. $\dfrac{2a - 3b}{a^2 + 4ab + 4b^2} \cdot \dfrac{4a^2 - 4b^2}{4a^2 - 9b^2} \cdot \dfrac{5a^2 + 10ab}{3ab - 3b^2} \quad \dfrac{20a^2 + 20ab}{6a^2b + 21ab^2 + 18b^3}$

34. $\dfrac{6x - 3y}{4x^2 + 4xy + y^2} \cdot \dfrac{2x + y}{4x^2 - 4xy + y^2} \quad \dfrac{6}{4x^2 - y^2}$

35. $\dfrac{5m + 5n}{m^2 - n^2} \cdot \dfrac{m^2 - mn}{(m + n)^2} \quad \dfrac{5m}{(m+n)^2}$

36. $\dfrac{x^2 - 3x - 18}{x^2 - x - 2} \cdot \dfrac{3x + 3}{x^2 - 2x - 15} \quad \dfrac{3x - 18}{x^2 - 7x + 10}$

37. $\dfrac{a^2 + 6a + 5}{a - 3} \cdot \dfrac{5a - 15}{a^2 + 4a - 5} \quad \dfrac{5(a+1)}{a-1}$

38. $\dfrac{3a + 9}{3a^2 - 5a + 2} \cdot \dfrac{6a^2 - 7a + 2}{2a^2 + 3a - 18}$

39. $\dfrac{4x^2 - 9y^2}{6x^2 - 9xy} \cdot \dfrac{6xy}{4xy + 6y^2} \quad 1$

40. $\dfrac{x^2 + 6x + 8}{x^2 + 4x + 14} \cdot \dfrac{x^2 + 5x + 6}{x^2 + 7x + 12} \quad \dfrac{(x + 2)^2}{x^2 + 4x + 14}$

41. $\dfrac{a^2 + a - 2}{a^2 - 3a - 10} \cdot \dfrac{a^2 - 2a - 8}{a^2 - 7a + 12} \quad \dfrac{a^2 + a - 2}{a^2 - 8a + 15}$

42. $\dfrac{x^2 - 2xb + b^2}{b - 1} \cdot \dfrac{b^2 - 5b + 4}{x^2 - b^2} \quad \dfrac{(x - b)(b - 4)}{x + b}$

43. $\dfrac{x^2 - x - 1}{x - 1} \cdot \dfrac{x^2 - 1}{x} \cdot \dfrac{x^2 - x - 1}{x - 1}$

C

44. $\dfrac{a^2 - 5a + 6}{6a^2 - 17a + 5} \cdot \dfrac{6a^2 + 7a - 3}{2a^2 - 7a + 3} \cdot \dfrac{2a^2 - 7a + 5}{a^2 - 3a + 2} \quad \dfrac{2a + 3}{2a - 1}$

45. $\dfrac{4x^2 + x - 14}{6xy - 14y} \cdot \dfrac{4x^2}{x^2 - 4} \cdot \dfrac{x - 2}{4x - 7} \cdot \dfrac{3x^2 - x - 14}{2x^2 - 14} \quad \dfrac{x^2(x + 2)}{y(x^2 - 7)}$

46. $\dfrac{(a + b)^2 - c^2}{a^2 + ab - ac} \cdot \dfrac{a}{(a + c)^2 - b^2} \cdot \dfrac{(a - b)^2 - c^2}{ab - b^2 - bc} \quad \dfrac{1}{b}$

47. $\dfrac{4b^2 - 16b + 15}{2b^2 + 3b + 1} \cdot \dfrac{b^2 - 6b - 7}{2b^2 - 17b + 21} \cdot \dfrac{4b^2 - 1}{4b^2 - 20b + 25} \quad \dfrac{2b - 1}{2b - 5}$

REVIEW CAPSULE FOR SECTION 10-5

Factor completely over the integers. *(Pages 322–323, 326–328, 335–336)*

1. $9y^2 - 4 \quad (3y + 2)(3y - 2)$
2. $m^3 - 7m^2 - 18m \quad m(m - 9)(m + 2)$
3. $6z^2 + z - 40$
4. $h^4 - 18h^2 + 81$
5. $2z^4 - 162 \quad 2(z^2 + 9)(z + 3)(z - 3)$
6. $2a^2 - 8b^2 + 16b - 8$
7. $x^2y - x^2z + 2x^2 \quad x^2(2 + y - z)$
8. $5x^2 - 2xy - 3y^2 \quad (5x + 3y)(x - y)$
9. $3x^2y + 6xy + 3y$
10. $4x^2 + 28x + 49 \quad (2x + 7)(2x + 7)$
11. $2ax + 4ay + 2a \quad 2a(x + 2y + 1)$
12. $2ax^4 + 2ax^2 - 4a \quad 2a(x^2 + 2)(x - 1)(x + 1)$

10–5 Division of Rational Expressions

Teaching Suggestions p. M-23

To divide by a real number, you multiply by the reciprocal of the divisor.

$$\frac{2}{3} \div \frac{1}{4} = \frac{2}{3} \cdot \frac{4}{1} = \frac{8}{3}, \text{ or } 2\frac{2}{3}.$$

The procedure for dividing by a rational expression is similar. It applies the following theorem.

Theorem 10–2

> **Division of Rational Expressions**
>
> To divide a rational expression $\frac{P}{Q}$ by a rational expression $\frac{R}{S}$, multiply $\frac{P}{Q}$ by the multiplicative inverse, or reciprocal, of $\frac{R}{S}$. That is, for $R \neq 0$,
>
> $$\frac{P}{Q} \div \frac{R}{S} = \frac{P}{Q} \cdot \frac{S}{R}.$$

EXAMPLE 1 Divide: $\frac{5y}{9xz^3} \div \frac{15y^3}{18x^2z^3}$. Express the answer in simplest form.

Solution: Multiply by the reciprocal of the divisor.

$$\frac{5y}{9xz^3} \div \frac{15y^3}{18x^2z^3} = \frac{5y}{9xz^3} \cdot \frac{18x^2z^3}{15y^3} \quad \longleftarrow \text{ By Theorem 10–2}$$

$$= \frac{5y}{9xz^3} \cdot \frac{\overset{1}{\cancel{18x^2z^3}}}{\underset{3 \cdot y^2}{\cancel{15y^3}}} \quad \longleftarrow \text{ Simplify.}$$

$$= \frac{2x}{3y^2} \quad \longleftarrow \text{ Simplest form}$$

When dividing rational expressions having numerators and denominators that are not monomials, look for polynomials that can be factored.

EXAMPLE 2 Divide: $\frac{x^2 - 4x + 4}{3x - 6} \div (x - 2)$

Solution: $\frac{x^2 - 4x + 4}{3x - 6} \div (x - 2) = \frac{x^2 - 4x + 4}{3x - 6} \cdot \frac{1}{x - 2} \quad \longleftarrow \text{ By Theorem 10–2}$

$$= \frac{\overset{1}{\cancel{(x - 2)}}\overset{1}{\cancel{(x - 2)}}}{3\underset{1}{\cancel{(x - 2)}}} \cdot \frac{1}{\underset{1}{\cancel{(x - 2)}}} \quad \longleftarrow \frac{1 \cdot 1 \cdot 1}{3 \cdot 1 \cdot 1} = \frac{1}{3}$$

$$= \frac{1}{3}$$

To simplify an expression such as

$$\frac{\dfrac{x^2}{y^2}}{\dfrac{x}{y}} \qquad \text{write it in the form} \qquad \frac{x^2}{y^2} \div \frac{x}{y}.$$

Then divide as shown in Examples 1 and 2.

A second method of simplifying such an expression uses the multiplicative inverse postulate. For example, to simplify the expression above, multiply both numerator and denominator by $\frac{y}{x}$, the multiplicative inverse of $\frac{x}{y}$. This will result in a denominator of 1.

$$\frac{\dfrac{x^2}{y^2}}{\dfrac{x}{y}} = \frac{\dfrac{x^2}{y^2} \cdot \dfrac{y}{x}}{\dfrac{x}{y} \cdot \dfrac{y}{x}} = \frac{\dfrac{x^2 \cdot y}{y^2 \cdot x}}{1} = \frac{x}{xy^2} = \frac{x}{y}$$

CLASSROOM EXERCISES

Divide. Express the answers in simplest form.

1. $\dfrac{x^2 y}{x} \div \dfrac{x}{y^2}$ y^3
2. $\dfrac{5a^2}{7b} \div \dfrac{15a^3}{14b^2}$ $\dfrac{2b}{3a}$
3. $\dfrac{x-y}{x+y} \div \dfrac{x^2-y^2}{2}$
4. $\dfrac{b^2-3b-10}{8b^2} \div \dfrac{2b-10}{16b^2}$

5. $8kn \div \dfrac{24k}{n}$ $\dfrac{n^2}{3}$
6. $\dfrac{6r^2t^2}{8s} \div 3rt$ $\dfrac{rt}{4s}$
7. $\dfrac{3c+12}{18} \div \dfrac{c-2}{2}$
8. $\dfrac{9}{t^2-1} \div \dfrac{3}{t+1}$ $\dfrac{3}{t-1}$

9. $\dfrac{1}{x} \div \dfrac{1}{x^2}$ x
10. $\dfrac{(n-1)^2}{4} \div (n-1)$
11. $\dfrac{a-x}{y} \div \dfrac{a^2-x^2}{xy}$
12. $\dfrac{9-z^2}{15} \div \dfrac{3-z}{5}$ $\dfrac{3+z}{3}$

WRITTEN EXERCISES

A   Divide. Express the answers in simplest form.

1. $\dfrac{x}{2} \div \dfrac{x}{4}$ 2
2. $\dfrac{x}{4} \div \dfrac{x}{a}$ $\dfrac{a}{4}$
3. $\dfrac{2}{x} \div \dfrac{4}{x}$ $\dfrac{1}{2}$
4. $\dfrac{4}{x} \div \dfrac{2}{x}$ 2
5. $\dfrac{x}{y} \div \dfrac{3}{y}$ $\dfrac{x}{3}$
6. $\dfrac{ad}{bc} \div \dfrac{a}{b}$

7. $\dfrac{a}{b} \div \dfrac{c}{d}$ $\dfrac{ad}{bc}$
8. $\dfrac{xy}{ab} \div \dfrac{xy}{bc}$ $\dfrac{c}{a}$
9. $\dfrac{1}{a} \div \dfrac{a}{b}$ $\dfrac{b}{a^2}$
10. $\dfrac{a}{x} \div \dfrac{c}{x}$ $\dfrac{a}{c}$
11. $\dfrac{1}{f} \div \dfrac{1}{g}$ $\dfrac{g}{f}$
12. $\dfrac{a}{x} \div \dfrac{x}{c}$

13. $\dfrac{8}{3a} \div 16$ $\dfrac{1}{6a}$
14. $\dfrac{9ab^2}{8xy^2} \div \dfrac{3b^2}{2xy}$ $\dfrac{3a}{4y}$
15. $\dfrac{14a^2}{10b^2} \div \dfrac{21a^2}{15b^2}$ 1

16. $\dfrac{5x}{12yz^2} \div \dfrac{15x^3}{18y^2z^2}$ $\dfrac{y}{2x^2}$
17. $\dfrac{4a-16}{3a} \div (3a-12)$ $\dfrac{4}{9a}$
18. $\dfrac{6z-27}{4z} \div (4z-18)$ $\dfrac{3}{8z}$

19. $\dfrac{x^2+x}{a} \div x^2$ $\dfrac{x+1}{ax}$
20. $\dfrac{(a-b)(a+b)}{(x-y)(x+y)} \div \dfrac{a-b}{x+y}$
21. $\dfrac{a^2-b^2}{x^2-y^2} \div \dfrac{a+b}{x-y}$ $\dfrac{a-b}{x+y}$

22. $\dfrac{(2x)^3}{(4yz)^3} \div \dfrac{16x^2}{8y^2z^3}$ $\dfrac{x}{16y}$
23. $\dfrac{3(x+y)^2}{x-y} \div 6(x+y)$
24. $\dfrac{x-y}{x+y} \div \dfrac{5x^2-5y^2}{3x-3y}$

25. $\dfrac{x^2+2x+1}{3x} \div (x+1)$
26. $\dfrac{a^3-6a^2+8a}{5a} \div \dfrac{2a-4}{10a-40}$
27. $\dfrac{5a^2-5ab}{ab+b^2} \div \dfrac{5a^2-5b^2}{b}$

28. $\dfrac{k}{k^2-6k+9} \div \dfrac{1}{k-3}$
29. $\dfrac{a^2-49}{(a+7)^2} \div \dfrac{3a-21}{2a+14}$ $\dfrac{2}{3}$
30. $(b^2-9) \div \dfrac{b^2+8b+15}{2b+10}$
$2(b-3)$

Additional Exercises
Classroom Exercises

3. $\dfrac{2}{(x+y)^2}$
4. $b+2$
7. $\dfrac{c+4}{3(c-2)}$
10. $\dfrac{n-1}{4}$
11. $\dfrac{x}{(a+x)}$

Assignment Guide
Minimal
Day 1 p. 366: 1–18
Day 2 p. 366: 19–30
Average
Day 1 p. 366: 1–22
Day 2 pp. 366–367: 23–30,
31–38 odd
Above Average
Day 1 p. 366: 1–27
Day 2 p. 366–367: 28–38,
39–44 odd

Additional Answers
Written Exercises

6. $\dfrac{d}{c}$
12. $\dfrac{ac}{x^2}$
20. $\dfrac{a+b}{x-y}$
23. $\dfrac{x+y}{2(x-y)}$
24. $\dfrac{3(x-y)}{5(x+y)^2}$
25. $\dfrac{x+1}{3x}$
26. $(a-4)^2$
27. $\dfrac{a}{(a+b)^2}$
28. $\dfrac{k}{k-3}$

B Write each expression as a problem in division using the division symbol. (The heavier line shows the main division.) Then divide and simplify.

31. $\dfrac{\dfrac{b}{a}}{b}$ $\dfrac{b^2}{a}$

32. $\dfrac{\dfrac{x}{4}}{\dfrac{3}{2}}$ $\dfrac{x}{6}$

33. $\dfrac{\dfrac{ab^2}{x}}{\dfrac{x^2}{ab}}$ $\dfrac{a^2b^3}{x^3}$

34. $\dfrac{\dfrac{3x}{y}}{\dfrac{5y^2}{2x^3}}$

35. $\dfrac{\dfrac{a^2b^2}{r}}{\dfrac{r^2}{ab}}$ $\dfrac{a^3b^3}{r^3}$

36. $\dfrac{\dfrac{x+y}{x}}{\dfrac{x^2-y^2}{x^2y}}$ $\dfrac{xy}{x-y}$

37. $\dfrac{\dfrac{x^2-25}{x}}{\dfrac{}{x-5}}$ $\dfrac{x+5}{x}$

38. $\dfrac{\dfrac{a+2}{2a}}{\dfrac{a-2}{a}}$

C Perform the indicated operations. Express the answers in simplest form.

39. $\dfrac{x^2-y^2}{x^2} \cdot \dfrac{x+y}{x-y} \div \dfrac{x^2-y^2}{yx}$ $\dfrac{y(x+y)}{x(x-y)}$

40. $\dfrac{a^2-2ab+b^2}{ab} \cdot \dfrac{a+b}{a-b} \div \dfrac{a^2-b^2}{a^2}$ $\dfrac{a}{b}$

41. $\dfrac{a^3b^3}{a^3-ab^2} \div \dfrac{abc}{a-b} \cdot \dfrac{ab+bc}{ab}$ $\dfrac{b^2(a+c)}{c(a+b)}$

42. $\dfrac{xy-xz-x^2}{xyz} \cdot \dfrac{x^2y^2z^3}{xy-xz} \div x^3$

43. $\dfrac{2x^3}{2a+b} \div \dfrac{10a^2}{4a^2+4ab+b^2} \cdot \dfrac{12a+3b}{2a^2+ab}$

44. $\dfrac{k+n}{k^2+n^2} \cdot \dfrac{k}{k-n} \div \dfrac{(k+n)^2}{k^4-n^4}$ k

---

CALCULATOR APPLICATIONS

Evaluating Rational Expressions

To evaluate a rational expression with a calculator, rewrite the numerator and denominator so that each exponent is 1.

EXAMPLE Evaluate $\dfrac{2x^3+3x^2-4x-5}{4x^2+5x-10}$ when $x=5$.

SOLUTION Factor using x: $\dfrac{(2x^2+3x-4)x+5}{(4x+5)x-10} = \dfrac{[(2x+3)x-4]x+5}{(4x+5)x-10}$

Evaluate the denominator first. Store its value.

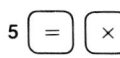   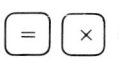

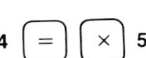  2.6956521

EXERCISES

Evaluate each expression below when the variable equals 6.

1. $\dfrac{3y^2+16y-35}{5y^2+33y-14}$ 0.4642857

2. $\dfrac{6d^3-4d^2-8d+2}{3d^2+d-2}$ 9.875

3. $\dfrac{2a^3+4a^2+3a+7}{a^3+2a^2-9a-18}$ 2.7824074

4. $\dfrac{z^3-5z^2-2z+8}{z^3-z^2-4z+4}$ 0.2

Rational Expressions   **367**

10-6 Least Common Denominator

To find the sum or difference of rational expressions such as

$$\frac{2}{a} + \frac{3}{a^2 b} \quad \text{and} \quad \frac{3}{5x - 10} - \frac{2}{x^2 - 4},$$

you replace the rational expressions with equivalent expressions having a *common denominator*. For example, $a^3 b^2$ is a common denominator of a and $a^2 b$ because $a^3 b^2$ is divisible by *both* a and $a^2 b$. For convenience, however, the *least common denominator*, or LCD, is most often used. The **LCD** of two or more rational expressions is the smallest positive common multiple (least common multiple) of the denominators of the rational expressions.

Procedure

> **To find the LCD of rational expressions:**
> 1. Express each denominator as a product of prime factors.
> 2. Write a product using each prime factor only once.
> 3. For each factor, write the greatest exponent used in any prime factorization.
> 4. Simplify where necessary. The result is the LCD.

Example 1 applies this procedure when the denominators are natural numbers.

EXAMPLE 1 Find the LCD of two rational expressions having 8 and 36 as denominators.

Solution:
1. Write the prime factorization of each number.

    $8 = 2 \cdot 2 \cdot 2$, or 2^3 $\qquad$ $36 = 2 \cdot 2 \cdot 3 \cdot 3$, or $2^2 \cdot 3^2$

2. Write a product using each prime factor only once. $\qquad$ $2 \cdot 3$
3. For each factor, write the greatest exponent used in $\qquad$ $2^3 \cdot 3^2$
the prime factorizations.
4. Simplify. $\qquad$ $2^3 \cdot 3^2 = 8 \cdot 9 = 72$ $\qquad$ **LCD: 72**

The method of Example 1 can be used when the denominators of the rational expressions contain variables.

EXAMPLE 2 Find the LCD of two rational expressions having $6x^5 y$ and $9x^2 y^2$ as denominators.

Solution:
1. $6x^5 y = 2 \cdot 3 \cdot x^5 \cdot y \qquad 9x^2 y^2 = 3^2 \cdot x^2 \cdot y^2$ ← **Write each prime factor only once.**
2. $2 \cdot 3 \cdot x \cdot y$ ← **Write the greatest exponent of each prime factor.**
3. $2 \cdot 3^2 \cdot x^5 \cdot y^2$
4. $18x^5 y^2$ ← **LCD**

368 *Chapter 10*

When one or more of the factors is a binomial, you can write the LCD in factored form.

EXAMPLE 3 Find the LCD of rational expressions having the given denominators.

$$a^2 - 9; \qquad 3a^2 + 3a - 18; \qquad a^2 - 4a + 4$$

Solution: $\boxed{1}$ $a^2 - 9 = (a + 3)(a - 3)$

$3a^2 + 3a - 18 = 3(a^2 + a - 6) = 3(a + 3)(a - 2)$

$a^2 - 4a + 4 = (a - 2)(a - 2),$ or $(a - 2)^2$

$\boxed{2}$ Product using each prime factor once: $\qquad 3(a + 3)(a - 3)(a - 2)$

$\boxed{3}$ Product having the greatest exponent for each factor:

$$3(a + 3)(a - 3)(a - 2)^2 \longleftarrow \textbf{Factored form}$$

Thus, the **LCD** is $3(a + 3)(a - 3)(a - 2)^2$.

Additional Examples
Example 3
Find the LCD of rational expressions having the given denominators.
1. $(a^2 - 36)$; $(2a^2 + 12a + 22)$; $(a^2 + 10a + 25)$
   Ans: $2(a + 6)(a - 6)(a + 5)^2$
2. $(a^2 + 5a)$; $(a^2 + 3a - 10)$; $(a^2 - 7a + 10)$
   Ans: $a(a + 5)(a - 2)(a - 5)$

CLASSROOM EXERCISES

In Exercises 1–11, find the LCD of the rational expressions having the given denominators.

1. 8; 12 24
2. 3; 7 21
3. 2; 3; 5 30
4. $6xy$; $9x^2$ $18x^2y$
5. $2a$; $3b$; $5c$ $30abc$
6. 14; $2s^2t$; $4t^3$ $28s^2t^3$
7. $8a^2b$; $6ab^3$; $12abc$ $24a^2b^3c$
8. $(a + b)$; $(a - b)^2$
9. $2(x + y)$; $3(x + y)$ $6(x + y)$
10. $a^2 - 4$; $(a + 2)^2(a - 2)(a + 2)^2$
11. $5r^2 - 15r$; $2r^2 + 6r$ $10r(r + 3)(r - 3)$

Additional Answers
Classroom Exercises
8. $(a + b)(a - b)^2$

WRITTEN EXERCISES

A Find the LCD of rational expressions having the given denominators.

1. 6; 12 12
2. 3; 4 12
3. 2; 15 30
4. 3; 19 57
5. 5; 6 30
6. 8; 12 24
7. a; b ab
8. x^2; x x^2
9. ab; b^2 ab^2
10. $2a^2$; $12b^2$ $12a^2b^2$
11. $2a$; $3a$ $6a$
12. $6x$; $3x$ $6x$
13. $6p$; $4p$ $12p$
14. $2x$; $3y$ $6xy$
15. ab^2; a^2b a^2b^2
16. 9; 2; 6 18
17. 8; 4; 3 24
18. 5; 2; 4 20
19. 5; 4; 10 20
20. 12; 2; 3 12
21. 16; 12; 3 48
22. x^2; y; y^2 x^2y^2
23. x; y; z xyz
24. x^2; xy; y^2
25. $(x - y)$; $(x + y)$ $(x + y)(x - y)$
26. $(x^2 - y^2)$; $(x - y)$ $(x + y)(x - y)$ x^2y^2
27. $(4a - 8b)$; $(3a - 6b)$ $12(a - 2b)$
28. $(9a^2 - 6)$; $(15a^2 - 10)$ $15(3a^2 - 2)$
29. $(2x + 2y)$; $(x + y)$ $2(x + y)$
30. $(x^2 - 4)$; $(x + 2)^2$ $(x - 2)(x + 2)^2$
31. $(x^2 - 5x + 6)$; $(x^2 - 4x + 3)$
32. $(6a^2 - 5a - 6)$; $(12a^2 + 11a + 2)$
33. $(x^2 - 2x - 8)$; $(x^2 - 6x + 8)$
34. $(a^2 + 12a + 36)$; $(a^2 + 3a - 18)$ $(a + 6)^2(a - 3)$

B

35. $(4x^2 - 9y^2)$; $(4x + 6y)$ $2(2x + 3y)(2x - 3y)$
36. $(r^2 - 25t^2)$; $(3r - 15t)$ $3(r + 5t)(r - 5t)$
37. $(2b^2 - b - 3)$; $(3b^2 + 5b + 2)$
38. $(3z^2 - 13z + 4)$; $(2z^2 - 5z - 12)$

Assignment Guide
Minimal p. 369: 2–34 even
Average p. 369: 2–38 even
Above Average: p. 369: 2–34 even, 35–38

Additional Answers
Written Exercises
31. $(x - 1)(x - 2)(x - 3)$
32. $(2a - 3)(3a + 2)(4a + 1)$
33. $(x + 2)(x - 2)(x - 4)$
37. $(2b - 3)(b + 1)(3b + 2)$
38. $(z - 4)(3z - 1)(2z + 3)$

Rational Expressions **369**

10-7 Rational Expressions: Addition/Subtraction

Teaching Suggestions p. M-23

Quick Quiz
Find the LCD of rational expressions having the given denominators.
1. 6; 28   **Ans: 84**
2. $6xy$; $8x^2y^3$ **Ans: $24x^2y^3$**
3. $27x^3y$; $15xy^2z$
   Ans: $135x^3y^2z$
4. $(a^2 - 49)$; $(2a^2 - 28a + 98)$;
   $(a^2 + 5a - 14)$
   Ans: $2(a + 7)(a - 2)(a - 7)^2$
5. $(a^2 + 5a + 6)$; $(a^2 + a - 2)$
   Ans: $(a + 3)(a + 2)(a - 1)$

Adding or subtracting rational expressions in algebra is similar to adding or subtracting fractions in arithmetic.

Arithmetic	**Algebra**
$\dfrac{1}{5} + \dfrac{3}{5} = \dfrac{1 + 3}{5} = \dfrac{4}{5}$	$\dfrac{2}{a} + \dfrac{4}{a} = \dfrac{2 + 4}{a} = \dfrac{6}{a}$

Theorem 10-3

> **Addition and Subtraction of Rational Expressions**
>
> If $\dfrac{P}{Q}$ and $\dfrac{R}{Q}$ are rational expressions, then
>
> $$\dfrac{P}{Q} + \dfrac{R}{Q} = \dfrac{P + R}{Q} \quad \text{and} \quad \dfrac{P}{Q} - \dfrac{R}{Q} = \dfrac{P - R}{Q}.$$

EXAMPLE 1   Add or subtract as indicated. Express answers in simplest form.

a. $\dfrac{a + 5}{x} + \dfrac{a - 2}{x}$ **b.** $\dfrac{3a}{2} - \dfrac{a + 7}{2}$

Solutions:

a. $\dfrac{a + 5}{x} + \dfrac{a - 2}{x} = \dfrac{a + 5 + a - 2}{x}$ ⟵ By Theorem 10-3

$= \dfrac{2a + 3}{x}$ ⟵ Simplest form

b. $\dfrac{3a}{2} - \dfrac{a + 7}{2} = \dfrac{3a - (a + 7)}{2}$ ⟵ By Theorem 10-3

$= \dfrac{3a - a - 7}{2}$ ⟵ $-(a + 7) = (-1)(a + 7) = -a - 7$

$= \dfrac{2a - 7}{2}$ ⟵ Simplest form

**Additional Examples
Example 1**
Add or subtract as indicated. Express answers in simplest form.
1.a. $\dfrac{x + 3}{a} + \dfrac{x - 5}{a}$
   Ans: $\dfrac{2x - 2}{a}$
b. $\dfrac{3x - 5}{2} + \dfrac{3x - 3}{2}$
   Ans: $3x - 4$
2.a. $\dfrac{4x}{3} - \dfrac{x + 5}{3}$
   Ans: $\dfrac{3x - 5}{3}$
b. $\dfrac{5a}{3x} - \dfrac{2a + 6}{3x}$
   Ans: $\dfrac{a - 2}{x}$

Adding or subtracting rational expressions with unlike denominators is similar to adding or subtracting fractions with unlike denominators.

Arithmetic	**Algebra**
$\dfrac{2}{3} + \dfrac{4}{5}$ ⟵ LCD: 15	$\dfrac{a}{3x} + \dfrac{c}{2y}$ ⟵ LCD: 6xy
$\dfrac{2}{3} + \dfrac{4}{5} = \left(\dfrac{2}{3} \cdot \dfrac{5}{5}\right) + \left(\dfrac{4}{5} \cdot \dfrac{3}{3}\right)$	$\dfrac{a}{3x} + \dfrac{c}{2y} = \left(\dfrac{a}{3x} \cdot \dfrac{2y}{2y}\right) + \left(\dfrac{c}{2y} \cdot \dfrac{3x}{3x}\right)$
$= \dfrac{10}{15} + \dfrac{12}{15}$	$= \dfrac{2ay}{6xy} + \dfrac{3cx}{6xy}$
$= \dfrac{22}{15}$, or $1\dfrac{7}{15}$	$= \dfrac{2ay + 3cx}{6xy}$

Procedure

> **To add or subtract rational expressions:**
> 1. Find the LCD of the denominators.
> 2. Write equivalent rational expressions having the LCD as denominators.
> 3. Add or subtract as indicated.
> 4. Write the answer in simplest form.

EXAMPLE 2 Add or subtract as indicated: $\dfrac{3}{x^2} + \dfrac{5}{2xy} - \dfrac{4}{3y^2}$

Solution: 1. Find the LCD.   LCD: $6x^2y^2$

2. Write equivalent expressions having $6x^2y^2$ as the denominator. That is,

multiply $\dfrac{3}{x^2}$ by $\dfrac{6y^2}{6y^2}$ because $(x^2)(6y^2) = 6x^2y^2$;

multiply $\dfrac{5}{2xy}$ by $\dfrac{3xy}{3xy}$ because $(2xy)(3xy) = 6x^2y^2$; and

multiply $\dfrac{4}{3y^2}$ by $\dfrac{2x^2}{2x^2}$ because $(3y^2)(2x^2) = 6x^2y^2$.

$$\dfrac{3}{x^2} + \dfrac{5}{2xy} - \dfrac{4}{3y^2} = \left(\dfrac{3}{x^2} \cdot \dfrac{6y^2}{6y^2}\right) + \left(\dfrac{5}{2xy} \cdot \dfrac{3xy}{3xy}\right) - \left(\dfrac{4}{3y^2} \cdot \dfrac{2x^2}{2x^2}\right)$$

$$= \dfrac{18y^2}{6x^2y^2} + \dfrac{15xy}{6x^2y^2} - \dfrac{8x^2}{6x^2y^2}$$

3. $$= \dfrac{18y^2 + 15xy - 8x^2}{6x^2y^2} \quad \longleftarrow \textbf{ By Theorem 10–3}$$

NOTE: Recall that multiplying a rational expression by an expression such as $\dfrac{6y^2}{6y^2}$ ($y \neq 0$) is equivalent to multiplying by 1.

EXAMPLE 3 Add or subtract as indicated: $\dfrac{x+1}{x^2-9} + \dfrac{4}{x+3} - \dfrac{x-1}{x-3}$

Solution: Factor the denominator, $x^2 - 9$. Then find the LCD.

$$\dfrac{x+1}{x^2-9} + \dfrac{4}{x+3} - \dfrac{x-1}{x-3} = \dfrac{x+1}{(x+3)(x-3)} + \dfrac{4}{x+3} - \dfrac{x-1}{x-3} \quad \longleftarrow \textbf{ LCD: } (x+3)(x-3)$$

$$= \dfrac{x+1}{(x+3)(x-3)} + \left(\dfrac{4}{x+3} \cdot \dfrac{x-3}{x-3}\right) - \left(\dfrac{x-1}{x-3} \cdot \dfrac{x+3}{x+3}\right)$$

$$= \dfrac{x+1}{(x+3)(x-3)} + \dfrac{4(x-3)}{(x+3)(x-3)} - \dfrac{(x-1)(x+3)}{(x+3)(x-3)}$$

$$= \dfrac{x+1 + 4(x-3) - (x-1)(x+3)}{(x+3)(x-3)} \quad \longleftarrow \textbf{ By Theorem 10–3}$$

Additional Examples
Example 2
Add or subtract as indicated.

1. $\dfrac{2}{x^2} - \dfrac{7}{3xy} + \dfrac{6}{5y^2}$

   Ans: $\dfrac{30y^2 - 35xy + 18x^2}{15x^2y^2}$

2. $\dfrac{5}{a^2} + \dfrac{6}{3ab} - \dfrac{3}{2b^2}$

   Ans: $\dfrac{10b^2 + 4ab - 3a^2}{2a^2b^2}$

Example 3
Add or subtract as indicated.

1. $\dfrac{x+3}{x^2-16} + \dfrac{5}{x+4} - \dfrac{x-2}{x-4}$

   Ans: $\dfrac{-x^2 + 4x - 9}{(x+4)(x-4)}$

2. $\dfrac{x+2}{x^2-9} - \dfrac{5}{x-3} + \dfrac{x-2}{x+3}$

   Ans: $\dfrac{x^2 - 9x - 7}{(x+3)(x-3)}$

$$= \frac{x + 1 + 4x - 12 - (x^2 + 2x - 3)}{(x + 3)(x - 3)} \longleftarrow \text{Simplify.}$$

$$= \frac{5x - 11 - x^2 - 2x + 3}{(x + 3)(x - 3)}$$

$$= \frac{-x^2 + 3x - 8}{(x + 3)(x - 3)} \longleftarrow \text{Simplest form}$$

Assignment Guide
Minimal
Day 1 p. 372: 1–18
Day 2 pp. 372–373: 19–57 odd
Average
Day 1 pp. 372–373: 1–57 odd
Day 2 p. 373: 58–72
Above Average
Day 1 pp. 372–373:
3, 6, 9, . . . 57, 59–72 odd
Day 2 p. 373: 73–81

CLASSROOM EXERCISES

Add or subtract as indicated. Write the answers in simplest form.

1. $\dfrac{2}{9} + \dfrac{5}{9}$ $\dfrac{7}{9}$

2. $\dfrac{9}{y} - \dfrac{7}{y}$ $\dfrac{2}{y}$

3. $\dfrac{1 + x}{z} - \dfrac{1 - x}{z}$

4. $\dfrac{4}{x} + \dfrac{6}{y}$ $\dfrac{4y + 6x}{xy}$

5. $\dfrac{a}{2b} - \dfrac{3c}{b^2d}$ $\dfrac{abd - 6c}{2b^2d}$

6. $\dfrac{5}{x} - \dfrac{2}{x + 1} + \dfrac{7}{y}$

WRITTEN EXERCISES

Ⓐ   Add or subtract as indicated. Write the answers in simplest form.

1. $\dfrac{7}{b} + \dfrac{9}{b}$ $\dfrac{16}{b}$

2. $\dfrac{10}{c} - \dfrac{3}{c}$ $\dfrac{7}{c}$

3. $\dfrac{27}{q} + \dfrac{23}{q} - \dfrac{1}{q}$ $\dfrac{49}{q}$

4. $\dfrac{3a}{2} + \dfrac{(a + 9)}{2}$ $\dfrac{4a + 9}{2}$

5. $\dfrac{17b}{3} + \dfrac{(2a - 6)}{3}$ $\dfrac{2a + 17b - 6}{3}$

6. $\dfrac{(2a + 6)}{4} + \dfrac{(3a - 9)}{4}$

7. $\dfrac{17m}{6} + \dfrac{(3m + 4)}{6}$ $\dfrac{10m + 2}{3}$

8. $\dfrac{(2a - 3)}{2} - \dfrac{(6a + 5)}{2}$ $-2a - 4$

9. $\dfrac{(2a + 9)}{4} - \dfrac{(2a - 6)}{4}$

10. $\dfrac{(3x - 2y)}{6} - \dfrac{(4x - 5y)}{6}$

11. $\dfrac{(2a - 7b)}{12} - \dfrac{(6a + 6b)}{12}$

12. $\dfrac{2a}{x + 5} + \dfrac{3a}{x + 5}$ $\dfrac{5a}{x + 5}$

13. $\dfrac{m}{x - y} + \dfrac{n}{x - y}$ $\dfrac{m + n}{x - y}$

14. $\dfrac{2a}{x - 4} - \dfrac{5a}{x - 4}$ $\dfrac{-3a}{x - 4}$

15. $\dfrac{7m}{2y + 5} - \dfrac{6m}{2y + 5}$

16. $\dfrac{q}{r - 7} - \dfrac{s}{r - 7}$ $\dfrac{q - s}{r - 7}$

17. $\dfrac{5q}{r + 6} - \dfrac{7q}{r + 6}$ $\dfrac{-2q}{r + 6}$

18. $\dfrac{x}{a - b} - \dfrac{y}{a - b}$

19. $\dfrac{x^2}{7} + \dfrac{x^2}{6}$ $\dfrac{13x^2}{42}$

20. $\dfrac{2x}{3} + \dfrac{5y}{2}$ $\dfrac{4x + 15y}{6}$

21. $\dfrac{x^2y}{6} + \dfrac{xy^2}{5}$ $\dfrac{5x^2y + 6xy^2}{30}$

22. $\dfrac{7ab}{10} - \dfrac{3a}{4}$ $\dfrac{14ab - 15a}{20}$

23. $\dfrac{2a + 3}{6} - \dfrac{5a - 7}{9}$ $\dfrac{-4a + 23}{18}$

24. $\dfrac{3x - 5}{4} + \dfrac{5x - 3}{3}$

25. $\dfrac{4n - 1}{5} - \dfrac{n + 2}{4}$ $\dfrac{11n - 14}{20}$

26. $\dfrac{x^2 - y^2}{3} - \dfrac{x^2 + y^2}{8}$ $\dfrac{5x^2 - 11y^2}{24}$

27. $\dfrac{3c}{8} + \dfrac{b + c}{3}$

28. $\dfrac{1}{a} + \dfrac{1}{b}$ $\dfrac{a + b}{ab}$

29. $\dfrac{2}{a} + \dfrac{3}{b}$ $\dfrac{3a + 2b}{ab}$

30. $\dfrac{1}{a} - \dfrac{1}{b}$ $\dfrac{b - a}{ab}$

31. $\dfrac{4}{x} - \dfrac{5}{y}$ $\dfrac{4y - 5x}{xy}$

32. $\dfrac{a}{b} - \dfrac{c}{d}$ $\dfrac{ad - bc}{bd}$

33. $\dfrac{3}{2c} + \dfrac{4}{6c}$ $\dfrac{13}{6c}$

See page 581 for the answers to Ex. 35-81 odd.

Add or subtract as indicated. Write the answers in simplest form.

34. $\dfrac{5}{4a} - \dfrac{3}{8a}$ $\dfrac{7}{8a}$

35. $\dfrac{7a}{10p} - \dfrac{2b}{5p}$

36. $\dfrac{5r}{4c} + \dfrac{4s}{5d}$

37. $\dfrac{3}{x} + \dfrac{5}{x^2}$

38. $\dfrac{4a}{b^2} - \dfrac{3a}{b}$ $\dfrac{4a - 3ab}{b^2}$

39. $\dfrac{3}{x} - \dfrac{5}{x^3} + \dfrac{2}{x^2}$

40. $\dfrac{a}{x^3} + \dfrac{b}{x^2} - \dfrac{c}{x}$ $\dfrac{a + bx - cx^2}{x^3}$

41. $\dfrac{5}{ab^2} - \dfrac{7}{a^2b}$

42. $\dfrac{2}{xy} + \dfrac{3}{yz}$

43. $\dfrac{9}{mn} + \dfrac{3}{mn^2}$

44. $\dfrac{8}{x} + \dfrac{3}{xy}$ $\dfrac{8y + 3}{xy}$

45. $\dfrac{1}{6p} - \dfrac{1}{4p} + \dfrac{1}{3p}$

46. $\dfrac{3}{b} + \dfrac{5}{2b} - \dfrac{11}{3b}$ $\dfrac{1}{6b}$

47. $\dfrac{a + b}{b} - \dfrac{a - b}{a}$

48. $\dfrac{x + 1}{2x} + \dfrac{2}{x}$ $\dfrac{x + 5}{2x}$

49. $\dfrac{2x - 1}{x} - \dfrac{x + 3}{3x}$

50. $\dfrac{1}{2a^2} - \dfrac{5}{6ab} + \dfrac{7}{12b^2}$

51. $\dfrac{x}{2b} + \dfrac{2x}{b} - \dfrac{1}{b^2}$

52. $\dfrac{x - 1}{3xy} + \dfrac{x^2 - x}{9x^2y^2}$

53. $\dfrac{3a + 5}{a} - \dfrac{2b - 3}{b}$

54. $\dfrac{3x - y}{x} + \dfrac{4x + 2y}{x}$

55. $\dfrac{4x + y}{x} - \dfrac{3x - 4y}{x^2}$

56. $\dfrac{2y - 3}{2y} + \dfrac{y - 4}{3y}$ $\dfrac{8y - 17}{6y}$

57. $\dfrac{5a - 2b}{-a^2} + \dfrac{4a + 3b}{-3a^2}$

B

58. $\dfrac{5}{x + 2} + \dfrac{3}{x - 2}$

59. $\dfrac{5}{x + 5} - \dfrac{3}{x - 5}$

60. $\dfrac{2}{a + 3} + \dfrac{5}{a + 5}$

61. $\dfrac{2x}{x - y} - \dfrac{3y}{x + y}$

62. $\dfrac{a}{2a + 2b} - \dfrac{b}{3a + 3b}$

63. $\dfrac{4a}{6a - 2b} + \dfrac{3b}{9a - 3b}$

64. $\dfrac{2}{3t + 3s} + \dfrac{3}{5t - 5s}$

65. $\dfrac{3x}{2y - 3} - \dfrac{2x}{3y - 2}$

66. $\dfrac{x + 3}{x - 5} + \dfrac{x - 5}{x + 3}$

67. $\dfrac{a - 2}{a + 3} - \dfrac{a - 3}{a + 5}$

68. $\dfrac{x + 3}{x^2 - 4} + \dfrac{x - 5}{x + 2}$

69. $\dfrac{3a + 2}{3a + 6} - \dfrac{a - 2}{a^2 - 4}$

70. $\dfrac{a + b}{ax + ay} - \dfrac{a + b}{bx + by}$

71. $\dfrac{a - b}{a + b} - \dfrac{a}{a^2 - b^2}$

72. $\dfrac{x - y}{x + y} + \dfrac{4xy}{x^2 - y^2}$

C

73. $\dfrac{4a}{2a + 6} - \dfrac{a - 1}{a + 3}$

74. $\dfrac{x - 6y}{2x^2 - 5xy + 2y^2} - \dfrac{7}{x + 2y}$

75. $\dfrac{7}{a^2 + a - 2} - \dfrac{5}{a^2 - 4a + 3}$

76. $\dfrac{2x}{x^2 - 25} - \dfrac{4(x - 5)}{x - 5}$

77. $\dfrac{3}{y^2 + y - 6} + \dfrac{2}{y^2 - 4y + 4}$

78. $\dfrac{5}{a^2 - 2ab + b^2} + \dfrac{6}{a - b}$

79. $\dfrac{5}{3x - 3} + \dfrac{x}{2x + 2} - \dfrac{3x^2}{x^2 - 1}$

80. $\dfrac{x^2}{a^2 - b^2} + \dfrac{x}{(a - b)^2}$

81. $\dfrac{r - s}{(r + s)^2} - \dfrac{1}{r - s} + \dfrac{s}{r^2 - s^2}$

─── **REVIEW CAPSULE FOR SECTION 10-8** ───

Perform the indicated operations. Simplify. *(Pages 97–99)*

1. $2(x + y) + 2x + 3y$ $4x + 5y$
2. $3r + 7 - 2(r^2 - 9)$
3. $10(c - 3) + c + 2$ $11c - 28$
4. $18(a - b) - (a - b)$ $17a - 17b$
5. $8 - 6(3x - 1) - 18x + 14$
6. $(a + 1)(a + 1) + 1$

Rational Expressions **373**

373

10–8 Mixed Expressions: Addition/Subtraction

Add or subtract as indicated. Express answers in simplest form.

1. $\dfrac{25}{a} + \dfrac{23}{a} - \dfrac{2}{a}$

Ans: $\dfrac{46}{a}$

2. $\dfrac{a}{y^3} - \dfrac{b}{y} + \dfrac{c}{y^2}$

Ans: $\dfrac{a - by^2 + cy}{y^3}$

3. $\dfrac{x+5}{x^2-4} - \dfrac{6}{x+2} + \dfrac{x-3}{x-2}$

Ans: $\dfrac{x^2 - 6x + 11}{(x+2)(x-2)}$

Additional Examples
Example 1
Add.

1. $a + \dfrac{3}{a}$ **Ans:** $\dfrac{a^2+3}{a}$

2. $2x + \dfrac{4}{x^2}$ **Ans:** $\dfrac{2x^3+4}{x^2}$

Example 2
Subtract.

1. $a + 2 - \dfrac{3}{a-2}$ **Ans:** $\dfrac{a^2-7}{a-2}$

2. $a + 5 - \dfrac{4}{a-3}$

Ans: $\dfrac{a^2 + 2a - 19}{a-3}$

Recall that numbers such as $4\frac{1}{2}$ and $5\frac{2}{3}$ are called **mixed numbers.** They indicate the sum of a whole number and a fraction.

$$4\tfrac{1}{2} = 4 + \tfrac{1}{2} \qquad 5\tfrac{2}{3} = 5 + \tfrac{2}{3}$$

The sum or difference of rational expressions where one rational expression has a denominator of 1 is called a **mixed expression.**

EXAMPLE 1 Add: $t + \dfrac{5}{2t}$

Solution: Write t as $\dfrac{t}{1}$. Then identify the LCD.

$$t + \frac{5}{2t} = \frac{t}{1} + \frac{5}{2t} \quad \longleftarrow \quad \text{LCD: } 2t$$

$$= \left(\frac{t}{1} \cdot \frac{2t}{2t}\right) + \frac{5}{2t}$$

$$= \frac{2t^2}{2t} + \frac{5}{2t}$$

$$= \frac{2t^2 + 5}{2t} \quad \longleftarrow \quad \text{Simplest form}$$

The method of Example 1 can also be used when the operation is subtraction.

EXAMPLE 2 Subtract: $a + 1 - \dfrac{1}{a-1}$

Solution: $a + 1 - \dfrac{1}{a-1} = \dfrac{a+1}{1} - \dfrac{1}{a-1} \quad \longleftarrow \quad \text{LCD: } (a-1)$

$$= \left(\frac{a+1}{1} \cdot \frac{a-1}{a-1}\right) - \frac{1}{a-1}$$

$$= \frac{(a+1)(a-1)}{1(a-1)} - \frac{1}{a-1}$$

$$= \frac{a^2-1}{a-1} - \frac{1}{a-1}$$

$$= \frac{a^2-1-1}{a-1} \quad \longleftarrow \quad \text{By Theorem 10–3}$$

$$= \frac{a^2-2}{a-1}$$

CLASSROOM EXERCISES

Add or subtract as indicated. Write the answers in simplest form.

1. $1 + \dfrac{1}{b}$ $\quad \dfrac{b+1}{b}$

2. $1 - \dfrac{1}{b}$ $\quad \dfrac{b-1}{b}$

3. $x + \dfrac{3}{x}$ $\quad \dfrac{x^2+3}{x}$

4. $x - \dfrac{3}{x}$ $\quad \dfrac{x^2-3}{x}$

5. $t + 1 + \dfrac{5}{t}$ $\quad \dfrac{t^2+t+5}{t}$

6. $\dfrac{10}{d} - 3$ $\quad \dfrac{10-3d}{d}$

7. $\dfrac{1}{a} - (a+1)$ $\quad \dfrac{1-a^2-a}{a}$

8. $\dfrac{1}{a} - (a-1)$ $\quad \dfrac{1-a^2+a}{a}$

WRITTEN EXERCISES

A Add or subtract as indicated. Write the answers in simplest form.

1. $3 + \dfrac{1}{a}$ $\quad \dfrac{3a+1}{a}$

2. $s - \dfrac{5}{3s}$ $\quad \dfrac{3s^2-5}{3s}$

3. $3 + \dfrac{a}{b}$ $\quad \dfrac{3b+a}{b}$

4. $1 + \dfrac{3}{x+1}$

5. $7 - \dfrac{4}{a-b}$ $\quad \dfrac{7a-7b-4}{a-b}$

6. $7 + \dfrac{2x}{y+z}$

7. $a + \dfrac{1}{a+1}$

8. $a - \dfrac{1}{a-1}$

9. $9 - \dfrac{2r}{r+s}$ $\quad \dfrac{7r+9s}{r+s}$

10. $\dfrac{4}{z-2} + 4$ $\quad \dfrac{4z-4}{z-2}$

11. $10 + \dfrac{c+2}{c-3}$

12. $18 - \dfrac{a+b}{a-b}$

13. $ax + \dfrac{b}{x}$ $\quad \dfrac{ax^2+b}{x}$

14. $2x - \dfrac{x+y}{y}$

15. $a - \dfrac{b}{c}$ $\quad \dfrac{ac-b}{c}$

16. $\dfrac{a}{x} - (a-1)$

17. $a^2 - \dfrac{1}{a}$ $\quad \dfrac{a^3-1}{a}$

18. $\dfrac{4a}{(a-2)^2} + 1$

19. $\dfrac{3r}{r^2-9} - 2$

20. $2 + \dfrac{2x+3y}{x+y}$

21. $(a+1) + \dfrac{1}{a+1}$

22. $6 + \dfrac{5}{4x-2}$ $\quad \dfrac{24x-7}{4x-2}$

23. $\dfrac{8}{3x-1} - 6$

24. $\dfrac{5}{t-1} - (t-1)$

B

25. $(x-5) - \dfrac{x}{x+3}$ $\quad \dfrac{x^2-3x-15}{x+3}$

26. $\dfrac{2a-1}{a+2} + (2a-3)$ $\quad \dfrac{2a^2+3a-7}{a+2}$

27. $(2t-1) - \dfrac{4t}{t+6}$

28. $\dfrac{x-7}{2x+5} + (x-4)$ $\quad \dfrac{2x^2-2x-27}{2x+5}$

29. $\dfrac{5t+1}{t-4} + (t+4)$ $\quad \dfrac{t^2+5t-15}{t-4}$

30. $(a+6) + \dfrac{3a-4}{a+6}$

31. $(a+2) + \dfrac{5}{a-2}$ $\quad \dfrac{a^2+1}{a-2}$

32. $4 - \dfrac{3}{t-1} - \dfrac{1}{t+1}$ $\quad \dfrac{4t^2-4t-6}{(t-1)(t+1)}$

33. $\dfrac{x}{x+2} + \dfrac{x}{x-2} - 1$

C

34. $\dfrac{x^2}{x+y} - \dfrac{y^2}{x-y} - (x-y)$ $\quad \dfrac{-2y^3}{(x+y)(x-y)}$

35. $\dfrac{7}{x-5} + (x^2+2x-3)$ $\quad \dfrac{x^3-3x^2-13x+22}{x-5}$

36. $(a^2+3a+1) + \dfrac{4}{a-5}$ $\quad \dfrac{a^3-2a^2-14a-1}{a-5}$

37. $\dfrac{7}{x-2} + x^2 + \dfrac{4}{x+2} + 4$ $\quad \dfrac{x^4+11x-10}{(x+2)(x-2)}$

38. $\dfrac{\frac{1}{2}-\frac{1}{3}}{\frac{1}{2}+\frac{1}{3}}$ $\quad \dfrac{1}{5}$

39. $\dfrac{\frac{3}{4}+\frac{2}{5}}{\frac{3}{4}-\frac{2}{5}}$ $\quad \dfrac{23}{7}$

40. $\dfrac{\frac{1}{a}-\frac{1}{2a}}{\frac{2}{a}}$ $\quad \dfrac{1}{4}$

41. $\dfrac{1-\frac{9}{x^2}}{x+3}$ $\quad \dfrac{x-3}{x^2}$

42. $\dfrac{\frac{a}{b}+1}{\frac{a}{b}-1}$ $\quad \dfrac{a+b}{a-b}$

43. $\dfrac{\frac{3a}{2}+1}{\frac{3a}{4}-\frac{1}{3a}}$ $\quad \dfrac{6a}{3a-2}$

44. $\dfrac{\frac{r^2+t^2}{rt}+2}{\frac{r^2-t^2}{2rt}}$ $\quad \dfrac{2r+2t}{r-t}$

45. $\dfrac{1+\frac{2r}{r^2+1}}{1-\frac{2r+2}{r^2+1}}$

Rational Expressions   **375**

Assignment Guide
Minimal p. 375: 2–24 even
Average p. 375: 2–33 even
Above Average p. 375: 3, 6, 9, . . . 33, 34–45 even

Additional Answers
Written Exercises

4. $\dfrac{x+4}{x+1}$

6. $\dfrac{7y+7z+2x}{y+z}$

7. $\dfrac{a^2+a+1}{a+1}$

8. $\dfrac{a^2-a-1}{a-1}$

11. $\dfrac{11c-28}{c-3}$

12. $\dfrac{17a-19b}{a-b}$

14. $\dfrac{2xy-x-y}{y}$

16. $\dfrac{a-ax+x}{x}$

18. $\dfrac{a^2+4}{(a-2)^2}$

19. $\dfrac{3r-2r^2+18}{r^2-9}$

20. $\dfrac{4x+5y}{x+y}$

21. $\dfrac{a^2+2a+2}{a+1}$

23. $\dfrac{14-18x}{3x-1}$

24. $\dfrac{-t^2+2t+4}{t-1}$

27. $\dfrac{2t^2+7t-6}{t+6}$

30. $\dfrac{a^2+15a-32}{a+6}$

33. $\dfrac{x^2+4}{(x+2)(x-2)}$

45. $\dfrac{r^2+2r+1}{r^2-2r-1}$

Divide. *(Pages 288–289)*

1. $8a \div 2$ $4a$ **2.** $9f \div f$ 9 **3.** $a^3b^2 \div ab^2$ a^2 **4.** $t^2y \div ty$ t

5. $21x^2y \div 7x$ $3xy$ **6.** $24z^4 \div 8z^2$ $3z^2$ **7.** $11x^2y^3 \div 11x^2y^3$ 1 **8.** $30z^5 \div 15z^4$ $2z$

OBJECTIVE: To divide one polynomial by another

10-9   Division of Polynomials

Teaching Suggestions p. M-23

Quick Quiz
Add or subtract as indicated.
Write the answers in simplest
form.

1. $5x + \dfrac{3}{x}$ **Ans:** $\dfrac{5x^2 + 3}{x}$

2. $7a - \dfrac{5}{b}$ **Ans:** $\dfrac{7ab - 5}{b}$

3. $a - 5 + \dfrac{4}{a - 3}$

Ans: $\dfrac{a^2 - 8a + 19}{a - 3}$

4. $x - 1 - \dfrac{3}{x - 2}$

Ans: $\dfrac{x^2 - 3x - 1}{x - 2}$

Division of one polynomial by another is similar to long division in arithmetic.

Arithmetic

$$\boxed{1} \; 28 \overline{)\; 537} \quad \longleftarrow \text{Think: } (28)(\underline{\;?\;}) \le 53$$

with $\dfrac{1}{28\,)\,537}$, $28 \longleftarrow 1 \cdot 28$, $25 \longleftarrow 53 - 28$

$$\boxed{2} \; 28 \overline{)\; 537}$$
$$\dfrac{28}{257} \quad \longleftarrow \text{Think: } (28)(\underline{\;?\;}) \le 257$$
$$\dfrac{252}{5} \quad \longleftarrow \text{Remainder}$$

Answer: $19 + \dfrac{5}{28}$, or $19\dfrac{5}{28}$

Algebra

$$\boxed{1} \; x + 3 \overline{)\; x^2 + x - 1} \quad \longleftarrow \text{Think: } (x)(\underline{\;?\;}) = x^2$$

quotient x; $x^2 + 3x \longleftarrow x(x + 3)$; $-2x \longleftarrow x - 3x$

$$\boxed{2} \; x + 3 \overline{)\; x^2 + x - 1}$$
$$\dfrac{x^2 + 3x}{-2x - 1} \quad \longleftarrow \text{Think: } (x)(\underline{\;?\;}) = -2x$$
$$\dfrac{-2x - 6}{5} \quad \longleftarrow \text{Remainder}$$

quotient $x - 2$

Answer: $x - 2 + \dfrac{5}{x + 3}$

As these examples show, a division problem can be expressed in general form.

$$\frac{\text{Dividend}}{\text{Divisor}} = \text{Quotient} + \frac{\text{Remainder}}{\text{Divisor}}, \text{ or}$$

$$\text{Dividend} = (\text{Divisor})(\text{Quotient}) + \text{Remainder}$$

Example 1 shows how to use this general form to check a division problem.

Additional Examples
Example 1
1. Divide $x^3 - 3x^2 - 2x + 10$
by $x - 1$.

Ans: $x^2 - 2x - 4 + \dfrac{6}{x - 1}$

2. Divide $a^2 - 13a - 22$
by $a - 2$.

Ans: $a - 11 - \dfrac{44}{a - 2}$

EXAMPLE 1   Divide $x^3 - x^2 - 2x + 10$ by $x + 2$.

Solution:

$$\boxed{1} \; x + 2 \overline{)\; x^3 - x^2 - 2x + 10} \quad \longleftarrow \text{Think: } (x)(\underline{\;?\;}) = x^3$$

quotient x^2

$$\dfrac{x^3 + 2x^2}{-3x^2 - 2x + 10}$$

$\longleftarrow x^2(x + 2)$

$\longleftarrow x^3 - x^2 - 2x + 10 - (x^3 + 2x^2)$

$$\boxed{2} \; x + 2 \overline{)\; x^3 - x^2 - 2x + 10} \quad \longleftarrow \text{Think: } x(\underline{\;?\;}) = -3x^2$$

quotient $x^2 - 3x$

$$\dfrac{x^3 + 2x^2}{-3x^2 - 2x + 10}$$
$$\dfrac{-3x^2 - 6x}{4x + 10}$$

$\longleftarrow (-3x)(x + 2)$

$\longleftarrow (-3x^2 - 2x + 10) - (-3x^2 - 6x)$

376   *Chapter 10*

$$\boxed{3} \quad x+2 \overline{)\begin{array}{r} x^2 - 3x + 4 \\ x^3 - x^2 - 2x + 10 \end{array}} \quad \longleftarrow \quad \textbf{Think: (x)(\underline{?}) = 4x}$$

$$\begin{array}{r}
\underline{x^3 + 2x^2} \\
-3x^2 - 2x + 10 \\
\underline{-3x^2 - 6x} \\
4x + 10 \\
\underline{4x + 8} \quad \longleftarrow \quad \textbf{4(x + 2)} \\
2 \quad \longleftarrow \quad \textbf{Remainder}
\end{array}$$

Thus, $x^3 - x^2 - 2x + 10 \div x + 2 = \mathbf{x^2 - 3x + 4 + \dfrac{2}{x + 2}}$.

Check: Dividend = (Divisor)(Quotient) + Remainder

$$x^3 - x^2 - 2x + 10 \overset{?}{=} (x + 2)(x^2 - 3x + 4) + 2$$
$$x^3 - x^2 - 2x + 10 \overset{?}{=} (x^3 - x^2 - 2x + 8) + 2$$
$$x^3 - x^2 - 2x + 10 \overset{?}{=} x^3 - x^2 - 2x + 10 \quad \text{Yes} \quad \text{✔}$$

When you divide polynomials, always be sure that the terms of each polynomial are arranged in descending order of the exponents of the variable. Also, when one of the terms in the dividend is "missing," insert 0 as the coefficient.

EXAMPLE 2   Divide $2a^2 + a^3 - 75$ by $a - 5$.

Solution: Write $2a^2 + a^3 - 75$ as $a^3 + 2a^2 + 0a - 75$. $\longleftarrow$ **Descending order of exponents**

$$a - 5 \overline{)\begin{array}{r} a^2 + 7a + 35 \\ a^3 + 2a^2 + 0a - 75 \end{array}}$$

$$\begin{array}{r}
\underline{a^3 - 5a^2} \\
7a^2 + 0a \\
\underline{7a^2 - 35a} \\
35a - 75 \\
\underline{35a - 175} \\
100
\end{array} \qquad \textbf{Answer: } a^2 + 7a + 35 + \dfrac{100}{a - 5}$$

The check is left for you.

Additional Examples
Example 2
1. Divide $3a^2 + a^3 - 25$ by $a - 5$.

    Ans: $a^2 + 8a + 40 + \dfrac{175}{a - 5}$

2. Divide $-3x + 8 + x^3$ by $x + 2$.

    Ans: $x^2 - 2x + 1 + \dfrac{6}{x + 2}$

CLASSROOM EXERCISES

Write the missing term to be inserted in the dividend before dividing. $0a$

1. $t + 5 \overline{)\, t^2 - 25}$ $0t$ 2. $x - 3 \overline{)\, x^2 - 12}$ $0x$ 3. $2a - 1 \overline{)\, 4a^3 - 8a^2 + 10}$

4. $x + 2 \overline{)\, x^3 + 8}$ $0x^2 + 0x$ 5. $2x^2 + 2x + 1 \overline{)\, 4x^4 + 1}$ 6. $3x - 1 \overline{)\, 12x^3 - 9x^2 + 7}$

                                       $0x^3 + 0x^2 + 0x$ $0x$

Write the terms of the dividend in descending order of the exponents of the variable.

7. $2r - 1 \overline{)\, 10r - 9r^2 + 5 + 2r^3}$ $2r^3 - 9r^2 + 10r + 5$ 8. $4k - 1 \overline{)\, 7 + 8k^2 - 30k}$ $8k^2 - 30k + 7$ 9. $z - 3 \overline{)\, 2 - 13z + 6z^2}$ $6z^2 - 13z + 2$

Rational Expressions   **377**

Assignment Guide
Minimal p. 378: 1–23 odd
Average p. 378: 1–31 odd
Above Average p. 378: 3, 6, 9, . . . 30, 32–41

Additional Answers
Written Exercises

4. $p - 6 + \dfrac{62}{p + 5}$

6. $2a - 7$

7. $4y + 15 + \dfrac{6}{y + 1}$

8. $3c + 15 + \dfrac{-36}{c - 3}$

9. $3x + 1$

11. $3a - 2 + \dfrac{1}{2a - 3}$

13. $5n + 2 + \dfrac{6}{3n + 2}$

15. $a^2 - 3a - 4$

17. $3x^2 + 5x - 2$

18. $2p^2 - p - 1 + \dfrac{-3}{4p + 1}$

19. $a^2 + 2ab + \dfrac{3ab^2}{3a + 2b}$

20. $2y^2 - 4y + 2 + \dfrac{-12}{3y + 1}$

24. $x^2 + 3x - 4$

25. $2x^2 + x + 1$

27. $x^2 - 5x + 29 + \dfrac{-148}{x + 5}$

33. $(3y + 2)(y + 2)$

34. $(y + 2)(y - 2)(y^2 - 2)$

35. $2t + 3$

36. No; when $r^3 - 2r^2 + 4r - 6$ is divided by $(r - 2)$, there is a remainder.

37. No; when $6n^3 - 22n + 1$ is divided by $(2n - 4)$, there is a remainder.

WRITTEN EXERCISES

A Divide the first polynomial by the second.

1. $x^2 + 10x + 21$; $x + 3$ $x + 7$
2. $y^2 + 13y + 22$; $y + 2$ $y + 11$
3. $c^2 - 3c - 28$; $c - 7$ $c + 4$

4. $p^2 - p + 32$; $p + 5$
5. $3n^2 + 14n + 8$; $n + 4$ $3n + 2$
6. $2a^2 - 11a + 14$; $a - 2$

7. $4y^2 + 19y + 21$; $y + 1$
8. $3c^2 - 24c + 9$; $c - 3$
9. $3x^2 - 8x - 3$; $x - 3$

10. $2x^2 - 11x - 40$; $2x + 5$ $x - 8$
11. $6a^2 - 13a + 7$; $2a - 3$

12. $8x^2 - 14x - 30$; $2x - 6$ $4x + 5$
13. $15n^2 + 16n + 10$; $3n + 2$

14. $x^2 + xy - 3y^2$; $x - y$ $x + 2y + \dfrac{-y^2}{x - y}$
15. $a^3 - 5a^2 + 2a + 8$; $a - 2$

16. $c^3 + 2c^2 - 2c + 24$; $c + 4$ $c^2 - 2c + 6$
17. $6x^3 + x^2 - 19x + 6$; $2x - 3$

18. $8p^3 - 2p^2 - 5p - 4$; $4p + 1$
19. $3a^3 + 8a^2b + 7ab^2$; $3a + 2b$

20. $6y^3 - 10y^2 + 2y - 10$; $3y + 1$
21. $x^2 + 25$; $x + 5$ $x - 5 + \dfrac{50}{x + 5}$

22. $6a^2 - ab + b^2$; $2a + b$ $3a - 2b + \dfrac{3b^2}{2a + b}$
23. $a^3 - 8b^3$; $a - 2b$ $a^2 + 2ab + 4b^2$

B

24. $2x^3 - 5x + 7x^2 - 4$; $2x + 1$
25. $8x + 13x^2 + 6x^3 + 5$; $3x + 5$

26. $8x^2 + 11x + 5x^3 - 6$; $5x - 2$ $x^2 + 2x + 3$
27. $x^3 + 4x - 3$; $x + 5$

28. $x^3 - 6x^2 + 1$; $x + 2$ $x^2 - 8x + 16 + \dfrac{-31}{x + 2}$
29. $x^3 - 2x - 21$; $x - 3$ $x^2 + 3x + 7$

30. $x^3 - 125$; $x - 5$ $x^2 + 5x + 25$
31. $x^3 + 27$; $x + 3$ $x^2 - 3x + 9$

32. Factor $x^2 - 8x - 9$ completely, given that $(x + 1)$ is a factor. $(x + 1)(x - 9)$

33. Factor $3y^2 + 8y + 4$ completely, given that $(3y + 2)$ is a factor.

34. One factor of $y^4 - 6y^2 + 8$ is $(y^2 - 4)$. Find the other factor. Then factor completely over the integers.

35. One factor of $2t^3 - t^2 - 4t + 3$ is $(t^2 + 1 - 2t)$. Find the other factor. Then factor completely over the integers.

36. Is $(r - 2)$ a factor of $r^3 - 2r^2 + 4r - 6$? Give a reason for your answer.

37. Is $(2n - 4)$ a factor of $6n^3 - 22n + 1$? Give a reason for your answer.

C

38. Find the value of k for which $(3t + 2)$ is a factor of $15t^2 - 2t + k$. $k = -8$

39. Find the value of k for which $(x - 3)$ is a factor of $2x^3 - x^2 - 17x + k$. $k = 6$

40. A rectangle of width $(4x - 9y)$ units has an area of $(12x^2 - 11xy - 36y^2)$ square units. Find the perimeter of the rectangle. $14x - 10y$ units

41. When $6p^3 - 22p + c$ is divided by $2p - 4$, the remainder is 5. Find c. $c = 1$

Puzzle ——— See the Solution Key.

A four-digit number is divided by a two-digit number to give a two-digit number, as shown.

Find the missing digits. (There is only one solution.)

```
        xx
5x) 1xxx
     x5x
     xxx
     400
```

BASIC: ADDING FRACTIONS

This section is optional. Each computer applications lesson relates directly to a topic covered within the given chapter. (See Section 10-7, pages 370–373)

A computer cannot handle fractions as you do. If you enter $2/5$ into a computer, the machine will divide 2 by 5 and return a decimal, 0.4. To program a computer to compute the sum of two fractions in fractional form, you must include the following algebra in the program.

$$\frac{a}{b} + \frac{c}{d} = \frac{ad}{bd} + \frac{bc}{bd} = \frac{ad + bc}{bd}$$

Problem: *Write a program which adds two fractions.*

Program:

```
100 PRINT "FOR THE FRACTIONS A/B AND C/D, WHAT"
110 PRINT "ARE A, B, C, AND D (NONE 0)";
120 INPUT A, B, C, D
130 IF A*B*C*D <> 0 THEN 160
140 PRINT "NO ZERO VALUES. TRY AGAIN."
150 GOTO 120
160 LET N = A*D + B*C
170 LET D1 = B*D
180 IF N = 0 THEN 310
190 LET N1 = ABS(N)
200 LET D2 = ABS(D1)
210 IF N1 > D2 THEN 240
220 LET S = N1
230 GOTO 250
240 LET S = D2
250 FOR Y = S TO 1 STEP -1
260 IF N1/Y <> INT(N1/Y) THEN 280
270 IF D2/Y = INT(D2/Y) THEN 290
280 NEXT Y
290 LET N = N/Y
300 LET D1 = D1/Y
310 PRINT "(";A;"/";B;") + (";C;"/";D;") = ";
320 IF ABS(D1) = 1 THEN 380
330 IF N * D1 < 0 THEN 360
340 PRINT ABS(N);"/";ABS(D1)
350 GOTO 390
360 PRINT "-";ABS(N);"/";ABS(D1)
370 GOTO 390
380 PRINT N * D1
390 PRINT
400 PRINT "ANY MORE FRACTIONS (1=YES, 0=NO)";
410 INPUT Z
420 IF Z = 1 THEN 120
430 END
```

Adding Fractions **379**

Output: RUN

```
FOR THE FRACTIONS A/B AND C/D, WHAT
ARE A, B, C, AND D (NONE 0)? 1,2,1,4
( 1 / 2 ) + ( 1 / 4 ) = 3 / 4

ANY MORE FRACTIONS (1=YES, 0=NO)? 1
? 7,-8,-5,9
( 7 /-8 ) + (-5 / 9 ) = - 103 / 72

ANY MORE FRACTIONS (1=YES, 0=NO)? 0
READY
```

Analysis

Statements 130–150: This is the bad data trap.

Statements 160–170: N and D1 are the numerator and denominator, respectively, for the sum. However, N/D1 must be reduced to lowest terms.

Statements 190–300: This section determines the greatest common factor (GCF) of N and D1. First (statements 190–200), the ABS (absolute value) function serves to make sure that, if either N or D1 is negative, the corresponding positive value (N1 or D2) is used when determining the GCF. Then (statements 210–240), S is set equal to the smaller of N1 and D2. In this way, the loop (statements 250–280) that finds the GCF can start at S and go backwards to 1. For each value of Y in this range, the INT function is used (statements 260–270) to decide whether Y is a factor of both N1 and D2. When such a Y value is found (and notice that, if all larger values fail, 1 will work), the computer jumps to statements 290 and 300, which reduce N/D1 to lowest terms by dividing each value by Y.

Statements 310–380: These steps print the sum in as "neat" a way as possible. Statements 320 and 380 handle cases where D1 is 1 or −1 so that, for example, 8 is not printed as 8 / 1 and −7 is not printed as 7 / -1. Statements 330 and 360 take care of negative sums so that, for instance, -3 / 4 is printed instead of 3 / -4.

EXERCISES

A   Rewrite the program on page 379 so that it does each of the following.

1. Subtract C/D from A/B.   2. Multiply A/B and C/D.   3. Divide A/B by C/D.

B   Write a BASIC program for each problem.   See the Solution Key.

4. Determine whether $\frac{a}{b}$ equals $\frac{c}{d}$. For example, $\frac{2}{4} = \frac{1}{2}$ but $\frac{2}{5} \neq \frac{1}{2}$.

5. Given two positive integers a and b, print the least common multiple (LCM) of a and b.

380   *Computer Applications*

Additional Answers
For Ex. 1–3 rewrite the indicated statements in the program on page 379.
1. 160 LET N = A·D − B·C
2. 160 LET N = A·C
170 LET D1 = B·D
3. 160 LET N = A·D
170 LET D1 = B·C

Review

Multiply. Write each product in simplest form. *(Section 10-4)*

1. $\dfrac{ah}{4x} \cdot \dfrac{x}{h}$ $\dfrac{a}{4}$

2. $(x + 1) \cdot \dfrac{x - 3}{x - 1}$

3. $\dfrac{x^2 - 3x - 10}{x^2 - 2x} \cdot \dfrac{x^2 - 3x + 2}{x^2 - 25}$

Divide. Write each answer in simplest form. *(Section 10-5)*

4. $\dfrac{x}{3} \div \dfrac{x}{a}$ $\dfrac{a}{3}$

5. $\dfrac{4ab}{x} \div \dfrac{8a^2}{x^2}$ $\dfrac{bx}{2a}$

6. $\dfrac{a^2 - 2a - 3}{a^2 + a - 2} \div \dfrac{a - 3}{2a^2 + 2a - 4}$ $2a + 2$

Find the LCD of the rational expressions having the given denominators. *(Section 10-6)*

7. $3; 11$ 33

8. $2ab^2; 4a^2$ $4a^2b^2$

9. $(x^2 - 2x - 8); (x^2 - 3x - 4)$ $(x - 4)(x + 1)(x + 2)$

Add or subtract as indicated. Write each answer in simplest form. *(Section 10-7)*

10. $\dfrac{2a + 4}{a + b} + \dfrac{3a - 5}{a + b}$ $\dfrac{5a - 1}{a + b}$

11. $\dfrac{3}{xy^2} + \dfrac{2}{x^2y}$ $\dfrac{3x + 2y}{x^2y^2}$

12. $\dfrac{x}{x^2 - 4} + \dfrac{1}{x^2 + 2x}$

(Section 10-8)

13. $2 + \dfrac{1}{x}$ $\dfrac{2x + 1}{x}$

14. $y - \dfrac{1}{2y}$ $\dfrac{2y^2 - 1}{2y}$

15. $(a + b) - \dfrac{2ab}{a + b}$

16. $\dfrac{1}{x - 1} - (x - 1)$

Divide the first polynomial by the second. *(Section 10-9)*

17. $x^2 - x - 6; x + 2$ $x - 3$

18. $9b^2 - 16; 3b - 4$ $3b + 4$

19. $x^2 + 13x + 36; x + 9$ $x + 4$

20. $16y^2 - 6y - 1; 2y - 1$ $8y + 1$

Chapter Summary

IMPORTANT TERMS

Extremes (p. 351)
Least common denominator, or LCD (p. 368)
Means (p. 351)
Mixed expression (p. 374)

Mixed number (p. 374)
Proportion (p. 350)
Ratio (p. 350)
Rational expression (p. 357)
Simplest form (p. 357)

IMPORTANT IDEAS

1. Multiplication Property of Proportions In a proportion, the product of the means equals the product of the extremes. That is,

$$\text{if } ad = bc, \text{ then } \frac{a}{b} = \frac{c}{d} \ (b \neq 0, d \neq 0).$$

Also,

$$\text{if } ad = bc, \text{ then } \frac{a}{b} = \frac{c}{d} \ (b \neq 0, d \neq 0).$$

Rational Expressions   **381**

Quiz Sections 10-4–10-9
After completing this Review you may want to administer a quiz covering the same sections. See page M-52 of the Teacher's Manual for the suggested quiz.

Additional Answers

2. $\dfrac{x^2 - 2x - 3}{x - 1}$

3. $\dfrac{x^2 + x - 2}{x^2 + 5x}$

12. $\dfrac{x - 1}{x(x - 2)}$, or $\dfrac{x - 1}{x^2 - 2x}$

15. $\dfrac{a^2 - 2ab - b^2}{a + b}$

16. $\dfrac{-x^2 + 2x}{x - 1}$

2. **Product of Rational Expressions Theorem** If $\dfrac{P}{Q}$ and $\dfrac{R}{S}$ are rational expressions, then

$$\frac{P}{Q} \cdot \frac{R}{S} = \frac{P \cdot R}{Q \cdot S}.$$

3. **Division of Rational Expressions Theorem** To divide a rational expression $\dfrac{P}{Q}$ by a rational expression $\dfrac{R}{S}$, multiply $\dfrac{P}{Q}$ by the multiplicative inverse, or reciprocal, of $\dfrac{R}{S}$. That is, for $R \neq 0$,

$$\frac{P}{Q} \div \frac{R}{S} = \frac{P}{Q} \cdot \frac{S}{R}.$$

4. **Steps for finding the LCD of rational expressions**
   [1] Express each denominator as a product of prime factors.
   [2] Write a product using each prime factor only once.
   [3] For each factor, write the greatest exponent used in any prime factorization.
   [4] Simplify where necessary. The result is the LCD.

5. **Addition and Subtraction of Rational Expressions Theorem**
   If $\dfrac{P}{Q}$ and $\dfrac{R}{Q}$ are rational expressions, then

$$\frac{P}{Q} + \frac{R}{Q} = \frac{P + R}{Q} \quad \text{and} \quad \frac{P}{Q} - \frac{R}{Q} = \frac{P - R}{Q}.$$

6. **Steps for Adding or Subtracting Rational Expressions**
   [1] Find the LCD of the denominators.
   [2] Write equivalent rational expressions having the LCD as denominators.
   [3] Add or subtract as indicated.
   [4] Write the answer in simplest form.

_____ Chapter Objectives and Review _____

Objective: *To solve proportions (Section 10–1)*

Solve each proportion.

1. $\dfrac{35}{84} = \dfrac{21}{x}$ $50\frac{2}{5}$

2. $\dfrac{17}{1.5} = \dfrac{y}{1.8}$ 20.4

3. $\dfrac{1}{b-3} = \dfrac{2}{b+6}$ 12

4. $n = \dfrac{n+8}{-3}$ -2

5. In a mixture of green paint, the ratio of blue paint to yellow paint is 4:3. How many gallons of blue paint should be mixed with 2 gallons of yellow paint to produce this shade of green? $2\frac{2}{3}$

6. Two candidates, Alio and Benton, ran for mayor. The voters elected Alio by a ratio of 5 to 3. A total of 2480 votes were cast. How many votes did each receive? Alio: 1550; Benton: 930

Objective: *To solve investment problems and mixture problems (Section 10-2)*

7. Enrico invested one third of his savings at 9% per year and the rest at 11% per year. The total yearly interest was $496. In all, how much money did he invest? $4800

8. Carol invested the same amount of money at 12% yearly interest and at 10%. She received a total of $330 in interest for the year. How much money did she invest at each rate? $1500

9. How many grams of salt must be added to 400 grams of a 15% salt solution to obtain a 20% salt solution? 25

10. How many kilograms of a 10% copper alloy must be melted with 20 kilograms of a 20% copper alloy to obtain an 18% copper alloy? 5

Objective: *To simplify rational expressions (Section 10-3)*

Simplify.

11. $\dfrac{39}{65}$ $\dfrac{3}{5}$

12. $\dfrac{12ab}{30b^2}$ $\dfrac{2a}{5b}$

13. $\dfrac{3(x+y)}{9(x-y)}$ $\dfrac{x+y}{3(x-y)}$

14. $\dfrac{6(c+2d)^2}{8(c+2d)}$

15. $\dfrac{5x}{5x+10}$ $\dfrac{x}{x+2}$

16. $\dfrac{2a-4b}{6a+4b}$ $\dfrac{a-2b}{3a+2b}$

17. $\dfrac{4x^2-16y^2}{8y^2-2x^2}$ -2

18. $\dfrac{6a^2-15ab+9b^2}{3b^2-4ab+a^2}$

Objective: *To multiply rational expressions (Section 10-4)*

Multiply. Write each product in simplest form.

19. $\dfrac{x^2}{2a}\cdot\dfrac{a}{x}$ $\dfrac{x}{2}$

20. $(2x+1)\cdot\dfrac{x+5}{6x+3}$ $\dfrac{x+5}{3}$

21. $\dfrac{3a+3}{4a-4}\cdot\dfrac{a-1}{a+1}$ $\dfrac{3}{4}$

22. $\dfrac{4x}{x^2-y^2}\cdot\dfrac{x-y}{2x^2+2xy}$ $\dfrac{2}{(x+y)^2}$

23. $\dfrac{2x}{x+2}\cdot\dfrac{x^2+5x+6}{2x+2}$

24. $\dfrac{3a+b}{a^2-b^2}\cdot\dfrac{a-b}{3a^2+4ab+b^2}$

Objective: *To divide rational expressions (Section 10-5)*

Divide. Write each answer in simplest form.

25. $\dfrac{3}{a}\div\dfrac{6}{b}$ $\dfrac{b}{2a}$

26. $\dfrac{ax}{by}\div\dfrac{x}{y}$ $\dfrac{a}{b}$

27. $\dfrac{6a^2b}{5c}\div\dfrac{3ac}{5b}$ $\dfrac{2ab^2}{c^2}$

28. $\dfrac{(5xy)^2}{12z}\div\dfrac{10x}{9z^3}$ $\dfrac{15xy^2z^2}{8}$

29. $\dfrac{x^2+xy}{a^2-b^2}\div\dfrac{x+y}{(a-b)^2}$

30. $(x^2-a^2)\div\dfrac{ax-a^2}{x+a}$

Objective: *To find the LCD of rational expressions (Section 10-6)*

Find the LCD of rational expressions having the given denominators.

31. $7; 9$ 63

32. $4; 10$ 20

33. $3x^2y^2; 9xy^2$ $9x^2y^2$

34. $(x+3); (x-3)$

35. $(a^2-b^2); (a+b)$ a^2-b^2

36. $(y^2+2y+1); (y^2-y-2)$

Objective: *To add and subtract rational expressions (Section 10-7)*

Add or subtract as indicated. Write each answer in simplest form.

37. $\dfrac{3x+5}{x+2}-\dfrac{2x+3}{x+2}$ 1

38. $\dfrac{a-1}{6}+\dfrac{a+1}{9}$ $\dfrac{5a-1}{18}$

39. $\dfrac{a+b}{ab}-\dfrac{3}{2a}$ $\dfrac{2a-b}{2ab}$

Rational Expressions **383**

42. $\dfrac{x-4}{x-2}$

45. $\dfrac{a^2+b^2}{a^2-b^2}$

51. $\dfrac{x^2+2x-3}{x+2}$

53. $\dfrac{a^2}{a-1}$

Add or subtract as indicated. Write each answer in simplest form.

40. $\dfrac{1-3y}{3xy}-\dfrac{2x-1}{6x^2y}$ $\dfrac{-6xy+1}{6x^2y}$ **41.** $\dfrac{2}{a+3}-\dfrac{1}{a-1}$ $\dfrac{a-5}{a^2+2a-3}$ **42.** $\dfrac{x}{x+2}-\dfrac{8}{x^2-4}$

43. $\dfrac{x-y}{3x+3y}-\dfrac{x-y}{2x+2y}$ $\dfrac{-x+y}{6x+6y}$ **44.** $\dfrac{x+1}{2xy}-\dfrac{2y-1}{4y^2}$ $\dfrac{2y+x}{4xy^2}$ **45.** $\dfrac{2ab}{a^2-b^2}+\dfrac{a-b}{a+b}$

Objective: *To add or subtract a polynomial and a rational expression (Section 10-8)*

Add or subtract as indicated. Write each answer in simplest form.

46. $3+\dfrac{x}{y}$ $\dfrac{3y+x}{y}$ **47.** $b+\dfrac{3}{2b}$ $\dfrac{2b^2+3}{2b}$ **48.** $x-\dfrac{2y}{3x}$ $\dfrac{3x^2-2y}{3x}$ **49.** $\dfrac{3}{x}+2x$ $\dfrac{3+2x^2}{x}$

50. $a-\dfrac{ab}{a+b}$ $\dfrac{a^2}{a+b}$ **51.** $x-\dfrac{3}{x+2}$ **52.** $1+\dfrac{2x+1}{x-1}$ $\dfrac{3x}{x-1}$ **53.** $(a+1)+\dfrac{1}{a-1}$

Objective: *To divide one polynomial by another (Section 10-9)*

Divide the first polynomial by the second.

54. $x^2+x-6;\ x+3$ $x-2$ **55.** $a^2-6a+9;\ a-3$ $a-3$

56. $4y^2-25;\ 2y-5$ $2y+5$ **57.** $4x^2-5x-6;\ 4x+3$ $x-2$

58. $b^3+4b+5;\ b+1$ b^2-b+5 **59.** $2n^3+3n^2+3n+1;\ 2n+1$ n^2+n+1

60. $y^3+3y^2+16;\ y+4$ y^2-y+4 **61.** $4a^3-4a^2-15a+1;\ 2a-3$
                                              $2a^2+a-6+\dfrac{-17}{2a-3}$

Chapter Test

A formal Chapter Test is provided in the Teacher's Manual. See p. M-73.

Solve each proportion.

1. $\dfrac{17}{26}=\dfrac{x}{78}$ 51 **2.** $\dfrac{2.5}{1}=\dfrac{0.5}{n}$ 0.2 **3.** $\dfrac{15-n}{2}=\dfrac{15+n}{3}$ 3

Perform the indicated operations. Express answers in simplest form.

4. $\dfrac{4x^2}{3y}\div\dfrac{x}{y}$ $\dfrac{4x}{3}$ **5.** $3-\dfrac{2}{a}$ $\dfrac{3a-2}{a}$ **6.** $\dfrac{9x^2}{4}\cdot\dfrac{2}{15x}$ $\dfrac{3x}{10}$ **7.** $\dfrac{3b^3}{4}\div\dfrac{26}{8}$ $\dfrac{3b^3}{13}$

8. $\dfrac{a^2+ab}{a^2-b^2}\cdot\dfrac{a-b}{a+ab}$ $\dfrac{1}{a+b}$ **9.** $\dfrac{2x+3y}{x-y}+\dfrac{x-6y}{x-y}$ 3 **10.** $\dfrac{x^2-y^2}{3xy}\div\dfrac{x^2-2xy+y^2}{6x}$

11. $\dfrac{c-d}{cd}+\dfrac{c+d}{c^2}$ $\dfrac{c^2+d^2}{c^2d}$ **12.** $\dfrac{3}{2x+2y}-\dfrac{x}{x^2-y^2}$ **13.** $\dfrac{x^2-9}{x^2+2x}\cdot\dfrac{x+2}{x^2+6x+9}$

14. $\dfrac{3}{a+1}+1$ $\dfrac{a+4}{a+1}$ **15.** $\dfrac{y^2-3y+2}{2y+2}\cdot\dfrac{y+1}{y-1}$ $\dfrac{y-2}{2}$ **16.** $\dfrac{a+1}{4a^2}-\dfrac{1-a}{2a}$ $\dfrac{2a^2-a+1}{4a^2}$

17. Divide x^2+5x+6 by $x+3$. $x+2$ **18.** Divide y^3-7y+6 by $y-2$. y^2+2y-3

19. A machine can fill 96 bottles of milk in one minute. At this rate, how many bottles can it fill in 60 minutes? 5760

20. How many kilograms of pure lead must be melted with 40 kilograms of a 10% lead alloy in order to make a 20% alloy? 5

───── More Challenging Problems ─────

Perform the indicated operations.

$a^4 + 3a^3 + 9a^2 + 27a + 81$

1. $(a^{n+1} + 5)(a^{n-1} + 5)$ $\quad a^{2n} + 5a^{n+1} + 5a^{n-1} + 25$ **2.** $(a^5 - 243) \div (a - 3)$

3. $(a^{\frac{n}{2}} + b^{\frac{n}{2}} + c^{\frac{n}{2}})^2$ **4.** $(c - 5)^3 - (c + 5)^2$

5. $(x - y)(x^{n-1} + x^{n-2}y + x^{n-3}y^2 + \cdots + x^2y^{n-3} + xy^{n-2} + y^{n-1})$ $\quad x^n - y^n$

Factor each polynomial. **6.** $(c + d - 3x + y)(c + d + 3x - y)$

6. $(c^2 + 2cd + d^2) - (9x^2 - 6xy + y^2)$ **7.** $(x^2 + 6x + 9) - (y - 1)^2$

8. $x^2(2x - 3) - 2x(2x - 3) + (2x - 3)$ **9.** $4a^2 + 4ab + b^2 - 9c^2 + 12cd - 4d^2$
$\quad (2a + b - 3c + 2d)(2a + b + 3c - 2d)$

Perform the indicated operations and simplify.

10. $\dfrac{x + y + \frac{y^2}{x}}{x + y + \frac{x^2}{y}}$ $\quad \dfrac{y}{x}$ **11.** $\dfrac{x + \frac{y^3}{x^2}}{\frac{y^2}{x^2} - \frac{y}{x} + 1}$ $\quad x + y$ **12.** $\dfrac{\frac{x^2}{y^2} - 1}{\frac{x^2}{y^2} + \frac{2x}{y} + 1}$ $\quad \dfrac{x - y}{x + y}$

13. $\dfrac{\frac{1 - 4x^2}{(2x + y)^2}\left[1 + \frac{y + 1}{2x - 1}\right]}{\frac{1}{2x + y} - \frac{1}{2x - y} + \frac{1}{4x^2 - y^2}}$

14. $\dfrac{x - 6 + \frac{4}{x - 2}}{\left(\frac{1}{x + 2} - \frac{x}{7x - 4}\right)\left(x - \frac{x + 8}{x - 1}\right)} - \dfrac{7x - 4}{x - 2}$

Additional Practice

You may wish to use all or some of these exercises, depending on how well students performed on the formal chapter test.

Skills

Solve each proportion. *(Section 10-1)*

1. $\dfrac{14}{91} = \dfrac{63}{x}$ $\quad 409\frac{1}{2}$ **2.** $\dfrac{5}{n} = \dfrac{4}{n - 1}$ $\quad 5$ **3.** $\dfrac{10}{y + 3} = \dfrac{4}{y - 1}$ $\quad 3\frac{2}{3}$

Simplify. No denominator equals zero. *(Section 10-3)*

4. $\dfrac{24a^2b}{56a}$ $\quad \dfrac{3ab}{7}$ **5.** $\dfrac{36xy}{60wx}$ $\quad \dfrac{3y}{5w}$ **6.** $\dfrac{3a + 3b}{3a^2 - 3b^2}$ $\quad \dfrac{1}{a - b}$ **7.** $\dfrac{x^2 - x - 6}{x^2 + x - 12}$

Multiply. Write each product in simplest form. *(Section 10-4)*

8. $\dfrac{x + y}{12} \cdot \dfrac{3}{x}$ $\quad \dfrac{x + y}{4x}$ **9.** $(2x - 3) \cdot \dfrac{x}{4x - 6}$ $\quad \dfrac{x}{2}$ **10.** $\dfrac{a^2 - b^2}{4a + 2b} \cdot \dfrac{2}{a - b}$

Divide. Write each answer in simplest form. *(Section 10-5)*

11. $\dfrac{18}{c} \div \dfrac{36}{c^2}$ $\quad \dfrac{c}{2}$ **12.** $\dfrac{9x^2 - 4y^2}{2x^2} \div \dfrac{3x - 2y}{8x}$ $\quad \dfrac{12x + 8y}{x}$ **13.** $\dfrac{n^2 + 2n + 1}{3n - 3} \div \dfrac{n + 1}{3}$

Rational Expressions **385**

Find the LCD of the rational expressions having the given denominators. *(Section 10–6)*

14. $8a$; $12a$ $24a$

15. $4xy^2$; $16x^2y$ $16x^2y^2$

16. $x^2 - 1$; $2x^2 + 2x$

Add or subtract as indicated. Write each answer in simplest form. *(Section 10–7)*

17. $\dfrac{3a + b}{a + b} - \dfrac{a - b}{a + b}$ 2

18. $\dfrac{x + 1}{6x} + \dfrac{4x}{8x^2}$ $\dfrac{x + 4}{6x}$

19. $\dfrac{x}{x^2 - x - 6} - \dfrac{1}{x^2 - 3x}$

(Section 10–8)

20. $3 + \dfrac{1}{2a}$ $\dfrac{6a + 1}{2a}$

21. $x - \dfrac{1}{x + 1}$ $\dfrac{x^2 + x - 1}{x + 1}$

22. $\dfrac{2}{y + 3} - (y - 3)$

Divide the first polynomial by the second. *(Section 10–9)*

23. $x^2 - 8x + 15$; $x - 3$ $x - 5$

24. $y^3 - 3y^2 - 4y$; $y + 1$ $y^2 - 4y$

25. $4a^2 - 25$; $2a - 5$ $2a + 5$

26. $n^3 - 8$; $n - 2$ $n^2 + 2n + 4$

27. $8y^3 - 12y + 5$; $2y - 1$ $4y^2 + 2y - 5$

28. $8a^3 + b^3$; $2a + b$ $4a^2 - 2ab + b^2$

29. $2x^3 - 9x^2 + 11x - 3$; $2x - 3$ $x^2 - 3x + 1$

30. $12b^2 - 11bc - 36c^2$; $4b - 9c$ $3b + 4c$

Applications

31. A vertical meter stick casts a shadow 1.6 meters long at the same time that a flagpole casts a 10.4-meter shadow. How tall is the flagpole?   6.5 m *(Section 10–1)*

32. A recipe for a casserole that serves 6 people calls for $2\frac{1}{2}$ cups of milk. How many cups of milk are necessary if the recipe is to serve 10 people? $4\frac{1}{6}$ cups *(Section 10–1)*

33. A truck travels 80 kilometers in 2 hours. How far will it travel in 5 hours at the same rate? *(Section 10–1)*   200 km

34. On a map, 2.5 centimeters represent 50 kilometers. How many centimeters represent 75 kilometers? *(Section 10–1)*

35. How many liters of concentrated plant food must be added to 11 liters of an 8% solution of the concentrate in order to obtain a 12% solution?   0.5 liter *(Section 10–2)*

36. How many milliliters of an 18%-ammonia solution must be added to 20 milliliters of a 12% ammonia solution to make a 15% solution? *(Section 10–2)*   20 mL

37. A 150-gram solution is 6% salt and 94% water. How many grams of water must be evaporated to obtain a solution that is 14% salt? *(Section 10–2)* $85\frac{5}{7}$ grams

38. Earl invested \$10,000, part at 12% per year and part at 14% per year. He wants to earn at least \$1310 on the investments in a year. How much should he invest at each rate? *(Section 10–2)*

39. Juanita invested \$12,000, part at 8% per year and the rest at 12% per year. The total yearly interest was \$1120. How much did she invest at each rate? *(Section 10–2)*   8%: \$8000; 12%: \$4000

40. Julian invested an amount of money at 9% per year and three times as much at 11% per year. The total yearly interest was \$168. How much did he invest at each rate? *(Section 10–2)*   9%: \$400; 11%: \$1200

CHAPTER **11** Applications of Rational Expressions

Teaching Suggestions p. M-24

11–1 Equations with Rational Expressions

Quick Quiz

Solve and check.

1. $6a + 3a = 10$

   Ans: $\{\frac{10}{9}\}$

2. $8(x - 3) - 4(x - 1) = 0$

   Ans: $\{5\}$

3. $x^2 - 7x + 6 = 0$

   Ans: $\{1, 6\}$

4. $x^2 - 8x - 9 = 0$

   Ans: $\{-1, 9\}$

5. $x^2 + 8x + 15 = 0$

   Ans: $\{-5, -3\}$

Additional Examples
Example 1

Solve and check.

1. $\frac{n}{5} + \frac{n}{3} = 1$

   Ans: $\{\frac{15}{8}\}$

2. $\frac{a}{6} - \frac{a}{3} = 2$

   Ans: $\{-12\}$

To solve equations containing rational expressions, follow these steps.

Procedure

> **Steps for Solving Equations with Rational Expressions**
>
> 1. Multiply **each side** of the equation by the LCD.
>
> 2. Follow the usual procedures to solve the resulting equation.

EXAMPLE 1   Solve: $\dfrac{n}{3} + \dfrac{n}{2} = 1$

Solution:

$$\frac{n}{3} + \frac{n}{2} = 1 \quad \longleftarrow \quad \begin{array}{l}\textbf{The LCD is 6.}\\ \textbf{Multiply each side by 6.}\end{array}$$

$$6\left(\frac{n}{3} + \frac{n}{2}\right) = 6(1)$$

$$6 \cdot \frac{n}{3} + 6 \cdot \frac{n}{2} = 6 \cdot 1 \quad \longleftarrow \quad \textbf{By the distributive postulate}$$

$$2n + 3n = 6 \quad \longleftarrow \quad \textbf{Solve for \textit{n}.}$$

$$5n = 6$$

$$n = \frac{6}{5}$$

Check: $\dfrac{n}{3} + \dfrac{n}{2} = 1$

$$\frac{\frac{6}{5}}{3} + \frac{\frac{6}{5}}{2} \stackrel{?}{=} 1$$

$$\frac{\frac{6}{5}}{3} = \frac{6}{5} \div 3 = \frac{6}{5} \cdot \frac{1}{3} \quad \text{and} \quad \frac{\frac{6}{5}}{2} = \frac{6}{5} \div 2 = \frac{6}{5} \cdot \frac{1}{2}.$$

$$\frac{6}{15} + \frac{6}{10} \stackrel{?}{=} 1$$

$$\frac{2}{5} + \frac{3}{5} \stackrel{?}{=} 1$$

$$1 \stackrel{?}{=} 1 \quad \text{Yes} \quad \text{✔} \qquad \text{Solution set: } \left\{\frac{6}{5}\right\}$$

REMEMBER: Multiply each side of an equation containing rational expressions by the LCD.

The equation in Example 2 contains rational expressions that have a variable in the denominator. Recall that values of the variable that could make a denominator equal zero must be excluded. Thus, in Example 2, x cannot equal 2 or 4.

EXAMPLE 2 Solve: $\dfrac{7}{x-4} - \dfrac{5}{x-2} = 0$

Solution: $\dfrac{7}{x-4} - \dfrac{5}{x-2} = 0$ ◀——— **The LCD is $(x-4)(x-2)$, $x \ne 4$, $x \ne 2$. Multiply each side by $(x-4)(x-2)$.**

$$(x-4)(x-2)\left(\dfrac{7}{x-4} - \dfrac{5}{x-2}\right) = (x-4)(x-2)(0)$$

$$7(x-2) - 5(x-4) = 0 \quad ◀\text{——— } \textbf{Simplify.}$$

$$7x - 14 - 5x + 20 = 0$$

$$2x + 6 = 0$$

$$2x = -6$$

$$x = -3 \quad ◀\text{——— } \textbf{Remember: } x \ne 2 \textbf{ and } x \ne 4$$

Check: $\dfrac{7}{x-4} - \dfrac{5}{x-2} = 0$ ◀——— **Replace x with -3.**

$$\dfrac{7}{-3-4} - \dfrac{5}{-3-2} \overset{?}{=} 0$$

$$\dfrac{7}{-7} - \dfrac{5}{-5} \overset{?}{=} 0 \quad ◀\text{——— } -\left(\dfrac{5}{-5}\right) = -(-1) = 1$$

$$-1 + 1 \overset{?}{=} 0 \quad \text{Yes} \; ✔ \quad \textbf{Solution set: } \{-3\}$$

Sometimes the number obtained as a solution to an equation does not check in the original equation. The number is only an **apparent solution** (not a solution at all). This is why it is important to check.

EXAMPLE 3 Solve: $\dfrac{x}{10} + \dfrac{1}{x-1} = \dfrac{x+1}{2x-2}$

Solution:

$$\dfrac{x}{10} + \dfrac{1}{x-1} = \dfrac{x+1}{2x-2} \quad ◀\text{——— } \textbf{Factor } 2x - 2.$$

$$\dfrac{x}{10} + \dfrac{1}{x-1} = \dfrac{x+1}{2(x-1)} \quad ◀\text{——— } \textbf{LCD: } 10(x-1), \; x \ne 1$$

$$10(x-1)\left(\dfrac{x}{10} + \dfrac{1}{x-1}\right) = [10(x-1)]\left[\dfrac{x+1}{2(x-1)}\right]$$

$$10(x-1)\left(\dfrac{x}{10}\right) + 10(x-1)\left(\dfrac{1}{x-1}\right) = 5(x+1)$$

$$(x-1)x + 10 = 5(x+1)$$

$$x^2 - x + 10 = 5x + 5 \quad ◀\text{——— } \textbf{Write in the form } x^2 + bx + c = 0.$$

$$x^2 - 6x + 5 = 0 \quad ◀\text{——— } \textbf{Factor } x^2 - 6x + 5.$$

$$(x-5)(x-1) = 0$$

$$x - 5 = 0 \quad \underline{\text{or}} \quad x - 1 = 0$$

$$x = 5 \quad \underline{\text{or}} \quad x = 1 \quad ◀\text{——— } \textbf{Remember: } x \ne 1$$

Applications of Rational Expressions **389**

Note what happens when you check both solutions.

Check: $\dfrac{x}{10} + \dfrac{1}{x-1} = \dfrac{x+1}{2x-2}$ ⟵ **Replace x with 5.**

$\dfrac{5}{10} + \dfrac{1}{4} \overset{?}{=} \dfrac{6}{8}$

$\dfrac{1}{2} + \dfrac{1}{4} \overset{?}{=} \dfrac{3}{4}$

$\dfrac{3}{4} \overset{?}{=} \dfrac{3}{4}$ Yes ✔   **Solution set: {5}**

$\dfrac{x}{10} + \dfrac{1}{x-1} = \dfrac{x+1}{2x-2}$ ⟵ **Replace x with 1.**

$\dfrac{1}{10} + \dfrac{1}{0} \overset{?}{=} \dfrac{2}{0}$

Since division by 0 is not defined, 1 is not a solution.

CLASSROOM EXERCISES

Solve each equation.

1. $\dfrac{2x}{3} - \dfrac{x}{2} = 2$ $x = 12$

2. $\dfrac{6p}{7} - \dfrac{p}{2} = 5$ $p = 14$

3. $\dfrac{2}{x} + \dfrac{3}{x} = 5$ $x = 1$

4. $\dfrac{3}{2a} - \dfrac{1}{4} = \dfrac{7}{8a}$ $a = 2\frac{1}{2}$

5. $\dfrac{6}{y-2} = \dfrac{3}{2}$ $y = 6$

6. $\dfrac{3}{n+2} = \dfrac{5}{n-1}$ $n = -6\frac{1}{2}$

7. $\dfrac{2}{x+3} = \dfrac{4}{x+1}$ $x = -5$

8. $\dfrac{x-4}{7} + \dfrac{2}{x-2} = 1$ $x = 4$ or $x = 9$

9. $\dfrac{1}{a} - \dfrac{2a}{a+1} = 0$ $a = -\frac{1}{2}$ or $a = 1$

WRITTEN EXERCISES

A   Solve each equation.

1. $\dfrac{a}{3} - \dfrac{a}{4} = 2$ $a = 24$

2. $\dfrac{b}{4} - \dfrac{b}{5} = 2$ $b = 40$

3. $\dfrac{3a}{5} + \dfrac{3}{2} = \dfrac{7a}{10}$ $a = 15$

4. $\dfrac{4d}{7} + \dfrac{5}{4} = \dfrac{17d}{28}$ $d = 35$

5. $\dfrac{3t}{4} + \dfrac{5}{3} = \dfrac{7t}{6}$ $t = 4$

6. $\dfrac{3m}{2} + \dfrac{5}{3} = \dfrac{7m}{6}$ $m = -5$

7. $\dfrac{2}{x} = 3$ $x = \frac{2}{3}$

8. $\dfrac{3}{a} = -4$ $a = -\frac{3}{4}$

9. $\dfrac{2}{3x} = \dfrac{1}{9}$ $x = 6$

10. $\dfrac{3}{2x} - \dfrac{1}{3} = \dfrac{5}{6x}$ $x = 2$

11. $\dfrac{5}{6x} + 3 = \dfrac{1}{2x}$ $x = -\frac{1}{9}$

12. $\dfrac{3}{10x} - \dfrac{3}{5} = \dfrac{2}{5x}$ $x = -\frac{1}{6}$

13. $\dfrac{5}{n} - \dfrac{1}{2} = 2$ $n = 2$

14. $\dfrac{4}{x} + \dfrac{3}{2x} = \dfrac{11}{6}$ $x = 3$

15. $\dfrac{2n+1}{2n} - \dfrac{3n-2}{3n} = \dfrac{7}{12}$ $n = 2$

16. $\dfrac{4}{2x} - 3 = \dfrac{-2}{5x} - \dfrac{3}{5}$ $x = 1$

17. $\dfrac{4}{3x} - \dfrac{5}{2x} = 5 - \dfrac{1}{6x}$ $x = -\frac{1}{5}$

18. $\dfrac{7}{4x} - 2 = \dfrac{3}{2x} - 4$ $x = -\frac{1}{8}$

19. $\dfrac{3}{2} = \dfrac{x}{x+2}$ $x = -6$

20. $\dfrac{b-2}{b+3} = \dfrac{3}{8}$ $b = 5$

21. $\dfrac{x-7}{x+2} = \dfrac{1}{4}$ $x = 10$

22. $\dfrac{5}{a+3} = \dfrac{2}{2}$ $a = 2$

23. $\dfrac{a-1}{a-2} = 1.5$ $a = 4$

24. $\dfrac{y}{y-3} = \dfrac{6}{3}$ $y = 6$

25. $\dfrac{2}{x+3} = \dfrac{5}{x}$ $x = -5$

26. $\dfrac{t+1}{t-1} = \dfrac{2}{t-1} + \dfrac{t}{8}$ $t = 8$

27. $\dfrac{b}{6} + \dfrac{1}{b-1} = \dfrac{b+1}{2b-2}$ $b = 3$

28. $\dfrac{x}{3} + \dfrac{2x^2}{3x-4} = \dfrac{9x-2}{9}$ 29. $\dfrac{2x-1}{2} - \dfrac{x+2}{2x+5} = \dfrac{6x-5}{6}$ 30. $\dfrac{7}{x-4} = \dfrac{5}{x-2}$

31. $\dfrac{10}{x-3} = \dfrac{9}{x-5}$ $x=23$ 32. $\dfrac{x+5}{x-3} + \dfrac{4}{x-3} = 5$ $x=6$ 33. $\dfrac{x+2}{x+4} = \dfrac{x+6}{x-8}$ $x=-2\tfrac{1}{2}$

34. $\dfrac{x-1}{x+1} = \dfrac{x+3}{x+10}$ $x=2\tfrac{3}{5}$ 35. $\dfrac{x-3}{x+5} = \dfrac{x-2}{x+2}$ $x=1$ 36. $\dfrac{x}{x-3} + \dfrac{2}{x+4} = 1$

37. $\dfrac{3x}{x-2} - 3 = \dfrac{4}{x+2}$ $x=-10$ 38. $\dfrac{2x}{x-4} - \dfrac{4}{x+5} = 2$ $x=-14$ 39. $\dfrac{5x}{x+1} - \dfrac{x}{x+6} = 4$

40. $\dfrac{x-1}{x+1} - \dfrac{2x}{x-1} = -1$ 41. $\dfrac{6}{4x} = \dfrac{x+2}{x^2-3x}$ $x=13$ 42. $6 + \dfrac{20}{x^2-1} = \dfrac{10}{x-1}$

43. $\dfrac{3}{3x^2-3x-28} = \dfrac{5}{5x^2-x-20}$ $x=-6\tfrac{2}{3}$ 44. $\dfrac{2x+1}{x-1} - \dfrac{3x}{x+2} = \dfrac{-x^2-2}{x^2+x-2}$ $x=-\tfrac{1}{2}$

45. $\dfrac{a}{a-2} = \dfrac{a+3}{a+2} - \dfrac{a}{a^2-4}$ $a=-3$ 46. $\dfrac{3(x-4)}{4x^2-9} = \dfrac{3x}{4x^2-16x+15}$ $x=1\tfrac{1}{4}$

47. For what value of k will the solution set of $\dfrac{a-2}{5a} = \dfrac{1}{k} - \dfrac{4}{15a}$ be $\{4\}$? $k=6$

48. For what value of k will the solution set of $\dfrac{k}{3t} = \dfrac{t-5}{t^2-4t}$ be $\left\{\tfrac{5}{2}\right\}$? $k=5$

Puzzle

See the Solution Key.

A six-digit number is divided by a three–digit number to give a three–digit number, as shown at the right.

Find the missing digits. (There is only one solution.)

```
              xxx
        _____
   xxx ) xxxxxx
          x0xx
          ____
          xxxx
          x50x
          ____
           xxx
           x4x
```

REVIEW CAPSULE FOR SECTION 11-2

Determine the slope of the line containing the given points. *(Pages 189–193)*

1. $P(1, 3)$; $Q(4, 9)$ 2   2. $R(-2, 5)$; $T(6, -1)$ $-\tfrac{3}{4}$ 3. $N(0, 0)$; $V(-5, 0)$ 0
4. $S(-3, -2)$; $T(4, 3)\tfrac{5}{7}$ 5. $R(12, 8)$; $P(-4, -10)$ $1\tfrac{1}{8}$ 6. $H(0, -2)$; $T(-1, -3)$ 1

In Exercises 7–10:
 a. Write each equation in the form $y = mx + b$.
 b. Give the slope and y intercept of the line. *(Pages 194–196)*

7. $3x + y = 6$ 8. $y - 5x = 9$ 9. $6x - 3y = 18$ 10. $10 - 6y = 21x$

Applications of Rational Expressions   **391**

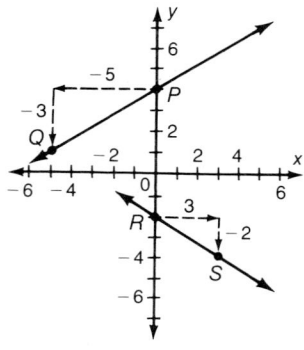
OBJECTIVE: To write the equation of a line, given its slope and the coordinates of a point on the line

11–2 Using Slope to Write a Linear Equation

When you know the slope and y intercept of a line, you can write the equation of the line. The equation will be in the form $y = mx + b$.

EXAMPLE 1 The slope of a line is 2 and its y intercept is 5. Write the equation of the line.

Solution: 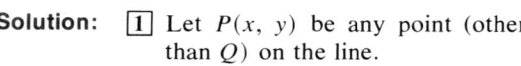 Replace m with 2 and b with 5.

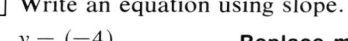

You can also determine the equation of a line when you know its slope and the coordinates of a point on the line.

EXAMPLE 2 A line with slope -3 passes through the point $Q(2, -4)$. Determine the equation of the line.

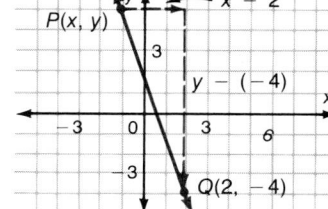

Solution: 1 Let $P(x, y)$ be any point (other than Q) on the line.

2 Write an equation using slope.

$\dfrac{y - (-4)}{x - 2} = m$ ← Replace m with -3.

$\dfrac{y + 4}{x - 2} = -3$

3 Solve the equation for y Multiply each side by the LCD $(x - 2)$.

$(x - 2)\left(\dfrac{y + 4}{x - 2}\right) = (x - 2)(-3)$ ← Remember: $x \neq 2$

$y + 4 = -3x + 6$ and $y = -3x + 2$

The equation of a line can also be determined from its graph.

EXAMPLE 3 Determine the equation of the line shown in the graph.

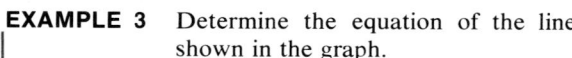

Solution: 1 Read the y intercept from the graph: $b = 3$

2 To find the slope m, choose two convenient points on the graph.

$P(0, 3); Q(3, -1)$

$m = \dfrac{-1 - 3}{3 - 0} = \dfrac{-4}{3},$ or $-\dfrac{4}{3}$

3 Write the equation as in Example 1. $y = -\dfrac{4}{3}x + 3$

CLASSROOM EXERCISES

In Exercises 1–6, a point on a line and the slope of the line are given. Write the equation of the line in the form $y = mx + b$. $y = \frac{1}{2}x + 4$

1. $P(0, 2)$; $m = 4$ $y = 4x + 2$ **2.** $Q(-1, 2)$; $m = 3$ $y = 3x + 5$ **3.** $R(4, 6)$; $m = \frac{1}{2}$

4. $A(-3, 1)$; $m = -2$ $y = -2x - 5$ **5.** $B(0, -3)$; $m = -\frac{1}{4}$ $y = -\frac{1}{4}x - 3$ **6.** $C(1, -1)$; $m = -1$

$y = -x$

WRITTEN EXERCISES

A

In Exercises 1–6, the slope and the y intercept of a line are given. Write the equation of the line in the form $y = mx + b$.

1. slope: 3; y intercept: 4 $y = 3x + 4$ **2.** slope: 2; y intercept: 1 $y = 2x + 1$

3. slope: $\frac{1}{2}$; y intercept: -3 $y = \frac{1}{2}x - 3$ **4.** slope: $\frac{2}{3}$; y intercept: -2 $y = \frac{2}{3}x - 2$

5. slope: -4; y intercept: $\frac{2}{3}$ $y = -4x + \frac{2}{3}$ **6.** slope: $-\frac{3}{8}$; y intercept: $-\frac{1}{2}$ $y = -\frac{3}{8}x - \frac{1}{2}$

In Exercises 7–15, one point on a line and the slope of the line are given. Write the equation of the line in the form $y = mx + b$.

$y = -3x + 17$

7. $D(2, 3)$; $m = 2$ $y = 2x - 1$ **8.** $G(0, 4)$; $m = 3$ $y = 3x + 4$ **9.** $P(4, 5)$; $m = -3$

10. $T(0, 0)$; $m = 1$ $y = x$ **11.** $H(-2, 1)$; $m = 1$ $y = x + 3$ **12.** $S(0, 0)$; $m = -1$

13. $N(-1, 1)$; $m = \frac{1}{2}$ $y = \frac{1}{2}x + 1\frac{1}{2}$ **14.** $Q(\frac{1}{2}, 3)$; $m = -\frac{2}{3}$ **15.** $V(-3, 4)$; $m = -\frac{1}{3}$

Determine the equation of each line from its graph.

16. 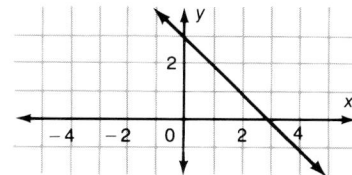 **17.**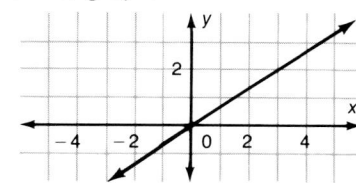

18. 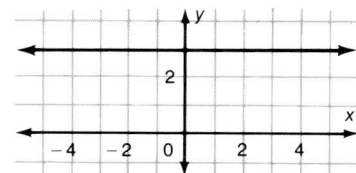 **19.**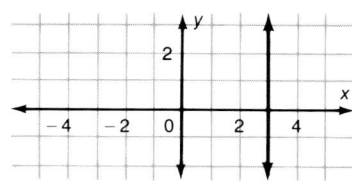

20. 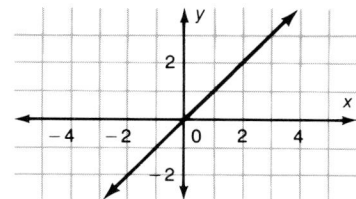 **21.**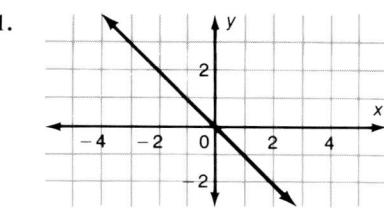

Assignment Guide
Minimal Omit
Average
pp. 393–394: 1–29 odd
Above Average
pp. 393–394: 1–37 odd

Additional Answers
Written Exercises
12. $y = -x$
14. $y = -\frac{2}{3}x + 3\frac{1}{3}$
15. $y = -\frac{1}{3}x + 3$
16. $y = -x + 3$
17. $y = \frac{2}{3}x$
18. $y = 3$
19. $x = 3$
20. $y = x$
21. $y = -x$

Applications of Rational Expressions   **393**

Determine the equation of each line from its graph.

22.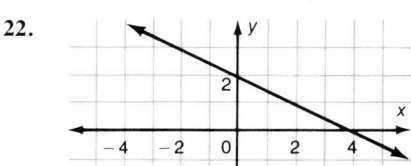

23.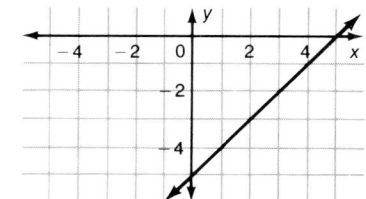

B   In Exercises 24–31, determine the equation of each line. Write the equation in the form $y = mx + b$. REMEMBER: Parallel lines have the same slope.

24. The line has -2 as its y intercept and is parallel to the line defined by the equation $3y = x - 9$. $y = \frac{1}{3}x - 2$

25. The line has 3 as its y intercept and is parallel to the line defined by the equation $3x - y + 6 = 0$. $y = 3x + 3$

26. The line passes through the point $(2, 3)$ and is parallel to the line defined by the equation $2y - 3x = 4$. $y = \frac{3}{2}x$

27. The line passes through the point $(2, 1)$ and is parallel to the line defined by the equation $2x - y = 8$. $y = 2x - 3$

28. The line has the same slope as the graph of $y + 3x = 7$ and the same y intercept as the graph of $y - 4x = 9$.
$y = -3x + 9$

29. The line has the same slope as the graph of $y + 4x = -8$ and the same y intercept as the graph of $2y - 6x = 10$.
$y = -4x + 5$

C
30. The line passes through the point $(3, 4)$ and is parallel to the x axis. $y = 4$

31. The line passes through the point $(3, 4)$ and is parallel to the y axis. $x = 3$

When two lines are perpendicular (meet at a 90°–angle), their slopes are negative reciprocals of each other.

Example: Determine the slope of a line perpendicular to $y = 2x + 9$.

Solution: Slope of $y = 2x + 9$: 2

Negative reciprocal of 2: $-\frac{1}{2}$ ⟵ $2(-\frac{1}{2}) = -1$

Slope of line perpendicular to $y = 2x + 9$: $-\frac{1}{2}$

In Exercises 32–35, write the equation of each line. Write the equation in the form $y = mx + b$.

32. The line has 4 as its y intercept and is perpendicular to the line defined by the equation $y = 2x - 3$. $y = -\frac{1}{2}x + 4$

33. The line passes through the point $(2, 3)$ and is perpendicular to the line defined by the equation $y + 4x = 5$. $y = \frac{1}{4}x + 2\frac{1}{2}$

34. The line passes through the point $(-1, 4)$ and is perpendicular to the line defined by $3y - 2x = 9$. $y = -\frac{3}{2}x + 2\frac{1}{2}$

35. The line passes through the point $(3, -2)$ and is perpendicular to the line defined by $4y + 3x = 7$. $y = \frac{4}{3}x - 6$

36. Show that the equation of a line with x intercept a and y intercept b is $\dfrac{x}{a} + \dfrac{y}{b} = 1$, $a \neq 0$, $b \neq 0$.

37. Show that the y intercept of the line with slope m and passing through a given point (x_1, y_1) is $y_1 - mx_1$.

Determine the slope of the line containing the given points. *(Pages 189–193)*

1. $P(7, 5)$; $R(-2, 4)$ $\frac{1}{9}$
2. $S(8, 6)$; $T(-3, 5)$ $\frac{1}{11}$
3. $V(9, -2)$; $S(-3, -4)$ $\frac{1}{6}$
4. $M(-7, -2)$; $Q(-5, -6)$ -2
5. $A(0, -4)$; $B(5, 5)$ $\frac{9}{5}$
6. $Q(5, 0)$; $R(0, 5)$ -1

Solve each equation for y in terms of x. *(Pages 162–164, 350–353)*

7. $\frac{y-5}{x+2} = \frac{3}{4}$ $y = \frac{3}{4}x + 6\frac{1}{2}$
8. $\frac{y-1}{x-3} = -\frac{1}{2}$
9. $\frac{y+3}{x-1} = -\frac{2}{5}$
10. $\frac{y-9}{x+3} = \frac{7}{8}$ $y = \frac{7}{8}x + 11\frac{5}{8}$
11. $\frac{y+2}{x} = -3$ $y = -3x - 2$
12. $\frac{y-2}{x+2} = -\frac{5}{6}$

OBJECTIVE: To write the equation of a line, given the coordinates of two points on the line

11–3 Using Two Points to Write a Linear Equation

When you know two points on a line, you can use these points to determine the equation of the line by expressing slope in two ways.

EXAMPLE 1 Determine the equation of the line passing through the points $Q(-3, 7)$ and $R(2, -9)$.

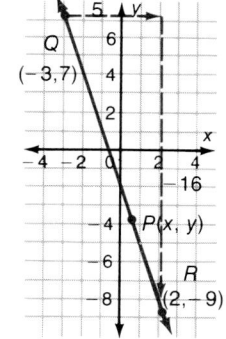

Solution:

$\boxed{1}$ Use the given points to find m.

$$m = \frac{-9 - 7}{2 - (-3)} = \frac{-16}{5}, \text{ or } -\frac{16}{5}$$

$\boxed{2}$ Let $P(x, y)$ be a third point on the line. Use the coordinates of P or Q to find m.

$$m = \frac{y - 7}{x - (-3)} = \frac{y - 7}{x + 3}$$

$\boxed{3}$ Since the slope of a line is *everywhere the same*, use the two expressions for m to write an equation.

$$\frac{y - 7}{x + 3} = -\frac{16}{5} \quad\longleftarrow\quad \text{LCD: } 5(x + 3),\ x \neq -3$$

$$5(x + 3)\left(\frac{y - 7}{x + 3}\right) = 5(x + 3)\left(-\frac{16}{5}\right)$$

$$5(y - 7) = (x + 3)(-16)$$

$$5y - 35 = -16x - 48$$

$$5y = -16x - 13$$

$$y = -\frac{16}{5}x - \frac{13}{5}$$

Additional Answers
8. $y = -\frac{1}{2}x + 2\frac{1}{2}$
9. $y = -\frac{2}{5}x - 2\frac{3}{5}$
12. $y = -\frac{5}{6}x + \frac{1}{3}$

Teaching Suggestions p. M-24

Quick Quiz
For each line described in Exercises 1–4, write the equation of the line in the form $y = mx + b$.
1. slope: -2; y intercept: 3
   Ans: $y = -2x + 3$
2. slope: $\frac{3}{4}$; y intercept: -5
   Ans: $y = \frac{3}{4}x - 5$
3. slope: -5; $P(-3, 4)$
   Ans: $y = -5x - 11$
4. slope: 4; $Q(4, -5)$
   Ans: $y = 4x - 21$
5. Determine the equation of each line from its graph.

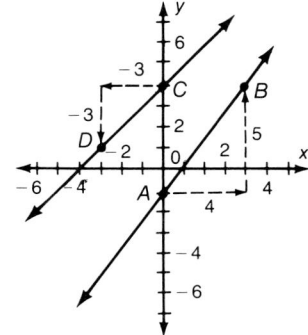

Ans: $\overleftrightarrow{AB}: y = \frac{5}{4}x - 1$
$\overleftrightarrow{CD}: y = x + 4$

Additional Examples
Example 1
Determine the equation of the line passing through the given points.
1. $M(2, 8)$; $N(-3, -4)$
   Ans: $y = \frac{12}{5}x + \frac{16}{5}$
2. $S(-3, 3)$; $T(5, -6)$
   Ans: $y = -\frac{9}{8}x - \frac{3}{8}$

Given two points on a line, you can also determine the equation of the line by finding the slope and y intercept.

EXAMPLE 2 Determine the equation of the line passing through the points $R(-3, 4)$ and $T(4, 7)$.

Solution:
$\boxed{1}$ Use the given points to find m.

$$m = \frac{7-4}{4-(-3)} = \frac{3}{7}$$

$\boxed{2}$ In $y = mx + b$, replace m with $\frac{3}{7}$.

$$y = \frac{3}{7}x + b$$

$\boxed{3}$ Since $T(4, 7)$ is on the line, replace x with 4 and y with 7.

$$7 = \frac{3}{7}(4) + b$$

$$7 = \frac{12}{7} + b$$

$$\frac{37}{7} = b$$

$\boxed{4}$ Write the equation with $m = \frac{3}{7}$ and $b = \frac{37}{7}$.

$$y = \frac{3}{7}x + \frac{37}{7}$$

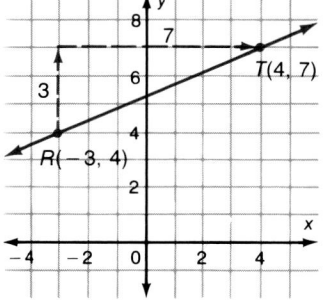

By multiplying each side of $y = \frac{3}{7}x + \frac{37}{7}$ by 7, the LCD, the equation can be written as

$$7y = 3x + 37, \quad \text{or} \quad -3x + 7y = 37. \longleftarrow \textbf{General form}$$

A linear equation written in the form

$$Ax + By = C$$

is said to be expressed in **general form**. Recall that the coefficients A, B, and C are real numbers and A and B cannot both equal zero. When writing a linear equation in general form, the coefficient, A, is usually expressed as a positive real number.

CLASSROOM EXERCISES

Determine the equation of the line passing through the given points. Write the equation in the form $y = mx + b$.

1. $P(2, 0)$ and $Q(0, 2)$
2. $E(2, 0)$ and $F(0, -2)$
3. $S(3, 0)$ and $T(-4, 0)$
4. $S(0, 0)$ and $R(3, -4)$
5. $V(6, 0)$ and $N(-1, -2)$
6. $M(-1, 2)$ and $E(-2, -3)$

396   *Chapter 11*

396

WRITTEN EXERCISES

Ⓐ Determine the equation of the line passing through the given points. Write the equation in the form $y = mx + b$.

1. $R(1, 1)$; $S(2, 3)$ $y = 2x - 1$
2. $T(0, 0)$; $V(-3, 4)$ $y = -\frac{4}{3}x$
3. $A(0, 1)$; $B(-1, 1)$ $y = 1$
4. $D(0, 0)$; $E(-1, -2)$ $y = 2x$
5. $F(3, 4)$; $N(-2, 5)$
6. $E(5, -1)$; $H(3, -2)$
7. $K(-3, -4)$; $P(-5, -6)$
8. $R(2, 3)$; $S(-1, 5)$
9. $T(4, -3)$; $N(6, 0)$
10. $C(2, 2)$; $N(3, 7)$ $y = 5x - 8$
11. $T(1, -4)$; $A(3, -6)$ $y = -x - 3$
12. $V(0, 4)$; $Y(4, 0)$ $y = -x + 4$

Determine the equation of the line passing through the given points. Write the equation in general form. $3x + y = 3$

13. $P(1, 4)$; $S(3, 9)$ $5x - 2y = -3$
14. $T(1, 0)$; $M(3, -6)$
15. $W(-3, -1)$; $Z(9, 7)$ $2x - 3y = -3$
16. $M(0, -1)$; $V(6, 8)$
17. $Z(1, -6)$; $B(6, 0)$
18. $Q(-2, -5)$; $R(-1, -2)$
19. $V(-3, 11)$; $C(6, 5)$ $2x + 3y = 27$
20. $D(0, 0)$; $F(-3, 5)$ $5x + 3y = 0$
21. $D(0, 3)$; $C(-4, -8)$ $11x - 4y = -12$

Ⓑ In Exercises 22–27, use the given slope and one point of a line. Then determine whether the other point lies on that line.

22. 6; $(2, 3)$; $(6, 9)$
23. $\frac{1}{2}$; $(4, 2)$; $(-2, -1)$
24. $-\frac{3}{5}$; $(-5, 7)$; $(0, 4)$
25. -4; $(2, 6)$; $(-1, 13)$ $y = -4x + 14$; No
26. 2; $(-1, -2)$; $(2, 4)$ $y = 2x$; Yes
27. -3; $(-2, 2)$; $(1, 6)$ $y = -3x - 4$; No

Ⓒ In each of Exercises 28–33, the coordinates of the vertices of a triangle are given. Write the equations of the lines forming the sides of each triangle. Write the equations in general form.

28. $A(2, 4)$; $B(6, 2)$; $C(3, -1)$
29. $D(6, 6)$; $E(8, 4)$; $F(1, 2)$
30. $F(3, 2)$; $G(-2, 3)$; $H(1, -2)$
31. $X(-3, 4)$; $Y(-2, -1)$; $Z(1, 1)$
32. $R(3, 3)$; $S(5, -1)$; $T(2, -2)$
33. $V(3, 6)$; $G(5, 4)$; $P(-1, 4)$
34. Show that if $P(x_1, y_1)$ and $Q(x_2, y_2)$ are different points on the graph of the equation $y = 4x - 2$, then $\frac{y_2 - y_1}{x_2 - x_1} = 4$.

_____ Review _____

Solve each equation. *(Section 11–1)* $b = -3 \text{ or } b = 4$

1. $\frac{a}{2} - \frac{a}{3} = 2$ $a = 12$
2. $\frac{9}{x} - 6 = \frac{15}{x}$ $x = -1$
3. $\frac{b + 2}{b + 4} = \frac{3}{b}$
4. $\frac{x}{2} = \frac{x}{x - 1}$ $x = 0 \text{ or } x = 3$
5. $\frac{x + 4}{2x + 3} = \frac{4}{x}$ $x = -2 \text{ or } x = 6$
6. $\frac{x}{2} = \frac{1}{x - 2} - \frac{x}{2x - 4}$ $x = -1$

One point on a line and the slope of the line are given. Write the equation of the line in the form $y = mx + b$. *(Section 11–2)* $y = -\frac{2}{3}x + \frac{1}{2}$

7. $A(0, 4)$; $m = 1$ $y = x + 4$
8. $P(0, -1)$; $m = -2$ $y = -2x - 1$
9. $C(0, \frac{1}{2})$; $m = -\frac{2}{3}$

Applications of Rational Expressions **397**

Determine the equation of the line passing through the given points. Write the equation in the form $y = mx + b$. *(Section 11–3)* $y = \frac{1}{5}x + \frac{3}{5}$

10. $A(4, 4)$; $B(-4, -4)$ $y = x$ **11.** $P(1, 2)$; $Q(0, -1)$ $y = 3x - 1$ **12.** $C(2, 1)$; $D(-3, 0)$

Determine the equation of the line passing through the given points. Write the equation in general form. *(Section 11–3)*

13. $M(0, 4)$; $N(4, 2)$ **14.** $S(2, -2)$; $T(-2, 10)$ **15.** $F(1, -1)$; $G(-3, 0)$

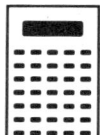 *CALCULATOR APPLICATIONS* _____

Checking Equations with Rational Expressions

You can use a calculator to check the solution set of an equation with rational expressions.

EXAMPLE Equation: $\dfrac{n}{3} + \dfrac{n}{2} = 1$ Solution set: $\left\{\dfrac{6}{5}\right\}$ (Example 1 on page 388)

$$\dfrac{\frac{6}{5}}{3} + \dfrac{\frac{6}{5}}{2} = 1 \quad \text{Evaluate the first term and store its value.}$$

6 $\div$ 5 $\div$ 3 $=$ $\boxed{M+}$ 6 $\div$ 5 $\div$ 2 $+$ $\boxed{MR}$ $=$ $\boxed{\qquad\qquad\qquad \textit{1.}}$

Since both sides of the equation have the same value, the solution checks.

EXERCISES

Use a calculator to check each given "solution set." Correct any incorrect answers.

1. $\dfrac{b}{3} + \dfrac{b}{4} = 21$; $\{36\}$ Yes   **2.** $\dfrac{n}{3} - \dfrac{2n}{3} = 1$; $\{3\}$ No; $n = -3$ **3.** $4m - \dfrac{6m + 3}{2} = 8$; $\{\frac{19}{2}\}$ Yes

4. $\dfrac{1}{3z} + \dfrac{1}{8} = \dfrac{4}{3z}$; $\{8\}$ Yes   **5.** $\dfrac{x}{2} - \dfrac{x}{6} = x - 16$; $\{24\}$ Yes   **6.** $\dfrac{10}{d} - 2 = \dfrac{5 - d}{4d}$; $\{-5\}$

No; $d = 5$

_____ **REVIEW CAPSULE FOR SECTION 11–4** _____

Write the reciprocal of each number. *(Pages 68–71)*

1. $\dfrac{5}{8}$ $\dfrac{8}{5}$ **2.** $-\dfrac{7}{3}$ $-\dfrac{3}{7}$ **3.** $-\dfrac{1}{9}$ -9 **4.** 12 $\dfrac{1}{12}$ **5.** $\dfrac{1}{a}$, $a \neq 0$ a **6.** $-z$

Solve and check each equation. *(Pages 350–353, 370–373)*

7. $\dfrac{6}{3y - 1} = \dfrac{3}{4}$ $y = 3$ **8.** $\dfrac{1 - t}{1 + t} = \dfrac{2}{3}$ $t = \frac{1}{5}$ **9.** $\dfrac{2}{s} = \dfrac{5}{3s - 1}$ $s = 2$ **10.** $\dfrac{n + 1}{3n - 2} = \dfrac{5}{2}$

11. $\dfrac{1}{x} + \dfrac{1}{2} = 5$ $x = \frac{2}{9}$ **12.** $\dfrac{3}{4} - \dfrac{1}{y} = 4$ $y = -\frac{4}{13}$ **13.** $\dfrac{1}{2y} - \dfrac{1}{3y} = 2$ $y = \frac{1}{12}$ **14.** $\dfrac{r + 3}{r - 2} = \dfrac{5}{3}$

Consumer Applications

Borrowing Money

It is important for the consumer to know the cost of borrowing money, or **interest**, particularly when buying a car or a home. The following formula can be used to determine the monthly payment for a given loan. With this, you can then compute the interest.

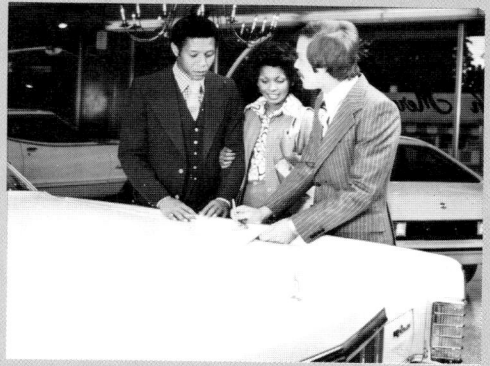

This section is optional. It applies the algebraic skill of evaluating a formula with the aid of a calculator.

$$m = \frac{A\left(\frac{r}{12}\right)\left(1 + \frac{r}{12}\right)^n}{\left(1 + \frac{r}{12}\right)^n - 1}$$

EXAMPLE Mr. and Mrs. Jones want to borrow $5000 to buy a car. The annual rate of interest is 14% and the loan is to be paid back over 48 months. Find **a.** the monthly payment **b.** the total interest.

Solution: **a.** $A = \$5000;\ r = 0.14;\ n = 48$

$$m = \frac{5000\left(\frac{0.14}{12}\right)\left(1 + \frac{0.14}{12}\right)^{48}}{\left(1 + \frac{0.14}{12}\right)^{48} - 1} \qquad \longleftarrow \qquad \frac{0.14}{12} = 0.0117$$

$$= \frac{5000(0.0117)(1.0117)^{48}}{(1.0117)^{48} - 1} \qquad \longleftarrow \qquad \text{Use a calculator.}$$

$$= \$136.73$$

b. Total Interest = Total of Payments − Cash Price of Car

$$= (48 \times 136.73) - 5000$$
$$= 6563.04 - 5000$$
$$= \$1563.04 \text{ interest}$$

EXERCISES

In Exercises 1–5, compute the missing amounts.

	Amount Borrowed	Rate	Months	Monthly Payments	Total Cost	Total Interest
1.	$ 3,000	12.5%	36	?	?	?
2.	$10,000	13%	48	?	?	?
3.	$15,000	12%	96	?	?	?
4.	$20,000	13.5%	120	?	?	?
5.	$ 2,000	18%	24	?	?	?

Borrowing Money   399

Additional Answers
1. $100.36; $3612.96; $612.96
2. $268.28; $12,877.44; $2877.44
3. $243.80; $23,404.80; $8404.80
4. $304.55; $36,546; $16,546
5. $99.85; $2396.40; $396.40

OBJECTIVE: To solve number problems involving rational expressions

11–4 Number Problems

Teaching Suggestions p. M-24

Quick Quiz
Determine the equation of the line passing through the given points.

1. $R(4, 6)$; $S(-2, 5)$
  Ans: $y = \frac{1}{6}x + \frac{32}{6}$

2. $T(3, 5)$; $U(-4, -1)$
  Ans: $y = \frac{6}{7}x + \frac{17}{7}$

3. $V(-2, -1)$; $W(3, -5)$
  Ans: $y = -\frac{4}{5}x - \frac{13}{5}$

4. $X(-6, 10)$; $Y(-4, 6)$
  Ans: $y = 2x + 2$

Additional Examples
Example 1
1. When the same number is subtracted from the numerator and the denominator of $\frac{18}{25}$ (Condition 1), the result is $\frac{2}{3}$ (Condition 2). What is the number?
Ans: 4

2. When the same number is added to both the numerator and denominator of $\frac{13}{15}$, the result is $\frac{9}{10}$. What is the number?
Ans: 5

Some number problems can be represented by equations involving rational expressions.

EXAMPLE 1 When the same number is subtracted from the numerator and added to the denominator of $\frac{17}{22}$ (Condition 1), the result is $\frac{5}{8}$ (Condition 2). What is the number?

Solution: ① Use Condition 1 to represent the unknown. Then represent the original fraction and the new fraction.

Let x = the number to be added and subtracted.

Original fraction: $\frac{17}{22}$ New fraction: $\frac{17 - x}{22 + x}$

② Use Condition 2 to write an equation for the problem.

$$\frac{17 - x}{22 + x} = \frac{5}{8} \quad \longleftarrow \text{ The new fraction equals } \tfrac{5}{8}.$$

③ Solve the equation. The LCD is $8(22 + x)$, $x \neq -22$.

$$8(22 + x)\left(\frac{17 - x}{22 + x}\right) = 8(22 + x)\left(\frac{5}{8}\right)$$

$$8(17 - x) = (22 + x)5 \quad \longleftarrow \text{ Multiply.}$$

$$136 - 8x = 110 + 5x \quad \longleftarrow \text{ Solve for x.}$$

$$26 = 13x$$

$$2 = x$$

Check: ④ $\dfrac{17 - 2}{22 + 2} \overset{?}{=} \dfrac{5}{8}$

$$\frac{15}{24} \overset{?}{=} \frac{5}{8} \quad \text{Yes } \checkmark$$

The number is **2**.

Recall that any two numbers whose product is 1 are *reciprocals* or *multiplicative inverses* of each other.

Thus, $\frac{2}{3}$ and $\frac{3}{2}$ are **reciprocals** because $\frac{2}{3} \cdot \frac{3}{2} = 1$.

Also, -5 and $-\frac{1}{5}$ are **reciprocals** because $-5\left(-\frac{1}{5}\right) = 1$.

EXAMPLE 2   One positive number is three times another (Condition 1). The difference of their reciprocals is $\frac{1}{6}$ (Condition 2). Find the numbers.

Solution: $\boxed{1}$ Let a = the smaller positive number.
Then $3a$ = the larger number.

Reciprocals: $\frac{1}{a}$ and $\frac{1}{3a}$, $a \neq 0$

$\boxed{2}$ Since $3a > a$, $\frac{1}{a} > \frac{1}{3a}$. Subtract $\frac{1}{3a}$ from $\frac{1}{a}$.

$$\frac{1}{a} - \frac{1}{3a} = \frac{1}{6} \longleftarrow \text{ LCD: } 6a, a \neq 0$$

$\boxed{3}$ $6a\left(\frac{1}{a} - \frac{1}{3a}\right) = 6a\left(\frac{1}{6}\right)$

$$6 - 2 = a$$
$$4 = a \longleftarrow \text{ Don't forget to find } 3a.$$
$$12 = 3a$$

Check: $\boxed{4}$ Does $12 = 3 \cdot 4$?   Yes ✔

Does $\frac{1}{4} - \frac{1}{12} = \frac{1}{6}$?   Yes ✔   The numbers are **4** and **12**.

CLASSROOM EXERCISES

In Exercises 1–4:
a. Use Condition 1 to represent the unknown(s).
b. Use Condition 2 to write an equation for the problem.

1. What number added to both numerator and denominator of the fraction $\frac{3}{7}$ (Condition 1) results in a fraction equal to $\frac{3}{5}$ (Condition 2)?

2. What number added to both the numerator and denominator of the fraction $\frac{4}{9}$ (Condition 1) results in a fraction equal to $\frac{2}{3}$ (Condition 2)?

3. One positive number is 4 times another (Condition 1). The difference of their reciprocals is $\frac{3}{8}$ (Condition 2). Find the numbers.

4. A positive number is twice another (Condition 1). The sum of their reciprocals is $\frac{1}{2}$ (Condition 2). Find the numbers.

WORD PROBLEMS

A   Solve each problem.

1. What number must be added to both the numerator and denominator of the fraction $\frac{5}{8}$ to make a fraction equal to $\frac{3}{4}$?   4

2. What number must be subtracted from both the numerator and denominator of the fraction $\frac{7}{12}$ to make a fraction equal to $\frac{1}{2}$?   2

Applications of Rational Expressions   **401**

Additional Examples
Example 2
1. One positive number is four times another (Condition 1). The difference of their reciprocals is $\frac{1}{4}$ (Condition 2). Find the numbers.
Ans: 3; 12
2. One positive number is five times another. The sum of their reciprocals equals $\frac{3}{5}$. Find the numbers.
Ans: 2; 10

Additional Answers
Classroom Exercises
1. **a.** Let x = number added
   b. $\frac{3 + x}{7 + x} = \frac{3}{5}$
2. **a.** Let x = number added
   b. $\frac{4 + x}{9 + x} = \frac{2}{3}$
3. **a.** Let x = smaller number, then $4x$ = larger number
   b. $\frac{1}{x} - \frac{1}{4x} = \frac{3}{8}$
4. **a.** Let x = smaller number, then $2x$ = larger number
   b. $\frac{1}{x} + \frac{1}{2x} = \frac{1}{2}$

Assignment Guide
Minimal Omit
Average
pp. 401–402: 2–18 even
Above Average
pp. 401–402: 2–18 even, 19, 20

3. One positive number is 5 times another number. The difference of their reciprocals is $\frac{2}{5}$. Find the numbers. 2, 10

4. One positive number is 3 times another number. The sum of their reciprocals is $\frac{2}{3}$. Find the numbers. 2, 6

5. What number must be added to the numerator and subtracted from the denominator of $\frac{17}{32}$ to make a fraction equal to $\frac{3}{4}$? 4

6. What number must be subtracted from the numerator and added to the denominator of $\frac{13}{23}$ to make a fraction equal to $\frac{1}{3}$? 4

7. The numerator of a fraction is 3 less than its denominator. If 2 is added to the numerator, the value of the fraction becomes $\frac{3}{4}$. What is the fraction? $\frac{1}{4}$

8. The denominator of a fraction is 4 more than its numerator. If 6 is added to the denominator, the value of the fraction becomes $\frac{1}{3}$. What is the fraction? $\frac{5}{9}$

9. One number is 4 more than another. The quotient of the larger divided by the smaller is $\frac{5}{2}$. Find the numbers. $2\frac{2}{3}, 6\frac{2}{3}$

10. One number is 7 less than another. The quotient of the larger divided by the smaller is $\frac{4}{3}$. Find the numbers. 28, 21

11. The sum of two fractions is $\frac{11}{16}$ and one of them is $\frac{5}{6}$ of the other. Find the fractions. $\frac{3}{8}, \frac{5}{16}$

12. The difference between two fractions is $\frac{1}{8}$. One fraction is $\frac{2}{3}$ of the other. Find the fractions. $\frac{3}{8}, \frac{1}{4}$

B

13. Two integers are consecutive. If 6 is added to the first and 2 is subtracted from the second, the quotient of the resulting integers is $4\frac{1}{2}$. Find them. 3, 4

14. Two integers are consecutive. If 5 is added to the first and 3 is subtracted from the second, the quotient of the resulting integers is $2\frac{2}{5}$. Find them. 7, 8

15. The sum of two numbers is 11. The sum of their reciprocals is $\frac{11}{30}$. Find the numbers. 5, 6

16. The difference of two numbers is 5. The difference of their reciprocals is $\frac{5}{126}$. Find the numbers. 9, 14

17. The sum of a positive number and its reciprocal is $\frac{41}{20}$. Find the number. $\frac{5}{4}$ or $\frac{4}{5}$

18. The difference of a positive number and its reciprocal is $\frac{24}{35}$. Find the number. $\frac{7}{5}$

C

19. The numerator of a fraction is 1 less than the denominator. The reciprocal of the fraction is $\frac{7}{12}$ more than the fraction. Find the fraction. $\frac{3}{4}$ or $-\frac{4}{3}$

20. The denominator of a fraction is 3 more than the numerator. The fraction is $\frac{21}{10}$ less than its reciprocal. Find the fraction. $\frac{2}{5}$ or $-\frac{5}{2}$

_____ **REVIEW CAPSULE FOR SECTION 11-5** _____

Solve and check each equation. *(Pages 388–391)*

1. $\frac{210}{y} = \frac{195}{y-5}$ $y = 70$

2. $\frac{1}{3} + \frac{1}{x} = \frac{1}{2}$ $x = 6$

3. $\frac{2}{t} = \frac{5}{3t-1}$ $t = 2$

4. $\frac{500}{r} = \frac{450}{r-5}$ $r = 50$

5. $\frac{x}{5} - \frac{x}{15} = 4$ $x = 30$

6. $\frac{48}{12-r} = 2\left(\frac{48}{12+r}\right)$ $r = 4$

Problem Solving and Applications

OBJECTIVE: To solve motion problems

11–5 Motion Problems

Motion problems are based on the distance/rate/time formula.

Distance = rate × time, or $d = rt$

EXAMPLE 1   David Blaisdell spends 5 hours traveling to and from work each day. If his average rate driving his moped to work is 18 miles per hour and his average rate returning is 12 miles per hour (Condition 1), how far is it from his home to his place of work (Condition 2)?

Solution: $\boxed{1}$ Organize the information in a table.
Use Condition 1 to represent the unknowns.

	Rate (r)	Time (t)	Distance $d = rt$
Going	18 mph	t	$18t$
Returning	12 mph	$5 - t$	$12(5 - t)$

$\boxed{2}$ Use the table and Condition 2 to write an equation.

Distance going = Distance returning ◄——— **Condition 2**

$$18t \quad = \quad 12(5 - t)$$

$\boxed{3}$ Solve the equation.

$$18t = 12(5 - t)$$
$$18t = 60 - 12t$$
$$30t = 60$$
$$t = 2 \quad \longleftarrow \quad \textbf{It takes 2 hours to drive to work.}$$

Check: $\boxed{4}$ **Condition 1**   Does $2 + 3 = 5$?   Yes ✔

Condition 2   Does $18 \cdot 2 = 12 \cdot 3$?   Yes ✔

The distance from home to work is $2 \cdot 18$, or **36 miles.**

Suppose that a boat travels at a rate of 30 kilometers per hour in still water and that the rate of the current is 4 kilometers per hour.

Then,

rate traveling upstream is 30 − 4,   or   26 km/h,

and

rate traveling downstream is 30 + 4,   or   34 km/h.

Applications of Rational Expressions   **403**

Teaching Suggestions p. M-24

Quick Quiz
1. What number must be subtracted from both the numerator and denominator of the fraction $\frac{9}{16}$ to make a fraction equal to $\frac{1}{2}$?
   Ans: 2
2. One positive number is six times another. The difference of their reciprocals is $\frac{1}{12}$. Find the numbers.
   Ans: 2; 12

Additional Examples
Example 1
1. Ruth Landers spends 5 hours traveling to and from work each day. If her average rate driving her moped to work is 30 kilometers per hour and her average rate returning is 20 kilometers per hour (Condition 1), how far is it from her home to her place of work (Condition 2)?
   Ans: 60 km
2. On Saturday, it took the Drakes 4 hours to travel to and from the beach by car. If their average rate driving to the beach was 40 miles per hour and their average rate returning was 24 miles per hour, how far is it from their home to the beach?
   Ans: 60 mi

Additional Examples
Example 2

1. A motorboat can travel at a rate of 15 miles per hour in still water. Find the rate of the current of a river if the boat takes $\frac{2}{3}$ as much time to travel 60 miles downstream as it takes to travel the same distance upstream.
Ans: 3 mph

2. Lee can row at a speed of 10 kilometers per hour in still water. Find the rate of the current of a river if Lee takes $\frac{1}{3}$ as much time to travel 30 kilometers downstream as it takes to travel the same distance upstream. **Ans: 5 km/n**

EXAMPLE 2 A motorboat can travel at a rate of 25 kilometers per hour in still water. Find the rate of the current of a river if the boat takes $\frac{2}{3}$ as much time to travel 100 kilometers downstream as it takes to travel the same distance upstream.

Solution: $\boxed{1}$ Let $x =$ the rate of the current.

	Rate (r)	**Distance (d)**	**Time** $t = d \div r$
Downstream	$25 + x$	100	$\dfrac{100}{25 + x}$
Upstream	$25 - x$	100	$\dfrac{100}{25 - x}$

$\boxed{2}$ **Time downstream $= \frac{2}{3}$ (Time upstream)**

$$\frac{100}{25 + x} = \frac{2}{3}\left(\frac{100}{25 - x}\right) \qquad \begin{array}{l}\text{LCD:} \\ \mathbf{3(25 + x)(25 - x)}\end{array}$$

$\boxed{3}$ $3(25 + x)(25 - x)\left(\dfrac{100}{25 + x}\right) = 3(25 + x)(25 - x)\left(\dfrac{2}{3}\right)\left(\dfrac{100}{25 - x}\right)$

$$3(25 - x)(100) = (25 + x)(2)(100)$$
$$300(25 - x) = 200(25 + x)$$
$$7500 - 300x = 5000 + 200x$$
$$2500 = 500x$$
$$5 = x$$

$\boxed{4}$ The check is left for you.   Rate of the current: **5 km/hr**

CLASSROOM EXERCISES

The rate of a jet plane in still air is 1100 kilometers per hour. The rate of the wind is 150 kilometers per hour. Use this information in Exercises 1–8.

1. What is the rate of the plane flying with the wind? 1250 km/h

2. What is the rate of the plane flying against the wind? 950 km/h

3. What is the rate of the plane flying with the wind if the rate of the wind decreases by w kilometers per hour? $1250 - w$

4. What is the rate of the plane flying against the wind if the rate of the wind increases by q kilometers per hour? $950 - q$

5. How far can the plane in Exercise 1 travel in 3 hours? 3750 km

6. How far can the plane in Exercise 2 travel in 3 hours? 2850 km

7. How long will it take the plane in Exercise 1 to travel 7500 kilometers? 6 hr

8. How long will it take the plane in Exercise 2 to travel 7600 kilometers?

8 hours

A jet had been flying for 2 hours when it encountered headwinds which reduced its speed by 64 kilometers per hour. If the plane took 5 hours to travel 2304 kilometers, what was its rate of speed before meeting the head winds?

Use this information in Exercises 9–11.

9. Complete the table.

	Rate (r)	Time (t)	Distance $d = rt$
Before headwinds	x	2	$\underline{}$? 2x
After headwinds	$\underline{}$? $x - 64$	$\underline{}$? 3	$\underline{}$? $3(x - 64)$

10. Write the equation you would use to find the plane's rate before encountering the headwinds?

$2x + 3(x - 64) = 2304$

11. What was the rate of the plane after encountering the headwinds?

435.2 km/h

WORD PROBLEMS

A   Solve each problem.

1. A tanker takes $\frac{1}{2}$ hour to go from a refinery to a delivery point and back. If its rate going is 30 mph and its rate returning is 40 mph, how far is it from the refinery to the delivery point? $8\frac{4}{7}$ mi

2. Laurie takes 3 hours to travel from Ahmes to Billings on her moped. Brian covers the same distance in 2 hours, traveling 10 kilometers per hour faster. How far is it from Ahmes to Billings?

3. Jim drove his car 500 kilometers in the same time that Ed drove his car 450 kilometers. Jim drove 5 kilometers an hour faster than Ed. Find the speed of each. Jim: 50 km/h; Ed: 45 km/h

4. A sight-seeing bus travels 90 kilometers to its destination. If the rate returning is twice the rate going and the time for a round trip is 3 hours, find the rate of travel each way.

5. Millan and Sharon work at the same store. Millan drives 24 miles to work and Sharon drives 18 miles. Both take the same time to get there since Millan drives 15 mph faster than Sharon. Find the speed of each person.

6. Karen can row at the speed of 10 kilometers per hour in still water. In a river where the current is 5 kilometers per hour, it takes her 4 hours longer to row x kilometers upstream than the same distance downstream. Find x

7. Tim can average 12 mph with his motor boat in still water. Find the rate of the current of a river if the boat takes twice as long to go 48 miles upstream as it does to travel the same distance downstream. 4 mph

8. A boat that sails at the rate of 30 kilometers per hour in still water can go 104 kilometers down a river in the same time it takes to travel 91 kilometers up the river. Find the rate of the current of the river. 2 km/h

Applications of Rational Expressions   **405**

Assignment Guide
Minimal Omit
Average p. 405: 1–8
Above Average
pp. 405–406: 2–16 even

Additional Answers
Word Problems
2. 60 km
4. Rate going: 45 km/h;
   rate returning: 90 km/h
5. Millan: 60 mph
   Sharon: 45 mph
6. 30 km

9. A boat goes 36 kilometers upstream in the same time that it takes to travel 45 kilometers downstream. The current is flowing at 3 kilometers per hour. Find the rate of the boat in still water. 27 km/h

B

11. Allan can drive his car over a route in 5 hours, and Carla can drive her car over the same route in 4 hours. How long would it take to meet if they started at opposite ends at the same time? $2\frac{2}{9}$ hr

13. An airplane flew 200 kilometers with a tailwind of 60 kilometers per hour. Then it returned against the wind. Find the rate of the plane in still air if the trip took 45 minutes. 540 km/h

C

15. Rhonda can swim in still water at twice the rate of the current in the river near her home. She swam one kilometer upstream and then back in 40 minutes. Find the rate of the current. 2 km/h

16. Two cars race on a 6.4-kilometer track. The faster car gains a lap in 40 minutes. The sum of the rates of the cars is 320 kilometers per hour. Find the rate of each car. faster car: 164.8 km/h; slower car: 155.2 km/h

10. A plane can fly 600 kilometers with the wind in the same time that it can fly 520 kilometers against the wind. The wind is blowing at 30 kilometers per hour. Find the rate of the plane in still air. 420 km/h

12. On a trip, June drove at a rate of 55 mph. She decided to return by a route that was 5 miles longer. Her rate returning was 45 mph. If it took her 1 hour longer returning, how long was the second route? 225 mi

14. A plane flies 852 kilometers with a tailwind in half the time it takes to fly 1560 kilometers against the same wind. If the rate in still air is 408 kilometers per hour, find the speed of the wind. 18 km/h

REVIEW CAPSULE FOR SECTION 11–6

Write each fraction in lowest terms.

1. $\frac{2}{30}$ $\frac{1}{15}$ **2.** $\frac{4}{60}$ $\frac{1}{15}$ **3.** $\frac{9}{54}$ $\frac{1}{6}$ **4.** $\frac{16}{50}$ $\frac{8}{25}$ **5.** $\frac{18}{90}$ $\frac{1}{5}$ **6.** $\frac{27}{81}$ $\frac{1}{3}$

Solve and check each equation. *(Pages 388–391)*

7. $\frac{n}{20} + \frac{n}{30} = 1$ $n = 12$

8. $\frac{1}{2} + \frac{w}{6} = 1$ $w = 3$

9. $\frac{20}{x} + \frac{20}{2x} = 1$

10. $\frac{a}{6} + \frac{a-2}{9} = 1$ $a = 4\frac{2}{5}$

11. $\frac{8}{x} + \frac{8}{3x} = 1$ $x = 10\frac{2}{3}$

12. $\frac{x+4}{9} + \frac{1}{4} = 1$

13. $\frac{1}{y} - \frac{1}{y-4} = 1$ $y = 2$

14. $\frac{-2}{x-2} + \frac{x}{x+2} = 1$ $x = 0$

15. $y - \frac{2}{y} = 1$

Additional Answers
Review Capsule
9. $x = 30$
12. $x = 2\frac{3}{4}$
15. $y = -1$ <u>or</u> $y = 2$

Problem Solving and Applications

OBJECTIVE: To solve work problems

11–6 Work Problems

Teaching Suggestions p. M-24

Work problems usually deal with persons or machines working at different rates of speed. The first step in solving these problems involves determining how much of the work an individual or a machine can do in a given unit of time, such as a minute, an hour, and so on.

For example suppose Freida takes 3 hours to type a term paper.

Part of job done in 1 hour: $\dfrac{1}{3}$

Part of job done in 2 hours: $\dfrac{1}{3} \cdot 2$, or $\dfrac{2}{3}$

Part of job done in n hours: $\dfrac{1}{3} \cdot n$, or $\dfrac{n}{3}$

Many work problems involve this formula.

rate of work × time = work done,   or

$$r \quad \cdot \quad t \quad = \quad w$$

EXAMPLE 1 Gloria can clear the snow from a sidewalk in 60 minutes. Marsha can clear the same area in 30 minutes. How long will it take them to do the job if they work together?

Solution: $\boxed{1}$ Represent the unknown. Organize the information in a table.

Let t = the number of minutes for both to do the job working together.

Worker	Rate of Work per Minute (r)	Time Spent Working Together (t)	Part of Work Done ($r \cdot t = w$)
Gloria	$\dfrac{1}{60}$	t	$\dfrac{1}{60}t$, or $\dfrac{t}{60}$
Marsha	$\dfrac{1}{30}$	t	$\dfrac{1}{60}t$, or $\dfrac{t}{60}$

$\boxed{2}$ Use the table to write an equation for the problem.

$$\underset{\dfrac{t}{60}}{\underbrace{\text{Work done by Gloria}}} \; + \; \underset{\dfrac{t}{30}}{\underbrace{\text{Work done by Marsha}}} \; = \; \underset{1}{\underbrace{\text{Total job}}}$$

$$\frac{t}{60} + \frac{t}{30} = 1$$

$\boxed{3}$ Solve the equation. The LCD is 60.

Applications of Rational Expressions   **407**

$$60\left(\frac{t}{60} + \frac{t}{30}\right) = 60(1)$$

$$60\left(\frac{t}{60}\right) + 60\left(\frac{t}{30}\right) = 60$$

$$t + 2t = 60 \longleftarrow \text{ Solve for } t.$$

$$3t = 60$$

$$t = 20 \longleftarrow \begin{array}{l}\textbf{Number of minutes they}\\\textbf{work together}\end{array}$$

Check: $\boxed{4}$ Gloria does $\frac{20}{60}$, or $\frac{1}{3}$ of the work in 20 minutes.

Marsha does $\frac{20}{30}$, or $\frac{2}{3}$ of the work in 20 minutes.

Total work done: $\frac{1}{3} + \frac{2}{3} = \frac{3}{3}$, or 1

Working together, Gloria and Marsha can complete the job in **20 minutes.**

REMEMBER: When a job is completed, the sum of the fractional parts of the job done by each worker equals 1.

EXAMPLE 2 Bill can do a certain job in 8 days. After working alone for 4 days, he is joined by Tony. Together they finish the job in 2 more days. How long would it take Tony to do the job alone?

Solution: $\boxed{1}$ Let $d =$ the number of days for Tony to do the job alone.

Then $\frac{1}{d} =$ Tony's rate of work.

Worker	Rate of Work Per Day	Time Working Alone	Time Working Together	Work Done $(r \cdot t = w)$
Bill	$\frac{1}{8}$	4 days	2 days	$\frac{1}{8}(4) + \frac{1}{8}(2) = \frac{3}{4}$
Tony	$\frac{1}{d}$	0 days	2 days	$\frac{1}{d} \cdot 2$, or $\frac{2}{d}$

$\boxed{2}$ $\underset{\downarrow}{\underline{\begin{array}{c}\textbf{Work done by}\\\textbf{Bill}\end{array}}} + \underset{\downarrow}{\underline{\begin{array}{c}\textbf{Work done by}\\\textbf{Tony}\end{array}}} = \underset{\downarrow}{\underline{\begin{array}{c}\textbf{Total}\\\textbf{job}\end{array}}}$

$$\frac{3}{4} \quad + \quad \frac{2}{d} \quad = \quad 1 \longleftarrow \textbf{LCD: } 4d$$

$\boxed{3}$
$$4d\left(\frac{3}{4} + \frac{2}{d}\right) = 4d(1)$$

$$4d\left(\frac{3}{4}\right) + 4d\left(\frac{2}{d}\right) = 4d$$

$$3d + 8 = 4d$$

$$8 = d \longleftarrow \begin{array}{l}\textbf{Number of days if}\\\textbf{Tony worked alone}\end{array}$$

Check: 4 Work done by Bill: $\frac{3}{4}$

Work done by Tony: $\frac{2}{d} = \frac{2}{8} = \frac{1}{4}$

Total work done: $\frac{3}{4} + \frac{1}{4} = 1$

It will take Tony **8 days** to do the job alone.

CLASSROOM EXERCISES

Clarence can mow a lawn in 80 minutes. Jim can mow the same lawn in 120 minutes. Use this information in Exercises 1–6.

1. What part of the lawn can Clarence mow in 1 minute? $\frac{1}{80}$

2. What part of the lawn can Jim mow in 1 minute? $\frac{1}{120}$

3. What part of the lawn can Clarence mow in 30 minutes? $\frac{3}{8}$

4. What part of the lawn can Jim mow in 90 minutes? $\frac{3}{4}$

5. What part of the lawn can Clarence mow in m minutes? $\frac{m}{80}$

6. What part of the lawn can Jim mow in y minutes? $\frac{y}{120}$

Pipe A can empty a pool in 5 hours. Pipe B can empty the pool in 3 hours. Use this information in Exercises 7–13.

7. What part of the pool can Pipe A empty in 1 hour? $\frac{1}{5}$

8. What part of the pool can Pipe A empty in 4 hours? $\frac{4}{5}$

9. What part of the pool can Pipe B empty in 1 hour? $\frac{1}{3}$

10. What part of the pool can Pipe B empty in 3 hours? 1

11. What part of the pool is drained in 1 hour by both pipes? $\frac{1}{5} + \frac{1}{3}$ or $\frac{8}{15}$

12. What part of the pool can be emptied in x hours by both pipes? $\frac{x}{5} + \frac{x}{3}$, or $\frac{8x}{15}$

13. Write an equation whose solution would give the number of hours that it would take both pipes to empty the pool. $\frac{x}{5} + \frac{x}{3} = 1$

WORD PROBLEMS

A Solve each problem.

1. Ken can build a fence in 4 days. His niece Sara can do it in 4.5 days. How long would it take them working together? $2\frac{2}{17}$ days

2. Jill can paint a house in 2 days. Her brother can paint it in 4 days. How long would it take them to paint the house if they work together? $1\frac{1}{3}$ days

3. A large pipe can empty a tank in 5 minutes, and a smaller pipe can empty it in 8 minutes. How long would it take both pipes to empty the tank? $3\frac{1}{13}$ minutes

4. Marge can do a piece of work in 3 days, Mae in 5 days, and Gina in 8 days. If all three work together, how long will it take them to do the work? $1\frac{41}{79}$ days

Assignment Guide
Minimal Omit
Average pp. 409–410: 1–10
Above Average
pp. 409–411: 3, 6, 9, 15, 16–20

Applications of Rational Expressions　**409**

5. To remove the dirt from a building foundation, a contractor is using a large diesel shovel and a small one. If the large shovel can do the entire job in 6 days and the small shovel can do it in 9 days, how long will it take them together? $3\frac{3}{5}$ days

6. Gwen Hall estimates that she can paint the Smiths' house in 6 days. Her brother Doug can paint it in 8 days and her sister Laura can paint it in 10 days. How long will it take all three working together? $2\frac{26}{47}$ days

7. Jim can shovel the driveway in 2 hours. Lucy can shovel it in 4 hours. Jim shovels for 1 hour and then Lucy helps him finish the job. How long does it take the two of them to finish? $\frac{2}{3}$ hour

8. If one pipe can fill a tank in 3 hours, a second pipe in 5 hours and a third pipe in 6 hours, how long will it take to fill the tank if all three pipes are being used? $1\frac{3}{7}$ hours

9. One machine can complete an order for bolts in 7 hours and another machine can do it in 5 hours. How long will it take both machines to finish the job after the slower machine has been working alone for $3\frac{1}{2}$ hours? $1\frac{11}{24}$ hours

10. Juan can paint a room in 3 hours. Anita can paint the same room in 5 hours. Anita paints alone for 2 hours and then Juan helps her finish. How long does it take them to finish painting the room? $1\frac{1}{8}$ hours

B

11. Kate can type a manuscript in 6 hours. If Mark helps her they can type the complete manuscript in 4 hours. How long would it take Mark if he did all the typing? 12 hours

$2\frac{1}{2}$ hours

12. Jacques can spade a garden in 5 hours. After working alone for 2 hours he is joined by Dave. Together they finish the job in 1 hour. How long would it take Dave to spade the garden alone?

13. It takes 10 minutes to fill a certain tank and 15 minutes to empty it when it is full. With the drain open and the tank empty, how long would it take to fill it?

30 min

14. Janette can make an afghan in 10 days, Bill in 6 days, and Sue in 15 days. Bill and Janette work for 3 days. How long will it take Janette and Sue to finish the afghan? $1\frac{1}{5}$ days

15. One card reader can read a deck of computer cards in twice the time it takes another reader. Together they can read the deck in 8 minutes. How long would it take each reader alone to read the deck? 12 min, 24 min

16. An old machine requires 3 times as many hours to complete a job as a new machine. When both machines work together, they require 9 hours to complete a job. How many hours would it take the new machine to finish the job alone? 12 hours

C

17. A swimming pool can be filled by a large pipe in 4 hours and by a small pipe in 6 hours. A third pipe can empty the pool in 3 hours. How long would it take to fill the pool if all three pipes were open at the same time? 12 hours

18. Jaime, Brigette, and Tom can prepare the ballots for a school election in 2 hours. If Jaime could prepare the ballots in 5 hours and Brigette could prepare them in 6 hours, how long will it take Tom to prepare the ballots alone?

$7\frac{1}{2}$ hours

19. Frank and Liz, working together, can assemble a ham radio kit in 12 hours. Frank requires 18 hours to do it alone. Frank and Liz work together for 4 hours and Liz leaves. How long will it take Frank to finish alone? 12 hours

20. It takes Louis 12 hours to repair a car's transmission. Tina came to help him after Louis had worked 6 hours alone. Together they finished the job in 3 more hours. How long would it take Tina to repair the transmission alone? 12 hours

---

Puzzle See the Solution Key.

Copy the puzzle at the right. Complete the puzzle by entering the solutions to the equations in the appropriate box(es).

Across

1. $\dfrac{n}{6} - \dfrac{n}{4} = 9$

9. $\dfrac{5}{7} = \dfrac{2+b}{6}$

3. $\dfrac{2}{5} = \dfrac{4}{r-4}$

10. $\dfrac{9}{x-3} = \dfrac{7}{x-5}$

4. $\dfrac{4}{12} = \dfrac{5}{d}$

11. $\dfrac{4}{y} = \dfrac{7}{y-6}$

5. $b^2 = 100$

12. $\dfrac{m}{28} = \dfrac{1}{4}$

8. $x^2 - 12x = -36$

16. $\dfrac{3f}{8} - \dfrac{1}{4} = \dfrac{f}{3} - \dfrac{11}{24}$

Down

2. $\dfrac{2}{k-7} = \dfrac{3}{k}$

6. $\dfrac{2p}{3} + \dfrac{3p}{4} = 51$

10. $\dfrac{2}{5} = \dfrac{w}{45}$

14. $\dfrac{g}{12} = \dfrac{5}{4}$

5. $\dfrac{1}{2} = \dfrac{50}{s}$

7. $\dfrac{3z}{4} - 12 = \dfrac{3(z-12)}{5}$

13. $\dfrac{6}{c-2} = \dfrac{5}{c-3}$

15. $x^2 - 18x = -81$

REVIEW CAPSULE FOR SECTION 11–7

In Exercises 1–4, write a formula to express the direct variation. Use k as the constant of variation. *(Pages 197–200)*

1. The perimeter, P, of an equilateral triangle varies directly as the length of a side, r. $P = 3r$

2. The length, r, of a person's shadow at a given time varies directly as the height, h, of the person. $r = kh$

3. The total income, T, at a fixed rate of pay per hour, varies directly as the number of hours worked, h. $T = kh$

4. For a car traveling at a constant rate of speed, the distance covered, d, varies directly as the time, t, that it travels.

5. If s varies directly as n, and $s = 60$ when $n = 2$, find s when $n = 7$. $s = 210$

6. If w varies directly as p, and $w = 5$ when $p = 10$, find p when $w = 12.5$.

Additional Answers
Review Capsule
4. $d = kt$
6. $p = 25$

Applications of Rational Expressions   **411**

11–7 Inverse Variation

The table below and the graph at the right illustrate the rate of speed required to travel 480 kilometers during various periods of time.

r	50	60	40	30	20	10	5
t	6	8	12	16	24	48	96

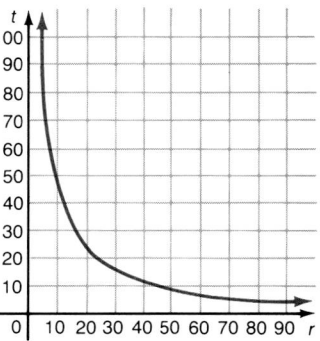

For a trip of 480 kilometers, the relationship between rate of travel (speed) and time can be defined by the equation $rt = 480$. The equation describes an *inverse variation*. It shows that r varies inversely as t or that t varies inversely as r. That is, as the values of r decrease, the values of t increase. Also, as the values of r increase, the values of t decrease.

Definition

> If the product of two variables is a nonzero constant, the variables are in **inverse variation.** The equation for the inverse variation may be written as
>
> $$xy = k \qquad \text{or} \qquad y = \frac{k}{x},$$
>
> where k is the **constant of variation.**

EXAMPLE 1 Determine whether each equation is an example of inverse variation.

  a. $bh = 40$ **b.** $t = \dfrac{100}{r}$

Solution: Compare each equation with $xy = k$ or $y = \dfrac{k}{x}$.

  a. $bh = 40$ has the same form as $xy = k$. Thus, it is an example of inverse variation.

  b. $t = \dfrac{100}{r}$ has the same form as $y = \dfrac{k}{x}$. Thus, it is an example of inverse variation.

NOTE: In $bh = 40$, the constant of variation is 40. In $t = \dfrac{100}{r}$, the constant of variation is 100.

When you are given that a function is an inverse variation and you know one ordered pair of the function, you can determine k, the constant of variation. Then you can write the equation that shows how x and y are related.

EXAMPLE 2   If x varies inversely as y, and $x = 4$ when $y = 5$, write the equation that shows how x and y are related.

Solution: $\boxed{1}$ Find k, the constant of variation.

$xy = k$ ◄——— **x varies inversely as y.**
            Replace x with 4 and y with 5.

$4 \cdot 5 = k$

$20 = k$ ◄——— **Write the equation. Use $k = 20$.**

$\boxed{2}$ Equation: $xy = 20$

Additional Examples
Example 2
In Exercises 1–2, y varies inversely as x. Write the equation that shows how x and y are related.
1. $x = 3$ when $y = 8$
   Ans: $xy = 24$
2. $x = 7$ when $y = -5$
   Ans: $xy = -35$

The graph of the inverse variation

$$xy = k, \text{ where } k > 0$$

is a **hyperbola.** Its branches are in the first and third quadrants as shown at the right.

$$xy = 4$$

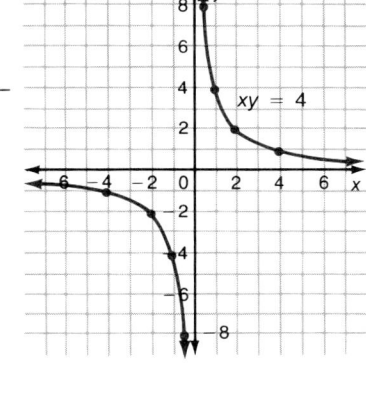

x	y
-4	-1
-2	-2
-1	-4
$-\frac{1}{2}$	-8

x	y
$\frac{1}{2}$	8
1	4
2	2
4	1

When $k < 0$, the branches of the hyperbola are in the second and fourth quadrants. In practical applications, only the branch in the first quadrant usually satisfies all the conditions of the problem.

EXAMPLE 3   The current in an electric circuit varies inversely as the resistance. When the current is 40 amps, the resistance is 12 ohms. Find the current when the resistance is 20 ohms.

Solution: $\boxed{1}$ Find the constant of variation.

$cr = k$ ◄——— **c varies inversely as r.**

$40 \cdot 12 = k$ and $k = 480$ **Equation: $cr = 480$**

$\boxed{2}$ Find c when $r = 20$.

$cr = 480$

$20c = 480$

$c = 24$ The current is **24 amps.**

Applications of Rational Expressions   **413**

Example 3
1. The current in an electric circuit varies inversely as the resistance. When the current is 40 amps, the resistance is 12 ohms. Find the current when the resistance is 60 amps.
Ans: 8 amps
2. The number of hours required to complete a certain job varies inversely as the number of workers on the job. If 8 workers require 9 hours to complete the job, how long should it take 24 workers?
Ans: 3 hours

Determine whether each equation is an example of inverse variation. Answer *Yes* or *No*.

1. $yz = 6$ Yes **2.** $y = x$ No **3.** $b + h = 40$ No **4.** $ab = \frac{1}{4}$ Yes

5. $\frac{x}{y} = \frac{1}{2}$ No **6.** $y = \frac{1}{x}$ Yes **7.** $x = \frac{200}{z}$ Yes **8.** $\frac{a}{5} = \frac{3}{b}$ Yes

In Exercises 9–12, use the equation $xy = 28$.

increases

9. If x increases, what happens to y? decreases **10.** If x decreases, what happens to y?

11. If a certain value of x is doubled, what happens to the value of y?
y is halved

12. If a certain value of y is multiplied by 4, what happens to the value of x?
x is divided by 4

WRITTEN EXERCISES

A Determine whether each of the following is an example of inverse variation. Answer *Yes* or *No*. Give a reason for each answer.

1. $xy = 6$ **2.** $x + y = 6$ **3.** $x - y = 6$ **4.** $x = 10y$

5. $\frac{x}{y} = 6$ **6.** $x = \frac{10}{y}$ **7.** $y = \frac{42}{x}$ **8.** $x + y = 10$

9. $y = 250x$ **10.** $y = 430x - 5$ **11.** $xy + y = 8$ **12.** $xy - y = 8$

In Exercises 13–18, y varies inversely as x. Write the equation that shows how x and y are related.

13. $y = 7$ when $x = 6$ $xy = 42$ **14.** $y = 4$ when $x = 12$ $xy = 48$ **15.** $y = \frac{3}{4}$ when $x = \frac{2}{3}$ $xy = \frac{1}{2}$

16. $y = -5$ when $x = 2$ $xy = -10$ **17.** $y = -8$ when $x = -5$ $xy = 40$ **18.** $y = -5\frac{1}{4}$ when $x = -8\frac{1}{3}$

19. If x varies inversely as y, and $x = 8$ when $y = 9$, find x when $y = 18$. $x = 4$

20. If p varies inversely as q, and $p = 50$ when $q = 4$, find p when $q = 40$. $p = 5$

21. If r varies inversely as t and $r = 80$ when $t = 0.25$, find r when $t = 2$. $r = 10$

22. If y varies inversely as z and $y = 6$ when $z = -4$, find y when $z = -3$. $y = 8$

23. If a varies inversely as b and $a = 60$ when $b = \frac{1}{2}$, find b when $a = 20$. $b = 1\frac{1}{2}$

24. If c varies inversely as d and $c = 0.40$ when $d = 100$, find d when $c = 1.6$. $d = 25$

WORD PROBLEMS

Solve each problem.

In Exercises 25–26, the current varies inversely as the resistance.

25. When the resistance in a certain electrical circuit is 10 ohms, the current is 24 amps. Find the current when the resistance is 20 ohms. 12 amps

26. A certain electrical circuit has a resistance of 12 ohms. The current is 15 amps. Find the current when the resistance is decreased to 4 ohms. 45 amps

Assignment Guide
Minimal Omit
Average Omit
Above Average
Day 1 pp. 414–415: 2–32 even
Day 2 p. 415: 33–44

Additional Answers
Written Exercises

1. Yes; corresponds to $xy = k$
2. No; does not correspond to $xy = k$ or $x = \frac{k}{y}$
3. No; does not correspond to $xy = k$ or $x = \frac{k}{y}$
4. No; does not correspond to $xy = k$ or $x = \frac{k}{y}$
5. No; does not correspond to $xy = k$ or $x = \frac{k}{y}$
6. Yes; corresponds to $x = \frac{k}{y}$
7. Yes; corresponds to $x = \frac{k}{y}$
8. No; does not correspond to $xy = k$ or $x = \frac{k}{y}$
9. No; does not correspond to $xy = k$ or $x = \frac{k}{y}$
10. No; does not correspond to $xy = k$ or $x = \frac{k}{y}$
11. No; does not correspond to $xy = k$ or $x = \frac{k}{y}$
12. No; does not correspond to $xy = k$ or $x = \frac{k}{y}$
18. $xy = 43\frac{3}{4}$

27. The number of days needed to finish repairing a sidewalk varies inversely as the number of people working. It takes 12 days for two people to repair the walk. How many people are needed to complete the job in 4 days? 6 people

28. The rent for an apartment varies inversely as the number of people sharing the cost. Four people sharing an apartment pay $120 each per month. How many people would be needed so that each would pay $80 per month? 6 people

29. The amount of time to make a trip varies inversely as the rate of travel. At 30 miles per hour it takes Jenny 4 hours to travel from her home to her vacation cottage. How long would it take if she drove at 50 miles per hour? $2\frac{2}{5}$ hours

30. A jet traveling at 2200 kilometers per hour took 4 hours to fly from Boston to Paris. The time varies inversely as the rate of speed. How long would it take a plane traveling at 2500 km/hr to make the same trip? $3\frac{13}{25}$ hours

31. The number of tomato plants in a row in George's garden varies inversely as the space between them. If the plants are spaced 15 centimeters apart, 60 plants fit in a row. How many can fit if he places them 25 centimeters apart?

B

36 plants

32. The number of days needed to paint the outside of a house varies inversely as the number of people painting the house. It takes 2 people 8 days to paint the house. How many days will it take 4 people to paint the house? 4 days

33. The number of square tiles on a floor varies inversely as the area of the tiles. It takes 108 tiles with an area of 1 square foot to cover a certain floor. How many tiles with an area of $\frac{9}{16}$ square feet would it take to cover the same floor? 192 tiles

34. When the tension on a wire is kept constant, the number of vibrations per second varies inversely as the length of the wire. A wire 400 centimeters long vibrates 160 times per second. How long should a wire be so that it will vibrate 240 times per second?

If y varies inversely as the square of x, then $y = \dfrac{k}{x^2}$, or $yx^2 = k$. Find the constant of variation and write the equation for each relation.

35. $y = 6$ when $x = 2$

36. $y = 2$ when $x = 1$

37. $y = 8$ when $x = 4$

38. $y = 4$ when $x = -3$

39. $y = -5$ when $x = -4$

40. $y = 3\frac{1}{2}$ when $x = 5\frac{3}{4}$

C

41. The frequency, f, of vibration of a wire (of uniform length and tension) varies inversely as the square root of its weight, w. Express this relation in a formula, using k to represent the constant of variation. Given that k is 508, what is f when w is 4?

42. The intensity, I, of a light varies inversely as the square of the distance, d, from the light. How far should a book be placed from a light to receive four times as much intensity of illumination as it received when it was 2 meters from the light? 1 meter

In Exercises 43–44, use the formula $fp = v$, where f is the frequency, p is the wavelength and v is the speed of sound (about 335 meters per second in air).

43. An open pipe produces a sound wave whose length is twice that of the pipe. What is the frequency of the sound from a pipe whose length is 1 meter? $167\frac{1}{2}$

44. A stopped pipe produces a sound wave whose length is four times that of the pipe. Find the length of a pipe that produces a sound with a frequency of 220.

Applications of Rational Expressions **415**

11-8   Joint Variation

Quick Quiz
The number of printing presses required to put out a newspaper varies inversely as the time the presses are in operation. If 12 presses can produce an edition of the paper in 3 hours, how long would it take 18 presses to put out an edition of the paper?
Ans: 2 hours

Additional Examples
Example 1
1. The volume, V, of a pyramid varies jointly as the area of its base, B, and its altitude, h. When $B = 15$ and $h = 4$, $V = 20$. Find V when $B = 8$ and $h = 18$.
Ans: 48 cubic units
2. If x varies jointly as y and z and $x = 180$ when $y = 20$ and $z = 3$, find x when $y = 12$ and $z = 10$.
Ans: 360

Example 2
1. If y varies directly as x and inversely as q, and $y = 3$ when $x = 8$ and $q = 24$, find y when $x = 6$ and $q = 3$.
Ans: 18
2. If a varies directly as b and inversely as c, and $a = 1$ when $b = 15$ and $c = 5$, find a when $b = 30$ and $c = 2$.
Ans: 5

When one variable varies directly as the product of two or more variables, the variation is called a **joint variation**.

EXAMPLE 1   The volume, V, of a pyramid varies jointly as the area of its base, B, and its altitude h. When $B = 18$ and $h = 4$, $V = 24$. Find V when $B = 7$ and $h = 12$.

Solution: $V = kBh$ ◄——— **V varies jointly as B and h.**

To find k, replace V with 24, B with 18, and h with 4.

$24 = k(18)(4)$

$24 = 72k$

$\dfrac{1}{3} = k$ ◄——— **Write the equation for the joint variation. Use $k = \dfrac{1}{3}$.**

Thus, $V = \dfrac{1}{3}Bh$. ◄——— **Replace B with 7 and h with 12.**

$V = \dfrac{1}{3}(7)(12)$

$V = \mathbf{28}$ **cubic units** ◄——— **Volume is measured in cubic units.**

When a variable varies directly as one variable and inversely as another, the variation is sometimes called **combined variation**. Thus, if x varies directly as y and inversely as z, then

$$x = ky\left(\dfrac{1}{z}\right) \qquad \text{or} \qquad x = \dfrac{ky}{z}.$$

EXAMPLE 2   Suppose that y varies directly as x and inversely as w. If $y = 2$ when $x = 7$ and $w = 14$, find y when $x = 10$ and $w = 8$.

Solution: $y = \dfrac{kx}{w}$ ◄——— **y varies directly as x and inversely as w.**

To find k, replace y with 2, x with 7, and w with 14.

$2 = \dfrac{7k}{14}$

$2 = \dfrac{1}{2}k$

$4 = k$ ◄——— **Write the equation for the variation.**

$y = \dfrac{4x}{w}$ ◄——— **Replace x with 10 and w with 8.**

$y = \dfrac{4 \cdot 10}{8}$

$y = \mathbf{5}$

CLASSROOM EXERCISES

Write a formula for each statement. Use k as the constant of variation.

1. a varies jointly as b and c. $a = kbc$
2. t varies jointly as s and v. $t = ksv$
3. m varies directly as n and inversely as p. $m = \dfrac{kn}{p}$
4. h varies directly as g and inversely as l.
5. s varies directly as t and inversely as the square of r. $s = \dfrac{kt}{r^2}$
6. x varies directly as the square of y and inversely as the cube of w. $x = \dfrac{ky^2}{w^3}$

WRITTEN EXERCISES

A

1. If t varies jointly as s and r, and $t = 120$ when $s = 15$ and $r = 4$, find t when $s = 12$ and $r = 9$. $t = 216$

2. If q varies jointly as n and p, and $q = 12$ when $n = 14$ and $p = 6$, find q when $n = 21$ and $p = 8$. $q = 24$

3. If x varies jointly as w, y, and z, and $x = 15$ when $w = 2$, $y = 10$, and $z = 3$, find x when $w = 8$, $y = 5$, and $z = 7$. $x = 70$

4. If a varies jointly as b, c, and d, and $a = 75$ when $b = 1$, $c = 5$, and $d = 5$, find a when $b = 3$, $c = 7$, and $d = 9$.

5. If q varies directly as h and inversely as j, and $q = 14$ when $h = 28$ and $j = 7$, find q when $h = 14$ and $j = 6$. $q = 8\frac{1}{6}$

6. If f varies directly as d^2 and inversely as b, and $f = 3$ when $d = 6$ and $b = 4$, find f when $d = 9$ and $b = 5$. $f = 5\frac{2}{5}$

7. If A varies directly as B and inversely as C^2, and $A = 9$ when $B = 9$ and $C = 4$, find A when $B = 5$ and $C = 2$. $A = 20$

8. If G varies directly as H^3 and inversely as F^2, and $G = 4$ when $H = 2$ and $F = 4$, find G when $H = 6$ and $F = 12$. $G = 12$

9. If m varies jointly as p and r^2, and $m = 28$ when $p = 7$ and $r = 8$, find m when $p = 10$ and $r = 4$. $m = 10$

10. If x varies jointly as y and z and inversely as m, and $x = 60$ when $y = 2$, $z = 5$, and $m = 4$, find x when $y = 3$, $z = 9$, and $m = 6$. $x = 108$

WORD PROBLEMS

11. The area of a triangle varies jointly as the base and the height. A triangle with a base of 5 inches and a height of 6 inches has an area of 15 square inches. Find the area when the base is 7 inches and the height is 4 inches. $14\ \text{in}^2$

12. The mass, m, of a rectangular sheet of wood varies jointly as the length, l, and the width, w. When l is 40 centimeters and w is 20 centimeters, m is 400 grams. Find m when l is 30 centimeters and w is 20 centimeters. 300 grams

13. The volume of a pyramid, V, varies jointly as the area of the base, B, and the height, h. When B is 12 square centimeters and h is 9 centimeters, V is 36 cubic centimeters. Find V when b is 14 square centimeters and h is 6 centimeters. $28\ \text{cm}^3$

14. The volume of a cone varies jointly as the area of the base, B, and the height, h. The volume is 50 cubic centimeters when the area of the base is 30 square centimeters and the height is 5 centimeters. Find V when $h = 9$ centimeters and $B = 40$ square centimeters. $120\ \text{cm}^3$

Applications of Rational Expressions   **417**

Additional Answers
Classroom Exercises

4. $h = \dfrac{kg}{l}$

Assignment Guide
Minimal Omit
Average Omit
Above Average
pp. 417–418: 1–18 odd

Additional Answers
Written Exercises
4. $a = 567$

15. The glide ability of a hang glider depends on a ratio called the **aspect ratio,** R. R varies directly as the square of the wingspread, S^2, and inversely as the wing area, A. When A is 30 square feet and, S is 9 feet, R is 2.7. Find R when A is 40 square feet and S is 10 feet. R = 2.5

16. The force of attraction, F, of a body varies directly as its mass, m, and inversely as the square of the distance, d, from the body. When m = 8 kilograms and d = 5 meters, F = 100 Newtons. Find F when m = 2 kilograms and d = 15 meters. F = $2\frac{7}{9}$ Newtons

17. The electrical resistance in a wire varies directly as its length, L, and inversely as the square of its diameter, d. A wire 5 kilometers long with a diameter of 6 millimeters has a resistance of 20 ohms. Find the resistance of a wire of the same material with a length of 6 kilometers and a diameter of 4 millimeters. 54 ohms

18. The crushing load, L, of a square wooden post varies directly as the fourth power of its thickness, t^4, and inversely as its length squared, L^2. A post 10 centimeters thick and 4 meters high is crushed by a load of 22.5 tons. What is the crushing load of a post 5 centimeters thick and 3 meters high? L = 2.5 tons

Quiz Sections 11-4–11-8
After completing this Review you may want to administer a quiz covering the same sections. See page M-53 of the Teacher's Manual for the suggested quiz.

Review

1. The sum of two fractions is $\frac{10}{3}$ and one of them is $\frac{1}{4}$ of the other. Find the fractions. *(Section 11-4)* $\frac{2}{3}, \frac{8}{3}$

2. One integer is $\frac{2}{3}$ of another integer. The sum of their reciprocals is $\frac{5}{36}$. Find the integers. *(Section 11-4)* 12, 18

3. It takes 12 hours to drive a truck to its delivery point and back. If the rate going is 50 kilometers per hour and the return rate is 70 kilometers per hour, how long is the round trip? *(Section 11-5)* 700 km

4. An airplane flies 99 miles with a tailwind of 20 miles per hour. It returns to its starting point flying against the wind. If the round trip takes one hour, what is the rate of the plane in still air? *(Section 11-5)* 200 km/h

5. One pipe can fill a tank in 20 minutes. A larger pipe can fill it in 12 minutes. If both pipes are used, how long will it take to fill the tank? *(Section 11-6)* $7\frac{1}{2}$ hours

6. Maria can make out the payroll in 6 hours. If Ted helps her, they can finish in 4 hours. How long would it take Ted to do the job alone? *(Section 11-6)* 12 hr

7. The current in an electrical circuit varies inversely as the resistance. When the resistance in a certain circuit is 12 ohms, the current is 30 amps. Find the current when the resistance is 18 ohms. *(Section 11-7)* 20 amps

8. The number of days needed to paint a house varies inversely as the number of people working. It takes 10 days for two people to paint the house. How many people are needed to complete the job in 5 days? *(Section 11-7)* 4

9. The area of a triangle varies jointly as the base and the height. A triangle with a base of 7 inches and a height of 8 inches has an area of 28 square inches. Find the area when the base is 5 inches and the height is 6 inches. *(Section 11-8)* 15 square inches

10. The mass, m, of a rectangular sheet of metal varies jointly as the length, l, and the width, w, When l is 4 meters and w is 2 meters, m is 2 kilograms. Find m when l is 5 meters and w is 3 meters. *(Section 11-8)* $3\frac{3}{4}$ kg

COMPUTER APPLICATIONS

BASIC: EQUATION OF A LINE

Problem: *Given the slope and the coordinates of a point on a line, write a program which prints the equation of the line in slope-intercept form.*

This section is optional. Each computer applications lesson relates directly to a topic covered within the given chapter. (See Section 11–2, pages 392–394)

```
100 PRINT "WHAT IS THE SLOPE OF THE LINE AND THE"
110 PRINT "COORDINATES OF A POINT ON THE LINE";
120 INPUT M, X1, Y1
130 LET B = Y1 - M*X1
140 PRINT "EQUATION IS Y = ";
150 IF M = 0 THEN 240
160 IF B = 0 THEN 200
170 IF B < 0 THEN 220
180 PRINT M;"X +";B
190 GOTO 250
200 PRINT M;"X"
210 GOTO 250
220 PRINT M;"X -";ABS(B)
230 GOTO 250
240 PRINT B
250 PRINT
260 PRINT "ANY MORE LINES (1=YES, 0=NO)";
270 INPUT Z
280 IF Z = 1 THEN 120
290 END
```

Output:
```
RUN
WHAT IS THE SLOPE OF THE LINE AND THE
COORDINATES OF A POINT ON THE LINE? 3,1,1
EQUATION IS Y = 3 X - 2

ANY MORE LINES (1=YES, 0=NO)? 1
? -2,4,-7
EQUATION IS Y = -2 X + 1

ANY MORE LINES (1=YES, 0=NO)? 1
? 0,15,-1
EQUATION IS Y = -1

ANY MORE LINES (1=YES, 0=NO)? 1
? 5,1,5
EQUATION IS Y = 5 X

ANY MORE LINES (1=YES, 0=NO)? 0
READY
```

Equation of a Line   **419**

Analysis

Statement 130: In the slope–intercept form of a linear equation ($y = mx + b$), b represents the y intercept. Statement 130 is derived by solving the equation for b, and substituting the coordinates of the sample point, (x_1, y_1).

$$y = mx + b$$
$$y - mx = b \quad \underline{\text{or}} \quad b = y - mx$$
$$b = y_1 - m(x_1)$$

Statements 140–240: The bulk of the program is concerned with printing the equation as neatly as possible.

Statements 150 and 240: If M = 0, no X term is printed. See the output for the third set of data in the sample run on page 419.

Statements 160 and 200: If B = 0, just the X term is printed. See the output for the last set of data in the sample run on page 419.

Statements 170 and 220: If B < 0, the equation is printed as Y = 3 X − 2 and not as Y = 3 X + −2.

EXERCISES

A Run the program on page 419, using the following values of slope and coordinates of a point on each line.

1. Slope: 2; Point: $(0, 3)$
2. Slope: 4; Point: $(-2, -1)$
3. Slope: 3; Point: $(1, -3)$
4. Slope: 7; Point: $(3, 6)$
5. Slope: −1; Point: $(4, 0)$
6. Slope: −3; Point: $(1, 3)$
7. Slope: −10; Point: $(6, 2)$
8. Slope: 12; Point: $(0, 8)$
9. Slope: 0; Point: $(2, -5)$
10. Slope: 0; Point: $(-1, -1)$

11. The program on page 419 does not handle vertical lines, since the slope of such lines is undefined. Add statements to the program so that a value of 999 for the slope is the code for a vertical line. Print the equation in the form $x = x_1$. See the Solution Key for the answers to Exercises 11-15.

B Write a BASIC program for each problem.

12. Given the coordinates of two points on a line, print the equation of the line in slope–intercept form.

13. Given the coordinates of a point on a line and the y intercept, print the equation of the line in slope–intercept form.

14. y varies inversely as x. Given the constant of variation and the smallest and largest x values, print a table of ordered pairs for x and y.

15. Given two ordered pairs, print whether the set of ordered pairs is an example of inverse variation.

IMPORTANT TERMS

Apparent solution (p. 389)
Combined variation (p. 416)
General form of a linear
  equation (p. 396)

Hyperbola (p. 413)
Inverse variation (p. 412)
Joint variation (p. 416)

IMPORTANT IDEAS

1. **Steps for Solving Equations with Rational Expressions**
   - ☐1 Multiply each side of the equation by the LCD.
   - ☐2 Follow the usual procedures to solve the resulting equation.

2. You can write the equation of a line if you know
   a. the slope and the y intercept,
   b. the slope and the coordinates of one point on the line, or
   c. the coordinates of two points on the line.

3. **Work formula:** rate of work × time = work done, or $r \cdot t = w$

_____ Chapter Objectives and Review _____

Objective: *To solve equations containing rational expressions (Section 11–1)*

Solve each equation.

1. $\dfrac{n}{2} - \dfrac{2n}{9} = 5$ $n = 18$

2. $\dfrac{24}{3x} = \dfrac{4}{9}$ $x = 18$

3. $\dfrac{12}{5x} - \dfrac{7}{5x} = \dfrac{1}{2}$ $x = 2$

4. $\dfrac{y}{6} = \dfrac{y}{2(2-y)}$ $y = -1$ or $y = 0$

5. $\dfrac{a}{3} = \dfrac{4}{a+4}$ $a = -6$ or $a = 2$

6. $\dfrac{1}{y} + \dfrac{1}{2y} = \dfrac{1}{y+2}$

7. $\dfrac{4}{x} = \dfrac{x}{x+1} - \dfrac{1}{x^2+x}$ $x = 5$

8. $\dfrac{3}{x-3} + \dfrac{4}{x} = \dfrac{x}{x-3}$ $x = 4$

9. $\dfrac{a}{1+3a} = \dfrac{2}{a+5}$

10. $\dfrac{x-1}{x+2} - \dfrac{6}{x^2+2x} = \dfrac{2}{x}$ $x = 5$

11. $\dfrac{y}{y+14} = \dfrac{2}{y+5}$

12. $\dfrac{n+1}{n} = \dfrac{2}{2n-3} + \dfrac{2}{n}$

Objective: *To write the equation of a line, given its slope and the coordinates of a point on the line (Section 11–2)*

The slope and the y intercept of a line are given. Write the equation of the line in the form $y = mx + b$.

13. slope: -3; y intercept: 4 $y = -3x + 4$

14. slope: 5; y intercept: 0 $y = 5x$

15. slope: $-\dfrac{1}{2}$; y intercept: $-\dfrac{3}{4}$ $y = -\dfrac{1}{2}x - \dfrac{3}{4}$

16. slope: $\dfrac{5}{8}$; y intercept: 8 $y = \dfrac{5}{8}x + 8$

One point on a line and the slope of the line are given. Write the equation of the line in the form $y = mx + b$.

17. $B(1, 4)$; $m = 2$ $y = 2x + 2$

18. $P(-2, 3)$; $m = \dfrac{1}{4}$

19. $Y(-4, -4)$; $m = -1$

20. $D(5, 0)$; $m = 6$ $y = 6x - 30$

21. $Q(3, -3)$; $m = \dfrac{3}{2}$

22. $G(-4, -4)$; $m = 4$

Applications of Rational Expressions **421**

Additional Answers
6. $y = -6$
9. $a = -1$ or $a = 2$
11. $y = -7$ or $y = 4$
12. $n = \dfrac{1}{2}$ or $n = 3$
18. $y = \dfrac{1}{4}x + \dfrac{7}{2}$
19. $y = -x - 8$
21. $y = \dfrac{3}{2}x - \dfrac{15}{2}$
22. $y = 4x + 12$

Objective: *To write the equation of a line, given the coordinates of two points on the line (Section 11–3)*

Determine the equation of the line passing through the given points. Write the equation in the form $y = mx + b$.

23. $M(0, 2)$; $N(3, 11)$ $y = 3x + 2$ 24. $P(2, 0)$; $Q(-4, 3)$ 25. $X(0, 0)$; $Y(-3, 15)$

26. $A(1, 2)$; $B(-1, -4)$ $y = 3x - 1$ 27. $F(2, -3)$; $G(-2, 5)$ 28. $J(3, 0)$; $K(-6, -12)$

Determine the equation of the line passing through the given points. Write the equation in general form.

29. $C(3, 5)$; $D(5, 3)$ $x + y = 8$ 30. $X(0, -4)$; $Y(1, -2)$ 31. $H(4, -1)$; $I(-6, 3)$

   $2x - y = 4$ $2x + 5y = 3$

Objective: *To solve number problems involving rational expressions (Section 11–4)*

32. The sum of two fractions is $\frac{11}{12}$. One fraction is $\frac{3}{8}$ of the other. Find the fractions. $\frac{1}{4}, \frac{2}{3}$

33. The sum of two positive integers is 14. The difference of their reciprocals is $\frac{1}{24}$. Find the integers.   6, 8

Objective: *To solve motion problems (Section 11–5)*

34. Miriam drove 400 kilometers in the same amount of time that it took Ruth to drive 320 kilometers. Miriam drove 15 kilometers per hour faster than Ruth. Find the speed of each.   Ruth: 60 km/h; Miriam: 75 km/h

35. Bob paddles his canoe at a rate of 6 kilometers per hour in still water. Find the rate of the current if it takes Bob twice as long to paddle 20 kilometers upstream as to paddle 20 kilometers downstream.   2 km/h

Objective: *To solve work problems (Section 11–6)*

36. An old machine can produce an order for bottle caps in 7.5 hours. A newer machine can produce the same number of caps in 5 hours. How long would it take to fill the order using both machines together?   3 hours

37. One outboard motor uses up a tank of fuel in 6 hours. A larger motor uses the same amount of fuel in 4 hours. How long can both motors be run if they are connected to the same tank that is filled to capacity? $2\frac{2}{5}$ hours

Objective: *To solve problems involving inverse variation (Section 11–7)*

y varies inversely as x. Write the equation that shows how x and y are related.

38. $y = 36$ when $x = -3$ $xy = -108$ 39. $y = 7$ when $x = 1$ $xy = 7$ 40. $y = 6$ when $x = 16$ $xy = 96$

41. $y = 9$ when $x = \frac{1}{2}$ $xy = 4\frac{1}{2}$ 42. $y = -2\frac{1}{2}$ when $x = 3$ $xy = -7\frac{1}{2}$ 43. $y = -\frac{9}{2}$ when $x = \frac{2}{3}$ $xy = -3$

44. A rectangular garden is to have a given area. When the length is 8 meters, the width is 3.5 meters. What is the width when the length is 5.6 meters?   5 meters

45. A rectangular box is to have a given volume. When the area of the base of the box is 144 square units, the height is 8 units. What is the height when the area of the base is 256 square units? $4\frac{1}{2}$ units

Objective: *To solve problems involving joint or combined variation*
(Section 11–8)

46. If c varies jointly as p and q, and $c = 84$ when $p = 3$ and $q = 7$, find c when $p = \frac{1}{2}$ and $q = 9$. $c = 18$

47. If r varies directly as w and inversely as y^2, and $r = 2$ when $w = 6$ and $y = 3$, find r when $w = 10$ and $y = 2$. $r = 7\frac{1}{2}$

48. If b varies jointly as c and d and inversely as f^2, and $b = 80$ when $c = 10$, $d = 2$, and $f = 4$, find b when $c = 5$, $d = 6$, and $f = 2$. $b = 480$

49. If h varies jointly as j^2 and k and inversely as g, and $h = 50$ when $j = 2$, $k = 5$, and $g = \frac{1}{2}$, find h when $j = 4$, $k = 10$, and $g = \frac{1}{4}$. $h = 800$

50. The interest, i, for one year varies jointly as the principal, p, and the rate, r. When p is \$500 and r is 6%, i is \$30. Find i when p is \$800 and r is 9%. (HINT: Write a decimal for 6% and 9%.) $i = \$72$

51. The attraction, F, between two objects varies jointly as their masses, a and b, and inversely as the square of the distance, d, between them. When $F = 4$, $a = 3$, $b = 4$, and $d = 6$. Find F when $a = 5$, $b = 15$, and $d = 20$. $F = 2\frac{1}{4}$

_____ Chapter Test _____

A formal Chapter Test is provided in the Teacher's Manual. See p. M-74.

Solve each equation.

1. $\frac{x}{6} + \frac{2x}{9} = 7$ $x = 18$

2. $\frac{3y}{y+9} + \frac{3}{4y} = 1$ $y = 1\frac{1}{8}$ or $y = 3$

3. $\frac{a}{a-2} = \frac{2}{a-3}$ $a = 1$ or $a = 4$

One point on a line and the slope of the line are given. Write the equation of the line in the form $y = mx + b$.

4. $A(0, 3)$; $m = -1$ $y = -x + 3$

5. $P(1, -2)$; $m = \frac{1}{3}$ $y = \frac{1}{3}x - \frac{7}{3}$

6. $F(-6, 5)$; $m = 3$ $y = 3x + 23$

Determine the equation of the line passing through the given points. Write the equation in the form $y = mx + b$.

7. $A(3, 5)$; $B(5, 3)$ $y = -x + 8$

8. $X(0, -4)$; $Y(1, -2)$ $y = 2x - 4$

9. $M(4, -1)$; $N(-6, 3)$ $y = -\frac{2}{5}x + \frac{3}{5}$

10. Jan drove 160 kilometers in the same time that Karen drove 150 kilometers. Jan drove 5 kilometers per hour faster than Karen. Find the speed of each.

11. It takes David 30 minutes to load a truck. Matthew can do the job in 20 minutes. How long will it take them to load the truck if they work together?

12. The sum of two fractions is $1\frac{1}{2}$. One fraction is $\frac{4}{5}$ of the other fraction. Find the two fractions. $\frac{2}{3}, \frac{5}{6}$

13. If p varies inversely as t, and $p = 3$ when $t = 6$, find p when $t = 9$. $p = 2$

14. If c varies inversely as d, and $c = 4$ when $d = -6$, find c when $d = 2$. $c = -12$

15. Given that c varies jointly as n and p and inversely as t, and $n = 4$, $p = 6$, and $t = 12$ when $c = 1$, find c when $n = 5$, $p = 18$, and $t = 15$. $c = 3$

Applications of Rational Expressions   **423**

Additional Answers
Chapter Test
10. Jan: 80 km/h; Karen: 75 km/h
11. 12 min

Additional Practice

You may wish to use all or some of these exercises depending on how well students performed on the formal chapter test.

Skills

Solve. *(Section 11–1)*

1. $\frac{y}{6} + \frac{y}{9} = 5$ $y = 18$

2. $\frac{2}{x} + \frac{3}{4} = \frac{4x + 5}{4x}$ $x = 3$

3. $\frac{n}{n+1} = \frac{3}{n-1} - \frac{6}{n^2 - 1}$ $n = 3$

One point on a line and the slope of the line are given. Write the equation of the line in the form $y = mx + b$. *(Section 11–2)*

4. $A(3, 4)$; $m = 4$ $y = 4x - 8$

5. $B(0, -6)$; $m = -2$ $y = -2x - 6$

6. $C(-2, -4)$; $m = 1$ $y = x - 2$

7. $D(-1, 5)$; $m = -\frac{1}{2}$

8. $E(3, 0)$; $m = \frac{2}{3}$ $y = \frac{2}{3}x - 2$

9. $F(0, 0)$; $m = -\frac{3}{4}$

Determine the equation of the line passing through the given points. Write the equation in the form $y = mx + b$. *(Section 11–3)*

10. $A(-2, 0)$; $D(0, 4)$ $y = 2x + 4$

11. $C(0, 0)$; $B(2, -3)$ $y = -\frac{3}{2}x$

12. $M(0, 5)$; $N(-1, -4)$ $y = 9x + 5$

13. $P(3, 2)$; $Q(-2, -3)$ $y = x - 1$

14. $R(4, -1)$; $S(-2, -2)$

15. $J(-1, -1)$; $K(1, 5)$

Determine the equation of the line passing through the given points. Write the equation in general form. *(Section 11–3)*

16. $S(6, -2)$; $T(0, 3)$

17. $F(-4, -1)$; $G(4, -2)$

18. $V(0, -3)$; $W(12, 0)$

(Section 11–7)

19. If y varies inversely as x, and $y = 6$ when $x = 8$, find y when $x = 12$. $y = 4$

20. If b varies inversely as h, and $b = 0.5$ when $h = 4$, find b when $h = 10$. $b = 0.2$

(Section 11–8)

21. If x varies jointly as y and z, and $x = 60$ when $y = 5$ and $z = 2$, find x when $y = 3$ and $z = 4$. $x = 72$

22. If p varies directly as q^2 and inversely as r, and $p = -4$ when $q = 4$ and $r = -2$, find p when $q = 3$ and $r = 6$. $p = \frac{3}{4}$

Applications

23. Two integers are consecutive. If 5 is subtracted from the lesser integer and added to the greater integer, their quotient is equal to $\frac{1}{2}$. Find the integers. *(Section 11–4)* 16, 17

24. Kim drove her car 100 kilometers in the same time that Sue drove her car 110 kilometers. Sue's average rate was 6 kilometers per hour faster than Kim's. Find the average rate for each person. *(Section 11–5)*

25. A plane can fly 1050 kilometers with a tailwind in the same time that it can fly 900 kilometers against the wind. If the wind speed is 25 kilometers per hour, what is the speed of the plane in still air? *(Section 11–5)* 325 km/h

26. Janet can type a manuscript in 6 days. After working alone one day, Ted helps her to complete the job. Together, they finish the typing in 3 more days. How long would it take Ted to do the job alone? *(Section 11–6)* 9 days

---

Additional Answers

7. $y = -\frac{1}{2}x + \frac{9}{2}$

9. $y = -\frac{3}{4}x$

14. $y = -\frac{1}{6}x - \frac{1}{3}$

15. $y = 3x + 2$

16. $5x + 6y - 18$

17. $x + 8y = -12$

18. $x - 4y = 12$

24. Kim: 60 km/h; Sue: 66 km/h

Review of Word Problems: Chapters 1–11

In this cumulative review of word problems, note that each problem is referenced to the related section.

1. Jill paid $19.53 for 45 liters of gasoline and one liter of oil. If the oil cost $1.93, what was the cost of one liter of gasoline? *(Section 3–4)*   39.1¢

2. The perimeter of a triangle is 75 inches. The first side is $\frac{2}{3}$ of the second side and the third side is $\frac{5}{6}$ of the second side. Find the length of each side of the triangle. *(Section 4–4)*   20 in; 25 in; 30 in

3. Alex is now four times as old as his sister, Louise. In 2 years, Alex will be three times as old as Louise will be then. How old are Alex and Louise now? *(Section 4–5)*   Louise: 4; Alex: 16

4. Ronald and Tony left the same place at the same time and drove in opposite directions. Ronald's rate was 8 miles per hour less than Tony's rate. After 2 hours they were 200 miles apart. Find the rate at which each was traveling. *(Section 5–2)*   Ronald: 46 mph; Tony: 54 mph

5. Which has the greater area, a rectangle with length $(a + 6)$ units and width $(a - 4)$ units or a rectangle with length $(a + 5)$ units and width $(a - 3)$ units? How much greater is it? *(Section 8–8)*

6. In how many ways can 126 seedlings be planted so that each row has the same number of seedlings and there are at least 6 rows and 6 columns? *(Section 9–1)*

7. The area of a rectangle is expressed as $(x^2 + 4x - 12)$ square units. Express the length and width of the rectangle as binomials. *(Section 9–5)*

8. The area of the carpet in a large reception room is 96 square meters. The length of the carpet is 4 meters more than its width. Find the length and width of the carpet. *(Section 9–9)*   length: 12 m; width: 8 m

9. A 3-meter pole casts a 2.4-meter shadow at the same time that a tree casts a 10.4-meter shadow. How tall is the tree? *(Section 10–1)*   13 m

10. Patricia Brancato invested some money at different yearly interest rates. Part was invested at 12%, twice that amount at 13%, and $200 less at 10% than at 12%. The total yearly income was $460. How much was invested at each rate? *(Section 10–2)*   12%: $1000; 13%: $2000; 10%: $800

11. The sum of two fractions is $\frac{14}{15}$. One fraction is $\frac{3}{25}$ of the other. Find the fractions. *(Section 11–4)* $\frac{5}{6}, \frac{1}{10}$

12. It took Marcia 4 hours to drive from her home to the airport and back. Her average rate going was 50 miles per hour. Her average rate returning was 30 miles per hour, since the traffic was heavy. How far is her home from the airport? *(Section 11–5)*   75 mi

13. Warren can weed a garden in 2 hours. His younger brother can weed the same garden in 6 hours. How long will it take them to weed the garden if they work together? *(Section 11–6)* $1\frac{1}{2}$ hours

14. The current in an electric circuit varies inversely as the resistance. When the resistance is 8 ohms, the current is 60 amps. Find the resistance when the current is 32 amps. *(Section 11–7)*   15 ohms

Additional Answers
5. rectangle with length $(a+5)$ units and width $(a-3)$ units; 9 square units greater
6. 6 rows, 21 columns; 7 rows, 18 columns; 9 rows, 14 columns; 14 rows, 9 columns; 18 rows, 7 columns; 21 rows, 6 columns
7. length: $(x+6)$ units; width: $(x-2)$ units

Cumulative Review: Chapters 8–11

The Test Booklet contains another form of the cumulative review.

1. Which expression equals xy^3? **a**

   a. $x \cdot y \cdot y \cdot y$ **b.** $x \cdot x \cdot x \cdot y \cdot y \cdot y$ **c.** $(x \cdot y)(x \cdot y)(x \cdot y)$ **d.** $x \cdot x \cdot x \cdot y$

2. Which expression equals $(y^2)^3$? **c**

   a. $3 \cdot y^2$ **b.** $y^2 \cdot y$ **c.** $y^2 \cdot y^2 \cdot y^2$ **d.** $y^{3 \cdot 3}$

3. For which numbers in the replacement set $\{-5, 0, 5\}$ is it true that $(3y^2)^3 = 27y^6$? **d**

   a. 0   **b.** -5 **c.** -5 and 5   **d.** $-5, 0$ and 5

4. Simplify: $\dfrac{(4m^2d^3)(3md^2)^3}{(3md^3)^2}$ **a**

   a. $12m^3d^3$ **b.** $(12md)^3$ **c.** $12m^3d^5$ **d.** $\dfrac{4m^2}{3d^3}$

5. Simplify: $(2)^{-3}$ **c**

   a. -6 **b.** $-\dfrac{1}{8}$ **c.** $\dfrac{1}{8}$ **d.** -8

6. Write 84,000,000 in scientific notation. **d**

   a. 8.4×10^6 **b.** 0.84×10^8 **c.** 0.84×10^6 **d.** 8.4×10^7

7. Subtract: $(7xy - 3xy^2 - 6) - (xy^2 - xy - 9)$ **d**

   a. $8xy - 4xy^2 - 3$ **b.** $6xy - 2xy^2 - 15$ **c.** $6xy - 4xy^2 - 15$ **d.** $8xy - 4xy^2 + 3$

8. Subtract: $7 - 4(3m - 5)$ **b**

   a. $9m + 20$ **b.** $-12m + 27$ **c.** $-12m - 13$ **d.** $9m - 5$

9. Which expression equals $(x - 3y)^2$? **b**

   a. $x^2 - 3xy + 9y^2$ **b.** $x^2 - 6xy + 9y^2$ **c.** $x^2 + 9y^2$ **d.** $x^2 - 9y^2$

10. Multiply: $(3y - 7x)(3y + 7x)$ **c**

    a. $9y^2 + 49x^2$ **b.** $3y^2 - 7x^2$ **c.** $9y^2 - 49x^2$ **d.** $9x^2 - 14xy + 49y^2$

11. Write the prime factorization of 72. **b**

    a. $4 \cdot 2 \cdot 3^2$ **b.** $2^3 \cdot 3^2$ **c.** $2 \cdot 6^2$ **d.** $2^3 \cdot 9$

12. Which of the following is *not* a factor of $12(x + y)(x - y)$? **c**

    a. $12(x - y)$ **b.** $x + y$ **c.** $(x - y)^2$ **d.** $12(x + y)$

13. Which of the following is a factor of $8(x + y) - 3(x + y)$? **a**

    a. $x + y$ **b.** 3   **c.** $5(x - y)$ **d.** $5x + 8y$

14. Which of the following is *not* a factor of $\dfrac{n^2}{25} - \dfrac{m^2}{36}$? **c**

    a. $\dfrac{n}{5} + \dfrac{m}{6}$ **b.** $\dfrac{n}{5} - \dfrac{m}{6}$ **c.** $\dfrac{n^2 - m^2}{25 \cdot 36}$ **d.** $(n - m)$

15. Find a factor of $6y^4 - 10y^3 + 4y^2$. **b**

    a. $3y + 1$ **b.** $2y^2$ **c.** $(3y + 2)(y - 1)$ **d.** $2y^2(y + 1)$

16. Which of the following is a perfect square trinomial? **c**

    a. $6a^2 + 6ab + 4b^2$ **b.** $3a^2 + 12ab + 4b^2$ **c.** $9a^2 + 12ab + 4b^2$ **d.** $9a^2 + 12ab + b^2$

17. Solve: $2x^2 = 18x$ **b**

 a. $\{0\}$ **b.** $\{0, 9\}$ **c.** $\{\ \}$ **d.** $\{\pm 3\}$

18. Solve: $2x^2 = x + 3$ **c**

 a. $\{1\}$ **b.** $\{3, -1\}$ **c.** $\{\frac{3}{2}, -1\}$ **d.** $\{\frac{2}{3}, -1\}$

19. The length of a rectangle is 2 centimeters more than the width. When the length and the width are each increased by 3 centimeters, the area is 80 square centimeters. Which equation will give the original width of the rectangle, w?

 a. $2(w + 2) = 80$ **b.** $(w + 3)(w + 5) = 80$ **b**

 c. $w(w + 2) + 80 = (w + 3)(w + 5)$ **d.** $w^2 + w(w + 2) = 80$

20. Solve for y: $\dfrac{y + 4}{2} = \dfrac{y - 3}{5}$ **a**

 a. $y = -8\frac{2}{3}$ **b.** $y = 8$ **c.** $y = -8$ **d.** $y = 0$

21. Carlo has $6000 invested, part at 6% and the rest at 11%. His total yearly interest is $460. If x is the amount at 6%, which equation expresses the total interest? **c**

 a. $0.11x + 0.06(6000 - x) = 460$ **b.** $0.11 - 6000 + 0.06x = 460$

 c. $0.06x + 0.11(6000 - x) = 460$ **d.** $0.06 + 0.11)(6000 - x) = 460$

22. Divide and simplify: $\dfrac{x - 2}{x^2 - 5x + 6} \div \dfrac{x^2 - 3x}{x^2 - 9}$ **c**

 a. $\dfrac{x - 1}{x}$ **b.** $\dfrac{x}{(x - 3)(x + 3)}$ **c.** $\dfrac{x + 3}{x(x - 3)}$ **d.** $-\dfrac{6}{x(x^2 + 1)}$

23. Subtract: $\dfrac{3y}{2} - \dfrac{y + 7}{6}$ **a**

 a. $\dfrac{8y - 7}{6}$ **b.** $\dfrac{2y - 7}{6}$ **c.** $\dfrac{8y + 7}{6}$ **d.** $8y - 7$

24. Divide: $(x^3 - 6x^2 - x + 30) \div (x + 2)$ **d**

 a. $x - 3$ **b.** $x^2 + 8x + 15$ **c.** $x - 5$ **d.** $x^2 - 8x + 15$

25. Solve: $\dfrac{7}{4y} - 2 = \dfrac{3}{2y} - 4$ **b**

 a. $y = \frac{5}{8}$ **b.** $y = -\frac{1}{8}$ **c.** $y = 0$ **d.** $y = \frac{1}{8}$

26. What is the equation of the line with slope -4 and containing the point $A(-5, 3)$? **d**

 a. $y - 4x = 17$ **b.** $y = -4x + 17$ **c.** $3y - 5x = -4$ **d.** $4x + y = -17$

27. The numerator of a fraction is 7 less than the denominator. If 2 is added to the numerator, the new fraction equals $\frac{3}{4}$. What is the denominator of the original fraction? **a**

 a. 20 **b.** 13 **c.** 4 **d.** 5

28. y varies directly as the square of x and inversely as z. When x is 3 and z is 1, then y is 63. Find y when x is 4 and z is 2. **c**

 a. 14 **b.** 7 **c.** 56 **d.** 112

Preparing for College Entrance Tests

Additional practice can be found in the Teacher's Manual.

Given a system of equations (or a compound sentence with "and"), you can sometimes answer questions on College Entrance tests without solving the system. The key is in recognizing a binomial product or the factors of such a product.

EXAMPLE: If $a + b = 5$ and $a - b = 3$, find $a^2 - b^2$.

      (a) 2   (b) 3   (c) 15   (d) 16

Think: $a^2 - b^2 = (a + b)(a - b)$

Solution: $a^2 - b^2 = (a + b)(a - b)$ ⟵ **From the given equations:** $a + b = 5; a - b = 3.$

                  $= (5)(3) = \mathbf{15}$ **Answer: c**

Choose the best answer. Choose a, b, c, or d.

1. If $x - y = 6$ and $x + y = -1$, find $x^2 - y^2$. a
   (a) -6 (b) 5   (c) 6   (d) 35

2. If $m + 2p = 4$ and $m - 2p = 6$, find $m^2 - 4p^2$. c
   (a) -8 (b) 10   (c) 24   (d) 26

3. If $3c - d = 1$ and $3c + d = \frac{1}{2}$, find $9c^2 - d^2$. a
   (a) $\frac{1}{2}$ (b) $\frac{3}{4}$ (c) $1\frac{1}{2}$ (d) 2

4. If $s^2 - t^2 = 6$ and $s + t = 3$, find $s - t$. a
   (a) 2   (b) 3   (c) 6   (d) 18

5. If $a - b = 2$ and $a^2 - b^2 = 12$, find $a + b$. b
   (a) $\frac{1}{6}$ (b) 6   (c) 14   (d) 24

6. If $4p^2 - 9r^2 = 3$ and $2p + 3r = 3$, find $2p - 3r$. b
   (a) -1 (b) 1   (c) 3   (d) 9

7. If $(a + b)^2 = 6$ and $ab = 8$, find $a^2 + b^2$. (HINT: $(a + b)^2 = a^2 + 2ab + b^2$.) d
   (a) 22   (b) 20   (c) -2 (d) -10

8. If $x + y = 8$ and $xy = 4$, find $x^2 + y^2$. b
   (a) 0   (b) 56   (c) 60   (d) 72

9. If $(a - b)^2 = 49$ and $ab = 30$, find $a^2 + b^2$. a
   (a) 109   (b) 79   (c) 67   (d) -11

10. If $xy = \frac{1}{2}$ and $x^2 + y^2 = 1\frac{1}{4}$, find $(x + y)^2$. d
   (a) $\frac{1}{4}$ (b) $\frac{5}{8}$ (c) $\frac{3}{4}$ (d) $2\frac{1}{4}$

11. If $x^2 + y^2 = 8$ and $xy = 4$, find $(x - y)^2$. a
   (a) 0   (b) 2   (c) 12   (d) 16

Preparing for College Entrance Tests

Additional practice can be found in the Teacher's Manual.

On College Entrance tests, it is important to recognize problems that can be solved by using proportions.

REMEMBER: Write the ratios of a proportion so that they compare the same units in the same order.

EXAMPLE: If c cans of stew make x servings, how many cans are needed to make y servings?

(a) $\dfrac{xy}{c}$ (b) $\dfrac{cx}{y}$ (c) $\dfrac{c}{xy}$ (d) $\dfrac{cy}{x}$

Think: $\dfrac{c \text{ cans}}{x \text{ servings}} = \dfrac{?}{y \text{ servings}}$

Solution: Let $n =$ the number of cans needed for y servings.

$\dfrac{c}{x} = \dfrac{n}{y}$ ← **Cans**
← **Servings**

$xn = cy$

$n = \dfrac{cy}{x}$ **Answer: d**

Choose the best answer. Choose a, b, c, or d.

1. If a machine fills c cans in h hours, how many hours will it take to fill d cans?   a

(a) $\dfrac{hd}{c}$ (b) $\dfrac{h}{cd}$ (c) $\dfrac{d}{hc}$ (d) $\dfrac{cd}{h}$

2. If Beth earns d dollars in h hours, how many dollars will she earn in 10 hours?   b

(a) $\dfrac{10h}{d}$ (b) $\dfrac{10d}{h}$ (c) $10 + \dfrac{d}{h}$ (d) $\dfrac{10 + d}{h}$

3. A car travels a kilometers in b hours. At that rate, how many hours will it take the car to go 200 kilometers?   d

(a) $200\dfrac{a}{b}$ (b) $\dfrac{b}{200a}$ (c) $\dfrac{200}{a} + b$ (d) $\dfrac{200b}{a}$

4. If c cups of flour are used to make p pie crusts, how many cups of flour are needed to make $2p$ pie crusts?   c

(a) $2p$ (b) $\dfrac{c}{2}$ (c) $2c$ (d) $\dfrac{2}{p}$

5. If p pounds of potatoes cost d dollars, how many pounds of potatoes can be bought with $3d$ dollars?   a

(a) $3p$ (b) $3d$ (c) $\dfrac{3d^2}{p}$ (d) $\dfrac{3p}{d} + 1$

6. A car uses x liters of gasoline every y kilometers it is driven. At that rate, how many kilometers can the car be driven with $x + 10$ liters of gasoline? **d**

(a) $y + \dfrac{10}{x}$ (b) $\dfrac{x^2 + 10x}{y}$ (c) $y(x + 10)$ (d) $\dfrac{y(x + 10)}{x}$

7. During p hours, a total of v vehicles pass through an intersection. At that rate, how many vehicles would pass through the intersection in $p - 1$ hours?

(a) $pv(p - 1)$ (b) $v - \dfrac{1}{p}$ (c) $\dfrac{pv - 1}{p}$ (d) $\dfrac{v(p - 1)}{p}$ **d**

8. Maria earns d dollars per hour. How many dollars does she earn in 40 hours?

(a) $\dfrac{40}{d}$ (b) $40d$ (c) $\dfrac{d}{40}$ (d) $d + 40$ **b**

9. If c crates can be carried on each boxcar, how many boxcars are needed to carry 500 crates?   **c**

(a) $500c$ (b) $500 - c$ (c) $\dfrac{500}{c}$ (d) $\dfrac{c}{500}$

10. An airplane travels m miles in h hours. At that rate, how many miles does it travel in 30 minutes?   **a**

(a) $\dfrac{m}{2h}$ (b) $\dfrac{1800h}{m}$ (c) $\dfrac{2m}{h}$ (d) $30mh$

11. Keith types w words per minute. At that rate, how many words does he type in h hours?   **c**

(a) $\dfrac{60w}{h}$ (b) $\dfrac{60h}{w}$ (c) $60wh$ (d) $\dfrac{wh}{60}$

12. For nonzero numbers a, b, and c, $2a = 4b$ and $8b = 6c$. Then $\dfrac{a}{c} = \underline{\quad?\quad}$
(HINT: Since $2a = 4b$, $4a = 8b$. But $8b = 6c$. Then $4a = 6c$.) **b**

(a) $\dfrac{2}{3}$ (b) $\dfrac{3}{2}$ (c) $\dfrac{8}{3}$ (d) $\dfrac{3}{1}$

13. For nonzero numbers x, y, and z, $3x = 2y$ and $6y = 4z$. Then $\dfrac{x}{z} = \underline{\quad?}$ **d**

(a) $\dfrac{9}{4}$ (b) $\dfrac{3}{4}$ (c) $\dfrac{2}{3}$ (d) $\dfrac{4}{9}$

14. For nonzero numbers r, s, and t, $4r = 8s$ and $4s = 5t$. Then $\dfrac{r}{t} = \underline{\quad?}$ **a**

(a) $\dfrac{5}{2}$ (b) $\dfrac{8}{5}$ (c) $\dfrac{5}{4}$ (d) $\dfrac{5}{8}$

15. The ratio of the length of a rectangle to its perimeter is $1 : 3$. What is the ratio of the length of the rectangle to its width?   **a**
(HINT: Perimeter of a rectangle $= 2l + 2w$)

(a) $2 : 1$ (b) $3 : 1$ (c) $3 : 2$ (d) $1 : 1$

CHAPTER 12 Radicals

Quick Quiz
Evaluate.
1. 11^2 **Ans: 121**
2. 15^2 **Ans: 225**
3. $(25x)^2$ **Ans: $625x^2$**
4. $(x^2yz^3)^2$ **Ans: $x^4y^2z^6$**
5. $(17ab^2c^4)^2$ **Ans: $289a^2b^4c^8$**

OBJECTIVE: To find the square roots of numbers or expressions that are perfect squares

12–1 **Roots of Numbers**

To square a number, you multiply it by itself. The inverse operation is taking the square root.

Since $5^2 = 25$, $\sqrt{25} = 5$. ◄———— **Read: "The square root of 25 is 5."**

In the expression $\sqrt{25}$, $\sqrt{}$ is the **radical symbol,** 25 is the **radicand,** and $\sqrt{25}$ is the **radical.**

Since $9^2 = 81$ and $(-9)^2 = 81$, the number 81 has two square roots, 9 and -9. Every positive real number has two square roots, one positive and one negative.

Definition

> The **principal square root** of a positive real number is the positive square root of the number. The principal square root is indicated by the radical symbol, $\sqrt{}$.

From the definition,

$$\sqrt{\frac{49}{9}} = \frac{7}{3} \quad \text{and} \quad \sqrt{0.36} = 0.6.$$

A negative square root is associated with the symbol, $-\sqrt{}$. The symbol, $\pm\sqrt{}$, indicates both square roots. Thus,

$$-\sqrt{81} = -9 \quad \text{and} \quad \pm\sqrt{81} = \pm 9.$$

Additional Examples
Example 1
Simplify.
1. a. $\sqrt{900}$ **Ans: 30**
   b. $\sqrt{256}$ **Ans: 16**
2. a. $\pm\sqrt{\dfrac{36}{121}}$ **Ans: $\pm\dfrac{6}{11}$**
   b. $\pm\sqrt{\dfrac{64}{169}}$ **Ans: $\pm\dfrac{8}{13}$**

EXAMPLE 1 Simplify: a. $\sqrt{400}$ b. $\pm\sqrt{\dfrac{49}{625}}$

Solutions: a. $\sqrt{400} = 20$ ◄———— **Since $(20)^2 = 400$**

b. $\pm\sqrt{\dfrac{49}{625}} = \pm\dfrac{7}{25}$ ◄———— **Since $\left(\dfrac{7}{25}\right)^2 = \dfrac{49}{625}$ and $\left(-\dfrac{7}{25}\right)^2 = \dfrac{49}{625}$**

A negative number has no real-number square root.

$$\sqrt{-225} \neq -15 \text{ because } (-15)^2 = 225.$$

Thus, for $\sqrt{a}$ to represent a nonnegative real number, a must be a positive real number or zero. Since $|a| \geq 0$ for all real numbers, absolute value notation can be used to ensure that $\sqrt{a^2}$ is a nonnegative real number.

Definition

> For any real number a,
> $$\sqrt{a^2} = |a|.$$

Example 2
Simplify.
1. a. $\sqrt{m^2n^2}$ **Ans: $|mn|$**
   b. $\sqrt{c^2d^2}$ **Ans: $|cd|$**
2. a. $\sqrt{64r^4}$ **Ans: $8r^2$**
   b. $\sqrt{196p^8}$ **Ans: $14p^4$**

EXAMPLE 2 Simplify: a. $\sqrt{r^2t^2}$ b. $\sqrt{81a^4}$

Solutions: a. $\sqrt{r^2t^2} = |rt|$ ◄———— **By definition**

b. $\sqrt{81a^4} = 9|a^2| = 9a^2$ ◄———— **Since a^2 cannot be negative**

NOTE: Since squaring a positive number and taking the square root are inverse operations, it follows that

$$(\sqrt{11})^2 = 11, \quad \text{and} \quad (\sqrt{a})^2 = a.$$

CLASSROOM EXERCISES

Write the two square roots of each number.

1. 64 ±8 2. 121 ±11 3. $\frac{25}{36}$ ±$\frac{5}{6}$ 4. $\frac{1}{4}$ ±$\frac{1}{2}$ 5. 10,000 ±100 6. $\frac{9}{100}$ ±$\frac{3}{10}$

Simplify.

7. $-\sqrt{36}$ −6 8. $\pm\sqrt{144}$ ±12 9. $-\sqrt{\frac{25}{169}}$ −$\frac{5}{13}$ 10. $-(\sqrt{7})^2$ −7 11. $-(\sqrt{18})^2$ −18 12. $(\sqrt{y})^2$ y

WRITTEN EXERCISES

Assignment Guide
Minimal p. 433: 2–40 even
Average
Day 1 p. 433: 1–40
Day 2 p. 433: 41–60
Above Average
Day 1 p. 433: 1–48
Day 2 p. 433: 49–72

A Simplify.

1. $\sqrt{16}$ 4 2. $-\sqrt{25}$ −5 3. $\sqrt{49}$ 7 4. $\pm\sqrt{144}$ ±12

5. $\pm\sqrt{100}$ ±10 6. $\pm\sqrt{81}$ ±9 7. $\sqrt{10,000}$ 100 8. $\sqrt{40,000}$ 200

9. $-\sqrt{4^2}$ −4 10. $\pm\sqrt{8^2}$ ±8 11. $\pm\sqrt{100^2}$ ±100 12. $\sqrt{125^2}$ 125

13. $\sqrt{\frac{9}{49}}$ $\frac{3}{7}$ 14. $\sqrt{\frac{4}{81}}$ $\frac{2}{9}$ 15. $\pm\sqrt{\frac{25}{36}}$ ±$\frac{5}{6}$ 16. $\pm\sqrt{\frac{121}{100}}$ ±$\frac{11}{10}$

17. $-\sqrt{\frac{64}{25}}$ −$\frac{8}{5}$ 18. $\pm\sqrt{\frac{144}{169}}$ ±$\frac{12}{13}$ 19. $\sqrt{\frac{81}{100}}$ $\frac{9}{10}$ 20. $\sqrt{\frac{196}{49}}$ 2

21. $(\sqrt{17})^2$ 17 22. $(\sqrt{13})^2$ 13 23. $(\sqrt{25})^2$ 25 24. $(\sqrt{46})^2$ 46

25. $\sqrt{b^2}$ $|b|$ 26. $\sqrt{c^4}$ c^2 27. $\pm\sqrt{t^{10}}$ ±$|t^5|$ 28. $\pm\sqrt{d^6}$ ±$|d^3|$

29. $\sqrt{c^4d^6}$ $c^2|d^3|$ 30. $-\sqrt{f^{10}t^4}$ −$|f^5|t^2$ 31. $-\sqrt{h^8s^{12}}$ −h^4s^6 32. $\sqrt{r^{12}t^6}$ $r^6|t^3|$

33. $\sqrt{9c^2}$ $3|c|$ 34. $\sqrt{81t^8}$ $9t^4$ 35. $-\sqrt{64c^6}$ −$8|c^3|$ 36. $-\sqrt{49b^4}$ −$7b^2$

37. $\pm\sqrt{25d^4}$ ±$5d^2$ 38. $\pm\sqrt{100r^{12}}$ ±$10r^6$ 39. $\sqrt{4x^2y^2}$ $2|xy|$ 40. $\sqrt{9a^2b^2}$ $3|ab|$

B

41. $\sqrt{0.49}$ 0.7 42. $\sqrt{0.25}$ 0.5 43. $-\sqrt{2.25}$ −1.5 44. $-\sqrt{1.44}$ −1.2

45. $\sqrt{0.64b^2}$ $0.8|b|$ 46. $\sqrt{1.69a^2}$ $1.3|a|$ 47. $\pm\sqrt{6.25t^4}$ ±$2.5t^2$ 48. $\pm\sqrt{4.41a^6}$

49. $\sqrt{25r^8s^{16}t^{12}}$ 50. $\pm\sqrt{49c^{10}d^6f^{12}}$ 51. $-\sqrt{81a^{12}b^8d^{16}}$ 52. $\sqrt{16f^4g^{10}h^{18}}$

53. $\pm\sqrt{\frac{49t^4}{25b^6}}$ ±$\frac{7t^2}{5|b^3|}$ 54. $\pm\sqrt{\frac{16d^8}{121f^2}}$ ±$\frac{4d^4}{11|f|}$ 55. $\sqrt{\frac{49a^4b^2}{9}}$ $\frac{7a^2|b|}{3}$ 56. $\sqrt{\frac{25x^2y^2}{36}}$ $\frac{5|xy|}{6}$

57. $\sqrt{(13c^3)^2}$ $13|c^3|$ 58. $\sqrt{(468d^7)^2}$ $468|d^7|$ 59. $\sqrt{(2a^2)^4}$ $4a^4$ 60. $\sqrt{(3b^3)^6}$ $27|b^9|$

C Examples: $\sqrt[3]{8} = 2$ ◄── Since $2^3 = 8$ $\sqrt[4]{81} = 3$ ◄── Since $3^4 = 81$

61. $\sqrt[3]{27}$ 3 62. $\sqrt[3]{125}$ 5 63. $\sqrt[4]{256}$ 4 64. $\sqrt[4]{625}$ 5

65. $\sqrt[3]{a^6b^3}$ a^2b 66. $\sqrt[3]{d^6t^9}$ d^2t^3 67. $\sqrt[3]{c^{12}f^{18}g^6}$ $c^4f^6g^2$ 68. $\sqrt[3]{r^9s^3t^6}$

69. $\sqrt[4]{(14b^2)^4}$ $14b^2$ 70. $\sqrt[3]{(23d^4)^3}$ $23d^4$ 71. $(\sqrt[3]{16f^6})^3$ $16f^6$ 72. $\sqrt[4]{(21t^3)^4}$

Additional Answers
Written Exercises
48. ±2.1$|a^3|$
49. $5r^4s^8t^6$
50. ±7$|c^5d^3|f^6$
51. $9a^6b^4d^8$
52. $4f^2|g^5h^9|$
68. $|r^3s|t^2$
72. 21$|t^3|$

Radicals **433**

Review Capsule
This Review Capsule reviews
the prior taught skills used in
Section 12-2. The reference is
to the pages where the skills
were taught.

——— **REVIEW CAPSULE FOR SECTION 12-2** ———

Classify each number as rational, *R*, or irrational, *Ir*. (Pages 25–29) *Ir*

1. $\sqrt{9}$ *R*   2. $\sqrt{121}$ *R*   3. $\sqrt{21}$ *Ir*   4. $\sqrt{5}$ *Ir*   5. $\sqrt{625}$ *R*   6. $\sqrt{37}$

Copy this table. Write *Yes* or *No* to identify the sets to which each number belongs. (Pages 25–29)

	Integers	Rational Numbers	Irrational Numbers	Real Numbers
7. -9	? Yes	? Yes	? No	? Yes
8. 64	? Yes	? Yes	? No	? Yes
9. 54	? Yes	? Yes	? No	? Yes
10. 1.25	? No	? Yes	? No	? Yes
11. 3.6	? No	? Yes	? No	? Yes
12. $\frac{1}{8}$	? No	? Yes	? No	? Yes

OBJECTIVE: To find rational approximations of square roots

12-2 Rational Approximations of Square Roots

Teaching Suggestions p. M-25

Quick Quiz
Simplify.
1. $\sqrt{324}$ **Ans: 18**
2. $\sqrt{441}$ **Ans: 21**
3. $\pm\sqrt{\frac{49}{225}}$ **Ans: $\pm\frac{7}{15}$**
4. $\pm\sqrt{\frac{256}{81}}$ **Ans: $\pm\frac{16}{9}$**
5. $\sqrt{a^2b^2}$ **Ans: $|ab|$**
6. $\sqrt{9x^2y^2}$ **Ans: $3|xy|$**
7. $\sqrt{81r^4x^8}$ **Ans: $9r^2x^4$**
8. $\sqrt{144a^{12}b^{20}}$ **Ans: $12a^6b^{10}$**

You learned in Chapter 1 that every rational number can be represented by an infinite repeating decimal or by a terminating decimal.

$$\frac{1}{3} = 0.333 \cdots, \text{ or } 0.\overline{3} \qquad 1\frac{3}{5} = \frac{8}{5} = 1.6$$

The bar indicates the digits that repeat.

You also learned that any rational number can be represented in the form $\frac{a}{b}$, where a is an integer and b is a natural number.

$$0 = \frac{0}{1} \qquad 5.61 = \frac{561}{100} \qquad 0.001 = \frac{1}{1000}$$

Example 1 shows how to represent an infinite repeating decimal in the form $\frac{a}{b}$.

Additional Examples
Example 1
Write each rational number
in the form $\frac{a}{b}$.
1. $0.\overline{6}$ **Ans: $\frac{2}{3}$**
2. $0.\overline{7}$ **Ans: $\frac{7}{9}$**

EXAMPLE 1   Write $0.\overline{3}$ in the form $\frac{a}{b}$.

Solution: Let $n = 0.\overline{3}$ ◄——— **Multiply each side by 10^1, or 10.**

$10n = 3.\overline{3}$ ◄——— **Subtract $n = 0.\overline{3}$ from this equation.**

$\underline{n = 0.\overline{3}}$

$9n = 3.0$ ◄——— **Solve for n.**

$n = \frac{3}{9}$, or $\frac{1}{3}$ Thus, $0.\overline{3} = \frac{1}{3}$.

434   *Chapter 12*

EXAMPLE 2 Write $9.\overline{18}$ in the form $\frac{a}{b}$.

Solution: Let $n = 9.\overline{18}$ ◄——— **Multiply each side by 10^2, or 100.**

$100n = 918.\overline{18}$ ◄——— **Subtract $n = 9.\overline{18}$ from this equation.**

$$\frac{\begin{array}{r} n = \quad 9.\overline{18} \end{array}}{99n = 909.00}$$

$n = \dfrac{909}{99} = \dfrac{101}{11}$ Thus, $9.\overline{18} = \dfrac{101}{11}$.

Recall that a rational number is a perfect square if it is the square of a rational number. A rational number that is not a perfect square has an **irrational square root.** Thus, the following numbers are irrational.

$$\sqrt{2} \qquad \sqrt{5} \qquad -\sqrt{17} \qquad \sqrt{31}$$

An irrational square root is often left in radical form. However, you can always approximate an irrational square root between consecutive integers.

$2 < \sqrt{7} < 3$ ◄——— **Since $\sqrt{4} < \sqrt{7} < \sqrt{9}$**

$9 < \sqrt{84} < 10$ ◄——— **Since $\sqrt{81} < \sqrt{84} < \sqrt{100}$**

You can use a calculator or the Table of Squares and Square Roots on page 541 to find a closer approximation to the square root of an irrational number.

EXAMPLE 3 The area of a square is 55 square meters. What is the length of each side to the nearest tenth of a meter?

Solution: Let s = the length of each side.

$s^2 = 55$ ◄——— **Area = s · s**

$s = \pm\sqrt{55}$ ◄——— **Since $s^2 = 55$, $s = \sqrt{55}$, or $s = -\sqrt{55}$.**

$s = \sqrt{55}$ ◄——— **s must be positive.**

Use the Table of Square Roots on page 541 to find $\sqrt{55}$.

$s \approx 7.416$ ◄——— **Round to the nearest tenth.**

$s \approx 7.4$ **meters**

No.	Square	Square Root
55	3025	7.416

CLASSROOM EXERCISES

Determine the consecutive integers x and y between which each square root lies.

1. $x < \sqrt{13} < y$ **2.** $x < \sqrt{26} < y$ **3.** $x < \sqrt{92} < y$ **4.** $x < \sqrt{32} < y$

Use the Table of Square Roots on page 541 to determine an approximation to each square root. Round each answer to the nearest tenth.

5. $\sqrt{8}$ 2.8 **6.** $\sqrt{21}$ 4.6 **7.** $\sqrt{13}$ 3.6 **8.** $\sqrt{26}$ 5.1 **9.** $\sqrt{92}$ 9.6 **10.** $\sqrt{59}$ 7.7

Radicals **435**

Additional Examples
Example 2
Write each rational number in the form $\frac{a}{b}$.
1. $9.\overline{12}$ **Ans:** $\frac{301}{33}$
2. $6.\overline{3}$ **Ans:** $\frac{19}{3}$

Example 3
1. The area of a square is 63 square meters. What is the length of each side to the nearest tenth of a meter? **Ans:** $\approx$ **7.9 m**
2. The area of a square is 41 square centimeters. What is the length of each side to the nearest tenth of a centimeter? **Ans:** $\approx$ **6.4 cm**

Additional Answers
1. $3 < \sqrt{13} < 4$
2. $5 < \sqrt{26} < 6$
3. $9 < \sqrt{92} < 10$
4. $5 < \sqrt{32} < 6$

WRITTEN EXERCISES

A   Write each rational number in the form $\frac{a}{b}$.

1. $0.\overline{4}$ $\frac{4}{9}$
2. $0.\overline{8}$ $\frac{8}{9}$
3. $0.\overline{15}$ $\frac{5}{33}$
4. $0.\overline{81}$

5. $0.\overline{72}$ $\frac{8}{11}$
6. $0.\overline{23}$ $\frac{23}{99}$
7. $0.\overline{186}$ $\frac{62}{333}$
8. $0.\overline{296}$

9. $0.\overline{543}$ $\frac{181}{333}$
10. $0.\overline{262}$ $\frac{262}{999}$
11. $1.\overline{2}$ $\frac{11}{9}$
12. $3.\overline{4}$ $\frac{31}{9}$

13. $2.\overline{51}$ $\frac{88}{33}$
14. $6.\overline{23}$ $\frac{617}{99}$
15. $3.\overline{14}$ $\frac{311}{99}$
16. $6.\overline{34}$

17. $1.3\overline{78}$ $\frac{91}{66}$
18. $4.2\overline{54}$ $\frac{234}{55}$
19. $3.70\overline{4}$ $\frac{1667}{450}$
20. $2.82\overline{9}$

Determine the consecutive integers x and y between which each square root lies.

21. $x < \sqrt{67} < y$
22. $x < \sqrt{47} < y$
23. $x < \sqrt{27} < y$

24. $x < \sqrt{101} < y$
25. $x < \sqrt{123} < y$
26. $x < \sqrt{150} < y$

27. $x < \sqrt{136} < y$
28. $x < \sqrt{46} < y$
29. $x < \sqrt{56} < y$

30. $x < \sqrt{14} < y$
31. $x < \sqrt{260} < y$
32. $x < \sqrt{901} < y$

33. $x < \sqrt{10,001} < y$
34. $x < \sqrt{1,000,001} < y$
35. $x < \sqrt{8101} < y$

APPLICATIONS: Using Approximations of Square Roots

Solve each problem.

Use the Table of Squares and Square Roots on page 541 or a calculator. Round answers to the nearest tenth.

36. The area of a square garden is 74 square meters. What is the length of one side of the garden?   8.6 m

37. The area of a square poster is 630 square centimeters. What is the length of a side of the poster?   25.1 cm

38. The area of a circle is 67 square centimeters. What is the radius of the circle? (HINT: Area $= \pi r^2$; use $\pi = 3.14$.)   4.6 cm

39. The area of a circular rug is 7 square meters. What is the diameter of the rug? (Use $\pi = 3.14$.)   3.0 m

B

40. The formula $d = 4.9t^2$ gives the approximate distance in meters traveled in t seconds by an object falling from rest. How long will an object take to fall 490 meters from rest?   10 seconds

41. The length of a rectangle is 5 times its width. The area of the rectangle is 204 square inches. Find the length and width of the rectangle.   6.4 in

42. The formula $D = 3.56\sqrt{a}$ gives the approximate distance to the horizon (in kilometers) from the viewpoint of an aircraft a meters above the ground. Find the distance to the horizon from the cockpit of an airplane 2025 meters off the ground. (HINT: Use the "Squares" column in the Tables of Squares and Square Roots.)   160.2 km

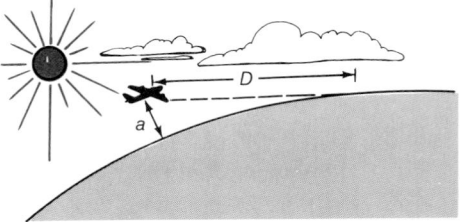

OBJECTIVE: To simplify radicals

12–3 Simplifying Radicals

Teaching Suggestions p. M-25

The following illustrates an important property of radicals.

$$\sqrt{9 \cdot 4} = \sqrt{36} = 6 \qquad\qquad \sqrt{9} \cdot \sqrt{4} = 3 \cdot 2 = 6$$

This suggests the following theorem.

Theorem 12–1

The square root of the product of two nonnegative numbers is the product of their square roots. That is, if a and b are real numbers and $a \geq 0$, $b \geq 0$, then $$\sqrt{ab} = \sqrt{a} \cdot \sqrt{b}.$$

Theorem 12–1 is used to simplify radicals. A radical is in **simplest form** when the radicand does not contain a perfect square factor other than 1.

EXAMPLE   Simplify.

  a. $\sqrt{50}$ **b.** $3\sqrt{8}$ **c.** $\sqrt{4d^5}$

Solutions: Identify the perfect square factors in the radicand.

  a. $\sqrt{50} = \sqrt{25 \cdot 2}$ ←——— **25 is the largest perfect square factor of 50.**

   $= \sqrt{25} \cdot \sqrt{2}$ ←——— $\sqrt{25 \cdot 2} = \sqrt{25} \cdot \sqrt{2}$

   $= 5\sqrt{2}$ ←——— **Simplest form**

  b. $3\sqrt{8} = 3\sqrt{4 \cdot 2}$

   $= 3 \cdot \sqrt{4} \cdot \sqrt{2}$ ←——— $\sqrt{4 \cdot 2} = \sqrt{4} \cdot \sqrt{2}$

   $= 3 \cdot 2 \cdot \sqrt{2}$

   $= 6\sqrt{2}$ ←——— **Simplest form**

  c. $\sqrt{4d^5} = \sqrt{4d^4 \cdot d}$ ←——— $4d^4$ **is the largest perfect square factor of** $4d^5$.

   $= \sqrt{4d^4} \cdot \sqrt{d}$

   $= 2d^2\sqrt{d}$ ←——— **Simplest form**

Quick Quiz
In Exercises 1–3, write each rational number in the form $\frac{a}{b}$.
1. $0.\overline{1}$ **Ans:** $\frac{1}{9}$
2. $0.\overline{16}$ **Ans:** $\frac{16}{99}$
3. $3.\overline{21}$ **Ans:** $\frac{106}{33}$
4. The area of a square is 75 square meters. What is the length of each side to the nearest tenth of a meter?
  Ans: $\approx$ **8.7 m**

Additional Examples
Simplify.
1. **a.** $\sqrt{75}$ **Ans:** $5\sqrt{3}$
  b. $\sqrt{72}$ **Ans:** $6\sqrt{2}$
2. **a.** $4\sqrt{12}$ **Ans:** $8\sqrt{3}$
  b. $5\sqrt{48}$ **Ans:** $20\sqrt{3}$
3. **a.** $\sqrt{9c^9}$ **Ans:** $3c^4\sqrt{c}$
  b. $\sqrt{49x^{13}}$ **Ans:** $7x^6\sqrt{x}$

CLASSROOM EXERCISES

Write each number as the product of the greatest possible perfect square integer and another factor.

1. $18 = \underline{\ ?\ } \times 2$ 9

2. $27 = \underline{\ ?\ } \times 3$ 9

3. $200 = \underline{\ ?\ } \times 2$ 100

4. $24 = \underline{\ ?\ } \times 6$ 4

5. $40 = \underline{\ ?\ } \times 10$ 4

6. $75 = \underline{\ ?\ } \times \underline{\ ?\ }$

7. $125 = \underline{\ ?\ } \times \underline{\ ?\ }$ 25 × 5

8. $288 = \underline{\ ?\ } \times \underline{\ ?\ }$ 144 × 2

9. $300 = \underline{\ ?\ } \times \underline{\ ?\ }$

10. $98 = \underline{\ ?\ } \times \underline{\ ?\ }$ 49 × 2

11. $243 = \underline{\ ?\ } \times \underline{\ ?\ }$ 81 × 3

12. $320 = \underline{\ ?\ } \times \underline{\ ?\ }$

Additional Answers
6. 25×3
9. 100×3
12. 64×5

Radicals   **437**

Assignment Guide
Minimal
Day 1 p. 438: 1–25
Day 2 p. 438: 26–48
Average
Day 1 p. 438: 1–18 odd, 19–36
Day 2 p. 438: 37–60
Above Average p. 438:
3, 6, 9, . . . 60, 61–66

Additional Answers
Written Exercises
29. $-20\sqrt{2}$
33. 3,000
34. 1,000,000
35. 30,000 $\sqrt{10}$
36. 400,000
45. $5q^5\sqrt{3q}$
48. $6c^4d^6\sqrt{2cd}$
63. $2(c^2 + d^2)\sqrt{7(c^2 + d^2)}$
64. $4(a^2 - b^2)^2\sqrt{3(a^2 - b^2)}$

Review Capsule
4. $a^2 - 2a + 1$
5. $a^2 + 2a + 1$
6. $4t^2 + 20t + 25$
12. 25
13. $a^2 = 119$
14. $a^2 = 207$
15. $a^2 = 57$
16. $a^2 = 148$
17. $a = -9$ or $a = 9$
18. $t = -6$ or $t = 6$
19. $a = -12$ or $a = 12$
20. $a = -11$ or $a = 11$

WRITTEN EXERCISES

A Simplify. Assume that all variables represent positive real numbers.

1. $\sqrt{8}$ $2\sqrt{2}$ **2.** $\sqrt{40}$ $2\sqrt{10}$ **3.** $\sqrt{20}$ $2\sqrt{5}$ **4.** $\sqrt{24}$ $2\sqrt{6}$

5. $\sqrt{12}$ $2\sqrt{3}$ **6.** $\sqrt{63}$ $3\sqrt{7}$ **7.** $\sqrt{75}$ $5\sqrt{3}$ **8.** $\sqrt{125}$ $5\sqrt{5}$

9. $\sqrt{100}$ 10 **10.** $\sqrt{98}$ $7\sqrt{2}$ **11.** $\sqrt{32}$ $4\sqrt{2}$ **12.** $2\sqrt{4}$ 4

13. $\sqrt{242}$ $11\sqrt{2}$ **14.** $\sqrt{64}$ 8 **15.** $\sqrt{196}$ 14 **16.** $\sqrt{28}$ $2\sqrt{7}$

17. $4\sqrt{72}$ $24\sqrt{2}$ **18.** $2\sqrt{20}$ $4\sqrt{5}$ **19.** $3\sqrt{28}$ $6\sqrt{7}$ **20.** $4\sqrt{49}$ 28

21. $\sqrt{56}$ $2\sqrt{14}$ **22.** $3\sqrt{18}$ $9\sqrt{2}$ **23.** $9\sqrt{50}$ $45\sqrt{2}$ **24.** $6\sqrt{72}$ $36\sqrt{2}$

25. $8\sqrt{12}$ $16\sqrt{3}$ **26.** $-6\sqrt{9}$ -18 **27.** $-3\sqrt{16}$ -12 **28.** $-2\sqrt{32}$ $-8\sqrt{2}$

29. $-5\sqrt{32}$ **30.** $4\sqrt{200}$ $40\sqrt{2}$ **31.** $3\sqrt{1000}$ $30\sqrt{10}$ **32.** $\sqrt{1 \text{ million}}$ 1,000

33. $3\sqrt{1 \text{ million}}$ **34.** $\sqrt{1,000,000,000,000}$ **35.** $3\sqrt{1,000,000,000}$ **36.** $4\sqrt{10,000,000,000}$

37. $\sqrt{10^2}$ 10 **38.** $\sqrt{10^4}$ 100 **39.** $\sqrt{10^7}$ $1000\sqrt{10}$ **40.** $\sqrt{9t^7}$ $3t^3\sqrt{t}$

41. $\sqrt{36b^3}$ $6b\sqrt{b}$ **42.** $\sqrt{25m^9}$ $5m^4\sqrt{m}$ **43.** $\sqrt{18p^5}$ $3p^2\sqrt{2p}$ **44.** $\sqrt{24c^7}$ $2c^3\sqrt{6c}$

45. $\sqrt{75q^{11}}$ **46.** $\sqrt{12r^5s^7}$ $2r^2s^3\sqrt{3rs}$ **47.** $\sqrt{32a^9b^3}$ $4a^4b\sqrt{2ab}$ **48.** $\sqrt{72c^9d^{13}}$

B Approximations for $\sqrt{2}$, $\sqrt{3}$, and $\sqrt{5}$ are given below.

$$\sqrt{2} \approx 1.414 \qquad \sqrt{3} \approx 1.732 \qquad \sqrt{5} \approx 2.236$$

Use these three approximations to name the nonnegative square root of each number below to the nearest hundredth.

Example: 300 $\sqrt{300} = \sqrt{100} \cdot \sqrt{3} = 10\sqrt{3} \approx 10(1.732) =$ **17.32**

49. 8 2.83 **50.** 12 3.46 **51.** 20 4.47 **52.** 45 6.71 **53.** 98 9.90 **54.** 50 7.07

55. 147 12.12 **56.** 320 17.89 **57.** 192 13.86 **58.** 216 14.69 **59.** 360 18.97 **60.** 200 14.14

C Simplify. Assume that all variables represent positive real numbers.

61. $\sqrt{3(x + y)^2}$ $(x + y)\sqrt{3}$ **62.** $\sqrt{5(t - r)^2}$ $(t - r)\sqrt{5}$ **63.** $\sqrt{28(c^2 + d^2)^3}$

64. $\sqrt{48(a^2 - b^2)^5}$ **65.** $\sqrt{x^2 + 2xy + y^2}$ $x + y$ **66.** $\sqrt{d^2 + 6d + 9}$ $d + 3$

_____ **REVIEW CAPSULE FOR SECTION 12-4** _____

Simplify. *(Pages 9–11, 304–305, 432–433)*

1. 10^2 100 **2.** 15^2 225 **3.** 7^2 49 **4.** $(a - 1)^2$ **5.** $(a + 1)^2$ **6.** $(2t + 5)^2$

7. $(\sqrt{2})^2$ 2 **8.** $(\sqrt{5})^2$ 5 **9.** $(\sqrt{9})^2$ 9 **10.** $(\sqrt{16})^2$ 16 **11.** $(\sqrt{7})^2$ 7 **12.** $(\sqrt{25})^2$

Solve for a^2. *(Pages 84–85)*

13. $a^2 + 25 = 144$ **14.** $18 + a^2 = 225$ **15.** $72 - a^2 = 15$ **16.** $21 = 169 - a^2$

Solve for a. *(Pages 337–338)*

17. $a^2 = 81$ **18.** $a^2 = 36$ **19.** $a^2 - 144 = 0$ **20.** $121 - a^2 = 0$

438 *Chapter 12*

12–4 The Pythagorean Theorem

Test each triangle below to determine whether the sum of the squares of the shorter sides equals the square of the longest side. (The symbol ⌐ means that an angle is a right angle.)

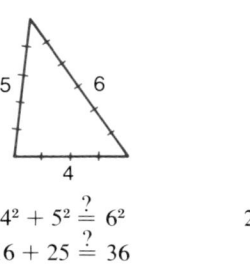
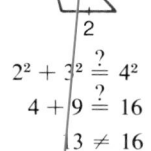
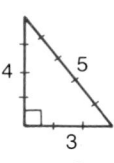

$$4^2 + 5^2 \overset{?}{=} 6^2$$
$$16 + 25 \overset{?}{=} 36$$
$$41 \neq 36$$

$$2^2 + 3^2 \overset{?}{=} 4^2$$
$$4 + 9 \overset{?}{=} 16$$
$$13 \neq 16$$

$$3^2 + 4^2 \overset{?}{=} 5^2$$
$$9 + 16 \overset{?}{=} 25$$
$$\mathbf{25 = 25}$$

The sentence is true for the third triangle only because it is a *right triangle*. A *right triangle* is a triangle with one angle of 90°. The relationship between the two shorter sides (legs) and the longest side (hypotenuse) of every right triangle is known as the *Pythagorean Theorem*.

Theorem 12–2

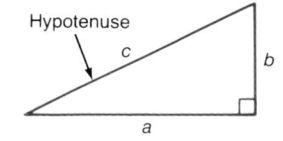

Pythagorean Theorem

If a, b, and c are the lengths of the sides of a right triangle and c is the length of the **hypotenuse** (longest side), then

$$a^2 + b^2 = c^2.$$

The proof of the Pythagorean Theorem is outlined in Exercises 35–38 on page 442.

EXAMPLE 1 The shorter sides of a right triangle are 12 and 5. Find the length of the hypotenuse.

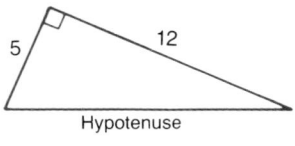

Solution: Since the triangle is a right triangle, use the Pythagorean Theorem.

$$a^2 + b^2 = c^2 \quad \longleftarrow \text{ \textbf{Replace }} a \text{ \textbf{with 5 and} } b \text{ \textbf{with 12.}}$$
$$5^2 + 12^2 = c^2$$
$$25 + 144 = c^2$$
$$169 = c^2 \quad \longleftarrow \text{ \textbf{Since } } c^2 = 169, c = 13 \textbf{ or } c = -13.$$
$$13 = c \quad \longleftarrow \text{ \textbf{The length of a side of the}}$$
$$\text{\textbf{triangle must be positive.}}$$

The length of the hypotenuse is **13**.

The Pythagorean Theorem is useful in solving problems related to right triangles.

Additional Examples
Example 2
1. The top of a 19-foot ladder reaches a window ledge. The ledge is 16 feet above the ground. To the nearest tenth of a foot, how far from the house is the foot of the ladder?
Ans: 10.2 ft
2. The top of a 10-meter ladder reaches a window ledge. The foot of the ladder is 2 meters away from the house. To the nearest tenth of a meter, how far above the ground is the window ledge?
Ans: 9.8 m

EXAMPLE 2 The top of a 6-meter ladder reaches a window ledge. The ledge is 5 meters above the ground. To the nearest tenth of a meter, how far from the house is the foot of the ladder?

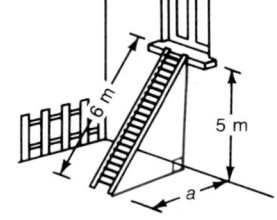

Solution: Since the ladder, the ground, and the side of the house form a right triangle, use the Pythagorean Theorem.

$$c^2 = a^2 + b^2 \quad\longleftarrow\quad \textbf{Replace } c \textbf{ with 6 and } b \textbf{ with 5.}$$
$$6^2 = a^2 + 5^2$$
$$36 = a^2 + 25 \quad\longleftarrow\quad \textbf{Solve for } a^2.$$
$$11 = a^2$$
$$\pm\sqrt{11} = a \quad\longleftarrow\quad \textbf{The distance, } a\textbf{, cannot be negative.}$$
$$a \approx 3.317 \quad\longleftarrow\quad \textbf{Use the Table of Square Roots or a calculator.}$$

The foot of the ladder is about **3.3 meters** from the house.

When you know the lengths of three sides of a triangle, you can use this theorem to determine whether it is a right triangle.

Theorem 12–3

> If the sum of the squares of the lengths of the two shorter sides (legs) of a triangle is equal to the square of the length of the longest side (hypotenuse), then the triangle is a right triangle.

Example 3
The lengths of the three sides of a triangle are given. State whether or not they form a right triangle.
1. 5, 6, 7 **Ans: No**
2. $\sqrt{3}$, $\sqrt{3}$, 6 **Ans: Yes**

EXAMPLE 3 Determine whether a triangle whose sides are 10, 15, and 20 units long is a right triangle.

Solution:
$$c^2 = a^2 + b^2 \quad\longleftarrow\quad \textbf{Replace } c \textbf{ with 20, } a \textbf{ with 10, and } b \textbf{ with 15.}$$
$$20^2 \stackrel{?}{=} 10^2 + 15^2$$
$$400 \stackrel{?}{=} 100 + 225$$
$$400 \neq 325 \qquad \text{The triangle is \textbf{not} a right triangle.}$$

CLASSROOM EXERCISES

Use the Pythagorean Theorem to find the unknown side.

1. $a = 3$, $b = 4$, $c = \underline{\ ?\ }$ 5
2. $a = 5$, $b = 12$, $c = \underline{\ ?\ }$ 13
3. $a = 12$, $c = 15$, $b = \underline{\ ?\ }$ 9
4. $b = 2$, $c = \sqrt{13}$, $a = \underline{\ ?\ }$ 3
5. $a = \sqrt{2}$, $b = \sqrt{2}$, $c = \underline{\ ?\ }$ 2
6. $a = 5\sqrt{3}$, $c = 10$, $b = \underline{\ ?\ }$ 5

WRITTEN EXERCISES

Assignment Guide
Minimal Omit
Average pp. 441–442: 2–32 even
Above Average pp. 441–442: 3, 6, 9, . . . 30, 33–41

A In Exercises 1–10, refer to the diagram at the right. Use the Pythagorean Theorem to find the unknown side. Use the Square Root Table on page 541 or a calculator. Round answers to the nearest tenth.

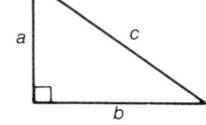

1. $a = 6$, $b = 8$, $c = \underline{\ ?\ }$ 10
2. $a = 24$, $b = 10$, $c = \underline{\ ?\ }$ 26
3. $a = 14$, $b = 7$, $c = \underline{\ ?\ }$ 15.7
4. $a = 9$, $b = 5$, $c = \underline{\ ?\ }$ 10.3
5. $a = 10$, $b = 12$, $c = \underline{\ ?\ }$ 15.6
6. $a = 8$, $b = 10$, $c = \underline{\ ?\ }$ 12.8
7. $a = 12$, $b = \underline{\ ?\ }$, $c = 17$ 12.0
8. $a = 10$, $b = \underline{\ ?\ }$, $c = 13$ 8.3
9. $a = \underline{\ ?\ }$, $b = 16$, $c = 25$ 19.2
10. $a = \underline{\ ?\ }$, $b = 10$, $c = 19$ 16.2

In Exercises 11–22, the lengths of three sides of a triangle are given. State whether or not they form a right triangle. Answer *Yes* or *No*.

11. 12, 5, 13   Yes
12. 9, 12, 15   Yes
13. 4, 5, 7   No
14. 3, 8, 12   No
15. 9, 40, 41   Yes
16. 16, 20, 24   No
17. 2, 8, 10   No
18. 3, 4, 5   Yes
19. 7, 10, 12   No
20. 1, 1, $\sqrt{2}$ Yes
21. $\sqrt{3}$, 1, 2   Yes
22. $\sqrt{2}$, $\sqrt{2}$, 4   No

APPLICATIONS: Using the Pythagorean Theorem

In Exercises 23–32, draw a sketch for each problem. Use the Table of Square Roots on page 541 or a calculator. Round answers to the nearest tenth.

23. Find the length of the diagonal of a rectangle whose length is 6 meters and whose width is 4 meters. 7.2 m

24. Find the length of the diagonal of a square whose sides each have a length of 3 meters. 4.2 m

25. A pipeline is built diagonally across a square field. Each side of the field is 7 kilometers long. What is the length of the pipeline? 9.9 km

26. A wire stretches from the top of a pole 22 feet high to a stake in the ground which is 10 feet from the foot of the pole. Find the length of the wire. 24.2 ft

27. A ladder 40 feet long leans against a building and reaches a ledge. The foot of the ladder is 16 feet from the building. How high is the ledge? 36.7 ft

28. Sean took a homing pigeon 10 kilometers due east of his home and then 5 kilometers north. When he let the pigeon go, it flew straight home. How far did it fly? 11.2 km

B

29. A diagonal of a square is 10 centimeters long. Find the length of each side of the square. 7.1 cm

30. The diagonal of a rectangle is 20 inches long. The rectangle's length is 3 times its width. Find the dimensions of the rectangle. length: 18.9 in; width: 6.3 in

Radicals   **441**

31. Two telephone poles, 30 feet and 39 feet high, respectively, are 60 feet apart. How long is the wire from the top of one pole to the top of the other pole? 60.7 ft

32. In a swimming pool 70 feet long and 25 feet wide, how many feet will be saved by swimming diagonally across the pool instead of along its sides? 20.7 ft

C

33. A rectangle of height 12 centimeters is inscribed in a circle with a radius of 10 centimeters. Find the area of the rectangle. 192 cm²

34. A man on a wharf 12 meters above the water pulls in a boat on the end of a rope. He had 20 meters of rope out and then pulled in 7 meters of rope. How far did he move the boat? 11 m

The figure at the right suggests a proof of the Pythagorean Theorem. Note that each side of the larger square is $(a + b)$ units long. The area of this square is made up of four triangles and a smaller square each of whose sides is c units long.

In Exercises 35–38, give a reason for each statement.

35. $(a+b)^2 = c^2 + 4\left(\frac{1}{2}ab\right)$ (Why?)

36. $a^2 + 2ab + b^2 = c^2 + 4\left(\frac{1}{2}ab\right)$ (Why?)

37. $a^2 + 4\left(\frac{1}{2}ab\right) + b^2 = c^2 + 4\left(\frac{1}{2}ab\right)$ (Why?)

38. $a^2 + b^2 = c^2$ (Why?)

39. Derive a formula for the length of the altitude, h, of the equilateral triangle shown at the right. $h = \sqrt{3}\left(\frac{s}{2}\right)$

40. Derive a formula for the area of an equilateral triangle in terms of a side, s. $A = \frac{s^2}{4}\sqrt{3}$

41. Prove: A triangle with sides $2pq$, $(p^2 - q^2)$, and $(p^2 + q^2)$ is a right triangle.

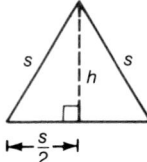

Additional Answers
Written Exercises
35. a whole is equal to the sum of its parts.
36. substitution principle (squared the binomial)
37. substitution principle [$2ab = 4\left(\frac{1}{2}ab\right)$]
38. addition property for equations
41. Use Theorem 12-3: $\overset{?}{}$
$(2pq)^2 + (p^2 - q^2)^2 \overset{?}{=}$
$(p^2 + q^2)^2$
$4p^2q^2 + p^4 - 2p^2q^2 + q^4 \overset{?}{=}$
$p^4 + 2p^2q^2 + q^4$
$p^4 + 2p^2q^2 + q^4 =$
$p^4 + 2p^2q^2 + q^4$

_____ **REVIEW CAPSULE FOR SECTION 12–5** _____

Evaluate. *(Pages 9–11, 47–50, 56–58)*

1. $|-18|$ 18   **2.** $|15 - 12|$ 3   **3.** $|-8 + 6|$ 2   **4.** $|-8 - (-7)|$ 1   **5.** $|9 - (-1)|$ 10

6. $[9 - (-7)]^2$ 256   **7.** $(21 - 8)^2$ 169   **8.** $(1 - 3)^2$ 4   **9.** $[7 - (-5)]^2$ 144   **10.** $[-3 - (-5)]^2$ 4

Evaluate $(x_2 - x_1)^2 + (y_2 - y_1)^2$ for the given values of (x_1, y_1) and (x_2, y_2). *(Pages 9–11, 56–58)*

11. $x_1 = 7$, $y_1 = 0$; $x_2 = 3$, $y_2 = -1$ 17   **12.** $x_1 = 0$, $y_1 = -1$; $x_2 = 3$, $y_2 = -1$ 9

13. $x_1 = -4$, $y_1 = -5$; $x_2 = -2$, $y_2 = -2$ 13   **14.** $x_1 = 2$, $y_1 = -5$; $x_2 = 4$, $y_2 = 2$ 53

OBJECTIVE: To find the distance between two points on the coordinate plane

12–5 The Distance Formula

Two points that lie on a line parallel to the x axis (horizontal line) have the same y coordinate. To find the distance between two such points, determine the absolute value of the difference of their x coordinates. Thus, in Figure 1,

$$AB = |-2 - 1| = |-3| = \mathbf{3}.$$

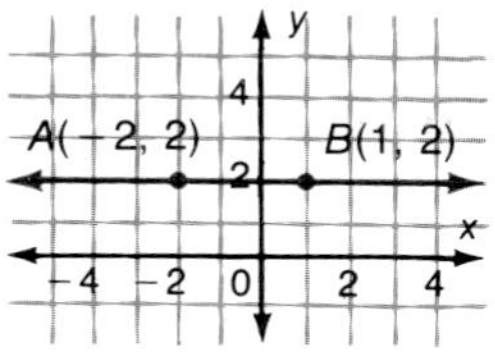

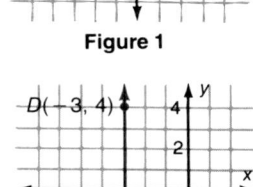

Figure 1

Similarly, two points that lie on a line parallel to the y axis (vertical line) have the same x coordinate. To find the distance between two such points, determine the absolute value of the difference of their y coordinates. Thus, in Figure 2,

$$CD = |4 - (-2)| = |4 + 2| = |6| = \mathbf{6}.$$

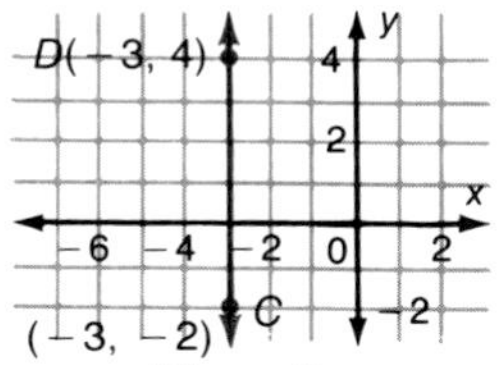

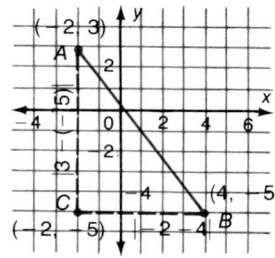

Figure 2

Suppose that you wish to find the distance between the points $A(-2, 3)$ and $B(4, -5)$ shown in Figure 3. First you draw the horizontal and vertical line segments intersecting at C to form right triangle ABC. After finding the lengths of AC and BC, you can use the Pythagorean Theorem to find the length of AB. Thus,

Figure 3

$BC = |-2 - 4| = |-6| = \mathbf{6}$ and $AC = |3 - (-5)| = |8| = \mathbf{8}$

$(AB)^2 = (BC)^2 + (AC)^2$ ← **By the Pythagorean Theorem**

$(AB)^2 = 6^2 + 8^2$

$(AB)^2 = 36 + 64$

$(AB)^2 = 100$ and $AB = 10$ Thus, AB is **10 units** long.

This procedure can be generalized as a formula to find the distance between any two points $P_1(x_1, y_1)$ and $P_2(x_2, y_2)$ in the coordinate plane. You are asked to prove this formula in the Exercises.

> **Distance Formula**
>
> If $P_1(x_1, y_1)$ and $P_2(x_2, y_2)$ are any two points in the coordinate plane, then the distance, d, between the points is given by the formula
>
> $$d = \sqrt{(x_2 - x_1)^2 + (y_2 - y_1)^2}.$$

Teaching Suggestions p. M-25

Quick Quiz

1. The shorter sides of a right triangle are 5 and 12. Find the length of the hypotenuse.
   Ans: 13
2. A pipeline is built diagonally across a square field. Each side of the field is 4 miles long. To the nearest tenth of a mile, what is the length of the pipeline?
   Ans: 5.6 mi

The lengths of the three sides of a triangle are given. State whether or not they form a right triangle.

3. 7, 10, 13 **Ans: No**
4. 12, 9, 15 **Ans: Yes**

EXAMPLE   Find the distance between $P(7, 3)$ and $Q(2, -5)$.

Solution: Use the Distance Formula.

$d = \sqrt{(x_2 - x_1)^2 + (y_2 - y_1)^2}$ ← **Replace x_2 with 2 and x_1 with 7.**
Replace y_2 with -5 and y_1 with 3.

$d = \sqrt{(2 - 7)^2 + (-5 - 3)^2}$

$d = \sqrt{(-5)^2 + (-8)^2}$

$d = \sqrt{25 + 64}$, or $\sqrt{89}$ ← **Simplest form**

It does not matter which point is considered (x_1, y_1) and which one is considered (x_2, y_2). The distance will be the same.

CLASSROOM EXERCISES

Find the distance between each pair of points.

1. $P(4, 3)$ and $Q(0, 0)$ 5
2. $A(0, 0)$ and $C(-5, 9)$ $\sqrt{106}$
3. $Q(-1, 2)$ and $R(8, -2)$ $\sqrt{97}$
4. $P(1, 4)$ and $S(6, 9)$ $5\sqrt{2}$
5. $T(-3, 2)$ and $R(2, -7)$ $\sqrt{106}$
6. $S(4, 0)$ and $V(4, 9)$ 9

WRITTEN EXERCISES

A   Find the distance between each pair of points.

1. $A(0, 0)$ and $B(-5, 0)$ 5
2. $P(0, 0)$ and $Q(0, -5)$ 5
3. $C(-3, 5)$ and $D(-3, -3)$ 8
4. $H(7, -8)$ and $J(-2, -8)$ 9
5. $K(9, 4)$ and $L(3, 4)$ 6
6. $B(5, 13)$ and $C(5, -1)$ 14
7. $D(6, 8)$ and $E(0, 0)$ 10
8. $M(0, 0)$ and $N(2, 3)$ $\sqrt{13}$
9. $S(1, 3)$ and $T(4, 7)$ 5
10. $U(5, 10)$ and $V(2, 6)$ 5
11. $X(2, 1)$ and $Y(-3, -4)$
12. $L(-2, 4)$ and $M(-1, 2)$
13. $C(3, 1)$ and $D(-1, 6)$ $\sqrt{41}$
14. $A(2, 2)$ and $B(2, -7)$ 9
15. $P(9, 6)$ and $R(-5, 6)$ 14
16. $N(-2, -3)$ and $T(1, 2)$
17. $E(3, 2)$ and $F(8, -10)$ 13
18. $J(-2, 4)$ and $K(7, -8)$ 15

APPLICATIONS: Using the Distance Formula

Use the given figure to answer each question.

19.

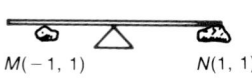

$M(-1, 1)$ $N(1, 1)$

What is the distance
between the objects on
the teeter-totter?   2

20.

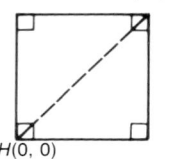

$S(90, 90)$

$H(0, 0)$

How far is it from
home plate to second
base? $90\sqrt{2}$

21. $T(13, 28)$

$R(6, 4)$

How long is the guy
wire of the radio
antenna?   25

444   *Chapter 12*

B   Find the perimeter of each triangle.

22.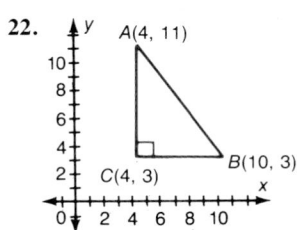

23.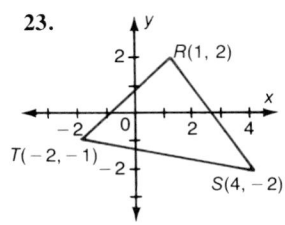

24.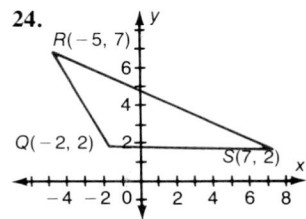

25.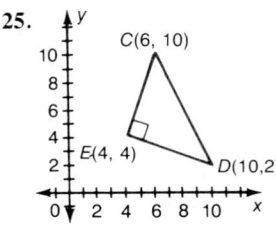

26.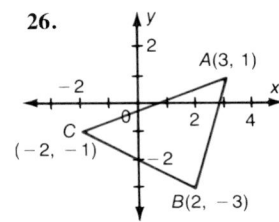

27.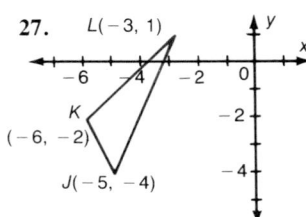

C

28. Use the Pythagorean Theorem to prove the Distance Formula.

_____ Review _____

Simplify. *(Section 12–1)*

1. $\sqrt{64}$ 8

2. $-\sqrt{400}$ −20

3. $\sqrt{100x^2}$ $10|x|$

4. $\pm\sqrt{a^8b^4}$ $\pm a^4b^2$

5. The area of a square is 7 square meters. What is the length of one side of the square to the nearest tenth of a meter? *(Section 12–2)* 2.6 m

6. The length of a rectangle is twice its width. The area of the rectangle is 218 square units. Find the dimensions to the nearest tenth. *(Section 12–2)*
width: 10.4 m; length: 20.8 m

Simplify. Variables represent positive numbers. *(Section 12–3)*

7. $\sqrt{28}$ $2\sqrt{7}$

8. $\sqrt{80}$ $4\sqrt{5}$

9. $-\sqrt{24x^5}$ $-2x^2\sqrt{6x}$

10. $2\sqrt{36d^3}$ $12d\sqrt{d}$

The lengths of the legs of a right triangle are a and b, and c is the length of the hypotenuse. Use the Pythagorean Theorem to find the length of the unknown side to the nearest tenth. *(Section 12–4)*

11. $a = 9$, $b = 12$, $c = \underline{\quad ? \quad}$ 15

12. $b = 5$, $c = 9$, $a = \underline{\quad ? \quad}$ 7.5

Find the distance between each pair of points. *(Section 12–5)*

13. $A(4, -6)$ and $B(1, -6)$ 3

14. $P(4, -2)$ and $Q(-2, 4)$ $6\sqrt{2}$

15. $K(7, 3)$ and $L(-4, -5)$ $\sqrt{185}$

Radicals   **445**

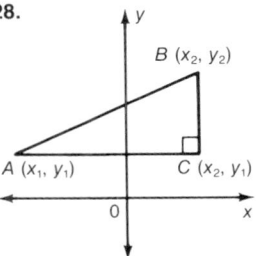

Career Applications

Space Technology

Reuben Ramos is an Engineer at NASA.

Aerospace engineers develop and design space-craft. These vehicles must be able to travel at great speeds so that they can either enter an orbit around the earth or escape the earth's gravitational field and travel to other parts of the universe.

The speed of the spacecraft determines whether it will come right back to the earth, orbit the earth, or travel into outer space. The following formulas give the orbital and escape speeds of a spacecraft at a specific height above the earth.

$$V_o = R\sqrt{\frac{g}{R + h}} \text{ and } V_e = \sqrt{2} \cdot V_o \longleftarrow \begin{array}{l} V_o = \text{orbital speed} \\ V_e = \text{escape speed} \end{array}$$

In the formula, R is the radius of the earth, 6.4×10^6 meters, g is the acceleration due to gravity on the earth, 9.8 m/sec², and h is the height above the surface of the earth at which the spacecraft is traveling.

EXAMPLE 1 Suppose that the U.S. space shuttle is to orbit the earth at an average height of 12.8×10^6 meters above its surface. Find the orbital speed and the escape speed of the shuttle orbiter.

Solution:

$$V_o = R\sqrt{\frac{g}{R + h}}$$

$$= 6.4 \times 10^6 \sqrt{\frac{9.8}{(6.4 \times 10^6) + (12.8 \times 10^6)}}$$

$$= 6.4 \times 10^6 \sqrt{\frac{9.8}{19.2 \times 10^6}} \longleftarrow \text{Use a calculator.}$$

$$= (6.4 \times 10^6) \cdot 0.707 \times 10^{-3}$$

$$\approx 4.5 \times 10^3 \text{ m/sec}$$

$$V_e = 2 \cdot 4.5 \times 10^3 = 1.4 \cdot 4.5 \times 10^3 = \mathbf{6.3 \times 10^3 \text{ m/sec}}$$

NOTE: If the speed of the spacecraft is less than V_o for a given height, it will return to earth. The vehicle will orbit the earth if its speed is between V_o and V_e. If the spacecraft's speed is greater than or equal to V_e, it will escape the earth's gravity and travel into outer space.

The shuttle orbiter was designed to land like a jet airplane. As the orbiter approaches the earth, the distance to the horizon becomes shorter. The following formula approximates this distance in kilometers.

$$D = 3.56\sqrt{A}$$ ← **A is the altitude of the orbiter in meters.**

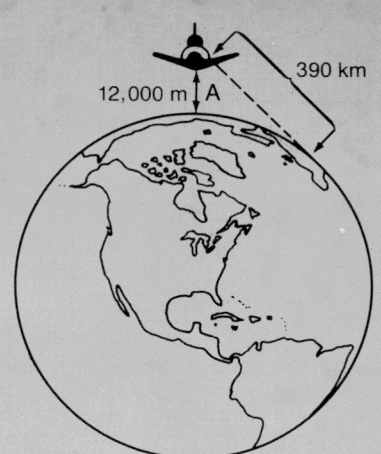

EXAMPLE 2 Find the distance to the horizon from the orbiter when its altitude is 12,000 meters.

Solution:
$$D = 3.56\sqrt{12,000}$$
$$= 3.56\sqrt{400} \cdot \sqrt{30}$$
$$= 3.56 \cdot 20 \cdot \sqrt{30}$$
$$\approx 390 \text{ kilometers}$$

EXERCISES

In Exercises 1–3, use the formulas on page 446 to find the orbital speed and the escape speed of a spacecraft at the given height above the earth.

1. 6.4×10^6 meters
2. 3.2×10^6 meters
3. 9.6×10^6 meters

In Exercises 4–5, state whether a spacecraft with the given speed at the given height would return to earth, orbit the earth, or travel into outer space.

4. Speed: 4.6×10^3 meters per second
   Height: 6.4×10^6 meters

5. Speed: 4.8×10^3 meters per second
   Height: 1.92×10^7 meters

6. On December 3, 1980, Janice Brown made the first solar-powered flight in the Solar Challenger. At one point in the flight the plane was 27 meters above the ground. How far could Janice see to the horizon? (nearest km)

7. On July 7, 1981, Stephen Ptacek flew the Solar Challenger across the English Channel. At one point in the flight, the plane was 50 meters high. Find the distance to the horizon. (nearest km)

8. Find the distance to the horizon from a plane that is 3000 meters above the earth. (nearest km)

9. Find the distance to the horizon from the shuttle when it is 4000 meters above the earth. (nearest km)

Space Technology 447

Quick Quiz
Find the distance between
each pair of points.
1. $P(5, 6)$ and $Q(-4, -3)$
    Ans: $9\sqrt{2}$
2. $R(-6, 4)$ and $S(-9, -8)$
    Ans: $3\sqrt{17}$

Additional Examples
Example 1
Multiply. Express the answer
in simplest form.
1. $-5\sqrt{6} \cdot 3\sqrt{2}$
    Ans: $-30\sqrt{3}$
2. $-6\sqrt{5} \cdot -7\sqrt{10}$
    Ans: $210\sqrt{2}$

Example 2
Multiply. Express the answer
in simplest form.
1. $\sqrt{12} \cdot \sqrt{6}$
    Ans: $6\sqrt{2}$
2. $\sqrt{50} \cdot \sqrt{40}$
    Ans: $20\sqrt{5}$

OBJECTIVE: To multiply radicals

12-6 Multiplication of Radicals

To multiply two radicals such as $4\sqrt{2}$ and $3\sqrt{5}$, you use the commutative and associative properties of multiplication.

EXAMPLE 1 Multiply: $-3\sqrt{6} \cdot 4\sqrt{3}$. Express the answer in simplest form.

Solution:
$$-3\sqrt{6} \cdot 4\sqrt{3} = (-3 \cdot 4) \cdot (\sqrt{6} \cdot \sqrt{3}) \quad \longleftarrow \quad \textbf{By the commutative and associative postulates}$$
$$= -12 \cdot \sqrt{6 \cdot 3}$$
$$= -12 \cdot \sqrt{18} \quad \longleftarrow \quad \sqrt{18} \textbf{ can be simplified.}$$
$$= -12 \cdot \sqrt{9} \cdot \sqrt{2} \quad \longleftarrow \quad \sqrt{18} = \sqrt{9} \cdot \sqrt{2}$$
$$= -12 \cdot 3 \cdot \sqrt{2}$$
$$= -36\sqrt{2} \quad \longleftarrow \quad \textbf{Simplest form}$$

When a radical can be simplified, it is usually easier to do this before multiplying by other factors.

EXAMPLE 2 Multiply: $\sqrt{8} \cdot \sqrt{6}$. Express the answer in simplest form.

Solution:
$$\sqrt{8} \cdot \sqrt{6} = \sqrt{4 \cdot 2} \cdot \sqrt{6} \quad \longleftarrow \quad \sqrt{8} \textbf{ can be simplified.}$$
$$= 2 \cdot \sqrt{2} \cdot \sqrt{6} \quad \longleftarrow \quad \sqrt{2} \cdot \sqrt{6} = \sqrt{12}$$
$$= 2 \cdot \sqrt{12} \quad \longleftarrow \quad \sqrt{12} \textbf{ can be simplified.}$$
$$= 2 \cdot \sqrt{4 \cdot 3}$$
$$= 2 \cdot \sqrt{4} \cdot \sqrt{3}$$
$$= 2 \cdot 2 \cdot \sqrt{3}$$
$$= 4\sqrt{3} \quad \longleftarrow \quad \textbf{Simplest form}$$

CLASSROOM EXERCISES

Multiply. Express your answers in simplest form.

1. $\sqrt{2} \cdot \sqrt{7}$ $\sqrt{14}$ 2. $\sqrt{2} \cdot \sqrt{8}$ 4 3. $\sqrt{2} \cdot \sqrt{9}$ $3\sqrt{2}$ 4. $\sqrt{15} \cdot \sqrt{3}$ $3\sqrt{5}$
5. $-\sqrt{2} \cdot \sqrt{18}$ -6 6. $3\sqrt{3} \cdot \sqrt{2}$ $3\sqrt{6}$ 7. $\sqrt{5} \cdot 5\sqrt{3}$ $5\sqrt{15}$ 8. $\sqrt{5} \cdot 5\sqrt{5}$ 25
9. $6\sqrt{8} \cdot 5\sqrt{6}$ $120\sqrt{3}$ 10. $\sqrt{300} \cdot \sqrt{3}$ 30 11. $2\sqrt{1000}$ $20\sqrt{10}$ 12. $5\sqrt{10} \cdot 4\sqrt{10}$
200

WRITTEN EXERCISES

A   Multiply and simplify.

1. $\sqrt{5} \cdot \sqrt{2}$ $\sqrt{10}$ 2. $\sqrt{3} \cdot \sqrt{5}$ $\sqrt{15}$ 3. $\sqrt{7} \cdot \sqrt{2}$ $\sqrt{14}$ 4. $\sqrt{6} \cdot \sqrt{2}$ $2\sqrt{3}$
5. $\sqrt{3} \cdot \sqrt{6}$ $3\sqrt{2}$ 6. $3\sqrt{3} \cdot \sqrt{2}$ $3\sqrt{6}$ 7. $\sqrt{5} \cdot \sqrt{10}$ $5\sqrt{2}$ 8. $\sqrt{8} \cdot \sqrt{2}$ 4

448   *Chapter 12*

Assignment Guide
Minimal
Day 1 pp. 448–449: 1–16
Day 2 p. 449: 17–32
Average
Day 1 pp. 448–449: 1–24
Day 2 p. 449: 25–48
Above Average pp. 448–449:
3, 6, 9, . . . 30, 33–54

9. $\sqrt{9} \cdot \sqrt{4}$ 6
10. $\sqrt{4} \cdot \sqrt{2}$ $2\sqrt{2}$
11. $\sqrt{3} \cdot \sqrt{12}$ 6
12. $\sqrt{10} \cdot \sqrt{20}$ $10\sqrt{2}$

13. $\sqrt{25} \cdot \sqrt{3}$ $5\sqrt{3}$
14. $\sqrt{50} \cdot \sqrt{2}$ 10
15. $\sqrt{7} \cdot \sqrt{7}$ 7
16. $\sqrt{30} \cdot \sqrt{3}$ $3\sqrt{10}$

17. $2\sqrt{3} \cdot \sqrt{2}$ $2\sqrt{6}$
18. $\sqrt{3} \cdot 5\sqrt{7}$ $5\sqrt{21}$
19. $4\sqrt{2} \cdot \sqrt{5}$ $4\sqrt{10}$
20. $3\sqrt{2} \cdot 4\sqrt{3}$ $12\sqrt{6}$

21. $5\sqrt{2} \cdot 3\sqrt{5}$ $15\sqrt{10}$
22. $4\sqrt{5} \cdot 3\sqrt{2}$ $12\sqrt{10}$
23. $7\sqrt{6} \cdot 2\sqrt{2}$ $28\sqrt{3}$
24. $8\sqrt{5} \cdot 3\sqrt{6}$ $24\sqrt{30}$

25. $-7\sqrt{12} \cdot 4\sqrt{3}$ -168
26. $8\sqrt{6} \cdot -3\sqrt{3}$
27. $3\sqrt{6} \cdot -4\sqrt{10}$
28. $-2\sqrt{12} \cdot -3\sqrt{2}$

29. $-8\sqrt{6} \cdot -3\sqrt{7}$
30. $-6\sqrt{8} \cdot -3\sqrt{6}$
31. $-9\sqrt{10} \cdot 7\sqrt{3}$
32. $-4\sqrt{14} \cdot 2\sqrt{7}$

B Multiply. Variables represent positive numbers.

33. $\sqrt{a} \cdot \sqrt{ab}$ $a\sqrt{b}$
34. $\sqrt{cd} \cdot \sqrt{c}$ $c\sqrt{d}$
35. $\sqrt{8bc} \cdot \sqrt{4bc}$
36. $\sqrt{6ax} \cdot \sqrt{9ax}$

37. $\sqrt{6m^4} \cdot \sqrt{3mn^2}$
38. $\sqrt{2a^2c} \cdot \sqrt{2c^2x}$
39. $\sqrt{a^3b} \cdot \sqrt{bc^3}$
40. $\sqrt{c^3} \cdot -\sqrt{5cd}$

41. $\sqrt[3]{4} \cdot \sqrt[3]{2}$ 2
42. $\sqrt[3]{9} \cdot \sqrt[3]{3}$ 3
43. $\sqrt[3]{4^2} \cdot \sqrt[3]{4}$ 4
44. $\sqrt[3]{7} \cdot \sqrt[3]{7^2}$ 7

45. $\sqrt[3]{10} \cdot \sqrt[3]{10^2}$ 10
46. $\sqrt[3]{8} \cdot \sqrt[3]{2}$ $2\sqrt[3]{2}$
47. $\sqrt[3]{12} \cdot \sqrt[3]{2}$ $2\sqrt[3]{3}$
48. $\sqrt[3]{24} \cdot \sqrt[3]{2}$ $2\sqrt[3]{6}$

C

49. $-3a\sqrt{ab} \cdot 2a\sqrt{ab}$ $-6a^3b$
50. $-2\sqrt{7y} \cdot 5\sqrt{2y}$ $-10y\sqrt{14}$
51. $y^2\sqrt{xy} \cdot 2x\sqrt{y}$

52. $3b\sqrt{b^2e} \cdot 2e\sqrt{be^2}$
53. $5t^2\sqrt{k^3} \cdot 2t\sqrt{k}$ $10k^2t^3$
54. $2\sqrt{r} \cdot 3\sqrt{r^3} \cdot 3\sqrt{r^5}$

$18r^4\sqrt{r}$

CALCULATOR APPLICATIONS

Evaluating the Product of Two Radicals

If you have a calculator with square root and memory keys, you can use the calculator to evaluate the product of two radicals.

EXAMPLE Multiply: $-3\sqrt{6} \cdot 4\sqrt{3}$ (See Example 1 on page 448.)

SOLUTION Rewrite the problem so that each radical is the first term in each factor.

$$-3\sqrt{6} \cdot 4\sqrt{3} = (\sqrt{6} \cdot -3)(\sqrt{3} \cdot 4)$$

6  3   3   4 -50.911687

EXERCISES

Multiply.

1. $2\sqrt{5} \cdot 6\sqrt{3}$
2. $-4\sqrt{8} \cdot 6\sqrt{2}$
3. $-6\sqrt{5} \cdot -3\sqrt{3}$
4. $5\sqrt{10} \cdot \sqrt{8}$

5. $4\sqrt{6} \cdot -2\sqrt{5}$
6. $-8\sqrt{3} \cdot 4\sqrt{7}$
7. $\sqrt{8} \cdot 4\sqrt{3}$
8. $-2\sqrt{5} \cdot 9\sqrt{2}$

——— REVIEW CAPSULE FOR SECTION 12-7 ———

Simplify. *(Pages 432-433, 448-449)*

1. $\sqrt{2} \cdot \sqrt{2}$ 2
2. $\sqrt{3} \cdot \sqrt{3}$ 3
3. $(\sqrt{5})^2$ 5
4. $(\sqrt{8})^2$
5. $(\sqrt{125})^2$ 125

6. $\dfrac{1}{\sqrt{2}} \cdot \dfrac{\sqrt{2}}{\sqrt{2}}$ $\dfrac{\sqrt{2}}{2}$
7. $\dfrac{1}{\sqrt{5}} \cdot \dfrac{\sqrt{5}}{\sqrt{5}}$ $\dfrac{\sqrt{5}}{5}$
8. $\dfrac{6}{\sqrt{3}} \cdot \dfrac{\sqrt{3}}{\sqrt{3}}$ $2\sqrt{3}$
9. $\dfrac{14}{\sqrt{7}} \cdot \dfrac{\sqrt{7}}{\sqrt{7}}$ $2\sqrt{7}$
10. $\dfrac{18}{\sqrt{2}} \cdot \dfrac{\sqrt{2}}{\sqrt{2}}$ $9\sqrt{2}$

Radicals **449**

12-7 Quotients of Radicals

Quick Quiz
Multiply and simplify.
1. $-4\sqrt{6} \cdot 3\sqrt{10}$
   Ans: $-24\sqrt{15}$
2. $5\sqrt{7} \cdot -4\sqrt{14}$
   Ans: $-140\sqrt{2}$
3. $\sqrt{18} \cdot \sqrt{3}$
   Ans: $3\sqrt{6}$
4. $\sqrt{2} \cdot \sqrt{20}$
   Ans: $2\sqrt{10}$

Since $\sqrt{\dfrac{16}{81}} = \dfrac{4}{9}$ and $\dfrac{\sqrt{16}}{\sqrt{81}} = \dfrac{4}{9}$, $\sqrt{\dfrac{16}{81}} = \dfrac{\sqrt{16}}{\sqrt{81}}$.

Since $\sqrt{\dfrac{4}{25}} = \dfrac{2}{5}$ and $\dfrac{\sqrt{4}}{\sqrt{25}} = \dfrac{2}{5}$, $\sqrt{\dfrac{4}{25}} = \dfrac{\sqrt{4}}{\sqrt{25}}$.

These statements suggest the following theorem.

Theorem 12-4

> **Division Theorem for Square Roots**
> If a and b are real numbers where $a \geq 0$ and $b > 0$, then
> $$\sqrt{\frac{a}{b}} = \frac{\sqrt{a}}{\sqrt{b}}.$$

Additional Examples
Example 1
Simplify.
1. a. $\sqrt{\dfrac{24}{121}}$ **Ans: $\dfrac{2\sqrt{6}}{11}$**

   b. $\sqrt{\dfrac{45}{64}}$ **Ans: $\dfrac{3\sqrt{5}}{8}$**

2. a. $5\sqrt{\dfrac{3}{25}}$ **Ans: $\sqrt{3}$**

   b. $8\sqrt{\dfrac{7}{64}}$ **Ans: $\sqrt{7}$**

EXAMPLE 1 Simplify: **a.** $\sqrt{\dfrac{8}{49}}$ **b.** $4\sqrt{\dfrac{5}{16}}$

Solutions: **a.** $\sqrt{\dfrac{8}{49}} = \dfrac{\sqrt{8}}{\sqrt{49}}$ ⟵ **By Theorem 12-4**

$\qquad\qquad = \dfrac{\sqrt{4 \cdot 2}}{7}$ ⟵ $\sqrt{8} = \sqrt{4 \cdot 2} = \sqrt{4} \cdot \sqrt{2}$

$\qquad\qquad = \dfrac{2\sqrt{2}}{7}$ ⟵ **Simplest form**

b. $4\sqrt{\dfrac{5}{16}} = 4 \cdot \dfrac{\sqrt{5}}{\sqrt{16}}$ ⟵ **By Theorem 12-4**

$\qquad\qquad = \overset{1}{\cancel{4}} \cdot \dfrac{\sqrt{5}}{\underset{1}{\cancel{4}}}$ ⟵ $\dfrac{1 \cdot \sqrt{5}}{1}$

$\qquad\qquad = \sqrt{5}$

The following definition will help you to determine whether a radical is in simplest form.

Definition

> **A radical is in simplest form when:**
> 1 The radicand contains no factor that is a perfect square.
> 2 The radicand does not contain a fraction.
> 3 No radical appears in a denominator.

To simplify a fraction such as $\dfrac{\sqrt{7}}{\sqrt{3}}$, you write an equivalent fraction having a rational denominator. This is called **rationalizing the denominator**.

EXAMPLE 2 Simplify: **a.** $\sqrt{\dfrac{7}{3}}$ **b.** $\dfrac{5\sqrt{2}}{2\sqrt{18}}$

Solutions: **a.** $\sqrt{\dfrac{7}{3}} = \dfrac{\sqrt{7}}{\sqrt{3}}$ ⟵———— **By Theorem 12–4**

$\qquad = \dfrac{\sqrt{7}}{\sqrt{3}} \cdot \dfrac{\sqrt{3}}{\sqrt{3}}$ ⟵———— **Multiplying by $\dfrac{\sqrt{3}}{\sqrt{3}}$ will give an equivalent fraction with no radical in the denominator.**

$\qquad = \dfrac{\sqrt{21}}{3}$ ⟵———— $\sqrt{3} \cdot \sqrt{3} = (\sqrt{3})^2 = 3$

b. $\dfrac{5\sqrt{2}}{2\sqrt{18}} = \dfrac{5\sqrt{2}}{2\sqrt{18}} \cdot \dfrac{\sqrt{2}}{\sqrt{2}}$ ⟵———— **Multiplying by $\dfrac{\sqrt{2}}{\sqrt{2}}$ will give an equivalent fraction with no radical in the denominator.**

$\qquad = \dfrac{5\sqrt{4}}{2\sqrt{36}}$

$\qquad = \dfrac{5 \cdot 2}{2 \cdot 6}$

$\qquad = \dfrac{10}{12}, \text{ or } \dfrac{5}{6}$

Follow the method of Example 2 to rationalize a denominator containing variables.

EXAMPLE 3 Simplify: **a.** $\sqrt{\dfrac{1}{b^5}}$ **b.** $\sqrt{\dfrac{2}{10x}}$

Solutions: **a.** $\sqrt{\dfrac{1}{b^5}} = \dfrac{\sqrt{1}}{\sqrt{b^5}}$ ⟵———— **By Theorem 12–4**

$\qquad = \dfrac{1}{\sqrt{b^5}} \cdot \dfrac{\sqrt{b}}{\sqrt{b}}$ ⟵———— **Multiplying by $\dfrac{\sqrt{b}}{\sqrt{b}}$ will give an equivalent rational expression with no radical in the denominator.**

$\qquad = \dfrac{\sqrt{b}}{\sqrt{b^6}}$

$\qquad = \dfrac{\sqrt{b}}{b^3}, \text{ or } \dfrac{1}{b^3}\sqrt{b}$

b. $\sqrt{\dfrac{2}{10x}} = \sqrt{\dfrac{1}{5x}}$ ⟵———— $\dfrac{2}{10} = \dfrac{1}{5}$

$\qquad = \dfrac{1}{\sqrt{5x}}$ ⟵———— **By Theorem 12–4**

$\qquad = \dfrac{1}{\sqrt{5x}} \cdot \dfrac{\sqrt{5x}}{\sqrt{5x}}$

$\qquad = \dfrac{\sqrt{5x}}{5x}$ ⟵———— $(\sqrt{5x} \cdot \sqrt{5x}) = (\sqrt{5x})^2 = 5x$

Radicals   **451**

Compare these two methods of approximating $\frac{1}{\sqrt{5}}$.

$$\frac{1}{\sqrt{5}} = \frac{\sqrt{5}}{5} \approx \frac{2.236}{5} = \textbf{0.447} \qquad\qquad \frac{1}{\sqrt{5}} \approx \frac{1}{2.236} = \textbf{0.447}$$

You can see that rationalizing the denominator *before dividing* makes it easier to evaluate $\frac{1}{\sqrt{5}}$.

CLASSROOM EXERCISES

Simplify.

1. $\sqrt{\dfrac{16}{25}}$ $\frac{4}{5}$
2. $\pm\sqrt{\dfrac{49}{100}}$ $\pm\frac{7}{10}$
3. $4\sqrt{\dfrac{32}{81}}$ $\frac{16\sqrt{2}}{9}$
4. $-2\sqrt{\dfrac{27}{144}}$ $-\frac{\sqrt{3}}{2}$
5. $\pm 3\sqrt{\dfrac{5}{49}}$ $\pm\frac{3\sqrt{5}}{7}$

Rationalize the denominators and simplify.

6. $\dfrac{1}{\sqrt{6}}$ $\frac{\sqrt{6}}{6}$
7. $\sqrt{\dfrac{3}{6}}$ $\frac{\sqrt{2}}{2}$
8. $\dfrac{\sqrt{6}}{\sqrt{5}}$ $\frac{\sqrt{30}}{5}$
9. $\dfrac{1}{\sqrt{8}}$ $\frac{\sqrt{2}}{4}$
10. $\dfrac{\sqrt{2}}{\sqrt{3}}$ $\frac{\sqrt{6}}{3}$
11. $\sqrt{\dfrac{2}{9}}$ $\frac{\sqrt{2}}{3}$
12. $\sqrt{\dfrac{1}{7}}$ $\frac{\sqrt{7}}{7}$
13. $\dfrac{4\sqrt{5}}{\sqrt{2}}$ $2\sqrt{10}$
14. $\dfrac{15\sqrt{3}}{3\sqrt{5}}$ $\sqrt{15}$
15. $\sqrt{\dfrac{1}{x^3}}$ $\frac{\sqrt{x}}{x^2}$

WRITTEN EXERCISES

A Simplify.

1. $\sqrt{\dfrac{4}{25}}$ $\frac{2}{5}$
2. $\sqrt{\dfrac{3}{49}}$ $\frac{\sqrt{3}}{7}$
3. $\sqrt{\dfrac{7}{36}}$ $\frac{\sqrt{7}}{6}$
4. $\sqrt{\dfrac{10}{81}}$ $\frac{\sqrt{10}}{9}$
5. $\sqrt{\dfrac{6}{16}}$
6. $2\sqrt{\dfrac{7}{25}}$ $\frac{2\sqrt{7}}{5}$
7. $5\sqrt{\dfrac{9}{196}}$ $\frac{15}{14}$
8. $3\sqrt{\dfrac{6}{100}}$ $\frac{3\sqrt{6}}{10}$
9. $7\sqrt{\dfrac{11}{144}}$ $\frac{7\sqrt{11}}{12}$
10. $6\sqrt{\dfrac{3}{64}}$
11. $2\sqrt{\dfrac{12}{225}}$ $\frac{4\sqrt{3}}{15}$
12. $7\sqrt{\dfrac{18}{49}}$ $3\sqrt{2}$
13. $5\sqrt{\dfrac{24}{121}}$ $\frac{10\sqrt{6}}{11}$
14. $9\sqrt{\dfrac{27}{169}}$ $\frac{27\sqrt{3}}{13}$
15. $7\sqrt{\dfrac{75}{625}}$

Rationalize the denominators and simplify. All variables represent positive numbers.

16. $\dfrac{3}{\sqrt{5}}$ $\frac{3\sqrt{5}}{5}$
17. $\dfrac{2}{\sqrt{3}}$ $\frac{2\sqrt{3}}{3}$
18. $\dfrac{5}{\sqrt{2}}$ $\frac{5\sqrt{2}}{2}$
19. $\dfrac{2}{\sqrt{6}}$ $\frac{\sqrt{6}}{3}$
20. $\dfrac{\sqrt{3}}{\sqrt{2}}$
21. $\dfrac{\sqrt{7}}{\sqrt{2}}$ $\frac{\sqrt{14}}{2}$
22. $\dfrac{\sqrt{8}}{\sqrt{3}}$ $\frac{2\sqrt{6}}{3}$
23. $\dfrac{\sqrt{7}}{\sqrt{5}}$ $\frac{\sqrt{35}}{5}$
24. $\dfrac{2\sqrt{3}}{\sqrt{2}}$ $\sqrt{6}$
25. $\dfrac{3\sqrt{2}}{\sqrt{3}}$
26. $\dfrac{4\sqrt{2}}{\sqrt{5}}$ $\frac{4\sqrt{10}}{5}$
27. $\dfrac{3\sqrt{3}}{\sqrt{2}}$ $\frac{3\sqrt{6}}{2}$
28. $\dfrac{5\sqrt{8}}{\sqrt{7}}$ $\frac{10\sqrt{14}}{7}$
29. $\dfrac{3\sqrt{9}}{\sqrt{2}}$ $\frac{9\sqrt{2}}{2}$
30. $\dfrac{2\sqrt{4}}{\sqrt{3}}$
31. $\dfrac{8\sqrt{5}}{\sqrt{15}}$ $\frac{8\sqrt{3}}{3}$
32. $\dfrac{3\sqrt{6}}{2\sqrt{2}}$ $\frac{3\sqrt{3}}{2}$
33. $\dfrac{2\sqrt{7}}{5\sqrt{3}}$ $\frac{2\sqrt{21}}{15}$
34. $\dfrac{5\sqrt{3}}{\sqrt{18}}$ $\frac{5\sqrt{6}}{6}$
35. $\dfrac{4\sqrt{2}}{3\sqrt{32}}$

Assignment Guide
Minimal
Day 1 p. 452: 1–15
Day 2 pp. 452–453: 16–50 even
Average
Day 1 p. 452: 1–30
Day 2 pp. 452–453: 32–50 even, 51–62
Above Average
Day 1 pp. 452–453: 1–50 even
Day 2 p. 453: 51–74

Additional Answers
Written Exercises

5. $\frac{\sqrt{6}}{4}$
10. $\frac{3\sqrt{3}}{4}$
15. $\frac{7\sqrt{3}}{5}$
20. $\frac{\sqrt{6}}{2}$
25. $\sqrt{6}$
30. $\frac{4\sqrt{3}}{3}$
35. $\frac{1}{3}$

36. $\dfrac{4}{\sqrt{a}}$ $\dfrac{4\sqrt{a}}{a}$ **37.** $\dfrac{7}{\sqrt{y}}$ $\dfrac{7\sqrt{y}}{y}$ **38.** $\dfrac{21}{\sqrt{2b}}$ $\dfrac{21\sqrt{2b}}{2b}$ **39.** $\dfrac{14}{\sqrt{4c}}$ $\dfrac{7\sqrt{c}}{c}$ **40.** $\dfrac{8}{\sqrt{2d}}$

41. $\sqrt{\dfrac{3}{b^3}}$ $\dfrac{\sqrt{3b}}{b^2}$ **42.** $\sqrt{\dfrac{4}{c^5}}$ $\dfrac{2\sqrt{c}}{c^3}$ **43.** $\sqrt{\dfrac{3}{12x^3}}$ $\dfrac{\sqrt{x}}{2x^2}$ **44.** $\sqrt{\dfrac{14}{8x^5}}$ $\dfrac{\sqrt{7x}}{2x^3}$ **45.** $\sqrt{\dfrac{21}{27d^3}}$

46. $\dfrac{\sqrt{ax}}{\sqrt{a}}$ $\sqrt{x}$ **47.** $\dfrac{\sqrt{b^3d^4}}{\sqrt{bd}}$ $bd\sqrt{d}$ **48.** $\dfrac{\sqrt{24b^3}}{\sqrt{6b}}$ $2b$ **49.** $\sqrt{\dfrac{60m^3n}{5m}}$ $2m\sqrt{3n}$ **50.** $\sqrt{\dfrac{x^2y}{xy^2}}$

B   Simplify.

51. $\sqrt{\dfrac{2}{3}}\cdot\sqrt{\dfrac{3}{4}}$ $\dfrac{\sqrt{2}}{2}$ **52.** $\sqrt{\dfrac{3}{5}}\cdot\sqrt{\dfrac{2}{5}}$ $\dfrac{\sqrt{6}}{5}$ **53.** $\sqrt{\dfrac{7}{2}}\cdot\sqrt{\dfrac{7}{5}}$ $\dfrac{7\sqrt{10}}{10}$ **54.** $\sqrt{\dfrac{7}{8}}\cdot\sqrt{\dfrac{3}{8}}$

55. $\sqrt{\dfrac{3}{5}}\cdot\sqrt{\dfrac{6}{7}}$ $\dfrac{3\sqrt{70}}{35}$ **56.** $\sqrt{\dfrac{10}{13}}\cdot\sqrt{\dfrac{1}{2}}$ $\dfrac{\sqrt{65}}{13}$ **57.** $\sqrt{\dfrac{6}{7}}\cdot\sqrt{\dfrac{7}{6}}$ 1 **58.** $\sqrt{\dfrac{3}{5}}\cdot\sqrt{\dfrac{3}{5}}$

59. $\sqrt{3-\dfrac{1}{2}}$ $\dfrac{\sqrt{10}}{2}$ **60.** $\sqrt{7+\dfrac{3}{4}}$ $\dfrac{\sqrt{31}}{2}$ **61.** $\sqrt{25-\dfrac{25}{4}}$ $\dfrac{5\sqrt{3}}{2}$ **62.** $\sqrt{4^2-\left(\dfrac{1}{4}\right)^2}$

C   Rationalize the denominators. Then use the values below to find a decimal approximation for each expression.

$$\sqrt{2}\approx 1.414 \qquad \sqrt{3}\approx 1.732 \qquad \sqrt{5}\approx 2.236$$

Example: $\dfrac{3}{\sqrt{2}}$ **Solution:** $\dfrac{3}{\sqrt{2}}=\dfrac{3\sqrt{2}}{\sqrt{2}\cdot\sqrt{2}}$

$$=\dfrac{3\sqrt{2}}{2}$$

$$\approx\dfrac{3\cdot 1.414}{2}=\textbf{2.121}$$

2.309$\overline{3}$ 3.535   0.866   1.414   0.6708   0.942$\overline{6}$

63. $\dfrac{4}{\sqrt{3}}$ **64.** $\dfrac{5}{\sqrt{2}}$ **65.** $\dfrac{3}{\sqrt{12}}$ **66.** $\dfrac{4}{\sqrt{8}}$ **67.** $\dfrac{3}{\sqrt{20}}$ **68.** $\dfrac{4}{\sqrt{18}}$

69. $\dfrac{5}{\sqrt{10}}$ **70.** $\dfrac{4}{\sqrt{15}}$ **71.** $\dfrac{7}{\sqrt{18}}$ **72.** $\dfrac{10}{\sqrt{24}}$ **73.** $\dfrac{7}{\sqrt{45}}$ **74.** $\dfrac{11}{\sqrt{30}}$

1.580852   1.0327338$\overline{6}$ 1.649$\overline{6}$ 2.04089$\overline{3}$ 1.0434$\overline{6}$ 2.00789282....

_____ **REVIEW CAPSULE FOR SECTION 12–8** _____

Simplify. *(Pages 437–438)*

1. $\sqrt{24}$ $2\sqrt{6}$ **2.** $\sqrt{80}$ $4\sqrt{5}$ **3.** $\sqrt{40}$ $2\sqrt{10}$ **4.** $\sqrt{128}$ $8\sqrt{2}$ **5.** $3\sqrt{32}$ $12\sqrt{2}$ **6.** $3\sqrt{64}$ 24

7. $5\sqrt{28}$ **8.** $-2\sqrt{18}$ **9.** $8\sqrt{50}$ **10.** $3\sqrt{12}$ **11.** $-4\sqrt{96}$ **12.** $7\sqrt{75}$
$\quad$ $10\sqrt{7}$ $\qquad\quad$ $-6\sqrt{2}$ $\qquad\quad$ $40\sqrt{2}$ $\qquad\quad$ $6\sqrt{3}$ $\qquad\quad$ $-16\sqrt{6}$ $\qquad\quad$ $35\sqrt{3}$

Multiply. Write the product in simplest form. *(Pages 448–449)*

13. $\sqrt{7}\cdot\sqrt{5}$ $\sqrt{35}$ **14.** $\sqrt{5}\cdot\sqrt{12}$ $2\sqrt{15}$ **15.** $\sqrt{3}\cdot\sqrt{2}$ $\sqrt{6}$ **16.** $5\sqrt{2}\cdot\sqrt{2}$ 10

17. $5\sqrt{2}\cdot 6\sqrt{2}$ 60 **18.** $\sqrt{7}\cdot\sqrt{7}$ 7 **19.** $\sqrt{8}\cdot\sqrt{8}$ 8 **20.** $2\sqrt{2}\cdot\sqrt{8}$ 8

Radicals   **453**

12–8 Addition and Subtraction of Radicals

Terms such as $-5x^3y^2$ and $3x^3y^2$ are like terms because their variable factors, x and y, are the same and they have the same exponents. Similarly, $2\sqrt{3}$ and $7\sqrt{3}$ are **like terms** because their radicals are the same.

Like Radicals	Unlike Radicals
$\sqrt{5}$ and $6\sqrt{5}$	$\sqrt{3}$ and $\sqrt{5}$
$3\sqrt{a}$ and $-2\sqrt{a}$	$3\sqrt{a}$ and $2\sqrt{b}$

To add or subtract like radicals, you apply the distributive postulate.
$$5\sqrt{y} + 7\sqrt{y} = (5 + 7)\sqrt{y} = 12\sqrt{y}$$

EXAMPLE 1   Add or subtract as indicated: $3\sqrt{5} + 6\sqrt{2} - \sqrt{5}$

Solution: Group the like terms.
$$3\sqrt{5} + 6\sqrt{2} - \sqrt{5} = (3\sqrt{5} - \sqrt{5}) + 6\sqrt{2}$$
$$= (3 - 1)\sqrt{5} + 6\sqrt{2} \longleftarrow \text{ By the distributive postulate}$$
$$= 2\sqrt{5} + 6\sqrt{2}$$

Always express each radical in simplest form before adding or subtracting. This will help you to identify like radicals.

EXAMPLE 2   Add or subtract as indicated: $\sqrt{48} + 6\sqrt{27} - 5\sqrt{12}$

Solution: Simplify the radicals before adding or subtracting.
$$\sqrt{48} + 6\sqrt{27} - 5\sqrt{12} = \sqrt{16 \cdot 3} + 6\sqrt{9 \cdot 3} - 5\sqrt{4 \cdot 3} \longleftarrow \begin{array}{l}\sqrt{9 \cdot 3} = 3\sqrt{3}; \\ \sqrt{4 \cdot 3} = 2\sqrt{3}\end{array}$$
$$= 4\sqrt{3} + 6 \cdot 3\sqrt{3} - 5 \cdot 2\sqrt{3}$$
$$= 4\sqrt{3} + 18\sqrt{3} - 10\sqrt{3}$$
$$= (4 + 18 - 10)\sqrt{3}$$
$$= 12\sqrt{3} \longleftarrow \text{ Simplest form}$$

You can also use the distributive postulate to simplify products of radical expressions.

EXAMPLE 3   Simplify each expression. **a.** $\sqrt{5}(3 + \sqrt{10})$ **b.** $(3 - \sqrt{5})(3 + \sqrt{5})$

Solutions: **a.** $\sqrt{5}(3 + \sqrt{10}) = \sqrt{5} \cdot 3 + \sqrt{5} \cdot \sqrt{10} \longleftarrow$ **By the distributive postulate**
$$= 3\sqrt{5} + \sqrt{50} \longleftarrow \textbf{Simplify.}$$
$$= 3\sqrt{5} + \sqrt{25 \cdot 2}$$
$$= 3\sqrt{5} + 5\sqrt{2} \longleftarrow \textbf{Simplest form}$$

   b. $(3 - \sqrt{5})(3 + \sqrt{5}) = (3)^2 - (\sqrt{5})^2 \longleftarrow \boldsymbol{(a + b)(a - b) = a^2 - b^2}$
$$= 9 - 5 = 4 \longleftarrow \boldsymbol{(\sqrt{5})^2 = 5}$$

In Example 3b, note that the product of $(3 - \sqrt{5})$ and $(3 + \sqrt{5})$ is a rational number. Expressions of the form $(a + \sqrt{b})$ and $(a - \sqrt{b})$ are called **conjugates**. Since

$$(a + \sqrt{b})(a - \sqrt{b}) = a^2 - b,$$

you can use conjugates to rationalize some binomial denominators. (See the Example for Exercises 48–51.)

CLASSROOM EXERCISES

Add or subtract as indicated.

1. $5\sqrt{3} - 2\sqrt{3} + \sqrt{3}$ $4\sqrt{3}$ 2. $-5\sqrt{6} + 2\sqrt{6} + 8\sqrt{6}$ $5\sqrt{6}$ 3. $2\sqrt{2} - \sqrt{8} + \sqrt{2}$ $\sqrt{2}$

4. $5\sqrt{2} + 2\sqrt{18} - 3\sqrt{72}$ $-7\sqrt{2}$ 5. $\sqrt{12} + \sqrt{3} - 2\sqrt{27}$ $-3\sqrt{3}$ 6. $6\sqrt{y} - 7\sqrt{y} + 13\sqrt{y}$ $12\sqrt{y}$

Simplify.

7. $\sqrt{2}(9 + \sqrt{5})$ $9\sqrt{2} + \sqrt{10}$ 8. $\sqrt{3}(3 - \sqrt{3})$ $3\sqrt{3} - 3$ 9. $\sqrt{5}(6 - 2\sqrt{5})$ $6\sqrt{5} - 10$ 10. $(1 + \sqrt{2})(1 - \sqrt{2})$ -1

WRITTEN EXERCISES

A   Add or subtract as indicated.

1. $3\sqrt{2} + 2\sqrt{2} - 4\sqrt{2}$ 2. $5\sqrt{3} - 2\sqrt{3} - 6\sqrt{3}$ 3. $6\sqrt{2} + 8\sqrt{2} - 9\sqrt{2}$
4. $-3\sqrt{3} + 4\sqrt{3} - 10\sqrt{3}$ 5. $5\sqrt{7} + 6\sqrt{7} - 11\sqrt{7}$ 6. $4\sqrt{3} + 2\sqrt{3} - 2\sqrt{2} + 7\sqrt{2}$
7. $8\sqrt{5} + 6\sqrt{5} + 2\sqrt{3} + 7\sqrt{3}$ 8. $10\sqrt{2} + 7\sqrt{3} - 4\sqrt{2} - 5\sqrt{3}$ 9. $\sqrt{4} + 3\sqrt{2} + 7 - 5\sqrt{2}$
10. $\sqrt{12} + 3\sqrt{3}$ 11. $\sqrt{8} + 5\sqrt{2} - 6\sqrt{2}$ 12. $\sqrt{20} - 3\sqrt{5} + 2\sqrt{5}$
13. $-6\sqrt{5} + 7\sqrt{5} - \sqrt{20}$ 14. $\sqrt{12} - \sqrt{27} + \sqrt{48}$ 15. $3\sqrt{18} - 7\sqrt{32} - 5\sqrt{50}$
16. $10\sqrt{8} - \sqrt{72} + 3\sqrt{98}$ 17. $10\sqrt{8} - 3\sqrt{98} + 6\sqrt{72}$ 18. $2\sqrt{8} + 4\sqrt{50} + 3\sqrt{18}$
19. $6\sqrt{54} - 3\sqrt{24} - 2\sqrt{6}$ 20. $\sqrt{125} + 2\sqrt{80} - 3\sqrt{20}$ 21. $2\sqrt{40} + \sqrt{90} + 5\sqrt{160}$

Simplify.

22. $\sqrt{2}(\sqrt{3} + 3)$ $\sqrt{6} + 3\sqrt{2}$ 23. $\sqrt{7}(\sqrt{2} + 5)$ $\sqrt{14} + 5\sqrt{7}$ 24. $\sqrt{3}(\sqrt{3} + 2)$ $3 + 2\sqrt{3}$
25. $\sqrt{4}(\sqrt{8} + 2)$ $4\sqrt{2} + 4$ 26. $\sqrt{8}(2\sqrt{3} - 5)$ $4\sqrt{6} - 10\sqrt{2}$ 27. $\sqrt{5}(\sqrt{2} - \sqrt{3})$ $\sqrt{10} - \sqrt{15}$
28. $(8 + \sqrt{7})(8 - \sqrt{7})$ 57 29. $(\sqrt{5} - 2)(\sqrt{5} + 2)$ 1 30. $(\sqrt{6} + 9)(\sqrt{6} - 9)$ -75

B   Add or subtract as indicated.

31. $\sqrt{\dfrac{2}{3}} + \sqrt{\dfrac{8}{3}}$ $\sqrt{6}$ 32. $5\sqrt{\dfrac{1}{6}} - 3\sqrt{\dfrac{3}{2}}$ $-\dfrac{2\sqrt{6}}{3}$ 33. $\sqrt{\dfrac{2}{3}} - 3\sqrt{\dfrac{1}{6}}$ $-\dfrac{\sqrt{6}}{6}$

34. $\sqrt{\dfrac{2}{36}} - 3\sqrt{\dfrac{2}{49}} - 6\sqrt{\dfrac{2}{25}}$ 35. $\sqrt{\dfrac{8}{9}} + 2\sqrt{\dfrac{1}{2}} - 3\sqrt{\dfrac{9}{8}}$ 36. $\sqrt{\dfrac{3}{4}} - 2\sqrt{\dfrac{19}{16}} + \sqrt{\dfrac{3}{8}}$

37. $\sqrt{100x} - \sqrt{9x}$ $7\sqrt{x}$ 38. $2a\sqrt{ab} + 4\sqrt{a^3b}$ $6a\sqrt{ab}$ 39. $3\sqrt{2b^3} - \sqrt{8b^3}$ $b\sqrt{2b}$
40. $4\sqrt{12r^2} + 2\sqrt{75r^2} - 3\sqrt{27r^2}$ $9r\sqrt{3}$ 41. $\sqrt{12a^3} - 2\sqrt{3a^3} + \sqrt{27a^3}$ $3a\sqrt{3a}$
42. $x\sqrt{xy^3} + xy\sqrt{xy} + y\sqrt{x^3y}$ $3xy\sqrt{xy}$ 43. $2b\sqrt{25b} + b\sqrt{4b} - 3b\sqrt{9b}$

Radicals   **455**

Assignment Guide
Minimal
Day 1 p. 455: 1–15
Day 2 p. 455 16–30
Average
Day 1 p. 455: 1–30
Day 2 pp. 455–456: 31–49
Above Average pp. 455–456: 3, 6, 9, . . . 51, 52–63

Additional Answers
Written Exercises
1. $\sqrt{2}$
2. $-3\sqrt{3}$
3. $5\sqrt{2}$
4. $-9\sqrt{3}$
5. 0
6. $6\sqrt{3} + 5\sqrt{2}$
7. $14\sqrt{5} + 9\sqrt{3}$
8. $6\sqrt{2} + 2\sqrt{3}$
9. $9 - 2\sqrt{2}$
10. $5\sqrt{3}$
11. $\sqrt{2}$
12. $\sqrt{5}$
13. $-\sqrt{5}$
14. $3\sqrt{3}$
15. $-44\sqrt{2}$
16. $35\sqrt{2}$
17. $35\sqrt{2}$
18. $33\sqrt{2}$
19. $10\sqrt{6}$
20. $7\sqrt{5}$
21. $27\sqrt{10}$

34. $-\dfrac{307\sqrt{2}}{210}$

35. $-\dfrac{7\sqrt{2}}{12}$

36. $\dfrac{2\sqrt{3} - 2\sqrt{19} + \sqrt{6}}{4}$

43. $(12b - 72)\sqrt{b}$

Write the conjugate of each radical expression.

44. $1 + \sqrt{2}$ $1 - \sqrt{2}$ **45.** $3 - \sqrt{5}$ $3 + \sqrt{5}$ **46.** $2\sqrt{3} + 5\sqrt{7}$ **47.** $1 - \sqrt{x}$

                                                                    $2\sqrt{3} - 5\sqrt{7}$ $1 + \sqrt{x}$

Rationalize the denominator.

Example: $\dfrac{5}{1 - 2\sqrt{5}} = \dfrac{5}{1 - 2\sqrt{5}} \cdot \dfrac{1 + 2\sqrt{5}}{1 + 2\sqrt{5}} = \dfrac{5 + 10\sqrt{5}}{1 - 4(5)} = \dfrac{\mathbf{5 + 10\sqrt{5}}}{\mathbf{-19}}$

48. $\dfrac{2}{1 + \sqrt{2}}$ **49.** $\dfrac{4}{\sqrt{7} - 2}$ **50.** $\dfrac{7}{5 - \sqrt{3}}$ **51.** $\dfrac{2}{\sqrt{6} - 3}$

C

52. $\dfrac{3\sqrt{5} + 2\sqrt{3}}{2\sqrt{5} - 5\sqrt{3}}$ **53.** $\dfrac{2\sqrt{5} + 3\sqrt{2}}{4\sqrt{5} - \sqrt{2}}$ **54.** $\dfrac{\sqrt{a} + \sqrt{b}}{\sqrt{a} - \sqrt{b}}$ **55.** $\dfrac{3\sqrt{x} - 1}{\sqrt{x} + 1}$

Factor over the real numbers.

Example: $x^2 - 5 = x^2 - (\sqrt{5})^2 = \mathbf{(x + \sqrt{5})(x - \sqrt{5})}$

56. $y^2 - 7$ **57.** $a^2 - 10$ **58.** $2b^2 - 12$ **59.** $5x^2 - 25$

60. $27 - r^2$ **61.** $1 - 2x^2$ **62.** $t^2 - 5v^2$ **63.** $a^2 - 2a\sqrt{5} + 5$

--- Puzzle ---

See if you can solve the following problems involving radicals.

1. Solve: $\sqrt{\sqrt{\sqrt{x + 37} + 2} + 6} = 3$

2. Three of the statements below are true. Which one is false?

    a. $\sqrt{1\frac{1}{3}} = 2\sqrt{\frac{1}{3}}$ **b.** $\sqrt{2\frac{2}{3}} = 2\sqrt{\frac{2}{3}}$ **c.** $\sqrt{3\frac{2}{3}} = 3\sqrt{\frac{2}{3}}$ **d.** $\sqrt{5\frac{1}{3}} = 4\sqrt{\frac{1}{3}}$

3. Show that this statement is true: $\sqrt{x + \dfrac{x}{x^2 - 1}} = x\sqrt{\dfrac{x}{x^2 - 1}}$.

    (HINT: Work on the left side only.)

--- **REVIEW CAPSULE FOR SECTION 12–9** ---

Simplify. *(Pages 432–433)*

1. $(\sqrt{5})^2$ 5   **2.** $(\sqrt{15})^2$ 15   **3.** $(\sqrt{11})^2$ 11   **4.** $(\sqrt{565})^2$ 565   **5.** $(\sqrt{x})^2$ x

6. $(\sqrt{a - 1})^2$ **7.** $(\sqrt{2b - 1})^2$ **8.** $(3\sqrt{x})^2$ **9.** $(4\sqrt{2b})^2$ **10.** $(5\sqrt{a - 1})^2$

Determine whether the given number is a solution of the given equation. Answer *Yes* or *No*. *(Pages 17–19)*

11. $2 + \sqrt{x} = 4$;   4   Yes   **12.** $2 - 4\sqrt{y} = 3$; $\frac{1}{16}$ No   **13.** $1 + \sqrt{x} = 0$; -1 No

14. $\sqrt{y} - 48 = 2$;   2500   Yes   **15.** $2\sqrt{a} - 14 = 0$;   7   No   **16.** $3\sqrt{b + 1} = 8$; $\frac{55}{9}$ Yes

Additional Answers
Written Exercises
48. $-2 + 2\sqrt{2}$

49. $\dfrac{4\sqrt{7} + 8}{3}$

50. $\dfrac{35 + 7\sqrt{3}}{22}$

51. $\dfrac{2\sqrt{6} + 6}{-3}$

52. $\dfrac{60 + 19\sqrt{15}}{-55}$

53. $\dfrac{23 + 7\sqrt{2}}{39}$

54. $\dfrac{a + 2\sqrt{ab} + b}{a - b}$

55. $\dfrac{3x - 3\sqrt{x} - 1}{x - 1}$

56. $(y + \sqrt{7})(y - \sqrt{7})$
57. $(a + \sqrt{10})(a - \sqrt{10})$
58. $2(b + \sqrt{6})(b - \sqrt{6})$
59. $5(x + \sqrt{5})(x - \sqrt{5})$
60. $(\sqrt{27} + r)(\sqrt{27} - r)$
61. $(1 + x\sqrt{2})(1 - x\sqrt{2})$
62. $(t + v\sqrt{5})(t - v\sqrt{5})$
63. $(a - \sqrt{5})^2$

Review Capsule
6. $a - 1$
7. $2b - 1$
8. $9x$
9. $32b$
10. $25a - 25$

12–9 Solving Radical Equations

Teaching Suggestions p. M-25

An equation such as $3 + \sqrt{x} = 6$ is a radical equation. A **radical equation** contains a radical that includes a variable.

EXAMPLE 1 Solve: $3 + \sqrt{x} = 6$

Solution: Add -3 to each side in order to get the radical alone on the left side.

$$3 + \sqrt{x} = 6$$
$$-3 + 3 + \sqrt{x} = -3 + 6$$
$$\sqrt{x} = 3 \quad \longleftarrow \quad \textbf{Now square both sides.}$$
$$(\sqrt{x})^2 = (3)^2 \quad \longleftarrow \quad (\sqrt{\textbf{x}})^2 = \textbf{x}$$
$$x = 9$$

Check:
$$3 + \sqrt{x} = 6 \quad \longleftarrow \quad \textbf{Replace x with 9.}$$
$$3 + \sqrt{9} \overset{?}{=} 6$$
$$3 + 3 \overset{?}{=} 6$$
$$6 \overset{?}{=} 6 \quad \text{Yes } \checkmark$$

Solution set: $\{9\}$

Quick Quiz
Add or subtract as indicated.
1. $3\sqrt{6} + 9\sqrt{5} - 2\sqrt{6}$
   Ans: $\sqrt{6} + 9\sqrt{5}$
2. $4\sqrt{12} - 8\sqrt{27} + 2\sqrt{48}$
   Ans: $-8\sqrt{3}$
Simplify each expression.
3. $\sqrt{5}\,(2 + \sqrt{8})$
   Ans: $2\sqrt{5} + 2\sqrt{10}$
4. $(\sqrt{14} - 6)\,(\sqrt{14} + 6)$
   Ans: -22

Additional Examples
Example 1
Solve and check.
1. $5 + \sqrt{x} = 9$ **Ans:** $\{16\}$
2. $8 + \sqrt{x} = 10$ **Ans:** $\{4\}$

In Example 2, the radicand of $3\sqrt{2a - 1}$ is a binomial.

EXAMPLE 2 Solve: $3\sqrt{2a - 1} + 4 = 7$

Solution:
$$3\sqrt{2a - 1} + 4 = 7 \quad \longleftarrow \quad \textbf{Add (−4) to each side.}$$
$$3\sqrt{2a - 1} + 4 + (-4) = 7 + (-4)$$
$$3\sqrt{2a - 1} = 3 \quad \longleftarrow \quad \textbf{Multiply each side by } \tfrac{1}{3}.$$
$$\sqrt{2a - 1} = 1 \quad \longleftarrow \quad \textbf{Square both sides.}$$
$$(\sqrt{2a - 1})^2 = 1^2$$
$$2a - 1 = 1 \quad \longleftarrow \quad \textbf{Solve for a.}$$
$$2a = 2$$
$$a = 1$$

The check is left for you.

Solution set: $\{1\}$

Example 2
Solve and check.
1. $5\sqrt{3a - 5} + 4 = 9$
   Ans: $\{2\}$
2. $8\sqrt{4a - 8} - 9 = 7$
   Ans: $\{3\}$

Squaring both sides of an equation sometimes results in an "apparent solution" that does not check in the original equation. An "apparent solution" is not a member of the solution set. This is why it is important to check all your answers in the original equation.

Additional Examples
Example 3
Solve and check.
1. $7 + \sqrt{x - 2} = 5$
   Ans: ϕ
2. $10 + \sqrt{x - 8} = 8$
   Ans: ϕ

EXAMPLE 3 Solve: $6 + \sqrt{x - 5} = 3$

Solution: $6 + \sqrt{x - 5} = 3$ ← **Add (−6) to each side.**

$\sqrt{x - 5} = -3$ ← **Square both sides.**

$(\sqrt{x - 5})^2 = (-3)^2$ ← $(\sqrt{x - 5})^2 = x - 5$

$x - 5 = 9$

$x = 14$

Check: $6 + \sqrt{x - 5} = 3$ ← **Replace x with 14.**

$6 + \sqrt{14 - 5} \overset{?}{=} 3$

$6 + \sqrt{9} \overset{?}{=} 3$ No ← **14 is not a solution.**

Solution set: ϕ

Additional Answers
Classroom Exercises
5. Divide both sides by 3.
6. Subtract 12 from both sides.
7. Subtract 4 from both sides.
8. Subtract 9 from both sides.

CLASSROOM EXERCISES

Solve.

1. $\sqrt{y} = \dfrac{2}{5}$ $y = \frac{4}{25}$
2. $\sqrt{3x - 2} = 7$ $x = 17$
3. $\sqrt{4x} = 10$ $x = 25$
4. $\sqrt{\dfrac{a}{4}} = 25$ $a = 2500$

State the first step you would use to solve each equation. Do *not* solve the equation.

5. $3\sqrt{y} = 1$
6. $12 + 3\sqrt{x} = 0$
7. $\sqrt{3x} + 4 = 7$
8. $\sqrt{x} + 9 = 20$

Assignment Guide
Minimal omit
Average
Day 1 p. 458: 1–30: even
Day 2 p. 459: 31–46
Above Average
Day 1 pp. 458–459: 1–36
Day 2 p. 459: 37–52

Additional Answers
Written Exercises
6. $x = 11$
9. $x = 14$
12. $x = \frac{25}{4}$, or $6\frac{1}{4}$

WRITTEN EXERCISES

A Solve and check each equation. If an apparent solution does not check in the original equation, give the solution set as ϕ.

1. $\sqrt{x} = 6$ $x = 36$
2. $\sqrt{x} = \dfrac{3}{4}$ $x = \frac{9}{16}$
3. $\sqrt{\dfrac{n}{5}} = 2$ $n = 20$
4. $8 = \sqrt{x - 9}$ $x = 73$
5. $8 = \sqrt{5r + 1}$ $r = \frac{63}{5}$ or $12\frac{3}{5}$
6. $\sqrt{x + 5} = 4$
7. $3 + \sqrt{x - 1} = 5$ $x = 5$
8. $6 + \sqrt{x} = 13$ $x = 49$
9. $6 - \sqrt{x - 5} = 3$
10. $5 + \sqrt{x} = 3$ ϕ
11. $8 + 2\sqrt{x} = 0$ ϕ
12. $2\sqrt{x} = 5$
13. $5\sqrt{x} = 2$ $x = \frac{4}{25}$
14. $-\sqrt{x} = 6$ ϕ
15. $-7 = \sqrt{y}$ ϕ
16. $-\sqrt{m} = -5$ $m = 25$
17. $-9 = -\sqrt{y}$ $y = 81$
18. $-\sqrt{x} = \dfrac{3}{4}$ ϕ
19. $\sqrt{x} = -3$ ϕ
20. $\sqrt{x} = \sqrt{5}$ $x = 5$
21. $-1 = \sqrt{x - 5}$ ϕ
22. $\sqrt{a - 1} = \sqrt{3}$ $a = 4$
23. $\sqrt{7 + 3x} = -4$ ϕ
24. $-9 = \sqrt{6 - x}$ ϕ
25. $\sqrt{3y + 2} = 2\sqrt{y}$ $y = 2$
26. $5 = \dfrac{15}{\sqrt{2a - 3}}$ $a = 6$
27. $\sqrt{\dfrac{9}{16}} = x$ $x = \frac{3}{4}$
28. $-\sqrt{\dfrac{81}{25}} = x$ $x = -\frac{9}{5}$, or $-1\frac{4}{5}$
29. $\sqrt{2x + 1} = \sqrt{x + 5}$ $x = 4$
30. $3\sqrt{5b + 1} + 5 = 8$ $b = 0$

APPLICATIONS: Using Radical Equations

31. Five times the square root of a number is 2. Find the number. $\frac{4}{25}$

32. Eight less than the square root of a number is 0. What is the number? 64

33. Three more than the square root of a number is 7. What is the number? 16

34. A number is increased by 3. The square root of this sum is 5. Find the number. 22

35. Twice a number is decreased by 3. The square root of this difference equals 6. Find the number. $\frac{39}{2}$, or $19\frac{1}{2}$

36. The quotient of the square root of a number and 5 equals $\frac{3}{4}$. What is the number? $\frac{225}{16}$, or $14\frac{1}{16}$

B

37. The formula

$$s = \sqrt{30fd}$$

can be used to estimate the speed, s, in miles per hour that a car was traveling when it skidded d feet after the brakes were applied. In the formula, f is the coefficient of friction. Find the distance a car will travel on a wet concrete road ($f = 0.4$) if the car is traveling 60 miles per hour when the brakes are applied. 300 ft

38. The formula

$$T = 2\pi\sqrt{\frac{L}{9.8}}$$

relates the time, T, in seconds that it takes for a pendulum to swing back and forth once with the length, L, of the pendulum in meters. What is the length of a pendulum that takes 3 seconds to swing back and forth once? Use $\pi = 3.14$. Round the answer to the nearest tenth. 2.2 m

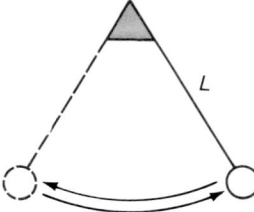

39. The formula

$$t = \sqrt{\frac{d^3}{216}}$$

relates the time, t, in hours that a storm with diameter, d, in miles will last. What is the diameter of a storm that lasts one hour? 6 mi

40. The time, t, in seconds that it takes a body to fall a distance of s feet from rest is given by the formula

$$t = \sqrt{\frac{2s}{g}}$$

where g is the acceleration due to gravity. Find s when $t = 6.25$ and $g = 32$.
$s = 625$ ft

Solve and check each equation.

41. $\sqrt{x^2 + 5} = x + 1$ $x = 2$

42. $\sqrt{x^2 - 5} = x - 5$ ϕ

43. $\sqrt{x^2 + 24} = x + 12$

44. $\sqrt{3b^2 - 5} = 11$ $b = \sqrt{42}$

45. $\sqrt{y^2 + 4y} = \sqrt{5}$

46. $\sqrt{a^2 - 7a} = \sqrt{18}$

C

47. $4\sqrt{2a + 2} - 9 = 2\sqrt{2a + 2}$

48. $\sqrt{4b - 3} - \sqrt{3b + 4} = 0$ $b = 7$

49. $5\sqrt{3t - 1} - 4 = 3\sqrt{3t - 1}$

50. $\sqrt{2q + 6} - \sqrt{5q} = 0$ $q = 2$

Determine whether each pair of equations is equivalent (has the same solution set). Give a reason for each answer.

51. $x^2 + y^2 = 1$; $y = \sqrt{1 - x^2}$

52. $x^2 + y^2 = 1$; $\sqrt{x^2 + y^2} = 1$

Radicals **459**

Write each product as a base with a single exponent. *(Pages 280–282)*

1. $x^3 \cdot x^4$ x^7 **2.** $a \cdot a^6$ a^7 **3.** $c^2 \cdot c$ c^3 **4.** $5^3 \cdot 5^2$ 5^5 **5.** $10^2 \cdot 10^5$ 10^7

Simplify. *(Pages 285–287)*

6. $(x^2)^2 x^4$ **7.** $(x^2)^3 x^6$ **8.** $(x^3)^2 x^6$ **9.** $(x^3)^3 x^9$ **10.** $(4b^3)^2$ $16b^6$

11. $(z^4)^3 z^{12}$ **12.** $(\frac{1}{2}z)^2 \frac{1}{4}z^2$ **13.** $(4t)^3$ $64t^3$ **14.** $(-4c^2)^3$ $-64c^6$ **15.** $(0.5d)^2$ $0.25d^2$

Write each expression with positive exponents. Simplify the result when possible. *(Pages 290–293)*

16. 5^{-3} $\frac{1}{125}$ **17.** $3b^{-2}$ $\frac{3}{b^2}$ **18.** $(3b)^{-2}$ $\frac{1}{9b^2}$ **19.** $(-4)^{-3}$ $-\frac{1}{64}$ **20.** 10^{-2} $\frac{1}{100}$

21. 6^{-1} $\frac{1}{6}$ **22.** $\frac{4}{b^{-2}}$ $4b^2$ **23.** $(-2)^{-4}$ $\frac{1}{16}$ **24.** $\left(\frac{1}{6}\right)^{-1}$ 6 **25.** $\left(-\frac{1}{2}\right)^{-4}$ 16

OBJECTIVE: To simplify expressions containing rational exponents

12–10   Rational Exponents

The properties of positive and negative integral exponents can be extended in order to define rational exponents. Consider the following.

You already know that
$$\sqrt{5} \cdot \sqrt{5} = (\sqrt{5})^2 = 5.$$

If the exponent theorems hold for rational exponents, then
$$5^{\frac{1}{2}} \cdot 5^{\frac{1}{2}} = 5^{\frac{1}{2}+\frac{1}{2}} = 5^1, \text{ or } 5.$$

Thus, it seems reasonable to define
$$\sqrt{5} = 5^{\frac{1}{2}}.$$

The following expresses the definition in general form.

Definition

Rational Exponents
For any positive integer n where n is odd and a is any real number, or for any positive integer n where n is even and $a \geq 0$, $$a^{\frac{1}{n}} = \sqrt[n]{a}.$$

EXAMPLE 1   Simplify: **a.** $81^{\frac{1}{2}}$ **b.** $-(81)^{\frac{1}{2}}$ **c.** $81^{\frac{1}{4}}$ **d.** $(-8)^{\frac{1}{3}}$

Solutions: **a.** $81^{\frac{1}{2}} = \sqrt{81}$ **b.** $-(81)^{\frac{1}{2}} = -\sqrt{81}$
                   $= 9$ $= -9$

          c. $81^{\frac{1}{4}} = \sqrt[4]{81}$ **d.** $(-8)^{\frac{1}{3}} = \sqrt[3]{-8}$
            $= 3$ ◄——— Since $3^4 = 81$ $= -2$

Teaching Suggestions p. M-25

Quick Quiz
Solve and check. If an apparent solution does not check in the original equation, give the solution set as ϕ.
1. $4 + \sqrt{x} = 8$ **Ans: {16}**
2. $3 + \sqrt{x} = 2$ **Ans: ϕ**
3. $3\sqrt{2x - 7} + 7 = 10$
    Ans: {4}
4. $8 - \sqrt{x - 4} = 5$
    Ans: {13}
5. $9 + \sqrt{a - 3} = 7$ **Ans: ϕ**
6. $6 - \sqrt{x - 5} = 9$ **Ans: ϕ**

Additional Examples
Example 1
Simplify.
1.a. $64^{\frac{1}{2}}$ **Ans: 8**

   b. $-(64)^{\frac{1}{2}}$ **Ans: −8**

   c. $16^{\frac{1}{4}}$ **Ans: 2**

   d. $(-64)^{\frac{1}{3}}$ **Ans: −4**

2.a. $49^{\frac{1}{2}}$ **Ans: 7**

   b. $-(49)^{\frac{1}{2}}$ **Ans: −7**

   c. $256^{\frac{1}{4}}$ **Ans: 4**

   d. $(-125)^{\frac{1}{3}}$ **Ans: −5**

By the definition of rational exponents, $\sqrt[5]{7} = 7^{\frac{1}{5}}$. Then, by the laws of exponents,

$$\sqrt[5]{7^3} = (7^3)^{\frac{1}{5}} = 7^{3 \cdot \frac{1}{5}} = 7^{\frac{3}{5}} \quad \text{Thus,} \quad \sqrt[5]{7^3} = 7^{\frac{3}{5}}.$$

When the conditions of the definition are satisfied, rational exponents may be viewed in two ways. Thus,

$$7^{\frac{3}{5}} = (\sqrt[5]{7})^3 \quad \text{or} \quad \sqrt[5]{7^3}.$$

Example 2 illustrates the value of taking the root first.

EXAMPLE 2 Simplify: **a.** $4^{\frac{3}{2}}$ **b.** $-(27)^{\frac{2}{3}}$ **c.** $(16)^{\frac{5}{4}}$

Solutions: **a.** $4^{\frac{3}{2}} = (4^{\frac{1}{2}})^3 = (\sqrt{4})^3 = 2^3 = \mathbf{8}$

   b. $-(27)^{\frac{2}{3}} = -(27^{\frac{1}{3}})^2 = -(\sqrt[3]{27})^2 = -3^2 = \mathbf{9}$

   c. $16^{\frac{5}{4}} = [(16)^{\frac{1}{4}}]^5 = (\sqrt[4]{16})^5 = (2)^5 = \mathbf{32}$

Example 2
Simplify.

1.a. $36^{\frac{3}{2}}$ **Ans: 216**

   b. $-(64)^{\frac{2}{3}}$ **Ans: −16**

   c. $81^{\frac{5}{4}}$ **Ans: 243**

2.a. $4^{\frac{5}{2}}$ **Ans: 32**

   b. $-(125)^{\frac{2}{3}}$ **Ans: −25**

   c. $27^{\frac{5}{3}}$ **Ans: 243**

CLASSROOM EXERCISES

Write using rational exponents.

1. $\sqrt{7}$ $7^{\frac{1}{2}}$ 2. $\sqrt[3]{2}$ $2^{\frac{1}{3}}$ 3. $\sqrt{5^3}$ $5^{\frac{3}{2}}$ 4. $\sqrt[5]{6^2}$ $6^{\frac{2}{5}}$ 5. $\sqrt[4]{9^3}$ $9^{\frac{3}{4}}$

Simplify.

6. $16^{\frac{1}{2}}$ 4   7. $(-64)^{\frac{1}{3}}$ −4   8. $-(4^{\frac{3}{2}})$ −8   9. $(8)^{\frac{5}{3}}$ 32   10. $243^{\frac{3}{4}}$ 27

WRITTEN EXERCISES

A   Simplify.

1. $9^{\frac{1}{2}}$ 3   2. $125^{\frac{1}{3}}$ 5   3. $16^{\frac{1}{4}}$ 2   4. $(-27)^{\frac{1}{3}}$ −3   5. $81^{\frac{1}{4}}$ 3

6. $625^{\frac{1}{4}}$ 5   7. $121^{\frac{1}{2}}$ 11   8. $144^{\frac{1}{2}}$ 12   9. $-36^{\frac{1}{2}}$ −6   10. $-(81)^{\frac{1}{4}}$ −3

11. $-(\frac{1}{4})^{\frac{1}{2}}$ $-\frac{1}{2}$ 12. $(\frac{1}{27})^{\frac{1}{3}}$ $\frac{1}{3}$ 13. $-(\frac{1}{27})^{\frac{1}{3}}$ $-\frac{1}{3}$ 14. $(-\frac{1}{27})^{\frac{1}{3}}$ $-\frac{1}{3}$ 15. $(\frac{1}{27})^{\frac{1}{3}}$ 3

16. $-(\frac{1}{27})^{\frac{1}{3}}$ −3   17. $(\frac{4}{9})^{\frac{1}{2}}$ $\frac{2}{3}$ 18. $(-\frac{8}{125})^{\frac{1}{3}}$ $-\frac{2}{5}$ 19. $-(\frac{8}{125})^{\frac{1}{3}}$ $-\frac{2}{5}$ 20. $-25^{\frac{1}{2}}$ −5

21. $-64^{\frac{1}{2}}$ −8   22. 15^0 1   23. $-(9)^{\frac{1}{2}}$ −3   24. $-(16)^{\frac{1}{4}}$ −2   25. $25^{\frac{1}{2}}$ 5

26. $81^{\frac{1}{2}}$ 9   27. $8^{\frac{1}{3}}$ 2   28. $64^{\frac{1}{3}}$ 4   29. $32^{\frac{1}{5}}$ 2   30. $-16^{\frac{1}{2}}$ −4

31. $64^{\frac{1}{2}}$ 8   32. $27^{\frac{1}{3}}$ 3   33. $-(49^{\frac{1}{2}})$ −7   34. $(-8)^{\frac{1}{3}}$ −2   35. $-(125)^{\frac{1}{3}}$ −5

36. $(\frac{1}{16})^{\frac{1}{2}}$ $\frac{1}{4}$ 37. $(\frac{4}{25})^{\frac{1}{2}}$ $\frac{2}{5}$ 38. $-(\frac{1}{36})^{\frac{1}{2}}$ $-\frac{1}{6}$ 39. $(-\frac{1}{8})^{\frac{1}{3}}$ $-\frac{1}{2}$ 40. $(\frac{1}{64})^{\frac{1}{3}}$ $\frac{1}{4}$

41. $27^{\frac{4}{3}}$ 81   42. $(\frac{1}{64})^{\frac{2}{3}}$ $\frac{1}{16}$ 43. $16^{\frac{3}{4}}$ 8   44. $4^{\frac{3}{2}}$ 8   45. $49^{\frac{3}{2}}$ 343

Use a radical to name each of the following. Variables represent positive integers.

46. $7^{\frac{1}{2}}$ $\sqrt{7}$ 47. $(-8)^{\frac{1}{3}}$ $\sqrt[3]{-8}$ 48. $16^{\frac{1}{4}}$ $\sqrt[4]{16}$ 49. $93^{\frac{1}{n}}$ $\sqrt[n]{93}$ 50. $x^{\frac{1}{2}}$ $\sqrt{x}$

51. $y^{\frac{1}{3}}$ $\sqrt[3]{y}$ 52. $a^{\frac{1}{4}}$ $\sqrt[4]{a}$ 53. $(x^2)^{\frac{1}{3}}$ $\sqrt[3]{x^2}$ 54. $(xy)^{\frac{1}{2}}$ $\sqrt{xy}$ 55. $(ab)^{\frac{1}{3}}$ $\sqrt[3]{ab}$

Assignment Guide
Minimal omit
Average omit
Above Average pp. 461–462
3, 6, 9, . . . 54, 56–65

Radicals   **461**

B   Evaluate each expression for $a = 8$, $b = 9$, and $c = 1$.

56. $a^{\frac{1}{3}} - b^{\frac{1}{2}}$ -1 57. $(a + c)^{\frac{1}{2}}$ 3   58. $-a^{\frac{1}{3}}$ -2 59. $-b^{\frac{1}{2}}$ -3 60. $a^{\frac{5}{3}}$ 32

61. $b^{\frac{3}{2}}$ 27   62. $-(bc)^{\frac{3}{2}}$ -27 63. $c^{\frac{1}{8}}$ 1   64. $(a - b)^{\frac{1}{3}}$ -1 65. $(ab + c)^{\frac{1}{2}}$
$73^{\frac{1}{2}}$ or $\sqrt{73}$

___ Review ___

Multiply and simplify. Variables represent positive numbers. *(Section 12–6)*

1. $\sqrt{3} \cdot \sqrt{12}$ 6   2. $-3\sqrt{14} \cdot 2\sqrt{6}$ $-12\sqrt{21}$ 3. $\sqrt{x} \cdot \sqrt{xy}$ $x\sqrt{y}$ 4. $\sqrt{6a} \cdot \sqrt{3a}$

Simplify. Variables represent positive numbers. *(Section 12–7)*

5. $\sqrt{\dfrac{4}{9}}$ $\dfrac{2}{3}$ 6. $\dfrac{1}{\sqrt{6}}$ $\dfrac{\sqrt{6}}{6}$ 7. $\sqrt{\dfrac{2}{5}}$ $\dfrac{\sqrt{10}}{5}$ 8. $\sqrt{\dfrac{5}{x^3}}$ $\dfrac{\sqrt{5x}}{x^2}$ 9. $\dfrac{\sqrt{18a^3}}{\sqrt{3ab^2}}$

Add or subtract as indicated. *(Section 12–8)*

10. $3\sqrt{5} + \sqrt{5} - 4\sqrt{5}$ 0   11. $6\sqrt{5} + \sqrt{8} - \sqrt{45}$ 12. $\sqrt{6r^2} + \sqrt{24r^2}$

Solve and check each equation. If an apparent solution does not check in the original equation, give the solution set as ϕ. *(Section 12–9)*

13. $\sqrt{x + 1} = 10$ $x = 99$ 14. $2 + \sqrt{x} = 7$ $x = 25$ 15. $3\sqrt{x - 2} = 6$
$x = 6$

Simplify. *(Section 12–10)*

16. $1000^{\frac{1}{3}}$ 10   17. $-(25)^{\frac{1}{2}}$ -5 18. $(-32)^{\frac{1}{5}}$ -2 19. $4^{\frac{5}{2}}$ 32   20. $(-8)^{\frac{2}{3}}$
4

CALCULATOR APPLICATIONS ___

Evaluating Formulas

You can use a calculator with a square root key to evaluate formulas that include radicals.

EXAMPLE Use the formula $T = 2\pi\sqrt{\dfrac{L}{9.8}}$ to find T when $L = 2.2$. Use $\pi = 3.14$. (See Exercise 38 on page 459.)

SOLUTION Evaluate the radical first.

2 . 2 $\div$ 9 . 8 $=$ $\sqrt{\ }$ $\times$ 2 $\times$ 3 . 1 4 $=$ 2.9754853

EXERCISES

Use the formula $T = 2\pi\sqrt{\dfrac{L}{9.8}}$ to find T for each value of L. Round your answers to the nearest tenth.

1. $L = 5$ 2. $L = 8.5$ 3. $L = 10.4$ 4. $L = 13$ 5. $L = 19.7$ 6. $L = 0.5$

BASIC: COMPUTING SQUARE ROOTS

BASIC has the SQR function for computing square roots. But how does a function like this work? The **algorithm** (step–by–step procedure) for approximating the square root of a positive real number is shown below.

This section is optional. Each computer applications lesson relates directly to a topic covered within the given chapter. (See Section 12–2, pages 434–436)

Procedure

> 1 Make an estimate, e, of the square root. For example, let e be the greatest integer less than or equal to $\frac{1}{2}x$.
>
> 2 Divide x by e. Call this quotient a.
>
> 3 Take the average of a and e. Let this average become e_2.
>
> 4 Repeat steps 2 and 3 until the difference between a and e becomes less than a specified tolerance (for example, 0.1). Then, that value of e is the approximate square root.

EXAMPLE Use the algorithm to approximate $\sqrt{17}$.

Solution:

1 Let $e_1 = 8$.

2 Then $a_1 = \dfrac{17}{8} \approx 2.13$.   3 $\dfrac{8 + 2.13}{2} \approx 5.07$ $e_2 = 5.07$

4 Repeat steps 2 and 3.

$a_2 = \dfrac{17}{5.07} \approx 3.35$ $e_3 = \dfrac{5.07 + 3.35}{2} = 4.21$

$a_3 = \dfrac{17}{4.21} \approx 4.04$ $e_4 = \dfrac{4.21 + 4.04}{2} \approx 4.13$

Since the difference between e_4 and a_3 is less than 0.1, **4.13** is a reasonable approximation of $\sqrt{17}$.

Problem: *Write a program to calculate the square root of any positive integer. Do not use the* SQR *function.*

```
100 PRINT "ENTER A POSITIVE REAL NUMBER."
110 INPUT X
120 IF X <= 0 THEN 100
130 LET E = INT(X/2)              ←——————— Step 1
140 LET A = X/E                   ←——————— Step 2
150 LET E = (A + E)/2             ←——————— Step 3
160 IF ABS(A - E) > .0001 THEN 140 ←——————— Step 4 (Tolerance: 0.0001)
170 PRINT "SQUARE ROOT OF";X;" = ";E
180 PRINT
190 PRINT "ANY MORE SQUARE ROOTS (1=YES, 0=NO)";
200 INPUT Z
210 IF Z = 1 THEN 100
220 END
```

Computing Square Roots   **463**

The following is the output from a sample run of the program on page 463.

Output:
```
RUN
ENTER A POSITIVE REAL NUMBER.
? 17
SQUARE ROOT OF 17 = 4.12311

ANY MORE SQUARE ROOTS (1=YES, 0=NO)? 1
ENTER A POSITIVE REAL NUMBER.
? -13
ENTER A POSITIVE REAL NUMBER.
? 89
SQUARE ROOT OF 89 = 9.43398

ANY MORE SQUARE ROOTS (1=YES, 0=NO)? 0
READY
```

EXERCISES

A   Run the program on page 463 for the following values of x.

1. $x = 5$ **2.** $x = 13$ **3.** $x = 26$ **4.** $x = 36$

5. $x = 42$ **6.** $x = 0$ **7.** $x = -7$ **8.** $x = 115$

9. Add statements to the program on page 463 so that the successive values of e and a are printed in two labeled columns.   See the Solution Key for the answers to Ex. 9-16.

Write a BASIC program for each problem.

10. Given the area of a square, compute and print the length of a side. (See Example 3 on page 435.)

11. Given the area of a circle, compute and print the length of the radius. (Use $\pi = 3.14$.) (See Exercise 38 on page 436.)

12. Given the lengths of the two legs of a right triangle, compute and print the length of the hypotenuse. (See Example 1 on page 439.)

13. Given the lengths of the hypotenuse and one leg of a right triangle, compute and print the length of the other leg. (See Example 2 on page 440.)

B

14. Given three positive real numbers a, b, and c, decide whether they could be the lengths of the sides of a right triangle. Do not assume that c will be the largest number.

15. Given the coordinates of two points, compute and print the distance between the points.

C

16. Given the coordinates of three points (not in a straight line), calculate and print the perimeter of the triangle formed by joining the points.

Chapter Summary

IMPORTANT TERMS
Conjugates (p. 455)
Hypotenuse (p. 439)
Irrational square root (p. 435)
Principal square root (p. 432)
Radical (p. 432)
Radical equation (p. 457)

Radical symbol, $\sqrt{\ }$ (p. 432)
Radicand (p. 432)
Rational exponent (p. 460)
Rationalizing the denominator (p. 450)
Right triangle (p. 439)

IMPORTANT IDEAS

1. For any real number a, $\sqrt{a^2} = |a|$.

2. If a and b are real numbers and $a \geq 0$, $b \geq 0$, *then*
$$\sqrt{ab} = \sqrt{a} \cdot \sqrt{b}.$$

3. **Pythagorean Theorem:** If a, b, and c are the lengths of the sides of a right triangle and c is the hypotenuse (longest side), then
$$a^2 + b^2 = c^2.$$

4. If the sum of the squares of the lengths of the two shorter sides (legs) of a triangle is equal to the square of the length of the longest side (hypotenuse), then the triangle is a right triangle.

5. **Distance Formula:** If $P_1(x_1, y_1)$ and $P_2(x_2, y_2)$ are any two points in the coordinate plane, then the distance, d, between the points is given by the formula
$$d = \sqrt{(x_2 - x_1)^2 + (y_2 - y_1)^2}.$$

6. If a and b are real numbers where $a \geq 0$ and $b > 0$, *then* $\sqrt{\dfrac{a}{b}} = \dfrac{\sqrt{a}}{\sqrt{b}}$.

7. A radical is in simplest form when

   $\boxed{1}$ The radicand contains no factor that is a perfect square.

   $\boxed{2}$ The radicand does not contain a fraction.

   $\boxed{3}$ No radical appears in a denominator.

8. For any positive integer n where n is odd and a is any real number, or for any positive integer n where n is even and $a \geq 0$, $a^{\frac{1}{n}} = \sqrt[n]{a}$.

Chapter Objectives and Review

Objective: *To find the square roots of numbers or expressions that are perfect squares (Section 12–1)*

Simplify.

1. $\sqrt{121}$ 11

2. $-\sqrt{y^{12}}$ $-y^6$

3. $\sqrt{9x^2y^6}$ $3|xy^3|$

4. $\sqrt{(37d^3)^2}$ $37|d^3|$

Objective: *To find rational approximations for square roots (Section 12–2)*

Write each rational number in the form $\dfrac{a}{b}$.

5. $0.\overline{5}$ $\frac{5}{9}$

6. $0.\overline{18}$ $\frac{2}{11}$

7. $0.\overline{16}$ $\frac{16}{99}$

8. $0.\overline{407}$ $\frac{11}{27}$

Radicals   **465**

9. The area of a square is 20 square meters. Find the length of a side to the nearest tenth of a meter. 4.5 m

10. The area of the face of an old coin is 6.28 square centimeters. Find the radius of the coin to the nearest tenth. (Use $A = \pi r^2$, where $\pi = 3.14$.) 1.4 cm

Objective: *To simplify radicals (Section 12–3)*

Simplify. All variables represent positive numbers.

11. $\sqrt{18}$ $3\sqrt{2}$ **12.** $6\sqrt{32}$ $24\sqrt{2}$ **13.** $\sqrt{54x^3}$ $3x\sqrt{6x}$ **14.** $-2\sqrt{4a^3b^5}$ $-4ab^2\sqrt{ab}$

Objective: *To find the length of a side of a right triangle using the Pythagorean Theorem (Section 12–4)*

The lengths of the legs of a right triangle are *a* and *b*, and *c* is the length of the hypotenuse. Use the Pythagorean Theorem to find the length of the unknown side to the nearest tenth.

15. $a = 12$, $b = 16$, $c = \underline{\ ?\ }$ 20.0

16. $a = \underline{\ ?\ }$, $b = 7$, $c = 10$ 7.1

17. A sidewalk is built diagonally across a rectangular park 200 meters long and 300 meters wide. Find the length of the sidewalk to the nearest meter. 361 m

18. The diagonal of a square rug is 3 meters in length. Find the length of each side of the square to the nearest tenth of a meter. 2.1 m

Objective: *To find the distance between two points on the coordinate plane (Section 12–5)*

Find the distance between each pair of points.

19. $C(3, -4)$ and $D(6, 0)$ 5 **20.** $R(6, 2)$ and $S(-1, 2)$ 7 **21.** $W(3, -6)$ and $X(-6, 3)$ $9\sqrt{2}$

Objective: *To multiply radicals (Section 12–6)*

Multiply and simplify. All variables represent positive numbers.

22. $\sqrt{2} \cdot \sqrt{6}$ **23.** $3\sqrt{8} \cdot -5\sqrt{12}$ **24.** $\sqrt{2a^2} \cdot \sqrt{2b^2}$ **25.** $-\sqrt{3n^3} \cdot \sqrt{6n^2}$

Objective: *To divide radicals (Section 12–7)*

Simplify. All variables represent positive real numbers.

26. $\pm\sqrt{\dfrac{36}{25}}$ $\pm\dfrac{6}{5}$ **27.** $\dfrac{1}{\sqrt{10}}$ $\dfrac{\sqrt{10}}{10}$ **28.** $\sqrt{2+\dfrac{1}{4}}$ $\dfrac{3}{2}$ **29.** $\sqrt{\dfrac{12}{8y^5}}$ **30.** $\dfrac{\sqrt{30a^3b}}{\sqrt{5a}}$

Objective: *To add and subtract radicals (Section 12–8)*

Add or subtract as indicated.

31. $6\sqrt{7} - 4\sqrt{7} - \sqrt{7}$ $\sqrt{7}$ **32.** $4\sqrt{18} + 5\sqrt{2}$ $17\sqrt{2}$ **33.** $4\sqrt{24x^2} - 2\sqrt{54x^2}$ $2x\sqrt{6}$

Rationalize the denominator.

34. $\dfrac{1}{3+\sqrt{2}}$ **35.** $\dfrac{3}{4-\sqrt{3}}$ **36.** $\dfrac{4}{\sqrt{5}+1}$ **37.** $\dfrac{2}{\sqrt{8}-4}$

Additional Answers

22. $2\sqrt{3}$

23. $6\sqrt{2} - 10\sqrt{3}$

24. $2ab$

25. $-3n^2\sqrt{n}$

29. $\dfrac{\sqrt{6y}}{2y^3}$

30. $a\sqrt{6b}$

34. $\dfrac{3-\sqrt{2}}{7}$

35. $\dfrac{12+3\sqrt{3}}{13}$

36. $\sqrt{5} - 1$

37. $-\dfrac{\sqrt{2}+2}{2}$

Objective: *To solve radical equations (Section 12–9)*

Solve and check each equation.

38. $\sqrt{x-3}=1$ $x=4$ **39.** $6+\sqrt{3x-5}=2$ $x=7$ **40.** $\sqrt{2x-1}=\sqrt{x+4}$ $x=5$

41. Nine more than the square root of a number is 14. Find the number.   25

42. Twelve, divided by the square root of a number, equals $1\frac{1}{2}$. Find the number.   64

Objective: *To simplify expressions containing rational exponents (Section 12–10)*

Simplify.

43. $100^{\frac{1}{2}}$ 10   **44.** $(-27)^{\frac{1}{3}}$ -3 **45.** $144^{\frac{1}{2}}$ 12   **46.** $625^{\frac{3}{4}}$ 125   **47.** $-(1000)^{\frac{2}{3}}$ -100

Chapter Test

A formal Chapter Test is provided in the Teacher's Manual. See p. M-75.

Simplify.

1. $\pm\sqrt{100}$ ±10 **2.** $\sqrt{\frac{9}{16}}$ $\frac{3}{4}$ **3.** $\sqrt{63}$ $3\sqrt{7}$ **4.** $-\sqrt{108}$ $-6\sqrt{3}$ **5.** $(-8)^{\frac{1}{3}}$ -2 **6.** $27^{\frac{2}{3}}$ 9

The lengths of the sides of a right triangle are a and b, and c is the length of the hypotenuse. Find the length of the unknown side.

7. $a=15$, $b=20$, $c=\underline{\;?\;}$ 25   **8.** $a=24$, $b=\underline{\;?\;}$, $c=25$ 7

Find the distance between each pair of points.

9. $A(3,6)$ and $B(0,2)$ 5   **10.** $K(6,-2)$ and $L(-3,-2)$ 9

Perform the indicated operations. Simplify the answers.

11. $\sqrt{5}\cdot\sqrt{8}$ $2\sqrt{10}$ **12.** $-3\sqrt{2}\cdot\sqrt{10}$ $-6\sqrt{5}$ **13.** $6\sqrt{2}+3\sqrt{8}$ $12\sqrt{2}$

14. $\dfrac{3\sqrt{12}}{2\sqrt{18}}$ $\dfrac{\sqrt{6}}{2}$ **15.** $\sqrt{2n}\cdot\sqrt{6n}$ $2n\sqrt{3}$ **16.** $6\sqrt{5x^2}-\sqrt{45x^2}$ $3x\sqrt{5}$

Solve and check each equation.

17. $\sqrt{x-2}=3$ $x=11$ **18.** $4\sqrt{x+6}=8$ $x=-2$

14. The length of a parking lot is 24 meters and the width is 10 meters. Find the length of a diagonal of the lot.   26m

20. Four less than the square root of a number is 6. What is the number?   100

Additional Practice

You may wish to use all or some of these exercises depending on how well students performed on the formal chapter test.

Skills

Simplify. *(Section 12–1)*

1. $-\sqrt{144}$ -12 **2.** $\sqrt{0.36}$ 0.6   **3.** $\pm\sqrt{19^2}$ ±19 **4.** $\sqrt{9a^2b^4}$ $3|a|b^2$ **5.** $\sqrt{\frac{64}{81}}$ $\frac{8}{9}$

Write each rational number in the form $\frac{a}{b}$. *(Section 12–2)*

6. $0.\overline{7}$ $\frac{7}{9}$ **7.** $0.\overline{81}$ $\frac{9}{11}$ **8.** $1.\overline{3}$ $\frac{4}{3}$ **9.** $0.\overline{297}$ $\frac{11}{37}$ **10.** $0.41\overline{6}$ $\frac{5}{12}$

Simplify. All variables represent positive numbers. *(Section 12–3)*

11. $\dfrac{\sqrt{54}}{3\sqrt{6}}$ **12.** $\dfrac{2\sqrt{75}}{10\sqrt{3}}$ **13.** $\dfrac{-3\sqrt{80x^3}}{-12x\sqrt{5x}}$ **14.** $\dfrac{4\sqrt{63}}{12\sqrt{7}}$ **15.** $\dfrac{5\sqrt{180a^4b^5}}{30a^2b^2\sqrt{5b}}$

The lengths of the sides of a right triangle are a and b, and c is the length of the hypotenuse. Find the length of the unknown side. *(Section 12–4)*

16. $a = 15, b = 36, c = \underline{\ \ ?\ \ }$ 39   **17.** $a = \underline{\ \ ?\ \ }, b = 12, c = 15$ 9

Find the distance between each pair of points. *(Section 12–5)*   13

18. $A(2, 3)$ and $B(2, -5)$ 8   **19.** $P(0, 3)$ and $Q(-8, -3)$ 10   **20.** $S(2, 12)$ and $T(-3, 0)$

Multiply and simplify. Variables represent positive numbers. *(Section 12–6)*

21. $\sqrt{6} \cdot \sqrt{18}$ $6\sqrt{3}$ **22.** $\sqrt{75} \cdot \sqrt{2}$ $5\sqrt{6}$ **23.** $\sqrt{14a} \cdot \sqrt{2a}$ $2a\sqrt{7}$ **24.** $\sqrt{15xy} \cdot \sqrt{3xy}$

Simplify. Variables represent positive numbers. *(Section 12–7)* $2x$

25. $\sqrt{\dfrac{3}{16}}$ $\dfrac{\sqrt{3}}{4}$ **26.** $\dfrac{3\sqrt{6}}{2\sqrt{3}}$ $\dfrac{3\sqrt{2}}{2}$ **27.** $\dfrac{\sqrt{6}}{\sqrt{8}}$ $\dfrac{\sqrt{3}}{2}$ **28.** $\sqrt{\dfrac{35a^2}{7}}$ $a\sqrt{5}$ **29.** $\dfrac{\sqrt{12x^3}}{\sqrt{3x}}$

Add or subtract as indicated. *(Section 12–8)* $17\sqrt{2}$

30. $2\sqrt{3} + \sqrt{3} + 4\sqrt{3}$ $7\sqrt{3}$ **31.** $3\sqrt{5} - 2\sqrt{20}$ $-\sqrt{5}$ **32.** $6\sqrt{8} + 3\sqrt{18} - \sqrt{32}$

Solve and check each equation. *(Section 12–9)* $x = \frac{5}{2}$

33. $\sqrt{x-2} = 5$ $x = 27$ **34.** $5 + \sqrt{x} = 12$ $x = 49$ **35.** $3\sqrt{2x+4} = 9$

Simplify. *(Section 12–10)*

36. $216^{\frac{1}{3}}$ 6   **37.** $-(49)^{\frac{1}{2}}$ -7 **38.** $(-64)^{\frac{1}{3}}$ -4 **39.** $16^{-\frac{1}{2}}$ $\frac{1}{4}$ **40.** $16^{\frac{3}{4}}$ 8

Applications

41. The length of a rectangle is twice its width. The area of the rectangle is 60 square meters. Find the length and width to the nearest tenth of a meter. *(Section 12–2)*   width: 5.5 m; length: 11 m

42. The foot of a ladder lies 1.5 meters from the base of a wall. The top lies against the wall, 3.5 meters above the ground. Find the length of the ladder (nearest tenth). *(Section 12–4)*   3.8 m

43. The diagonal of a square measures 12 centimeters. Find the length of each side of the square to the nearest tenth of a centimeter. *(Section 12–4)*   8.5 cm

44. The diagonal of the floor of a tent measures 4 meters. The tent is twice as long as it is wide. Find the dimensions to the nearest tenth. *(Section 12–4)*

45. Five less than the square root of a number is 4. Find the number.   81 *(Section 12–9)*

46. Twice a number is increased by 6. The square root of this sum is 8. Find the number. *(Section 12–9)*   29

CHAPTER 13 Quadratic Functions and Equations

13–1 Quadratic Equations

Teaching Suggestions p. M-26

Quick Quiz

State the two square roots of each of the following.

1. 36   **Ans: −6; 6**
2. 100   **Ans: −10; 10**
3. $\frac{4}{9}$ **Ans: −$\frac{2}{3}$; $\frac{2}{3}$**
4. $\frac{1}{4}$ **Ans: −$\frac{1}{2}$; $\frac{1}{2}$**
5. 19   **Ans: −$\sqrt{19}$; $\sqrt{19}$**
6. 72   **Ans: −6$\sqrt{2}$; 6$\sqrt{2}$**

Equations such as the following are *quadratic equations*.

$$a^2 = 5 \qquad g^2 - 9 = 0 \qquad y^2 + 5y = 0 \qquad x^2 - 4x + 4 = 0$$

Definition

> A **quadratic equation** is an equation that can be written in the form (**standard form**)
> $$ax^2 + bx + c = 0$$
> where a, b, and c are real numbers and $a \neq 0$.

In Chapter 9, you solved certain quadratic equations by factoring. Quadratic equations of the form $x^2 = k$ where $k \geq 0$ can be solved by factoring or by taking the square root of each side of the equation. This last procedure results in two linear equations which *together* are equivalent to the original quadratic equation.

> If $x^2 = k$, then $x = \sqrt{k}$ <u>or</u> $x = -\sqrt{k}$ for any real number k, $k \geq 0$.

Additional Examples
Example 1
Solve and check.
1. $x^2 - 11 = 0$
   Ans: $\{-\sqrt{11}, \sqrt{11}\}$
2. $x^2 - 8 = 0$
   Ans: $\{-2\sqrt{2}, 2\sqrt{2}\}$

EXAMPLE 1   Solve: $x^2 - 7 = 0$

Solution: **Method 1**   By factoring

$$x^2 - 7 = 0$$
$$(x - \sqrt{7})(x + \sqrt{7}) = 0 \longleftarrow \text{ **By the Zero-Product Theorem**}$$
$$x = \sqrt{7} \quad \underline{\text{or}} \quad x = -\sqrt{7}$$

Method 2   By taking the square root

$$x^2 - 7 = 0$$
$$x^2 = 7$$
$$x = \pm\sqrt{7}$$

Check:

Replace x with $\sqrt{7}$.

$$x^2 - 7 = 0$$
$$(\sqrt{7})^2 - 7 \overset{?}{=} 0$$
$$7 - 7 \overset{?}{=} 0$$
$$0 \overset{?}{=} 0 \quad \text{Yes} ✔$$

Replace x with $-\sqrt{7}$.

$$x^2 - 7 = 0$$
$$(-\sqrt{7})^2 - 7 \overset{?}{=} 0$$
$$7 - 7 \overset{?}{=} 0$$
$$0 \overset{?}{=} 0 \quad \text{Yes} ✔$$

Thus, the **solution set** is $\{-\sqrt{7}, \sqrt{7}\}$.

Quadratic equations such as $(x - 5)^2 = 36$ can also be solved by taking the square root of each side of the equation.

470   *Chapter 13*

EXAMPLE 2   Solve: $(x - 5)^2 = 36$

   Solution: $(x - 5)^2 = 36$ ◄──────── **Take the square root of both sides.**

   $x - 5 = \pm 6$

   $x - 5 = 6$ <u>or</u> $x - 5 = -6$

   $x = 11$ <u>or</u> $x = -1$

   The check is left for you.   **Solution set:** $\{-1, 11\}$

CLASSROOM EXERCISES

1. $x = -5$ <u>or</u> $x = 5$ **2.** $x = -2\sqrt{2}$ or $x = 2\sqrt{2}$

Solve each equation.

1. $x^2 = 25$ **2.** $x^2 - 8 = 0$ **3.** $(x - 2)^2 = 9$ **4.** $(x + 5)^2 = 16$

$x = -1$ <u>or</u> $x = 5$ $x = -9$ <u>or</u> $x = -1$

5. $(x - \frac{1}{2})^2 = \frac{1}{4}$ **6.** $(x + 1)^2 = 81$ **7.** $3a^2 = 36$ **8.** $3y^2 = 4$

$x = 0$ <u>or</u> $x = 1$ $x = -10$ <u>or</u> $x = 8$ $a = -2\sqrt{3}$ <u>or</u> $a = 2\sqrt{3}$ $y = -\frac{2\sqrt{3}}{3}$ <u>or</u> $y = \frac{2\sqrt{3}}{3}$

WRITTEN EXERCISES See pages 587-588 for the answers to Exercises 1-64 odd.

A   Solve each equation.

$y = -2$ <u>or</u> $y = 2$ $n = -\sqrt{19}$ <u>or</u> $n = \sqrt{19}$

1. $x^2 = 16$ **2.** $y^2 - 4 = 0$ **3.** $x^2 - 11 = 0$ **4.** $n^2 - 7 = 12$

5. $m^2 + 2 = 3$ **6.** $7 - 2x^2 = -15$ **7.** $4x^2 = 36$ **8.** $3x^2 + 5 = 26$

9. $2r^2 = 200$ **10.** $2s^2 - 18 = 0$ **11.** $z^2 = 32$ **12.** $y^2 - 19 = 0$

13. $x^2 - \frac{1}{4} = 0$ **14.** $2x^2 = \frac{1}{2}$ **15.** $99 = b^2 - 22$ **16.** $3n^2 - n = 15 - n$

17. $4m^2 - 3 = 9$ **18.** $3y^2 - 9 = 0$ **19.** $3z^2 = \frac{12}{9}$ **20.** $r - r^2 = 5r^2 + r$

21. $(x - 2)^2 = 0$ **22.** $(x + 5)^2 = 16$ **23.** $(x - 3)^2 = 25$ **24.** $(x - 1)^2 = 1$

25. $(x + 7)^2 = 49$ **26.** $(x + 6)^2 = 100$ **27.** $(x - \frac{1}{2})^2 = 4$ **28.** $(x + 17)^2 = 49$

29. $3(a + 6)^2 = 27$ **30.** $5(b - 2)^2 = 125$ **31.** $3(z - 6)^2 = 48$ **32.** $3(t + 9)^2 = 27$

B $b = -3$ <u>or</u> $b = 7$ $t = -12$ <u>or</u> $t = -6$

33. $(b + \frac{3}{4})^2 = 16$ **34.** $(c + \frac{3}{2})^2 = \frac{1}{4}$ **35.** $(x - \frac{1}{4})^2 = \frac{1}{16}$ **36.** $(t - \frac{8}{3})^2 = \frac{1}{9}$

37. $(x + \frac{3}{7})^2 = \frac{1}{49}$ **38.** $(2m + 4)^2 = 1$ **39.** $(2k - 6)^2 = 16$ **40.** $(2q - 9)^2 = 25$

41. $(2n - 5)^2 = 49$ **42.** $(3p - 7)^2 = 1$ **43.** $(4r - 8)^2 = 16$ **44.** $(6s - 1)^2 = 25$

45. $5(2y - 1)^2 = 80$ **46.** $4(3x - 2)^2 = 36$ **47.** $3(2v + 7)^2 = 27$ **48.** $10(3a + 7)^2 = 1000$

$a = -5\frac{2}{3}$ <u>or</u> $a = 1$

C   Solve for x where a, b, and c are nonnegative constants.

49. $x^2 = a + b$ **50.** $\dfrac{x^2}{a} = 1$ **51.** $\dfrac{x^2}{a} = b$ **52.** $x^2 - 2a = 0$

53. $4x^2 = a^2$ **54.** $\dfrac{ax^2}{b} = 1$ **55.** $\dfrac{ax^2}{b} = ac$ **56.** $\dfrac{ab^2}{x^2} = 1$

57. $(x + a)^2 = b$ **58.** $(x - a)^2 = b$ **59.** $(2x + a)^2 = b$ **60.** $(3x - c)^2 = d$

61. $(ax + b)^2 = c$ **62.** $(ax - b)^2 = d$ **63.** $(ax - b)^2 = 4$ **64.** $(ax + c)^2 = 3d$

$x = \dfrac{b - \sqrt{d}}{a}$ <u>or</u> $x = \dfrac{b + \sqrt{d}}{a}$

Quadratic Functions and Equations   **471**

Express each trinomial as the square of a binomial. When a trinomial is not a perfect square, write *NP*. *(Pages 326–328)*

1. $m^2 - 4m + 4$ $\quad(m - 2)^2$
2. $v^2 + 4v + 8$ $\quad NP$
3. $h^2 + h + 1$ $\quad NP$
4. $t^2 + 0.2t + 0.01$ $\quad(t + 0.1)^2$
5. $q^2 - 0.6q + 0.09$ $\quad(q - 0.3)^2$
6. $p^6 - 12p^3 + 36$
7. $r^2 + \frac{2}{3}r + \frac{1}{9}$ $\quad(r + \frac{1}{3})^2$
8. $y^2 - \frac{7}{6}y + \frac{49}{36}$ $\quad NP$
9. $b^2 - \frac{7}{2}b + \frac{49}{16}$
10. $t^2 - \frac{1}{3}t + \frac{1}{36}$ $\quad(t - \frac{1}{6})^2$
11. $a^2 + \frac{6}{5}a + \frac{9}{25}$ $\quad(a + \frac{3}{5})^2$
12. $c^2 + \frac{3}{4}c + \frac{9}{64}$ $\quad(c + \frac{3}{8})^2$

OBJECTIVE: To solve quadratic equations by completing the square

13–2 Completing the Square

When a quadratic equation cannot be easily solved by factoring or by taking the square root of each side, a method called **completing the square** can be used. Recall that

$$(x + 7)^2 = x^2 + 2 \cdot 7 \cdot x + 49 = x^2 + 14x + 49.$$

Note that the last term, 49, is the square of one-half the coefficient of the middle term, $14x$. That is,

$$49 = \left(\frac{1}{2} \cdot 14\right)^2.$$

EXAMPLE 1 Complete the square.

a. $a^2 + 8a$

b. $x^2 - 10x$

Solutions:
a. **Think:** What is $\left(\frac{1}{2} \cdot 8\right)^2$?

$$\left(\frac{1}{2} \cdot 8\right)^2 = 4^2 = 16$$

$$a^2 + 8a + 16 = (a + 4)^2$$

b. **Think:** What is $\left[\frac{1}{2}(-10)\right]^2$?

$$\left[\frac{1}{2}(-10)\right]^2 = (-5)^2 = 25$$

$$x^2 - 10x + 25 = (x - 5)^2$$

The following procedure summarizes the steps for completing the square of $x^2 + bx$.

Procedure

> **To complete the square of $x^2 + bx$:**
> 1. Find one-half the coefficient of x. $\longrightarrow \frac{b}{2}$
> 2. Square the result of step 1. $\longrightarrow \left(\frac{b}{2}\right)^2 = \frac{b^2}{4}$
> 3. Add the result of step 2 to $x^2 + bx$. $\longrightarrow x^2 + bx + \frac{b^2}{4}$

You can find the solutions of a quadratic equation by completing the square. Example 2 shows the steps you use to solve an equation by this method.

EXAMPLE 2 Solve $x^2 + 6x + 8 = 0$ by completing the square.

Solution: $\boxed{1}$ Write the equation in the form $x^2 + bx = c$.

$$x^2 + 6x + 8 = 0$$
$$x^2 + 6x = -8$$

$\boxed{2}$ Complete the square for $x^2 + 6x$.

Think: $\left(\frac{1}{2} \cdot 6\right)^2 = 9$

Add this number to each side of the equation.

$$x^2 + 6x + 9 = -8 + 9$$
$$x^2 + 6x + 9 = 1$$

$\boxed{3}$ Write the left member as a perfect square. Solve the equation.

$$(x + 3)^2 = 1$$
$$x + 3 = 1 \quad \text{or} \quad x + 3 = -1$$
$$x = -2 \qquad\qquad x = -4$$

$\boxed{4}$ The check is left for you.

Solution set: $\{-4, -2\}$

Before attempting to solve a quadratic equation by completing the square, be sure that the equation is in the form $x^2 + bx + c = 0$, where the coefficient of the x^2-term is **1**.

EXAMPLE 3 Solve $4x^2 - 4x - 7 = 0$ by completing the square.

Solution: Since the coefficient of $4x^2$ is not 1, divide *each side* of the equation by 4, the coefficient of $4x^2$.

$$4x^2 - 4x - 7 = 0 \quad \longleftarrow \quad \textbf{Divide each side by 4.}$$

$$x^2 - x - \frac{7}{4} = 0 \quad \longleftarrow \quad \textbf{Add } \left(\frac{7}{4}\right) \textbf{ to each side.}$$

$$x^2 - x = \frac{7}{4} \quad \longleftarrow \quad \left[\frac{1}{2}(-1)\right]^2 = \frac{1}{4}. \textbf{ Add } \frac{1}{4} \textbf{ to each side.}$$

$$x^2 - x + \frac{1}{4} = \frac{7}{4} + \frac{1}{4} \quad \longleftarrow \quad \frac{7}{4} + \frac{1}{4} = \frac{8}{4} = 2$$

$$\left(x - \frac{1}{2}\right)^2 = 2$$

$$x - \frac{1}{2} = \sqrt{2} \quad \text{or} \quad x - \frac{1}{2} = -\sqrt{2}$$
$$x = \frac{1}{2} + \sqrt{2} \qquad\qquad x = \frac{1}{2} - \sqrt{2}$$

Check:

$$4x^2 - 4x - 7 = 0 \qquad\qquad\qquad 4x^2 - 4x - 7 = 0$$
$$4(\tfrac{1}{2} + \sqrt{2})^2 - 4(\tfrac{1}{2} + \sqrt{2}) - 7 \overset{?}{=} 0 \qquad 4(\tfrac{1}{2} - \sqrt{2})^2 - 4(\tfrac{1}{2} - \sqrt{2}) - 7 \overset{?}{=} 0$$
$$4(\tfrac{1}{4} + \sqrt{2} + 2) - 2 - 4\sqrt{2} - 7 \overset{?}{=} 0 \qquad 4(\tfrac{1}{4} - \sqrt{2} + 2) - 2 + 4\sqrt{2} - 7 \overset{?}{=} 0$$
$$1 + 4\sqrt{2} + 8 - 2 - 4\sqrt{2} - 7 \overset{?}{=} 0 \qquad 1 - 4\sqrt{2} + 8 - 2 + 4\sqrt{2} - 7 \overset{?}{=} 0$$
$$0 \overset{?}{=} 0 \quad \text{Yes} \qquad\qquad\qquad 0 \overset{?}{=} 0 \quad \text{Yes}$$

Solution set: $\left\{\frac{1}{2} + \sqrt{2}, \frac{1}{2} - \sqrt{2}\right\}$

Additional Examples
Example 2
Solve by completing the square.
1. $x^2 + 8x + 7 = 0$
   Ans: $\{-1, -7\}$
2. $x^2 - 12x + 11 = 0$
   Ans: $\{1, 11\}$

Example 3
Solve by completing the square.
1. $4x^2 - 4x - 11 = 0$
   Ans: $\{\frac{1}{2} + \sqrt{3}, \frac{1}{2} - \sqrt{3}\}$
2. $9x^2 - 18x - 36 = 0$
   Ans: $\{1 + \sqrt{5}, 1 - \sqrt{5}\}$

Assignment Guide
Minimal Omit
Average
Day 1 p. 474: 1–12, 13–39 odd
Day 2 p. 474: 40–54
Above Average
Day 1 p. 474: 1–54 odd
Day 2 p. 474: 55–66

Additional Answers
Written Exercises
4. 1; $(a + 1)^2$
8. $\frac{1}{4}$; $(a + \frac{1}{2})^2$
15. $n = 3$ or $n = 5$
18. $x = -6$ or $x = -2$
21. $x = 4$ or $x = 10$
24. $c = -5$ or $c = 3$
27. $a = 1$ or $a = 2$
30. $a = -2$ or $a = 5$
33. $x = -2$ or $x = 3$
36. $y = -4$ or $y = 1$
45. $n = \frac{1}{4}$ or $n = 4$
48. $a = -1\frac{2}{3}$ or $a = -1$
49. $a = -1\frac{1}{2}$ or $a = 4$
51. $p = \frac{1 - \sqrt{3}}{2}$ or $p = \frac{1 + \sqrt{3}}{2}$
52. $a = \frac{-3 - \sqrt{145}}{4}$
    or $a = \frac{-3 + \sqrt{145}}{4}$
53. $x = \frac{1 - \sqrt{73}}{12}$ or $x = \frac{1 + \sqrt{73}}{12}$
54. $x = 1 - \sqrt{5}$ or $x = 1 + \sqrt{5}$
56. $x = \frac{-7 - \sqrt{41}}{2}$
    or $x = \frac{-7 + \sqrt{41}}{2}$
57. $x = \frac{5 - \sqrt{57}}{4}$ or $x = \frac{5 + \sqrt{57}}{4}$
58. $x = \frac{-b - \sqrt{b^2 - 4}}{2}$ or
    $x = \frac{-b + \sqrt{b^2 - 4}}{2}$
59. $x = \frac{-b - \sqrt{b^2 - 4c}}{2}$ or
    $x = \frac{-b + \sqrt{b^2 - 4c}}{2}$
60. $x = \frac{b - \sqrt{b^2 - 4ac}}{2a}$ or
    $x = \frac{b + \sqrt{b^2 - 4ac}}{2a}$
63. $t = 5\frac{1}{2}$ or $t = 4$
64. $a = 1\frac{1}{3}$ or $a = 4$

474

CLASSROOM EXERCISES

Write the term needed to complete the square.

1. $x^2 + 4x + \underline{\ ?\ }$ 4
2. $x^2 - 2x + \underline{\ ?\ }$ 1
3. $x^2 + 8x + \underline{\ ?\ }$ 16
4. $c^2 - 14c + \underline{\ ?\ }$ 49
5. $x^2 - x + \underline{\ ?\ }$ $\frac{1}{4}$
6. $d^2 - \frac{4}{5}d + \underline{\ ?\ }$ $\frac{4}{25}$
7. $t^2 + \frac{1}{2}t + \underline{\ ?\ }$ $\frac{1}{16}$
8. $x^2 + bx + \underline{\ ?\ }$ $\frac{b^2}{4}$
9. $x^2 - \frac{b}{a}x + \underline{\ ?\ }$ $\frac{b^2}{4a^2}$

WRITTEN EXERCISES

A   Complete the square. Then write the trinomial as the square of a binomial.

1. $x^2 + 10x$ 25; $(x + 5)^2$
2. $y^2 - 8y$ 16; $(y - 4)^2$
3. $m^2 + 4m$ 4; $(m + 2)^2$
4. $a^2 + 2a$
5. $r^2 - r$ $\frac{1}{4}$; $(r - \frac{1}{2})^2$
6. $x^2 + 12x$ 36; $(x + 6)^2$
7. $r^2 - 20r$ 100; $(r - 10)^2$
8. $a^2 + a$
9. $x^2 + 5x$ $\frac{25}{4}$; $(x + \frac{5}{2})^2$
10. $x^2 - 11x$ $\frac{121}{4}$; $(x - \frac{11}{2})^2$
11. $x^2 - \frac{2}{5}x$ $\frac{1}{25}$; $(x - \frac{1}{5})^2$
12. $y^2 + 7y$
    $\frac{49}{4}$; $(y + \frac{7}{2})^2$

Solve by completing the square.

13. $x^2 + 4x = 12$ $x = -6$ or $x = 2$
14. $x^2 + 6x = 27$ $x = -9$ or $x = 3$
15. $n^2 - 8n = -15$
16. $n^2 - 2n - 8 = 0$ $n = -2$ or $n = 4$
17. $a^2 - 6a + 8 = 0$ $a = 2$ or $a = 4$
18. $x^2 + 8x = -12$
19. $a^2 + 4a = 5$ $a = -5$ or $a = 1$
20. $b^2 + 10b = -16$
21. $x^2 - 14x = -40$
22. $x^2 - 12x = -35$ $x = 5$ or $x = 7$
23. $x^2 - 10x = -24$ $x = 4$ or $x = 6$
24. $c^2 + 2c = 15$
25. $x^2 - 16x = -60$ $x = 6$ or $x = 10$
26. $x^2 - 16x = 17$ $x = -1$ or $x = 17$
27. $a^2 - 3a = -2$
28. $x^2 - 7x + 10 = 0$ $x = 2$ or $x = 5$
29. $x^2 - 9x = -18$ $x = 3$ or $x = 6$
30. $a^2 - 3a = 10$
31. $n^2 + 6 = -5n$ $n = -3$ or $n = -2$
32. $n^2 - 12 = n$ $n = -3$ or $n = 4$
33. $x^2 - x = 6$
34. $x^2 + x = 6$ $x = -3$ or $x = 2$
35. $x^2 - x = 30$ $x = -5$ or $x = 6$
36. $y^2 + 3y = 4$
37. $y^2 - y = 2$ $y = -1$ or $y = 2$
38. $p^2 + 5p = 0$ $p = -5$ or $p = 0$
39. $x^2 = 3x$
    20. $b = -8$ or $b = -2$ $x = 0$ or $x = 3$

B   Solve by completing the square. Irrational solutions may be left in radical form.
    $n = \frac{1}{5}$ or $n = 2$

40. $3n^2 - 2n = 1$ $n = -\frac{1}{3}$ or $n = 1$
41. $2n^2 = n + 3$ $n = -1$ or $n = 1\frac{1}{2}$
42. $5n^2 + 2 = 11n$
43. $3x^2 - 2x = 8$ $x = -1\frac{1}{3}$ or $x = 2$
44. $2y^2 - 3y = 35$ $y = -3\frac{1}{2}$ or $y = 5$
45. $4n^2 + 4 = 17n$
46. $6p^2 - 9p = 27$ $p = -1\frac{1}{2}$ or $p = 3$
47. $2x^2 - 7x + 3 = 0$ $x = \frac{1}{2}$ or $x = 3$
48. $3a^2 + 8a + 5 = 0$
49. $2a^2 - 5a - 12 = 0$
50. $3x^2 - x - 2 = 0$
51. $2p^2 - 2p - 1 = 0$
52. $2a^2 + 3a = 17$
53. $3 = 6x^2 - x$ $x = -\frac{2}{3}$ or $x = 1$
54. $7x^2 - 14x = 28$

C $x = 3 - \sqrt{13}$ or $x = 3 + \sqrt{13}$

55. $\frac{1}{4}x^2 - \frac{3}{2}x - 1 = 0$
56. $1 + \frac{7}{x} + \frac{2}{x^2} = 0$
57. $2x = 5 + \frac{4}{x}$
58. $x^2 + bx + 1 = 0$
59. $x^2 + bx = -c$
60. $ax^2 + bx + c = 0$
61. $\frac{5x + 7}{x - 1} = 3x + 2$ $x = -1$ or $x = 3$
62. $\frac{5x - 1}{x + 1} = \frac{3x}{2}$ $x = \frac{1}{3}$ or $x = 2$
63. $\frac{3t - 8}{t - 2} = \frac{5t - 2}{t + 5}$
64. $\frac{a + 3}{2a - 7} - \frac{2a - 1}{a - 3} = 0$
65. $\frac{1}{3 - b} - \frac{4}{5} = \frac{1}{9 - 2b}$
66. $\frac{5}{d - 2} - \frac{4}{d} = \frac{3}{d + 6}$
    $b = 2$ or $b = 4\frac{7}{8}$ $d = -2$ or $d = 12$

Simplify. *(Pages 437–438)*

1. $\sqrt{54}$ $3\sqrt{6}$ 2. $-\sqrt{24}$ $-2\sqrt{6}$ 3. $9\sqrt{48}$ $36\sqrt{3}$ 4. $5\sqrt{18}$ $15\sqrt{2}$ 5. $-2\sqrt{32}$ $-8\sqrt{2}$

6. $7\sqrt{50}$ $35\sqrt{2}$ 7. $-\sqrt{8}$ $-2\sqrt{2}$ 8. $-3\sqrt{40}$ $-6\sqrt{10}$ 9. $-4\sqrt{50}$ $-20\sqrt{2}$ 10. $5\sqrt{44}$ $10\sqrt{11}$

Evaluate $b^2 - 4ac$ for the given values of a, b, and c. *(Pages 5–8)*

11. $a = 3$, $b = 5$, $c = 1$ 13   12. $a = 2$, $b = -1$, $c = 3$ -23 13. $a = -8$, $b = 7$, $c = 1$ 81

14. $a = 1$, $b = -6$, $c = 0$ 36   15. $a = 2$, $b = 0$, $c = -5$ 40   16. $a = 5$, $b = -8$, $c = -2$ 104

OBJECTIVE: To solve quadratic equations using the quadratic formula

13-3   The Quadratic Formula

By completing the square of the standard form of the quadratic equation,

$$ax^2 + bx + c = 0.$$

you can determine the **solutions** or **roots** of the equation.

Compare the method for the specific case shown on the left with that for the general case shown on the right.

Specific Case

$3x^2 - 2x - 2 = 0$

$\longleftarrow$ **Divide each side by the coefficient of the x^2-term.** $\longrightarrow$ Solve $ax^2 + bx + c = 0$. **General Case**

$x^2 - \frac{2}{3}x - \frac{2}{3} = 0$

$x^2 + \frac{b}{a}x + \frac{c}{a} = 0$

$x^2 - \frac{2}{3}x = \frac{2}{3}$

$x^2 + \frac{b}{a}x = -\frac{c}{a}$

$\frac{1}{2}\left(-\frac{2}{3}\right) = -\frac{1}{3}; \left(-\frac{1}{3}\right)^2 = \frac{1}{9}$ $\longleftarrow$ $\left[\frac{1}{2}(\text{coefficient of } x)\right]^2$ $\longrightarrow$ $\frac{1}{2}\left(\frac{b}{a}\right) = \frac{b}{2a}; \left(\frac{b}{2a}\right)^2 = \frac{b^2}{4a^2}$

$x^2 - \frac{2}{3}x + \frac{1}{9} = \frac{2}{3} + \frac{1}{9}$ $\longleftarrow$ **Complete the square.** $\longrightarrow$ $x^2 + \frac{b}{a}x + \frac{b^2}{4a^2} = \frac{b^2}{4a^2} - \frac{c}{a}$

$\left(x - \frac{1}{3}\right)^2 = \frac{7}{9}$

$\left(x + \frac{b}{2a}\right)^2 = \frac{b^2 - 4ac}{4a^2}$

$x - \frac{1}{3} = \pm\sqrt{\frac{7}{9}}$ $\longleftarrow$ **Solve for x.** $\longrightarrow$ $x + \frac{b}{2a} = \pm\sqrt{\frac{b^2 - 4ac}{4a^2}}$

$x = \frac{1}{3} \pm \frac{\sqrt{7}}{3}$

$x = -\frac{b}{2a} \pm \frac{\sqrt{b^2 - 4ac}}{2a}$

$x = \frac{1 \pm \sqrt{7}}{3}$

$x = \frac{-b \pm \sqrt{b^2 - 4ac}}{2a}$

The check is left for you.   The check is left for you.

Solution set: $\left\{\dfrac{1 + \sqrt{7}}{3}, \dfrac{1 - \sqrt{7}}{3}\right\}$ Solution set: $\left\{\dfrac{-b + \sqrt{b^2 - 4ac}}{2a}, \dfrac{-b - \sqrt{b^2 - 4ac}}{2a}\right\}$

Quadratic Functions and Equations   **475**

Teaching Suggestions p. M-26

Quick Quiz
Complete the square.
1. $x^2 - x$
   Ans: $x^2 - x + \frac{1}{4}$
2. $a^2 + 12a$
   Ans: $a^2 + 12a + 36$
Solve by completing the square.
3. $x^2 + 8x + 15 = 0$
   Ans: $\{-5, -3\}$
4. $x^2 - 4x - 5 = 0$
   Ans: $\{-1, 5\}$
5. $8x^2 - 8x - 6 = 0$
   Ans: $\{\frac{1}{2} + \sqrt{2}, \frac{1}{2} - \sqrt{2}\}$
6. $7x^2 - 14x - 35 = 0$
   Ans: $\{1 + \sqrt{6}, 1 - \sqrt{6}\}$

The solutions for the general equation are usually referred to as the *quadratic formula.*

> **Quadratic Formula**
>
> For the quadratic equation $ax^2 + bx + c = 0$, where a, b, and c are real numbers and $a \neq 0$,
> $$x = \frac{-b \pm \sqrt{b^2 - 4ac}}{2a}.$$

EXAMPLE   Use the quadratic formula to solve $3x^2 + 2x - 3 = 0$.

Solution: Identify a, b, and c. Then use the quadratic formula.

$3x^2 + 2x - 3 = 0$ ⟵   **a = 3; b = 2; c = −3**

$x = \dfrac{-b \pm \sqrt{b^2 - 4ac}}{2a}$ ⟵   **Quadratic formula**

$x = \dfrac{-2 \pm \sqrt{(2)^2 - 4(3)(-3)}}{2(3)}$

$x = \dfrac{-2 \pm \sqrt{4 + 36}}{6}$

$x = \dfrac{-2 \pm \sqrt{40}}{6}$ ⟵   **Simplify $\sqrt{40}$.**

$x = \dfrac{-2 \pm 2\sqrt{10}}{6}$ ⟵   **Factor the numerator.**

$x = \dfrac{2(-1 \pm \sqrt{10})}{6}$ ⟵   **Simplify.**

$x = \dfrac{-1 \pm \sqrt{10}}{3}$ ⟵   **The check is left for you.**

Solution set: $\left\{ \dfrac{-1 + \sqrt{10}}{3}, \dfrac{-1 - \sqrt{10}}{3} \right\}$

Be sure to express a quadratic equation in the form $ax^2 + bx + c = 0$ before using the quadratic formula. For example, to solve $2x^2 - x = 3$, first write the equation in the form

$$2x^2 - x - 3 = 0.$$

Then identify a, b, and c and use the quadratic formula.

CLASSROOM EXERCISES

For each quadratic equation, identify a, b, and c.

1. $x^2 - 4x - 5 = 0$ **2.** $3x^2 - 5x - 4 = 0$ **3.** $4x^2 + 12x = 7$

4. $3x^2 = 7 + 3y$ **5.** $7 - a^2 = 3a$ **6.** $4t^2 = 9 + 2t$

7. $3x^2 = 45$ **8.** $5b^2 = 3b + 2$ **9.** $5y^2 - 1 = 2y$

WRITTEN EXERCISES See page 588 for the answers to Exercises 1-56 odd.

A   Use the quadratic formula to solve each equation. Write irrational roots in simplest radical form.

1. $x^2 - 4x = 21$

2. $x^2 + 6x = 16$ $x = -8$ or $x = 2$

3. $2x^2 - x - 3 = 0$

4. $x^2 = 3x$ $x = 0$ or $x = 3$

5. $p^2 - 4p = 0$

6. $n^2 - 2n - 8 = 0$

7. $a^2 + 4a = 5$

8. $6a^2 + 13a + 6 = 0$

9. $n^2 + 6 = -5n$

10. $2y^2 = 5y - 3$

11. $2x^2 + x = 3$

12. $y^2 + 3y = 4$

13. $y^2 - y = 2$

14. $10b^2 + 7b - 12 = 0$

15. $x^2 + 6x = -9$

16. $x^2 - 2x = 4$

17. $x^2 + 2x = 1$

18. $x^2 + 4x = -2$

19. $x^2 + 6x + 3 = 0$

20. $x^2 - x - 1 = 0$

21. $x^2 + 3x + 1 = 0$

22. $2x^2 - 4x - 3 = 0$

23. $2x^2 + x - 5 = 0$

24. $3x^2 - 2x = 1$

25. $2x^2 + 7x + 2 = 0$

26. $6x^2 - 3x - 4 = 0$ $x = \frac{1}{4} - \frac{\sqrt{105}}{12}$ or $x = \frac{1}{4} + \frac{\sqrt{105}}{12}$

27. $3x^2 + 10x + 5 = 0$ $x = \frac{1 - \sqrt{22}}{3}$ or $x = \frac{1 + \sqrt{22}}{3}$

B

28. $2x^2 - 7x + 2 = 0$

29. $2x^2 - x - 1 = 0$

30. $3x^2 - 2x = 7$

31. $2y^2 - 3y = 4$

32. $4n^2 - 4 = n$

33. $7x^2 - 3x - 1 = 0$

34. $9n^2 + 2 + 9n = 0$

35. $8n^2 + 7n - 2 = 0$

36. $4a^2 - 5 = 3a$

37. $4 + \frac{9}{b^2} - \frac{12}{b} = 0$

38. $\frac{6d + 10}{d} = -\frac{3}{d^2}$

39. $\frac{3}{t - 1} - 4 = \frac{1}{t + 1}$

In Exercises 40–45, use the quadratic formula to solve each equation. Use the Table of Square Roots on page 541 or use a calculator to approximate irrational roots to the nearest tenth.

40. $3n^2 - 2n = 2$

41. $3x^2 - x - 3 = 0$

42. $2a^2 - 5a - 1 = 0$ $a = -0.2$ or $a = 2.7$

43. $2n^2 = n + 2$

44. $5n^2 + 3 = 11n$ $n = 0.3$ or $n = 1.9$

45. $3b^2 + 5b + 1 = 0$

C   In Exercises 46–51, use the quadratic formula to solve each equation. Write irrational roots in simplest radical form.

46. $\frac{1}{a}x^2 + \frac{1}{b}x + \frac{1}{c} = 0$

47. $\frac{1}{c}x^2 + dx = 2c$

48. $3gx^2 - 2hx + k = 0$

49. $\frac{1}{4}x^2 = \frac{1}{2}x - \frac{1}{4}$

50. $(2r + 1)^2 = (r + 1)^2 + 6$

51. $(a - 5)^2 = (a - 5) + 4$

In Exercises 52–53, refer to the quadratic equation $ax^2 + bx + c = 0$, where $a \neq 0$ and $b^2 - 4ac > 0$.

52. Show that the sum of the roots of the equation is $-\frac{b}{a}$.

53. Show that the product of the roots of the equation is $\frac{c}{a}$.

54. Write a quadratic equation whose roots are $1 \pm \sqrt{3}$. (HINT: Use the results of Exercises 52 and 53 to find the sum and product of the roots and thus to find the relationship between a, b, and c.)
$x^2 - 2x - 2 = 0$

55. Write a quadratic equation whose roots are $2 \pm \sqrt{5}$.

56. Write two quadratic equations whose solutions are $2 \pm \sqrt{3}$. Answers will
$x^2 - 4x + 1 = 0;\ 2x^2 - 8x + 2 = 0$ vary.

Quadratic Functions and Equations   **477**

Assignment Guide
Minimal Omit
Average
Day 1 p. 477: 1–27 odd
Day 2 p. 477: 28–45
Above Average
Day 1 p. 477: 1–39 odd
Day 2 p. 477: 40–56

Additional Answers

6. $n = -2$ or $n = 4$

8. $a = -1\frac{1}{2}$ or $a = -\frac{2}{3}$

10. $y = 1$ or $y = 1\frac{1}{2}$

12. $y = -4$ or $y = 1$

14. $b = -1\frac{1}{2}$ or $b = \frac{4}{5}$

16. $x = 1 - \sqrt{5}$ or $x = 1 + \sqrt{5}$

18. $x = -2 - \sqrt{2}$ or $x = -2 + \sqrt{2}$

20. $x = \frac{1 - \sqrt{5}}{2}$ or $x = \frac{1 + \sqrt{5}}{2}$

22. $x = 1 - \frac{\sqrt{10}}{2}$ or $x = \frac{1 + \sqrt{10}}{2}$

24. $x = -\frac{1}{3}$ or $x = 1$

28. $x = \frac{7 - \sqrt{33}}{4}$ or $x = \frac{7 + \sqrt{33}}{4}$

32. $n = \frac{1 - \sqrt{65}}{8}$ or $n = \frac{1 + \sqrt{65}}{8}$

34. $n = -\frac{2}{3}$ or $n = -\frac{1}{3}$

36. $a = \frac{3 - \sqrt{89}}{8}$ or $a = \frac{3 + \sqrt{89}}{8}$

38. $d = \frac{-5 - \sqrt{7}}{6}$ or $d = \frac{-5 + \sqrt{7}}{6}$

40. $n = -0.5$ or $n = 1.2$

46. $x = \frac{-a}{2b} - \sqrt{\frac{a^2}{4b^2} - \frac{a}{c}}$
or $x = \frac{-a}{2b} + \sqrt{\frac{a^2}{4b^2} - \frac{a}{c}}$

48. $x = \frac{h - \sqrt{h^2 - 3gk}}{3g}$ or
$x = \frac{h + \sqrt{h^2 - 3gk}}{3g}$

50. $r = \frac{-1 - \sqrt{19}}{3}$ or
$r = \frac{-1 + \sqrt{19}}{3}$

52. $\frac{-b + \sqrt{b^2 - 4ac}}{2a} + \frac{-b - \sqrt{b^2 - 4ac}}{2a} = $
$\frac{-b + (-b) + \sqrt{b^2 - 4ac} - \sqrt{b^2 - 4ac}}{2a}$
$= \frac{-2b}{2a} = \frac{-b}{a} = -\frac{b}{a}$

In Exercises 1–6, use one variable to represent the unknowns.
(Pages 107–109, 125–128)

1. Three consecutive integers $n, n + 1, n + 2$

2. Two consecutive odd integers $n, n + 2$

3. The reciprocal of a certain number

4. Five less than a number's reciprocal

5. The number of seats in a row is ten fewer than the number of rows.

6. The denominator of a fraction is one more than twice the numerator.

Problem Solving and Applications

OBJECTIVE: To solve problems using quadratic equations

13-4 Using Quadratic Equations

When the conditions of a problem can be represented by a quadratic equation, the equation can then be solved by one of the methods you have learned.

EXAMPLE 1 In a school auditorium, the number of seats in each row is 8 fewer than the number of rows (Condition 1). The auditorium seats 609 persons (Condition 2). How many seats are there in each row?

Solution: $\boxed{1}$ Use Condition 1 to represent the unknowns.

Let s = the number of seats in each row.
Then $s + 8$ = the number of rows.

$\boxed{2}$ Use Condition 2 to write an equation.

$$s(s + 8) = 609 \longleftarrow \left(\begin{matrix} \text{Number of} \\ \text{Rows} \end{matrix} \right) \left(\begin{matrix} \text{Number of Seats} \\ \text{per Row} \end{matrix} \right) = \begin{matrix} \text{Total} \\ \text{Seats} \end{matrix}$$

$\boxed{3}$ $\quad s^2 + 8s = 609 \longleftarrow$ Solve for s.

$s^2 + 8s - 609 = 0 \longleftarrow a = 1, b = 8, c = -609.$

$$s = \frac{-b \pm \sqrt{b^2 - 4ac}}{2a}$$

$$s = \frac{-8 \pm \sqrt{64 + 2436}}{2}$$

$$s = \frac{-8 \pm \sqrt{2500}}{2}$$

$$s = \frac{-8 + 50}{2} \longleftarrow \text{The number of seats cannot be negative.}$$

$$s = \frac{-8 + 50}{2} = \frac{42}{2}, \text{ or } 21 \longleftarrow \text{Number of seats per row}$$

$\boxed{4}$ The check is left for you.   There are **21 seats** per row.

When the solutions to a quadratic equation are irrational numbers, use the Table of Square Roots on page 541 or use a calculator to approximate the solutions to the nearest tenth, to the nearest hundredth, and so on, as directed.

EXAMPLE 2 The **Golden Rectangle,** discovered by the Greeks in the fifth century B.C., was considered to have the most "pleasing" shape. In a golden rectangle, the length is about 1.6 times the width (Condition 1). Find, to the nearest tenth, the dimensions of the golden rectangle with an area of 48 square centimeters.

Solution: $\boxed{1}$ Let $w =$ the width.
Then $1.6w =$ the length.

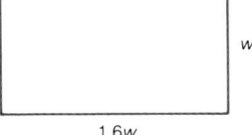

$\boxed{2}$ $w(1.6w) = 48$

$\boxed{3}$ $1.6w^2 = 48$

$w^2 = 30$

$w = \pm\sqrt{30}$ ◄——— **The width cannot be negative.**

$w \approx 5.5$ ◄——— **Don't forget to find the length.**

$1.6w \approx 8.8$

Check: $\boxed{4}$ Is $(5.5)(8.8) \approx 48$? Yes ✔

The width is about **5.5 centimeters**; the length is about **8.8 centimeters**.

CLASSROOM EXERCISES

In Exercises 1–6:
a. Use Condition 1 to represent the variables.
b. Use Condition 2 to write an equation for the problem.

1. The length of a rectangle is 3 meters longer than the width. The area is 40 square meters.

2. The base of a triangle is 3 feet longer than the altitude. The area is 44 square feet.

3. The product of two consecutive odd integers is 35.

4. A certain number exceeds its square by 15.

5. The square of a number is 10 more than three times the number.

6. The sum of a number and six times its reciprocal is 5.

WORD PROBLEMS

A Use a quadratic equation to represent the conditions of each problem. Then solve the equation. Approximate irrational roots to the nearest hundredth.

1. In a theater, the number of seats in each row is 16 fewer than the number of rows. How many seats are in each row of a 1161-seat theater? 27 seats

2. The length of a rectangular piece of sheet metal is 3 times its width. What is its length if its area is 192 square centimeters? 24 cm

Quadratic Functions and Equations **479**

Additional Examples
Example 2
1. Find, to the nearest tenth, the dimensions of the golden rectangle with an area of 80 square centimeters.
Ans: width: $\approx$ **7.1 cm; length:** $\approx$ **11.4 cm**
2. The length of a rectangular lot is 5 times its width. What is the length of the lot if the area is 80 square meters?
Ans: 20 m

Additional Answers
Classroom Exercises
1. **a.** Let $w =$ width, then $w + 3 =$ length.
b. $w(w + 3) = 40$
2. **a.** Let $a =$ altitude, then $a + 3 =$ base.
b. $\frac{1}{2}a(a + 3) = 44$
3. **a.** Let $n =$ first integer, then $n + 2 =$ second integer.
b. $n(n + 2) = 35$
4. **a.** Let $n =$ number, then $n^2 =$ square of number.
b. $n - n^2 = 15$
5. **a.** Let $n =$ number, then $n^2 =$ square of number.
b. $n^2 = 3n + 10$
6. **a.** Let $n =$ number, then $\frac{1}{n} =$ the reciprocal.
b. $n + 6\left(\frac{1}{n}\right) = 5$

Assignment Guide
Minimal Omit
Average
Day 1 pp. 479–480: 1–7, 11, 14
Day 2 p. 480: 15–20
Above Average
Day 1 pp. 479–480: 2–16 even
Day 2 p. 480–481: 17–22

3. Find the dimensions of a golden rectangle with an area of 40 square centimeters. width: 5 cm; length: 8 cm

4. One number is 3 more than another. The product of the numbers is 54. Find the numbers. −9 and −6, or 6 and 9

5. The square of a number is 56 more than the number itself. What is the number? 8, or −7

6. The length of a rectangle is 3 meters longer than its width. Its area is 40 square meters. Find its dimensions.

7. The perimeter of a rectangle is 30 meters and its area is 54 square meters. What are its dimensions?

8. What is the length of the diagonal of a square if it is 3 centimeters longer than a side of the square? 10.24 cm

9. A number exceeds its square by $\frac{2}{9}$. Find the number. $\frac{2}{3}$, or $\frac{1}{3}$

10. The square of a number exceeds the number by 42. Find the number. 7, or −6

11. The hypotenuse of a right triangle is 2 centimeters longer than one side and 4 centimeters longer than the other side. How long is the hypotenuse? 10 cm

12. A rectangular strip of asphalt paving is 5 meters longer than it is wide. Its area is 300 square meters. Find the length and width of the strip.

13. The difference in the squares of two consecutive odd integers is 56. What are the integers? 13 and 15, or −13 and −15

14. If a number is decreased by 18 times its reciprocal, the difference will be 7. What is the number? 9, or −2

15. A rectangular city lot has an area of 1000 square meters. If the length of the lot is 10 meters more than twice its width, find its length and width.

16. There are two numbers such that one is 3 more than half the other. The difference of the squares of the two numbers is 495. What are the numbers?
28 and 17, or −24 and −9

B

17. The numerator of a fraction is 1 less than its denominator. If the fraction is increased by 2 times its reciprocal, the sum will be $3\frac{5}{12}$. Find the numerator and the denominator.

18. The denominator of a fraction is 2 more than its numerator. If the fraction is increased by 3 times its reciprocal, the sum will be $5\frac{3}{5}$. Find the numerator and the denominator.

19. The figure below shows a rectangular park with a border of chestnut trees. The border has an area of 225 square meters. How wide is this border if the outside length is 25 meters and the outside width is 15 meters? 3.39 m

20. A box is to be made by cutting squares measuring 4 centimeters on a side from the square piece of cardboard shown below. If the volume of the box is to be 100 cubic centimeters, find the length of a side of the original square. 13 cm

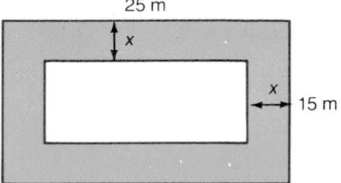

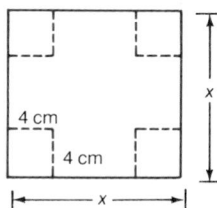

C

21. Sam and his mother drove 294 miles to the State Fair. Sam drove the farm truck at an average speed of 7 miles per hour slower than his mother drove the family car. It took Sam an hour longer than it took his mother. What was Sam's rate?   42 mi/h

22. Mrs. and Mr. Murphy can do a piece of work together in 5 hours. Alone Mrs. Murphy can do the job in 3 hours less than Mr. Murphy can do it alone. How many hours, to the nearest tenth, will it take each to do the job?
Mr. Murphy: 11.7; Mrs. Murphy: 8.7

Review

Solve each equation. Irrational solutions may be left in simplified radical form. *(Section 13-1)*

1. $x^2 = 64$ $x = -8$ or $x = 8$
2. $y^2 + 6 = 7$ $y = -1$ or $y = 1$
3. $3x^2 = 36$ $x = -2\sqrt{3}$ or $x = 2\sqrt{3}$
4. $4n^2 + 5 = 21$ $n = 2$ or $n = -2$
5. $(x - 4)^2 = 0$ $x = 4$
6. $4(a - 5)^2 = 16$ $a = 7$ or $a = 3$

Solve by completing the square. Irrational solutions may be left in simplified form. *(Section 13-2)*

7. $x^2 - 2x - 15 = 0$ $x = -3$ or $x = 5$
8. $x^2 + 5x + 6 = 0$ $x = -3$ or $x = -2$
9. $n^2 - 2n = 8$ $n = -2$ or $n = 4$
10. $a^2 - a = 2$ $a = -1$ or $a = 2$
11. $2t^2 + t - 6 = 0$ $t = -2$ or $t = 1\frac{1}{2}$
12. $3s^2 - 6s = 1$

Use the quadratic formula to solve each equation. Irrational solutions may be left in simplified radical form. *(Section 13-3)*

13. $a^2 - 4a - 21 = 0$ $a = -3$ or $a = 7$
14. $c^2 = 4c$ $c = 0$ or $c = 4$
15. $y^2 - 2y = 8$ $y = -2$ or $y = 4$
16. $3b^2 + 2b = 3$
17. $2x^2 + 4x = 1$
18. $2y^2 = y + 2$

Solve each problem. Approximate irrational roots to the nearest tenth. *(Section 13-4)*

19. On a pegboard, the number of pegs in each row is 4 more than the number of rows. There are 96 pegs in all. How many pegs are in each row?   12

20. The hypotenuse of a right triangle is one meter longer than one leg and 3 meters longer than the other leg. How long is the hypotenuse?   6.4 m

REVIEW CAPSULE FOR SECTION 13-5

Complete the table of ordered pairs for each function. *(Pages 181-184)*

1. $y = x^2 - x + 6$

x	−2	−1	0	1	2	3
y	?	?	?	?	?	?
	12	8	6	6	8	12

2. $y = 2x^2 - 9x + 11$

x	−4	−2	0	2	4	6
y	?	?	?	?	?	?
	79	37	11	1	7	29

Quadratic Functions and Equations   **481**

Quiz Sections 13-1–13-4
After completing this Review you may want to administer a quiz covering the same sections. See page M-55 of the Teacher's Manual for the suggested quiz.

Additional Answers
Review
12. $s = \frac{3 - 2\sqrt{3}}{3}$ or $s = \frac{3 + 2\sqrt{3}}{3}$

16. $b = \frac{-1 - \sqrt{10}}{3}$ or $b = \frac{-1 + \sqrt{10}}{3}$

17. $x = \frac{-2 - \sqrt{6}}{2}$ or $x = \frac{-2 + \sqrt{6}}{2}$

18. $y = \frac{1 - \sqrt{17}}{4}$ or $y = \frac{1 + \sqrt{17}}{4}$

Career Applications
Meteorology

Meteorologists study the atmosphere, its physical composition, its motions, and its processes. Specialists in weather forecasting, called **synoptic meteorologists**, are the most well-known of these scientists. They use present and past data to predict future weather patterns.

One item of the weather forecast that is very important is the **wind chill** factor. Wind chill results from the combination of cold air and strong winds that often occurs in cold weather. It is the temperature a person feels rather than the actual temperature.

The National Weather Service publishes a table for estimating wind chill. Part of that table is shown below.

Penny Griego, Weather Forecaster

Winds in MPH	Temperatures in °F																
	35	30	25	20	15	10	5	0	−5	−10	−15	−20	−25	−30	−35	−40	−45
5	33	27	21	19	12	7	0	−5	−10	−15	−21	−26	−31	−36	−42	−47	−52
10	22	16	10	3	−3	−9	−15	−22	−27	−34	−40	−46	−52	−58	−64	−71	−77
15	16	9	2	−5	−11	−18	−25	−31	−38	−45	−51	−58	−65	−72	−78	−85	−92
20	12	4	3	−10	−17	−24	−31	−39	−46	−53	−60	−67	−74	−81	−88	−95	−103
25	8	1	7	−15	−22	−29	−36	−44	−51	−59	−66	−74	−81	−88	−96	−103	−110
30	6	−2	−10	−18	−25	−33	−41	−49	−56	−64	−71	−79	−86	−93	−101	−109	−116
35	4	−4	−12	−20	−27	−35	−43	−52	−58	−67	−74	−82	−89	−97	−105	−113	−120
40	3	−5	−13	−21	−29	−37	−45	−53	−60	−69	−76	−84	−92	−100	−107	−115	−123
45	2	−6	−14	−22	−30	−38	−46	−54	−62	−70	−78	−85	−93	−102	−109	−117	−125

EXAMPLE 1   Find the wind chill temperature when the actual temperature is 5°F and the wind speed is 30 miles per hour.

Solution: Find 30 in the "Winds" column. Look directly to the right to the number in the "5" column. The wind chill temperature is **−41°F**.

The following formula has been developed for approximating the wind chill temperature in Celsius degrees.

$$C = 33 - \frac{(10\sqrt{r} + 10.45 - r)(33 - t)}{22.1}$$

C = wind chill temperature in °C
t = actual temperature in °C
r = wind speed in meters/second

482   Career Applications

EXAMPLE 2 Use a scientific calculator to find the wind chill temperature when the actual temperature is 3.2°C and the wind speed is 18.5 meters per second.

Solution: $C = 33 - \dfrac{(10\sqrt{18.5} + 10.45 - 18.5)(29.8)}{22.1}$ ◄——— (33 − 3.2)

$$\boxed{3\,3}\ \boxed{-}\ \boxed{(}\ \boxed{(}\ \boxed{1\,0}\ \boxed{\times}\ \boxed{1\,8\,.\,5}\ \boxed{\sqrt{}}\ \boxed{+}\ \boxed{1\,0\,.\,4\,5}\ \boxed{-}\ \boxed{1\,8\,.\,5}\ \boxed{)}\ \boxed{\times}$$

$$\boxed{(}\ \boxed{2\,9\,.\,8}\ \boxed{)}\ \boxed{\div}\ \boxed{2\,2\,.\,1}\ \boxed{)}\ \boxed{=} \qquad \boxed{-14.142826}$$

Thus, the wind chill temperature is **−14.1°C**. Subtracting the actual temperature from the wind chill temperature,

$$-14.1 - 3.2 = -17.3$$

it feels **17.3°C** colder than the actual temperature.

EXERCISES

In Exercises 1–8, use the table on page 482 to find the wind chill temperature.

	Winds in MPH	Temperature	Wind Chill
1.	20	25°F	?
2.	15	−10°F	?
3.	35	15°F	?
4.	40	−20°F	?

	Winds in MPH	Temperature	Wind Chill
5.	25	5°F	?
6.	10	−10°F	?
7.	45	−5°F	?
8.	30	0°F	?

In Exercises 9–14,

a. Use the formula in Example 2 to find the wind chill temperature to the nearest tenth of a degree.

b. State how much colder the wind chill temperature makes it feel.

	Winds in Meters per Second	Temperature	Wind Chill
9.	9.2	−5.2°C	?
10.	10.3	2.0°C	?
11.	8.9	−10.8°C	?
12.	4.6	3.9°C	?
13.	16.3	−5.8°C	?
14.	21.2	−19.3°C	?

Louis B. C. Fong served as Deputy Director of Meteorological Services at NASA.

Meteorology   483

13-5 Graphing Quadratic Functions

Each of these equations defines a *quadratic function.*

$$y = 2x^2 \qquad\qquad y = -3x^2 + 5 \qquad\qquad y = 2x^2 + 5x - 9$$

Definition

> A **quadratic function** is a function defined by the equation $y = ax^2 + bx + c$, where a, b, and c are real numbers and $a \neq 0$.

The graph of a quadratic function is a **parabola.** To sketch the graph of a parabola, make a table of ordered pairs. Then graph the points and draw a smooth curve connecting them.

EXAMPLE 1 Graph the function $y = x^2 - 2x - 3$.

Solution: ☐1 Make a table of values.

x	$x^2 - 2x - 3$	y
-2	$(-2)^2 - 2(-2) - 3$	5
-1	$(-1)^2 - 2(-1) - 3$	0
0	$0^2 - 2(0) - 3$	-3
1	$1^2 - 2(1) - 3$	-4
2	$2^2 - 2(2) - 3$	-3
3	$3^2 - 2(3) - 3$	0

☐2 Graph the ordered pairs. Draw a smooth curve.

x	y
-2	5
-1	0
0	-3
1	-4
2	-3
3	0

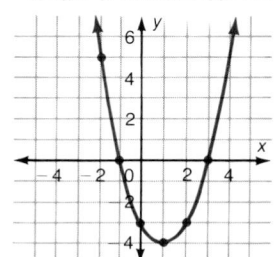

The x coordinate of a point where the curve intersects the x axis is called an **x intercept.** Thus, in Example 1, the x intercepts are -1 and 3.

To find the *zeros* of a function, you find the values of x that make y equal to 0. This can be done by graphing to find the x intercepts.

Definition

> The **zeros** of a function are the values of x for which the function equals zero.

EXAMPLE 2 Graph the function $y = 2x - x^2$.

Determine the zeros of the function.

Solution:

x	-2	-1	0	1	2	3
y	-8	-3	0	1	0	-3

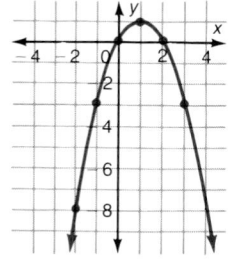

The zeros of the function are **0** and **2.**

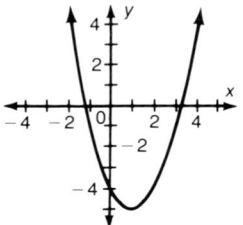
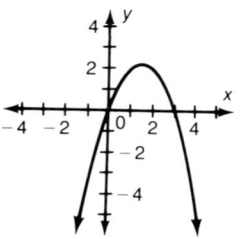

CLASSROOM EXERCISES

Write *Yes* or *No* to indicate whether each function is quadratic.

1. $y = -5x$ No
2. $y = 3x^2$ Yes
3. $y = -5x^2 + 9$ Yes
4. $x + 2y - 3 = 0$ No
5. $3x^2 + 5x - 7 = y$ Yes
6. $x^2 + x = 2 + y$ Yes
7. $y = 4$ No
8. $x^2 + x = y$ Yes

WRITTEN EXERCISES

See the Solution Key for the graphs of Ex 1-12, 19-33.
See page 589 for the coordinates of several points
for the odd Exercises 1-12, 19-33.

A Graph each quadratic function.

1. $y = x^2 + 8x + 12$
2. $y = x^2 + 6x + 8$
3. $y = x^2 - 6x + 8$
4. $y = x^2 - 8x + 12$
5. $y = x^2 - 2x - 8$
6. $y = x^2 - 2x - 24$
7. $y = x^2 - 16$
8. $y = x^2 - 25$
9. $y = x^2 - x - 6$
10. $y = x^2 + 2x - 3$
11. $y = x^2 + 6x + 8$
12. $y = x^2 - 49$

In Exercises 13–18:
 a. Determine the x intercepts from the graph of the function.
 b. Write the zeros of the function.

13.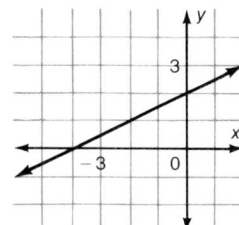
14.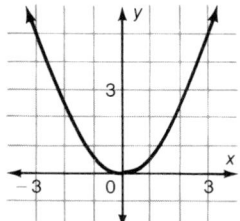
15.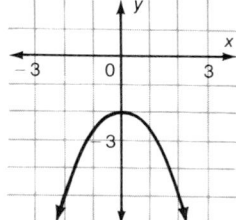

16.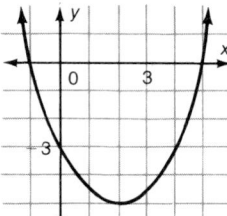
17.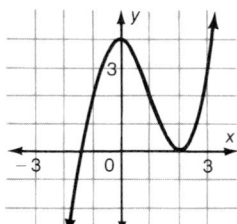
18.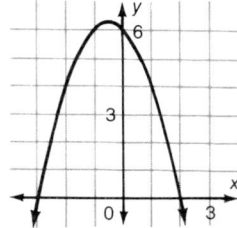

Graph each function. Determine the zeros of each function.

19. $y = x^2 + x - 6$
20. $y = x^2 - 15x + 54$
21. $y = x^2 - 9$
22. $y = x^2 + 3x - 10$
23. $y = x^2 + 2x + 1$
24. $y = x^2 - 5x - 36$
25. $y = 13 + 12x - x^2$
26. $y = 10 + 3x - x^2$
27. $y = 5 - 4x - x^2$
28. $y = 2x^2 - x - 15$
29. $y = 3x^2 - x - 2$
30. $y = 2x^2 - 9x - 11$
31. $y = x^2 + \frac{1}{4}x - \frac{3}{8}$
32. $y = x^2 - 0.5x - 8.4$
33. $y = 15 - 4x - 4x^2$

Quadratic Functions and Equations **485**

Assignment Guide
Minimal Omit
Average p. 485: 1–27 odd
Above Average
p. 485: 3, 6, 9, 12, 13–33 odd

Additional Answers
Written Exercises
The coordinates of several
points are given for Ex. 2–12.
2. $(-6, 8)$, $(-7, 3)$, $(-4, 0)$,
   $(-3, -1)$, $(-2, 0)$, $(-1, 3)$,
   $(0, 8)$
4. $(0, 12)$, $(1, 5)$, $(2, 0)$,
   $(4, -4)$, $(6, 0)$, $(7, 5)$
6. $(-5, 11)$, $(-4, 0)$, $(0, -24)$,
   $(6, 0)$, $(1, -25)$, $(2, -24)$,
   $(7, 11)$
8. $(-6, 11)$, $(-4, 0)$,
   $(-2, -21)$, $(0, -24)$,
   $(2, -21)$, $(5, 0)$, $(6, 11)$
10. $(-4, 5)$, $(-3, 0)$, $(-2, -3)$,
    $(-1, -4)$, $(0, -3)$, $(1, 0)$,
    $(2, 5)$
12. $(-8, 15)$, $(-7, 0)$,
    $(-3, -40)$, $(0, -48)$,
    $(3, -40)$, $(7, 0)$, $(8, 15)$
13. **a.** -4 **b.** -4
14. **a.** 0 **b.** 0
15. **a.** none **b.** none
16. **a.** -1 and 5 **b.** -1 and 5
17. **a.** $-1\frac{1}{2}$ and 2
    b. $-1\frac{1}{2}$ and 2
18. **a.** -3 and 2
    b. -3 and 2
For Exercises 19–33, the
zeroes are given.
19. -3 and 2
20. 6 and 9
21. -3 and 3
22. -5 and 2
23. -1
24. -4 and 9
25. -1 and 13
26. -2 and 5
27. -5 and 1
28. $-2\frac{1}{2}$ and 3
29. $-\frac{2}{3}$ and 1
30. -1 and $5\frac{1}{2}$
31. $-\frac{3}{4}$ and $\frac{1}{2}$
32. -2.65 and 3.15
33. $-2\frac{1}{2}$ and $1\frac{1}{2}$

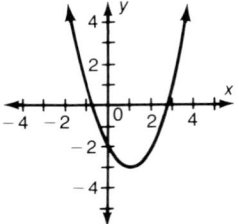
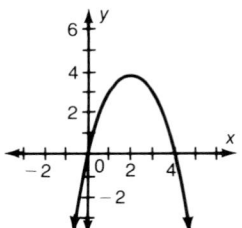
Classify each number as *rational* or *irrational*. *(Pages 25–29)*

1. $-\frac{1}{2}$ 2. $\sqrt{5}$ 3. $\sqrt{81}$ 4. $-\sqrt{100}$ 5. $2\sqrt{3}$ 6. $5 - 6\sqrt{2}$

Solve each quadratic equation by factoring. *(Pages 332–334)*

7. $a^2 - 121 = 0$ $a = -11$ or $a = 11$ 8. $16x^2 = 9$ $x = -\frac{3}{4}$ or $a = \frac{3}{4}$ 9. $12y^2 + 11y + 2 = 0$

10. $3b^2 - 10b + 3 = 0$ $b = \frac{1}{3}$ or $b = 3$ 11. $29d + 7 = -4d^2$ $d = -7$ or $d = -\frac{1}{4}$ 12. $4t^2 + 25 = 20t$ $t = 2\frac{1}{2}$

Use the quadratic formula to solve each equation. *(Pages 475–477)*

13. $x^2 - 10x + 25 = 0$ $x = 5$ 14. $9 = b^2 - 6b$ 15. $r^2 = 5$

16. $3z - 5z^2 + 1 = 0$ 17. $2q^2 - 3q - 1 = 0$ 18. $5d^2 + 7d = 10$

OBJECTIVE: To state the nature of the solutions of a quadratic equation by evaluating the discriminant

13–6 The Discriminant

Note where the zeros occur in each of these functions.

Two x Intercepts	One x Intercept	No x Intercepts
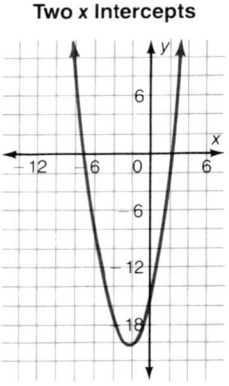	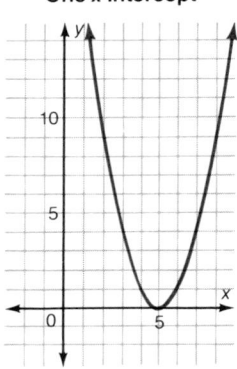	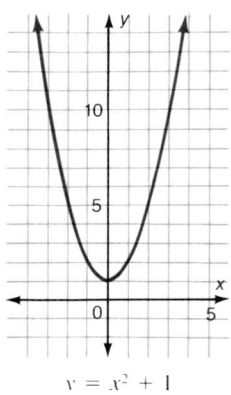
$y = x^2 + 5x - 14$	$y = x^2 - 10x + 25$	$y = x^2 + 1$

Function	x Intercepts	Nature of the Solutions
$y = x^2 + 5x - 14$	Two distinct points	Two real zeros
$y = x^2 - 10x + 25$	One point	One real zero
$y = x^2 + 1$	None	No real zeros

The number and kind of solutions of quadratic equations can be determined from a part of the quadratic formula, that is, from

$$b^2 - 4ac.$$

This portion of the formula that determines the nature of the solutions of a quadratic equation is called the **discriminant**.

Equation	$\sqrt{b^2 - 4ac}$	Nature of $b^2 - 4ac$	Solutions
$x^2 + 5x - 14 = 0$	$\sqrt{25 + 56}$	Positive: two real-number solutions	$\{2, -7\}$
$x^2 - 10x + 25 = 0$	$\sqrt{100 - 100}$	Zero: one real-number solution	$\{5\}$
$x^2 + 1 = 0$	$\sqrt{0 - 4}$	Negative: no real-number solutions	ϕ

For convenience, the solutions of $x^2 - 10x + 25 = 0$ are often said to be equal since factoring $x^2 - 10x + 25 = 0$ as $(x - 5)(x - 5) = 0$ gives $+5$ and $+5$ as solutions. However, there is only one distinct solution, 5.

For $x^2 + 1 = 0$, there is no solution in the set of real numbers. The number $\sqrt{0 - 4}$, or simply $\sqrt{-4}$, is not a real number.

Nature of the solutions of $ax^2 + bx + c = 0$

1. If $b^2 - 4ac > 0$, there are two distinct, real solutions.
2. If $b^2 - 4ac = 0$, there is one, distinct real solution.
3. If $b^2 - 4ac < 0$, there are no real solutions.

EXAMPLE   Use the discriminant to determine the nature of the solutions of each equation.

   a. $3x^2 - 11 = 0$ **b.** $-x^2 + x - 5 = 0$ **c.** $-x^2 + 6x - 9 = 0$

Solutions: **a.** $3x^2 - 11 = 0$ ← $a = 3, b = 0, c = -11$

   $b^2 - 4ac = 0 - 4(3)(-11)$

   $= 132$

   Since $b^2 - 4ac > 0$ there are **two real-number solutions.**

   b. $-x^2 + x - 5 = 0$ ← $a = -1, b = 1, c = -5$

   $b^2 - 4ac = 1 - 4(-1)(-5)$

   $= -19$

   Since $b^2 - 4ac < 0$, there are **no real-number solutions.**

   c. $-x^2 + 6x - 9 = 0$ ← $a = -1, b = 6, c = -9$

   $b^2 - 4ac = 6^2 - 4(-1)(-9)$

   $= 0$

   Since $b^2 - 4ac = 0$, there is **one distinct real-number solution.**

CLASSROOM EXERCISES

Evaluate $b^2 - 4ac$ for each equation. Then state the number of solutions.

1. $2x^2 - 3x - 1 = 0$ **2.** $n^2 - 2n + 4 = 0$ **3.** $x^2 - 6x + 9 = 0$

4. $3y^2 - y = -1$ **5.** $b^2 + b + 1 - 0$ **6.** $2a^2 + 1 = 4a$

Quadratic Functions and Equations   **487**

WRITTEN EXERCISES

A   Evaluate $b^2 - 4ac$ for each equation.

1. $x^2 + 9x + 5 = 0$ 61
2. $x^2 + 8x - 4 = 0$ 80
3. $x^2 + 6x + 9 = 0$ 0

4. $x^2 - 4x + 4 = 0$ 0
5. $2x^2 + x + 6 = 0$ −47
6. $2x^2 + 7x + 9 = 0$

7. $x^2 - 9 = 0$ 36
8. $x^2 - 16 = 0$ 64
9. $x^2 + 12 = 0$ −48

10. $3x^2 + 6x - 7 = 0$ 120
11. $-5x^2 - 2x - 3 = 0$ −56
12. $-4x^2 + 3x + 7 = 0$
                                                                            121

Without solving, give the nature of the solutions of each equation.

13. $x^2 + 2x + 8 = 0$
14. $3x^2 - 3x - 4 = 0$
15. $3y^2 - \frac{1}{3}y = \frac{2}{5}$

16. $x^2 = 5x + 5$
17. $3x^2 + 4x - \frac{3}{4} = 0$
18. $2y^2 - 4y = -2$

19. $x^2 - x + \frac{6}{25} = 0$
20. $20x = x^2 + 100$
21. $\frac{1}{2}x^2 - 16x + 132 = 0$

22. $4x^2 + 2x - 9 = 0$
23. $x^2 - 5x + 6 = 0$
24. $-x^2 + 7x - 15 = 0$

B

25. For what values of k will the equation $x^2 + kx + 25 = 0$ have only one solution?

26. For what values of k are the solutions of $x^2 + 4x + k = 0$ real numbers?

27. For what values of k will the equation $x^2 + kx + 3 = 0$ have two real solutions?

28. For what values of k are the solutions of $x^2 + 6x + k = 0$ not real numbers?

C   In Exercises 29–32, describe the solutions of the quadratic equation $ax^2 + bx + c = 0$ according to the given conditions.

29. $b^2 = 4ac$ one real solution
30. $a \ne 0$, $b \ne 0$, $c = 0$ two real solutions

31. $b = 0$, a and c have opposite signs
    two real solutions
32. $b = 0$, a and c have the same sign
    no real solutions

ᴄᴀᴌᴄᴜᴌᴀᴛᴏʀ ᴀᴘᴘᴌɪᴄᴀᴛɪᴏɴs ——————————————

Evaluating Irrational Solutions

To evaluate an irrational solution on a calculator, you use the square root and memory keys.

EXAMPLE   Evaluate $\dfrac{-1 - \sqrt{10}}{3}$ to the nearest hundredth (Example, page 476).

SOLUTION   First evaluate the numerator. To do this, first find $\sqrt{10}$ and store.

1 0 [√] [M+] 1 [+/−] [−] [MR] [=] [÷] 3 [=] $\boxed{-1.3874258}$

To the nearest hundredth, the answer is **−1.39**.

EXERCISES

Evaluate each of the following to the nearest hundredth.

1. $\dfrac{-1 + \sqrt{10}}{3}$
2. $\dfrac{1 - \sqrt{25}}{12}$
3. $\dfrac{1 + \sqrt{41}}{4}$
4. $\dfrac{3 - \sqrt{29}}{10}$
5. $\dfrac{-4 - \sqrt{33}}{6}$
6. $\dfrac{-7 + \sqrt{249}}{10}$

13–7 Maximum and Minimum

Teaching Suggestions p. M-26

In the graph below, the dashed line through the **turning point**, or **vertex**, of the parabola $P(1, -4)$ is called the **axis of symmetry**. The equation of the axis of symmetry is $x = 1$. If the parabola were folded along this line, the left side of the parabola would fit exactly over the right side. The axis of symmetry is halfway between any two points on the parabola that have the same y coordinate. Thus, the line $x = 1$ is halfway between the points $(-1, 0)$ and $(3, 0)$ and the points are said to be **mirror images** of each other.

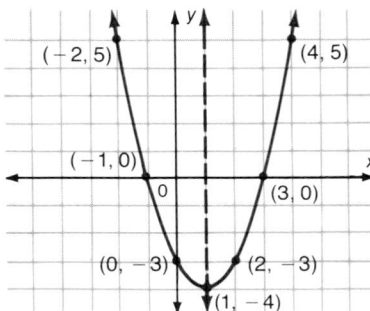

The minimum (least) value of the quadratic function shown above is the value of y on the axis of symmetry. Thus, the minimum value is -4.

The axis of symmetry for the quadratic function $y = ax^2 + bx + c$ is midway between the two roots. To find this point, find the *mean*, or *average*, of the roots.

$$\frac{\dfrac{-b + \sqrt{b^2 - 4ac}}{2a} + \dfrac{-b - \sqrt{b^2 - 4ac}}{2a}}{2} = -\frac{b}{2a}$$

Thus, the axis of symmetry is a line parallel to the y axis; its equation is $x = -\dfrac{b}{2a}$.

> For the quadratic function, $y = ax^2 + bx + c$, the equation of the axis of symmetry is $x = -\dfrac{b}{2a}$.

NOTE: The maximum or minimum point of a quadratic function is the *only* point of the function that lies on the axis of symmetry; it occurs at the *vertex*, or *turning point*, of the parabola, where $x = -\dfrac{b}{2a}$.

Quadratic Functions and Equations **489**

Additional Examples
Example 1

1. For the parabola $y = x^2 + x - 2$, find each of the following.

  a. The equation of the axis of symmetry.
  Ans: $x = -\frac{1}{2}$

  b. The coordinates of the vertex. **Ans:** $(-\frac{1}{2}, -2\frac{1}{4})$

  c. The minimum value of the function. **Ans:** $-2\frac{1}{4}$

2. For the parabola $y = -x^2 + 3x - 2$, find each of the following.

  a. The equation of the axis of symmetry.
  Ans: $x = 1\frac{1}{2}$

  b. The coordinates of the vertex. **Ans:** $(1\frac{1}{2}, \frac{1}{4})$

  c. The maximum value of the function. **Ans:** $\frac{1}{4}$

Example 2
Use the information from Example 1 and the zeros of the function to graph each function in Example 1.

1. Ans:

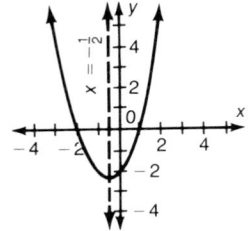

2. Ans:

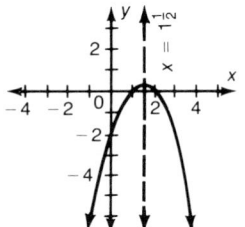

EXAMPLE 1 For the parabola $y = x^2 + x - 6$, find each of the following.

  a. The equation of the axis of symmetry
  b. The coordinates of the vertex
  c. The minimum value of the function

Solutions: **a.** Equation of axis of symmetry: $x = -\dfrac{b}{2a}$

  $x = -\frac{1}{2}$ ⟵ $a = 1; b = 1$

  b. Since the vertex of the parabola lies on the axis of symmetry, find y when $x = -\frac{1}{2}$.

  $y = x^2 + x - 6$

  $y = (-\frac{1}{2})^2 - \frac{1}{2} - 6$

  $y = \frac{1}{4} - \frac{1}{2} - 6 = -6\frac{1}{4}$

  Coordinates of vertex: $(-\frac{1}{2}, -6\frac{1}{4})$

  c. **Minimum value:** $-6\frac{1}{4}$

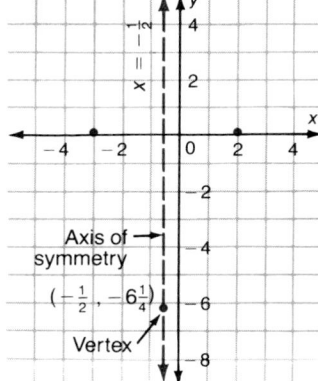

Axis of symmetry

$(-\frac{1}{2}, -6\frac{1}{4})$

Vertex

You can use the results of Example **1a** and **1b** to sketch the graph.

EXAMPLE 2 Sketch the graph of $y = x^2 + x - 6$.

  Solution: Use the information from Example 1 and the zeros of the function.

  Axis of symmetry: $x = -\dfrac{1}{2}$

  Vertex: $\left(-\dfrac{1}{2}, -6\dfrac{1}{4}\right)$

  Zeros of the function: $(-3, 0)$ and $(2, 0)$

  Sketch the parabola.

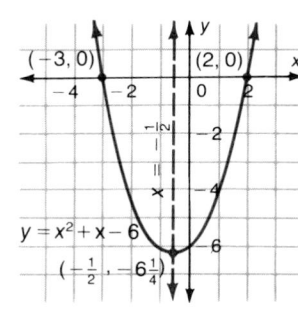

$(-3, 0)$ $(2, 0)$

$y = x^2 + x - 6$

$(-\frac{1}{2}, -6\frac{1}{4})$

When the coefficient of the square term of a quadratic function is positive, the graph of the function opens upward; when the coefficient is negative, the graph opens downward.

$y = x^2 - 4x + 3$

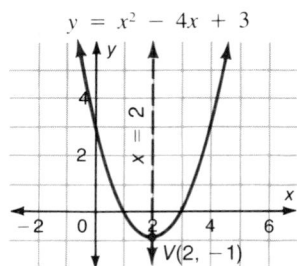

$V(2, -1)$

$y = 4x - x^2$

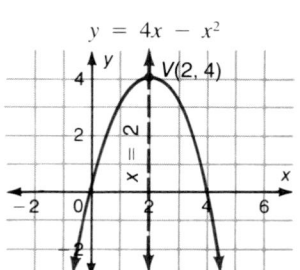

$V(2, 4)$

For the quadratic function $y = ax^2 + bx + c$, the graph opens **upward** when $a > 0$, and the graph opens **downward when $a < 0$.**

CLASSROOM EXERCISES

State whether each function will have a maximum value or a minimum value.

3. maximum

1. $y = 3x^2$ minimum
2. $y = 2x + x^2$ minimum
3. $y = 6 + x - x^2$

4. $y = 9 + x^2$ minimum
5. $y = -(1 - x)^2$ maximum
6. $y = (x + 1)^2$

minimum

WRITTEN EXERCISES

Assignment Guide
Minimal Omit
Average Omit
Above Average
p. 493: 3, 6, 9, . . . 27, 29, 31

A

For each parabola in Exercises 1–15:
  a. Write the equation of the axis of symmetry.
  b. Write the coordinates of the vertex and tell whether it is a maximum or minimum point.
  c. Sketch the parabola. See the Solution Key.

1. $y = 2x^2$
2. $y = 4x^2$
3. $y = x^2 + 4$

4. $y = x^2 - 6x + 5$
5. $y = x^2 + 8x + 7$
6. $y = x^2 - 2x - 8$

7. $y = x^2 - 3x$
8. $y = x^2 + 2x - 8$
9. $y = x^2 - 2x$

B

10. $y = -2x^2$
11. $y = -x^2 + 1$
12. $y = -x^2 + 3x$

13. $y = -x^2 - 2x + 8$
14. $y = -x^2 - 2x + 3$
15. $y = -x^2 + 3x - 2$

16. Find the minimum value of y if $y = x^2 - 6x + 8$. -1

17. Find the maximum value of y if $y = 5 - x^2$. 5

18. Find the maximum value of y if $y = -x^2 + 3x - 2$. $\frac{1}{4}$

19. Find the minimum value of y if $y = x^2 - 2x - 24$. -25

Additional Answers
Written Exercises
  1. a. $x = 0$ **b.** $(0, 0)$
  2. a. $x = 0$ **b.** $(0, 0)$
  3. a. $x = 0$ **b.** $(0, 4)$
  4. a. $x = 3$ **b.** $(3, -4)$
  5. a. $x = -4$ **b.** $(-4, -9)$
  6. a. $x = 1$ **b.** $(1, -9)$
  7. a. $x = 1\frac{1}{2}$ **b.** $(1\frac{1}{2}, -2\frac{1}{4})$
  8. a. $x = -1$ **b.** $(-1, -9)$
  9. a. $x = 1$ **b.** $(1, -1)$
  10. a. $x = 0$ **b.** $(0, 0)$
  11. a. $x = 0$ **b.** $(0, 1)$
  12. a. $x = 1\frac{1}{2}$ **b.** $(1\frac{1}{2}, 2\frac{1}{4})$
  13. a. $x = -1$ **b.** $(-1, 9)$
  14. a. $x = -1$ **b.** $(-1, 4)$
  15. a. $x = 1\frac{1}{2}$ **b.** $(1\frac{1}{2}, \frac{1}{4})$

APPLICATIONS: Maximum and Minimum

Myra wishes to use 100 feet of fencing to build a rectangular pen for her dog. The sum of the length and width of the yard will be 50 feet. The area, y, of the yard will equal $x(50 - x)$.

x

$50 - x$

20. Find x so that the area, y, is a maximum.   25 ft

21. Find the maximum area.   625 ft²

22. A farmer uses 250 feet of fence to enclose a rectangular garden. What should be the length and width of the garden if the farmer is to have the maximum area to plant?   length: $62\frac{1}{2}$ ft; width: $62\frac{1}{2}$ ft

Quadratic Functions and Equations   **491**

Quick Quiz

For the parabola $y = x^2 + 2x - 3$

a. Find the equation of the axis of symmetry.
Ans: $x = -1$

b. Find the coordinates of the vertex.
Ans: $(-1, -4)$

c. Find the minimum value of the function.
Ans: -4

d. Find the zeros of the function. **Ans:** $-3; 1$

e. Sketch the graph of the function.
Ans:

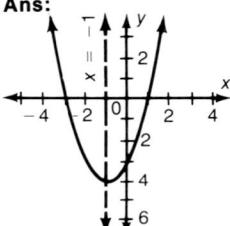

Additional Examples

1. Graph: $y > x^2 + 2$
Ans:

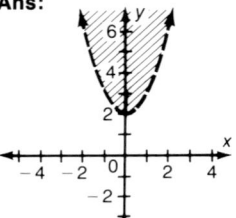

2. Graph: $y \geq x^2 - 4$
Ans:

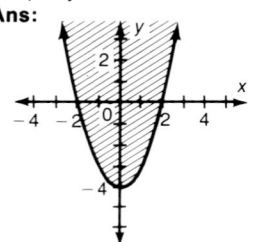

A homeowner wishes to make a rectangular garden surrounded on three sides by a decorative fence. (The house forms the fourth side.) The owner buys 60 feet of fence.

23. If x represents the width of the garden, represent the second width and the length in terms of x. second width: x; length: $60 - 2x$

24. Find the width that will make the area a maximum. 15 ft

25. What is the maximum area that can be enclosed with the fence? 450 ft²

26. Suppose the homeowner in Exercises 23–25 had 40 feet of fence. What would be the dimensions of the garden that would make the area a maximum?

width: 10 ft; length: 20 ft

Ⓒ

27. Determine a formula that will give the maximum or minimum value of the quadratic function $y = ax^2 + bx + c$. maximum, or minimum, $= \left[-\dfrac{b}{2a}, f\left(-\dfrac{b}{2a} \right) \right]$

OBJECTIVE: To solve quadratic inequalities

13-8 Quadratic Inequalities

The graph of an equation such as $y = -x^2 + 1$ divides the coordinate plane into three sets of points: the set of points on the curve, the set of points inside the curve, and the set of points outside the curve. The solution of an inequality such as $y > -x^2 + 1$ is made up of one or two of these sets of points.

To determine the solution set of $y > -x^2 + 1$, first graph $y = -x^2 + 1$. Then test points inside and outside the curve to find those that satisfy the inequality.

EXAMPLE Graph: $y > -x^2 + 1$

Solutions: ① Graph $y = -x^2 + 1$.

Use a dashed line to show that the solutions of $y > -x^2 + 1$ are *not* on the graph of $y = -x^2 + 1$.

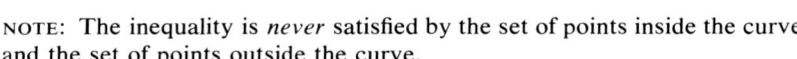

② Test points inside and outside the parabola.

Inside: Test $(0, 0)$	Outside: Test $(0, 3)$
$y > -x^2 + 1$	$y > -x^2 + 1$
$0 > 0 + 1$?	$3 > 0 + 1$?
$0 > 1$? No	$3 > 1$? Yes ✔

③ Shade the region outside the parabola.
The graph of $y > -x^2 + 1$ is the **set of points outside the parabola.**

NOTE: The inequality is *never* satisfied by the set of points inside the curve and the set of points outside the curve.

You can test points inside and outside the graph of $y = -x^2 + 1$ to show that the shaded region on each graph below represents the given set of points.

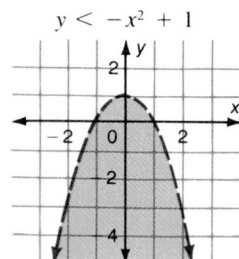
$y < -x^2 + 1$

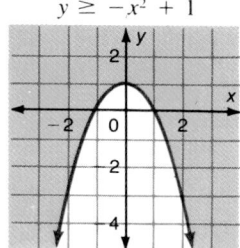
$y \geq -x^2 + 1$

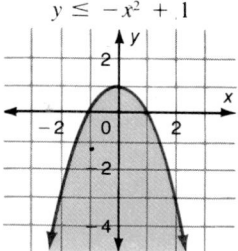
$y \leq -x^2 + 1$

CLASSROOM EXERCISES

For each parabola in Exercises 1–8:
a. State whether the graph will include a solid, S, or a dashed, D, curve.
b. State whether the graph includes the region inside the curve or outside the curve.

1. $y > x^2$
  a. D
  b. inside

2. $y \geq x^2$
  a. S
  b. inside

3. $y \leq x^2 - 1$
  a. S
  b. outside

4. $y < x^2 - 1$
  a. D
  b. outside

5. $y \geq 2x - x^2$
  a. S
  b. outside

6. $y \leq 1 - x^2$
  a. S
  b. inside

7. $y < x^2 - 3x$
  a. D
  b. outside

8. $y > x^2 + 5x + 6$
  a. D
  b. inside

WRITTEN EXERCISES

A   Graph each inequality. See the Solution Key for the graphs of Ex. 1-16.

1. $y \leq x^2$
2. $y > x^2 - 1$
3. $y \geq x^2 + 4$
4. $y < -x^2$

5. $y > -2x^2$
6. $y > x^2 - 2x$
7. $y \leq x^2 - 3x$
8. $y \geq 1 - x^2$

9. $y \leq x^2 - 4x + 4$
10. $y \geq x^2 - 2x + 1$
11. $y < 2 - x^2$
12. $y \leq -x^2 + 3$

13. $y > x^2 + 2x - 8$
14. $y \leq x^2 - 5x - 6$
15. $y \geq 6 - x^2$
16. $y \geq 5 - x^2$

B   Graph the solution set of each system. See p. 590 for Ex. 17-32 odd.
                                         See the Solution Key for Ex. 17-32 even.

17. $\begin{cases} y \geq x^2 \\ y < 4 \end{cases}$
18. $\begin{cases} y \geq x^2 \\ x \leq 0 \end{cases}$
19. $\begin{cases} y < -x^2 + 1 \\ y \geq 0 \end{cases}$
20. $\begin{cases} y \geq -x^2 \\ x \geq 0 \end{cases}$

21. $\begin{cases} y > x^2 - 3 \\ y < x \end{cases}$
22. $\begin{cases} y > -x^2 + 4 \\ y = x \end{cases}$
23. $\begin{cases} y \leq x^2 + 2 \\ y \geq x \end{cases}$
24. $\begin{cases} y \leq 2x^2 \\ y \geq 2x - 3 \end{cases}$

25. $\begin{cases} y > x^2 - 4 \\ y \leq 4 \end{cases}$
26. $\begin{cases} y < x^2 + 5 \\ y < 5 \end{cases}$
27. $\begin{cases} y < -x^2 + 5 \\ y \geq 0 \end{cases}$
28. $\begin{cases} y > -x^2 + 2 \\ y \geq -5 \end{cases}$

C

29. $\begin{cases} y \geq x^2 \\ y \leq -x^2 \end{cases}$
30. $\begin{cases} y \geq x^2 - 2 \\ y \leq -x^2 + 4 \end{cases}$
31. $\begin{cases} y \geq x^2 - 4 \\ y \leq \frac{1}{4}x^2 \end{cases}$
32. $\begin{cases} y \leq 1 - x^2 \\ y \leq x^2 + 1 \end{cases}$

Quadratic Functions and Equations   **493**

Assignment Guide
Minimal Omit
Average Omit
Above Average
p. 493: 3, 6, 9, . . . 27, 29, 31

Additional Answers
Written Exercises
For Exercises 1–16, the coordinates of several points are given. D represents a dashed curve and S represents a solid curve. The terms inside and outside indicate whether the graph includes the region inside or outside the curve.

1. $(-2, 4)$, $(-1, 1)$, $(0, 0)$, $(1, 1)$, $(2, 4)$; S; outside

2. $(-2, 2)$, $(-1, 0)$, $(0, -1)$, $(1, 0)$, $(2, 3)$; D; inside

3. $(-2, 8)$, $(-1, 5)$, $(0, 4)$, $(1, 5)$, $(2, 8)$; S; inside

4. $(-2, -4)$, $(-1, -1)$, $(0, 0)$, $(1, -1)$, $(2, -4)$; D; inside

5. $(-2, -8)$, $(-1, -2)$, $(0, 0)$, $(1, -2)$, $(2, -8)$; D; outside

6. $(-1, 3)$, $(0, 0)$, $(1, -1)$, $(2, 0)$, $(3, 3)$; D; inside

7. $(-1, 4)$, $(0, 0)$, $(1\frac{1}{2}, -2\frac{1}{4})$, $(3, 0)$, $(4, 4)$; S; outside

8. $(-2, -3)$, $(-1, 0)$, $(0, 1)$, $(1, 0)$, $(2, -3)$; S; outside

9. $(0, 4)$, $(1, 1)$, $(2, 0)$, $(3, 1)$, $(4, 4)$; S; outside

10. $(-1, 4)$, $(0, 1)$, $(1, 0)$, $(2, 1)$, $(3, 4)$; S; inside

11. $(-2, -2)$, $(-\sqrt{2}, 0)$, $(0, 2)$, $(\sqrt{2}, 0)$, $(2, -2)$; D; inside

12. $(-2, -1)$, $(-1, 2)$, $(0, 3)$, $(1, 2)$, $(2, -1)$; S; inside

13. $(-4, 0)$, $(-3, -5)$, $(-1, -9)$, $(1, -5)$, $(2, 0)$; S; inside

14. $(-1, 0)$, $(0, -6)$, $(2\frac{1}{2}, -12\frac{1}{4})$, $(5, -6)$, $(6, 0)$+ S+ outside

15. $(-3, -3)$, $(-\sqrt{6}, 0)$, $(0, 6)$, $(\sqrt{6}, 0)$, $(3, -3)$; S; outside

16. $(-3, -4)$, $(-\sqrt{5}, 0)$, $(-1, 4)$, $(0, 5)$, $(1, 4)$, $(\sqrt{5}, 0)$, $(3, -4)$; S; outside

BASIC: SOLVING QUADRATIC EQUATIONS

Problem: *Write a program which solves quadratic equations of the form* $ax^2 + bx + c = 0$ *($a \neq 0$). If the equation has no real roots, print* NO REAL ROOTS.

```
100 PRINT "FOR THE EQUATION A*X↑2 + B*X + C = 0,"
110 PRINT "WHAT ARE A,B,C";
120 INPUT A, B, C
130 LET D = B↑2 - 4*A*C
140 IF D = 0 THEN 200
150 IF D < 0 THEN 230
160 LET X1 = (-B + SQR(D))/(2*A)
170 LET X2 = (-B - SQR(D))/(2*A)
180 PRINT "THE TWO ROOTS ARE ";X1;"AND ";X2
190 GOTO 240
200 LET X = -B/(2*A)
210 PRINT "DOUBLE ROOT IS ";X
220 GOTO 240
230 PRINT "NO REAL ROOTS"
240 PRINT
250 PRINT "ANY MORE EQUATIONS TO SOLVE (1=YES, 0=NO)";
260 INPUT Z
270 IF Z = 1 THEN 120
280 END
```

The following is the output from a sample run of the program above.

Output:
```
RUN
FOR THE EQUATION A*X↑2 + B*X + C = 0,
WHAT ARE A,B,C? 1,0,-16
THE TWO ROOTS ARE  4 AND -4

ANY MORE EQUATIONS TO SOLVE (1=YES, 0=NO)? 1
? 1,1,-6
THE TWO ROOTS ARE  2 AND -3

ANY MORE EQUATIONS TO SOLVE (1=YES, 0=NO)? 1
? 5,4,2
NO REAL ROOTS

ANY MORE EQUATIONS TO SOLVE (1=YES, 0=NO)? 1
? 2,-3,-35
THE TWO ROOTS ARE  5 AND -3.5
```

```
ANY MORE EQUATIONS TO SOLVE (1=YES, 0=NO)? 1
? 1,-4,4
DOUBLE ROOT IS   2

ANY MORE EQUATIONS TO SOLVE (1=YES, 0=NO)? 0
READY
```

Analysis

Statements *130–150:*	D is the discriminant of the equation. If D = 0, there is a double root. If D < 0, there are no real roots.
Statements *160–180:*	These steps compute and print the two real roots, X1 and X2. The only difference between the roots is that X1 is computed using the positive square root of the discriminant, while X2 uses the negative square root.
Statements *200–210:*	These statements, which compute the double root when D = 0, could be combined into the following single statement.

```
200   PRINT "DOUBLE ROOT IS"; -B/(2*A)
```

EXERCISES

A   Run the program on page 494 for the following values of *a*, *b*, and *c*.

1. $a = 1; b = 1; c = -6$
2. $a = 1; b = -8; c = 15$
3. $a = 1; b = 8; c = -42$
4. $a = 3; b = 12; c = 10$
5. $a = -4; b = 2; c = -3$
6. $a = 4; b = -20; c = 25$

Write each equation in the form $ax^2 + bx + c = 0$. Then use the program on page 494 to find the roots.

7. $x^2 + 5x = 7$
8. $3x^2 = 8 + 2x$
9. $12x = 4x^2 + 9$
10. $4x = 3x^2 + 6$
11. $4x^2 = 5x$
12. $24x^2 = 18$
13. $2x^2 = 7x - 6$
14. $6x^2 + 3 = 7x$
15. $13x = 2x^2 + 15$

16. The program on page 494 assumes that $a \neq 0$. Add statements to the program to print NOT A QUADRATIC EQUATION if 0 is entered for *a*.
   See the Solution Key for the answers to Ex. 16-19.
   Write a BASIC program for each problem.

17. For a function of the form $y = ax^2 + bx + c$, enter *a*, *b*, and *c* $(a \neq 0)$. Print whether the function has 0, 1, or 2 real zeros.

B

18. Solve equations of the form $(ax + b)^2 = c$. If $c < 0$, print NO REAL ROOTS.

19. Given *a* and *b* of $ax^2 + bx$, find *c*, if possible, in order to complete the square $ax^2 + bx + c$. Print the complete trinomial.

Solving Quadratic Equations   **495**

_____ Review _____

Graph each quadratic function. Determine the zeros of each function. *(Section 13-5)*   See the Solution Key for the graphs.

1. $y = x^2 + 5x + 6$ **2.** $y = x^2 - 1$ **3.** $y = -x^2 + 4x - 4$

Without solving, give the nature of the solutions of each equation. *(Section 13-6)*

4. $3y^2 - 3y - 4 = 0$ **5.** $x^2 + 2x + 8 = 0$ **6.** $2a^2 - 4a = -3$
two distinct real solutions   no real solutions   no real solutions

For each parabola in Exercises 7–9:   See the Solution Key for the graphs.
  a. Write the equation of the axis of symmetry.
  b. Write the coordinates of the vertex and tell whether it is a maximum or a minimum point.
  c. Sketch the parabola. *(Section 13-7)*

7. $y = -2x^2$ **8.** $y = x^2 + 6$ **9.** $y = x^2 - 8x + 7$

Graph each inequality. *(Section 13-8)* See the Solution Key for the graphs.

10. $y > -2x^2$ **11.** $y < x^2 + 2$ **12.** $y \geq -x^2 + 2x$

_____ Chapter Summary _____

IMPORTANT TERMS

Completing the square (p. 472)
Discriminant (p. 486)
Parabola (p. 484)
Quadratic equation (p. 470)

Quadratic function (p. 484)
Roots of an equation (p. 475)
Zeros of a function (p. 484)

IMPORTANT IDEAS

1. If $x^2 = k$, then $x = \sqrt{k}$ <u>or</u> $x = -\sqrt{k}$ for any real number k, $k \geq 0$.

2. **Steps for Completing the Square of $x^2 + bx$**
   - $\boxed{1}$ Find one-half the coefficient of x.
   - $\boxed{2}$ Square the result of Step 1.
   - $\boxed{3}$ Add the result of Step 2 to $x^2 + bx$.

3. **Quadratic Formula:** For the quadratic equation $ax^2 + bx + c = 0$, where a, b, and c are real numbers and $a \neq 0$,
$$x = \frac{-b \pm \sqrt{b^2 - 4ac}}{2a}.$$

4. **The Nature of the Solutions of $ax^2 + bx + c = 0$**
   - $\boxed{1}$ If $b^2 - 4ac > 0$, there are two distinct, real solutions.
   - $\boxed{2}$ If $b^2 - 4ac = 0$, there is one distinct real solution.
   - $\boxed{3}$ If $b^2 - 4ac < 0$, there are no real solutions.

Chapter Objectives and Review _____

Additional Answers

Objective: *To solve quadratic equations by factoring or by taking the square root of each side of the equation (Section 13–1)*

Solve each equation. Irrational solutions may be left in simplified radical form.

1. $x^2 = 121$ $x = -11$ or $x = 11$
2. $4n^2 = 32$ $n = 2\sqrt{2}$ or $n = -2\sqrt{2}$
3. $2y^2 - 8 = 10$ $y = 3$ or $y = 3$
4. $(y - 5)^2 = 0$ $y = 5$
5. $6(t + 3)^2 = 24$ $t = -5$ or $t = -1$
6. $(3b - 1)^2 = 81$
7. $(6y + 3)^2 = 1$ $y = -\frac{2}{3}$ or $y = -\frac{1}{3}$
8. $(x - \frac{3}{4})^2 = \frac{9}{16}$ $x = 0$ or $x = 1\frac{1}{2}$
9. $2(x - 3)^2 = \frac{8}{25}$

Objective: *To solve quadratic equations by completing the square (Section 13–2)*

Solve by completing the square. Irrational solutions may be left in simplified radical form.

10. $x^2 + 6x = 7$ $x = -7$ or $x = 1$
11. $a^2 - 6a - 7 = 0$ $a = -1$ or $a = 7$
12. $y^2 + 3y = 4$ $y = -4$ or $y = 1$
13. $x^2 - x = 30$ $x = -5$ or $x = 6$
14. $r^2 + 4r = -2$
15. $b^2 = 3b + 10$
16. $2n^2 - 4n + 3 = 0$ ϕ
17. $3c^2 + 8c = -5$ $c = -1\frac{2}{3}$ or $c = -1$
18. $2x^2 - x = 3$ $x = -1$ or $x = 1\frac{1}{2}$

Objective: *To solve quadratic equations using the quadratic formula (Section 13–3)*

Use the quadratic formula to solve each equation. Irrational solutions may be left in simplified radical form.

19. $y^2 + 6y - 16 = 0$
20. $x^2 - 3x = 0$ $x = 0$ or $x = 3$
21. $b^2 = 5 - 4b$ $b = -5$ or $b = 1$
22. $c^2 + 6c - 1 = 0$
23. $2x^2 + 11x + 5 = 0$ $x = -5$ or $x = -\frac{1}{2}$
24. $2y^2 - 7y + 4 = 0$
25. $9c^2 + 2 + 9c = 0$
26. $x^2 + 4x - 2 = 0$
27. $3d^2 + 5 = 16d$ $d = \frac{1}{3}$ or $d = 5$

Objective: *To solve problems using quadratic equations (Section 13–4)*

Solve each problem. Approximate irrational roots to the nearest tenth.

28. The sum of a positive number and its square is 72. Find the number. 8

29. The sum of the squares of two consecutive positive integers is 85. Find the integers. 6 and 7

30. The perimeter of a rectangle is 32 meters, and its area is 48 square meters. What are its dimensions? width: 4 m; length: 12 m

31. The length of a rectangular sign is one meter longer than its width. Its area is 11 square meters. Find its dimensions. width: 2.9 m; length: 3.9 m

Objective: *To graph quadratic functions and read the zeros of each function from its graph (Section 13–5)* See the Solution Key for the graphs.

Graph each quadratic function. Write the zeros of the function.

32. $y = x^2 + 2x - 8$
33. $y = x^2 - 3x$
34. $y = x^2 + 4x + 4$
35. $y = x^2 - 5x + 4$
36. $y = x^2 - 4$
37. $y = -x^2 + 6x - 9$

Quadratic Functions and Equations **497**

Additional Answers
6. $b = -2\frac{2}{3}$ or $b = 3\frac{1}{3}$
9. $x = 2\frac{3}{5}$ or $x = 3\frac{2}{5}$
14. $r = -2 - \sqrt{2}$ or $r = -2 + \sqrt{2}$
15. $b = -2$ or $b = 5$
19. $y = -8$ or $y = 2$
22. $c = -3 - \sqrt{10}$ or $c = -3 + \sqrt{10}$
24. $y = \frac{7 - \sqrt{17}}{4}$ or $y = \frac{7 + \sqrt{17}}{4}$
25. $c = -\frac{2}{3}$ or $c = -\frac{1}{3}$
26. $x = -2 - \sqrt{6}$ or $x = -2 + \sqrt{6}$
32. The graph is a parabola, opening upward, with vertex at $(-1, -9)$ and y intercept at $(0, -8)$; zeros: $-4, 2$.
33. The graph is a parabola, opening upward, with vertex at $(1.5, -2.25)$ and y intercept at the origin; zeros: $0, 3$.
34. The graph is a parabola, opening upward, with vertex at $(-2, 0)$ and y intercept at $(0, 4)$; zero: -2.
35. The graph is a parabola, opening upward, with vertex at $(2.5, -2.25)$ and y intercept at $(0, 4)$; zeros: $1, 4$.
36. The graph is a parabola, opening upward, with vertex at $(0, -4)$ and y intercept at $(0, -4)$; zeros: $-2, 2$.
37. The graph is a parabola, opening downward, with vertex at $(3, 0)$ and y intercept at $(0, -9)$; zero: 3.

Objective: *To state the nature of the solutions of a quadratic equation by evaluating the discriminant (Section 13–6)*

Without solving, give the nature of the solutions of each equation.

38. $x^2 - 5x - 5 = 0$
39. $2x^2 - 3x = 0$
40. $y^2 - 20y + 100 = 0$
41. $3y^2 = 1 + 2y$
42. $x^2 - 14x + 48 = 0$
43. $a^2 + 2 = 2a$
44. $x^2 = 8x - 16$
45. $3n = 4n^2 + 1$
46. $x^2 + x + \frac{1}{4} = 0$

47. For what values of k will the equation $x^2 + kx + 64 = 0$ have only one real solution? $k = -16$ <u>or</u> $k = 16$

48. For what values of k will the equation $x^2 + x + k = 0$ have two real solutions? $k < \frac{1}{4}$

_____ Chapter Test _____

A formal Chapter Test is provided in the Teacher's Manual. See p. M-76.

Solve each equation. Irrational solutions may be left in simplified radical form.

1. $2x^2 + 3 = 11$ $x = -2$ <u>or</u> $x = 2$
2. $(y - 1)^2 = 9$ $y = -2$ <u>or</u> $y = 4$
3. $3(x + 4)^2 = 48$
4. $x^2 + 3x + 2 = 0$ $x = -2$ <u>or</u> $x = -1$
5. $x^2 - 9x = -18$ $x = 3$ <u>or</u> $x = 6$
6. $a^2 + 6 = -5a$
7. $y^2 + 3y - 4 = 0$ $y = -4$ <u>or</u> $y = 1$
8. $n^2 + 32 = 12n$ $n = 4$ <u>or</u> $n = 8$
9. $c^2 - 4c + 2 = 0$
10. $4y^2 - 2y - 1 = 0$
11. $x^2 - 8x + 16 = 0$ $x = 4$
12. $3x^2 - 6x + 1 = 0$

Write the zeros of the functions graphed below.

13.

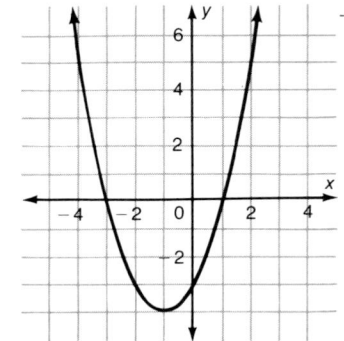

$-3, 1$

14.

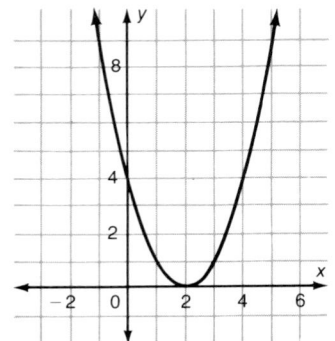

2

Without solving, give the nature of the solutions of each equation.

15. $x^2 - 8x + 16 = 0$
16. $x^2 + 5x + 8 = 0$
17. $6x^2 + 13x - 5 = 0$
18. $9x^2 + 1 = 6x$

19. The width of a picture window is 2 feet more than its height. If the area of the window is 24 square feet, what are its width and height? width: 6 ft; height: 4 ft

20. In a right triangle, one leg is 2 meters shorter than the hypotenuse. The other leg is 4 meters shorter than the hypotenuse. Find the length of the hypotenuse.
10 m

Additional Practice

You may wish to use all or some of these exercises depending on how well students performed on the formal chapter test.

Skills

Solve each equation. Irrational solutions may be left in simplified radical form. *(Section 13–1)*

1. $y^2 = 81$ $y = -9$ or $y = 9$
2. $x^2 - 100 = 0$ $x = -10$ or $x = 10$
3. $2x^2 + 5 = 155$ $x = -5\sqrt{3}$ or $x = 5\sqrt{3}$
4. $(x - 3)^2 = 4$ $x = 1$ or $x = 5$
5. $2(x + 1)^2 = 18$ $x = -4$ or $x = 2$
6. $7(y - 4)^2 = 343$ $y = -3$ or $y = 11$

Solve by completing the square. Irrational solutions may be left in radical form. *(Section 13–2)*

7. $x^2 - 4x = 0$ $x = 0$ or $x = 4$
8. $x^2 - 6x = 0$ $x = 0$ or $x = 6$
9. $x^2 + 2x - 4 = 0$ $x = -1 - \sqrt{5}$ or $x = -1 + \sqrt{5}$
10. $x^2 - 8x = 9$ $x = -1$ or $x = 9$
11. $x^2 = 5x$ $x = 0$ or $x = 5$
12. $y^2 = 4y + 2$ $y = 2 - \sqrt{6}$ or $y = 2 + \sqrt{6}$

Use the quadratic formula to solve each equation. Irrational solutions may be left in radical form. *(Section 13–3)*

13. $x^2 - 3x = 40$ $x = -5$ or $x = 8$
14. $y^2 + 64 = 16y$ $y = 8$
15. $2a^2 - a = 3$ $a = -1$ or $a = 1\frac{1}{2}$
16. $3r^2 + 2r = 4$
17. $4p^2 - 3p - 1 = 0$ $p = -\frac{1}{4}$ or $p = 1$
18. $2x^2 - 6x = 0$ $x = 0$ or $x = 3$

Graph each quadratic function. Determine the zeros of each function. *(Section 13–5)* See the Solution Key for the graphs.

19. $y = x^2 - 3x - 4$
20. $y = x^2 + 2x + 1$
21. $y = x^2 - 36$
22. $y = x^2 - 3x$
23. $y = x^2 - 4x + 4$
24. $y = -x^2 - 5x + 6$

Without solving, give the nature of the solutions of each equation. *(Section 13–6)*

25. $x^2 + 2x - 48 = 0$
26. $x^2 + 18x + 81 = 0$
27. $x^2 + 3x + 4 = 0$
28. $x^2 = 8x + 20$
29. $x^2 + 5 = x$
30. $x^2 + 15x + 36 = 0$

Applications

Solve each problem. *(Section 13–4)*

31. In a theater, the number of seats in each row is 2 more than the number of rows. The theater seats 624 people. How many seats are there in each row?

32. A driveway is 10 meters longer than it is wide. Its area is 35 square meters. Find its length and width to the nearest tenth of a meter.

33. The combined areas of two square flower gardens is 65 square meters. Each side of the larger garden is 3 feet longer than a side of the smaller garden. Find the length of a side of each garden.

34. A small city lot is in the shape of a right triangle. The hypotenuse is 40 meters longer than one leg and 5 meters longer than the other leg. Find the length of each side of the lot.

Quadratic Functions and Equations   **499**

Additional Answers

16. $r = \dfrac{-1 - \sqrt{13}}{3}$ or $r = \dfrac{-1 + \sqrt{13}}{3}$

19. Parabola opens upward; vertex: $(1\frac{1}{2}, -6\frac{1}{4})$; y intercept: $(0, -4)$; zeros: -1, 4

20. Parabola opens upward; vertex: $(-1, 0)$; y intercept: $(0, 1)$; zero: -1

21. Parabola opens upward; vertex: $(0, -36)$; y intercept: $(0, -36)$; zeros: -6, 6

22. Parabola opens upward; vertex: $(1\frac{1}{2}, -2\frac{1}{4})$; y intercept: $(0, 0)$; zeros: 0, 3

23. Parabola opens upward; vertex: $(2, 0)$; y intercept: $(0, 4)$; zero: 2

24. Parabola opens downward; vertex: $(2\frac{1}{2}, \frac{1}{4})$; y intercept: $(0, -6)$; zeros: 2, 3

25. two distinct, real solutions
26. one distinct, real solution
27. no real solution
28. two distinct, real solutions
29. no real solutions
30. two distinct, real solutions
31. 26 seats
32. length: 12.7m; width: 2.7m
33. smaller garden: 4ft; larger garden: 7ft
34. hypotenuse: 65m; legs: 25m, 60m

Review of Word Problems: Chapters 1–13

1. José is saving money in order to buy a lawn mower. He has already saved $138 which is 60% of the price of the mower. What is the price of the mower? *(Section 3–7)* $230

2. In triangle ABC, the measure of angle A is three times that of angle B. The measure of angle C is 12° greater than that of angle A. Find the measure of each of the three angles. *(Section 4–4)* A: 72°; B: 24°; C: 84°

3. Jeff's earnings vary directly with the number of hours that he works. One week he earned $110.50 for 26 hours of work. How much did he earn in a week during which he worked 32 hours? *(Section 5–10)* $136

4. The length of a rectangle is 18 centimeters more than its width. The perimeter is 128 centimeters. What are its length and width? *(Section 6–4)* length: 41 cm; width: 23 cm

5. The sum of an integer and three times its square is 114. Find the integer. *(Section 9–9)* 6

6. Table tennis is played on a rectangular table top with an area of 45 square feet and a perimeter of 28 feet. What are the length and width of the table top? *(Section 9–9)* length: 9 ft; width: 5 ft

7. A house painter and his assistant agree to share the money earned on a job in the ratio 4:3. If they are paid $1288 for the job, how much money will each receive? *(Section 10–1)* painter: $736; assistant: $552

8. A boat can travel at a rate of 40 kilometers per hour in still water. It takes $1\frac{1}{2}$ times as long for the boat to travel 80 kilometers upstream as to travel the same distance downstream. Find the rate of the current. *(Section 11–3)*

9. Linda drove 73 kilometers in the same time that Bob drove 68 kilometers. Linda's average rate was 5 kilometers per hour greater than Bob's. Find the average rate for each person. *(Section 11–5)* Linda: 73 km/h; Bob: 68 km/h

10. The area of a square sign is 6 square meters. What is the length of a side of the sign, to the nearest tenth of a meter? *(Section 12–2)* 2.4 m

11. A 17–meter wire stretches from the top of a vertical pole to a hook in the ground 8 meters from the base of the pole. Find the height of the pole. *(Section 12–4)* 15 m

12. Twice the square root of a number, plus 8, is 14. Find the number. *(Section 12–9)* 9

13. A rectangular garden is 6 meters long and 4 meters wide. It is surrounded by a walk of uniform width. If the area of the walk is 39 square meters, how wide is the walk? *(Section 13–4)* $1\frac{1}{2}$ m

14. The hypotenuse of a right triangle is 4 centimeters longer than one leg and 8 centimeters longer than the other leg. How long is the hypotenuse? *(Section 13–4)* 20 cm

15. There are two numbers such that one is 6 less than twice the other. The difference of the squares of the two numbers is 1311. What are the two numbers? *(Section 13–4)* 25 and 44, or −40 and −17

Cumulative Review: Chapters 1–13

The Test Booklet contains another form of the cumulative review.

Choose the best answer. Choose a, b, c, or d.

1. Find A in $A = P(1 + 0.09t)$ when $P = \$800$ and $t = 3.5$ years. b
   - **a.** $1000
   - **b.** $1052
   - **c.** $600
   - **d.** $3052

2. Which statement is true? c
   - **a.** $Q \subset N$
   - **b.** $Ir \subset Q$
   - **c.** $N \subset W$
   - **d.** $R \subset Ir$

3. Solve: $-a = 12$ c
   - **a.** $\{0\}$
   - **b.** $\{12\}$
   - **c.** $\{-12\}$
   - **d.** $\{4\}$

4. Which number is rational? b
   - **a.** $\sqrt{2}$
   - **b.** $\sqrt{9}$
   - **c.** π
   - **d.** $\sqrt{28}$

5. Simplify: $2[4 + 6(2 - 7)]$ a
   - **a.** -52
   - **b.** 52
   - **c.** -63
   - **d.** 63

6. Evaluate $3b - 5c + 6$ when $b = 3.2$ and $c = 2$. d
   - **a.** -5.6
   - **b.** 4
   - **c.** -6.4
   - **d.** 5.6

7. Simplify: $3.4a + 2b - 6a + 5b$ b
   - **a.** $4.4ab$
   - **b.** $-2.6a + 7b$
   - **c.** $-2.6a^2 + 7b^2$
   - **d.** $2.6a - 7b$

8. Solve: $4b - 6 = 22$ d
   - **a.** $\{4\}$
   - **b.** $\{6\frac{1}{2}\}$
   - **c.** $\{-7\}$
   - **d.** $\{7\}$

9. At an average speed of 80 kilometers per hour, how many hours will it take to travel 680 kilometers? b
   - **a.** 8
   - **b.** $8\frac{1}{2}$
   - **c.** $\frac{2}{17}$
   - **d.** 7

10. The length of a rectangle is 4 times its width. If the perimeter of the rectangle is 100 centimeters, how many centimeters are in the length? c
    - **a.** 10
    - **b.** 50
    - **c.** 40
    - **d.** 30

11. Solve: $-2(3x + 6) = -8x - 6$ d
    - **a.** $\{0\}$
    - **b.** $\{-3\}$
    - **c.** $\{6\}$
    - **d.** $\{3\}$

12. Solve: $n - 8 < -18$ a
    - **a.** $n < -10$
    - **b.** $n < -26$
    - **c.** $n > -10$
    - **d.** $n > -26$

13. Solve: $-3x + 7 > 2x + 32$ b
    - **a.** $x < 5$
    - **b.** $x < -5$
    - **c.** $x > 5$
    - **d.** $x > -5$

14. Solve for w: $P = 2(l + w)$ d
    - **a.** $w = P - l$
    - **b.** $w = 2P - l$
    - **c.** $w = l - P$
    - **d.** $w = \frac{P}{2} - l$

15. What is the slope of the line containing the points $A(5, 6)$ and $B(-2, -3)$? b
    - **a.** $-\frac{9}{7}$
    - **b.** $\frac{9}{7}$
    - **c.** $\frac{7}{9}$
    - **d.** $-\frac{7}{9}$

16. What is the slope of the graph of $3x - y = 8$? a
    - **a.** 3
    - **b.** -3
    - **c.** 8
    - **d.** -8

Cumulative Review: Chapters 1–13   **501**

17. What is the y intercept of the graph of $2x + 3y = 7$? c

    a. 7   **b.** $\frac{3}{7}$ **c.** $\frac{7}{3}$ **d.** -7

18. If y varies directly as x, and $y = 14$ when $x = 4$, find y when $x = 6$. d

    a. 7   **b.** 12   **c.** 8   **d.** 21

19. Solve this system: $\begin{cases} x + y = 8 \\ x - y = 28 \end{cases}$ b

    a. $(-10, 18)$ **b.** $(18, -10)$ **c.** $(18, 10)$ **d.** $(10, -18)$

20. Solve this system: $\begin{cases} 2x + 3y = 20 \\ 3x - 4y = -21 \end{cases}$ a

    a. $(1, 6)$ **b.** $(6, 1)$ **c.** $(-6, -1)$ **d.** $(-1, -6)$

21. The sum of two numbers is 28. Three times the smaller is 4 more than the larger. What are the numbers? c

    a. 10 and 18   **b.** 13 and 15   **c.** 20 and 8   **d.** 16 and 12

22. Louise has $0.85 in nickels and dimes. She has 5 more nickels than dimes. How many nickels does she have? b

    a. 4   **b.** 9   **c.** 10   **d.** 8

23. Almonds at $4.00 per pound are mixed with walnuts at $2.00 per pound to make a mixture worth $3.50 per pound. If there are 20 pounds of the mixture, how many pounds of almonds are there? b

    a. 10   **b.** 15   **c.** 5   **d.** 12

24. Which of the following is equivalent to $3n \geq 17$? b

    a. $3n > 17$ and $3n = 17$ **b.** $3n > 17$ or $3n = 17$

    c. $3n < 17$ or $3n = 17$ **d.** $3n < 17$ and $3n = 17$

25. Solve: $|3(x + 2) - 9| = 6$ d

    a. $\{3\}$ **b.** $\{-1\}$ **c.** $\{-3, 1\}$ **d.** $\{3, -1\}$

26. What is the maximum value of $2x - y$ in the system $\begin{cases} x \geq 0 \\ y \geq 0 \\ x + y \leq 6 \end{cases}$ c

    a. 3   **b.** -6 **c.** 12   **d.** -12

27. Simplify: $\dfrac{(9a^2b^3)(8a^3b^4)}{(6ab^2)^2}$ c

    a. $4ab^3$ **b.** a^2b^2 **c.** $2a^3b^3$ **d.** $(2ab)^3$

28. Write in scientific notation: 0.000046 b

    a. 4.6×10^5 **b.** 4.6×10^{-5} **c.** 4.6×10^3 **d.** 4.6×10^6

29. Subtract: $(3xy + 7xy^2 - 4) - (9xy^2 - 4xy + 8)$ d

    a. $-7xy + 2xy^2 - 12$ **b.** $xy - 2xy^2 + 12$ **c.** $-xy - 2xy^2 + 12$ **d.** $7xy - 2xy^2 - 12$

30. Subtract: $6 - 8(3b + 6)$ a

    a. $-24b - 42$ **b.** $24b + 12$ **c.** $24b$ **d.** $-24b - 48$

31. What does $(a + 2b)^2$ equal? b

    a. $a^2 - 4ab + 4b^2$ **b.** $a^2 + 4ab + 4b^2$ **c.** $a^2 + 4b^2$ **d.** $a^2 - 4b^2$

32. Multiply: $(2x - 4y)(2x + 4y)$ **a**

    a. $4x^2 - 16y^2$ **b.** $4x^2 + 8xy + 16y^2$ **c.** $4x^2 + 16y^2$ **d.** $2x^2 - 4y^2$

33. Multiply: $(3c - 2d)(4c + 3d)$ **a**

    a. $12c^2 + cd - 6d^2$ **b.** $12c^2 - cd - 6d^2$ **c.** $12c^2 - 17cd + 6d^2$ **d.** $12c^2 + cd + 6d^2$

34. Write the prime factorization of 75. **c**

    a. $3 \cdot 5$ **b.** $3^2 \cdot 5^2$ **c.** $3 \cdot 5^2$ **d.** $3^2 \cdot 5$

35. Which of the following is a perfect square trinomial? **a**

    a. $x^2 + 6x + 9$ **b.** $2x^2 + 6x + 9$ **c.** $4x^2 - 8x - 25$ **d.** $x^2 - 9x + 16$

36. Solve: $2x^2 = 50x$ **b**

    a. $\{0\}$ **b.** $\{0.25\}$ **c.** $\{25\}$ **d.** $\{0, -25\}$

37. Solve: $3x^2 = 13x + 10$ **b**

    a. $\{-\frac{2}{3}, -5\}$ **b.** $\{-\frac{2}{3}, 5\}$ **c.** $\{0, -5\}$ **d.** $\{-\frac{2}{3}, 0\}$

38. Solve: $\dfrac{a+7}{3} = \dfrac{a+8}{4}$ **d**

    a. $a = 8$ **b.** $a = 4$ **c.** $a = 16$ **d.** $a = -4$

39. Divide and simplify: $\dfrac{x^2 - 1}{x^2 + 3x + 2} \div \dfrac{x^2 + 4x - 5}{x^2 - 4}$ **a**

    a. $\dfrac{x - 2}{x + 5}$ **b.** $\dfrac{x + 5}{x - 2}$ **c.** $\dfrac{x - 1}{x + 5}$ **d.** $\dfrac{x + 2}{x + 1}$

40. Simplify: $\sqrt{x^2 y^6}$ **a**

    a. xy^3 **b.** $\pm xy^3$ **c.** xy^4 **d.** $\pm xy^4$

41. What is the greatest integer for x that will make $x < \sqrt{125}$ a true statement? **b**

    a. 10   **b.** 11   **c.** 12   **d.** 124

42. Simplify: $\sqrt{80}$ **d**

    a. 20   **b.** $4\sqrt{20}$ **c.** $2\sqrt{20}$ **d.** $4\sqrt{5}$

43. Multiply and simplify: $-2\sqrt{10} \cdot 3\sqrt{6}$ **c**

    a. $-8\sqrt{15}$ **b.** $-5\sqrt{60}$ **c.** $-12\sqrt{15}$ **d.** $-6\sqrt{60}$

44. Which of the following is *not* equivalent to the other three? **c**

    a. $\dfrac{1}{\sqrt{6}}$ **b.** $\sqrt{\dfrac{2}{12}}$ **c.** $\dfrac{\sqrt{6}}{1}$ **d.** $\dfrac{\sqrt{6}}{6}$

45. Simplify: $2\sqrt{8} - 5\sqrt{2} + 4$ **a**

    a. $-\sqrt{2} + 4$ **b.** $3\sqrt{2}$ **c.** $-3\sqrt{6} + 4$ **d.** $6\sqrt{8} - 5\sqrt{2}$

46. The lengths of the sides of a rectangle are 5 centimeters and 12 centimeters. What is the length of the diagonal? **b**

    a. 17 cm   **b.** 13 cm   **c.** 34 cm   **d.** 60 cm

47. Solve: $4\sqrt{3y - 2} - 1 = 19$ **a**

    a. $\{9\}$ **b.** $\{\pm 9\}$ **c.** $\{34\}$ **d.** $\{9, 34\}$

48. Simplify: $(-8)^{\frac{1}{3}}$ **c**

    a. $-2\frac{2}{3}$ **b.** 2   **c.** -2 **d.** ± 2

49. A square has each of its vertices on the x or the y axes. One vertex is at $(0, 5)$. How long is each side of the square? **a**

  a. 5   **b.** $2\sqrt{5}$ **c.** 10   **d.** $\sqrt{5}$

50. Solve: $9x^2 = x$ **d**

  a. $\{0\}$ **b.** $\{\frac{1}{9}\}$ **c.** $\{\pm 3\}$ **d.** $\{0, \frac{1}{9}\}$

51. For which equation is $\{8, -2\}$ *not* the solution set?   **b**

  a. $(x - 3)^2 = 25$ **b.** $(x - 8)(x + 1) = 0$

  c. $x^2 - 6x = 16$ **d.** $x^2 - 6x - 16 = 0$

52. What must be added to each side of $x^2 + 8x = 7$ to make the left side a perfect square?   **a**

  a. 16   **b.** 4   **c.** $4x$ **d.** 23

53. Which equation has $\left\{\dfrac{-5 \pm \sqrt{17}}{4}\right\}$ as its solution set?   **b**

  a. $2x^2 - 5x + 1 = 0$ **b.** $2x^2 + 5x + 1 = 0$

  c. $2x^2 + 5x - 1 = 0$ **d.** $x^2 + 5x + 1 = 0$

54. When is the solution of $ax^2 + bx + c = 0$ two different real numbers?   **d**

  a. When $b - 4ac > 0$ **b.** When $b^2 - 4ac = 0$

  c. When $b^2 - 4ac < 0$ **d.** When $b^2 - 4ac > 0$

55. A quadratic function crosses the x axis at $(3, 0)$ and $(-4, 0)$. What are the zeros of the function?   **c**

  a. 0, 3   **b.** 0, 4   **c.** 3, -4 **d.** 3, 5

56. When is the graph of $y = ax^2 + bx + c$ tangent to the x axis?   **a**

  a. When $b^2 - 4ac = 0$ **b.** When $b^2 - 4ac$ is positive

  c. When $-b \pm \sqrt{b^2 - 4ac} = 0$ **d.** When $b = \sqrt{b^2 - 4ac}$

57. The width of a rectangle is 5 centimeters less than the length. The area is 104 square centimeters. What is the length of the rectangle?   **d**

  a. 8 cm   **b.** 28.5 cm   **c.** 23.5 cm   **d.** 13 cm

58. The vertex of the graph of $y = 3x^2 - 5x + 8$ occurs at what value of x?   **d**

  a. $x = 5$ **b.** $x = -\frac{5}{6}$ **c.** $x = -5$ **d.** $x = \frac{5}{6}$

59. Find the minimum value of y in $y = x^2 + 6x + 5$.   **b**

  a. 5   **b.** -4 **c.** -6 **d.** $\frac{5}{6}$

60. The equation $x^2 = 49$ is equivalent to   **b**

  a. $x = 7$ and $x = -7$ **b.** $x = 7$ or $x = -7$

  c. $(x - 7)^2 = 0$ **d.** $x = \sqrt{49}$

61. The graph of which of the following has no points on the x axis?   **a**

  a. $y = 3x^2 + x + 1$ **b.** $y = 3x^2 + 3x$

  c. $y = 3x^2 - 4x + 1$ **d.** $y = 16x^2$

62. Find the equation for the axis of symmetry for $y = x^2 - 2x - 8$.   **c**

  a. $x = -1$ **b.** $x = 2$ **c.** $x = 1$ **d.** $x = -2$

504   *Cumulative Review: Chapters 1–13*

Preparing for College Entrance Tests

Instead of solving a given equation, it is sometimes easier to try each of the given "solutions" to see which one makes the equation true.

REMEMBER: Watch for clues that will enable you to eliminate one or more of the possibilities without extensive calculations.

EXAMPLE: Which of the following numbers is in the solution set for $3x^2 - 14x + 16 = 0$?

    (a) 4   (b) 2   (c) -4 (d) -8

Think: If $3x^2 - 14x + 16 = 0$, then $3x^2 = 14x - 16$.
But $3x^2$ is positive. Therefore, $14x - 16$ must be positive.
Thus, $14x - 16 > 0$, or $14x > 16$ and $x > 1$.
This eliminates choices (c) and (d). Test choices (a) and (b).

Solution: Test (a): $3(4)^2 - 14(4) + 16 = 8 \neq 0$ ⟵ 4 is not a solution.
Test (b): $3(2)^2 - 14(2) + 16 = 0$ ⟵ 2 is a solution. **Answer: b**

Choose the best answer. Choose a, b, c, or d.

1. Which of the following numbers is in the solution set for $x^2 + 13x + 12 = 0$? **b**
  (a) -4 (b) -1 (c) 1   (d) 6

2. Which of the following numbers is in the solution set for $x^2 - 14x + 24 = 0$? **c**
  (a) -12 (b) -2 (c) 2   (d) 8

3. Which of the following numbers is in the solution set for $2x^2 + 11x + 12 = 0$? **a**
  (a) -4 (b) -1 (c) 2   (d) 4

4. Which of the following numbers is in the solution set for $3x^2 + 4x - 4 = 0$? **b**
  (a) -4 (b) -2 (c) $\frac{1}{3}$ (d) 4

5. Which of the following numbers is in the solution set for $x^2 + 16x - 36 = 0$? **a**
  (a) -18 (b) -1 (c) 4   (d) 6

6. Which of the following numbers is in the solution set for $6x^2 - 23x - 4 = 0$? **d**
  (a) -4 (b) -1 (c) $\frac{1}{2}$ (d) 4

7. If $\dfrac{1}{2+\frac{1+x}{2}} = \frac{1}{2}$, what is the value of x? (HINT: $\frac{1+x}{2}$ must equal 0.) **b**
  (a) -2 (b) -1 (c) 0   (d) 1

8. If $\dfrac{2}{3+\frac{2+x}{3}} = \frac{2}{3}$, what is the value of x? **a**
  (a) -2 (b) -1 (c) 0   (d) 1

Preparing for College Entrance Tests

Some items on College Entrance tests are designed so that one or more of several given statements are correct, or no statement is correct. In such cases, you must examine each of the possibilities before deciding on the answer.

EXAMPLE: If n is a rational number, which of the following must be rational numbers?

$$\text{I. } \sqrt{n} \qquad \text{II. } n^2 \qquad \text{III. } \sqrt{n^2}$$

(a) II only   (b) I and II only

(c) II and III only   (d) I, II, and III

Solution: I is not always true. (For example, $\sqrt{2}$ is not rational.)
II is true, since n^2 means $n \cdot n$, and the product of two rational numbers is rational.
III is true, since $\sqrt{n^2} = |n|$, which is rational when n is rational.
Answer: c

Choose the best answer. Choose a, b, c, or d.

1. If x is an integer greater than 1, which of the following statements are true? **a**

   $\text{I. } \sqrt{x} < x$ $\text{II. } \sqrt{x} < x^2$ $\text{III. } \dfrac{1}{x} < \sqrt{x}$

   (a) I and II only   (b) I and III only   (c) II and III only   (d) I, II, and III

2. If y is an integer less than 0, which of the following statements are true? **a**

   $\text{I. } \sqrt[3]{y} < 0$ $\text{II. } \sqrt{1-y} < 0$ $\text{III. } \sqrt{1+y^2} < 0$

   (a) I only   (b) II only   (c) I and III only   (d) None of these

3. If $\sqrt{p}$ is a rational number, which of the following must be rational numbers? **d**

   $\text{I. } \sqrt{p+1}$ $\text{II. } \sqrt{p+4}$ $\text{III. } \sqrt{p+9}$

   (a) II only   (b) III only   (c) I and II only   (d) None of these

4. If k is an integer, which of the following must be integers? **b**

   $\text{I. } \dfrac{k}{2}$ $\text{II. } k-2$ $\text{III. } \sqrt{k}$

   (a) I only   (b) II only   (c) I and II only   (d) II and III only

5. If x is a nonzero real number, which of the following statements must be true? **d**

   $\text{I. } \left(\dfrac{x}{x}\right)^x = 1$ $\text{II. } x^{\frac{x}{x}} = 1$ $\text{III. } x^{x-x} = 1$

   (a) I only   (b) II only   (c) I and II only   (d) I and III only

6. Which of the following statements are true? **c**

   $\text{I. } \sqrt{9 \cdot 16} > \sqrt{9} \cdot \sqrt{16}$ $\text{II. } \sqrt{9} \cdot \sqrt{16} > \sqrt{9} + \sqrt{16}$ $\text{III. } \sqrt{9} + \sqrt{16} > \sqrt{9+16}$

   (a) II only   (b) I and III only   (c) II and III only   (d) I, II, and III

OBJECTIVE: To use algebra to find the complement and supplement of an angle

14–1 Angles and Algebra

The following table shows some basic geometric figures that you will study when you take a course in geometry.

Geometric Figure	Name	Description
G •———————• K	Segment *GK*: $\overline{GK}$ or Segment *KG*: $\overline{KG}$	Consists of two **endpoints,** *G* and *K*, and all the points between them.
(ray A to B)	Ray *AB*: $\overrightarrow{AB}$	Extends without end in one direction from its one endpoint, *A*.
(line R–S)	Line *RS*: $\overleftrightarrow{RS}$	Extends without end in two opposite directions.
(angle with vertex X, rays to W and Y)	Angle *WXY*: $\angle WXY$ or Angle *YXW*: $\angle YXW$	Two different rays that have the same endpoint. $\overrightarrow{XW}$ and $\overrightarrow{XY}$ are the **sides** of the angle. The common endpoint, *X*, is the **vertex.**

Angles can be classified according to their measures. The unit of measure is the **degree,** °. The degree measure of $\angle ABC$ is 1° or m $\angle ABC = 1°$.

Geometric Figure	Name	Description
(right angle)	**Right angle**	An angle whose measure is 90°. NOTE: Two lines, rays, or segments that form a right angle are **perpendicular** to each other.
(acute angle)	**Acute angle**	An angle whose measure is less than 90°.
(obtuse angle)	**Obtuse angle**	An angle whose measure is greater than 90° and less than 180°.

Angle pairs that occur often in geometry have special names.

Model	Name	Description
(20° angle A; B 70° angle)	**Complementary angles**	Two angles whose measures have a sum of 90°. Each angle is a **complement** of the other.
(P 50° angle; 130° angle Q)	**Supplementary angles**	Two angles whose measures have a sum of 180°. Each angle is a **supplement** of the other.

508 *Chapter 14*

Algebra plays an important part in geometry, as the Example shows.

EXAMPLE The measure of an angle is 20° less than its supplement.

a. Find the measures of the angle and its supplement.

b. Find the measure of its complement.

Solutions: a. Let x = the measure of the angle.
Let y = the measure of its supplement.
Then $x = y - 20$.

$x + y = 180$ ◄————— **Definition of supplementary angles**

$y - 20 + y = 180$ ◄————— **Replace x with $y - 20$.**

$2y = 200$

$y = 100$ ◄————— **The measure of the supplement is 100°.**

$y - 20 = 100 - 20$

$y - 20 = 80$ ◄————— **The measure of the angle is 80°.**

b. The measure of the complement is $(90° - 80°) = 10°$.

WORD PROBLEMS

A Solve. angle: 60°; complement: 30°

1. The measure of an angle is 30° more than its complement. Find the measures of the angle and its complement.

2. The measure of an angle is 50° less than its supplement. Find the measures of the angle and its supplement. angle: 65°; supplement: 115°

3. Find the measure of the supplement of the angle in Exercise 1. 120°

4. Find the measure of the complement of the angle in Exercise 2. 25°

5. The measure of an angle is the same as its complement. Find the measure of the angle. 45°

6. The measure of an angle is $\frac{2}{3}$ the measure of its supplement. Find the measure of the angle. 72°

7. Find the measure of the supplement of the angle in Exercise 5. 135°

8. Find the measure of the complement of the angle in Exercise 6. 18°

9. The measure of an angle is twice that of its supplement. Find the measures of the angle and its supplement.
angle: 120°; supplement: 60°

10. The measure of an angle is $\frac{3}{4}$ the measure of its complement. Find the measures of the angle and its complement.
angle: $38\frac{4}{7}°$; complement: $51\frac{3}{7}°$

B Choose one of the given measures to complete each statement.

11. Angles A and B are supplementary. If m$\angle A = x$, then m$\angle B = $ __?__ . $180 - x$
$(90 - x, 90 + x, 180 - x, 180 + x)$

12. Angles C and D are complementary. If m$\angle C = y - 10$, then m$\angle D = $ __?__ . $100 - y$
$(80 - y, 100 - y, y + 80, y + 100)$

13. Angle A is supplementary to angle B, and angle B is supplementary to angle C. If m$\angle A = x$, then m$\angle C = $ __?__ .
$(90, x, 180 + x, 180 - x)$ x

14. Angle F is supplementary to angle G, and angle G is complementary to angle H. If m$\angle F = x$, then m$\angle H = $ __?__ .
$(x - 90, x, 2x, 180 - x)$ $x - 90$

Other Applications of Algebra **509**

14–2 Triangles and Algebra

OBJECTIVE: To find the measures of the angles of a triangle, given a relationship between the measures of the angles

The study of triangles is an important part of geometry. You use the following theorem and your knowledge of algebra (solving equations) to find the measures of angles in triangles.

Theorem 14–1

> **Triangle – Sum Theorem**
>
> The sum of the measures of the angles of a triangle is 180°.

The symbol "m $\angle A$" represents the "measure of angle A." In the following Example, you use Theorem 14–1 to write an equation for the problem.

EXAMPLE 1 In Triangle RST, the measure of $\angle S$ is three times the measure of $\angle R$, and $\angle T$ is 40° more than the measure of $\angle R$. Find the measure of each angle.

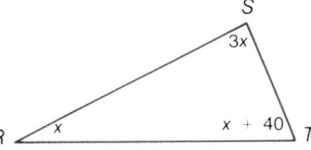

Solution:
$\boxed{1}$ Let x = the measure of $\angle R$.
Then $3x$ = the measure of $\angle S$, and $x + 40$ = the measure of $\angle T$. ⟵ **Condition 1**

$\boxed{2}$ $x + 3x + x + 40 = 180$ ⟵ **Use Theorem 14–1 (Condition 2) to write an equation.**

$$5x = 140$$
$$x = 28$$
$$3x = 84$$
$$x + 40 = 68$$

Thus, **m $\angle R$ = 28°, m $\angle S$ = 84°, and m $\angle T$ = 68°.**

You have used the Pythagorean Theorem (page 439) to find the length of an unknown side of a right triangle. By applying the following definition, you can use the Pythagorean Theorem to find the length of an unknown side in an **isosceles triangle** (a triangle with two sides of equal measure). The third side is called the **base**.

Definition

> An **altitude of a triangle** is a segment drawn from any vertex perpendicular to the opposite side.

In an isosceles triangle the angle opposite the base is the **vertex angle**.

EXAMPLE 2 In an isosceles triangle, the altitude (height) drawn from the vertex angle to the base bisects the base. Find the height, BD, of $\triangle ABC$. Write the answer in simplest radical form.

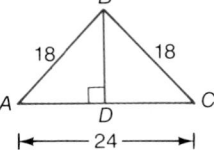

Solution: Use the Pythagorean Theorem.

$$AD^2 + BD^2 = AB^2 \longleftarrow \textbf{Pythagorean Theorem}$$

$$\left(\tfrac{1}{2}AC\right)^2 + BD^2 = 18^2$$

$$12^2 + BD^2 = 18^2$$

$$BD^2 = 180$$

$$BD = \sqrt{180}$$

$$BD = \sqrt{36 \cdot 5} = 6\sqrt{5}$$

Additional Examples
Example 2
1. Each of the equal sides of an isosceles triangle is 20 meters long and the base is 28 meters long. Find the length of the altitude to the base. Write the answer in simplest radical form.
Ans: $2\sqrt{51}$ m
2. Each of the equal sides of an isosceles triangle is 28 feet long and the base is 32 feet long. Find the length of the altitude to the base. Write the answer in simplest radical form.
Ans: $4\sqrt{33}$ ft

CLASSROOM EXERCISES

In Exercises 1–4, measures of angles in $\triangle ABC$ are given. Find the measure of $\angle C$.

1. $m\angle A = 60°$, $m\angle B = 70°$ $50°$

2. $m\angle A = 120°$, $m\angle B = 34°$ $26°$

3. $m\angle B = 60°$, $m\angle C = 60°$ $60°$

4. $m\angle B = 90°$, $m\angle A = 25°$ $65°$

Use the Pythagorean Theorem to replace each __?__ with the correct length. Refer to the figure. Write answers in simplest form.

5. $a = 1$, $b = 1$, $c = $ __?__ $\sqrt{2}$

6. $a = 1$, $c = 2$, $b = $ __?__ $\sqrt{3}$

7. $b = 3$, $c = 5$, $a = $ __?__ 4

8. $b = 2$, $a = 2$, $c = $ __?__ $2\sqrt{2}$

9. $b = 2$, $c = 4$, $a = $ __?__ $2\sqrt{3}$

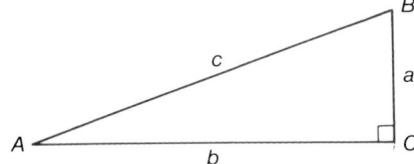

WORD PROBLEMS

A $\angle G: 100°; \angle H: 40°; \angle K: 40°$

1. In triangle KGH, the measure of $\angle K$ is the same as the measure of $\angle H$. The measure of $\angle G$ is $2\tfrac{1}{2}$ times the measure of $\angle K$. Find the measure of each angle.

$\angle X: 41°; \angle Y: 57°; \angle Z: 82°$

2. In triangle XYZ, the measure of $\angle Y$ is $25°$ less than the measure of $\angle Z$. The measure of $\angle X$ is $\tfrac{1}{2}$ the measure of $\angle Z$. Find the measure of each angle.

3. In triangle ABC, the measure of $\angle A$ is $\tfrac{2}{3}$ the measure of $\angle C$. The measure of $\angle B$ is $5°$ more than the measure of $\angle A$. Find the measure of each angle.
$\angle A: 50°; \angle B: 55°; \angle C: 75°$

4. In triangle PQR, the measure of $\angle P$ is $\tfrac{1}{3}$ the measure of $\angle Q$. The measure of $\angle R$ is $9°$ less than the measure of $\angle Q$. Find the measure of each angle.
$\angle P: 27°; \angle Q: 81°; \angle R: 72°$

Other Applications of Algebra   **511**

Assignment Guide
Minimal Omit
Average Omit
Above Average
pp. 511–512: 1–10 even, 11–14

5. The figure at the right shows a ferry traveling between points A, B, and C. The measure of $\angle A$ is 10° more than 4 times the measure of $\angle C$. The measure of $\angle B$ is 10° more than 5 times the measure of $\angle C$. Find the measure of each angle.

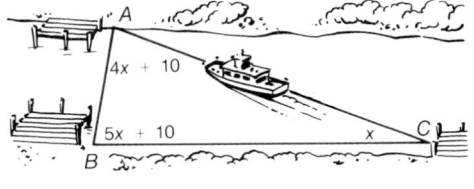

6. The flight path of an airplane around a storm is shown at the right. The measure of $\angle Q$ is 2° less than 6 times the measure of $\angle P$. The measure of $\angle R$ is $1\frac{2}{3}$ times the measure of $\angle P$. Find the measure of each angle.

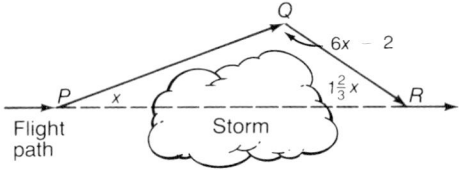

7. A telephone pole is supported by two guy wires that form an isosceles triangle with the ground. Each guy wire is 6 meters long, and the two wires are anchored 4 meters apart. Find the height of the pole. $4\sqrt{2}$ m

8. The two sides of a tent are each 2 meters long. If the tent is pitched so that the sides meet in a right angle at the top, find w, the width of the tent, and p, the height of the center pole.

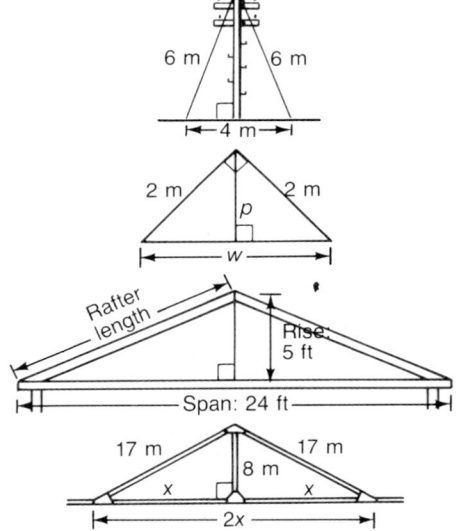

9. The **span** of a roof (see the figure at the right) is 24 feet long and the **rise** is 5 feet long. Find the length of each rafter. 13 ft

10. A truss for a footbridge has equal sides 17 meters long, and a vertical tie rod 8 meters long, as shown at the right. Find the length of the footbridge. 30 m

B

11. The length of a side of an equilateral A-frame house is 30 feet. Find the height of the house. $15\sqrt{3}$ ft

12. Compute the length of the altitude to the shortest side of a triangle whose sides are 17, 25, and 26 centimeters long. 24 cm

13. Compute the length of the altitude to the longest side of a triangle whose sides are 10, 6, and 12 decimeters long.

14. Write a formula that can be used to find the altitude of an equilateral triangle with side s. Use the figure at the right to solve for h in terms of s.

OBJECTIVE: To find the unknown lengths in similar triangles

14-3 Similar Triangles and Algebra

Your knowledge of ratio and proportion will be useful in geometry in solving problems that deal with <u>similar triangles</u>. **Similar triangles** have the same shape; that is, corresponding angles have equal measures. In similar triangles, corresponding sides are opposite <u>congruent angles</u>. **Congruent angles** are angles that have the same measure.

Similar Triangles	Corresponding Angles	Corresponding Sides
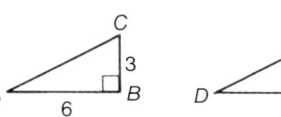	$\angle A$ and $\angle D$	$\overline{AB}$ and $\overline{DE}$
	$\angle B$ and $\angle E$	$\overline{BC}$ and $\overline{EF}$
	$\angle C$ and $\angle F$	$\overline{AC}$ and $\overline{DF}$
	$\angle K$ and $\angle X$	$\overline{KL}$ and $\overline{XZ}$
	$\angle L$ and $\angle Z$	$\overline{LM}$ and $\overline{YZ}$
	$\angle M$ and $\angle Y$	$\overline{KM}$ and $\overline{XY}$

EXAMPLE 1   **a.** Find the ratio of each pair of corresponding sides in these similar right triangles.

   b. Compare the ratios.

Solutions: **a.** $\dfrac{AB}{DE} = \dfrac{6}{8} = \dfrac{3}{4};$ $\dfrac{BC}{EF} = \dfrac{3}{4}$

$AC^2 = 6^2 + 3^2$ $DF^2 = 8^2 + 4^2$

$AC^2 = 36 + 9$ $DF^2 = 64 + 16$

$AC = \sqrt{45}$ $DF = \sqrt{80}$

$AC = \sqrt{9 \cdot 5} = 3\sqrt{5}$ $DF = \sqrt{16 \cdot 5} = 4\sqrt{5}$

$\dfrac{AC}{DF} = \dfrac{3\sqrt{5}}{4\sqrt{5}} = \dfrac{3}{4}$

   b. Each of the three ratios equals $\dfrac{3}{4}$.

This example suggests the following theorem.

Theorem 14-2   If two triangles are similar, then their corresponding sides are proportional.

Thus, when you know that two triangles are similar, you can write a proportion to find the length of an unknown side.

Other Applications of Algebra   **513**

 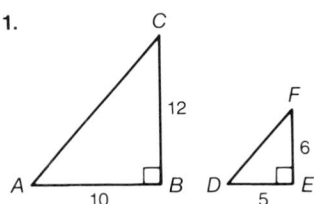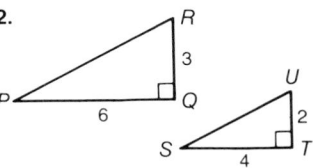

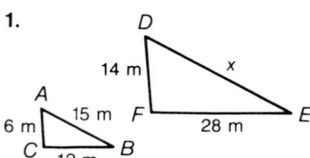
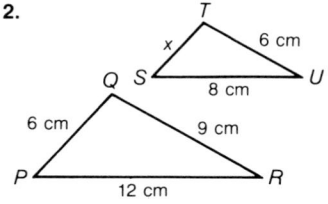
EXAMPLE 2   Find the unknown length in these similar triangles.

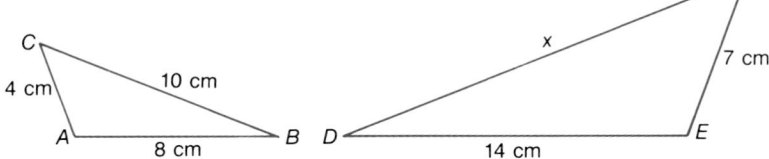

Solutions: [1] Write a ratio of an unknown side to the corresponding known side.

$$\frac{DF}{BC} = \frac{x}{10} \quad \longleftarrow \quad \frac{\triangle DEF}{\triangle ABC} \text{ is the } \underline{\text{order.}}$$

[2] Write a ratio of known corresponding sides in the same order as in step 1.

$$\frac{DE}{BA} = \frac{14}{8} = \frac{7}{4} \quad \longleftarrow \quad \frac{\triangle DEF}{\triangle ABC} \text{ is the same order, not } \frac{\triangle ABC}{\triangle DEF}.$$

[3] Use the two ratios to write a proportion and solve.

$$\frac{x}{10} = \frac{7}{4}$$
$$4x = 70$$
$$x = 17.5 \text{ cm}$$

CLASSROOM EXERCISES

In Exercises 1–4, each pair of triangles is similar. In Exercises 1–2, find the ratio comparing corresponding known sides of each pair.

1.

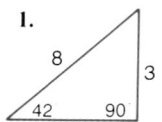

$\frac{8}{4}$

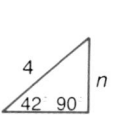

2.

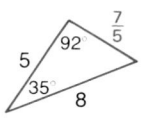

$\frac{7}{5}$

Write a proportion comparing corresponding sides of each pair.

3.

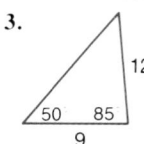

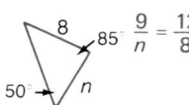
$\frac{9}{n} = \frac{12}{8}$

4.

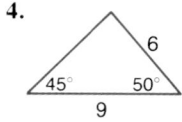

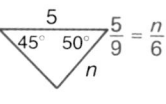
$\frac{5}{9} = \frac{n}{6}$

WRITTEN EXERCISES

A   In Exercises 1–2, each pair of triangles is similar. Find the unknown length.

1.

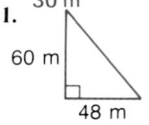

2.

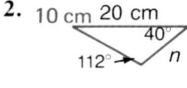

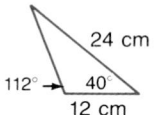

514   *Chapter 14*

APPLICATIONS: Using Similar Triangles

3. Norman is 1.8 meters tall. On a sunny day, Patty measured Norman's shadow and the shadow of the school. Use the similar triangles shown below to find the height of the school to the nearest tenth. **6.4 m**

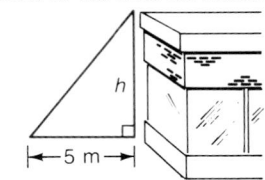

4. On the same sunny day, the shadow of a tree was 12 meters long. Use the similar triangles below to find the height of the tree to the nearest tenth. **15.4 m**

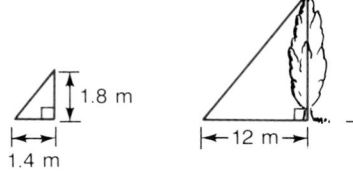

5. Jorge found the height of a street lamp by placing a mirror on the sidewalk. Then he walked backwards until he saw the top of the streetlight in the mirror. The figure below shows how he formed similar triangles. Find the height of the street lamp to the nearest tenth. **3.8 m**

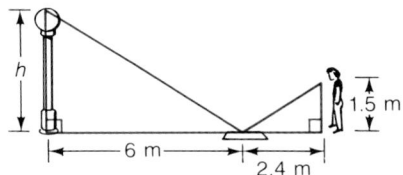

6. Find the distance across this lake to the nearest tenth of a meter. **100 m**

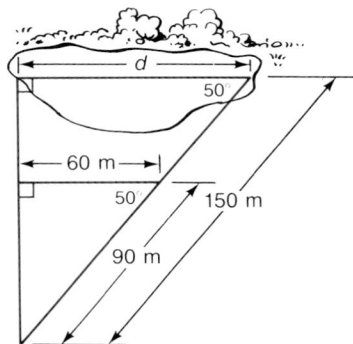

──── Review ────

Solve each problem.

1. The measure of an angle is 55° less than its complement. Find the measures of the angle, its supplement, and its complement. *(Section 14-1)*

2. The measure of an angle is $\frac{2}{5}$ the measure of its supplement. Find the measures of the angle, its supplement, and its complement. *(Section 14-1)*

3. In $\triangle ABC$, the measure of $\angle A$ is $\frac{1}{3}$ the measure of $\angle B$. The measure of $\angle C$ is 5° more than the measure of $\angle B$. Find the measures of the angles. *(Section 14-2)*

4. A road sign in the shape of an equilateral triangle is 60 centimeters long on each side. Find the height of the sign. Write your answer in simplest form. *(Section 14-2)* $30\sqrt{3}$ cm

Find the unknown length in each pair of similar triangles. *(Section 14-3)*

5. $6\frac{3}{4}$

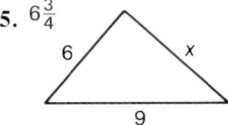
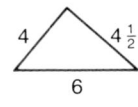

6. $6\frac{2}{3}$

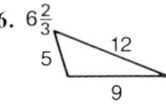
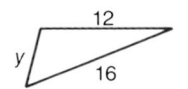

Other Applications of Algebra **515**

Quiz Sections 14-1–14-3
After completing this Review you may want to administer a quiz covering the same sections. See page M-56 of the Teacher's Manual for the suggested quiz.

Additional Answers
Review
1. angle: 17.5°;
   complement: 72.5°;
   supplement: 162.5
2. angle: $51\frac{3}{7}$°;
   complement: $38\frac{4}{7}$°;
   supplement: $128\frac{4}{7}$°
3. $\angle A$: 25°;
   $\angle B$: 75°;
   $\angle C$: 80°

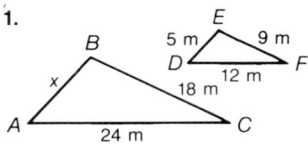
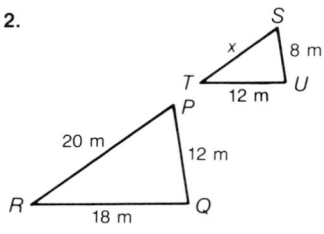
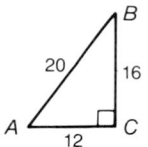
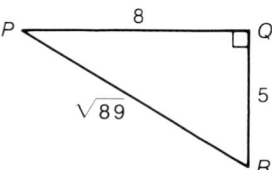
OBJECTIVE: To define and use the tangent ratio

14-4   The Tangent Ratio

These three right triangles are similar.

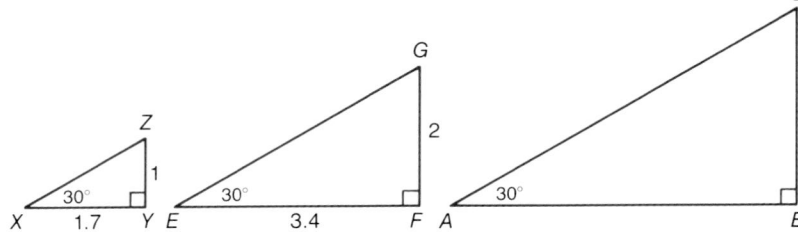

Since $\dfrac{YZ}{FG} = \dfrac{XY}{EF}$, the following proportion is true.

$$\frac{YZ}{XY} = \frac{FG}{EF}$$

Thus, for the above triangles,

$$\frac{1}{1.7} = \frac{2}{3.4} = \frac{BC}{AB}.$$

The ratio $\dfrac{BC}{AB}$ in *any* right triangle *ABC*, where $\angle B$ is a right angle, is the
tangent of angle C.

Definition

> In a right triangle, the **tangent of an acute angle** is the ratio
> $$\frac{\textbf{length of the leg opposite the angle}}{\textbf{length of the leg adjacent to the angle}}.$$

Tangent of angle *A* is abbreviated tan *A*.

EXAMPLE 1   Find each ratio. Write a decimal
for the ratio.

a. tan *A*   **b.** tan *B*

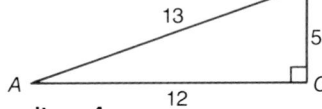

Solutions: **a.** $\tan A = \dfrac{BC}{AC}$ ⟵ *BC* is opposite $\angle$ *A.*
                                                        AC is adjacent to $\angle$ *A.*

$\tan A = \dfrac{5}{12}$

$\tan A = .4167$ ⟵ Rounded to 4 decimal places.

b. $\tan B = \dfrac{AC}{BC}$ ⟵ *AC* is opposite $\angle$ *B.*
                                    BC is adjacent to $\angle$ *B.*

$\tan B = \dfrac{12}{5}$

$\tan B = 2.4$

A ratio of the lengths of two sides of a right triangle is a **trigonometric ratio**. The study of trigonometry originated in connection with real-world measurement problems that involve right triangles.

A trigonometric ratio depends only on the measure of an acute angle, *not* on the size of the right triangle. The **Table of Sines, Cosines, and Tangents** on page 542 gives these values for acute angles.

Although most values are approximations for the ratios, the "=" symbol is used because it is more convenient. Thus, in Example 1, write tan A = .4167 instead of tan $A \approx$ .4167.

EXAMPLE 2 Find the tangent of 41°.

Solution: Find 41 in the **Angle**-column. Move directly right to the **Tangent**-column.

tan 41° = **.8693**

Angle	Sine	Cosine	Tangent
40°	.6428	.7660	.8391
41	.6561	.7547	.8693
42	.6691	.7431	.9004

Additional Examples
Example 2
Use the table on page 542 to find the tangent of each angle measure.
1. 33° **Ans: .6494**
2. 67° **Ans: 2.3559**

You use the tangent to find the measure of an angle.

EXAMPLE 3 What is the measure of the angle whose tangent is 1.1106?

Solution: Find 1.1106 in the **Tangent**-column. Move directly left to the **Angle**-column.

The measure of the angle whose tangent is 1.1106 is **48°**.

Angle	Sine	Cosine	Tangent
47°	.7314	.6820	1.0724
48	.7431	.6691	1.1106
49	.7547	.6561	1.1504

Example 3
Find the measure of the angle whose tangent is as indicated.
1. 3.0777 **Ans: 72°**
2. .8098 **Ans: 39°**

You also use the tangent to find the measure of a side.

EXAMPLE 4 A flagpole is side BC in triangle ABC pictured at the right. Point A is 14 meters from point C and $\angle A$ is 47°. How high is the flagpole to the nearest meter?

Solution:

$$\tan 47° = \frac{BC}{14}$$

$$1.0724 = \frac{BC}{14} \longleftarrow \text{ From the table, tan } 47° = 1.0724$$

$$14(1.0724) = BC \longleftarrow \text{ Solve for } BC.$$

$$15.0136 = BC$$

The height of the flagpole is about **15 meters**.

Example 4
1. A tree is side BC in triangle ABC. Point A is 25 feet from point C and $\angle A$ is 63°. How tall is the tree to the nearest foot?
Ans: $\approx$ **49 ft**
2. The side of a house is side BC in triangle ABC. Point A is 3 meters from point C and $\angle A$ is 74°. How high is the house to the nearest meter?
Ans: $\approx$ **10 m**

CLASSROOM EXERCISES

In Exercises 1–3, find tan A and tan B.

1.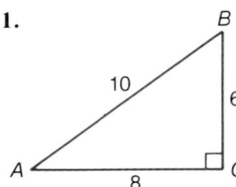

2.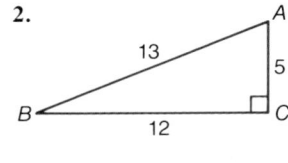

3.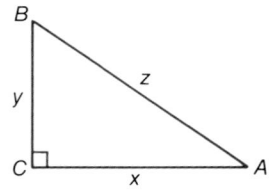

Use the table of values on page 542 to find x.

4. tan 76° = x 4.0108

5. tan 10° = x .1763

6. tan x = 1.3270   53°

WRITTEN EXERCISES

🅐   Use the table on page 542 to find the tangent of each angle measure.

1. 20° .3640
2. 40° .8391
3. 22° .4040
4. 45° 1.0000
5. 55° 1.4281
6. 70° 2.7475

7. 5° .0875
8. 25° .4663
9. 37° .7536
10. 80° 5.6713
11. 85° 11.4301
12. 89° 57.2900

Find x.

13. tan x = .5774   30°
14. tan x = 1.7321   60°
15. tan x = .1228   7°

16. tan x = .6009   31°
17. tan x = 1.6003   58°
18. tan x = 2.2460   66°

19. Refer to the table to complete the following sentence.

   As the measure of an angle increases from 0° to 89°, the tangent of the angle
   measure __?__ (increases or decreases) from .0000 to __?__ .
   increases   57.2900

APPLICATIONS: Using the Tangent Ratio

20. The triangle at the right is a right triangle. Use the tangent ratio to find
   the distance between Tom's home and
   John's home, directly through the park.
   1120 m

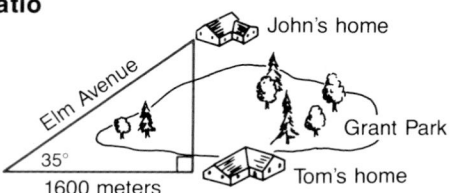

Find x.

21.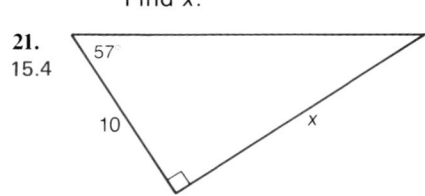
   15.4

22.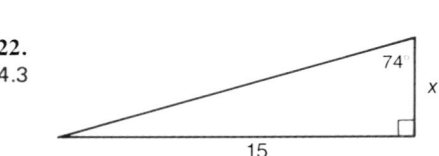
   4.3

23. In right triangle XYZ, $m \angle X$ is $45°$. Since the sum of $\angle X$, $\angle Y$, and $\angle Z$ is $180°$, $m \angle Y$ is also $45°$. If two angles of a triangle have the same measure, the sides opposite these angles have the same length and the triangle is isosceles.

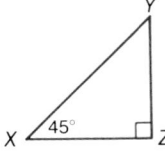

Triangle XYZ is isosceles and $XZ = YZ$. 1; 1; 1.0000

$\tan X = \dfrac{YZ}{XZ} = \underline{\quad?\quad}$ $\tan Y = \dfrac{XZ}{YZ} = \underline{\quad?\quad}$ $\tan 45° = \underline{\quad?\quad}$

24. To the nearest foot, how long is $\overline{DF}$ in $\triangle DEF$ below? 482 ft

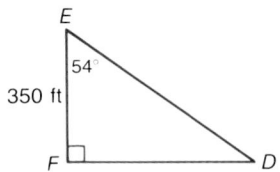

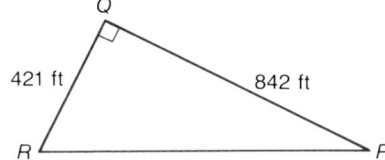

25. In $\triangle PQR$ above, what is $m \angle P$, to the nearest degree? $27°$

26. Use Figure 1 below to find the length of $\overline{BC}$ to the nearest foot. 35 ft

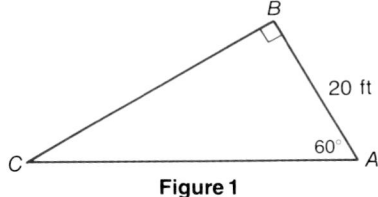

Figure 1

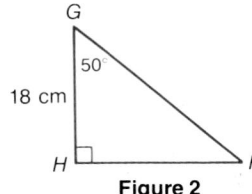

Figure 2

27. In Figure 2 at the right above, find the length of $\overline{HF}$ to the nearest centimeter. 21 cm

28. In the figure at the right, angle C is the right angle of $\triangle ABC$. What measurements could you make to find BC, the distance across the pond?

29. Using the figure for Exercise 28, find BC if $\angle A$ is $42°$ and AC is 80 meters. 72 m

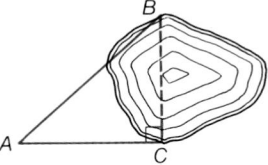

30. The figure below shows a television tower and support cables. Find $m \angle A$ to the nearest degree. 55°

31. A surveyor is measuring the width of a valley, as shown below. Find w to the nearest meter. 201 m

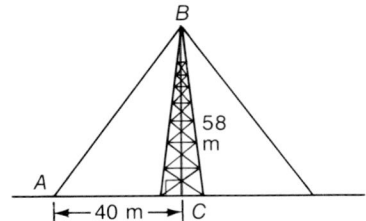

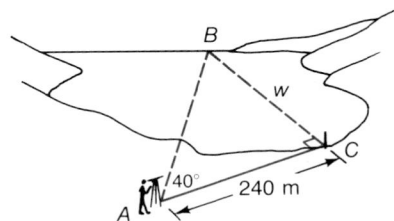

Other Applications of Algebra   **519**

1. Find each ratio. Write a
decimal for the ratio.

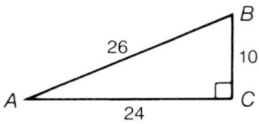

a. tan A   **Ans: .4167**
b. tan B   **Ans: 2.4**

In Exercises 2–5 use the
table on page 542 to find x.
2. tan 24° = x   **Ans: .4452**
3. tan x = .8693   **Ans: 41°**
4. tan 59° = x   **Ans: 1.6643**
5. tan x = 2.7475   **Ans: 70°**

Additional Examples
Example 1

1. Use the figure below to
determine sin A and cos A
for each of the triangles
ABC, ADE, and AFG, where
AB = 5, AD = 10, and AF
= 15.

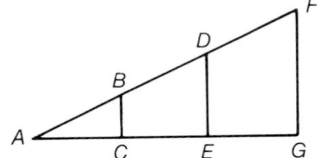

Ans: △ABC: sin A = $\frac{3}{5}$;
cos A = $\frac{4}{5}$; △ADE: sin A =
$\frac{3}{5}$. cos A = $\frac{4}{5}$; △AFG: sin A
$\frac{3}{5}$; cos A = $\frac{4}{5}$

2. Use the information and
the figure above to find
sin B and cos B for each
of the triangles ABC, ADE,
and AFG.

Ans: △ABC: sin B = $\frac{4}{5}$;
cos B = $\frac{3}{5}$; △ADE: sin B =
$\frac{4}{5}$; cos B = $\frac{3}{5}$; △AFG:
sin B = $\frac{4}{5}$; cos B = $\frac{4}{5}$

520

OBJECTIVE: To define and use the sine and cosine ratios

14–5   The Sine and Cosine Ratios

Suppose you wanted to determine the height of a plane or the distance across
a pond as shown below.

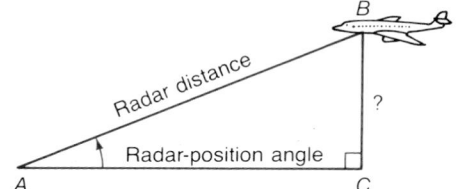
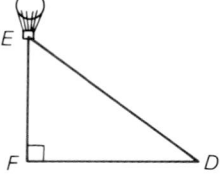

If both situations are represented by right triangles, where you know the
length of the hypotenuse and the measure of one acute angle, you still would
not be able to find either BC or FD using the tangent ratio. There are two
other ratios, the *sine ratio* and the *cosine ratio*, that you can use.

Definitions

> In a right triangle, the **sine of an acute angle** is the ratio
>
> $$\frac{\text{opposite side}}{\text{hypotenuse}}.$$
>
> In a right triangle, the **cosine of an acute angle** is the ratio
>
> $$\frac{\text{adjacent side}}{\text{hypotenuse}}.$$

The abbreviation for sine is sin (pronounced "sign"). The abbreviation for
cosine is cos (pronounced "co-sign").

EXAMPLE 1   Use the figure at the right to determine sin A and cos A for each of the
triangles ABC, ADE and AFG, where
AB = 5, AD = 10, and AF = 15.

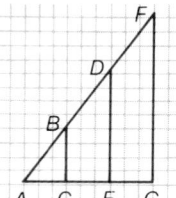

Solutions:

Triangle	sin A = $\dfrac{\text{opposite side}}{\text{hypotenuse}}$	cos A = $\dfrac{\text{adjacent side}}{\text{hypotenuse}}$
ABC	sin A = $\dfrac{BC}{AB} = \dfrac{4}{5}$	cos A = $\dfrac{AC}{AB} = \dfrac{3}{5}$
ADE	sin A = $\dfrac{DE}{AD} = \dfrac{8}{10} = \dfrac{4}{5}$	cos A = $\dfrac{AE}{AD} = \dfrac{6}{10} = \dfrac{3}{5}$
AFG	sin A = $\dfrac{FG}{AF} = \dfrac{12}{15} = \dfrac{4}{5}$	cos A = $\dfrac{AG}{AF} = \dfrac{9}{15} = \dfrac{3}{5}$

Since the triangles in Example 1 are similar, the ratios of corresponding sides are equal. Thus, for each of the triangles,

$$\sin A = \frac{4}{5} \quad \text{and} \quad \cos A = \frac{3}{5}.$$

Now you can solve the problems mentioned at the beginning of this section.

EXAMPLE 2 The distance from the tower to the plane is 40 kilometers and the measure of angle A is 12°. Find the height of the plane to the nearest tenth.

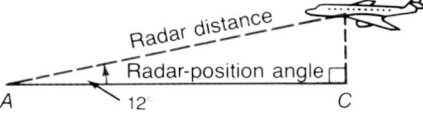
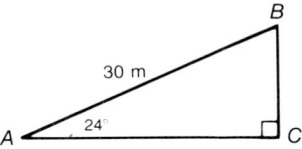

Solution: Since you know the measure of $\angle A$ and of the hypotenuse, and you want to find the side opposite $\angle A$, use $\sin A$.

$$\sin A = \frac{BC}{AB}$$

$$\sin 12° = \frac{BC}{40} \quad \longleftarrow \quad \textbf{Find sin 12° in the table.}$$

$$.2079 = \frac{BC}{40} \quad \longleftarrow \quad \textbf{Solve for BC.}$$

$$BC = 40(.2079)$$

$$BC = 8.3160$$

The height of the plane is about **8.3 kilometers.**

EXAMPLE 3 Find the distance across the pond shown at the right to the nearest meter.

Solution: Since you know the measure of $\angle D$ and of the hypotenuse, and you want to find the side adjacent to $\angle D$, use $\cos D$.

$$\cos D = \frac{FD}{ED}$$

$$\cos 35° = \frac{FD}{650} \quad \longleftarrow \quad \textbf{Find cos 35° in the table.}$$

$$.8192 = \frac{FD}{650} \quad \longleftarrow \quad \textbf{Solve for FD.}$$

$$FD = 650(.8192)$$

$$FD = 532.48$$

The distance is about **532 meters.**

Other Applications of Algebra **521**

Additional Examples
Example 2
1. A guy wire 30 meters long is attached to the top of a telephone pole and makes an angle of 24° with the ground.

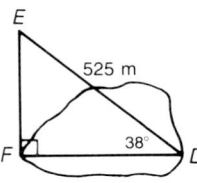

Find the height of the pole to the nearest tenth.
Ans: $\approx$ **12.2 m**
2. A 100-foot ladder, leaning against a building, makes an angle of 42° with the ground. To the nearest tenth, find the height at which the ladder touches the building.
Ans: $\approx$ **66.9 ft**

Example 3
1. Find the distance across the pond to the nearest meter.

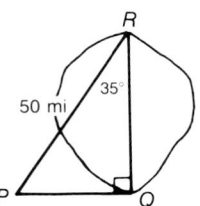

Ans: $\approx$ **414 m**
2. Find the distance across the lake to the nearest mile.

Ans: $\approx$ **41 mi**

CLASSROOM EXERCISES

Use the table on page 542 to find the following.

1. sin 12° .2079   **2.** cos 63° .4540   **3.** cos 45° .7071

In Exercises 4–6, find the sine and cosine of angle A.

4. 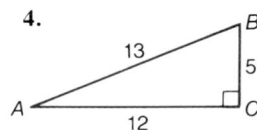   **5.** 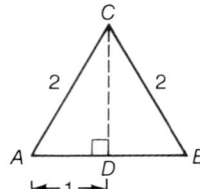   **6.**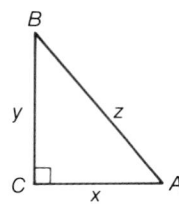

WRITTEN EXERCISES

A   Use the table of values on page 542 to find approximations for the sine and the cosine of the following angles.

1. 35°   **2.** 42°   **3.** 54°   **4.** 83°   **5.** 72°   **6.** 61°

Find x.

7. sin x = .1392   8°   **8.** sin x = .3907   23°   **9.** sin x = .6561   41°

10. sin x = .7547   49°   **11.** sin x = .9135   66°   **12.** sin x = .9962   85°

13. Look at your results for Exercises 7–12. As the size of an acute angle increases, does the sine ratio increase or decrease?   increase

Find x.

14. cos x = .9336   21°   **15.** cos x = .7660   40°   **16.** cos x = .5299   58°

17. cos x = ,1736   80°   **18.** cos x = .0175   89°   **19.** cos x = .9877   9°

20. Look at the cosine values in the table. As the size of an acute angle increases, does the value of the cosine increase or decrease?   decrease

APPLICATIONS: Using the Sine and Cosine Ratios

21. Bea's kite string is 60 meters long and makes an angle of 42° with the horizontal in the figure below. How high above the ground is the kite? 40.146 m

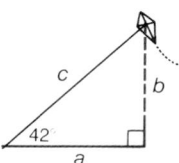   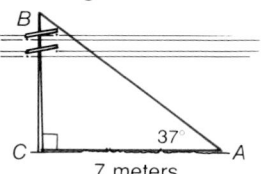

22. In the figure above, $\overline{AB}$ represents a wire supporting a pole, $\overline{BC}$. Find AB.   8.8 m

B

23. The railroad that runs to the summit of Pike's Peak makes, at the steepest place, an angle of 27° with the horizontal. How many meters would you rise in walking 30 meters up the railroad track? 13.6 m

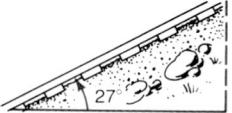

24. In △ABC below, c is 25 meters and ∠A is 65°. How long is b? 10.6 m

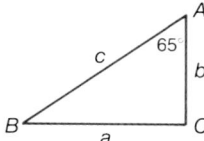

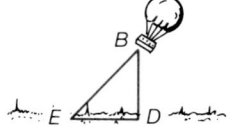

25. In the figure at the right above, the balloon at B is anchored to the ground at a point E by a wire. The wind blows the balloon so the wire makes an angle of 48° with the ground. If point D, directly under the balloon, is 85 meters from E, how long is the wire? 127.0 m

26. How far above the ground is the balloon in Exercise 25? 94.4 m

27. The scouts of the Lynx Patrol want to know the distance across a pond. They laid off $\overline{CA}$ at right angles to $\overline{BC}$. They extended $\overline{CA}$ until they came to a point A from which they could measure $\overline{AB}$. They measured $\overline{AB}$ and angle A. If AB is 195 meters and ∠A is 57°, find BC. 163.5 m

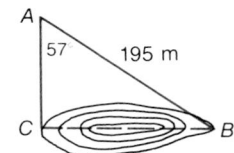

Exercises 28–31 refer to right triangles. Make a drawing for each. In triangle ABC, a is the side opposite ∠A, b is the side opposite ∠B, and c is the side opposite ∠C, a right angle.

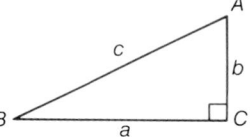

28. Find c when a is 26 centimeters and ∠A is 54°. 32.1 cm

29. Find c when a is 8.4 centimeters and ∠A is 62°. 9.5 cm

30. Find a when c is 65 meters and ∠A is 45°. 46.0 m

31. Find b when c is 100 meters and ∠A is 35°. 81.9 m

32. If XY is 110 feet and m∠YXZ is 27°, how long is d in Figure 1 below? 123.5 ft

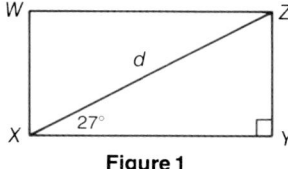

Figure 1

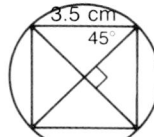

Figure 2

C

33. The diagonals of a square are perpendicular to each other, as shown in Figure 2 above. If a circle is circumscribed about the square, the diagonals are also diameters of the circle. Use the cosine ratio to find the radius of a circle circumscribed about a square whose side is 3.5 centimeters. 2.47485 cm

34. Use the Pythagorean Theorem to check your answer to Exercise 33.

Additional Answers
34. $a^2 + b^2 = c^2$;
$(2.47485)^2 + (2.47485)^2 = (3.5)^2$; $6.1248825 + 6.1248825 = 12.25$; $12.249765 \approx 12.25$

Other Applications of Algebra **523**

Problem Solving and Applications

OBJECTIVE: To use the sine, cosine, and tangent ratios to solve word problems

14-6 Using the Sine, Cosine, and Tangent Ratios

An important step in using trigonometric ratios to solve problems is deciding which ratio to use. When no figure is given, you should first draw one, carefully labeling what is known and what is to be found. The ratio that involves both the known parts and the part to be found is the one to use in solving the problem.

Known and Unknown Sides of the Right Triangle	Ratios to Use
opposite and adjacent	tangent
opposite and hypotenuse	sine
adjacent and hypotenuse	cosine

To describe the angles found by lines of sight to objects, two angles are used. They are the **angle of elevation** and the **angle of depression.**

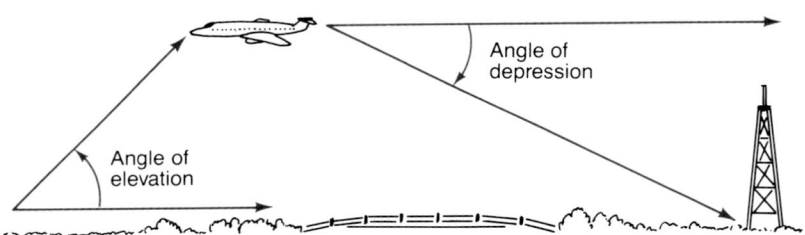

EXAMPLE 1 To find the height of a tree, a girl measures 9 meters along a straight line from its base. From the end of this line, she finds the angle of elevation to the top of tree to be 41°. How high is the tree (to the nearest meter)?

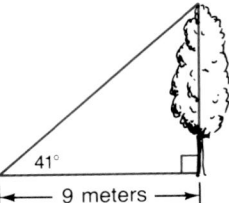

Solution: Let y = the height of the tree.

$$\tan 41° = \frac{y}{9}$$ ◄——— **The opposite side is unknown; the adjacent side is known. Use the tangent ratio.**

$$.8693 = \frac{y}{9}$$ ◄——— **tan 41° = .8693**

$$y = 9(.8693)$$
$$y = 7.8237$$

The tree is about **8 meters** tall.

EXAMPLE 2 The diagonal of a rectangle is 8 centimeters long and makes an angle of 25° with the longer side of the rectangle. Find the length of the base to the nearest centimeter.

Solution:

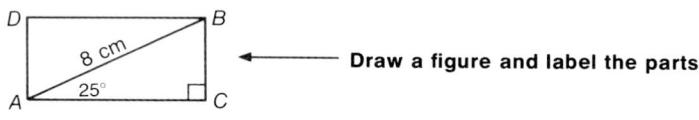

Draw a figure and label the parts.

$$\cos A = \frac{AC}{AB}$$

The hypotenuse is known; the adjacent side is unknown. Use the cosine ratio.

$$\cos 25° = \frac{AC}{8}$$

Find cos 25° from the table.

$$.9063 = \frac{AC}{8}$$

Solve for **AC**.

$$AC = 8(.9063)$$

$$AC = 7.2504 \quad \text{The base is about } \textbf{7 centimeters} \text{ long.}$$

Additional Examples
Example 1
1. The diagonal of a rectangle is 10 centimeters long and makes an angle of 35° with the longer side of the rectangle. Find the length of the base to the nearest centimeter.
Ans: ≈ **8 cm**
2. The diagonal of a rectangle is 25 meters long and makes an angle of 56° with the longer side of the rectangle. Find the length of the base to the nearest meter.
Ans: ≈ **14 m**

CLASSROOM EXERCISES

Use each figure to tell which trigonometric ratio could be used to find *x*.

1. tan   **2.** cos   **3.** sin   **4.** tan   **5.** cos

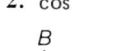 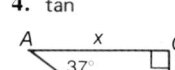 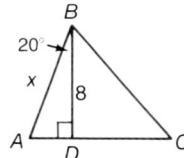

WORD PROBLEMS

A   Solve each problem.

1. To find the distance across a pond between two points, *M* and *N*, Fred measured off 250 meters on a line *MR* perpendicular to segment *MN*. He found ∠*MRN* to be 35°. Find *MN*.   about 175 m

2. Some girl scouts measured the height of a mound. They stretched a string from a point, *A*, at the bottom of the mound to the top, *T*, finding *AT* to be 24 meters. The measure of the angle of elevation of the top from point *A* was 35°. How high was the mound?   about 14 m high

3. If *AB* and *BC* in the figure at the right are each 30 meters, and *BD* is 18 meters, what is the measure of angle *A*?   about 37°

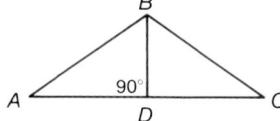

Assignment Guide
Minimal Omit
Average Omit
Above Average
pp. 525–526: 1–9

Other Applications of Algebra   **525**

4. You are given rectangle $ABCD$ with diagonal AC drawn. The measure of the angle between $\overline{AD}$ and AC is 31° and AD is 16.3 centimeters. How long is $\overline{AC}$?

5. Find the angle of elevation of the sun to the nearest degree when a church steeple 200 feet high casts a shadow 80 feet long. about 68°

6. From the top of a cliff 1200 meters above a lake, the angle of depression of the nearest shore is 18°. Find the distance from the top of the cliff to the edge of the lake. about 3883 m

7. In the figure at the right, AB is 215 centimeters, $\angle A$ is 35°, $\angle C$ is 65°, and the angles at D are right angles. How long are $\overline{BD}$ and $\overline{BC}$?

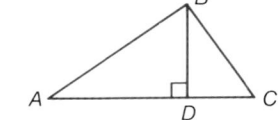

8. Use your own height in meters to find how long a shadow you will cast if the angle of elevation of the sun is 37°.

9. A tower that is 50 meters high has a support wire that makes an angle of 35° with the ground. How long is the wire? How far from the foot of the tower is the support wire attached to the ground? length of wire: about 87 m; distance: about 71 m

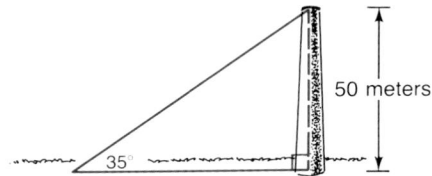

Review

In Exercises 1–16, use the table on page 542.
Complete. *(Section 14-4)*

1. $\tan 32° = \underline{\ ?\ }$ .6249
2. $\tan 47° = \underline{\ ?\ }$ 1.0724
3. $\tan 15° = \underline{\ ?\ }$ .2679
4. $\tan 86° = \underline{\ ?\ }$ 14.3007

5. $\tan x = .4040$; $x = \underline{\ ?\ }$ 22°
6. $\tan x = 2.1445$; $x = \underline{\ ?\ }$ 65°
7. $\tan x = 8.1443$; $x = \underline{\ ?\ }$ 83°

8. In the figure at the right, point B is 60 meters from the base of the water tower and in $\angle B$ is 41°. Find side AC, the height of the tower, to the nearest meter. *(Section 14-4)* 52 m

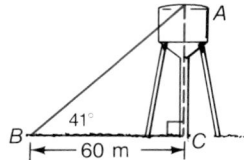

Complete. *(Section 14-5)*

9. $\sin 25° = \underline{\ ?\ }$ .4226
10. $\cos 63° = \underline{\ ?\ }$ .4540
11. $\sin 84° = \underline{\ ?\ }$ .9945
12. $\cos 13° = \underline{\ ?\ }$ .9744

13. $\sin x = .3090$; $x = \underline{\ ?\ }$ 18°
14. $\cos x = .8387$; $x = \underline{\ ?\ }$ 33°
15. $\sin x = .9613$; $x = \underline{\ ?\ }$ 74°

16. An airplane approaching an airport is 800 meters above the control tower. The angle of elevation from the tower to the plane is 8°. Find the distance between the plane and the tower to the nearest meter. 5747 m *(Section 14-6)*

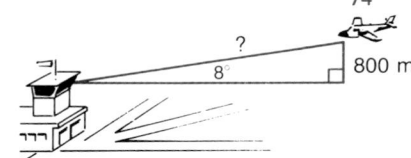

526 *Chapter 14*

OBJECTIVE: To test whether a given finite set of numbers under two given operations satisfies the postulates for a field

14–7 The Field Postulates

As you will discover in geometry, a **postulate** is a mathematical statement that is accepted without proof—just as in algebra. (See page 30.) Postulates are an important part of the structure of geometry. As the following illustrates, postulates are also important in the structure of algebra.

If it is nine o'clock, then five hours from now it will be two o'clock. Although $9 + 5 = 14$, in *clock arithmetic*

$$9 + 5 = 2.$$

In clock arithmetic you only use the whole numbers 1 through 12.

$$C = \{1, 2, 3, 4, 5, 6, 7, 8, 9, 10, 11, 12\}$$

Set C is a **finite set** because you can count the number of elements and the counting comes to an end.

Here is the procedure for adding numbers in clock arithmetic.

Procedure

> If the sum of any two numbers named in C is greater than 12, you subtract 12 to find the clock sum.

Here is the addition table for C.

+	1	2	3	4	5	6	7	8	9	10	11	12
1	2	3	4	5	6	7	8	9	10	11	12	1
2	3	4	5	6	7	8	9	10	11	12	1	2
3	4	5	6	7	8	9	10	11	12	1	2	3
4	5	6	7	8	9	10	11	12	1	2	3	4
5	6	7	8	9	10	11	12	1	2	3	4	5
6	7	8	9	10	11	12	1	2	3	4	5	6
7	8	9	10	11	12	1	2	3	4	5	6	7
8	9	10	11	12	1	2	3	4	5	6	7	8
9	10	11	12	1	2	3	4	5	6	7	8	9
10	11	12	1	2	3	4	5	6	7	8	9	10
11	12	1	2	3	4	5	6	7	8	9	10	11
12	1	2	3	4	5	6	7	8	9	10	11	12

EXAMPLE 1 Find the clock sums: **a.** $8 + 5$ **b.** $7 + 9$

Solutions: **Method 1: Using the Procedure**

a. $8 + 5 = 13$ and $13 - 12 = 1$ **b.** $7 + 9 = 16$ and $16 - 12 = 4$

Method 2: Using the Table

a. Find 8 in the + column. Look directly right to the 5–column.

$$8 + 5 = \mathbf{1}$$

b. Find 7 in the + column. Look directly right to the 9–column.

$$7 + 9 = \mathbf{4}$$

Teaching Suggestions p. M-27

Quick Quiz
1. From a point 50 meters from the base of a tower, the angle of elevation of the top of the tower is 46°. Find the height of the tower to the nearest meter.
   Ans: $\approx$ **52 m**
2. The diagonal of a rectangle is 45 centimeters long and makes an angle of 28° with the longer side of the rectangle. Find the length of the base to the nearest centimeter.
   Ans: $\approx$ **40 m**

Additional Examples
Example 1
Find the clock sums.
1. **a.** $8 + 7$ **Ans: 3**
   b. $9 + 4$ **Ans: 1**
2. **a.** $6 + 8$ **Ans: 2**
   b. $9 + 11$ **Ans: 8**

The following is the procedure for multiplying numbers in clock arithmetic.

Procedure

> If the product of any two numbers named in C is greater than 12, you subtract 12 or a multiple of 12 to find the clock product.

Here is the multiplication table for C.

×	1	2	3	4	5	6	7	8	9	10	11	12
1	1	2	3	4	5	6	7	8	9	10	11	12
2	2	4	6	8	10	12	2	4	6	8	10	12
3	3	6	9	12	3	6	9	12	3	6	9	12
4	4	8	12	4	8	12	4	8	12	4	8	12
5	5	10	3	8	1	6	11	4	9	2	7	12
6	6	12	6	12	6	12	6	12	6	12	6	12
7	7	2	9	4	11	6	1	8	3	10	5	12
8	8	4	12	8	4	12	8	4	12	8	4	12
9	9	6	3	12	9	6	3	12	9	6	3	12
10	10	8	6	4	2	12	10	8	6	4	2	12
11	11	10	9	8	7	6	5	4	3	2	1	12
12	12	12	12	12	12	12	12	12	12	12	12	12

Additional Examples
Example 2
Find the clock products.
1. **a.** 8×2 **Ans: 4**
   b. 11×2 **Ans: 10**
2. **a.** 9×3 **Ans: 3**
   b. 7×9 **Ans: 3**

EXAMPLE 2 Find the clock products: **a.** 9×2 **b.** 8×4

Solutions:

Method 1: Using the Procedure

a. $9 \times 2 = 18$ and $18 - 12 = 6$

b. $8 \times 4 = 32$ and $32 - 24 = 8$

Method 2: Using the Table

a. Find 9 in the ×–column. Look directly right to the 2–column.
$$9 \times 2 = 6$$

b. Find 8 in the ×–column. Look directly right to the 4–column.
$$8 \times 4 = 8$$

Note that in the finite set C under the operations of clock arithmetic, 12 acts the same as 0 does in the set of real numbers. That is, 12 is the additive identity element and 12 times any number is 12. Therefore, if the clock had been labeled as shown below, the pattern for addition and multiplication would be the same with 12 being replaced by 0.

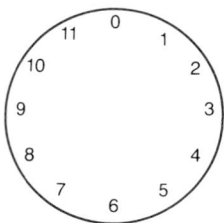

A set of numbers together with two operations for which the eleven postulates given below hold is called a **field,** F.

To determine if C is a field, check each postulate with the addition and multiplication tables for C.

Field Postulates	Does C satisfy the postulate?
Closure	
1. $a + b$ is an element of the set.	1–2. Yes. The sum or product of any two numbers is in C.
2. $a \times b$ is an element of the set.	
Commutativity	
3. $a + b = b + a$	3–4. Yes. All cases can be checked. Draw a diagonal from upper left to lower right of the table. The pattern on either side of the diagonal is the same. This shows commutativity.
4. $a \times b = b \times a$	
Associativity	
5. $a + (b + c) = (a + b) + c$	5–6. Yes. Check a few cases. All cases should be checked to show that these postulates hold.
6. $a \times (b \times c) = (a \times b) \times c$	
Identity Element	
7. There is an identity element, 0, such that $a + 0 = a$.	7. Yes. The identity element is 12. 12 added to any number in C gives that number.
8. There is an identity element, 1, such that $a \times 1 = a$.	8. Yes. The identity element is 1. 1 times any number in C gives that number.
Inverse Element	
9. For each element a in F, there is an inverse element, $-a$, such that $a + -a = 0$.	9. Yes. The additive identity element, 12, appears in each column. So each number in C has an additive inverse.
10. For each element a in F, there is an inverse element, $\frac{1}{a}$, $a \neq 0$, such that $a \times \frac{1}{a} = 1$.	10. No. There is no number in C by which to multiply 2, 3, 4, 6, 8, 9, 10, or 12 to get the identity element 1.
Distributive	
11. $a \times (b + c) = a \times b + a \times c$	11. Yes. Try a few cases. All combinations could be checked.

If one postulate is not satisfied, then the set of numbers is not a field. Thus, you could have stopped after finding that Postulate 10 did not hold. The set of clock numbers is *not* a field.

Additional Answers

1. $1+1=2; 1+2=3; 1+3=0;$
   $2+2=0; 2+3=1; 3+1=0;$
   $3+2=1$
2. $1 \times 1=1; 1 \times 2=2; 1 \times 3=3;$
   $2 \times 2=0; 2 \times 3=2; 3 \times 1=3;$
   $3 \times 2=2$
3. No; each element does not have a multiplicative inverse; there is no number by which to multiply 0 or 2 to get the identity number, 1
4. $1+1=2; 1+2=3; 1+3=4;$
   $1+4=5; 2+1=3; 2+3=5;$
   $2+4=0; 2+5=1; 3+1=4;$
   $3+2=5; 3+3=0; 3+4=1;$
   $4+1=5; 4+2=0; 4+3=1;$
   $4+5=3; 5+1=0; 5+3=2;$
   $5+4=3; 5+5=4$
5. $1 \times 1=1; 1 \times 3=3; 1 \times 4=4;$
   $1 \times 5=5; 2 \times 1=2; 2 \times 2=4;$
   $2 \times 3=0; 2 \times 4=2; 2 \times 5=4;$
   $3 \times 1=3; 3 \times 2=0; 3 \times 3=3;$
   $3 \times 5=3; 4 \times 2=2; 4 \times 3=0;$
   $4 \times 4=4; 5 \times 1=5; 5 \times 3=3;$
   $5 \times 4=2$
6. No; 2, 3, and 4 do not have multiplicative inverses
7. Yes; a "two-hour clock" is a field
8. $0+1=1; 0+2=2; 1+0=1;$
   $1+2=0; 2+0=2; 2+1=0$
9. $1 \times 1=1; 1 \times 2=2; 2 \times 1=2;$
   $2 \times 2=1$

WRITTEN EXERCISES

A   Complete the following tables for a "four-hour clock."

1.
+	0	1	2	3
0	0	1	2	3
1	1	?	?	?
2	2	3	?	?
3	3	?	?	2

2.
×	0	1	2	3
0	0	0	0	0
1	0	?	?	?
2	0	2	?	?
3	0	?	?	1

3. Does the set of numbers on a "four-hour clock" meet all the requirements for a field? If not, which postulate(s) is (are) not satisfied? Give examples.

Complete the following tables for a "six-hour clock."

4.
+	0	1	2	3	4	5
0	0	1	2	3	4	5
1	1	?	?	?	?	0
2	2	?	4	?	?	?
3	3	?	?	?	?	2
4	4	?	?	?	2	?
5	5	?	1	?	?	?

5.
×	0	1	2	3	4	5
0	0	0	0	0	0	0
1	0	?	2	?	?	?
2	0	?	?	?	?	?
3	0	?	?	?	0	?
4	0	4	?	?	?	2
5	0	?	4	?	?	1

6. Does the set of numbers on a "six-hour clock" meet all the requirements for a field? Explain.

7. Is any set of numbers on an "even-number clock" a field? Explain.

Complete the following tables for a "three-hour clock."

8.
+	0	1	2
0	0	?	?
1	?	2	?
2	?	?	1

9.
×	0	1	2
0	0	0	0
1	0	?	?
2	0	?	?

10. Is the set of numbers on a "three-hour clock" a field? Yes

11. Is the set of numbers on a "five-hour clock" a field? Yes

12. Addition and multiplication tables for the finite set $S = \{E, O\}$ are shown below. Is set S a field? Yes

+	E	O
E	E	O
O	O	E

×	E	O
E	E	E
O	E	O

14–8 Logic and Algebra

Teaching Suggestions p. M-27

The study of geometry is an application of logical reasoning. An understanding of some of the elementary aspects of logic can prove to be helpful to you in geometry and in your next algebra course, particularly when dealing with theorems that are often stated in the *if–then* form.

In mathematics, a statement in the *if–then* form is a **conditional statement.** You can think of a conditional statement as a *promise.*

> If it is cold, then I wear my coat.

If you keep your promise, then the conditional is true; if you do not, it is false.

In the following table, T stands for *True* and F stands for *False.*

It is cold.	You wore your coat.	You kept your promise.	
T	T	T	
F	T	T	← You did not say that you wouldn't wear your coat if it wasn't cold. Thus, you kept your promise.
F	F	T	← This case is *True* because you didn't break your promise.
T	F	F	← This case is *False* because you broke your promise.

Notice that the only case where the conditional is false is when the if–part is true and the then–part is false. This analysis of a conditional statement suggests the truth table below. The symbol for the conditional is $p \rightarrow q$, where the $\rightarrow$ connects the then–part, q, with the if–part, p.

p	q	$p \rightarrow q$
T	T	T
F	T	T
F	F	T
T	F	F

The symbol "$\sim$" is read **"not."** Thus, in Example 1, $\sim q$ is the negation of the then–part of the statement, q.

EXAMPLE 1 Tell when the conditional is false if p is true and q is true.

If it is raining, then I will use my umbrella.

Solution: Keep p true and make q false.

p	$\sim q$
It is raining	I will *not* use my umbrella

Additional Examples
Example 1
Tell when each conditional
is false.
1. If it is snowing, then I
   will wear my boots.
   **Ans: If it is snowing, then
   I will not wear my boots.**
2. If you work, then you get
   paid.
   **Ans: If you work, then you
   do not get paid.**

A conditional statement is a **compound statement** since it is formed by combining two *simple* statements.

EXAMPLE 2 Combine these two simple statements or the negatives of these statements to form a true conditional.

<u>3 is an even number.</u>   <u>3 is a real number.</u>

Solution:

		p	q	$p \rightarrow q$
There are three ways to do this.				
If 3 is an even number, then 3 is a real number.		F	T	T
If 3 is an even number, then 3 is *not* a real number.		F	F	T
If 3 is *not* an even number, then 3 is a real number.		T	T	T

Additional Examples
Example 2
Combine these statements to
form a true conditional.
1. 15 is an odd number; 15 is
a real number.
**Ans: If 15 is an odd
number, then 15 is a real
number. Or, if 15 is not
an odd number, then 15
is a real number. Or, if
15 is not an odd number,
then 15 is not a real
number.**

The **converse** of a conditional statement is formed by interchanging the p and q statements.

EXAMPLE 3 Write the converse for each of the true conditionals in Example 2.

Solution:

		q	p	$q \rightarrow p$
If 3 is a real number, then 3 is an even number.		T	F	F
If 3 is *not* a real number, then 3 is an even number.		F	F	T
If 3 is a real number, then 3 is *not* an even number.		T	T	T

Example 3
Write the converse.
1. If B is a bird, then B is
a robin.
**Ans: If B is a robin, then
B is a bird.**

As Example 3 shows, the converse of a true conditional is not always true. However, for a definition, *both* the conditional and its converse must be true.

Example 4
Write the definition as a
conditional and its converse.
1. A square is a rectangle
with four equal sides.
**Ans: Conditional: If a
rectangle is a square, then
it has four equal sides.
Converse: If a rectangle
has four equal sides, then
it is a square.**

EXAMPLE 4 Write the definition as a conditional and its converse.

<u>An even number is a number divisible by 2.</u>

Solution:

If a number is an even number, then it is divisible by 2. ◄——— **Conditional**

If a number is divisible by 2, then it is an even number. ◄——— **Converse**

Additional Answers

2. Conditional: If a triangle
is an isosceles triangle,
then it has two equal sides.
Converse: If a triangle
has two equal sides, then
it is an isosceles triangle.

4. Conditional: If a mathematical sentence is an
inequality, then it contains
$>$, $<$ or $\neq$. Converse: If a
mathematical sentence
contains $>$, $<$ or $\neq$, then
it is an equality.

CLASSROOM EXERCISES See page 592 for the answers to Ex. 1 and 3.

Write each definition as a conditional and its converse.

1. A right triangle is a triangle with one right angle.
2. An isosceles triangle is a triangle with two equal sides.
3. An odd number is a number that is not divisible by two.
4. An inequality is a mathematical sentence that contains $>$, $<$ or $\neq$.

532 *Chapter 14*

WRITTEN EXERCISES See page 592 for the answers to the odd Exercises 1-4, 10-24.

A Tell when each conditional is *false*.

1. If you have no more than 2 errors, then you get an A.
2. If our team wins this game, then our team goes to the Rose Bowl.
3. If I drive over the speed limit, then I break the law.
4. If the sun is shining, then I cast a shadow.
   If the sun is shining, then I do not cast a shadow.

Write *True* or *False* for each conditional.

5. If 7 is a whole number, then 7 is an even number. *False*
6. If $\sqrt{2}$ is an irrational number, then $\sqrt{2}$ is an even number. *False*
7. If $2 \times 3 = 8$, then $2 + 3 = 5$. *True*
8. If $4 + 7 > 6$, then $7 > 6 - 4$. *True*
9. If $25 + 60 = 85$, then $85 - 60 = 25$. *True*

Combine each pair of statements to form a true conditional.

10. $\sqrt{2}$ is irrational; 7 is an even number.
11. 15 is a real number; 15 is a rational number.
12. 9 is a factor of 12; 3 is a factor of 12.

Write the converse of each conditional.

13. If I work hard, then I get tired.
14. If x is a rose, then x is a flower. If x is a flower, then x is a rose.
15. If Q is a triangle, then Q has exactly three sides and three angles.

Write each definition as a conditional and its converse.

16. An equilateral triangle is a triangle with three equal sides. See below.
17. An irrational number is a number that cannot be expressed as the ratio of an integer and a natural number.
18. An acute angle is an angle whose measure is less than 90°.
19. An obtuse angle is an angle whose measure is greater than 90° and less than 180°.
20. Perpendicular lines are lines that meet at right angles.
21. Equivalent equations are equations that have the same solution set.
22. A set is a subset of a second set if all its members are also members of the second set.

B   16. Cond. If a triangle is equilateral, then it has 3 equal sides.
        Conv. If a triangle has three equal sides, then it is equilateral.

23. A binomial is a polynomial of two terms.
24. A compound statement is formed by combining two simple statements.

Other Applications of Algebra   **533**

Assignment Guide
Minimal Omit
Average Omit
Above Average p. 533: 1–24

Additional Answers

2. If our team wins this game, then our team does not go to the Rose Bowl.
10. If $\sqrt{2}$ is not irrational, then 7 is not an even number; If $\sqrt{2}$ is not irrational, then 7 is an even number; If $\sqrt{2}$ is irrational, then 7 is not an even number
12. If 9 is not a factor of 12, then 3 is a factor of 12; If 9 is a factor of 12, then 3 is not a factor of 12; If 9 is a factor of 12, then 3 is a factor of 12.
18. Conditional: If an angle is an acute angle, then its measure is less than 90°. Converse: If the measure of an angle is less than 90°, then the angle is an acute angle.
20. Conditional: If two lines are perpendicular, then they meet at right angles. Converse: If two lines meet at right angles, then they are perpendicular.
22. Conditional: If a set is a subset of a second set, then all its members are also members of the second set. Converse: If all members of a set are also members of a second set, then the set is a subset of the second set.
24. Conditional: If a statement is a compound sentence, then it is formed by combining two simple sentences. Converse: If a statement is formed by combining two simple sentences, then it is a compound sentence.

14-9 Direct Proof and Algebra

As was indicated in the previous section, theorems are often stated as conditionals. One way to prove a theorem is by a *direct proof*. **A direct proof** shows that the then-statement follows from the if-statement. In a proof, the if-statement is called the **hypothesis** and is always taken to be true. The then-statement is called the **conclusion.** It is the statement that is to be proved true.

Each statement in a proof must be justified by a reason. The reason may be the hypothesis, a definition, postulate, or a theorem.

Not only will you write proofs when you study geometry, you may also be asked to prove theorems like the following in your next algebra course.

EXAMPLE 1 Prove the following theorem.

If x, y, and z are any real numbers, then $(x + y)z = xz + yz$.

Proof: **Hypothesis:** x, y, and z are any real numbers.

Conclusion: $(x + y)z = xz + yz$

Statements	Reasons
1. x, y, and z are any real numbers.	1. Given (hypothesis)
2. $(x + y)z = z(x + y)$	2. Commutative postulate for multiplication
3. $z(x + y) = zx + zy$	3. Distributive postulate
4. $zx + zy = xz + yz$	4. Commutative postulate for multiplication
5. $(x + y)z = xz + yz$	5. Substitution principle

NOTE: Statements that have been proved may be used in later proofs.

To prove the next theorem, you will need these definitions.

Definitions

An **even number** is a number of the form $2n$, where n is an integer.

An **odd number** is a number of the form $2n + 1$, where n is an integer.

For example,

20 is an even number, because $20 = 2 \cdot 10$.

$2k + 2$ is an even number, because $2k + 2 = 2(k + 1)$.

21 is an odd number, because $21 = (2 \cdot 10) + 1$.

$2k + 3$ is an odd number, because $2k + 3 = 2(k + 1) + 1$.

Quick Quiz

1. Tell when the conditional is false: If it is later than 10:00 P.M., then I am asleep.
   Ans: If it is later than 10:00 P.M., then I am not asleep.
2. Write the converse: If *r* is a rectangle, then *r* has exactly four sides and four angles.
   Ans: If *r* has exactly four sides and four angles, then *r* is a rectangle.
3. Write the definition as a conditional and its converse: A number whose units digit is 0 or 5 is divisible by 5.
   Ans: Conditional: If a number's units digit is 0 or 5, then the number is divisible by 5. Converse: If a number is divisible by 5, then the number's units digit is 0 or 5.

Additional Example
Example 1
Prove: If *x*, *y*, and *z* are any real numbers, then $(x - y)z = xz - yz$.
Ans: Hyp: *x*, *y*, and *z* are any real numbers. Concl: $(x - y)z = xz - yz$. Proof:
1. *x*, *y*, and *z* are any real numbers. (Given) 2. $(x - y)z = z(x - y)$. (Comm. post. for mult.) 3. $z(x - y) = zx - zy$. (Distrib. post.) 4. $zx - zy = xz - yz$. (Comm. post. for mult.) 5. $(x - y)z = xz - yz$. (Subst. prin.)

EXAMPLE 2 Prove the following theorem.

If two numbers are odd numbers, then their sum is an even number.

Proof: **Hypothesis:** a and b are any two odd numbers.

Conclusion: $a + b$ is an even number.

Statements	Reasons
1. a and b are odd numbers.	1. Given
2. Let $a = 2k + 1$; let $b = 2p + 1$; $a + b = 2k + 1 + 2p + 1$	2. Definition of odd number
3. $2k + 1 + 2p + 1 = 2k + 2p + 2$	3. Addition
4. $2k + 2p + 2 = 2(k + p + 1)$	4. Distributive postulate
5. $k + p + 1$ is an integer.	5. Closure postulate for addition
6. $2(k + p + 1)$ is an even number.	6. Definition of even number
7. $a + b$ is an even number.	7. Substitution

WRITTEN EXERCISES See pages 592-593 for the answers to the odd Exercises 1-18.

A Prove each of the following.

1. $2x + 3x = 5x$

2. $n + n = 2n$

3. $3x + (5y + 7x) = 10x + 5y$

4. $3(4x) = 12x$

5. $(-2a)(-3a) = 6a^2$

6. $a(b + c + d) = ab + ac + ad$ See p. 536.

7. $(x + 3)(x + 4) = x^2 + 7x + 12$

8. $(x + y)^2 = x^2 + 2xy + y^2$ See p. 536.

Write a proof for each statement. Statements that have been proved may be used in later proofs.

9. The square of an even number is even.

10. The square of an odd number is odd. See p. 537.

11. The sum of two even numbers is an even number. (HINT: Let $2n$ be one even number and let $2k$ be the other. Then find $2n + 2k$.)

12. The sum of an even number and an odd number is an odd number. See p. 537.

13. The product of two odd numbers is an odd number.

14. The product of two even numbers is an even number. See p. 538.

15. The product of an even number and an odd number is an even number.

16. The sum of two multiples of 3 is a multiple of 3. (HINT: A multiple of 3 is a number of the form $3n$, where n is an integer.) See p. 538.

17. The product of two multiples of 3 is a multiple of 3.

18. The sum of two multiples of 6 is a multiple of 6. See p. 539.

Other Applications of Algebra **535**

Additional Example
Example 2
Prove: If two numbers are odd numbers, then their difference is an even number.
Ans: Hyp: a and b are any two odd numbers. Concl: $a - b$ is an even number. Proof:
1. a and b are odd numbers. (Given) 2. Let $a = 2k + 1$. let $b = 2p + 1$; $a - b = 2k + 1 - (2p + 1)$. (Def. of odd number) 3. $2k + 1 - (2p + 1) = 2k - 2p$. (Subtraction) 4. $2k - 2p = 2(k - p)$. (Distrib. post.) 5. $k - p$ is an integer. (Clos. post. for subtr.) 6. $2(k - p)$ is an even number. (Def. of even number) 7. $a - b$ is an even number. (Subst. prin.)

Assignment Guide
Minimal Omit
Average Omit
Above Average
pp. 535–536: 1–27 odd

Additional Answers
2. Hypothesis: n is any number.
   Conclusion: $n + n = 2n$
   Proof:
   1. n is any number. (Given)
   2. $n + n = 1 \cdot n + 1 \cdot n$ (Mult. identity)
   3. $1 \cdot n + 1 \cdot n = (1 + 1)n$ (Dist. post.)
   4. $(1 + 1)n = 2n$ (Addition)
   5. $n + n = 2n$ (Substitution)
4. Hypothesis: x is any number.
   Conclusion: $3(4x) = 12x$
   Proof:
   1. x is any number. (Given)
   2. $3(4x) = (3 \cdot 4)x$ (Assoc. post. for mult.)
   3. $(3 \cdot 4)x = 12x$ (Multiplication)
   4. $3(4x) = 12x$ (Substitution)

See page 593 for the answers to the odd Exercises 19-27.

19. If a number is divisible by 6, then it is divisible by 2. (HINT: Show that a number divisible by 6 is a multiple of 2.)

20. If a number is divisible by 6, then it is divisible by 3. See the Solution Key for Ex. 20-26 even.

21. The product of two multiples of 5 is a multiple of 5.

22. If a number is even, then the cube of the number is even.

B

23. For all real numbers a and b, $a - b$ and $b - a$ are opposites. (HINT: Prove that $(a - b) + (b - a) = 0$ is true. Then refer to the meaning of opposites.)

24. If a number is odd, then the cube of the number is odd. (HINT: $(2n + 1)^3 = (2n + 1)^2 (2n + 1)$)

25. If one of two given numbers is even and the other is odd, then the square of their sum is an odd number.

26. If one of two given numbers is even and the other is odd, then the sum of the square of their sum and the odd number is an even number. (HINT: Let x be the even number and y the odd number. Prove that $(x + y)^2 + y$ is an even number.)

27. If a number is not a multiple of 4, then its square is not a multiple of 8. (HINT: Numbers that are not multiples of 4 have the form $4n + 1$, $4n + 2$, or $4n + 3$, where n is an integer.)

Additional Answers
Written Exercises p. 535
6. Hypothesis: a, b, c and d are any numbers.
Conclusion: $a(b + c + d) = ab + ac + ad$
Proof:
1. a, b, c and d are any numbers. (Given)
2. $a(b + c + d) = a[(b + c) + d]$ (Assoc. post. for add.)
3. $a[(b + c) + d] = a(b + c) + ad$ (Dist. post.)
4. $a(b + c) + ad = ab + ac + ad$ (Dist. post.)
5. $a(b + c + d) = ab + ac + ad$ (Substitution)
8. Hypothesis: x and y are any numbers.
Conclusion: $(x + y)^2 = x^2 + 2xy + y^2$
Proof:
1. x and y are any numbers. (Given)
2. $(x + y)^2 = (x + y)(x + y)$ (Def. of exponents)
3. $(x + y)(x + y) = x^2 + 2xy + y^2$ (Mult. of binomials)
4. $(x + y)^2 = x^2 + 2xy + y^2$ (Substitution)

Quiz Sections 14-7–14-9
After completing this Review you may want to administer a quiz covering the same sections. See page M-57 of the Teacher's Manual for the suggested quiz.

_____ Review _____

See p. 593 for the answers to Ex. 1-10.

Using clock addition and multiplication, determine whether each finite set under these operations determines a field. If it does not, give an example to show that at least one postulate is not satisfied. *(Section 14–7)*

1. $\{0, 2, 4\}$ 2. $\{0, 1, 2, 3, 4, 5\}$ 3. $\{0, 1\}$ 4. $\{0, 2, 4, 6\}$

In Exercises 5–7, combine each pair of statements to form a true conditional. *(Section 14–8)*

5. A number is an odd number; a number is a rational number.

6. The sky is not cloudy; it is sunny outside.

7. The electricity is working; the lights are shining.

8. Write the converse of each conditional in Exercises 5–7. Then write *True* or *False* for each converse. *(Section 14–8)*

Write a direct proof for each of the following. *(Section 14–9)*

9. If a number is odd, then the cube of the number is odd.

10. The sum of three odd numbers is an odd number.

Chapter Summary

IMPORTANT TERMS

Acute angle (p. 508)
Altitude (p. 510)
Angle (p. 508)
Angle of depression (p. 524)
Angle of elevation (p. 524)
Base (p. 510)
Complementary angles (p. 508)
Compound statement (p. 532)
Conclusion (p. 534)
Conditional (p. 531)
Congruent angles (p. 513)
Converse (p. 532)
Cosine ratio (p. 520)
Degree (p. 508)
Direct proof (p. 534)
Endpoint (p. 508)
Field (p. 529)

Field postulates (p. 529)
Finite set (p. 527)
Hypothesis (p. 534)
Isosceles triangle (p. 510)
Line (p. 508)
Obtuse angle (p. 508)
Perpendicular (p. 508)
Ray (p. 508)
Right angle (p. 508)
Segment (p. 508)
Similar triangles (p. 513)
Sine ratio (p. 520)
Supplementary angles (p. 508)
Tangent ratio (p. 516)
Vertex (p. 508)
Vertex angle (p. 510)

IMPORTANT IDEAS

1. **Triangle—Sum Theorem**
   The sum of the measures of the angles of a triangle is 180°.

2. If two triangles are similar, then the corresponding sides are proportional.

3. A trigonometric ratio depends only on the measure of an acute angle, *not* on the size of the right triangle.

4. In using trigonometric ratios to solve problems, use the ratio that involves both the known parts and the part to be solved.

5. For a given set to be a field, it must satisfy the field postulates.

6. Each statement in a proof must be justified by a reason. The reason may be the hypothesis, a definition, a postulate, or a previously proved theorem.

Chapter Objectives and Review

Objective: *To use algebra to find the complement and supplement of an angle*
(*Section 14–1*)

1. The measure of an angle is 10° more than its complement. Find the measures of the angle, its complement, and its supplement. $50°; 40°; 130°$

2. The measure of an angle is 30° less than its supplement. Find the measures of the angle, its supplement and its complement. $75°; 105°; 15°$

Other Applications of Algebra   **537**

Additional Answers
Written Exercises p. 535

10. Hypothesis: n is an odd number.
    Conclusion: n^2 is an odd number.
    Proof:
    1. n is an odd number (Given)
    2. Let $n = 2k + 1$, then $n^2 = (2k + 1)^2$ (Def. of odd numbers)
    3. $(2k + 1)^2 = 4k^2 + 4k + 1$ (Squaring a binomial (Ex. 8))
    4. $4k^2 + 4k + 1 = 2(2k^2 + 2k) + 1$ (Dist. post.)
    5. $2k^2 + 2k$ is an integer (Closure post. for add. and mult.)
    6. $2(2k^2 + 2k) + 1$ is an odd number (Def. of odd number)
    7. n^2 is an odd number (Substitution)

12. Hypothesis: a is any even number and b is any odd number.
    Conclusion: $a + b$ is an odd number.
    Proof:
    1. a is even, b is odd (Given)
    2. Let $a = 2k$, $b = 2p + 1$. Then $a + b = 2k + 2p + 1$ (k and p are integers) (Def. of even and odd numbers)
    3. $2k + 2p + 1 = 2(k + p) + 1$ (Dist. post.)
    4. $k + p$ is an integer (Closure post. for add.)
    5. $2(k + p) + 1$ is an odd number (Def. of odd numbers)
    6. $a + b$ is an odd number (Substitution)

Objective: *To find the measures of the angles of a triangle, given a relationship between the measures of the angles (Section 14–2)*

3. In triangle FGH, the measure of $\angle F$ is $\frac{1}{2}$ the measure of $\angle G$. The measure of $\angle H$ is 20° less than the measure of $\angle F$. Find the measure of each angle.
$\angle G$: 100°; $\angle F$: 50°; $\angle H$: 30°

4. In triangle CDE, the measure of $\angle E$ is 5° less than the measure of $\angle C$. The measure of $\angle D$ is 3 times the measure of $\angle C$. Find the measure of each angle.
$\angle C$: 37°; $\angle D$: 111°; $\angle E$: 32°

Objective: *To find the length of an unknown side in an isosceles (or equilateral) triangle, using the altitude of the triangle (Section 14–2)*

5. In the baseball diamond shown at the right, the distance between each base is 90 feet. Find the distance between home plate and second base. Write your answer in simplest form. $90\sqrt{2}$ ft

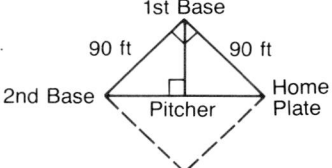

Objective: *To find the unknown lengths in similar triangles (Section 14–3)*

6. Triangles MRT and QSH are similar, with $MR = 7$, $RT = 6$, $MT = 4$ and $QH = 12$. Find HS and QS.
$\overline{QS}$: 21; $\overline{HS}$: 18

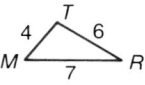
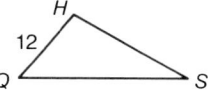

Objective: *To define and use the sine, cosine, and tangent ratios (Sections 14–4, 14–5, 14–6)*

Use triangle ABC to determine each ratio.

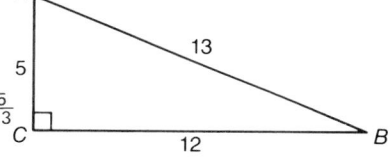

7. $\tan A$ $\frac{12}{5}$

8. $\tan B$ $\frac{5}{12}$

9. $\sin A$ $\frac{12}{13}$

10. $\cos A$ $\frac{5}{13}$

11. $\sin B$ $\frac{5}{13}$

12. $\cos B$ $\frac{12}{13}$

In each triangle, find *x* and *y*. Round answers to the nearest tenth.

13. $x = 14.0$
$y = 24.4$

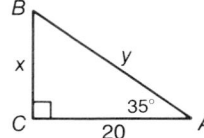

14. $x = 7.3$
$y = 6.8$

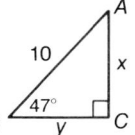

In each triangle, find the measure of $\angle A$. Round answers to the nearest degree.

15. 49°

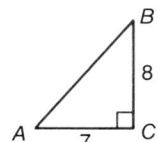

16. 60°

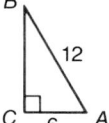

17. If you want the top of the 10-meter ladder shown below to be 8 meters from the ground, what must be the measure of angle B? **53°**

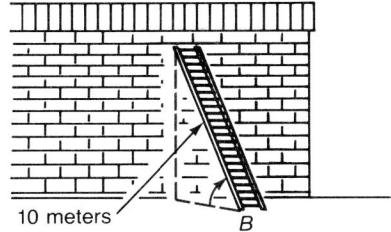

10 meters

B

18. If you want the bottom of the ladder above to be 7 meters from the building, what must be the measure of angle B? **46°**

Objective: *To test whether a given finite set of numbers under two given operations satisfies the postulates for a field (Section 14–7)*

Using clock addition and multiplication, determine whether each finite set under these operations determines a field. If it does not, show by an example that at least one postulate is not satisfied.

19. $\{0, 1, 2\}$ Yes **20.** $\{0, 1, 2, 3\}$ **21.** $\{0, 1, 2, 3, 4\}$

No; 2 has no mult. inv. Yes

Objective: *To determine when a conditional is false (Section 14–8)*

22. Under what conditions is the following statement false?

If I use an umbrella, then it is raining.

If I use an umbrella, then it is not raining.

Objective: *To combine two statements to make a true conditional (Section 14–8)*

23. Combine these two statements to make a true conditional.

6 is a factor of 12; 6 is a factor of 24.

If 6 is a factor of 12, then 6 is a factor of 24.

Objective: *To state the converse of a conditional (Section 14–8)*

24. State the converse of the conditional in Exercise 23. When is the converse false? If 6 is a factor of 24, then 6 is a factor of 12. If 6 is a factor of 24, then 6 is not a factor os 12.

Objective: *To relate definitions to conditionals and their converses (Section 14–8)*

25. Write this definition as a conditional and its converse. See page 594.

An odd number is a natural number that is not divisible by two.

Objective: *To write a direct proof (Section 14–9)*

Write a direct proof for each of the following.

26. $(3x^2)(-7x^3) = -21x^5$

27. The sum of two multiples of 4 is a multiple of 4. See page 594.

Other Applications of Algebra **539**

A formal Chapter Test is provided in the Teacher's Manual. See p. M-77.

Additional Answers

14. If today is Saturday, then Saturday is the last day of the week.

15. If a figure is a square, then the figure is a rectangle.

18. Hypothesis: n is an odd integer.
Conclusion: n^2 is an odd integer.
Proof:
1. n is an odd integer (Given)
2. Let $n = 2k + 1$ (Def. of odd numbers)
3. $n^2 = (2k + 1)(2k + 1)$ (Def. of exponent)
4. $(2k + 1)(2k + 1) = 2k(2k + 1) + 1(2k + 1)$ (Dist. post.)
5. $2k(2k + 1)$ is an even number (The product of an even number and an odd number is even. (Ex. 15, page 535))
6. $1(2k + 1) = 2k + 1$ (Identity post.)
7. $2k + 1$ is an odd number (Def. of odd numbers)
8. $2k(2k + 1) + (2k + 1)$ is odd (Sum of an even number and an odd number is odd. (Ex. 12, page 535))
9. n^2 is an odd number (Substitution)

20. Hypothesis: x is any number.
Conclusion: $5(x + 2) = 10 + 5x$
Proof:
1. $5(x + 2)$ (Given)
2. $5(x + 2) = 5(2 + x)$ (Comm. post.)
3. $5(2 + x) = 10 + 5x$ (Dist. post.)
4. $5(x + 2) = 10 + 5x$ (Substitution)

540

1. The measure of an angle is $\frac{1}{2}$ the measure of its supplement. Find the measures of the angle, its complement, and its supplement. angle: 60°; complement: 30°; supplement: 120°

2. In $\triangle XYZ$, m $\angle X$ is 10° more than m $\angle Y$ and m $\angle Z$ is 6° less than twice m $\angle Y$. Find the measures of the angles. $\angle X$: 54°; $\angle Y$: 44°; $\angle Z$: 82°

3. Two identical bookends are back-to-back, as shown at the right. Each base is 8 centimeters long, and each angled side is 15 centimeters long. Find the height of each bookend. 12.7 cm

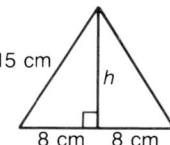

Find the unknown lengths in each pair of similar triangles.

4. 12

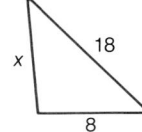
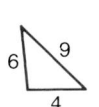

5. 2.625

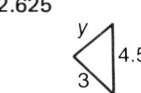
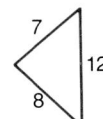

Use triangle ABC to write each ratio.

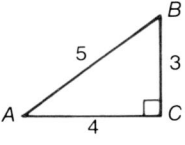

6. $\sin A$ $\frac{3}{5}$

7. $\tan A$ $\frac{3}{4}$

8. $\cos A$ $\frac{4}{5}$

9. $\tan B$ $\frac{4}{3}$

10. $\sin B$ $\frac{4}{5}$

11. $\cos B$ $\frac{3}{5}$

12. One angle of a right triangle measures 70° and the side adjacent to it measures 19 meters. To the nearest tenth of a meter, what is the measure of the side opposite the 70° angle? 52.2 m

Combine each pair of statements to form a true conditional.

13. 5 is a whole number; 5 is a rational number. If 5 is a whole number then 5 is a rational number.

14. Today is Saturday; Saturday is the last day of the week.

15. A figure is a square; a figure is a rectangle.

16. His name is Joe Junior; his father's name is Joe. If his name is Joe Junior, then his father's name is Joe.

17. Write the converse of each conditional in Exercises 13–16. Then write *True* or *False* for each converse. See page 594.

18. Prove: **If n is an odd integer, then n^2 is an odd integer.**

19. Determine whether the set of integers is a field under the usual definitions of addition and multiplication. Explain your answer. No. There is no inverse element.

20. Prove: $5(x + 2) = 10 + 5x$

540 *Chapter 14*

Table of Squares and Square Roots

No.	Square	Square Root	No.	Square	Square Root	No.	Square	Square Root
1	1	1.000	51	2601	7.141	101	10,201	10.050
2	4	1.414	52	2704	7.211	102	10,404	10.100
3	9	1.732	53	2809	7.280	103	10,609	10.149
4	16	2.000	54	2916	7.348	104	10,816	10.198
5	25	2.236	55	3025	7.416	105	11,025	10.247
6	36	2.449	56	3136	7.483	106	11,236	10.296
7	49	2.646	57	3249	7.550	107	11,449	10.344
8	64	2.828	58	3364	7.616	108	11,664	10.392
9	81	3.000	59	3481	7.681	109	11,881	10.440
10	100	3.162	60	3600	7.746	110	12,100	10.488
11	121	3.317	61	3721	7.810	111	12,321	10.536
12	144	3.464	62	3844	7.874	112	12,544	10.583
13	169	3.606	63	3969	7.937	113	12,769	10.630
14	196	3.742	64	4096	8.000	114	12,996	10.677
15	225	3.873	65	4225	8.062	115	13,225	10.724
16	256	4.000	66	4356	8.124	116	13,456	10.770
17	289	4.123	67	4489	8.185	117	13,689	10.817
18	324	4.243	68	4624	8.246	118	13,924	10.863
19	361	4.359	69	4761	8.307	119	14,161	10.909
20	400	4.472	70	4900	8.367	120	14,400	10.954
21	441	4.583	71	5041	8.426	121	14,641	11.000
22	484	4.690	72	5184	8.485	122	14,884	11.045
23	529	4.796	73	5329	8.544	123	15,129	11.091
24	576	4.899	74	5476	8.602	124	15,376	11.136
25	625	5.000	75	5625	8.660	125	15,625	11.180
26	676	5.099	76	5776	8.718	126	15,876	11.225
27	729	5.196	77	5929	8.775	127	16,129	11.269
28	784	5.292	78	6084	8.832	128	16,384	11.314
29	841	5.385	79	6241	8.888	129	16,641	11.358
30	900	5.477	80	6400	8.944	130	16,900	11.402
31	961	5.568	81	6561	9.000	131	17,161	11.446
32	1024	5.657	82	6724	9.055	132	17,424	11.489
33	1089	5.745	83	6889	9.110	133	17,689	11.533
34	1156	5.831	84	7056	9.165	134	17,956	11.576
35	1225	5.916	85	7225	9.220	135	18,225	11.619
36	1296	6.000	86	7396	9.274	136	18,496	11.662
37	1369	6.083	87	7569	9.327	137	18,769	11.705
38	1444	6.164	88	7744	9.381	138	19,044	11.747
39	1521	6.245	89	7921	9.434	139	19,321	11.790
40	1600	6.325	90	8100	9.487	140	19,600	11.832
41	1681	6.403	91	8281	9.539	141	19,881	11.874
42	1764	6.481	92	8464	9.592	142	20,164	11.916
43	1849	6.557	93	8649	9.644	143	20,449	11.958
44	1936	6.633	94	8836	9.695	144	20,736	12.000
45	2025	6.708	95	9025	9.747	145	21,025	12.042
46	2116	6.782	96	9216	9.798	146	21,316	12.083
47	2209	6.856	97	9409	9.849	147	21,609	12.124
48	2304	6.928	98	9604	9.899	148	21,904	12.166
49	2401	7.000	99	9801	9.950	149	22,201	12.207
50	2500	7.071	100	10,000	10.000	150	22,500	12.247

Table of Sines, Cosines, and Tangents

Angle	Sin	Cos	Tan	Angle	Sin	Cos	Tan
0°	.0000	1.0000	.0000	45°	.7071	.7071	1.0000
1	.0175	.9998	.0175	46	.7193	.6947	1.0355
2	.0349	.9994	.0349	47	.7314	.6820	1.0724
3	.0523	.9986	.0524	48	.7431	.6691	1.1106
4	.0698	.9976	.0699	49	.7547	.6561	1.1504
5	.0872	.9962	.0875	50	.7660	.6428	1.1918
6	.1045	.9945	.1051	51	.7771	.6293	1.2349
7	.1219	.9925	.1228	52	.7880	.6157	1.2799
8	.1392	.9903	.1405	53	.7986	.6018	1.3270
9	.1564	.9877	.1584	54	.8090	.5878	1.3764
10	.1736	.9848	.1763	55	.8192	.5736	1.4281
11	.1908	.9816	.1944	56	.8290	.5592	1.4826
12	.2079	.9781	.2126	57	.8387	.5446	1.5399
13	.2250	.9744	.2309	58	.8480	.5299	1.6003
14	.2419	.9703	.2493	59	.8572	.5150	1.6643
15	.2588	.9659	.2679	60	.8660	.5000	1.7321
16	.2756	.9613	.2867	61	.8746	.4848	1.8040
17	.2924	.9563	.3057	62	.8829	.4695	1.8807
18	.3090	.9511	.3249	63	.8910	.4540	1.9626
19	.3256	.9455	.3443	64	.8988	.4384	2.0503
20	.3420	.9397	.3640	65	.9063	.4226	2.1445
21	.3584	.9336	.3839	66	.9135	.4067	2.2460
22	.3746	.9272	.4040	67	.9205	.3907	2.3559
23	.3907	.9205	.4245	68	.9272	.3746	2.4751
24	.4067	.9135	.4452	69	.9336	.3584	2.6051
25	.4226	.9063	.4663	70	.9397	.3420	2.7475
26	.4384	.8988	.4877	71	.9455	.3256	2.9042
27	.4540	.8910	.5095	72	.9511	.3090	3.0777
28	.4695	.8829	.5317	73	.9563	.2924	3.2709
29	.4848	.8746	.5543	74	.9613	.2756	3.4874
30	.5000	.8660	.5774	75	.9659	.2588	3.7321
31	.5150	.8572	.6009	76	.9703	.2419	4.0108
32	.5299	.8480	.6249	77	.9744	.2250	4.3315
33	.5446	.8387	.6494	78	.9781	.2079	4.7046
34	.5592	.8290	.6745	79	.9816	.1908	5.1446
35	.5736	.8192	.7002	80	.9848	.1736	5.6713
36	.5878	.8090	.7265	81	.9877	.1564	6.3138
37	.6018	.7986	.7536	82	.9903	.1392	7.1154
38	.6157	.7880	.7813	83	.9925	.1219	8.1443
39	.6293	.7771	.8098	84	.9945	.1045	9.5144
40	.6428	.7660	.8391	85	.9962	.0872	11.4301
41	.6561	.7547	.8693	86	.9976	.0698	14.3007
42	.6691	.7431	.9004	87	.9986	.0523	19.0811
43	.6820	.7314	.9325	88	.9994	.0349	28.6363
44	.6947	.7193	.9657	89	.9998	.0175	57.2900
45	.7071	.7071	1.0000	90	1.0000	.0000	

GLOSSARY

Abscissa In an ordered pair, the first number, or x coordinate, is the *abscissa*. (Page 169)

Absolute value The *absolute value* of a real number x is the distance of x from 0. It is written $|x|$. (Page 47)

Acute angle An *acute angle* is an angle whose measure is less than $90°$. (Page 508)

Additive inverses *Additive inverses* are the same distance from zero on the number line. Their sum is zero. (Page 47)

Algebraic expression An *algebraic expression* contains at least one variable. (Page 2)

Altitude of a triangle The *altitude of a triangle* is a segment drawn from any vertex perpendicular to the opposite side. (Page 510)

Angle Two different rays that have the same endpoint form the sides of an *angle*. (Page 508)

Arithmetic mean The *arithmetic mean* of a set of numbers, scores, and so on, is the sum of the elements in the set divided by the number of elements. (Page 69)

Axis of symmetry A parabola can be folded so that its right side fits exactly over its left side. The line on which this fold can be made is called the *axis of symmetry*. (Page 489)

Binomial A *binomial* is the sum or difference of two monomials. (Page 296)

Combining like terms To *combine like terms* means to add or subtract the like terms. (Page 60)

Complementary angles Two angles whose measures have a sum of $90°$ are *complementary angles*. (Page 508)

Composite number A *composite number* is any integer greater than 1 that is not prime. (Page 316)

Compound sentence A *compound sentence* can be written as two simple sentences joined by a connective, such as <u>and</u> or <u>or</u>. (Page 250)

Conditional statement In mathematics, a statement in the if-then form is a *conditional statement*. (Page 531)

Congruent angles *Congruent angles* are angles that have the same measure. (Page 513)

Conjunction A compound sentence with <u>and</u> is a *conjunction*. (Page 250)

Consistent system A system of equations that has a solution set is a *consistent system*. (Page 213)

Constant of variation In the direct variation $y = kx$, k is called the *constant of variation*. (Page 197)

Converse The *converse* of a conditional statement is formed by interchanging the if- and then-statements. (Page 532)

Coordinate plane A plane that associates number pairs or coordinates with points is called a *coordinate plane*. The x and y axes separate the coordinate plane into four regions or quadrants. (Page 169)

Cosine ratio In a right triangle, the *cosine* of an acute angle is the ratio $\dfrac{\text{adjacent side}}{\text{hypotenuse}}$. (Page 520)

Counting numbers The set of *counting numbers* or natural numbers is the set of numbers whose members are 1 and every number found by adding 1 to a member of the set. (Page 22)

Direct proof A *direct proof* of a theorem shows that the then-statement follows from the if-statement. (Page 534)

Direct variation The equation $y = kx$, where k is a constant, expresses *direct variation* between x and y. (Page 197)

Discriminant The *discriminant* of the quadratic equation $ax^2 + bx + c = 0$ is the number $b^2 - 4ac$. (Page 486)

Disjunction A compound sentence with <u>or</u> is a *disjunction*. (Page 250)

Distance Formula If $P_1(x_1, y_1)$ and $P_2(x_2, y_2)$ are any two points in the coordinate plane, then the *distance*, d, between the points is given by the formula $d = \sqrt{(x_2 - x_1)^2 + (y_2 - y_1)^2}$. (Page 443)

Domain For ordered pairs of a relation, the set of all first coordinates is the *domain* of the relation. (Page 177)

Equation A mathematical sentence that contains the symbol "=" is an *equation*. (Page 18)

Equivalent equations *Equivalent equations* have the same solutions for the same replacement set. (Page 84)

Equivalent inequalities Inequalities that have the same solution set are called *equivalent inequalities*. (Page 140)

Equivalent systems Systems of equations that have the same solution set are *equivalent systems*. (Page 217)

Evaluate To *evaluate* means to find the value. (Page 5)

Even number An *even number* is a number of the form $2n$, where n is an integer. (Page 534)

Exponent The second power of 3 is written as 3^2. The raised two is called an *exponent*. The *exponent* indicates how many times a number is multiplied by itself. (Page 9)

Factor Since $35 = 7 \cdot 5$, 7 and 5 are *factors* of 35. (Page 9)

Field A set of numbers for which the field postulates hold for addition and multiplication is called a *field*. (Page 529)

Formula In a *formula*, variables and symbols are used to represent words. (Page 9)

Function A *function* is a relation for which no two ordered pairs have the same first element. (Page 177)

Half-plane If a line is drawn on the coordinate plane, a *half-plane* is the set of points that is on one side of the line. (Page 254)

Hypotenuse In a right triangle, the longest side is the *hypotenuse*. (Page 439)

Hypothesis In a proof, the if-statement is called the *hypothesis*. It is always taken to be true. (Page 534)

Inconsistent system A system of equations having no solution is called an *inconsistent system*. (Page 213)

Inequality A mathematical sentence that uses $>$, $<$, or $\neq$ is an *inequality*. (Page 18)

Integers The set of *integers* consists of the set of whole numbers and their opposites. (Page 22)

Intersection of two lines The *intersection of two lines* is the set of points common to both lines. (Page 212)

Inverse variation If the product of two variables is a nonzero constant, the variables are in *inverse variation*. The equation for the inverse variation may be written as $xy = k$ or $y = \frac{k}{x}$, where k is the constant of variation. (Page 412)

Irrational number *Irrational numbers* cannot be represented in the form $\frac{a}{b}$, where a is an integer and b is a natural number. (Page 26)

Joint variation When one variable varies directly as the product of two or more variables, the variation is called *joint variation*. Joint variation can be expressed by the equation $x = kyz$. (Page 416)

Least common denominator The *least common denominator* (LCD) of two or more rational expressions is the least common multiple of the denominators of the rational expressions. (Page 368)

Like radicals Radicals with the same radicands are *like radicals*. (Page 454)

Like terms *Like terms* have the same variables. In like terms, corresponding variables have the same exponents. (Page 60)

Linear equation An equation that can be written in the form $Ax + By = C$, where A, B, and C are real numbers and A and B are not both zero, is a *linear equation* in two variables. (Page 182)

Linear function A function whose ordered pairs satisfy a linear equation is a *linear function*. (Page 182)

Monomial A *monomial* is a term that is the product of numbers and variables with nonnegative integral exponents. (Page 283)

Numerical expression A *numerical expression* contains at least one of the operations of addition, subtraction, multiplication, and division. (Page 3)

Obtuse angle An *obtuse angle* is an angle whose measure is greater than $90°$ and less than $180°$. (Page 508)

Odd number An *odd number* is a number of the form $2n + 1$, where n is an integer. (Page 534)

Open sentence An equation that contains a variable is an *open sentence*. (Page 18)

Ordered pair An *ordered pair* is a pair of numbers, one of which is desginated as first and the other as second. (Page 169)

Ordinate In an ordered pair, the second number, or the y coordinate, is the *ordinate*. (Page 169)

Origin In the coordinate plane, the axes cross at the point $(0, 0)$, called the *origin*. (Page 169)

Per cent *Per cent* means per hundred or hundredths. (Page 103)

Perfect square A rational number is a *perfect square* if it is the square of a rational number. (Page 435)

Perimeter The *perimeter* of a geometric figure is the distance around it. To find this *perimeter*, add the lengths of the sides. (Page 129)

Perpendicular Two lines that are *perpendicular* to each other meet at right angles. (Page 169)

Polynomial A *polynomial* is a monomial or the sum of monomials. (Page 296)

Postulate A *postulate* is a statement that is accepted as true. (Page 30)

Prime factorization When a composite number is written as a product of prime-number factors or of powers of prime-number factors, the number is in *prime-factorization* form. (Page 316)

Prime number A *prime number* is an integer greater than 1 that has exactly two positive integral factors, itself and 1. (Page 316)

Prime polynomial When a polynomial has no polynomial factors with integral coefficients except itself and 1, it is a *prime polynomial* with respect to the integers. (Page 319)

Proportion A *proportion* is a statement that shows that two ratios are equal. (Page 350)

Quadrant A *quadrant* is one of four regions formed by the axes of a coordinate plane. (Page 169)

Quadratic equation An equation that can be written in the form $ax^2 + bx + c = 0$, where a, b, and c are real numbers and $a \neq 0$, is a *quadratic equation*. (Page 470)

Quadratic formula For any quadratic equation $ax^2 + bx + c = 0$, the solutions are

$$x = \frac{-b \pm \sqrt{b^2 - 4ac}}{2a}.$$ This is called the *quadratic formula*. (Page 476)

Quadratic function A *quadratic function* is a function defined by the equation $y = ax^2 + bx + c$, where a, b, and c are real numbers and $a \neq 0$. (Page 484)

Radical symbol In the expression $\sqrt{25}$, $\sqrt{}$ is the *radical symbol*. (Page 432)

Radicand In the expression $\sqrt{25}$, 25 is the *radicand*. (Page 432)

Range For ordered pairs, the set of all second coordinates is the *range*. (Page 177)

Ratio A *ratio* is a comparison of two numbers by division. (Page 350)

Rational expression A *rational expression* is an expression of the form $\frac{P}{Q}$, where P and Q

are polynomials and $Q \neq 0$. (Page 357)

Rational number A *rational number* is a number that can be expressed in the form $\frac{a}{b}$, where a is an integer and b is a natural number. (Page 22)

Rationalizing the denominator Eliminating the radical in the denominator of a fraction is called *rationalizing the denominator*. (Page 450)

Real numbers The union of the set of rational numbers and the set of irrational numbers is the set of *real numbers*. (Page 26)

Reciprocals Any two numbers whose product is 1 are called *reciprocals*, or multiplicative inverses, of each other. (Page 68)

Relation A *relation* is a set of ordered pairs. (Page 176)

Replacement set The *replacement set* is the set of numbers from which replacements for the variable are chosen. (Page 9)

Right angle An angle whose measure is 90° is a *right angle*. (Page 508)

Scientific notation When a number is represented as the product of some power of 10 and a number from 1 to 10, it is expressed in *scientific notation*. (Page 290)

Simplest form When the numerator and denominator of a rational expression have no common factors except 1 and −1, the expression is in *simplest form*. (Page 357)

Simplified radical A radical is in simplest form when the radicand does not contain a perfect square factor. (Page 437)

Sine ratio In a right triangle, the *sine* of an acute angle is the ratio $\frac{\text{opposite side}}{\text{hypotenuse}}$. (Page 520)

Slope The *slope* of a line is the ratio of the vertical change to the horizontal change between any two points on the line. That is, $\text{slope} = \frac{\text{vertical change}}{\text{horizontal change}}$, (horizontal change $\neq 0$). (Page 189)

Slope-intercept form of a linear equation The

equation $y = mx + b$ is called the *slope-intercept form of the linear equation*. (Page 195)

Solution set A *solution set* of an open sentence is the set of numbers that makes the sentence true. (Page 18)

Solve an equation To *solve an equation* means to find the number or numbers that will make the equation true. (Page 87)

Supplementary angles Two angles whose measures have a sum of 180° are *supplementary angles*. (Page 508)

System of linear equations Two or more linear equations in the same two variables form a *system of linear equations*. (Page 212)

Tangent ratio In a right triangle, the *tangent* of an acute angle is the ratio $\frac{\text{opposite side}}{\text{adjacent side}}$. (Page 516)

Term A *term* is a real number, a variable, or the product of real numbers and variables. (Page 60)

Theorem A *theorem* is a statement that can be proved from postulates and definitions. (Page 51)

Trinomial A polynomial with three terms is called a *trinomial*. (Page 296)

Unit price The *unit price* is the cost per gram, per ounce, and so on. (Page 12)

Variable A *variable* is a letter representing one or more numbers. (Page 2)

Whole numbers The set of *whole numbers* is the set of counting numbers and zero. (Page 22)

x intercept The x coordinate of a point where the line intersects the x axis is called an *x intercept*. (Page 484)

y intercept The y coordinate at which a line crosses the y axis is called the *y intercept*. (Page 194)

Zeros of a function The *zeros of a function* are the values for which the function equals zero. (Page 484)

INDEX

Boldfaced numerals indicate the pages that contain formal or informal definitions.

ANSWERS TO SELECTED EXERCISES

Answers to Selected Exercises

CHAPTER 1: USES OF ALGEBRA

Page 3 Classroom Exercises 1. d   3. b   5. c   7. 34   9. 7

Page 3 Written Exercises 1. 5 subtracted from q   3. q subtracted from 5   5. q multiplied by 5   7. q divided by 5   9. s multiplied by r   11. 4 subtracted from s   13. s multiplied by 16   15. n divided by t   17. $d + \ell$ 19. $d + i$ 21. $180 - a$ 23. $150 - s$ 25. 4.50h   27. 3c   29. $\frac{t}{24}$ 31. $\frac{s}{40}$ 33. 26   35. 13   37. 20   39. 0   41. 0   43. 48   45. 1   47. 16   49. The sum of a and b, divided by 5   51. The difference of a and b, multiplied by 9

Page 4 Review Capsule for Section 1-2 1. $\frac{2}{3}$ 2. $\frac{1}{4}$ 3. $\frac{1}{3}$ 4. $\frac{3}{4}$ 5. $\frac{2}{3}$ 6. $\frac{7}{8}$ 7. $\frac{1}{6}$ 8. $\frac{1}{5}$ 9. $\frac{4}{15}$ 10. $2\frac{5}{8}$ 11. $2\frac{2}{3}$ 12. 8.97   13. 25.17   14. 60.637   15. 5.4   16. 5.36   17. 3.0672   18. 190.6   19. 84.1   20. 0.064   21. 65.333   22. 1880   23. 0.138   24. 6.2   25. 35   26. 45

Page 6 Classroom Exercises 1. 10   3. 30   5. 22   7. 14   9. 340   11. 32   13. $2\frac{3}{5}$ 15. 1

Page 7 Written Exercises 1. 69   3. 84   5. 18   7. 57   9. 23   11. 12   13. 0   15. 184   17. 100   19. 360   21. 7   23. $\frac{6}{7}$ 25. $\frac{4}{9}$ 27. $\frac{1}{11}$ 29. $\frac{3}{8}$ 31. 34   33. 160   35. 24   37. 44   39. $\frac{4}{23}$ 41. 130   43. 18   45. 19   47. 1   49. 8   51. 9.99   53. 42.2   55. $2\frac{4}{5}$ 57. 2.25   59. $(1 + 9) \cdot (2 + 7)$ 61. $2(5 + 7 + 9)$ 63. $(2 \cdot 12) \div (2 + 6)$ 65. $25 + 11t$ 67. $475 - 15w$

Page 8 Puzzle See Solution Key.

Page 8 Review Capsule for Section 1-3 1. 0.08   2. 0.02   3. 0.12   4. 1.28   5. 0.045   6. 0.005   7. 9.982   8. 29.230   9. 2.1504   10. 0.01   11. 6.25   12. $\frac{1}{9}$ 13. $\frac{125}{512}$ 14. $\frac{8}{9}$ 15. $1\frac{1}{2}$ 16. $1\frac{5}{8}$ 17. $1\frac{13}{28}$ 18. $6\frac{1}{2}$ 19. $10\frac{3}{10}$ 20. $12\frac{3}{4}$ 21. $16\frac{21}{40}$ 22. $\frac{7}{30}$ 23. $\frac{11}{20}$ 24. $\frac{7}{24}$ 25. $\frac{29}{63}$ 26. $4\frac{3}{4}$ 27. $4\frac{11}{24}$ 28. $2\frac{17}{48}$ 29. $\frac{17}{40}$ 30. $4\frac{5}{12}$ 31. $1\frac{5}{24}$ 32. $4\frac{1}{3}$ 33. $2\frac{11}{12}$

Page 10 Classroom Exercises 1. $0.54; $0.72; $1.20   3. 64   5. $\frac{1}{25}$ 7. $\frac{1}{16}$ 9. $0; \frac{1}{2}; 6$ 11. 0; 2; 24

Page 10 Written Exercises 1. $0.80; $2; $4   3. $1; $2.50; $5   5. 4; 8; 12   7. 0; 1; 2   9. 6; 9; 14   11. $\frac{1}{3}; \frac{2}{3}; 1$ 13. 16; 20; 24   15. 18; 22; 26   17. $8\frac{1}{2}; 10\frac{1}{2}; 12\frac{1}{2}$ 19. 11; 12; 13   21. $5\frac{1}{2}; 6\frac{1}{2}; 7\frac{1}{2}$ 23. 512; 1000; 1728   25. 32   27. 0.01   29. 1.44   31. 0.0016   33. 0.000064   35. $\frac{16}{81}$ 37. 1.0404   39. 100,000   41. $\frac{1}{4}; \frac{1}{100}; \frac{9}{100}$ 43. 0.0225; 0.0625; 2.0449   45. $\frac{1}{2000}; \frac{1}{1000}; \frac{1}{10}; 1; 10$ 47. 180; 360; 540; 720   49. Represents even numbers only   51. Does not represent even numbers only   53. 0.25   55. 1   57. 0.0625   59. 0.015625   61. 0

Page 11 Puzzle See Solution Key.

Page 11 Review Capsule for Section 1-4 1. 4340   2. 8160   3. 78,480   4. 184,000   5. 0.9   6. 1.1   7. 37.5   8. 0.5   9. 101.0   10. 0.0   11. 1.9   12. 333.3   13. 0.0   14. $\frac{5}{12}$ 15. $51\frac{3}{5}$ 16. $58\frac{9}{40}$

Page 13 Classroom Exercises 1. $2800   3. 4.5¢

Page 13 Written Exercises 1. $1950   3. $1060   5. $1191.016 ≈ $1191.02   7. $0.007   9. $1.913   11. $0.124   13. 946-ml bottle   15. 24-ounce container   17. 60 cubic in   19. 2160 cubic cm   21. 168 cubic ft   23. 3.6 cubic m   25. 115 square units   27. 15 sq units   29. 1 square unit   31. 10%   33. $33\frac{1}{3}$%   35. 30%   37. $3112.50   39. $12,812.50   41. $C = 40\pi$, $A = 400\pi$ 43. $C = 80\pi$, $A = 1600\pi$ 45. $C \approx 62.8$ units, $A \approx 314$ square units   47. $C \approx 628$ units, $A \approx 31,400$ square units   49. a. $12, $15

b. 3   51. a. 280, 560, 1120, 2240   b. 7A   53. a. $352.75, $365.50, $378.25, $391, $403.75
b. 340 + 12.75h   55. a. 11 m, 16.5 m, 22 m, 24.75 m, 27.5 m   b. 5.5, 5.5 · $\frac{r}{16}$

Page 16   Review Capsule for Section 1-5   1. 16   2. 10   3. 5   4. 52   5. 30.5   6. 2.5   7. 1, 9, 17, 25,
33   8. 3, 17, 31, 45, 59   9. 1, 201, 401, 601, 801   10. 2, $\frac{14}{11}, \frac{22}{19}, \frac{10}{9}, \frac{38}{35}$ 11. 6, 14, 22, 30, 38
12. 1, 1, 1, 1, 1

Page 17   Consumer Application   1. $5691; 28.5¢   3. $6168.25; 29.4¢

Page 19   Classroom Exercises   1. F; $1\frac{7}{8} \neq 13\frac{1}{3}$ 3. F; 0 = 0   5. F; $\frac{57}{60} < \frac{67}{60}$ 7. {5}   9. {3, 7, 9, 11}

Page 19   Written Exercises   1. T   3. F; 16 ≠ 18   5. T   7. T   9. T   11. F; 56 > 55   13. {8}
15. {10}   17. {2, 4, 6, 8, 10}   19. {4}   21. {2, 4, 6, 8, 10}   23. {2}   25. {0, 1, 2, 3, 4, 5}   27. {5}
29. ϕ   31. {4, 5}   33. ϕ   35. {20}   37. {5, 10, 15, 20}   39. {0, 10, 15, 20}   41. {15}   43. {2}
45. {1}   47. {1, 2}   49. ϕ   51. T   53. F; $1^2 \not> 1 + 1$ 55. T   57. T   59. T   61. F; $2 \cdot \frac{1}{2} = 1$ and $\frac{1}{2}$ is
not a whole number.   63. F; $(0.2)^3 \not> (0.2)^2$

Page 20   Review   1. 3 · d, or 3d   2. m ÷ 15, or $\frac{m}{15}$ 3. 22   4. 7   5. $\frac{9}{40}$ 6. 4   7. 0   8. 11   9. 10;
38; 54   10. $2\frac{1}{2}$; 6; 8   11. $\frac{1}{8}$; 64; 216   12. 30; 72; 96   13. 135   14. 0.042   15. $\frac{1}{3}$ 16. {1, 2}
17. {1, 2, 3, 5}   18. {3, 4, 5}   19. {1, 2}

Page 21   Calculator Exercises   1. 20   3. 100   5. 37   7. 7.39216   9. 9.866

Page 21   Review Capsule for Section 1-6   1. 2   2. 6   3. 15   4. 70   5. 15   6. 43   7. 76   8. 45

Page 23   Classroom Exercises   1. whole number, integer, rational number   3. rational number   5. rational
number   7. $\frac{0}{1}$ 9. $\frac{50}{3}$ 11. $\frac{-52}{10}$

Page 23   Written Exercises   1. F; it is not a positive integer   3. T   5. T   7. T   9. T   11. F; it includes
positive and negative rational numbers and zero.   13. $\frac{4}{10}$ 15. $\frac{37}{100}$ 17. $\frac{-19}{3}$ 19. $\frac{15}{4}$ 21. $\frac{6725}{100}$ 23. $\frac{0}{1}$
25. 6   27. ⁻462   29. 525   31. ⁻155   33. 12   35. ⁻15   37. $4\frac{1}{2}$ 39. ⁻6   41. ⁻1   43. $2\frac{3}{4}$
45. ⁻31   47. 73.20   49. ⁻250   51. ⁻3.5   53. ⁻315   55. ⁻500   57. F; negative integers are not
whole numbers.   59. F; zero is not a natural number.   61. F; fractions are not integers.   63. F; fractions
and negative natural numbers are not whole numbers.   65. F; zero is not a natural number.

Page 25   Review Capsule for Section 1-7   1. 0.66666   2. 0.27272   3. 0.22222   4. 0.58333   5. 0.16666
6. 60   7. 70, 0.7   8. 95   9. 100, 0.46   10. 100, 0.72   11. 525, 5.25   12. 7.5   13. 0.75   14. 0.2,
8.2

Page 27   Classroom Exercises   1. Ir; there is no positive integer n such that n · n = 5.   3. Ir; there is no
positive integer n such that n · n = 21.   5. Q; $\sqrt{144}$ = 12 and 12 is a rational number.   7. N, W, I, Q, R
9. Q, R   11. Q, R   13. 4.359   15. 10.050   17. 12.207

Page 27   Written Exercises   1. $0.\overline{6}$ 3. $5.\overline{3}$ 5. 7.1875   7. 1.375   9. 0.15   11. $⁻0.\overline{27}$ 13. Ir; there
there is no positive integer n such that n · n = 7.   15. Ir; there is no positive integer n such that n · n = 11.
17. Q; $\sqrt{625}$ = 25 and 25 is a rational number.   19. Ir; there is no positive integer n such that n · n = 83.
21. Q; $\sqrt{\frac{36}{16}} = \frac{6}{4}$ and $\frac{6}{4}$ is a rational number.   23. Q; $\sqrt{100}$ = 10 and 10 is a rational number.   25. Q, R
27. Ir, R   29. Ir, R   31. I, Q, R   33. Q, R   35. A: 2; B: ⁻3; C: ⁻5; D: ⁻2; E: ⁻4   37. K: $\sqrt{3}$;
L: $\frac{1}{3}$; M: $\frac{-1}{3}$; O: $\frac{5}{6}$; P: $\frac{-5}{6}$ 39. 4.243   41. 10.488   43. 4.123   45. 8.944   47. 8.718   49. The
point would be close to 4.1.   51. The point would be close to 8.7.   53. 8   55. 16   57. 9   59. 20
61. 25   63. 39   65. 3.141666   67. 3.141600   69. ⊄   71. ⊂   73. ⊄   75. ⊄   77. ⊂   79. natural,
whole, rational, irrational   81. real

Page 29   Puzzle   See Solution Key.

Page 32 Classroom Exercises 1. Dist. post. 3. Comm. post. for mult. 5. Identity post. for add.
7. Identity post. for mult. 9. Comm. post. for add. 11. Closure post. for mult.

Page 32 Written Exercises 1. Comm. post. for add. 3. Comm. post. for mult. 5. Assoc. post. for
mult. 7. Comm. post. for add. 9. Comm. post. for add. 11. Dist. post. 13. Closure post. for add.
15. 12, Comm. post. for mult. 17. 10, Comm. post. for add. 19. 0, Ident. post. for add. 21. 32
23. 8365 25. 24 27. 190 29. 12,000 31. 2600 33. 48 35. 19 37. 940 39. 56 41. 670
43. 63 45. 2255 47. 430 49. 260 51. 260 53. Assoc. post. for mult., Comm. post. for mult.
55. Dist. post., Comm. post. for mult. 57. 5x; 50; 110; 1340 59. 2; 0 61. 16; 12 63. No 65. No;
$6 \div 2 \neq 2 \div 6, 3 \neq \frac{1}{3}$ 67. F; $6 \div (3 \cdot 1) \neq (6 \div 3) \cdot (6 \div 1), 2 \neq 12$ 69. F; $6 - (3 + 1) \neq (6 - 3) + (6 - 1)$,
$2 \neq 8$ 71. F; $6 - (3 - 1) \neq (6 - 3) - (6 - 1), 4 \neq ^-2$

Page 36 Computer Exercises See Solution Key.

Page 37 Review 1. $^-12\frac{1}{2}$ 2. 1.25 3. True 4. False; fractions and negative numbers are not natural
numbers. 5. True 6. True 7. True 8. Q 9. Ir; there is no positive integer n such that n · n = 33 10. Q
11. Q 12. Ir; there is no positive integer n such that n · n = 18 13. Ir; there is no positive integer n such
that n · n = 50 14. 14 15. 6 16. 13 17. Comm. post. for mult. 18. Comm. post. for add.
19. Dist. post. 20. 19 21. 19.2 22. 56

Page 37 Chapter Objectives and Review 1. 5x 3. $\frac{a}{4}$ 5. 5 7. 5 9. 55 11. 16 13. $\frac{1}{3}$ 15. 176
17. 75 19. 2 21. 0.21; 0.35; 0.49 23. 4; 5; 6 25. $\frac{9}{64}$ 27. 1 29. {3} 31. {12} 33. T 35. T
37. T 39. $^-3$ 41. 10 43. I, Q, R 45. Ir, R 47. Q, R 49. Ir, R 51. $^-1\frac{1}{4}$ 53. $\sqrt{2}$ 55. 2.646
57. 10.630 59. Comm. post. for add. 61. Assoc. post. for mult. 63. $\frac{1}{8}$; Assoc. post. for mult. 65. 6

Page 41 Chapter Test 1. $b - v$ 3. 7.55y 5. 12 7. 4 9. 11.6 11. 35 13. {0, 1, 2} 15. T
17. F; the opposite of 2 is $^-2$. 19. $^-105.1$ 21. I, Q, R 23. Ir, R 25. 7300

Page 42 Additional Practice 1. 10 3. 6 5. $\frac{2}{21}$ 7. $\frac{1}{3}$ 9. 11; 14; 17 11. 19; 28; 39 13. {9}
15. {4} 17. $\frac{3}{10}$ 19. $\frac{7}{3}$ 21. $\frac{^-38}{1}$ 23. Ir; there is no positive integer n such that n · n = 5 25. Q
27. Ir; there is no positive integer n such that n · n = 52. 29. 5.385 31. 10.536 33. 8.660 35. Ident.
post. for add. 37. Comm. post. for add. 39. C = 12p + 7 41. 270 cubic in

CHAPTER 2: OPERATIONS WITH REAL NUMBERS

Page 45 Classroom Exs. 1. $^-2$ 3. 7.8 5. $^-7\frac{1}{3}$ 7. $\frac{1}{7}$ 9. $^-0$ 11. q = $^-6$ 13. q = 6 15. > 17. >

Page 45 Classroom Exercises 1. $^-2$ 3. 7.8 5. $^-7\frac{1}{3}$ 7. $\frac{1}{7}$ 9. $^-0$ 11. q = $^-6$ 13. q = 6 15. > 17. >

Page 45 Written Exercises 1. $^-6$ 3. $^-9$ 5. $6\frac{1}{2}$ 7. $^-9.02$ 9. $\frac{2}{3}$ 11. 9.001 13. $^-5$ 15. $^-3.14$
17. $\frac{5}{6}$ 19. $^-9$ 21. $^-0.9$ 23. $^-1.2$ 25. $^-0$ 27. $^-3$ 29. t 31. m 33. x = $^-9$ 35. x = $^-0$
37. y = $^-3.25$ 39. a = $\frac{3}{4}$ 41. < 43. < 45. > 47. > 49. > 51. > 53. > 55. > 57. <
59. < 61. 27 = $^-(^-27)$ 63. $^-20 = ^-(20)$ 65. $^-(^-200) = 200$ 67. $^-1\frac{1}{4} = ^-(1\frac{1}{4})$ 69. $^-(^-500)$
$= 500$ 71. $^-(2\frac{3}{4}) = ^-2\frac{3}{4}$ 73. negative 75. positive 77. x = 4 79. x = 0 81. x < 0 83. t > $^-4$

Page 48 Classroom Exercises 1. $^-6.5$ 3. m 5. $^-0$ 7. 7 9. $^-7$ 11. 3 13. < 15. >

Page 49 Written Exercises 1. $^-6$ 3. $3\frac{1}{5}$ 5. 6.8 7. π 9. $\sqrt{2}$ 11. $^-5$ 13. $^-4$ 15. $^-0.9$ 17. 12
19. $^-15\frac{1}{2}$ 21. 0 23. r 25. a 27. ^-x 29. 6 31. π 33. 15 35. 0 37. 100 39. 462
41. 22,000 43. 7.25 45. $\sqrt{5}$ 47. 7.6 49. $\sqrt{7}$ 51. $^-19$ 53. 12 55. 15 57. 12 59. 21
61. $\frac{7}{6}$ 63. 251 65. 0 67. 0 69. = 71. > 73. > 75. = 77. < 79. = 81. T 83. T
85. F; | $^-35$ | = 35, and 35 $\not>$ 35 87. F; | $^-17.9$ | = 17.9, and 17.9 $\not<$ 17.9 89. F; | $^-\frac{1}{3}$ | = $\frac{1}{3}$, and $\frac{1}{3} > \frac{1}{4}$
91. T 93. 7 = a 95. $^-2\frac{2}{3}$ = y 97. y = ±4 99. x = ±2 101. > 103. T 105. T

Page 50 Calculator Exercises 1. 6 3. 6 5. 6 7. 4

Page 50 Review Capsule for Section 2-3 1. 115 2. 1230 3. 5565 4. 0.76 5. 20.67 6. 55.996
7. $\frac{2}{3}$ 8. $8\frac{3}{5}$ 9. $1\frac{5}{8}$ 10. $\frac{7}{24}$ 11. $13\frac{1}{2}$ 12. $4\frac{1}{2}$ 13. $17\frac{3}{10}$ 14. $15\frac{23}{24}$

Page 53 Classroom Exercises 1. Negative 3. Negative 5. Positive 7. Positive 9. −15 11. −1
13. 1 15. 4 17. −7.3 19. $\frac{5}{6}$ 21. −25 23. 13

Page 53 Written Exercises 1. 3 3. −9 5. 3 7. −3 9. −13 11. 4 13. 4 15. 5 17. −14
19. 9 21. −1 23. 1 25. 15 27. −1 29. −9 31. $1\frac{1}{4}$ 33. $11\frac{1}{2}$ 35. $1\frac{3}{4}$ 37. −2.1 39. −13.2
41. 6 43. 4.9 45. −7.6 47. −4 + 5 + 7; 8 yards 49. 52 + (−4) + 2; $50 51. 250 + (−75) + (−40)
+ 110; $245 53. −15,890 + 5750 + 30,765; net profit: $26,625 55. −10 57. 10 59. 17 61. 12
63. −1 65. −9 67. −2 69. $1\frac{2}{5}$ 71. 38 73. −25 75. 16 77. −17 79. −40
81. 1. Renaming 17 as 11 + 6 2. Assoc. post. for add. 3. Additive inv. post. 4. Ident. post. for add.
83. Theorem 2-1 **85.** 1. −9 + 7 = [−2 + (−7)] + 7 (Th. 2-1) 2. [−2 + (−7)] + 7 = −2 + [(−7) + 7]
(Assoc. post. for add.) 3. −2 + [(−7) + 7] = −2 + 0 (Add. inv. post.) 4. −2 + 0 = −2 (Ident. post. for
add.)

Page 55 Review Capsule for Section 2-4 1. 21 2. 17 3. 358 4. 128 5. 5.4 6. 3.8 7. 14.11
8. 3.3 9. $\frac{7}{10}$ 10. $14\frac{3}{8}$ 11. $\frac{0}{12}$ or 0 12. $\frac{1}{2}$ 13. $2\frac{1}{2}$ 14. $2\frac{5}{8}$ 15. $\frac{7}{24}$ 16. $6\frac{17}{24}$

Page 57 Classroom Exercises 1. 6 + (−3) 3. −10 + (−5) 5. −5 + 2 7. 8 + 4 9. 23 11. −5
13. −8.4 15. $\frac{1}{4}$

Page 57 Written Exercises 1. 3 + (−6) 3. 5 + 9 5. 0 + (2) 7. −5 + 5 9. −2 + (−8) 11. −3 + 9
13. $-2\frac{1}{2} + \frac{1}{2}$ 15. 2.9 + (−3.8) 17. −6 19. −9 21. −8 23. 10 25. −10 27. −12 29. 31
31. 0 33. −19 35. −11.8 37. −7.8 39. 1 41. −40 43. 5.6 45. 19.0 47. 6.7 49. 5.6
51. 0 53. 12° 55. 3 m 57. −26° 59. −5 61. 3 63. 11 65. $-\frac{1}{2}$ 67. −17 69. 18 71. 2
73. 2 75. 0 77. 16 79. 14 81. F; $-\frac{2}{3} - (-\frac{2}{3}) = 0, 0 \neq \frac{1}{3}$ 83. F; 0.24 − (−0.24) = 0.48, 0 ≠ 0.48
85. T 87. T 89. T 91. T

Page 58 Review 1. 1.5 2. −600 3. −37 4. −3.6 5. 3 6. −(−15) 7. 18 8. $\sqrt{13}$ 9. 7
10. 0 11. x = 6 12. m = −8 13. y = 9 or y = −9 14. a = 3 or a = −3 15. −3 16. −5 17. 5
18. −11 19. −2.51 20. −8

Page 59 Consumer Applications 1. $93 profit 3. $1790.30 loss

Page 61 Classroom Exercises 1. Like; same variable, x, with same exponent, 1. 3. Unlike; different
exponents for y. 5. Like; same variables, x and y, with same exponents, 1. 7. 2 9. −0.05 11. 1
13. 5x 15. 4m

Page 61 Written Exercises 1. Like; same variable, x, with same exponent, 1. 3. Unlike; number, 9, has no
variable. 5. Unlike; different exponents for x. 7. Unlike; different variables. 9. Like; same variable, t,
with same exponent, 1. 11. Like; same variable, x, with same exponent, 4. 13. 10x 15. 21.2m
17. 14mn 19. 10x 21. $5m^2$ 23. 20m 25. −8y 27. −6.4y 29. −17t 31. m 33. 3x 35. 3x
37. −7a 39. 3m 41. −5r 43. 5a + 4 45. 21y + 3 47. 6x + 6 49. 12x − 6y 51. −4x − 15
53. m 55. 5x + 3y + 57 57. 6xy + x 59. $14\frac{1}{12}xy$ 61. 7.37r 63. 7.52q + 4.87 65. 8h
67. $w^2 + 5w + 25$ 69. F; if m = 1, then 3 + 1 = 1 and this is false. 71. F; if m = 0, then 0 − 0 + 5 = 11
and this is false. 73. F; if a = 1 and b = 2, then 4(1)(2) + 1 = 5(1)(2) or 9 = 10 and this is false. 75. T
77. F; if x = 1, then 5 + 2 + 9 = 21 and this is false. 79. $A = 8h - \frac{1}{2}(3h)$, $A = 6\frac{1}{2}h$ 81. $A = \frac{1}{2}(13h) - \frac{1}{2}(8h)$,
$A = \frac{5}{2}h$ 83. $\frac{11}{56}c + \frac{1}{20}d$ 85. $\frac{1}{2}c - 1\frac{1}{2}d$ 87. 4x − 4y 89. −2x − 8y 91. $6x^2 - 6y^2$ 93. 2a − 2b
95. (x − y) 97. (7 + 6) 99. (c − d)

Page 63 Review Capsule for Section 2-6 1. 486 2. 2268 3. 300,884 4. 455,005 5. 0.56

6. 45.92 7. 4059 8. 1.9544 9. $\frac{1}{5}$ 10. $\frac{4}{15}$ 11. $\frac{21}{8}$ 12. $35\frac{119}{160}$

Page 65 Classroom Exercises 1. Negative 3. Positive 5. Negative 7. Positive 9. −56 11. 72
13. 20 15. 0

Page 65 Written Exercises 1. −18 3. −10 5. −10 7. 0 9. −12 11. $-\frac{1}{2}$ 13. 10 15. −15
17. 12 19. 0.25 21. 25 23. −18 25. −2 27. −72 29. −5 31. −8 33. −6200 35. $-\frac{33}{25}$
37. 0 39. −18 41. 20 43. −20 45. 0 47. −7 49. 1 51. 6.0 53. −1 55. −60 57. −20
59. −0.001 61. −1 63. $-\frac{7}{2}$ 65. $\frac{8}{27}$ 67. −1 69. −40 71. −120 73. 120 75. 0 77. −8
79. 16 81. 1 83. −1 85. = 87. > 89. = 91. = 93. = 95. −6 97. 6 99. 0 101. 18
103. −11 105. −4 107. 9 109. 0 111. Negative 113. Positive **115.** 1. 4 + (−4) = 0 (Add. inv.
post.) 2. 3[4 + (−4)] = 3 · 0 (Mult. prop. for equations) 3. 3[4 + (−4)] = 0 (Zero mult. theorem)
4. 3 · 4 + 3(−4) = 0 (Dist. post. of mult. over add.) 5. Hence, 3 · 4 and 3(−4) are additive inverses.
(Add. inv. post.) 6. 3(−4) = −(3 · 4) or −12 (Add. inv. post.)

Page 67 Review Capsule for Section 2-7 1. 5 2. 81 3. 5 4. 7 5. 0.9 6. 9.7 7. 0.0594 8. 70
9. $\frac{1}{3}$ 10. $\frac{3}{16}$ 11. 92 12. $\frac{46}{95}$ 13. $\frac{50}{3}$ 14. $\frac{303}{260}$ 15. 1 16. $\frac{25}{18}$ 17. 1.6 18. 0.4 19. 0.0
20. 21.4 21. 158.0 22. 7.0 23. 14.5 24. 76.1 25. 1.0 26. 0.0

Page 69 Classroom Exercises 1. Neg. 3. Pos. 5. $\frac{1}{7}$ 7. $-\frac{3}{2}$ 9. 0 11. 1 13. −1 15. 81

Page 70 Written Exercises 1. Neg. 3. Neg. 5. −4 7. 4 9. 0 11. −50 13. −1 15. −1
17. −6 19. −36 21. −0 23. $\frac{9}{8}$ 25. 3.2 27. −18 29. −7.85 31. $-\frac{16}{9}$ 33. + $7,600

35. −0.8 37. 0.4 39. 5 41. $\frac{1}{3}$ 43. $\frac{2}{11}$ 45. −3 47. −1 49. −9 51. −17 53. −22.5

Page 71 Review Capsule for Section 2-8 1. $\frac{13}{2}$ 2. $\frac{31}{4}$ 3. $-\frac{25}{4}$ 4. $-\frac{39}{4}$ 5. $\frac{11}{10}$ 6. $-\frac{29}{8}$ 7. $\frac{3}{2}$

8. −26 9. $\frac{363}{8}$ 10. $-\frac{119}{4}$ 11. 0 12. 0 13. −1.5 14. $\frac{2}{3}$ 15. 1 16. 1 17. −12 18. $-\frac{4}{3}$

Page 73 Classroom Exercises 1. −10 3. −2 5. 36 7. 12 9. 12 11. $-\frac{1}{4}$ 13. $-\frac{3}{2}$ 15. 1
17. 9 19. 1

Page 73 Written Exercises 1. −25 3. −30 5. 150 7. 225 9. 325 11. 0 13. 0 15. 5
17. −5 19. 15 21. $\frac{3}{2}$ 23. 0 25. 1 27. y 29. −y 31. −y 33. −5a 35. a 37. -15b
39. $-\frac{3}{8}$q 41. −4x 43. −15p 45. 15p 47. $\frac{7}{9}; \frac{7}{9}(\frac{9}{7}y) = (\frac{7}{9} \cdot \frac{9}{7})y = y$ 49. $-\frac{1}{8}; -\frac{1}{8}(-8y) = [-\frac{1}{8}(-8)]y$
= y 51. $-5; -5(-\frac{1}{5}y) = [-5(-\frac{1}{5})]y = y$ 53. $-\frac{5}{2}; -\frac{5}{2}(-\frac{2}{5}y) = [-\frac{5}{2}(-\frac{2}{5})]y = y$ 55. $-\frac{8}{3}; -\frac{8}{3}(-\frac{3}{8}y)$
$= [-\frac{8}{3}(-\frac{3}{8})]y = y$ 57. $-1; -1(-y) = [-1(-1)]y = y$ 59. $1; 1(1y) = (1 \cdot 1)y = y$ 61. $\frac{4}{13}; \frac{4}{13}(3\frac{1}{4}y)$
$= (\frac{4}{13} \cdot \frac{13}{4})y = y$ 63. $-\frac{2}{17}; -\frac{2}{17}(-8\frac{1}{2}y) = [-\frac{2}{17}(-\frac{17}{2})]y = y$ 65. $-10; -10(-\frac{y}{10}) = [-10(-\frac{1}{10})]y = y$
67. $-1; x + 1 + (-1) = x + [1 + (-1)] = x + 0 = x$ 69. $9; x + (-9) + 9 = x + [(-9) + 9] = x + 0 = x$
71. $4; x + (-4) + 4 = x + [(-4) + 4] = x + 0 = x$ 73. $12; (-12) + 6 + x = [(-12) + 12] + x = 0 + x = x$
75. $-21; 21 + (-21) + x = [21 + (-21)] + x = 0 + x = x$ 77. $6; x + (-9 + 3) = x + (-6)$, so add 6;
$x + (-6) + 6 = x + (-6 + 6) = x + 0 = x$ 79. $4; (-3 - 1) + x = [-3 + (-1)] + x = -4 + x$, so add 4;
$-4 + 4 + x = (-4 + 4) + x = 0 + x = x$ 81. $5; x + (8 - 13) = x + [8 + (-13)] = x + (-5)$, so add 5;
$x + (-5) + 5 = x + (-5 + 5) = x + 0 = x$ 83. $x - 15 = x + (-15)$ Opposite of (−15): 15 Therefore, add 15.
85. $x - 23 = x + (-23)$ Opposite of (−23): 23 Therefore, add 23. 87. $x - \frac{1}{5} = x + (-\frac{1}{5})$ Opposite of
$(-\frac{1}{5}): \frac{1}{5}$ Therefore, add $\frac{1}{5}$. 89. $x - (-2) = x + 2$ Opposite of 2: (−2) Therefore, add −2. 91. −30
93. −43 95. 59 97. 20,000 99. $-\frac{1}{2}$ 101. 1

Page 74   Review   1. $5 + 8a$ **2.** $-2.5x$ **3.** $\frac{1}{4}x + \frac{1}{15}y$ **4.** 18   **5.** $-\frac{9}{16}$ **6.** -0.008 **7.** 25   **8.** 0
9. -64 **10.** 1.4   **11.** $-8\frac{16}{23}$ **12.** Add -21.   **13.** Multiply by -3.   **14.** Multiply by $\frac{1}{13}$.   **15.** Add -4.

Page 77   Computer Exercises   See Solution Key.

Page 78   Chapter Objectives and Review   1. -2 **3.** $\sqrt{5}$ **5.** $6\frac{1}{2}$ **7.** 3.72   **9.** -16.7 **11.** -7 **13.** π
15. $<$ **17.** $<$ **19.** 18   **21.** $\sqrt{7}$ **23.** $-\frac{1}{3}$ **25.** -7 **27.** a   **29.** 42,000   **31.** 256   **33.** $<$ **35.** $<$
37. 15   **39.** $-1\frac{1}{2}$ **41.** $-2°C$ **43.** -6 **45.** $\frac{2}{5}$ **47.** $37°$ **49.** $14g$ **51.** $-24rt$ **53.** $15x + 11$
55. $29n + 6mn$ **57.** -24 **59.** -0.62 **61.** -1 **63.** $1\frac{1}{3}$ **65.** $-\frac{23}{40}$ **67.** $84\frac{1}{2}$ **69.** -112 **71.** $-m$
73. $-36x$ **75.** $-7x^2$ **77.** -9 **79.** $-\frac{4}{31}$ **81.** -11 **83.** 4   **85.** -5

Page 80   Chapter Test   1. -19 **3.** 617.25   **5.** 102   **7.** $<$ **9.** $=$ **11.** 7   **13.** 9   **15.** -18 **17.** $221
19. $27gt + 7$ **21.** $-0.7°$ **23.** $32\frac{2}{3}r$ **25.** 26

Page 81   Additional Practice   1. -4 **3.** -3 **5.** x   **7.** 0   **9.** π **11.** $<$ **13.** $>$ **15.** $<$ **17.** $<$
19. 14   **21.** 7.5   **23.** 0   **25.** -1.3 **27.** -3 **29.** 8.2   **31.** 0   **33.** 5   **35.** $-\frac{2}{5}$ **37.** 126   **39.** -7
41. -2 **43.** $-3r$ **45.** $12bc - 7b$ **47.** $25x$ **49.** $11x + 10$ **51.** $-1.9p - 7$ **53.** $25a + 3b$ **55.** 0
57. 90   **59.** 0   **61.** $3x$ **63.** $3g$ **65.** $\frac{3}{2}$ **67.** $-\frac{1}{3}$ **69.** $-\frac{3}{10}$ **71.** 3   **73.** 11   **75.** -500 **77.** 2 yd
79. $35°$ **81.** 12 w square units   **83.** $800 loss

CHAPTER 3: SOLVING EQUATIONS

Page 85   Classroom Exercises   1. -2 **3.** 9   **5.** -6 **7.** -9 **9.** $x = 2$ **11.** $t = 24$ **13.** $a = 13$
15. $x = 51$

Page 85   Written Exercises   1. $x = 6$ **3.** $n = -3$ **5.** $y = 20$ **7.** $y = 17$ **9.** $n = -6$ **11.** $y = -9$
13. $x = 19$ **15.** $t = 1.1$ **17.** $z = 38$ **19.** $m = -2$ **21.** $t = -5$ **23.** $a = 15$ **25.** $r = 3.5$ **27.** $z = 3.6$
29. $a = 2.78$ **31.** $x = 2.18$ **33.** $z = 2$ **35.** $c = -\frac{1}{2}$ **37.** $r = 6\frac{1}{2}$ **39.** $y = 3\frac{1}{4}$ **41.** 14   **43.** 6   **45.** 9
47. 0.1   **49.** $x = 2$ or $x = -2$ **51.** $n = 0$

Page 86   Review Capsule for Section 3-2   1. y   **2.** $-t$ **3.** $-q$ **4.** t   **5.** n   **6.** $\frac{3}{2}$ **7.** $\frac{8}{5}$ **8.** -2 **9.** $-\frac{4}{3}$
10. $-\frac{1}{9}$ **11.** $\frac{1}{7}$ **12.** $\frac{1}{2}$ **13.** $\frac{1}{8}$ **14.** $-\frac{4}{3}$ **15.** -4 **16.** $\frac{6}{5}$ **17.** -1

Page 88   Classroom Exercises   1. $\frac{1}{3}$ **3.** $-\frac{5}{4}$ **5.** 5   **7.** -1 **9.** $x = 7$ **11.** $y = 16$ **13.** $z = 60$
15. $t = -20$

Page 88   Written Exercises   1. $x = 4$ **3.** $b = -2$ **5.** $x = 28$ **7.** $s = -2$ **9.** $n = 6$ **11.** $n = 18$
13. $v = -7\frac{1}{5}$ **15.** $x = 0$ **17.** $t = -24\frac{1}{2}$ **19.** $y = -6$ **21.** $r = -\frac{1}{4}$ **23.** $n = -\frac{1}{32}$ **25.** $t = -32$
27. $t = \frac{2}{15}$ **29.** $y = 4$ **31.** $c = 0.0075$ **33.** $n = -1\frac{2}{3}$ **35.** $x = 6$ **37.** $y = -2\frac{1}{2}$ **39.** $y = 1\frac{2}{3}$ **41.** 20
43. 100   **45.** -21 **47.** 37   **49.** 11   **51.** F; true only for $x = 1$.   **53.** F; true only for $x = \frac{1}{2}$.

Page 90   Classroom Exercises   1. -7 **3.** 5   **5.** 12   **7.** -10 **9.** $x = 2$ **11.** $t = 2$

Page 90   Written Exercises   1. $n = 6$ **3.** $n = 4$ **5.** $t = -4$ **7.** $n = 6$ **9.** $n = 7$ **11.** $a = -6$ **13.** $a = 6$
15. $b = 9$ **17.** $a = -9$ **19.** $x = -2$ **21.** $t = 4\frac{1}{3}$ **23.** $x = -4$ **25.** $a = 9$ **27.** $y = -12$ **29.** $t = -3\frac{2}{3}$
31. $w = 2$ **33.** $n = 6$ **35.** $n = -30$ **37.** $x = 40$ **39.** $x = 28$ **41.** $t = 105$ **43.** $n = 96$ **45.** $n = 100$
47. $x = -45$ **49.** $x = 172$ **51.** $z = -0.09$ **53. 1.** Additive inverse post.   **2.** Comm. post. for add.
3. Additive inverse post.   **4.** Additive inverse post.   **55. 1.** Reflexive post. of equality   **3.** Substitution
principle   **4.** Comm. post. for add.   **5.** Substitution principle

Page 91   Calculator Exercises   1. $n = -5$ **3.** $y = \frac{16}{7}$

Page 93 Consumer Applications 1. $81 3. $120 5. $45 7. $226.80 9. −1806 Btu's
11. −1960 Btu's

Page 95 Classroom Exercises 1. $1250 3. $5600 5. $90.90

Page 95 Word Problems 1. 9 3. $\frac{1}{3}$ inch 5. 63 7. $1849 9. $8000 11. $5500 13. $80,000
15. $200,000

Page 96 Review 1. x = −2 2. n = 19 3. v = 0.9 4. a = 6 5. x = 2 6. b = −4 7. n = 4
8. y = $-\frac{25}{2}$, or $-12\frac{1}{2}$ 9. a = 3 10. n = −2 11. x = 2 12. m = 2 13. x = −2 14. a = 6
15. y = −24 16. r = −2 17. 240 kilometers 18. $\frac{1}{20}$ hour, or 3 minutes

Page 97 Review Capsule for Section 3-5 1. 16x + 2 2. 9y − 9 3. 5a 4. 5a − 9 5. t + 1 6. 2y
7. −32 − 5r 8. −7 + 5b

Page 98 Classroom Exercises 1. 9x − 9 3. −14x − 7 5. −2x − 2 7. −5x + 5 9. a = 1 11. b = 2
13. x = 12

Page 98 Written Exercises 1. 2x − 6 3. 6x + 3 5. 20x − 28 7. 4b − 24 9. −4x + 36 11. −20
+ 4n 13. −12 + 4x 15. −9 + 4m 17. x = 2 19. y = 6 21. x = 3 23. n = −4 25. x = −1
27. x = −2 29. x = 7 31. x = 2 33. n = 4 35. b = 28 37. x = 11 39. a = 9 41. x = 10
43. m = $-\frac{1}{3}$ 45. x = $7\frac{1}{2}$ 47. b = 1 49. m = −4 51. m = −9 53. x = 2 55. a = $4\frac{3}{4}$ **57.** 2. Add.
post. for equations 3. Assoc. post. for add. 4. Additive inverse post. 5. Identity post. for add. 59. No
61. No

Page 100 Classroom Exercises 1. 30°; 60°; 90° 3. 30°; 30°; 120° 5. 45°; 60°; 75°

Page 101 Written Exercises 1. 42.5°; 52.5°; 85° 3. 75°; 15° 5. 60°; 60°; 60° 7. 90°; 90°; 90°; 90°
9. 66°; 66°; 114°; 114° 11. 60°; 120°; 115°; 65° 13. 20°; 40°; 120° 15. 50°; 65°; 65° 17. 31°;
59° 19. 72°; 108° 21. 45°; 45°; 135°; 135° 23. 22.5°; 67.5°

Page 102 Puzzle See Solution Key.

Page 103 Review Capsule for Section 3-7 1. 0.70 2. 0.60 3. 0.75 4. 5.50 5. 7.25 6. 8.30
7. $\frac{9}{20}$ 8. $\frac{16}{25}$ 9. $\frac{1}{4}$ 10. $\frac{1}{2}$ 11. $\frac{7}{10}$ 12. $\frac{1}{8}$

Page 104 Classroom Exercises 1. 90 3. 75% 5. 86.1 7. 60% 9. 27 11. 40% 13. $70 15. $5\frac{5}{9}$%

Page 105 Written Exercises 1. 9.8 3. 75% 5. 75 7. 36 9. 900 11. 80% 13. $975 15. 6%
17. $66\frac{2}{3}$g 19. $175 21. 8% 23. $460 25. $133\frac{1}{3}$% 27. 70% 29. $1680 31. $24,000
33. $15,625 35. $432

Page 106 Calculator Exercises 1. 15

Page 108 Classroom Exercises 1. 19; 20; 21; 22 3. 1; 2; 3; 4 5. 0; 1; 2; 3 7. 14; 16; 18; 20
9. −10; −8; −6; −4 11. q + 2; q + 4; q + 6; q + 8 13. 11; 13; 15; 17 15. −19; −17; −15; −13
17. k + 2; k + 4; k + 6; k + 8 19. n; n + 1; n + (n + 1) = 43 21. n; n + 2; n + (n + 2) = 0

Page 109 Word Problems 1. −9; −8 3. −34; −33; −32; −31 5. 15; 16; 17 7. −37; −35; −33
9. −3; −1; 1; 3 11. No 13. 3; 4 15. 64; 65; 66; 67 17. 55; 57 19. even 21. 2h 23. 4(3) + 1,
4(4) + 1, 4(7) + 1 25. 37, 41

Page 110 Computer Exercises See Solution Key.

Page 112 Review 1. x = 3 2. y = 2 3. a = 2 4. m = 2 5. x = $5\frac{3}{25}$ 6. a = −5 7. 95° 8. 30°; 30°
9. 12 10. $56\frac{1}{4}$% 11. $200 12. 10% 13. 9; 10; 11 14. 22; 24 15. 41; 42; 43; 44 16. −15, −13

Page 113 Chapter Objectives and Review 1. x = 6 3. t = 21 5. r = 5 7. x = 3 9. x = 0.2

11. $m = -\frac{4}{9}$ 13. $x = 4$ 15. $t = 4$ 17. $754.80   19. $-m - 6$ 21. $-25 + 5a$ 23. $b = 7$ 25. $k = 0$
27. $r = 3$ 29. $40°; 60°; 80°$ 31. 17   33. 150%   35. $360   37. 20%   39. 40, 42, 44

Page 115   Chapter Test   1. $z = 18$ 3. $t = -4.3$ 5. $x = 14\frac{1}{4}$ 7. $p = 6$ 9. $y = -105$ 11. $b = 4$
13. $d = 1\frac{1}{3}$ 15. $g = 0$ 17. $35°; 55°; 90°$ 19. 34, 36

Page 115   Additional Practice   1. $x = 8$ 3. $s = -3.1$ 5. $y = 2\frac{3}{4}$ 7. $n = 4$ 9. $v = -\frac{7}{8}$ 11. $d = -12.9$
13. $g = 5$ 15. $j = 15$ 17. $w = 3.2$ 19. 24   21. $6x - 54$ 23. $72 - 6y$ 25. $12 - 16y$ 27. -12
$+ 15a$ 29. $y = -5$ 31. $b = -6$ 33. $c = 17$ 35. 14   37. 54   39. $\frac{3}{5}$ in   41. 220   43. $40°; 60°; 80°$
45. $45°; 45°; 90°$ 47. $4.50   49. $-17; -15$

CHAPTER 4: EQUATIONS AND INEQUALITIES

Page 119   Classroom Exercises   1. $-6y$ 3. $6 + y$ or $y + 6$ 5. $y - 6$ 7. $6y$ 9. $6 - y$ 11. $y - 6$
13. $\frac{-6}{y}$ 15. $\frac{y}{-6}$ 17. $\frac{6}{2y}$

Page 120   Word Problems   1. $25 - n$ 3. $x + (-6\frac{1}{4})$ 5. $-9 - b$ 7. $\frac{1}{2} + (-a)$ 9. $t - (-100)$
11. $n + \frac{4}{5}$ 13. $r - 4$ 15. $5 - s$ 17. $m - (-30)$ 19. $12 - |y|$ 21. $q + 9\frac{1}{2}$ 23. $r - (-0.5)$
25. $-0.5 - r$ 27. $\frac{9}{x}$ 29. $7q$ 31. $2p$ 33. $\frac{212}{-t}$ 35. $\frac{1}{5}z$ or $\frac{z}{5}$ 37. $\frac{z}{5}$ or $z \div 5$ 39. $-1p$ or $-p$
41. $r(\frac{1}{12})$ or $\frac{r}{12}$ 43. w = width of rectangle, $w + 5$ 45. p = perimeter of base, $\frac{1}{3}(p)$ 47. c = cost of
dinner, $c + 5.45$ 49. c = cost of new car, $c - 1200$ 51. a = air distance, $2a$ 53. c = cost of tennis racquet,
$c = 6.90$ 55. q = number of qts. of oil, $1.10q$ 57. a = amount of Jeff's checking account, $a + 20$ 59. $6k$
61. $\frac{1200}{m}$ or $1200 \div m$ 63. $\frac{3500}{m}$ or $3500 \div m$

Page 121   Calculator Exercises   1. 6 in   3. 1573 in

Page 123   Classroom Exercises   1. $\frac{2p}{7}$ 3. $150 + 3p$ 5. $2d + 25$ 7. $z + 1\frac{3}{4} = 20$ 9. $200 - t = 71\frac{3}{4}$
11. $9 + \frac{n}{2} = 29$

Page 123   Word Problems   1. $3a - 2$ 3. $2r - 20$ 5. $\frac{4\ell}{5}$ or $4\ell \div 5$ 7. $\frac{25n}{100}$ or $25n \div 100$ 9. $b + 0.15b$
11. $t + 19 = 42.6$ 13. $\frac{n}{14} = 9$ 15. $4z - 3 = 35$ 17. $\frac{t}{3} + 7 = 23$ 19. $\frac{5b}{3} = 100$ 21. $12c - 6 = 60$
23. $\frac{q}{6} - 14 = 4$ 25. $4s - 8 = -4$ 27. $359.70   29. $31.30   31. $142.50   33. $82.50   35. 40
37. 60   39. 6

Page 125   Review Capsule for Section 4-3   1. $59y + 36$ 2. $5p - 8$ 3. $-18z + 12$ 4. $d = \frac{23}{5}$ or $4\frac{3}{5}$
5. $x = 11$ 6. $x = -6$ 7. $t = \frac{7}{2}$ or $3\frac{1}{2}$ 8. $t = 15$ 9. $x = 1$

Page 126   Classroom Exercises   1. e   3. h   5. a   7. d

Page 127   Word Problems   1. 12; 60   3. 12; 8   5. 9; 27   7. 30; 20   9. 33; 43   11. 42; 14; 16
13. 8; 32; 33   15. $13 = Dan's earnings; $39 = Bob's earnings   17. $62.90 = cost of dress; $98.40 = cost of
coat   19. 325 = persons on Wed.; 560 = persons on Thurs.   21. $56.22 = gas bill; $41.41 = electric bill
23. $50 = list price; $10 = discount   25. $113 = list price; $22.60 = discount   27. $70 = list price; $24.50
= discount   29. 25 of each coin   31. 18 cm; 20 cm; 22 cm

Page 130   Classroom Exercises   1. $s = 9$ m   3. $a = 81$ m; $2a = 162$ m; $a + 299 = 380$ m   5. $2t = 6$ yd;
$t - 1 = 2$ yd   7. $\ell = 3$ cm; $w = 1.6$ cm   9. $b = 14$ m; $b - 5 = 9$ m; $b - 7.5 = 6.5$ m; $b + 12.5 = 26.5$ m

Page 130   Word Problems   1. $\ell = 28$ cm; $w = 4$ cm   3. 8 in; 24 in; 20 in   5. $\ell = 40$ in; $w = 16$ in
7. 6 cm; 6 cm; 15 cm   9. 499 km   11. 8.4 m; 7.2 m   13. AC = BC = 482.4 m; AB = 964.8 m
15. $m\angle A = 30°$; $m\angle B = 60°$; $m\angle C = 90°$ 17. $m\angle A = 46°$; $m\angle B = 100°$; $m\angle C = 34°$ 19. $m\angle D = 20°$;

m∠E = 100°; m∠F = 60°   21. 4 m   23. 8 cm

Page 132 Puzzle See Solution Key.

Page 132 Review Capsule for Section 4-5 1. −8t − 20   2. −12y + 15   3. −6 + 18r   4. −4 + 6n
5. −6 + m   6. −x − 9   7. 1 − b   8. 2x + 3

Page 133 Classroom Exercises 1. −x   3. 9y   5. −3a   7. 2t   9. 9d   11. 5m   13. x = −11   15. n = 3

Page 134 Written Exercises 1. x = 4   3. y = 4   5. a = 3   7. x = −3   9. ϕ 11. a = 6   13. m = $\frac{3}{4}$
15. x = −26   17. a = $\frac{2}{3}$ 19. r = 10   21. r = 4   23. y = 20   25. a = 4   27. k = 10$\frac{1}{2}$ 29. y = −2
31. x = 5   33. p = 6   35. y = −5   37. x = 9   39. ϕ 41. x = $\frac{7}{2}$ 43. x = 4   45. n = 6   47. {1}
49. {−4}   51. $\left\{1\frac{1}{5}\right\}$ 53. {5}   55. {−2}   57. $\left\{2\frac{1}{2}\right\}$

Page 136 Classroom Exercises 1. x + 12   3. 2z + 2   5. 2r + 6   7. t + 6   9. t − 5

Page 136 Word Problems 1. Anna: 8; Ramon: 2   3. Skip: 20; Paul: 10   5. Andy: 35; Bob: 10
7. 18; 19   9. electrician: 20 yr; apprentice: 4 yr   11. Mr. Connors: 25; Mr. Saito: 40   13. 41
15. 12 yr   17. 8 yr

Page 137 Review 1. −6m   2. $\frac{x}{12}$ 3. 2$\frac{1}{4}$ + k   4. 4.6 − n   5. $16.25   6. 36; 24   7. Bob: 97 shares;
Jane: 31 shares   8. ℓ = 60 m; w = 20 m   9. g = 1   10. n = 2   11. b = −6   12. n = −3   13. ϕ
14. c = 1   15. Maria: 7; Ann: 10

Page 138 Career Applications 1. 60.5 ft   3. 49.5 ft   5. 59.4 ft   7. 162 ft   9. 90.5 ft   11. 42.9 ft;
33 ft; 75.9 ft   13. 49.5 ft; 112.5 ft; 162 ft

Page 140 Review Capsule for Section 4-7 1. {−4, −3, −2, −1, 0, 1, 2}   2. {3, 4}   3. {2, 3, 4}
4. {−4, −3, −2, −1, 0, 1, 2, 3, 4}   5. {−4, −3, −2, −1, 0}   6. {−4, −3, −2, −1, 0}   7. {−4, −3, −2,
2, 3, 4}   8. {−3, −2, −1, 0, 1, 2, 3}

Page 141 Classroom Exercises 1. >   3. >   5. >; >   7. >; >   9. <; <

Page 141 Written Exercises 1. t > −3; all points to the right of and not including, −3   3. y > 12; all
points to the right of, and not including, 12   5. r < 7; all points to the left of, and not including, 7
7. r < 5; all points to the left of, and not including, 5   9. c < −7; all points to the left of, and not including,
−7   11. z > 16; all points to the right of, and not including, 16   13. x < 6; all points to the left of, and
not including, 6   15. x ≥ −8; all points to the right of, and including, −8   17. r < −19; all points to the
left of, and not including, −19   19. n ≥ −2; all points to the right of, and including, −2   21. −5 < z; all
points to the right of, and not including, −5   23. −1 ≥ y; all points to the left of, and including, −1
25. q ≤ −18; all points to the left of, and including, −18   27. x > −31; all points to the right of, and not
including, −31   29. x ≤ 0; all points to the left of, and including, 0   31. >   33. z   35. 0   37. −5
39. a   41. 3   43. Let a = 6, b = 5, c = 4, and d = 1. Then a − c = 6 − 4 = 2 and b − d = 5 − 1 = 4. Thus,
a − c > b − d is not true because 2 is not greater than 4.

Page 142 Review Capsule for Section 4-8 1. {0, 2}   2. {4}   3. ϕ 4. {−2, −1, 0, 1}   5. {−3, −1, 1,
3}   6. {−6, −3}

Page 144 Classroom Exercises 1. >   3. <   5. >   7. >; >   9. >; >

Page 144 Written Exercises 1. x < 4; all points to the left of, and not including, 4   3. q > 2; all points to
the right of, and not including, 2   5. d > −2; all points to the right of, and not including, −2   7. x ≥ 0;
all points to the right of, and including, 0   9. t ≥ 4; all points to the right of, and including, 4   11. z > 6;
all points to the right of, and not including, 6   13. a > 4; all points to the right of, and not including, 4
15. h ≤ 3; all points to the left of, and including, 3   17. y < 2; all points to the left of, and not including, 2
19. t < 5   21. x < −$\frac{5}{2}$ 23. r ≤ 5$\frac{3}{5}$ 25. a ≤ −$\frac{3}{4}$ 27. m > 11   29. y ≥ −$\frac{15}{2}$ 31. x > −15

33. $x > -\frac{7}{5}$ 35. $x < \frac{4}{3}$ 37. $y < -3$ 39. $x > -\frac{5}{13}$ 41. $k \geq 16$ 43. $r \geq -4$ 45. $z \geq -\frac{3}{5}$ 47. $d < \frac{4}{3}$
49. $>$ 51. $<$ 53. F; If $x = 8$ and $y = 7$, then $7 \not> 8$. 55. T 57. F; If $x = 2$ and $y = -2$, then $2(-2)$ $\not> 0$. 59. F; If $x = 10$ and $y = 3$, then $3^2 \not> 10$. 61. T

Page 145 Calculator Exercises 1. Correct 3. Correct 5. Incorrect

Page 145 Review Capsule for Section 4-9 1. $x =$ smaller integer; $x + (x + 2)$ 2. $p =$ number of pens; $p + 7$
3. $n =$ second number; $3n + 36$ 4. $r =$ Room 201's students; $2r + 5$ 5. $a =$ advertising part; $4a - 10$
6. $\ell =$ length of each side of the square; $2\ell - 4$

Page 147 Classroom Exercises 1. $x =$ number of pipe sections; $8x > 110$ 3. $x =$ score on third test;
$\frac{82 + 91 + x}{3} \geq 90$

Page 147 Word Problems 1. \$124.99 3. 89 5. 101 7. \$620.01 9. 1 and 2, or 2 and 3, or 3 and
4, or 4 and 5 11. 27 and 29 13. 12 15. $x : x > 4$ 17. 24 and 26

Page 148 Review 1. $n < 3$; all points to the left of, and not including, 3 2. $x < -2.5$; all points to the
left of, and not including, -2.5 3. $g \leq -5$; all points to the left of, and including, -5 4. $a > -3$
5. $a \geq -4$ 6. $p < 0$ 7. $h > 3$; all points to the right of, and not including, 3 8. $y \geq -1$; all points to the
right of, and including, -1 9. $s > 1$; all points to the right of, and not including, 1 10. $b > -1$
11. $t \geq -3$ 12. 89 13. 12 and 60

Page 150 Computer Exercises See Solution Key.

Page 151 Chapter Objectives and Review 1. $4.5 - w$ 3. $5 + x$ 5. \$41.50 7. 413 9. 44; 31
11. last month: \$1600; this month: \$2700 13. length: 50 m; width: 30 m 15. 27; 29; 31 17. $x = 3$
19. $n = -2$ 21. Tony: 6; Jim: 18 23. 10; 12 25. $y > 6$; all points to the right of, and not including, 6
27. $b < 5$; all points to the left of, and not including, 5 29. $f \geq 2$ 31. ϕ 33. $r < -2$; all points to the
left of, and not including, -2 35. $y \geq 5$ 37. 249 mi

Page 153 Chapter Test 1. $t + 9$ 3. $\frac{-6}{w}$ 5. $d = 2$ 7. $y = 1$ 9. $x < -1$; all points to the left of, and
not including, -1 11. $r \leq 1$; all points to the left of, and including, 1 13. $x > -2$ 15. $y > 3$ 17. 500
19. length: 166 cm; width: 140 cm

Page 154 More Challenging Problems 1. $\frac{5}{16}$ 3. $x = \frac{22b + 35d}{5}$ 5. $3y + f + \frac{i}{12}$ 7. $7\frac{1}{2}x + 2\frac{1}{2}y + 13\frac{5}{6}z$
9. 6 11. $6\frac{2}{3}$ 13. gain of \$1000

Page 155 Additional Practice 1. $6.5 - x$ 3. $\frac{28}{c}$ 5. $a = 1$ 7. $x = 3$ 9. $y = 2$ 11. $x > 10$
13. $a \leq -7$ 15. $x \geq 4$ 17. $n > \frac{1}{2}$ 19. \$14 21. Emily: 45; Jean: 65 23. $A = 20°$; $B = 60°$; $C = 100°$
25. 179 ft

Page 156 Review of Word Problems 1. $946 -$ mL bottle 3. $7°C$ 5. \$5400 7. 5% 9. 29, 31, 33
11. \$76 13. length: 32 m; width: 21 m 15. \$57

Page 157 Cumulative Review 1. b 3. a 5. c 7. d 9. a 11. d 13. c 15. c 17. c 19. b
21. b 23. c 25. a 27. c 29. c

Page 159 Preparing for College Entrance Tests 1. a 3. a 5. c 7. a

Page 160 Preparing for College Entrance Tests 1. b 3. c 5. c 7. a 9. c

CHAPTER 5: GRAPHING RELATIONS AND FUNCTIONS

Page 163 Classroom Exercises 1. $x = 7 - b$ 3. $x = t + 2$ 5. $x = \frac{a}{3}$

Page 163 Written Exercises 1. $x = 144$; $x = ab$ 3. $x = \frac{10}{3}$ or $3\frac{1}{3}$; $x = \frac{bc}{a}$ 5. $x = \frac{6}{5}$; $x = \frac{b - a}{5}$ 7. $x = -\frac{4}{3}$
or $-1\frac{1}{3}$; $x = \frac{b}{3} - a$ 9. $x = 3$; $x = \frac{b - a}{-2}$ 11. $d = \frac{C}{\pi}$ 13. $h = \frac{2A}{b}$ 15. $r = \frac{d}{t}$ 17. $r = \frac{i}{pt}$ 19. $F = \frac{9}{5}C + 32$

564 *Answers to Selected Exercises*

21. $d = \frac{C}{\pi}$; $d = 22.6$ 23. $\ell = \frac{P - 2w}{2}$; $\ell = 22$ 25. $w = \frac{A}{\ell}$; $w = 2.8$ 27. $n = \frac{b - a}{2}$ 29. $n = 3a + b$
31. $n = 5b - 3a$ 33. $n = b + c - a$ 35. $n = 4b$ 37. $n = \frac{b + c}{a}$ 39. $b = \frac{c}{a} - n$ 41. $a = \frac{c}{n} - b$
43. $b = \frac{2A}{h} - b'$

Page 164   Puzzle   See Solution Key.

Page 166   Classroom Exercises   1. Hiker A: r, 6, 6r; Hiker B: 2r, 6, 12r   **3.** Passenger: 2r, 3, 6r; Freight: r, 3, 3r

Page 167   Word Problems   1. 3 hr   **3.** 12 hr   **5.** 3 hours   **7.** 240 km/hr; 480 km/hr   **9.** 10 hours
11. 3 hours   **13.** 240 km   **15.** 8 km   **17.** 4.5 km

Page 170   Classroom Exercises   1. 6   **3.** 3   **5.** −4   **7.** 0   **9.** 8   **11.** 0   **13.** y axis   **15.** I   **17.** II
19. y axis   **21.** II

Page 170   Written Exercises   1. Start at the origin and make the moves given for each point. **a.** Left 3, up 4
b. Right 5, up 2   **c.** Right 4, down 3   **d.** Left 5, down 4   **e.** Right 6   **f.** Down 4   **g.** Up 5   **h.** Down 3
i. Left 4, down 4   **j.** The origin   **3.** abscissa: −3; ordinate: 4   **5.** abscissa: 0; ordinate: 5   **7.** abscissa: 0; ordinate: 0   **9.** 0   **11.** III   **13.** II   **15.** IV   **17.** y axis   **19.** II   **21.** I   **23.** IV   **25.** The picture is an elephant.   **27.** The graph is a horizontal line 4 units below the x axis.   **29.** The graph is a vertical line coinciding with the y axis.   **31.** The graph is a diagonal line passing through the origin at a 45° angle.
33. A horizontal line parallel to the x axis.   **35.** A half-plane with the y axis as its right-hand boundary.
37. (−4, 5)   **39.** (0, −4)   **41.** (−3, −3)   **43.** (−10, 5), (−4, 5), (−4, 1)   **45.** (2, 10), (2, 4), (4, 4)
47. (−13, 7), (1, 9), (−3, 3)

Page 173   Review   1. $x = 36$ **2.** $x = 17$ **3.** $x = -3$ **4.** $x = 5\frac{1}{2}$ **5.** $2\frac{1}{2}$ hours   **6.** 150 km   **7.** Start at the origin and make the moves given for each point. **a.** Right 10   **b.** Right 12, down 5   **c.** Right 4, down 9
d. Left 4, down 9   **e.** Left 9   **f.** Left 9, up 4   **g.** Right 4, up 9   **h.** Up 9   **i.** Right 10   **j.** Right 12, up 5
9. Abscissa: A: 10; B: 12; C: 4; D: −4; E: −9; F: −9; G: 4; H: 0; I: 0; J: 12   Ordinate: A: 0; B: −5; C: −9; D: −9; E: 0; F: 4; G: 9; H: 9; I: 10; J: 5

Page 173   Puzzle   See Solution Key.

Page 175   Career Applications   1. London   **3.** London   **5.** Calcutta and Chicago   **7.** Paris   **9.** 0
11. −6   **13.** −10   **15.** +3   **17.** 6 hours   **19.** 14 hours   **21.** 1:30 P.M.

Page 178   Classroom Exercises   1. D = $\{0, 2, 4, 6\}$; R = $\{1, 3, 5, 7\}$ **3.** D = $\{0, 1, 2, 3\}$; R = $\{-2\}$
5. Not a function; (1, 2) and (1, 3) have the same first element.   **7.** Is a function

Page 178   Written Exercises   1. D = $\{1, 2, 3, 4, 5\}$; R = $\{50, 100, 150, 200, 250\}$ **3.** D = $\{1, 2, 3, 4, 5\}$;
R = $\{\pi, 4\pi, 9\pi, 16\pi, 25\pi\}$ **5.** $\{(-4, -2), (-2, -3), (-1, 1), (1, -2), (1, 3), (2, 1), (4, 2)\}$ **7.** D = $\{-4, -2, -1, 1, 2, 4\}$; R = $\{-2, -3, 1, 3, 2\}$ **9.** $\{(-3, -3), (-2, -3), (-1, -3), (1, -3), (2, -3), (3, -3)\}$;
D = $\{-3, -2, -1, 1, 2, 3\}$; R = $\{-3\}$ **11.** D = $\{1, 2, 3, 4, 5\}$; R = $\{50, 100, 150, 200, 250\}$ **13.** D = $\{1, 2, 3, 4, 5\}$; R = $\{\pi, 4\pi, 9\pi, 16\pi, 25\pi\}$ **15.** Yes   **17.** No   **19.** No   **21.** Yes   **23.** Yes   **25.** No; All ordered pairs have the same first element.   **27.** Yes   **29.** $\{(1976, 11,000), (1978, 12,000), (1980, 13,000), (1982, 15,000), (1984, 16,000)\}$; D = $\{1976, 1978, 1980, 1982, 1984\}$; R = $\{11,000, 12,000, 13,000, 15,000, 16,000\}$ **31.** $\{(4, 256), (6, 576), (8, 1024), (10, 1600)\}$; D = $\{4, 6, 8, 10\}$;
R = $\{256, 576, 1024, 1600\}$ **33.** $\{(1, 4), (2, 33), (3, 113), (5, 523)\}$; D = $\{1, 2, 3, 5\}$; R = $\{4, 33, 113, 523\}$ **35.** All are functions.   **37. a.** 40, 40, 40, 60, 60, 80, 80, 100   **b.** 0, 20, 40, 60, 80, 100
c.

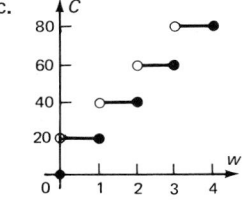

Page 182 Classroom Exercises 1. 8, 12 3. −6, −9 5. 4, 6, 10 7. 14, 11, 8, 5, 2 9. No 11. Yes 13. No 15. Yes 17. Yes 19. No 21. Yes 23. Yes 25. Yes 27. No 29. Yes

Page 183 Written Exercises For Exercises 1-28, each graph is a straight line containing the given points. 1. (0, −3), (1, 1) 3. (−2, 0), (0, −4) 5. (0, −5), (5, 0) 7. (0, 10), (10, 0) 9. (0, 0), (2, 1) 11. (0, 0), (4, −1) 13. (0, 4), (2, 0) 15. (0, 2), (3, 0) 17. (0, −4), (2, 0) 19. (0, −4), (4, −4) 21. (0, −9), (9, −9) 23. $(6\frac{1}{2}, 0)$, $(6\frac{1}{2}, 6)$ 25. (−2, 3), (0, 3), (2, 3) 27. (−4, 0), (0, 0), (4, 0) 29. x axis; x axis 31. one real number In Exercises 32-35, the graph is a line parallel to the y axis and contains the given points. 33. (8, −3), (8, 0), (8, 4) 35. (−9, −2), (−9, 0), (−9, 2) 37. the set of real numbers 39. each ordered pair has the same first element 41. $(0, 2\frac{8}{9})$, (−13, 0) 43. (0, 4), $(1\frac{1}{3}, 0)$ 45. (0, −1), $(\frac{1}{3}, 0)$ 47. Not a linear function.
$D = \{x : x \in R, x \neq 0\}$
$R = \{y : y \leq 0, y \in R\}$

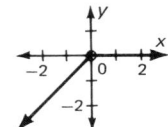

49. Not a linear function.
$D = \{ \text{real numbers} \}$
$R = \{y : y \geq 0, y \in R\}$

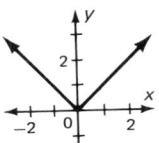

Page 185 Classroom Exercises 1. (0, 6), (2, 8), (3, 9) 3. $8\frac{1}{2}$

Page 186 Word Problems 1. (0, 0), (4, 6), (6, 9) 3. 0.75 km 5. $2\frac{2}{3}$ seconds 7. To draw the graph, use multiples of 3 for the d axis and multiples of 16 for the r axis. 9. 12.8 m 11. 5, 10, 15 13. $2.50 15. $20 17. $11.25 19. S = 20t 21. (0, 5) is the endpoint. To draw the graph, use multiples of 5 for the C axis and multiples of 1 for the h axis. 23. $17.50 25. $18 27. 100, 200, 300 29. 150 feet 31. 125 feet 33. A = 50t 35. 20, 37, 54, 71, 88, 105, 122, 139, 156, 173, 190, 207

Page 188 Review 1. D = {1, 2, 3, 4, 5, 6}; R = {12, 14, 8, 4, 6, −2} 2. D = {1, 2, 3, 4, 5, 6}; R = {10, 15, 25, 40, 60, 85} 3. D = {1, 2, 3, 4}; R = {$\pi, \frac{3\pi}{2}, 2\pi, \frac{5\pi}{2}, 3\pi$} 4. 1: Yes; 2: Yes; 3: No For Exercises 5-8, each graph is a straight line containing the given points. 5. (0, 0), (2, 4) 6. (0, −7), (2, −3) 7. (0, −3), (3, −3) 8. (2, 0), (2, 2) 9. (9, 4), (18, 8), (36, 16) 10. (0, 0) is the endpoint. The graph contains (9, 4), (18, 8), and (36, 16). 11. 7 units

Page 188 Review Capsule for Section 5-7 1. −5 2. −3 3. 5 4. −9 5. −10 6. 2 7. 10 8. 3 9. $-\frac{1}{3}$ 10. −8 11. −3 12. 0 13. 0 14. 0 15. −4 16. $\frac{5}{4} = 1\frac{1}{4}$

Page 191 Classroom Exercises 1. Positive 3. ND 5. $-\frac{3}{4}$ 7. $\frac{4}{5}$ 9. $-\frac{8}{7}$ 11. $-\frac{1}{2}$ 13. −1

Page 191 Written Exercises 1. 1 3. $\frac{1}{2}$ 5. $-\frac{1}{3}$ 7. 0 9. 2 11. $-\frac{3}{4}$ 13. $\frac{1}{2}$ 15. $\frac{9}{4}$ 17. $-\frac{1}{3}$ 19. 0 21. AB: 1; AC: $-\frac{2}{3}$; BC: −4 23. PQ and SR: $\frac{3}{7}$; PS and QR: 4 25. HD and FE: $\frac{2}{3}$; DE and HF: $-\frac{2}{3}$ 27. Yes 29. No 31. 14 33. −1 35. $m = \frac{y_2 - y_1}{x_2 - x_1}, x_2 \neq x_1$ 37. $x_1 = x_2$ 39. undefined

Page 193 Calculator Exercises 1. $-18\frac{1}{2}$, −17, $-16\frac{1}{2}$, −15 3. $-19\frac{1}{2}$, −15, $5\frac{1}{4}$, 12

Page 193 Review Capsule for Section 5-8 1. y = 3x − 4 2. $y = \frac{5}{2}x + 2\frac{1}{2}$ 3. $y = \frac{4}{3}x$ 4. $y = -\frac{2}{3}x + 2\frac{1}{3}$ 5. $y = 4\frac{1}{2}$ 6. y = 3 7. y = 2 8. y = −2

Page 196 Classroom Exercises 1. 2; 5 3. 3; 2 5. $\frac{2}{3}; \frac{1}{2}$ 7. 0; 3

Page 196 Written Exercises 1. y = −2x + 4; −2; 4 3. y = −5x − 3; −5; −3 5. y = 2x − 4; 2; −4

566 *Answers to Selected Exercises*

5. $y = 2x - 4; 2; -4$ 7. $y = -2x - \frac{5}{2}; -2; -\frac{5}{2}$ 9. $y = -x + 3; -1; 3$ 11. $y = -4; 0; -4$ For Exercises 13-30, each graph is a straight line containing the given points.   13. $(-1, -3), (0, 6)$ 15. $(0, 1), (1, 4)$ 17. $(0, 0), (3, -2)$ 19. $(0, -2), (1, -2)$ 21. $(-5, 1), (0, -1)$ 23. $(-1, 6), (0, 0)$ 25. $(0, 4), (1, 6)$ 27. $(0, -6), (1, -3)$ 29. $(0, 3), (4, 8)$ 31. Yes   33. Yes   35. No   37. $-\frac{3}{4}$ 39. $y = -\frac{1}{3}x + 5$ 41. $y = -\frac{A}{B}x + \frac{C}{B}$

Page 198   Classroom Exercises   1. Yes   3. Yes   5. No   7. No   9. No   11. No   13. -4 15. 2

Page 198   Written Exercises   1. Yes; P is always 4 times s.   3. Yes; Yes; y is always $\frac{5}{2}$ times x.   5. 20; Yes; doubled   7. Yes   9. Yes   11. No   13. Yes   15. $y = kx$ 17. $r = ks$ 19. $\frac{3}{2}$ 21. -2 23. $\frac{4}{3}$ 25. 3, 3   27. 15   29. -6 31. The slope of the line increases.   33. The y intercept of an equation expressing direct variation is 0, and if $y = 0$, then $x = 0$.   35. 20π; twice   37. decreases   39. multiplied by n

Page 200   Calculator Exercises   1. Yes; $y = \frac{1}{2}x$ 3. Yes; $y = 6\frac{3}{4}x$ or $y = \frac{27}{4}x$

Page 201   Classroom Exercises   1. $108.80   3. 2000   5. $8832.96

Page 202   Word Problems   1. $522   3. 125   5. 70   7. 420 mi   9. $4.50   11. 9 min   13. 240 lb

Page 203   Review   1. 1   2. -1 3. $-\frac{15}{11}$ 4. 0   5. $y = -3x + 5; -3; 5$ 6. $y = \frac{3}{2}x - 4; \frac{3}{2}; -4$ 7. $y = -8; 0; -8$ 8. $y = -\frac{3}{5}x; -\frac{3}{5}; 0$ 9. slope: -2; y intercept: 8; the graph contains $(0, 8)$ and $(4, 0)$ 10. Yes   11. Yes   12. Yes   13. No   14. 160   15. 4¢

Page 203   Puzzle   See Solution Key.

Page 204   Computer Exercises   See Solution Key.

Page 207   Chapter Objectives and Review   1. $n = st$ 3. $n = a - 2b$ 5. $n = \frac{3h - g}{2}$ 7. $h = \frac{A}{b}$ 9. slower runner: 8 km/hr; faster runner: 10 km/hr   11. Start at the origin and make the moves given for each point.   a. Right 3, down 7   b. Left 3, up 7   c. Down 2   d. Right 6, down 5   e. Left 6, down 6   f. Right 7, up 5   g. Right $6\frac{1}{2}$ h. Left 2, down 5   i. Left 1, up 4   j. Right $3\frac{1}{2}$, down 5   13. $(-5, 3)$ 15. D: $\{-2, -1, 0, 1, 2\}$; R: $\{-1, -\frac{1}{2}, 0, \frac{1}{2}, 1\}$ **17.** 14. No; 15. Yes; 16. Yes   For Exercises 18-21, the graph is a straight line containing the given points.   19. $(0, 0), (1, -4)$ 21. $(3, 0), (3, 3)$ 23. To draw the graph, use multiples of $400 for the t axis and multiples of $10,000 for the p axis.   25. -2 27. 0   29. $y = -x; -1; 0$ For Exercises 31-36, the graph is a straight line through the given points.   31. $(0, 2), (-2, 0)$ 33. $(0, -2), (-4, 0)$ 35. $(0, 6), (-1, 2)$ 37. Yes   39. Yes   41. $y = -18$ 43. $98   45. 4.3 m

Page 209   Chapter Test   1. $x = kp$ 3. $x = y - z$ 5. D: $\{0, 1, 2, 3, 4, 5\}$; R: $\{0, 1, 2, 3\}$; function   7. 0   9. $-\frac{9}{7}$ 11. $y = -\frac{3}{4}x + 1; -\frac{3}{4}; 1$ 13. The graph is a straight line containing $(0, 4)$ and $(-4, 0)$.   15. Yes   17. No   19. $2\frac{1}{2}$ hours

Page 210   Additional Practice   1. $n = \frac{a}{b}$ 3. $n = \frac{d - c}{3}$ For Exercises 4-8, start at the origin and make the moves given for each point.   5. Down 6   7. Right 6, up 7   9. D: $\{-13, -12, 0, 5, 12\}$; R: $\{-13, 0, 5, 12, 13\}$; not a function   For Exercises 11-14, the graph is a straight line containing the given points.   11. $(0, 0), (1, -3)$ 13. $(6, 0), (6, 6)$ 15. 2   17. $-\frac{1}{2}$ 19. $y = -2x + 5; -2; 5$ 21. $y = -12$ 23. $10   25. 35 km

CHAPTER 6: SYSTEMS OF SENTENCES

Page 213   Classroom Exercises   1. $x + y = 5$: 5, 4, 3, 2, 1; $x - y = 3$: $-3, -2, -1, 0, 1$; $(4, 1)$ 3. No   5. No   7. an infinite number   9. one solution   11. an infinite number of solutions

Page 214   Written Exercises 1. (7, 3)   3. (4, 0)   5. (5, 1)   7. (5, 1)   9. (1, 3)   11. (−2, 4)
13. (3, −4)   15. (1, 3)   17. (3, 2)   19. (0, 1)   21. (4, −2)   23. one   25. none   27. none
29. none   31. none   33. infinitely many   35. none   37. none   39. infinitely many   41. All equal
43. Each graph is a straight line. Solar heat contains (1, 10,000) and (11, 12,000). Oil heat contains
(1, 4000) and (11, 12,000).   45. 10 years   47. $600   49. 2 hours   51. more than 2 hours   53. none
55. one

Page 216   Review Capsule for Section 6-2   1. $x + 2y$ 2. $4y$ 3. $x + 2y$ 4. $-3a$ 5. $18r - 11t$
6. $-2.5r + 2.2s$

Page 218   Classroom Exercises   1. $x + y = 1$ 3. $2q = -1$

Page 218   Written Exercises   1. (3, −1)   3. (−1, 4)   5. (−1, 3)   7. $(2, 1\frac{2}{3})$ 9. $(1\frac{3}{4}, -\frac{1}{2})$ 11. (15, 7)
13. $(2\frac{3}{4}, \frac{1}{8})$ 15. $(3, -\frac{2}{3})$ 17. $(-3\frac{5}{6}, -6)$ 19. $(7\frac{1}{5}, 5\frac{2}{5})$ 21. $(6\frac{1}{2}, 1\frac{3}{4})$ 23. $(1, 2\frac{1}{2})$

Page 219   Puzzle   See Solution Key.

Page 219   Review Capsule for Section 6-3   1. −21   2. 9   3. 0   4. 11   5. −18.3   6. $\frac{1}{3}$ 7. $6x - 4y$
8. $-18a - 3b$ 9. $-2w + 3s$ 10. $-r - 3t$ 11. $v - 7g$ 12. $-7g + 9$ 13. $-2r + 3p$ 14. $-s + 9t$

Page 221   Classroom Exercises   1. Equation 2: 2   3. Equation 2: 9   5. Equation 1: 5; Equation 2: −2
7. Equation 1: 5; Equation 2: 3

Page 221   Written Exercises   1. (8, −15)   3. (−4, 3)   5. (−1, −2)   7. (6, −2)   9. (2, −1)
11. (−1, −1)   13. (4, 2)   15. (1, −2)   17. (0, 2)   19. $(1\frac{2}{5}, \frac{1}{5})$ 21. $(-\frac{1}{14}, 1\frac{2}{7})$ 23. $(\frac{2}{3}, \frac{1}{2})$
25. $(\frac{1}{3}, -\frac{1}{2})$ 27. (0.8, 5.5)   29. (8, 4)   In Exercises 31-34, answers may vary.   31. $r = -3; s = 1$
33. $r = 1; s = 4$ 35. (−2, 2)   37. (2, −4)   39. (5.216, 12.24)   41. $(2\frac{1}{3}, 3\frac{1}{2})$ 43. To prove the
statement, first write each equation in slope-intercept form. $Ax + By = C, By = -Ax + C, y = -\frac{A}{B}x + \frac{C}{B};$
$Ax + By = D, By = -Ax + D, y = -\frac{A}{B}x + \frac{D}{B}$ The two lines have the same slope, $-\frac{A}{B}$. But, since $C \neq D$
(given), their y intercepts are different. Thus, the two lines are parallel, and do not intersect. The system
has no solution set.

Page 222   Review Capsule for Section 6-4   1. x = amount Hal invested; $x + 2100$ 2. x = Roger's age; $\frac{1}{2}x$
3. x = no. of Jim's shirts; $3x$ 4. x = Joe's money; $x + 4$ 5. x = width of bookcase; $2x$ 6. x = no. of
Cindy's mother's shoes; $x - 3$ 7. x = Bakers' children; $2x + 1$ 8. ℓ = length of pool; $\frac{2}{3}\ell$

Page 224   Classroom Exercises   1. $x + y = 16$ 3. $x - y = 4$ 5. $x = y + 105$ 7. $\ell = 2w$ 9. $a + p = 5000$

Page 224   Word Problems   1. 16, 36   3. 9, 27   5. 5, 9   7. length: 21 in; width: 15 in   9. 404 miles
11. $13\frac{1}{3}$ in; $13\frac{1}{3}$ in; $8\frac{1}{3}$ in   13. 50°, 130°   15. 8, −4   17. father: 40 yr; Enrico: 20

Page 227   Classroom Exercises   1. $\begin{cases} t + u = 12 \\ 10t + u = 12t \end{cases}$ 3. $\begin{cases} t + u = 10 \\ t = u + 4 \end{cases}$ 5. $\begin{cases} u = 2t \\ 10t + u = 5u + 6 \end{cases}$

Page 227   Word Problems   1. $\begin{cases} t + u = 12 \\ 10t + u = 12t \end{cases}; 48$ 3. $\begin{cases} u = 2t \\ u - t = 4 \end{cases}; 48$ 5. $\begin{cases} u = 2t - 11 \\ 10t + u = 7(t + u) - 6 \end{cases}; 85$
7. $\begin{cases} t + u = 9 \\ 10t + u = 10u + t + 27 \end{cases}; 63$ 9. $\begin{cases} t + u = 11 \\ 10t + u + 45 = 10u + t \end{cases}; 38$ 11. $\begin{cases} 10t + u = 5(t + u) \\ u = t + 1 \end{cases}; 45$
13. $\begin{cases} h + t + u = 8 \\ t = h - 2 \\ u = 3h \end{cases}; 206$ 15. $9t - 9u$ 17. $9t - 9u = 9(t - u)$; therefore, 9 is always a factor.
19. $100h + 10t + u - (100u + 10t + h) = 100h + 10t + u - 100u - 10t - h$
$= 99h - 99u = 99(h - u)$ Therefore, 99 is always a factor.

Page 228   Review   1. (4, 0)   2. (7, 2)   3. (3, −4)   4. one   5. infinitely many   6. one   7. (3, −5)
8. (1, −2)   9. (−3, 5)   10. (1, 5)   11. (1, −2)   12. (7, −10)   13. length: 65 cm; width: 38 cm

14. Karl: 16 yr; brother: 7 yr 15. 84 16. 78

Page 229 Calculator Exercises 1. Checks 3. Does not check; (2, 5)

Page 229 Review Capsule for Section 6-6 1. $x = -2y + 3$ 2. $x = 3y - 7$ 3. $x = -\frac{5}{3}y + 3$ 4. $x = 2y - 1$
5. $x = -y + 3$ 6. $x = 3y$ 7. $x = y + 3$ 8. $x = -\frac{7}{12}y$

Page 230 Consumer Applications 1. $329 3. $467.50 5. $450 7. $167.40 9. 6000 Btu's
11. 5500 Btu's 13. 5500 Btu's 15. 6500 Btu's 17. 7000 Btu's

Page 232 Classroom Exercises 1. (1, 2) 3. (−1, −4) 5. (5, −3)

Page 233 Written Exercises 1. (6, 2) 3. (24, 3) 5. $(-\frac{5}{49}, -\frac{25}{49})$ 7. (2, −2) 9. (0, 4) 11. (2, 1)
13. (5, −5) 15. (−2, −3) 17. (5, −5) 19. (3, 5) 21. $(3, \frac{1}{2})$ 23. $(2\frac{1}{2}, 3\frac{1}{2})$ 25. (3, −4) 27. infinite number of solutions 29. (−h, −4h)

Page 233 Review Capsule for Section 6-7 1. 5k 2. 25t 3. $\frac{1}{2}b$ 4. 5k 5. 20m 6. 1000p
7. 25q + 10d 8. 10d + 5n 9. 2.5r + 5t 10. 100b + 1000q

Page 236 Classroom Exercises 1. Total value of dimes: $0.10x; value of each quarter: $0.25; total value of quarters: $0.25y; total number of coins: 12; total value: $1.95; $\begin{cases} x + y = 12 \\ 0.10x + 0.25y = 1.95 \end{cases}$

3. Total wages for first job: $4.50x; hourly wage for second job: $4.75; total wages for second job: $4.75y; total number of hours: 37; total wages: $260.75; $\begin{cases} x + y = 37 \\ 4.50x + 4.75y = 260.75 \end{cases}$

Page 237 Word Problems 1. 21 quarters; 24 dimes 3. $900 invested at 9%; $4100 invested at 7%
5. 5000 tickets at $5.50; 2500 tickets at $7.00 7. 23 ten-dollar bills; 73 five-dollar bills 9. 19 calculators at $15.95; 12 calculators at $22.75 11. $0.15 for first day; $0.10 each day thereafter

Page 239 Classroom Exercises 1. Total value of cashews: $6.50x; total value of almonds: $8.00y; weight of mixture: 100 kg; total value of mixture: $7.40(100); $\begin{cases} x + y = 100 \\ 6.50x + 8.00y = 7.40 \end{cases}$

Page 240 Word Problems 1. 18 lb of $1.70 cookies; 27 lb of $0.95 cookies 3. $\frac{1}{2}$ oz of each type of seed
5. 100 g of the 8% solution; 300 g of the 4% solution 7. 4 kg of alloy that is 65%; 16 kg of alloy that is 35% copper 9. 16 g of 40% acid; 24 g of 15% acid 11. 20 g

Page 241 Review 1. (5, 5) 2. (−1, 2) 3. (5, 2) 4. (1, −1) 5. (2, −3) 6. $(\frac{1}{2}, -\frac{1}{2})$ 7. nickels: 32; dimes: 34 8. ten−dollar bills: 9; twenty-dollar bills: 8 9. 10%: $500; 9.5%: $1000 10. $9.50 per pound: 10 lb; $2.25 per pound: 40 lb 11. 12% alloy: 10 kg; 18% alloy: 5 kg 12. 8% solution: $7\frac{1}{2}$ liters; 12% solution: $2\frac{1}{2}$ liters

Page 241 Puzzle See Solution Key.

Page 242 Computer Exercises See Solution Key.

Page 245 Chapter Objectives and Review 1. $x - y = 2$ contains (0, −2) and (2, 0); $2x + y = 4$ contains (0, 4) and (2, 0); intersection: (2, 0) 3. $2x + y = -3$ contains (0, −3) and (−2, 1); $3x + 4y = 3$ contains (1, 0) and (−3, 3); intersection: (−3, 3) 5. none 7. $(-\frac{1}{2}, 4\frac{1}{2})$ 9. $(6, -\frac{1}{2})$ 11. $(-3\frac{1}{2}, -3)$ 13. 14, 8
15. 58 17. (1, 5) 19. $(1, \frac{1}{3})$ 21. 12%: $3000; 15%: $1000 23. Solution A: 4 liters; Solution B: 6 liters

Page 246 Chapter Test 1. $2x - y = 8$ contains (0, −8) and (4, 0); $x + y = 1$ contains (1, 0) and (0, 1); intersection: (3, −2) 3. (1, 0) 5. (3, −2) 7. Carl: 26 hours; Tony: 32 hours 9. small: 16; large: 8

Page 247 More Challenging Problems 1. $(7, -4)$ 3. ϕ 5. $(\dfrac{a^3 - ab^2}{b^2 - a^2}, \dfrac{a^2b - b^3}{b^2 - a^2})$ 7. $7:54\frac{6}{11}$ P.M. or $7:21\frac{9}{11}$ P.M.

Page 247 Additional Practice 1. $x + y = 5$ contains $(5, 0)$ and $(0, 5)$; $2x - y = 4$ contains $(2, 0)$ and $(0, -4)$; intersection: $(3, 2)$ 3. $x - 2y = 8$ contains $(0, -4)$ and $(8, 0)$; $2x + y = 6$ contains $(0, 6)$ and $(3, 0)$; intersection: $(4, -2)$ 5. none   7. $(5, -9)$ 9. $(\frac{1}{2}, \frac{5}{8})$ 11. $(-2\frac{4}{5}, 2)$ 13. $(1, 1)$ 15. $(-5, 5)$ 17. $(3, 2)$ 19. $(3, -2)$ 21. $(1\frac{5}{8}, -\frac{1}{4})$ 23. $(3, 7)$ 25. line contains $(0, 550)$ and $(4, 890)$; line contains $(0, 650)$ and $(4, 890)$ 27. District A: 3289; District B: 3143   29. 49   31. 12%: \$6500; 14%: \$3500 33. 10%: 15 liters; 5%: 10 liters

CHAPTER 7: INEQUALITIES

Page 251 Classroom Exercises 1. $x = 3$ <u>or</u> $x < 3$ 3. $x = -1$ <u>or</u> $x > -1$ 5. $3y = 12$ <u>or</u> $3y < 12$ 7. $x + 2 = 8$ <u>or</u> $x + 2 < 8$ 9. $x \leq 5$ 11. $x \leq -3$ 13. $4 > x > 1$ 15. $-1 < t < 3$ 17. c   19. d   21. b

Page 252 Written Exercises 1. $3x - 1 = 11$ <u>or</u> $3x - 1 < 11$ 3. $3 < y$ <u>and</u> $2x < 10$ 5. $t - \frac{1}{2} = 3\frac{1}{2}$ or $t - \frac{1}{2} > 3\frac{1}{2}$ 7. $-3 < x + 2$ and $x + 2 < 1$ 9. $-9 < 3k$ and $3k < 15$ 11. All points between, and not including, -2 and 2   13. All points between, and not including, 3 and 5   15. All points to the right of, and not including, 0   17. All points to the left of, and including, -1 19. $x \geq 7$ 21. $-2\frac{1}{2} < x < 5$ 23. $4 > x \geq 2$ 25. $-3 < t \leq 6$ 27. $y \leq 3$ 29. $c \geq 2\frac{1}{2}$ 31. $x \leq -1$ 33. $-3 \leq m < 0$ 35. $1 \leq m \leq 6$ 37. 130, 205   39. $76 < y \leq 81$ 41. $58 < y \leq 60$ 43. $\{51\frac{1}{4}, 51\frac{3}{8}, 51\frac{1}{2}, 51\frac{5}{8}, 51\frac{3}{4}, 51\frac{7}{8}, 52, 52\frac{1}{8}, 52\frac{1}{4}, 52\frac{3}{8}, 52\frac{1}{2}, 52\frac{5}{8}\}$ 45. $y < -3$ or $y \geq -3$ 47. $2 < n < 3$ 49. $-5 > x \geq -8$ 51. $n < 7$

Page 253 Puzzle See Solution Key.

Page 253 Review Capsule for Section 7-2 1. No   2. Yes   3. Yes   4. Yes   5. Yes   6. Yes   7. $y = 5x$ 8. $y = -\frac{1}{2}x + 3$ 9. $y = 2x - 1$ 10. $y = 5x + 3$ 11. 0; 5   12. $\frac{3}{4}$; -3 13. $-\frac{1}{2}, \frac{1}{2}$ 14. $\frac{2}{3}$; 2

Page 255 Classroom Exercises 1. Yes   3. No   5. Yes

Page 255 Written Exercises 1. none   3. none   5. $(1, 0)$, $(0, 1)$ 7. $(1, -1)$, $(0, 0)$ 9. $(9, 2)$, $(-1, -7)$ Each graph in Exercises 11-30 is an open half-plane. The location of each half-plane with respect to the related dashed line is given along with two points for the line.   11. Above the line that contains $(0, -3)$ and $(1, -2)$ 13. To the left of the line that contains $(0, -4)$ and $(1, -1)$ 15. To the right of the line that contains $(0, 0)$ and $(1, -3)$ 17. To the left of the line that contains $(0, -4)$ and $(1, -6)$ 19. Above the line that contains $(0, 4)$ and $(1, 3)$ 21. Above the line that contains $(0, 2)$ and $(3, 0)$ 23. Above the line that contains $(0, 4)$ and $(2, 4)$ 25. Below the line that contains $(0, -4)$ and $(2, -4)$ 27. To the left of the line that contains $(8, 0)$ and $(8, 2)$ 29. To the left of the line that contains $(-4, 0)$ and $(-4, 2)$ 31. The closed half-plane above the line that contains $(0, -4)$ and $(2, -4)$ 33. The closed half-plane to the right of the line that contains $(1, -6)$ and $(0, -9)$ 35. The closed half-plane below the line that contains $(0, -5)$ and $(2, -5)$ 37. The closed half-plane to the left of the line that contains $(0, 6)$ and $(1, 8)$ 39. $x > 2$ 41. $y < x$ 43. A closed half-plane   45. A closed half-plane   47. A straight line   49. A closed half-plane

Page 256 Review Capsule for Section 7-3 1. $(4, -1)$ 2. $(3, 6)$ 3. $(1, -5)$ 4. $(-1\frac{1}{2}, -3)$ 5. Yes 6. Yes   7. No

Page 257 Classroom Exercises 1. c   3. a

Page 257 Written Exercises

1.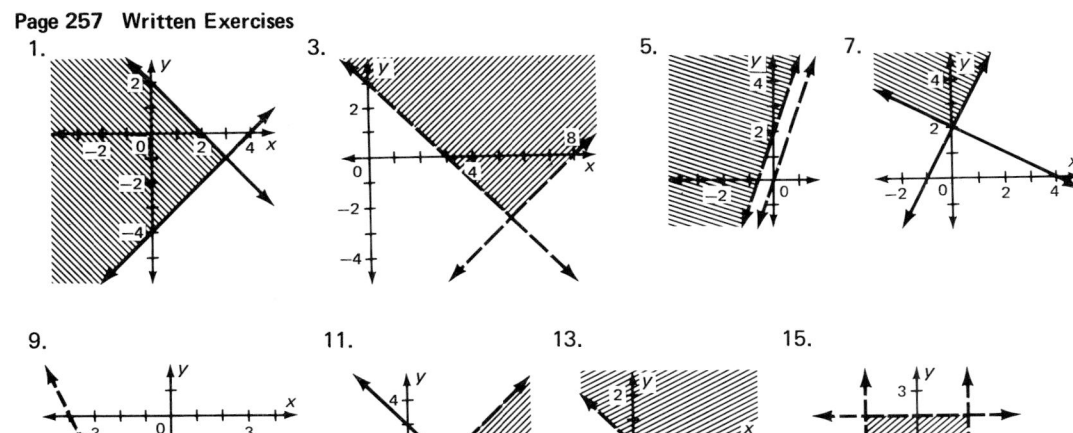

3.

5.

7.

9.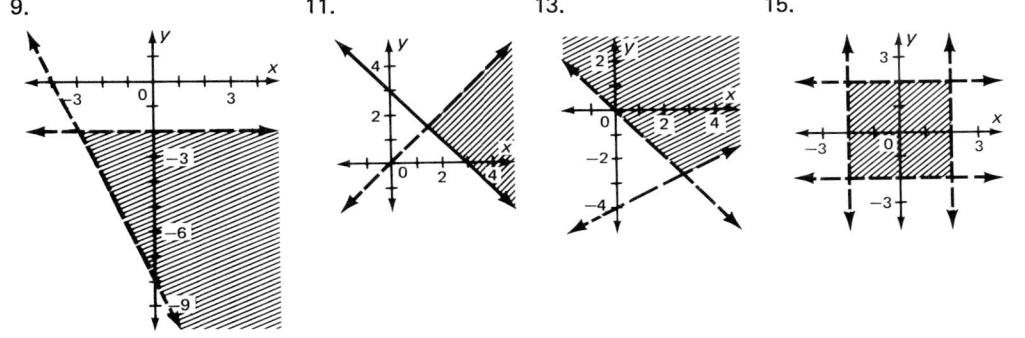

11.

13.

15.

17.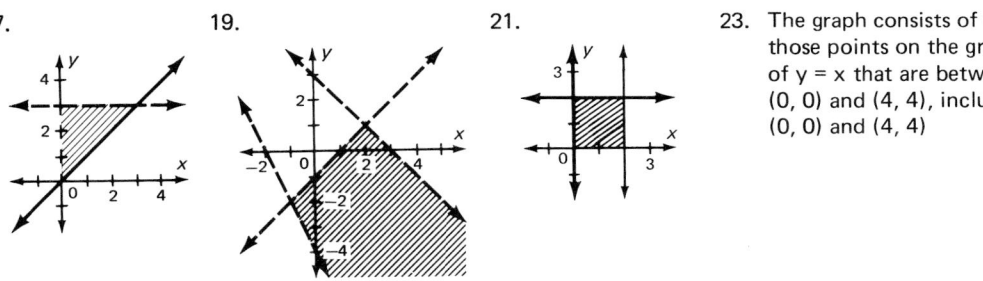

19.

21.

23. The graph consists of only those points on the graph of y = x that are between (0, 0) and (4, 4), including (0, 0) and (4, 4)

Page 258 Calculator Exercises See the answers to the Classroom Exercises on page 255.

Page 260 Classroom Exercises 1. 24; 0   3. 24; 0

Page 260 Word Problems 1. 40; 0   3. 60; 0   5. a. (0, 0), (0, 4), (4, 0) b. 0   7. a. (0, 0), (0, 5), (4, 1), (4, 0) b. 0   9. $15x + 18y$ 11. Coordinates of the polygonal region: (50, 80), (50, 150), (120, 80) 13. $3450   15. $\begin{cases} x + y \leq 4 \\ x \geq 0 \\ y \geq 0 \end{cases}$ 17. (0, 4), (0, 0), (4, 0)

Page 261 Review 1. $n \geq 3$; all points to the right of, and including, 3   2. $-3 < x < 2$; all points between, and not including, -3 and 2   3. $y \geq -2$; all points to the right of, and including, -2 4. The closed half-plane to the right of the line that contains (2, 1) and (2, -2)   5. The open half-plane below the line that contains (2, -2) and (3, -1)   6. The open half-plane to the left of the line that contains (-2, 1) and (-1, 3)   7. The open half-plane to the left of the line that contains (1, -1) and (2, 1)

8. 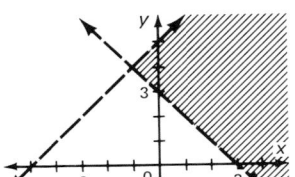 9. 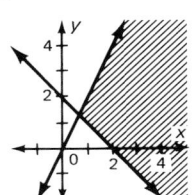 10. 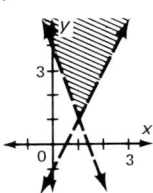 11.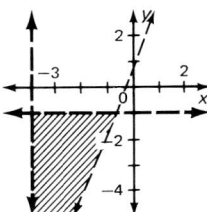

12. $25x + 36y$ 13. $\begin{cases} x + y \le 10 \\ 2x + 3y \le 24 \\ x \ge 0 \\ y \ge 0 \end{cases}$ 14. 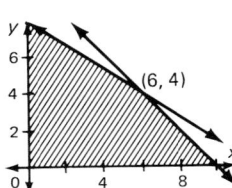   15. 6 plain, 4 fancy

Page 262   Consumer Applications   1. 5   3. 20   5. 11.4   7. 7.8   9. 10.5   11. 12.6   13. $275°\,F$
15. Solution C: $-12°\,F$; Solution D: $-2°\,F$ 17. Solution A: $-20°\,C$; Solution B: $-8°\,C$

Page 264   Review Capsule for Section 7-5   1. 6   2. 3   3. 0   4. -7 5. -10 6. -11 7. 1   8. -2
9. 9   10. -1 11. $x = 5$ or $x = -5$ 12. $y = 4$ 13. $n = -5.7$ 14. $n = 2$ or $n = -2$ 15. $r = 1$

Page 265   Classroom Exercises   1. $x = -15$ or $x = 5$ 3. $t = -2$ or $t = 2$ 5. $n = -2$ or $n = 2$ 7. $y = 2$
9. $q = -2\frac{3}{4}$ or $q = 3\frac{1}{4}$ 11. $k = 4$ or $k = 5$

Page 265   Written Exercises   1. $a = -5$ or $a = -1$ 3. $y = -2$ or $y = 2$ 5. $k = 1\frac{1}{3}$ or $k = 2\frac{2}{3}$ 7. $x = -9$ or
$x = 15$ 9. $k = -13$ or $k = 17$ 11. $t = -10$ or $t = 8$ 13. $t = -4\frac{2}{5}$ or $t = 5\frac{1}{5}$ 15. $k = -1\frac{5}{6}$ or $k = -\frac{1}{6}$
17. $y = -\frac{1}{8}$ or $y = \frac{1}{8}$ 19. $m = -3\frac{1}{3}$ or $m = -\frac{2}{3}$ 21. $x = -1$ or $x = 1$ 23. $w = -3\frac{1}{3}$ or $w = 3\frac{1}{3}$ 25. $y = -\frac{2}{3}$
or $y = 2$ 27. $k = -20$ or $k = 22$ 29. $t = \frac{2}{3}$ or $t = 4$ 31. $x \le -5$ or $x \ge 5$; all points to the left of, and
including, -5 all points to the right of, and including, 5   33. $-1 < n < 5$; all points between, and not
including, -1 and 5   35. $-4 \le x \le 5$; all points between, and including, -4 and 5   37. $1 \le n \le 5$; all
points between, and including, 1 and 5

Page 265   Review Capsule for Section 7-6   1. $x = -5$ 2. $x = 0$ 3. $y = -3x$ 4. $y = 5$ 5. $y = \frac{1}{2}x + 2$
6. 15, 5, 0, -5, -15 7. 7, 5, 4, 3, 1

Page 267   Classroom Exercises   1. 4, 2, 0, 2, 4   3. 1, 0, -1, -2, -1, 0

Page 267   Written Exercises   1. Two vertical lines, one through $(-2, 0)$ and the other through $(2, 0)$
3. Two horizontal lines, one through $(-3, 0)$, and the other through $(3, 0)$ Each graph in Exercises 5-20
consists of two rays. Their initial point and the coordinates of another point on each ray is given.
5. Initial point: $(0, 0)$; one ray: $(-1, 2)$; other ray: $(1, 2)$ 7. Initial point: $(0, 0)$; one ray: $(-2, -2)$;
other ray: $(2, 2)$ 9. Initial point: $(0, -4)$; one ray: $(-2, -2)$; other ray: $(2, -2)$ 11. Initial point:
$(0, 7)$; one ray: $(-1, 10)$; other ray: $(1, 10)$ 13. Initial point: $(0, 0)$; one ray: $(1, 1)$; other ray: $(1, -1)$
15. Initial point: $(-6, 0)$; one ray: $(-8, 1)$; other ray: $(-8, -1)$ 17. Initial point: $(0, 0)$; one ray:
$(-3, 1)$; other ray: $(-3, -1)$ 19. Initial point: $(6, 0)$; one ray: $(7, 1)$; other ray: $(7, -1)$ 21. The graph
consists of four rays. The initial point of two of the rays is $(-5, 0)$. One ray also contains $(-6, 1)$ and the
other ray also contains $(-6, -1)$. The initial point of the other two rays is $(5, 0)$. One ray also contains
$(6, 1)$ and the other ray also contains $(6, -1)$.   23. The graph consists of two lines that intersect at $(0, 0)$.
One line also contains $(1, 1)$ and the other line contains $(1, -1)$.   25. The graph consists of two parallel lines.
One line contains $(0, 3)$ and the other line contains $(0, 5)$.   27. The graph consists of one point: $(0, 0)$

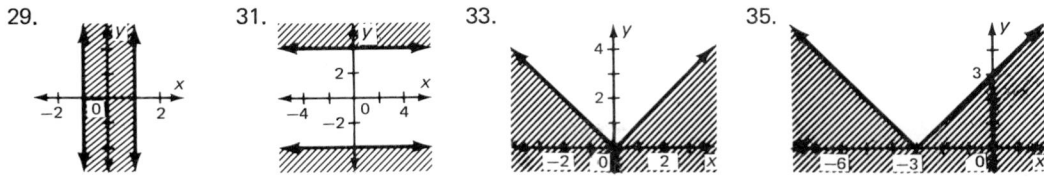

29.   31.   33.   35.

Page 267   Review   1. $x = -7$ or $x = 3$ **2.** $y = -12$ or $y = 12$ **3.** $m = -\frac{1}{3}$ or $m = \frac{1}{3}$ **4.** $q = -2$ or $q = 2$
5. $s = 1$ **6.** $n = 2$ or $n = 2\frac{1}{2}$ **7.** $z = -1$ or $z = 1$ **8.** $w = -1\frac{1}{2}$ or $w = 1$ **9.** $t = -\frac{1}{4}$ or $t = 1\frac{3}{4}$
10. The graph consists of two parallel lines, one four units to the right on the y axis, and the other four units to the left on the y axis.   **11.** The graph consists of two rays with their initial point at the origin. The ray in Quadrant I also passes through (3, 9), and the ray in Quadrant II also passes through (−3, 9).   **12.** The graph consists of two rays with their initial point at the origin. The ray in Quadrant III also passes through (−3, −9), and the ray in Quadrant IV also passes through (3, −9).   **13.** The graph consists of two rays with their initial point at (0, 5). The ray in Quadrant I also passes through (3, 8), and the ray in Quadrant II also passes through (−3, 8).   **14.** The graph consists of four rays with their initial point at the origin. The ray in Quadrant I also passes through (2, 4), and the ray in Quadrant IV also passes through (2, −4). The ray in Quadrant II also passes through (−2, 4), and the ray in Quadrant III also passes through (−2, −4).   **15.** The graph consists of two parallel lines, one four units above the x axis, and the other two units below the x axis.

Page 268   Computer Exercises   See Solution Key.

Page 270   Chapter Objectives and Review   1. $5x = -10$ or $5x > -10$ **3.** $-5 < y$ and $y < 0$ **5.** $6s - 8 = 4$ or $6s - 8 > 4$ **7.** All points between, and not including, −2 and 5   **9.** All points between −1 and 1, including −1 but not including 1   **11.** All points between, and including, −5 and 4   **13.** The open half-plane to the right of the line that contains (0, 0) and (2, −8).   **15.** The open half-plane to the left of the line that contains (−2, 0) and (1, −3).   **17.** The closed half-plane below the x axis.   **19.** The closed half-plane to the right of the line that contains (0, −3) and (2, −7).   **21.** d   **23.** b
25.   **27.**   **29.** maximum: 12; minimum: 0
31. maximum: 36; minimum: 0
33. maximum: 24; minimum: −8
35. $4x + 6y$
37. Coordinates of the polygonal region: (0, 0), (0, 4), (3, 2), (3, 0)
39. 28
41. $x = -1$ or $x = 1$
43. $p = -8$ or $p = 8$
45. $a = -11$ or $a = -1$

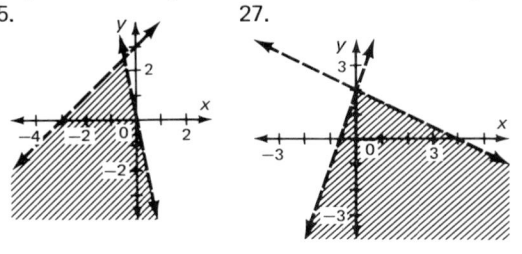

47. The graph consists of two parallel lines, one 1 unit to the right of the y axis, and the other one unit to the left of the y axis.   **49.** The graph consists of two rays, one in Quadrant I and one in Quadrant II, with their initial point at the origin. The ray in Quadrant I also passes through (2, 2), and the ray in Quadrant II also passes through (−2, 2).   **51.** The graph consists of two rays, one in Quadrant I and one in Quadrant II, with their initial point at the origin. The ray in Quadrant I also passes through (2, 6), and the ray in Quadrant II also passes through (−2, 6).   **53.** The graph consists of two parallel lines, one two units above the x axis, and one two units below the x axis.

Page 272   Chapter Test   1. $x - 3 = 9$ or $x - 3 > 9$ **3.** $-8 < 2n + 6$ and $2n + 6 < -2$ **5.** The graph shows all real numbers between −4 and 4.   **7.** Exercise 7 is located at the top of the following page.
9. $\begin{cases} x \geq 110 \\ y \geq 60 \\ x + y \leq 300 \end{cases}$ **11.** (240, 60), (110, 60), (110, 90)   **13.** $x = -5$ or $x = 5$ **15.** The graph consists of two rays, one in Quadrant I and one in Quadrant II, with their initial point at (0, 0). The ray in Quadrant I also passes through (2, 6), and the ray in Quadrant II also passes through (−2, 6).

7.

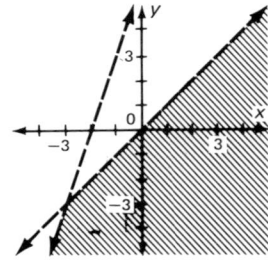

Page 273 **Additional Practice** 1. $2y = 5$ <u>or</u> $2y > 5$ 3. $-6 < 4a + 6$ <u>and</u> $4a + 6 < -2$ 5. $0 \geq p > -4$; all points between 0 and -4, including 0 and not including -4 7. The open half-plane above the line contains $(0, -1)$ and $(2, 1)$ 9. The open half-plane below the line that contains $(0, -4)$ and $(-4, 0)$

11.

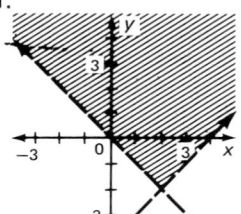

13.

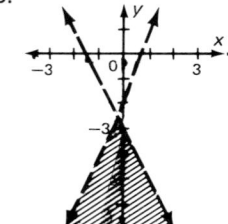

15. $x = -2$ <u>or</u> $x = 4$ 17. $x = -1\frac{1}{3}$ <u>or</u> $x = 4$

19. The graph consists of two parallel lines, one 1 unit above the x axis, and the other two units below the x axis.

21. $15 \leq s \leq 100$

23. $200x + 140y$

25. $(2, 6), (4, 3), (4, 6)$; \$1220

Page 274 **Review of Word Problems** 1. \$60.90 3.

s	100	200	300
t	6	12	18

5. \$15 7. 936 mi 9. 52 11. $0.08x + 0.10y$ 13. Coordinates of the polygonal region: $(150, 75), (150, 150), (225, 75)$

Page 275 **Cumulative Review Chapters 5-7** 1. b 3. b 5. a 7. b 9. c 11. c 13. c 15. d 17. a 19. c 21. c 23. d 25. d

Page 277 **Preparing for College Entrance Tests** 1. c 3. b 5. a 7. a 9. b 11. d 13. c 15. c 17. c 19. c

CHAPTER 8: EXPONENTS AND POLYNOMIALS

Page 281 **Classroom Exercises** 1. $10; 6; 10 \cdot 10 \cdot 10 \cdot 10 \cdot 10 \cdot 10$ 3. $3^4; 3 \cdot 3 \cdot 3 \cdot 3$ 5. $x^6; x; 6$

Page 282 **Written Exercises** 1. $5; 6; 5 \cdot 5 \cdot 5 \cdot 5 \cdot 5 \cdot 5$ 3. $2; 6; 2 \cdot 2 \cdot 2 \cdot 2 \cdot 2 \cdot 2$ 5. 10^5; $10 \cdot 10 \cdot 10 \cdot 10 \cdot 10$ 7. $10^4; 10; 4$ 9. $x^1; x; 1$ 11. 10,000 13. 100,000 15. 10,000,000,000 17. a 19. -1 21. -1 23. -1 25. 1 27. 1 29. 1 31. 10^5 33. 10^6 35. 10^3 37. 10^9 39. 10^{12} 41. 2^7 43. 10^4 45. 2^6 47. 2^{17} 49. a^6 51. m^8 53. 1 55. 2 57. 9 59. -6 61. 18 63. -24

Page 283 **Review Capsule for Section 8-2** 1. 200 2. -378 3. -54 4. 1 5. 0 6. 3600 7. -280 8. -1

Page 284 **Classroom Exercises** 1. x^{10} 3. $-x^5$ 5. a^9 7. $10a^5b^{10}$

Page 284 **Written Exercises** 1. x^7 3. $-y^3$ 5. x^9 7. m^7 9. n^7 11. a^2 13. b^5 15. $-b^2$ 17. $-x^3$ 19. y^4 21. p^5 23. $3^{10} = 59{,}049$ 25. $2^8 = 256$ 27. $(-5)^7 = -78{,}125$ 29. $20x^3y^2$ 31. $-24m^3n^2y^4$ 33. $-36x^8$ 35. x^4 37. 10^9 39. 10^{15} 41. 6×10^6 43. 3×10^9 45. $2.8a \times 10^{11}$ 47. N 49. N 51. N 53. x^{a+2} 55. x^{a+b} 57. x^{5a} 59. 3^{x+2} 61. 2^{9a+1} 63. $(x + 2)^{a+6}$

Page 286 **Classroom Exercises** 1. x^6 3. $9x^8$ 5. $-a^9b^6$ 7. $\frac{9}{16}$

Page 286 **Written Exercises** 1. x^6 3. x^8 5. a^{12} 7. x^{21} 9. x^{36} 11. y^9 13. b^{24} 15. y^{32}

574   *Answers to Selected Exercises*

17. x^2y^2 19. $25x^2$ 21. $x^4y^4z^4$ 23. 36   25. x^4 27. y^2 29. $27b^3$ 31. $9a^4b^2$ 33. $-27b^3$
35. $8x^9y^6$ 37. $64x^9y^6$ 39. x^8y^4 41. $64a^{12}c^6d^9$ 43. $64x^{18}y^{12}$ 45. x^8y^6 47. 4×10^6
49. 1.331×10^{18} 51. $\dfrac{x^2}{y^2}$ 53. $\dfrac{8}{27}$ 55. $\dfrac{c^7}{d^7}$ 57. $\dfrac{x^4}{y^6}$ 59. $\dfrac{b^4}{a^2}$ 61. $\dfrac{a^6}{b^9}$ 63. $\dfrac{x^6}{y^4}$ 65. d   67. a
69. f   71. i   73. $\dfrac{a^8}{b^4c^{12}}$ 75. $\dfrac{a^9b^6}{c^{12}}$ 77. $-6a^7b^8$ 79. $\dfrac{-27x^6}{64y^6}$ 81. x^{n^2} 83. $\dfrac{m^k}{n^k}$ 85. $\dfrac{3^c x^{cn}}{5^c y^{cm}}$
87. $\dfrac{3^k a^{km} b^{kn}}{2^k x^k y^k}$

Page 287   Calculator Exercises   1. 225   3. 2025   5. 3645   7. 1,000,000   9. 36,400,000
11. 160,000   13. 107,374.18   15. 11,805,916

Page 287   Review Capsule for Section 8-4   1. 1   2. 0   3. -1 4. 4   5. $-\dfrac{1}{4}$ 6. $-z$ 7. $-8x$ 8. 1

Page 288   Classroom Exercises   1. x^6 3. $-xy^2$ 5. $8^2 = 64$

Page 289   Written Exercises   1. 2^2 or 4   3. 5^3 or 125   5. a^5 7. x   9. ay^2 11. a^2b^3 13. k^2m
15. $5x^5y$ 17. $9r^2s^2$ 19. 4×10^2 21. P   23. P   25. N   27. P   29. $-2b$ 31. $\dfrac{3ab^3}{2}$ 33. $-125a^3$
35. 25×10^4 37. b   39. $a^{t-v}b^{w-25}$ 41. $x^{u-4v}y$ 43. $a^{2x-1}b^{3y-1}c^{k-1}$ 45. x^{3a+3} 47. x^{9a-39}

Page 289   Review Capsule for Section 8-5   1. 1000   2. 100,000   3. 1,000,000   4. 10   5. 10,000
6. 10,000,000   7. $\dfrac{1}{100}$ 8. $\dfrac{1}{1000}$ 9. 1   10. $\dfrac{1}{1000}$ 11. $\dfrac{1}{100,000}$ 12. $\dfrac{1}{10,000}$

Page 291   Classroom Exercises   1. $\dfrac{1}{16}$ 3. $\dfrac{1}{-4}$ 5. $\dfrac{1}{9b^2}$ 7. 7×10^9 9. 6.3×10^{-5} 11. 7.89×10^2
13. 2.107×10^1

Page 292   Written Exercises   1. 16   3. 1   5. 1000   7. 1   9. $-\dfrac{1}{8}$ 11. $\dfrac{64}{27}$ 13. 16   15. $-\dfrac{64}{27}$
17. $\dfrac{1}{1000}$ 19. $\dfrac{9}{4}$ 21. $\dfrac{1}{a^3}$ 23. $\dfrac{3}{x^5}$ 25. $\dfrac{1}{m}$ 27. $\dfrac{1}{4y}$ 29. $\dfrac{b^2}{a^3}$ 31. $\dfrac{1}{27y^3}$ 33. 4.6×10^3
35. 6.7×10^7 37. 2.4×10^{13} 39. 5.7×10^{-4} 41. 2×10^{-5} 43. 8×10^{-4} 45. 2×10^{-4}
47. 6×10^6 49. 3×10^3 51. 4×10^7 53. 5×10^{-3} 55. 2.976×10^5 km per second
57. 1×10^5 light years   59. 1×10^{11} stars   61. 1.5×10^8 km   63. 1×10^{-8} gm   65. 1×10^{15}
67. 6000   69. 0.000000022   71. $\dfrac{1}{a^8}$ 73. $\dfrac{b^2}{a^2}$ 75. x^4 77. x

Page 293   Review   1. -9 2. 3   3. -48 4. 64   5. 36   6. n^4 7. $-x^5$ 8. $-(12a^7)$ 9. $6c^3d^4$
10. y^8 11. a^8b^4 12. 4×10^8 13. $\dfrac{r^6}{s^3t^3}$ 14. a^2 15. y   16. $-3bc^2$ 17. $-4b^2$ 18. $\dfrac{1}{3^4} = \dfrac{1}{81}$
19. -64 20. $\dfrac{1}{(-\frac{2}{3})^3} = -\dfrac{1}{\frac{8}{27}} = -\dfrac{27}{8} = -3\dfrac{3}{8}$ 21. $\dfrac{3}{y^2}$ 22. $\dfrac{1}{(-3)^3} = \dfrac{1}{-27} = -\dfrac{1}{27}$ 23. 6×10^6
24. 4×10^{-2} 25. 7×10^{-4} 26. 1.5555×10^4

Page 293   Review Capsule for Section 8-6   1. $-2n$ 2. $2n$ 3. $-2x + 5$ 4. $3x^2 + 4x$ 5. $7a^2 + 3a - 4$
6. $2x + (-3x + 5)$ 7. $3a + (-2a + 3b)$ 8. $-3y + (6y + 3y - 4)$ 9. $3a + (-4a - 3b)$ 10. $t + (-4)$
$+ (-2t + 1)$ 11. $9 + (-r) + (-7r + 6)$

Page 294   Career Applications   1. 156   3. 75   5. 3.36×10^{18} 7. 3.31×10^{18} 9. 3.37×10^{18}
11. 81.99×10^{-15} 13. 81.4×10^{-9} cm^3

Page 297   Classroom Exercises   1. $12a + 2b$ 3. $2r + 6s$ 5. $-3x^3 + 6x^2 + 5x + 2$

Page 297   Written Exercises   1. $12a + 2b - 4c$ 3. $-p + 4t + 7x$ 5. $14x + y - 4z$ 7. $-5a^2 - 2ab - 4b^2$
9. $7ab - 3ac$ 11. $4x^2 + 15x - 7$ 13. $6a + 8b - 11c + 2d$ 15. $2x + 4y + 2$ 17. $12a + 20b - 12$
19. $6x + 11y - 8$ 21. $-3b + 3$ 23. $9x + 6$ 25. $-3m^2 + n$ 27. $-2b + 2c$ 29. $a + b$ 31. $-x^2 + 2x$
$+ 8$ 33. $x^2 - 6x - 7$ 35. $3x + 2y$ 37. $x^2 - 9y^2$ 39. $2x^2 - 2xy - 4y^2$ 41. $-9a + 3b - 6c + 3d$
43. $2x^2 + 8xy - 2y^2$ 45. $4xy$ 47. $-3x + 3y$ 49. $a + 2b + c + 1$ 51. The perimeter of the square is 2
meters larger.

Page 299 Review Capsule for Section 8-7   1. $6a + 15b - 12$ 2. $-14x + 7y - 35$ 3. $-2a + 6b - 1$
4. $20k - 15s + 10$ 5. $-21 + 5t + 3r$ 6. $6u - 10w + 11z$ 7. a^9 8. q^3 9. $-t^7$ 10. a^{10}
11. $-27x^3y^6$ 12. $a - b + 3$ 13. $8b + 3c + 2$ 14. $9n + 2$

Page 300 Classroom Exercises   1. $3x^2 + 27x$ 3. $7x^2 + 25x + 12$ 5. $-12n^4 - 30n^2$ 7. $a^2 + 11a + 18$
9. $-r^2s + 2rs - 7s$ 11. $x^2 - y^2$

Page 300 Written Exercises   1. $2a^2 + 3a$ 3. $3y^2 - 24y$ 5. $-2y^2 - 12y$ 7. $5m^2 - 2m$ 9. $7s^2 - 8s$
11. $-12a^2 + 20ab$ 13. $2a^3 - 8a^2 + 6a$ 15. $y^4 - 6y^3 + 3y^2$ 17. $-3x^5y - 12x^3y^2 + 15x^2y^3$
19. $a^2 + 10a + 21$ 21. $2a^2 + 14a + 20$ 23. $a^2 - a - 12$ 25. $6a^2 - 11a - 10$ 27. $6a^2 + 5a - 6$
29. $ac + ad + bc + bd$ 31. $ac - ad - bc + bd$ 33. $9b^2 - 16c^2$ 35. $16x^2 - 25$ 37. $9x^2 - 24x + 16$
39. $15x^2 + 11xy - 12y^2$ 41. $x^2 - \frac{3}{2}xy - y^2$ 43. $0.32n^2 - 9.8n + 45$ 45. $x^4 - y^4$ 47. $8s^3 - 6s^2$
$+ 12s - 9$ 49. $6x^4 + 13x^2y^2 + 6y^4$ 51. $4x^2 + 12xy + 9y^2$ 53. $6x + 35$ 55. $2y^2 - 4y - 48$
57. $16x^2 - 4y^2$ 59. $-5x + 2$ 61. $x^2 + 4x + 4$ 63. $\frac{h^2 + 3h}{2}$ 65. $\frac{1}{8}\pi(9x^2 - 6x + 1)$ 67. square's
area is 1 square unit larger   69. square's area is 1 square unit larger   71. $x^3 + 3x^2 + 3x + 1$ 73. $n^5 - 7n^4$
$+ 10n^3 + 2n^2 - 4n$ 75. $x^3 - 9x^2y + 9xy + 18xy^2 - 27y^3$ 77. $-2c^3 - 3c^2 + 5c + 6$
79. $x^4 - 4x^3 + 6x^2 - 4x + 1$

Page 302 Review Capsule for Section 8-8   1. $9c^2$ 2. $15x^5$ 3. $12a^2b^2$ 4. $6x^4$ 5. $8a^5$ 6. $36b^3c^4d^3$
7. $3x^4y^3z^7$ 8. $-x^6y^{12}z$

Page 302 Classroom Exercises   1. h   3. b   5. a   7. j   9. g

Page 303 Written Exercises   1. $x^2 + 8x + 15$ 3. $x^2 - 4$ 5. $a^2 + a - 6$ 7. $b^2 - 4b - 21$ 9. p^2
$+ 20p + 99$ 11. $d^2 + d - 20$ 13. $12y^2 + 17y + 6$ 15. $2x^2 + 13x + 21$ 17. $9x^2 - 16$ 19. $b^2 + 8b$
$+ 16$ 21. $m^2 - 4m - 77$ 23. $a^2 - 4c^2$ 25. $3x^2 - x - 2$ 27. $y^4 + 6y^2 + 9$ 29. $16y^2 - 24y + 9$
31. $4a^2 + 16a + 15$ 33. $5x^2 + 8x + 3$ 35. $35b^2 + 3b - 2$ 37. $24x^2 - 23x - 12$ 39. $6c^2 - 43c + 72$
41. $x^4 - 16$ 43. $7a^2 + 54a - 16$ 45. $6x^2 - xy - 15y^2$ 47. $\frac{7}{2}x^2 - 17x - 24$ 49. $\frac{1}{12}t^2 + 4t + 48$
51. $\frac{1}{35}x^2 - 2x + 35$ 53. $0.36uw + 0.9w - 0.48u - 1.2$ 55. $s^2 + 8s + 16$ 57. rectangle with length
$(a + 2)$ units and width $(a + 1)$ units; 6 square units larger

Page 303 Review Capsule for Section 8-9   1. 4   2. x^2 3. $-x^2$ 4. $x^2y^2z^2$ 5. a^4 6. a^4 7. $-a^4$
8. $4a^2$ 9. $-4a^2$ 10. $-4a^8$

Page 305 Classroom Exercises   1. $x^2 - 20x + 100$ 3. $x^2 - 4xy + 4y^2$ 5. $4p^2 - 4pq + q^2$ 7. m^4
$- 12m^2 + 36$

Page 305 Written Exercises   1. $a^2 + 6a + 9$ 3. $a^2 + 10a + 25$ 5. $a^2 - 10a + 25$ 7. $x^2 - 2xy + y^2$
9. $4a^2 + 4a + 1$ 11. $25m^2 - 10m + 1$ 13. $n^2 + 6n + 9$ 15. $9x^2 - 6xy + y^2$ 17. $4x^2 - 12x + 9$
19. $4x^2 + 4xy + y^2$ 21. $4x^2 - 12xy + 9y^2$ 23. $100a^2 + 40a + 4$ 25. $4x^4 + 12x^2y^2 + 9y^4$
27. $a^4 - 6a^2b^2 + 9b^4$ 29. $a^4 - 6a^2 + 9$ 31. $121a^4 + 22a^2c^2 + c^4$ 33. 361   35. 2704   37. 441
39. 998,001   41. 10,201   43. $x^2 + x + \frac{1}{4}$ 45. $x^2 - \frac{1}{3}x + \frac{1}{36}$ 47. $36b^2 + 6b + \frac{1}{4}$ 49. $x^2 - ax + \frac{a^2}{4}$
51. $x^2 + xy + \frac{y^2}{4}$

Page 307 Classroom Exercises   1. $x^2 - 1$ 3. $4r^2 - 25$ 5. $9h^2 - 16s^2$

Page 307 Written Exercises   1. $p^2 - 49$ 3. $p^2 - 64$ 5. $b^2 - c^2$ 7. $4p^2 - 9$ 9. $R^2 - r^2$
11. $25x^2 - 16y^2$ 13. $36x^4 - 49y^2$ 15. $a^2b^2 - c^2$ 17. $\frac{1}{4} - 4x^2$ 19. $4c^2 - d^2$ 21. $25y^2 - 16$
23. $x^4 - y^4$ 25. 399   27. 10,096   29. 75   31. 396   33. 2499   35. $\frac{1}{2}x^2 - \frac{9}{2}$ 37. square is 16
square units greater   39. $1 - y^{4a}$ 41. $a^4b^{16} - 25$ 43. $b^{2n} - c^{4n}$

Page 310 Review   1. $5a - 2b$ 2. $4x^2y + 7xy^2$ 3. $3d^2 - 3d - 4$ 4. $x^3 - 4x$ 5. $12x - 3$
6. $4y^3 + 8y^2$ 7. $2c^2 - 7c - 4$ 8. $4c^2 + 12c + 9$ 9. $4a^4 - 6a^2c + 2c^2$ 10. $b + 3$ 11. $y^2 - y - 6$
12. $6b^2 + 11b + 3$ 13. $3m^4 - 8m^2n - 3n^2$ 14. $x^4 + 3x^2 - 10$ 15. $a^4 - b^2$ 16. $3a^2b^2 - 7ab + 4$
17. $a^2 - 4a + 4$ 18. $9y^2 + 30y + 25$ 19. $4b^2 - 24bd + 36d^2$ 20. $r^4s^2 + 2r^2st + t^2$ 21. $b^2 - 4$

22. $r^2 - s^2$ 23. $1 - p^2$ 24. $9y^2 - 4$ 25. $9c^2 - 4d^2$ 26. $x^4 - 36$

Page 311   Chapter Objectives and Review   1. -8 3. 1 5. -1 7. 32 9. -128 11. a^{12} 13. p^5
15. 10^6, or $1,000,000$ 17. $3m^3n$ 19. x^{15} 21. $27y^3$ 23. $27c^3d^{12}$ 25. $\frac{m^6}{p^3n^6}$ 27. 3 29. $3ab^3$
31. $3x^3y$ 33. $s^{2x-1}t^{3y-2}$ 35. $\frac{1}{3^4} = \frac{1}{81}$ 37. $\frac{1}{y^6}$ 39. $\frac{3}{n^2}$ 41. 2.9×10^{10} 43. $4x - 2y$ 45. $3m^2$
$+ 5m$ 47. $30y + 15$ 49. $2x^2 + 7xy - 4y^2$ 51. $-x^2 + 2xy - y^2$ 53. $p^2 - 3p - 4$ 55. $6a^2 + ab$
$- 12b^2$ 57. $2d^2 + 5dh - 3h^2$ 59. $c^2 + 12c + 36$ 61. $x^4 + 6x^2 + 9$ 63. $d^2 - 25$ 65. $f^2 - g^2$
67. $25m^2 - 4n^2$

Page 313   Chapter Test   1. 2 3. -32 5. $-5ac^2$ 7. 6.5×10^8 9. 7.0×10^6 11. $4x - 5$
13. $m - n - p + 1$ 15. $x^2 - 8x + 16$ 17. $-w^7$ 19. $6b^2 - 3b$ 21. $3y^2 - 7xy - 6x^2$ 23. $3c^2 - 5cd$
$+ 2d^2$ 25. $4a^2 - b^2$

Page 313   Additional Practice   1. -2 3. -10 5. 400 7. $-12x^2$ 9. $18mn^4$ 11. a^3b^{12} 13. $\frac{a^5b^{15}}{c^{20}}$
15. ab^2 17. p^{2k+3} 19. 3.2×10^8 21. 6.52×10^{-5} 23. $7m^2n^2 - 3mn$ 25. $a^2 - 4a - 5$
27. $y^2 + 11y + 24$ 29. $3n^4 - 14n^2 + 15$ 31. $4n^2 - 12n + 9$ 33. $36y^2 - 8y + \frac{4}{9}$ 35. $x^2y^2 - 1$
37. $(8b + 12)$ units   39. square; 4 square units greater   41. rectangle with length $(2a + 1)$ units and width
$(2a - 1)$ units; 3 square units greater

CHAPTER 9: FACTORING POLYNOMIALS

Page 317   Classroom Exercises   1. Yes   3. No   5. C   7. P   9. C   11. $2^2 \cdot 5$ 13. $2^3 \cdot 5^2$
15. 41 is prime

Page 317   Written Exercises   1. Yes   3. Yes   5. No   7. No   9. Yes   11. Yes   13. P   15. C   17. C
19. P   21. P   23. C   25. $2 \cdot 3^2$ 27. $3 \cdot 7$ 29. $2 \cdot 3 \cdot 7$ 31. $3^2 \cdot 5$ 33. 5^2 35. $3 \cdot 11$
37. $2^2 \cdot 5^3$ 39. $2^2 \cdot 3 \cdot 5^2$ 41. $2^6 \cdot 3 \cdot 5$ In Exercises 43-54, answers may vary.   43. $2 \cdot 2$
45. $1 \cdot 3$ 47. $1 \cdot 7$ 49. $2 \cdot 4$ 51. $\frac{1}{2} \cdot \frac{1}{4}$ 53. $\frac{1}{2} \cdot \frac{1}{5}$ 55. 6 by 12; 8 by 9   57. 5 rows of 20 plants
each; 10 rows of 10 plants each

Page 318   Calculator Exercises   1. 3   3. 31   5. 131,071

Page 318   Review Capsule for Section 9-2   1. $x^2 + 3x$ 2. $-2a + 8$ 3. $a^2b - 2ab$ 4. $x^3y^2 + 7x^2y$
5. $ab + ac - ad$ 6. $-2xy^2 + 12xy - 6x$ 7. $4x + 4y$ 8. $pqr - psq$ 9. $a^2 - 2a + ab - 2b$
10. $xz + 2z + 3x + 6$ 11. $ty - t + 5y - 5$

Page 320   Classroom Exercises   1. 8   3. $3x$ 5. $a + b^2$ 7. $ab - 4bc + 2ac$ 9. $x - y$ 11. $14(p + q)$
13. $t(x + y)$ 15. $13t(s - 2)$ 17. $(a + b)(t + w)$ 19. $(4 + e)(d + 1)$

Page 320   Written Exercises   1. x 3. b 5. $x, 2y$ 7. 3 9. $1, 3y$ 11. 5 13. $4m$ 15. $8x, 1$
17. $4a, 1$ 19. $2m, 1$ 21. 4 23. x 25. $4a, 1$ 27. 5 29. $1, 7y$ 31. a, b 33. $2, 5$ 35. $7(x + y)$
37. $4(2x - y)$ 39. $x(3 - aw)$ 41. $c(4 + a + b)$ 43. $d(d + 2 + a)$ 45. $5(x - 2y + 3z^2)$ 47. $2\pi r(r + h)$
49. $cdh(h^2 + c + c^2dh)$ 51. $(a + d)(b - c)$ 53. $(a - s)(q - r)$ 55. $(k + r)(p - n)$ 57. $(x + y)(x - y)$
$(2a + b)$ 59. $7ab(a - 1)$ 61. prime   63. $7(2x^2 + xy + 3y^2)$ 65. prime   67. $7(2x^2 + xy + 3y^2)$
69. prime   71. $3x(9x^3 + x^2 + 3a)$ 73. $25x(y - 2z + 4)$ 75. $x(3x + 6y - 2x^2$ 77. $21(1 - 2p)$
79. $4x(2x - 3y - 4z)$ 81. $3x(x^2 - 5x - 2)$ 83. $a^2(3 + 4a - 5a^2b)$ 85. $x^3 + 1$ 87. $2w$

Page 322   Review Capsule for Section 9-3   1. $b^2 - 25$ 2. $4a^2 - 1$ 3. $9x^2 - 4$ 4. $x^4 - y^4$ 5. $\frac{1}{4}x^2$
$- y^2$ 6. $81 - p^2q^2$

Page 322   Classroom Exercises   1. $(m + 1)(m - 1)$ 3. $(2r + 1)(2r - 1)$ 5. $(a + 12)(a - 12)$
7. $(y + 2)(y - 2)$ 9. $(b + \frac{1}{5})(b - \frac{1}{5})$ 11. $(4t + \frac{1}{7})(4t - \frac{1}{7})$

Page 323   Written Exercises   1. $(y + 3)(y - 3)$ 3. $(x + 5)(x - 5)$ 5. $(2x + 3)(2x - 3)$ 7. $(4y + 6)$
$(4y - 6)$ 9. $(xy + a)(xy - a)$ 11. $(3x^2y + b)(3x^2y - b)$ 13. $(xy + z)(xy - z)$ 15. prime
17. $4(x^2 + 4y^2)$ 19. $(5x + 7)(5x - 7)$ 21. $(\frac{1}{3}x + 4)(\frac{1}{3}x - 4)$ 23. $(\frac{2}{3}x + \frac{5}{6}y)(\frac{2}{3}x - \frac{5}{6}y)$

25. $(x + \frac{1}{7})(x - \frac{1}{7})$ 27. $(\frac{1}{8}b + 5)(\frac{1}{8}b - 5)$ 29. a^2; b^2; $a^2 - b^2$; $(a + b)(a - b)$ 31. $\pi R^2 - 4\pi r^2$; $\pi(R + 2r)(R - 2r)$ 33. $(c + a + b)(c - a - b)$ 35. $(r + s + t + u)(r + s - t - u)$ 37. $(2x - 2a + 3y + 3b)$ $(2x - 2a - 3y - 3b)$

Page 324   Review   1. Yes   2. Yes   3. No   4. $3^2 \cdot 5$ 5. $2^4 \cdot 3$ 6. $2^3 \cdot 7$ 7. $2 \cdot 3 \cdot 13$ 8. $2 \cdot 5^3$
9. $2^4 \cdot 3^2 \cdot 5$ 10. $5(a + 2b)$ 11. $x(3 + a + d)$ 12. $pr(r - p)$ 13. $y(y^2 + 3)$ 14. Prime
15. $s^2 t(st + t^2 - 1)$ 16. $(a - 2)(b + c)$ 17. $(k + w)(x + y)$ 18. $(x + 2)(y + 2)$ 19. $(1 + m)(1 - m)$
20. $(a + 3)(a - 3)$ 21. $(3b + 4)(3b - 4)$ 22. $(9x + 1)(9x - 1)$ 23. Prime   24. $(2a + b^2)(2a - b^2)$
25. $(xy + 3)(xy - 3)$ 26. $(p^3 + q^4)(p^3 - q^4)$ 27. $(x + \frac{1}{2})(x - \frac{1}{2})$ 28. $(2t + \frac{1}{3})(2t - \frac{1}{3})$
29. $(\frac{2}{5}p + 1)(\frac{2}{5}p - 1)$ 30. $(\frac{n}{4} + \frac{m}{2})(\frac{n}{4} - \frac{m}{2})$, or $(\frac{1}{4}n + \frac{1}{2}m)(\frac{1}{4}n - \frac{1}{2}m)$

Page 324   Puzzle   See Solution Key.

Page 324   Review Capsule for Section 9-4   1. $a^2 - 6a + 9$ 2. $x^2 + 8x + 16$ 3. $4x^2 - 20x + 25$
4. $81 + 18b + b^2$ 5. $4a^2 + 20at + 25t^2$ 6. $9p^4 - 12p^2 + 4$ 7. $0.01 + 0.2z + z^2$ 8. $\frac{1}{4} - bc + b^2c^2$

Page 325   Consumer Applications   1. about 131 pounds   3. about 178 pounds

Page 327   Classroom Exercises   1. Yes   3. Yes   5. Yes   7. 2b   9. 1   11. 3t

Page 327   Written Exercises   1. Yes   3. No   5. Yes   7. 5   9. 5   11. 1   13. —   15. —   17. $(x + 3)^2$
19. $(n + 7)^2$ 21. $(2x + 3y)^2$ 23. $(1 + 4x)^2$ 25. $(a + 4)^2$ 27. $(2x + 1)^2$ 29. $(3y + 2)^2$ 31. $(b - 3)^2$
33. $(3a - 2)^2$ 35. $(7a - 6)^2$ 37. $(x - 9)^2$ 39. $(1 - 3b)^2$ 41. $(a + b + c)(a + b - c)$
43. $(x - y + 3)(x - y - 3)$ 45. $(a + b + 3)(a + b - 3)$

Page 328   Calculator Exercises   1. 28   3. 231   5. 1711   7. 125,751

Page 328   Review Capsule for Section 9-5   1. $a^2 + 3a + 2$ 2. $x^2 - 5x + 6$ 3. $y^2 + y - 12$ 4. $10 - 3t$ $- t^2$ 5. $y^2 - 3yz - 10z^2$ 6. $d^2 + 3dg - 88g^2$ 7. $r^2 + 4rs - 21s^2$ 8. $x^2 - 7xy - 18y^2$
9. $w^2 + wz - 2z^2$

Page 330   Classroom Exercises   1. 4, 3   3. 8, −3   5. −3, −3   7. −6, −3   9. −8, 4   11. 9, −8

Page 330   Written Exercises   1. $(x + 4)(x + 3)$ 3. $(y + 5)(y + 3)$ 5. $(a + 4)(a - 1)$ 7. $(y + 8)(y - 1)$
9. $(x - 3)(x - 2)$ 11. $(x - 9)(x - 4)$ 13. $(x - 5)(x + 3)$ 15. $(x - 9)(x + 8)$ 17. $(x + 8)(x - 3)$
19. $(x + 8)(x - 4)$ 21. $(x - 7)(x - 3)$ 23. $(x + 8)(x + 6)$ 25. $(x + 4)(x + 2)$ 27. $(x + 4)(x - 2)$
29. $(y - 11)(y - 6)$ 31. $(y - 13)(y + 12)$ 33. $(y + 12)(y - 6)$ 35. $(10 + v)(2 + v)$ 37. $(17 - k)(3 - k)$
39. $(r - 4t)(r - 2t)$ 41. $(a - 12b)(a - 2b)$ 43. $(x - 6y)(x + y)$ 45. $(x + 9y)(x - 2y)$ 47. $(a + 6b)$ $(a + 2b)$ 49. $(r + 5t)(r + 3t)$ 51. $(x - 15y)(x + 4y)$ 53. r^2 55. $(x + 12)(x + 1)$

Page 331   Puzzle   See Solution Key.

Page 331   Review Capsule for Section 9-6   1. $6x^2 + 17x + 12$ 2. $3b^2 - 8b - 35$ 3. $5y^2 - 2y - 16$
4. $25a^2 + 50ab + 21b^2$ 5. $6a^2 - 7ab - 3b^2$ 6. $7c^2 + 33cd - 10d^2$ 7. $15y^2 - 17y + 4$
8. $44p^2 + 25p - 6$ 9. $12x^2 - 13xy + 3y^2$

Page 333   Classroom Exercises   1. d   3. e   5. c   7. 5   9. 4   11. 3

Page 334   Written Exercises   1. 3   3. 1   5. 8n, 5n   7. 7, 1   9. 1, 2   11. $2(x + 2)(x + 1)$
13. $(3y + 2)(3y - 1)$ 15. $(3y - 4)(2y - 3)$ 17. $(3x + 4)(2x - 1)$ 19. $(5x - 1)(x - 3)$ 21. $(3y + 7)$ $(y - 1)$ 23. $(2y + 5)(y + 1)$ 25. $(3x - 2)(x - 3)$ 27. $(3a + 5)(a - 5)$ 29. $(2t - 1)(t + 3)$
31. $(2x + 5)(x - 8)$ 33. $(5q + 3)(q - 9)$ 35. $(4x - 3y)(2x - y)$ 37. $(6 + 7y)(3 - 5y)$ 39. $(2x + 3)$ $(x + 2)$ 41. $(4x - 7y)(3x - 2y)$ 43. $(4a + 7b)^2$ 45. $(8a + 7b)^2$

Page 334   Review Capsule for Section 9-7   1. s   2. 3   3. r   4. 5x   5. 9   6. $7a^2b$ 7. 2   8. t   9. N
10. D   11. P   12. N   13. D   14. N   15. P   16. P

Page 336   Classroom Exercises   1. $2(x + 1)^2$ 3. $6(t + 6)(t - 1)$ 5. $x(a + b + c)$

Page 336 Written Exercises 1. $5(b + 6)(b - 2)$ 3. $3(2x + 1)(x - 4)$ 5. $2(3x + 2)(2x - 3)$ 7. $3(x + y)$ $(x - y)$ 9. $3b(b - 1)$ 11. $2m(m - 9)(m - 1)$ 13. $2a(a + 1)(a - 1)$ 15. $3(4m - 1)(m + 3)$ 17. $3(x + 4)(x - 2)$ 19. $2(x + 10)(x - 4)$ 21. $2(t - 7)^2$ 23. $x^2(x + 3)(x - 3)$ 25. $2(a + 4)(a + 3)$ 27. $s(t - 5)(t + 4)$ 29. $3(x^2 + 4x + 15)$ 31. $3t^2(2 - 5t)$ 33. $a(b - 9)(b + 8)$ 35. $(3a - 2)(a + 1)$ 37. prime 39. $2(x - 4)(x - 3)$ 41. $(7c + 5)^2$ 43. $x(x + 1)(x - 1)$ 45. $(1 + 2y)(1 - 2y)$ 47. $2y(x + z) + (z + y)(z - y)$ 49. $(x + 4)(x - 4)(a + b)$ 51. $[5r(r + 1) + 8](r - 6)$ 53. $(x - y - 3)$ $(x - y)$ 55. $(z + 2)(z - 2)(z + 9q)(z - 9q)$ 57. $[-1(x + 4)(5 - x)][(x - 5)(x + 6)]$ 59. $4xy$ 61. $(k + 1)(k + 1)(k - 1)$ 63. $(t^2 + 2)(t + 1)(t - 1)$ 65. $(h + a - 3)(h - a + 3)$ 67. $(3a + 2)(a + 4)$ 69. $(5x + 5y)(-3x - 3y) + 63$

Page 338 Classroom Exercises 1. $b = 0$ or $b = 1$ 3. $q = 3$ or $q = 7$ 5. $t = -3$ or $t = 1$ 7. $x = -3$ or $x = 3$ 9. $y = 1\frac{1}{2}$ or $y = 3$

Page 338 Written Exercises 1. $x = -1$ or $x = 6$ 3. $x = -2$ or $x = 5$ 5. $n = -1$ or $n = 0$ 7. $y = -1$ or $y = 9$ 9. $c = -7$ or $c = 7$ 11. $y = -2$ or $y = 6$ 13. $a = -1$ or $a = \frac{2}{5}$ 15. $a = -\frac{2}{3}$ or $a = \frac{1}{2}$ 17. $n = 0$ or $n = 7$ 19. $n = -2\frac{1}{3}$ or $n = 0$ 21. $a = 0$ or $a = 2\frac{1}{4}$ 23. $a = -2\frac{1}{4}$ or $a = 1\frac{1}{6}$ 25. $w = -\frac{1}{3}$ or $w = 0$ or $w = \frac{2}{3}$ 27. $y = -\frac{1}{2}$ 29. $y = 0$ or $y = 16$ 31. $r = -1$ or $r = 1$ 33. $w = -3$ or $w = 0$ or $w = 5$ 35. $b = -3$ or $b = 4$ 37. $z = -5$ or $z = -4$ 39. $x = -3$ or $x = 0$ or $x = 3$ 41. $a = -14$ or $a = -4$ 43. $a = 3$ or $a = 4$ 45. $z = 1$ or $z = 2$ 47. $a = -2\frac{2}{3}$ or $a = 2$

Page 338 Puzzle See Solution Key.

Page 340 Classroom Exercises 1. a. Let w = width of hallway, then $4w$ = length b. $(4w)(w) = 144$ 3. a. Let first integer = n, then second integer = $n + 1$ b. $n(n + 1) = 182$

Page 340 Word Problems 1. 7, 5 3. 15, 14 or $-14, -15$ 5. $-8, -7$ 7. 9 or -8 9. width = 24 m; length = 44 m 11. $-5, -3$ 13. 15 rows 15. 8 players 17. width = 4 cm; length = 12 cm 19. width = 6 cm; length = 8 cm 21. width = 18 cm; length = 22 cm 23. 2 meters 25. width = 20 ft; length = 50 ft

Page 342 Review 1. $(x + 4)(x + 4)$, or $(x + 4)^2$ 2. $(8 - a)(8 - a)$, or $(8 - a)^2$ 3. $(3x + 1)(3x + 1)$, or $(3x + 1)^2$ 4. $(x + 3)(x + 1)$ 5. $(b - 2)(b - 4)$ 6. $(r - 4)(r + 3)$ 7. $(5x + 1)(x - 2)$ 8. $(7y - 1)$ $(y - 1)$ 9. $(3y + 2)(2y + 3)$ 10. $(3b + 1)(b - 2)$ 11. $(a - 4)(2a + 3)$ 12. $(15t - 2)(2t + 3)$ 13. $4(a - 1)(a + 1)$ 14. $3(d + 4)(d + 4)$, or $3(d + 4)^2$ 15. $4(n - 1)(n - 1)$, or $4(n - 1)^2$ 16. $x(x - 8)$ $(x + 1)$ 17. $2y(2y - 1)(y + 3)$ 18. $2b^2(3b + 1)(b - 2)$ 19. $x = -4$ or $x = 0$ 20. $y = 0$ or $y = 7$ 21. $n = -2$ or $n = 3$ 22. $a = -4$ or $a = 4$ 23. $p = -3$ 24. $r = -1\frac{1}{2}$ or $r = 1\frac{1}{3}$ 25. -2 26. width: 15 m; length: 24 m

Page 343 Computer Exercises See Solution Key.

Page 345 Chapter Objectives and Review 1. 3^3 3. $2 \cdot 47$ 5. $2^3 \cdot 3^2 \cdot 5$ 7. 3, 5, 9, 15 9. 2, 7, 14, 49 11. $3(a - 2b)$ 13. Prime 15. $n(4 + m - n)$ 17. $(3 + x)(3 - x)$ 19. $(n - 1)(n + 1)$ 21. $4(5 - 2x)(5 + 2x)$ 23. $(mn - c)(mn + c)$ 25. $(\frac{3}{4} - y)(\frac{3}{4} + y)$ 27. $(5 - \frac{1}{5}r)(5 + \frac{1}{5}r)$ 29. $(y - 5)$ $(y - 5)$, or $(y - 5)^2$ 31. $(4x - 3)(4x - 3)$, or $(4x - 3)^2$ 33. $(2m - n)(2m - n)$, or $(2m - n)^2$ 35. $(a + 2)(a + 4)$ 37. $(s - 5)(s + 2)$ 39. $(y - 2)(y + 8)$ 41. $(n + 9)(n - 4)$ 43. $(t + 5s)(t - 3s)$ 45. $(y - 2)(5y - 3)$ 47. $(8x - 1)(x - 3)$ 49. $(8n + 3)(2n - 1)$ 51. $(8t - 5)(3t + 2)$ 53. $2(h + 1)$ $(h + 1)$, or $2(h + 1)^2$ 55. $4(p - 2)(p - 2)$, or $4(p - 2)^2$ 57. $5(c - 5)(c + 5)$ 59. $y(y + 4)(y - 2)$ 61. $n^2(4n - 3)(2n + 3)$ 63. $y = -4$ or $y = 0$ 65. $b = -3$ or $b = 3$ 67. $t = -12$ or $t = 2$ 69. $y = -6$ or $y = 0$ or $y = 6$ 71. 3, 4, 5 73. 22 75. 14

Page 347 Chapter Test 1. $2^5 \cdot 3$ 3. 13 5. $2^2 \cdot 5 \cdot 11$ 7. $(3b - 1)(3b + 1)$ 9. $(y + 3)(y + 8)$ 11. $a^2b(b^2 - a)$ 13. $(n + 8)(n - 7)$ 15. $2(3b - 1)(b + 1)$ 17. $(ab - 4c)(ab + 4c)$ 19. $a(a - 3)(a + 2)$ 21. $x = -5$ or $x = 3$ 23. $p = -3$ or $p = 1$ 25. width: 4 cm; length: 12 cm

Page 348 Additional Practice   1. $3^2 \cdot 7$ **3.** $-2^2 \cdot 3 \cdot 5$ **5.** $-3 \cdot 5^3$ **7.** $3a(5 - 4a)$ **9.** $9a^2(1 - 2a)$
11. $(4m - 7n)(4m + 7n)$ **13.** $(x^5 - y)(x^5 + y)$ **15.** $(2x + 3)(2x + 3)$, or $(2x + 3)^2$ **17.** $(x - 7)(x + 2)$
19. $(a + 4b)(a - 3b)$ **21.** $2(2x + 5)(x - 1)$ **23.** $5(x - 3)(x + 3)$ **25.** $2n(3n - 2)(3n + 1)$ **27.** $n = -4$
or $n = 6$ **29.** 10 rows, 24 chairs; 12 rows, 20 chairs; 15 rows, 16 chairs; 16 rows, 15 chairs; 20 rows,
12 chairs; 24 rows, 10 chairs   **31.** width: $(x - 9)$ units; length: $(x + 4)$ units   **33.** 6

CHAPTER 10: RATIONAL EXPRESSIONS

Page 351 Classroom Exercises   1. $33\frac{1}{3}\%$ **3.** $\frac{3}{8}$ **5.** $\frac{3}{1}$, or 3   **7.** 25%   **9.** $\frac{1}{8}$

Page 352 Written Exercises   1. $x = 35$ **3.** $x = 2$ **5.** $x = 63$ **7.** $x = 10.5$ **9.** $x = 1$ **11.** $b = \frac{1}{2}$
13. $r = 10$ **15.** $s = -\frac{1}{2}$ **17.** $a = -31$ **19.** $x =$ miles in 6 hrs; $\frac{90}{1\frac{1}{2}} = \frac{x}{6}$ **21.** $d =$ distance on map; $\frac{1}{500}$
$= \frac{d}{1500}$ **23.** $3\frac{3}{4}$ cups   **25.** 240 km   **27.** 2.1 cm   **29.** 6 runs   **31.** about 5.5 hr   **33.** 3200 min
35. $96   **37.** Sally: $72; Tom: $48   **39.** length: 132 m; width: 48 m   **41.** $x = \frac{1}{3}$ **43.** $x = 4$
45. $x = -4$ or $x = 4$ **47.** $a : b = 4 : 7$ **49.** $(p + q) : q = 6 : 5$

Page 353 Review Capsule for Section 10-2   1. 132   **2.** 147.6   **3.** 64   **4.** 38   **5.** 13   **6.** 60

Page 355 Classroom Exercises   1. $0.12(\$8000)$ **3.** $0.115(y + 8000)$ **5.** $0.04(20)$ **7.** $0.6(30 - d)$

Page 356 Word Problems   1. $2000 at 6%; $6000 at 9%   **3.** 40 grams   **5.** $2500 at 10%; $10,000 at 12%
7. 55.125 liters   **9.** about 8.57 quarts   **11.** 20 milliliters   **13.** 10%: $950; 12%: $1900; 8%: $1400
15. 9%: $38,000; 12%: $19,000

Page 358 Classroom Exercises   1. $\frac{6}{11}$ **3.** $\frac{y}{3x}$ **5.** 1   **7.** -2

Page 358 Written Exercises   1. $\frac{5}{4}$ **3.** xy **5.** $\frac{2}{3}$ **7.** $\frac{a}{b}$ **9.** $\frac{4}{5y}$ **11.** $\frac{3x}{4}$ **13.** $\frac{4}{7}$ **15.** $\frac{1}{2}$ **17.** $\frac{8}{5(x + y)}$
19. $3(x - y)$ **21.** $\frac{(x - 6y)^2}{x}$ **23.** $\frac{5(a + b)}{2(2a + b)}$ **25.** $\frac{x - 2y}{3x + 4y}$ **27.** $\frac{b(2a + b)}{(a + b)(a - b)}$ **29.** 1   **31.** $\frac{1}{a + b}$
33. $\frac{1}{x + 1}$ **35.** $a + 1$ **37.** -1 **39.** $\frac{1}{9 - b}$ **41.** $-\frac{t - 1}{t + 1}$ **43.** $-\frac{1}{(n - k)^2}$ **45.** $2x$ **47.** $\frac{x + 2}{2(x - 4)}$
49. $\frac{6}{x - 3}$ **51.** $-3(a + 1)$ **53.** $\frac{R - r}{3}$ **55.** prime   **57.** $\frac{3(x + 3)}{x - 8}$ **59.** $x + y - 1$ **61.** $\frac{a + 2}{a - 5}$

Page 359 Review   1. $x = 8$ **2.** $x = 12$ **3.** $y = 3.25$ **4.** $t = 6$ **5.** 38.4 columns   **6.** 12%: $2000;
10%: $4000   **7.** 7.5 ounces   **8.** $\frac{4}{7d}$ **9.** $\frac{1}{2a - b}$ **10.** $\frac{3}{x + y}$ **11.** $\frac{3x - 2y}{x - 2y}$

Page 362 Review Capsule for Section 10-4   1. $12n^2$ **2.** $2a^4b^4$ **3.** $-2c^{10}$ **4.** $12x^3y^3z^8$ **5.** x^{10}
6. $\frac{1}{4b^2}$ **7.** $\frac{2rt^2}{5s}$ **8.** $\frac{x^3}{36}$ **9.** $\frac{9b^2}{2a^3}$ **10.** $\frac{36a}{7b^6}$ **11.** $6y$ **12.** $\frac{9y^3}{4x^4b^6}$ **13.** $x^2y^2(3x - y)$ **14.** $(10z + 1)$
$(10z - 1)$ **15.** $4x(2x + 1)(2x - 1)$ **16.** $9(t + 1)^2$ **17.** $(z - 9)(z + 2)$ **18.** $(4q - 1)(q + 3)$

Page 363 Classroom Exercises   1. $\frac{a^2}{c}$ **3.** $\frac{a^2 + ab}{b}$ **5.** 1

Page 363 Written Exercises   1. $\frac{m}{n}$ **3.** $\frac{c}{d}$ **5.** $\frac{1}{a^2by}$ **7.** $\frac{2z}{7y}$ **9.** 3   **11.** $\frac{4x^2 + 16x + 15}{2x - 5}$ **13.** 1
15. $\frac{n^2 + 6n + 9}{n + 5}$ **17.** $\frac{4xy}{1 + y}$ **19.** $\frac{n}{m}$ **21.** $\frac{a^2}{a^2 - a - 20}$ **23.** $\frac{x + 4}{x + 3}$ **25.** x **27.** $x - 1$ **29.** $\frac{1}{x - 4}$
31. 1   **33.** $\frac{20a^2 + 20ab}{6a^2b + 21ab^2 + 18b^3}$ **35.** $\frac{5m}{(m + n)^2}$ **37.** $\frac{5(a + 1)}{a - 1}$ **39.** 1   **41.** $\frac{a^2 + a - 2}{a^2 - 8a + 15}$
43. $\frac{(x + 1)(x^2 - x - 1)^2}{x(x - 1)}$ **45.** $\frac{x^2(x + 2)}{y(x^2 - 7)}$ **47.** $\frac{2b - 1}{2b - 5}$

Page 364 **Review Capsule for Section 10-5** 1. $(3y + 2)(3y - 2)$ 2. $-6m(m^2 + 3)$ 3. $(3z + 8)(2z - 5)$
4. $(h + 3)^2(h - 3)^2$ 5. $2(z^2 + 9)(z + 3)(z - 3)$ 6. $2(a + 2b - 2)(a - 2b + 2)$ 7. $x^2(2 + y - z)$
8. $(5x + 3y)(x - y)$ 9. $3y(x + 1)(x + 1)$ 10. $(2x + 7)(2x + 7)$ 11. $2a(x + 2y + 1)$
12. $2a(x^2 - 2)(x^2 + 1)$

Page 366 **Classroom Exercises** 1. y^3 3. $\dfrac{2}{(x + y)^2}$ 5. $\dfrac{n^2}{3}$ 7. $\dfrac{c + 4}{3(c - 2)}$ 9. x 11. $\dfrac{ax}{y(a + x)}$

Page 366 **Written Exercises** 1. 2 3. $\dfrac{1}{2}$ 5. $\dfrac{x}{3}$ 7. $\dfrac{ad}{bc}$ 9. $\dfrac{b}{a^2}$ 11. $\dfrac{g}{f}$ 13. $\dfrac{1}{ba}$ 15. 1 17. $\dfrac{4}{9a}$

19. $\dfrac{x + 1}{ax}$ 21. $\dfrac{a - b}{x + y}$ 23. $\dfrac{x + y}{2(x - y)}$ 25. $\dfrac{x + 1}{3x}$ 27. $\dfrac{a}{(a + b)^2}$ 29. $\dfrac{2}{3}$ 31. $\dfrac{b^2}{a}$ 33. $\dfrac{a^2 b^3}{x^3}$ 35. $\dfrac{a^3 b^3}{r^3}$

37. $\dfrac{x + 5}{x}$ 39. $\dfrac{y(x + y)}{x(x - y)}$ 41. $\dfrac{b^2(a + c)}{c(a + b)}$ 43. $\dfrac{3x^3(4a + b)}{5a^3}$

Page 367 **Calculator Exercises** 1. 0.4642857 3. 2.7824074

Page 369 **Classroom Exercises** 1. 24 3. 30 5. 30abc 7. $24a^2 b^3 c$ 9. $6(x + y)$ 11. $10r(r + 3)(r - 3)$

Page 369 **Written Exercises** 1. 12 3. 30 5. 30 7. ab 9. ab^2 11. 6a 13. 12p 15. $a^2 b^2$
17. 24 19. 20 21. 48 23. xyz 25. $(x + y)(x - y)$ 27. $12(a - 2b)$ 29. $2(x + y)$ 31. $(x - 1)$
$(x - 2)(x - 3)$ 33. $(x + 2)(x - 2)(x - 4)$ 35. $2(2x + 3y)(2x - 3y)$ 37. $(2b - 3)(b + 1)(3b + 2)$

Page 372 **Classroom Exercises** 1. $\dfrac{7}{9}$ 3. $\dfrac{2x}{z}$ 5. $\dfrac{abd - 6c}{2b^2 d}$

Page 372 **Written Exercises** 1. $\dfrac{16}{b}$ 3. $\dfrac{49}{q}$ 5. $\dfrac{2a + 17b - 6}{3}$ 7. $\dfrac{10m + 2}{3}$ 9. $\dfrac{15}{4}$ 11. $\dfrac{-4a - 13b}{12}$

13. $\dfrac{m + n}{x - y}$ 15. $\dfrac{m}{2y + 5}$ 17. $\dfrac{-2q}{r + 6}$ 19. $\dfrac{13x^2}{42}$ 21. $\dfrac{5x^2 y + 6xy^2}{30}$ 23. $\dfrac{-4a + 23}{18}$ 25. $\dfrac{11n - 14}{20}$

27. $\dfrac{8b + 17c}{24}$ 29. $\dfrac{3a + 2b}{ab}$ 31. $\dfrac{4y - 5x}{xy}$ 33. $\dfrac{13}{6c}$ 35. $\dfrac{7a - 4b}{10p}$ 37. $\dfrac{3x + 5}{x^2}$ 39. $\dfrac{3x^2 + 2x - 5}{x^3}$

41. $\dfrac{5a - 7b}{a^2 b^2}$ 43. $\dfrac{9n + 3}{mn^2}$ 45. $\dfrac{1}{4p}$ 47. $\dfrac{a^2 + b^2}{ab}$ 49. $\dfrac{5x - 6}{3x}$ 51. $\dfrac{5bx - 2}{2b^2}$ 53. $\dfrac{3a + ab + 5b}{ab}$

55. $\dfrac{4x^2 - 3x + xy + 4y}{x^2}$ 57. $\dfrac{3b - 19a}{3a^2}$ 59. $\dfrac{2x - 40}{(x + 5)(x - 5)}$ 61. $\dfrac{2x^2 - xy + 3y^2}{(x + y)(x - y)}$ 63. $\dfrac{2a + b}{3a - b}$

65. $\dfrac{5xy}{(2y - 3)(3y - 2)}$ 67. $\dfrac{3a - 1}{(a + 3)(a + 5)}$ 69. $\dfrac{3a - 1}{3(a + 2)}$ 71. $\dfrac{a^2 - 2ab + b^2 - a}{(a + b)(a - b)}$ 73. $\dfrac{a + 1}{a + 3}$

75. $\dfrac{2a - 31}{(a - 1)(a + 2)(a - 3)}$ 77. $\dfrac{5y}{(y + 3)(y - 2)^2}$ 79. $\dfrac{-15x^2 + 7x + 10}{6(x + 1)(x - 1)}$ 81. $\dfrac{-3rs + s^2}{(r + s)^2(r - s)}$

Page 373 **Review Capsule for Section 10-8** 1. $4x + 5y$ 2. $-2r^2 + 3r + 25$ 3. $11c - 28$ 4. $17a - 17b$
5. $-18x + 14$ 6. $a^2 + 2a + 2$

Page 375 **Classroom Exercises** 1. $\dfrac{b + 1}{b}$ 3. $\dfrac{x + 3}{x}$ 5. $\dfrac{t^2 + t + 5}{t}$ 7. $\dfrac{1 - a^2 - a}{a}$

Page 375 **Written Exercises** 1. $\dfrac{3a + 1}{a}$ 3. $\dfrac{3b + a}{b}$ 5. $\dfrac{7a - 7b - 4}{a - b}$ 7. $\dfrac{a^2 + a + 1}{a + 1}$ 9. $\dfrac{7r + 9s}{r + s}$

11. $\dfrac{11c - 28}{c - 3}$ 13. $\dfrac{ax^2 + b}{x}$ 15. $\dfrac{ac - b}{c}$ 17. $\dfrac{a^3 - 1}{a}$ 19. $\dfrac{3r - 2r^2 + 18}{r^2 - 9}$ 21. $\dfrac{a^2 + 2a + 2}{a + 1}$

23. $\dfrac{14 - 18x}{3x - 1}$ 25. $\dfrac{x^2 - 3x - 15}{x + 3}$ 27. $\dfrac{2t^2 + 7t}{t + 6}$ 29. $\dfrac{t^2 + 5t - 15}{t - 4}$ 31. $\dfrac{a^2 + 1}{a - 2}$ 33. $\dfrac{x^2 + 4}{(x + 2)(x - 2)}$

35. $\dfrac{x^3 - 3x^2 - 13x + 22}{x - 5}$ 37. $\dfrac{x^4 + 11x - 10}{(x + 2)(x - 2)}$ 39. $\dfrac{23}{7}$ 41. $\dfrac{x - 3}{x^2}$ 43. $\dfrac{6a}{3a - 2}$ 45. $\dfrac{r^2 + 2r + 1}{r^2 - 2r - 1}$

Page 376 **Review Capsule for Section 10-9** 1. 4a 2. 9 3. a^2 4. t 5. 3xy 6. $3z^2$ 7. 1 8. 2z

Page 377 **Classroom Exercises** 1. 0t 3. 0a 5. $0x^3 + 0x^2 + 0x$ 7. $2r^3 - 9r^2 + 10r + 5$
9. $6z^2 - 13z + 2$

Page 378 **Written Exercises** 1. $x + 7$ 3. $c + 4$ 5. $3n + 2$ 7. $4y + 15 + \dfrac{6}{y + 1}$ 9. $3x + 1$

11. $3a - 2 + \dfrac{1}{2a - 3}$ 13. $5n + 2 + \dfrac{6}{3n + 2}$ 15. $a^2 - 3a - 4$ 17. $3x^2 + 5x - 2$ 19. $a^2 + 2ab + \dfrac{3ab^2}{3a + 2b}$

21. $x - 5 + \dfrac{50}{x + 5}$ 23. $a^2 + 2ab + 4b^2$ 25. $2x^2 + x + 1 + \dfrac{-5}{3x + 5}$ 27. $x^2 - 5x + 29 + \dfrac{-148}{x + 5}$

29. $x^2 + 3x + 7$ 31. $x^2 - 3x + 9$ 33. $(3y + 2)(y + 2)$ 35. $2t + 3$ 37. No; when $6n^3 - 22n + 1$ is divided by $(2n - 4)$, there is a remainder.   39. $k = 6$ 41. $c = 1$

Page 378   Puzzle   See Solution Key.

Page 380   Computer Exercises   See Solution Key.

Page 381   Review   1. $\dfrac{a}{4}$ 2. $\dfrac{x^2 - 2x - 3}{x - 1}$ 3. $\dfrac{x^2 + x - 2}{x^2 + 5x}$ 4. $\dfrac{a}{3}$ 5. $\dfrac{bx}{2a}$ 6. $2a + 2$ 7. 33   8. $4a^2 b^2$

9. $(x - 4)(x + 1)(x + 2)$ 10. $\dfrac{5a - 1}{a + b}$ 11. $\dfrac{3x + 2y}{x^2 y^2}$ 12. $\dfrac{x - 1}{x(x - 2)}$ 13. $\dfrac{2x + 1}{x}$ 14. $\dfrac{4y^2 - 1}{2y}$

15. $\dfrac{a^2 - 2ab - b^2}{a + b}$ 16. $\dfrac{x^2 + 2x}{x - 1}$ 17. $x - 3$ 18. $3b + 4$ 19. $x + 4$ 20. $8y - 1$

Page 382   Chapter Objectives and Review   1. $50\dfrac{2}{5}$ 3. 12   5. $2\dfrac{2}{3}$ 7. \$4800   9. 25   11. $\dfrac{3}{5}$

13. $\dfrac{x + y}{3(x - y)}$ 15. $\dfrac{x}{x - 2}$ 17. $\dfrac{2(x - y)(x + y)}{(2y + x)(2y - x)}$ 19. $\dfrac{x}{2}$ 21. $\dfrac{3}{4}$ 23. $\dfrac{x^3 + 5x^2 + 6x}{x^2 - 3x + 2}$ 25. $\dfrac{b}{2a}$ 27. $\dfrac{18a^3}{25}$

29. $\dfrac{x(a - b)}{a + b}$ 31. 63   33. $9x^2 y^2$ 35. $a^2 - b^2$ 37. 1   39. $\dfrac{2a - b}{2ab}$ 41. $\dfrac{a - 5}{a^2 + 2a - 3}$ 43. $\dfrac{-x + y}{6x + 6y}$

45. $\dfrac{a^2 + b^2}{a^2 - b^2}$ 47. $\dfrac{2b^2 + 3}{2b}$ 49. $\dfrac{3 + 2x^2}{x}$ 51. $\dfrac{x^2 + 2x - 3}{x + 2}$ 53. $\dfrac{a^2}{a - 1}$ 55. $a - 3$ 57. $x - 2$

59. $n^2 + n + 1$ 61. $2a^2 + a - 6 + \dfrac{-17}{2a - 3}$

Page 384   Chapter Test   1. 51   3. 3   5. $\dfrac{3a - 2}{a}$ 7. $\dfrac{3x^3}{13}$ 9. 3   11. $\dfrac{c^2 + d^2}{c^2 d}$ 13. $\dfrac{x - 3}{x^2 + 3x}$ 15. $\dfrac{y - 2}{2}$

17. $x + 2$ 19. 5760

Page 385   More Challenging Problems   1. $a^{2n} + 5a^{n+1} + 5a^{n-1} + 25$ 3. $a^n + b^n + c^n + 2a^{\frac{n}{2}} b^{\frac{n}{2}} + 2a^{\frac{n}{2}} c^{\frac{n}{2}}$

$+ 2b^{\frac{n}{2}} c^{\frac{n}{2}}$ 5. $x^n - y^n$ 7. $(x + 3 - y + 1)(x + 3 + y - 1)$ 9. $(2a + b - 3c + 2d)(2a + b + 3c - 2d)$

11. $x + y$ 13. $\dfrac{-4x^2 + 2xy - 2x + y}{2y + 1}$

Page 385   Additional Practice   1. $409\dfrac{1}{2}$ 3. $3\dfrac{2}{3}$ 5. $\dfrac{3y}{5w}$ 7. $\dfrac{x + 2}{x + 4}$ 9. $\dfrac{x}{2}$ 11. $\dfrac{c}{2}$ 13. $\dfrac{n + 1}{n - 1}$

15. $16x^2 y^2$ 17. 2   19. $\dfrac{x^2 - x - 2}{x^3 - x^2 - 6x}$ 21. $\dfrac{x^2 + x - 1}{x + 1}$ 23. $x - 5$ 25. $2a + 5$ 27. $4y^2 + 2y - 5$

29. $x^2 - 3x + 1$ 31. 6.5 m   33. 200 km   35. 0.5 liter   37. $85\dfrac{5}{7}$ grams   39. 8%: \$8000; 12%: \$4000

CHAPTER 11: APPLICATIONS OF RATIONAL EXPRESSIONS

Page 390   Classroom Exercises   1. $x = 12$ 3. $x = 1$ 5. $y = 6$ 7. $x = -5$ 9. $a = -\dfrac{1}{2}$ or $a = 1$

Page 390   Written Exercises   1. $a = 24$ 3. $a = 15$ 5. $t = 4$ 7. $x = \dfrac{2}{3}$ 9. $x = 6$ 11. $x = -\dfrac{1}{9}$ 13. $n = 2$

15. $n = 2$ 17. $x = -\dfrac{1}{5}$ 19. $x = -6$ 21. $x = 10$ 23. $a = 4$ 25. $x = -5$ 27. $b = 3$ 29. $x = -1$

31. $x = 23$ 33. $x = -2\dfrac{1}{2}$ 35. $x = 1$ 37. $x = -10$ 39. $x = 24$ 41. $x = 13$ 43. $x = -6\dfrac{2}{3}$ 45. $a = -3$

47. $k = 6$

Page 391   Puzzle   See Solution Key.

Page 391 Review Capsule for Section 11-2   1. 2   2. $-\frac{3}{4}$ 3. 0   4. $\frac{5}{7}$ 5. $1\frac{1}{8}$ 6. 1   7. a. $y = -3x$ + 6   b. $-3; 6$ 8. a. $y = 5x + 9$ b. $5; 9$ 9. a. $y = 2x - 6$ b. $2; -6$ 10. a. $y = -\frac{7}{2}x + 1\frac{2}{3}$ b. $-\frac{7}{2}; 1\frac{2}{3}$

Page 393 Classroom Exercises   1. $y = 4x + 2$ 3. $y = \frac{1}{2}x + 4$ 5. $y = -\frac{1}{4}x - 3$

Page 393 Written Exercises   1. $y = 3x + 4$ 3. $y = \frac{1}{2}x - 3$ 5. $y = -4x + \frac{2}{3}$ 7. $y = 2x - 1$ 9. $y = -3x$ + 17   11. $y = x + 3$ 13. $y = \frac{1}{2}x + 1\frac{1}{2}$ 15. $y = -\frac{1}{3}x + 3$ 17. $y = \frac{2}{3}x$ 19. $x = 3$ 21. $y = -x$
23. $y = x - 5$ 25. $y = 3x + 3$ 27. $y = 2x - 3$ 29. $y = -4x + 5$ 31. $x = 3$ 33. $y = \frac{1}{4}x + 2\frac{1}{2}$
35. $y = \frac{4}{3}x - 6$ 37. Substitute (x_1, y_1) into $y = mx + b$: $y_1 = mx_1 + b$; $y_1 - mx_1 = mx_1 - mx_1 + b$; $b = y_1 - mx_1$

Page 395 Review Capsule for Section 11-3   1. $\frac{1}{9}$ 2. $\frac{1}{11}$ 3. $\frac{1}{6}$ 4. -2 5. $\frac{9}{5}$ 6. -1 7. $y = \frac{3}{4}x + 6\frac{1}{2}$
8. $y = -\frac{1}{2}x + 2\frac{1}{2}$ 9. $y = -\frac{2}{5}x - 2\frac{3}{5}$ 10. $y = \frac{7}{8}x + 11\frac{5}{8}$ 11. $y = -3x - 2$ 12. $y = -\frac{5}{6}x + \frac{1}{3}$

Page 396 Classroom Exercises   1. $y = -x + 2$ 3. $y = 0$ 5. $y = \frac{2}{7}x - 1\frac{5}{7}$

Page 397 Written Exercises   1. $y = 2x - 1$ 3. $y = 1$ 5. $y = -\frac{1}{5}x + 4\frac{3}{5}$ 7. $y = x - 1$ 9. $y = \frac{3}{2}x - 9$
11. $y = -x - 3$ 13. $5x - 2y = -3$ 15. $2x - 3y = -3$ 17. $6x - 5y = 36$ 19. $2x + 3y = 27$
21. $11x - 4y = -12$ 23. $y = \frac{1}{2}x$; Yes   25. $y = -4x + 14$; No   27. $y = -3x - 4$; No   29. $x + y = 12$;
$4x - 5y = -6$; $2x - 7y = -12$ 31. $5x + y = -11$; $3x + 4y = 7$; $2x - 3y = -1$ 33. $x + y = 9$; $x - 2y = -9$;
$y = 4$

Page 397 Review   1. $a = 12$ 2. $x = -1$ 3. $b = -3$ or $b = 4$ 4. $x = 0$ or $x = 3$ 5. $x = -2$ or $x = 6$
6. $x = -1$ 7. $y = x + 4$ 8. $y = -2x - 1$ 9. $y = -\frac{2}{3}x + \frac{1}{2}$ 10. $y = x$ 11. $y = 3x - 1$ 12. $y = \frac{1}{5}x + \frac{3}{5}$
13. $\frac{1}{2}x + y = 4$, or $x + 2y = 8$ 14. $3x + y = 4$ 15. $\frac{1}{4}x + y = -\frac{3}{4}$, or $x + 4y = -3$

Page 398 Calculator Exercises   1. Yes   3. Yes   5. Yes

Page 398 Review Capsule for Section 11-4   1. $\frac{8}{5}$ 2. $-\frac{3}{7}$ 3. -9 4. $\frac{1}{12}$ 5. a   6. $-\frac{1}{z}$, $z \neq 0$ 7. $y = 3$
8. $t = \frac{1}{5}$ 9. $s = 2$ 10. $n = \frac{12}{13}$ 11. $x = \frac{2}{9}$ 12. $y = -\frac{4}{13}$ 13. $y = \frac{1}{12}$ 14. $r = 9\frac{1}{2}$

Page 399 Consumer Applications   1. $100.36; $3612.96; $612.96   3. $243.80; $23,404.80; $8404.80
5. $99.85; $2396.40; $396.40

Page 401 Classroom Exercises   1. a. Let x = number added.   b. $\frac{3 + x}{7 + x} = \frac{3}{5}$ 3. a. Let x = smaller number,
then $4x$ = larger number.   b. $\frac{1}{x} - \frac{1}{4x} = \frac{3}{8}$

Page 401 Word Problems   1. 4   3. 2, 10   5. 4   7. $\frac{1}{4}$ 9. $2\frac{2}{3}$, $6\frac{2}{3}$ 11. $\frac{3}{8}, \frac{5}{16}$ 13. 3, 4   15. 5, 6
17. $\frac{5}{4}$ or $\frac{4}{5}$ 19. $\frac{3}{4}$ or $-\frac{4}{3}$

Page 402 Review Capsule for Section 11-5   1. $y = 70$ 2. $x = 6$ 3. $t = 2$ 4. $r = 50$ 5. $x = 30$
6. $r = 4$

Page 404 Classroom Exercises   1. 1250 km/hr   3. $1250 - w$ 5. 3750 km   7. 6 hr   9. Distance before headwinds: $2x$; rate after headwinds: $x - 64$; time after headwinds: 3; distance after headwinds: $3(x - 64)$
11. 435.2 km/hr

Page 405 Word Problems   1. $8\frac{4}{7}$ mi   3. Jim: 50 km/hr; Ed: 45 km/hr   5. Millan: 60 mi/hr; Sharon:
45 mi/hr   7. 4 mi/hr   9. 27 km/hr   11. $2\frac{2}{9}$ hr   13. 540 km/hr   15. 2 km/hr

Page 406 Review Capsule for Section 11-6 1. $\frac{1}{15}$ 2. $\frac{1}{15}$ 3. $\frac{1}{6}$ 4. $\frac{8}{25}$ 5. $\frac{1}{5}$ 6. $\frac{1}{3}$ 7. $n = 12$
8. $w = 3$ 9. $x = 30$ 10. $a = 4\frac{2}{5}$ 11. $x = 10\frac{2}{3}$ 12. $x = 2\frac{3}{4}$ 13. $y = 2$ 14. $x = 0$ 15. $y = -1$ or $y = 2$

Page 409 Classroom Exercises 1. $\frac{1}{80}$ 3. $\frac{3}{8}$ 5. $\frac{m}{80}$ 7. $\frac{1}{5}$ 9. $\frac{1}{3}$ 11. $\frac{1}{5} + \frac{1}{3}$, or $\frac{8}{15}$ 13. $\frac{x}{5} + \frac{x}{3} = 1$

Page 409 Word Problems 1. $2\frac{2}{17}$ days 3. $3\frac{1}{13}$ minutes 5. $3\frac{3}{5}$ days 7. $\frac{2}{3}$ hour 9. $1\frac{11}{24}$ hours
11. 12 hours 13. 12 min, 24 min 15. 30 min 17. 12 hours 19. 12 hours

Page 411 Puzzle See Solution Key.

Page 411 Review Capsule for Section 11-7 1. $P = 3r$ 2. $r = kh$ 3. $T = kh$ 4. $d = kt$ 5. $s = 210$
6. $p = 25$

Page 414 Classroom Exercises 1. Yes 3. No 5. No 7. Yes 9. y decreases 11. y is divided in half

Page 414 Written Exercises 1. Yes; corresponds to $xy = k$ 3. No; does not correspond to $xy = k$ or
$x = \frac{k}{y}$ 5. No; does not correspond to $xy = k$ or $x = \frac{k}{y}$ 7. Yes; corresponds to $x = \frac{k}{y}$ 9. No; does not
correspond to $xy = k$ or $x = \frac{k}{y}$ 11. No; does not correspond to $xy = k$ or $x = \frac{k}{y}$ 13. $xy = 42$ 15. $xy = \frac{1}{2}$
17. $xy = 40$ 19. $x = 4$ 21. $r = 10$ 23. $b = 1\frac{1}{2}$ 25. 12 amps 27. 6 people 29. $2\frac{2}{5}$ hours 31. 36
plants 33. 192 tiles 35. 24; $yx^2 = 24$ 37. 128; $yx^2 = 128$ 39. -80; $yx^2 = -80$ 41. $f\sqrt{w} = k$ or
$f = \frac{k}{\sqrt{w}}$; 254 43. $167\frac{1}{2}$

Page 417 Classroom Exercises 1. $a = kbc$ 3. $m = \frac{kn}{p}$ 5. $s = \frac{kt}{r^2}$

Page 417 Written Exercises 1. $t = 216$ 3. $x = 70$ 5. $q = 8\frac{1}{6}$ 7. $A = 20$ 9. $m = 10$ 11. 28 cm^3
13. 14 in^2 15. $R = 2.5$ 17. 54 ohms

Page 418 Review 1. $\frac{2}{3}, \frac{8}{3}$ 2. 12, 18 3. 700 km 4. 200 km/hr 5. $7\frac{1}{2}$ hours 6. 12 hours
7. 20 amps 8. 4 9. 15 square inches 10. $3\frac{3}{4}$ kg

Page 420 Computer Exercises See Solution Key.

Page 421 Chapter Objectives and Review 1. $n = 18$ 3. $x = 2$ 5. $a = -6$ or $a = 2$ 7. $x = 5$ 9. $a = 1$
or $a = 2$ 11. $y = -7$ or $y = 4$ 13. $y = -3x + 4$ 15. $y = -\frac{1}{2}x - \frac{3}{4}$ 17. $y = 2x + 2$ 19. $y = -x - 8$
21. $y = \frac{3}{2}x - \frac{15}{2}$ 23. $y = 3x + 2$ 25. $y = -5x$ 27. $y = -2x + 1$ 29. $x + y = 8$ 31. $2x + 5y = 3$
33. 6, 8 35. 2 km/hr 37. $2\frac{2}{5}$ hours 39. $xy = 7$ 41. $xy = 4\frac{1}{2}$ 43. $xy = -3$ 45. $4\frac{1}{2}$ units
47. $r = 7\frac{1}{2}$ 49. $h = 800$ 51. $F = 2\frac{1}{4}$

Page 423 Chapter Test 1. $x = 18$ 3. $a = 1$ or $a = 4$ 5. $y = \frac{1}{3}x - \frac{7}{3}$ 7. $y = -x + 8$ 9. $y = -\frac{2}{5}x + \frac{3}{5}$
11. 12 min 13. $p = 2$ 15. $c = 3$

Page 424 Additional Practice 1. $y = 18$ 3. $n = 3$ 5. $y = -2x - 6$ 7. $y = -\frac{1}{2}x + \frac{9}{2}$ 9. $y = -\frac{3}{4}x$
11. $y = -\frac{3}{2}x$ 13. $y = x - 1$ 15. $y = 3x + 2$ 17. $x + 8y = -12$ 19. $y = 4$ 21. $x = 72$ 23. 16, 17
25. 325 km/hr

Page 425 Review of Word Problems: Chapters 1-11 1. 39.1¢ 3. Louise: 4; Alex: 16 5. rectangle with

584   *Answers to Selected Exercises*

length (a + 5) units and width (a − 3) units; 9 square units greater   7. length: (x + 6) units; width: (x − 2) units   9. 13 m   11. $\frac{5}{6}, \frac{1}{10}$ 13. $1\frac{1}{5}$ hours

Page 426   Cumulative Review: Chapters 8-11   1. a   3. a   5. c   7. d   9. b   11. b   13. a   15. b   17. b   19. b   21. c   23. a   25. b   27. a

Page 428   Preparing for College Entrance Tests   1. a   3. a   5. b   7. d   9. a   11. a

Page 429   Preparing for College Entrance Tests   1. a   3. d   5. a   7. d   9. c   11. c   13. d   15. a

CHAPTER 12: RADICALS

Page 433   Classroom Exercises   1. ±8   3. $\pm\frac{5}{6}$ 5. ±100   7. −6   9. $-\frac{5}{13}$ 11. −18

Page 433   Written Exercises   1. 4   3. 7   5. ±10   7. 100   9. −4   11. ±100   13. $\frac{3}{7}$ 15. $\pm\frac{5}{6}$ 17. $-\frac{8}{5}$ 19. $\frac{9}{10}$ 21. 17   23. 25   25. b   27. $\pm t^5$ 29. $c^2 d^3$ 31. $-h^4 s^6$ 33. 3c   35. $-8c^3$ 37. $\pm 5d^2$ 39. 2xy   41. 0.7   43. −1.5   45. 0.8b   47. $2.5t^2$ 49. $5r^4 s^8 t^6$ 51. $9a^6 b^4 d^8$ 53. $\pm\frac{7t^2}{5b^3}$ 55. $\frac{7a^2 b}{3}$ 57. $13c^3$ 59. $4a^4$ 61. 3   63. 4   65. $a^2 b$ 67. $c^4 f^6 g^2$ 69. $14b^2$ 71. $16f^6$

Page 434   Review Capsule for Section 12-2   1. R   2. R   3. Ir   4. Ir   5. R   6. Ir   7. Yes; Yes; No; Yes   8. Yes; Yes; No; Yes   9. Yes; Yes; No; Yes   10. No; Yes; No; Yes   11. No; Yes; No; Yes   12. No; Yes; No; Yes

Page 435   Classroom Exercises   1. $3 < \sqrt{13} < 4$ 3. $9 < \sqrt{92} < 10$ 5. 2.8   7. 3.6   9. 9.6

Page 436   Written Exercises   1. $\frac{4}{9}$ 3. $\frac{5}{33}$ 5. $\frac{8}{11}$ 7. $\frac{62}{333}$ 9. $\frac{181}{333}$ 11. $\frac{11}{9}$ 13. $\frac{83}{33}$ 15. $\frac{283}{90}$ 17. $\frac{91}{66}$ 19. $\frac{1667}{450}$ 21. $8 < \sqrt{67} < 9$ 23. $5 < \sqrt{27} < 6$ 25. $11 < \sqrt{123} < 12$ 27. $11 < \sqrt{136} < 12$ 29. $7 < \sqrt{56} < 8$ 31. $16 < \sqrt{260} < 17$ 33. $100 < \sqrt{10,001} < 101$ 35. $90 < \sqrt{8101} < 91$ 37. 25.1 cm   39. 3.0 m   41. 6.4 in

Page 437   Classroom Exercises   1. 9   3. 100   5. 4   7. 25 × 5   9. 100 × 3   11. 81 × 3

Page 438   Written Exercises   1. $2\sqrt{2}$ 3. $2\sqrt{5}$ 5. $2\sqrt{3}$ 7. $5\sqrt{3}$ 9. 10   11. $4\sqrt{2}$ 13. $11\sqrt{2}$ 15. 14   17. $24\sqrt{2}$ 19. $6\sqrt{7}$ 21. $2\sqrt{14}$ 23. $45\sqrt{2}$ 25. $16\sqrt{3}$ 27. −12   29. $-20\sqrt{2}$ 31. $30\sqrt{10}$ 33. 3,000   35. $30,000\sqrt{10}$ 37. 10   39. $1000\sqrt{10}$ 41. $6b\sqrt{b}$ 43. $3p^2\sqrt{2p}$ 45. $5q^5\sqrt{3q}$ 47. $4a^4 b\sqrt{2ab}$ 49. 2.83   51. 4.47   53. 9.90   55. 12.12   57. 13.86   59. 18.97   61. $(x + y)\sqrt{3}$ 63. $2(c^2 + d^2)\sqrt{7(c^2 + d^2)}$ 65. x + y

Page 438   Review Capsule for Section 12-4   1. 100   2. 225   3. 49   4. $a^2 − 2a + 1$ 5. $a^2 + 2a + 1$ 6. $4t^2 + 20t + 25$ 7. 2   8. 5   9. 9   10. 16   11. 7   12. 25   13. $a^2 = 119$ 14. $a^2 = 207$ 15. $a^2 = 57$ 16. $a^2 = 148$ 17. a = −9 or a = 9   18. t = −6 or t = 6   19. a = −12 or a = 12   20. a = −11 or a = 11

Page 440   Classroom Exercises   1. 5   3. 9   5. 2

Page 441   Written Exercises   1. 10   3. 15.7   5. 15.6   7. 12.0   9. 19.2   11. Yes   13. No   15. Yes   17. No   19. No   21. Yes   23. 7.2 m   25. 9.9 km   27. 36.7 ft   29. 7.1 cm   31. 60.7 ft   33. 192 cm²   35. A whole is equal to the sum of its parts.   37. substitution principle $[2ab = 4(\frac{1}{2}ab)]$ 39. h = $\sqrt{3}(\frac{s}{2})$ 41. Use Theorem 12-3: $(2pq)^2 + (p^2 − q^2)^2 \overset{?}{=} (p^2 + q^2)^2$; $4p^2 q^2 + p^4 − 2p^2 q^2 + q^4 \overset{?}{=} p^4 + 2p^2 q^2 + q^4$; $p^4 + 2p^2 q^2 + q^4 = p^4 + 2p^2 q^2 + q^4$

Page 442   Review Capsule for Section 12-5   1. 18   2. 3   3. 2   4. 1   5. 10   6. 256   7. 169   8. 4   9. 144   10. 4   11. 17   12. 9   13. 13   14. 53

Page 444   Classroom Exercises   1. 5   3. $\sqrt{97}$ 5. $\sqrt{106}$

Page 444   Written Exercises   1. 5   3. 8   5. 6   7. 10   9. 5   11. $5\sqrt{2}$ 13. $\sqrt{41}$ 15. 14   17. 2

19. 2   21. 25   23. $5 + \sqrt{37} + 3\sqrt{2}$ 25. $4\sqrt{10} + 4\sqrt{5}$ 27. $3\sqrt{2} + \sqrt{5} + \sqrt{29}$

Page 445   Review   1. 8   2. −20   3. 10x   4. $\pm a^4 b^2$ 5. 2.6 m   6. width: 10.4 m; length: 20.8 m
7. $2\sqrt{7}$ 8. $4\sqrt{5}$ 9. $-2x^2\sqrt{6x}$ 10. $12d\sqrt{d}$ 11. 15   12. 7.5   13. 3   14. $6\sqrt{2}$ 15. $\sqrt{185}$

Page 446   Career Applications   1. $V_o = 5.6 \times 10^3$ m/sec; $V_e = 7.9 \times 10^3$ m/sec   3. $V_o = 5.0 \times 10^3$ m/sec;
$V_e = 7.1 \times 10^3$ m/sec   5. Orbit the earth   7. 25.2 km   9. 225.2 km

Page 448   Classroom Exercises   1. $\sqrt{14}$ 3. $3\sqrt{2}$ 5. −6   7. $5\sqrt{15}$ 9. $120\sqrt{3}$ 11. $20\sqrt{10}$

Page 448   Written Exercises   1. $\sqrt{10}$ 3. $\sqrt{14}$ 5. $3\sqrt{2}$ 7. $5\sqrt{2}$ 9. 6   11. 6   13. $5\sqrt{3}$ 15. 7
17. $2\sqrt{6}$ 19. $4\sqrt{10}$ 21. $15\sqrt{10}$ 23. $28\sqrt{3}$ 25. −168   27. $-24\sqrt{15}$ 29. $24\sqrt{42}$
31. $-63\sqrt{30}$ 33. $a\sqrt{b}$ 35. $4bc\sqrt{2}$ 37. $3m^2n\sqrt{2m}$ 39. $abc\sqrt{ac}$ 41. 2   43. 4   45. 10
47. $2\sqrt[3]{6}$ 49. $-6a^3b$ 51. $2xy^3\sqrt{x}$ 53. $10k^2t^3$

Page 449   Calculator Exercises   1. 46.4758   3. 69.7137   5. −43.817805   7. 19.595918

Page 449   Review Capsule for Section 12-7   1. 2   2. 3   3. 5   4. 8   5. 125   6. $\frac{\sqrt{2}}{2}$ 7. $\frac{\sqrt{5}}{5}$
8. $2\sqrt{3}$ 9. $2\sqrt{7}$ 10. $9\sqrt{2}$

Page 452   Classroom Exercises   1. $\frac{4}{5}$ 3. $\frac{16\sqrt{2}}{9}$ 5. $\pm\frac{3\sqrt{5}}{7}$ 7. $\frac{\sqrt{2}}{2}$ 9. $\frac{\sqrt{2}}{4}$ 11. $\frac{\sqrt{2}}{3}$ 13. $2\sqrt{10}$
15. $\frac{\sqrt{x}}{x^2}$

Page 452   Written Exercises   1. $\frac{2}{5}$ 3. $\frac{\sqrt{7}}{6}$ 5. $\frac{\sqrt{6}}{4}$ 7. $\frac{15}{14}$ 9. $\frac{7\sqrt{11}}{12}$ 11. $\frac{4\sqrt{3}}{15}$ 13. $\frac{10\sqrt{6}}{11}$
15. $\frac{7\sqrt{3}}{5}$ 17. $\frac{2\sqrt{3}}{3}$ 19. $\frac{\sqrt{6}}{3}$ 21. $\frac{\sqrt{14}}{2}$ 23. $\frac{\sqrt{35}}{5}$ 25. $\sqrt{6}$ 27. $\frac{3\sqrt{6}}{2}$ 29. $\frac{9\sqrt{2}}{2}$ 31. $\frac{8\sqrt{3}}{3}$
33. $\frac{2\sqrt{21}}{15}$ 35. $\frac{1}{3}$ 37. $\frac{7\sqrt{y}}{y}$ 39. $\frac{7\sqrt{c}}{c}$ 41. $\frac{\sqrt{3b}}{b^2}$ 43. $\frac{\sqrt{x}}{2x^2}$ 45. $\frac{\sqrt{7d}}{3d}$ 47. $bd\sqrt{d}$ 49. $2m\sqrt{3n}$
51. $\frac{\sqrt{2}}{2}$ 53. $\frac{7\sqrt{10}}{10}$ 55. $\frac{3\sqrt{70}}{35}$ 57. 1   59. $\frac{\sqrt{10}}{2}$ 61. $\frac{5\sqrt{3}}{2}$ 63. $2.309\overline{3}$ 65. 0.866   67. 0.6708
69. 1.580852   71. $1.649\overline{6}$ 73. $1.0434\overline{6}$

Page 453   Review Capsule for Section 12-8   1. $2\sqrt{6}$ 2. $4\sqrt{5}$ 3. $2\sqrt{10}$ 4. $8\sqrt{2}$ 5. $12\sqrt{2}$
6. 24   7. $10\sqrt{7}$ 8. $-6\sqrt{2}$ 9. $40\sqrt{2}$ 10. $6\sqrt{3}$ 11. $-16\sqrt{6}$ 12. $35\sqrt{3}$ 13. $\sqrt{35}$
14. $2\sqrt{15}$ 15. $\sqrt{6}$ 16. 10   17. 60   18. 7   19. 8   20. 8

Page 455   Classroom Exercises   1. $4\sqrt{3}$ 3. $\sqrt{2}$ 5. $-3\sqrt{3}$ 7. $9\sqrt{2} + \sqrt{10}$ 9. $6\sqrt{5} - 10$

Page 455   Written Exercises   1. $\sqrt{2}$ 3. $5\sqrt{2}$ 5. 0   7. $14\sqrt{5} + 9\sqrt{3}$ 9. $9 - 2\sqrt{2}$ 11. $\sqrt{2}$
13. $-\sqrt{5}$ 15. $-44\sqrt{2}$ 17. $35\sqrt{2}$ 19. $10\sqrt{6}$ 21. $27\sqrt{10}$ 23. $\sqrt{14} + 5\sqrt{7}$ 25. $4\sqrt{2} + 4$
27. $\sqrt{10} - \sqrt{15}$ 29. 1   31. $\sqrt{6}$ 33. $-\frac{\sqrt{6}}{6}$ 35. $-\frac{7\sqrt{2}}{12}$ 37. $7\sqrt{x}$ 39. $b\sqrt{2b}$ 41. $3a\sqrt{3a}$
43. $(12b - 72)\sqrt{b}$ 45. $3 + \sqrt{5}$ 47. $1 + \sqrt{x}$ 49. $\frac{4\sqrt{7} + 8}{3}$ 51. $\frac{2\sqrt{6} + 6}{-3}$ 53. $\frac{23 + 7\sqrt{2}}{39}$
55. $\frac{3x - 3\sqrt{x} - 1}{x - 1}$ 57. $(a + \sqrt{10})(a - \sqrt{10})$ 59. $5(x + \sqrt{5})(x - \sqrt{5})$ 61. $(1 + x\sqrt{2})(1 - x\sqrt{2})$
63. $(a - \sqrt{5})^2$

Page 456   Puzzle   See Solution Key.

Page 456   Review Capsule for Section 12-9   1. 5   2. 15   3. 11   4. 565   5. x   6. $a - 1$ 7. $2b - 1$
8. 9x   9. 32b   10. $25a - 25$ 11. Yes   12. No   13. No   14. Yes   15. No   16. Yes

Page 458   Classroom Exercises   1. $y = \frac{4}{25}$ 3. $x = 25$ 5. Divide both sides by 3.   7. Subtract 4 from
both sides.

Page 458 **Written Exercises** 1. $x = 36$ 3. $n = 20$ 5. $r = \frac{63}{5}$, or $12\frac{3}{5}$ 7. $x = 5$ 9. $x = 14$ 11. ϕ

13. $x = \frac{4}{25}$ 15. ϕ 17. $y = 81$ 19. $x = 4$ 21. ϕ 23. ϕ 25. $y = 2$ 27. $x = \frac{3}{4}$ 29. $x = 4$ 31. $\frac{4}{25}$

33. 16 35. $\frac{39}{2}$, or $19\frac{1}{2}$ 37. 300 ft 39. 6 mi 41. $x = 2$ 43. $x = -5$ 45. $y = -5$ or $y = 1$

47. $a = \frac{73}{8}$, or $9\frac{1}{8}$ 49. $t = \frac{5}{3}$, or $1\frac{2}{3}$ 51. Yes; squaring both sides of the second equation produces the first.

Page 460 **Review Capsule for Section 12-10** 1. x^7 2. a^7 3. c^3 4. 5^5 5. 10^7 6. x^4 7. x^6

8. x^6 9. x^9 10. $16b^6$ 11. z^{12} 12. $\frac{1}{4}z^2$ 13. $64t^3$ 14. $-64c^6$ 15. $0.25d^2$ 16. $\frac{1}{125}$ 17. $\frac{3}{b^2}$

18. $\frac{1}{9b^2}$ 19. $\frac{1}{-64}$ 20. $\frac{1}{100}$ 21. $\frac{1}{6}$ 22. $4b^2$ 23. $\frac{1}{16}$ 24. 6 25. 16

Page 461 **Classroom Exercises** 1. $7^{\frac{1}{2}}$ 3. $5^{\frac{3}{2}}$ 5. $9^{\frac{3}{4}}$ 7. -4 9. 32

Page 461 **Written Exercises** 1. 3 3. 2 5. 3 7. 11 9. -6 11. $-\frac{1}{2}$ 13. $-\frac{1}{3}$ 15. 3 17. $\frac{2}{3}$

19. $-\frac{2}{5}$ 21. -8 23. $\frac{1}{81}$ 25. 5 27. 2 29. 2 31. 8 33. -7 35. -5 37. $\frac{2}{5}$ 39. $-\frac{1}{2}$ 41. 81

43. 8 45. 343 47. $\sqrt[3]{-8}$ 49. $\sqrt[n]{93}$ 51. $\sqrt[3]{y}$ 53. $\sqrt[3]{x^2}$ 55. $\sqrt[n]{ab}$ 57. 3 59. -3 61. 27

63. 1 65. $73^{\frac{1}{2}}$ or $\sqrt{73}$

Page 462 **Review** 1. 6 2. $-12\sqrt{21}$ 3. $x\sqrt{y}$ 4. $3a\sqrt{2}$ 5. $\frac{2}{3}$ 6. $\frac{\sqrt{6}}{6}$ 7. $\frac{\sqrt{10}}{5}$ 8. $\frac{\sqrt{5x}}{x^2}$

9. $\frac{a\sqrt{6}}{b}$ 10. 0 11. $\sqrt{5} + 2\sqrt{2}$ 12. $3r\sqrt{6}$ 13. $x = 99$ 14. $x = 25$ 15. $x = 6$ 16. 10 17. -5

18. -2 19. 32 20. 4

Page 462 **Calculator Exercises** 1. 4.4857143 3. 6.4693891 5. 8.9038886

Page 464 **Computer Exercises** See Solution Key.

Page 465 **Chapter Objectives and Review** 1. 11 3. $3xy^3$ 5. $\frac{5}{9}$ 7. $\frac{16}{99}$ 9. 4.5 m 11. $3\sqrt{2}$

13. $3x\sqrt{6x}$ 15. 20.0 17. 361 m 19. 5 21. $9\sqrt{2}$ 23. $6\sqrt{2} - 10\sqrt{3}$ 25. $-3n^2\sqrt{n}$ 27. $\frac{\sqrt{10}}{10}$

29. $\frac{\sqrt{6y}}{2y^3}$ 31. $\sqrt{7}$ 33. $2x\sqrt{6}$ 35. $\frac{12 + 3\sqrt{3}}{13}$ 37. $-\frac{\sqrt{2} + 2}{2}$ 39. $x = 7$ 41. 25 43. 10 45. 12

47. -100

Page 467 **Chapter Test** 1. ±10 3. $3\sqrt{7}$ 5. -2 7. 25 9. 5 11. $2\sqrt{10}$ 13. $12\sqrt{2}$ 15. $2n\sqrt{3}$

17. $x = 11$ 19. 26 m

Page 467 **Additional Practice** 1. -12 3. ±19 5. $\frac{8}{9}$ 7. $\frac{9}{11}$ 9. $\frac{11}{37}$ 11. $3\sqrt{6}$ 13. $-12x\sqrt{5x}$

15. $30a^2b^2\sqrt{5b}$ 17. 9 19. 10 21. $6\sqrt{3}$ 23. $2a\sqrt{7}$ 25. $\frac{\sqrt{3}}{4}$ 27. $\frac{\sqrt{3}}{2}$ 29. $2x$ 31. $-\sqrt{5}$

33. $x = 27$ 35. $x = \frac{5}{2}$, or $2\frac{1}{2}$ 37. -7 39. $\frac{1}{4}$ 41. width: 5.5 m; length: 11 m 43. 2.4 cm 45. 81

CHAPTER 13: QUADRATIC FUNCTIONS AND EQUATIONS

Page 471 **Classroom Exercises** 1. $x = -5$ or $x = 5$ 3. $x = -1$ or $x = 5$ 5. $x = 0$ or $x = 1$
7. $a = -2\sqrt{3}$ or $a = 2\sqrt{3}$

Page 471 **Written Exercises** 1. $x = -4$ or $x = 4$ 3. $x = -\sqrt{11}$ or $x = \sqrt{11}$ 5. $m = -1$ or $m = 1$

7. $x = -3$ or $x = 3$ 9. $r = -10$ or $r = 10$ 11. $z = -4\sqrt{2}$ or $z = 4\sqrt{2}$ 13. $x = -\frac{1}{2}$ or $x = \frac{1}{2}$ 15. $b = -11$

or $b = 11$ 17. $m = -\sqrt{3}$ or $m = \sqrt{3}$ 19. $z = -\frac{2}{3}$ or $z = \frac{2}{3}$ 21. $x = 2$ 23. $x = -2$ or $x = 8$

25. $x = -14$ or $x = 0$ 27. $x = -1\frac{1}{2}$ or $x = 2\frac{1}{2}$ 29. $a = -9$ or $a = -3$ 31. $z = 2$ or $z = 10$ 33. $b = -4\frac{3}{4}$ or $b = 3\frac{1}{4}$ 35. $x = 0$ or $x = \frac{1}{2}$ 37. $x = -\frac{4}{7}$ or $x = -\frac{2}{7}$ 39. $k = 1$ or $k = 5$ 41. $n = -1$ or $n = 6$ 43. $r = 1$ or $r = 3$ 45. $y = -1\frac{1}{2}$ or $y = 2\frac{1}{2}$ 47. $v = -5$ or $v = -2$ 49. $x = -\sqrt{a + b}$ or $x = \sqrt{a + b}$ 51. $x = -\sqrt{ab}$ or $x = \sqrt{ab}$ 53. $x = -\frac{a}{2}$ or $x = \frac{a}{2}$ 55. $x = -\sqrt{bc}$ or $x = \sqrt{bc}$ 57. $x = -a - \sqrt{b}$ or $x = -a + \sqrt{b}$ 59. $x = \frac{-a - \sqrt{b}}{2}$ or $x = \frac{-a + \sqrt{b}}{2}$ 61. $x = \frac{-b - \sqrt{c}}{a}$ or $x = \frac{-b + \sqrt{c}}{a}$ 63. $x = \frac{-2 + b}{a}$ or $x = \frac{2 + b}{a}$

Page 472   Review Capsule for Section 13-2   1. $(m - 2)^2$ 2. NP   3. NP   4. $(t + 0.1)^2$ 5. $(q - 0.3)^2$ 6. $(p^3 - 6)^2$ 7. $(r + \frac{1}{3})^2$ 8. NP   9. $(b - \frac{7}{4})^2$ 10. $(t - \frac{1}{6})^2$ 11. $(a + \frac{3}{5})^2$ 12. $(c + \frac{3}{8})^2$

Page 474   Classroom Exercises   1. 4   3. 16   5. $\frac{1}{4}$ 7. $\frac{1}{16}$ 9. $\frac{b^2}{4a^2}$

Page 474   Written Exercises   1. 25; $(x + 5)^2$ 3. 4; $(m + 2)^2$ 5. $\frac{1}{4}$; $(r - \frac{1}{2})^2$ 7. 100; $(r - 10)^2$ 9. $\frac{25}{4}$; $(x + \frac{5}{2})^2$ 11. $\frac{1}{25}$; $(x - \frac{1}{5})^2$ 13. $x = -6$ or $x = 2$ 15. $n = 3$ or $n = 5$ 17. $a = 2$ or $a = 4$ 19. $a = -5$ or $a = 1$ 21. $x = 4$ or $x = 10$ 23. $x = 4$ or $x = 6$ 25. $x = 6$ or $x = 10$ 27. $a = 1$ or $a = 2$ 29. $x = 3$ or $x = 6$ 31. $n = -3$ or $n = -2$ 33. $x = -2$ or $x = 3$ 35. $x = -5$ or $x = 6$ 37. $y = -1$ or $y = 2$ 39. $x = 0$ or $x = 3$ 41. $n = -1$ or $n = 1\frac{1}{2}$ 43. $x = -1\frac{1}{3}$ or $x = 2$ 45. $n = \frac{1}{4}$ or $n = 4$ 47. $x = \frac{1}{2}$ or $x = 3$ 49. $a = -1\frac{1}{2}$ or $a = 4$ 51. $p = \frac{1 - \sqrt{3}}{2}$ or $p = \frac{1 + \sqrt{3}}{2}$ 53. $x = \frac{1 - \sqrt{73}}{12}$ or $x = \frac{1 + \sqrt{73}}{12}$ 55. $x = 3 - \sqrt{13}$ or $x = 3 + \sqrt{13}$ 57. $x = \frac{5 - \sqrt{57}}{4}$ or $x = \frac{5 + \sqrt{57}}{4}$ 59. $x = \frac{-b - \sqrt{b^2 - 4c}}{2}$ or $x = \frac{-b + \sqrt{b^2 - 4c}}{2}$ 61. $x = -1$ or $x = 3$ 63. $t = 5\frac{1}{2}$ or $t = 4$ 65. $b = 2$ or $b = 4\frac{7}{8}$

Page 475   Review Capsule for Section 13-3   1. $3\sqrt{6}$ 2. $-2\sqrt{6}$ 3. $36\sqrt{3}$ 4. $15\sqrt{2}$ 5. $-8\sqrt{2}$ 6. $35\sqrt{2}$ 7. $-2\sqrt{2}$ 8. $-6\sqrt{10}$ 9. $-20\sqrt{2}$ 10. $10\sqrt{11}$ 11. 13   12. -23 13. 81   14. 36   15. 40   16. 104

Page 476   Classroom Exercises   1. $a = 1$; $b = -4$; $c = -5$ 3. $a = 4$; $b = 12$; $c = -7$ 5. $a = 1$; $b = 3$; $c = -7$ 7. $a = 3$; $b = 0$; $c = -45$ 9. $a = 5$; $b = -2$; $c = -1$

Page 477   Written Exercises   1. $x = -3$ or $x = 7$ 3. $x = -1$ or $x = 1\frac{1}{2}$ 5. $p = 0$ or $p = 4$ 7. $a = -5$ or $a = 1$ 9. $n = -3$ or $n = -2$ 11. $x = -1\frac{1}{2}$ or $x = 1$ 13. $y = -1$ or $y = 2$ 15. $x = -3$ 17. $x = -1 - \sqrt{2}$ or $-1 + \sqrt{2}$ 19. $x = -3 - \sqrt{6}$ or $x = -3 + \sqrt{6}$ 21. $x = \frac{-3 - \sqrt{5}}{2}$ or $x = \frac{-3 + \sqrt{5}}{2}$ 23. $x = \frac{-1 - \sqrt{41}}{4}$ or $x = \frac{-1 + \sqrt{41}}{4}$ 25. $x = \frac{-7 - \sqrt{33}}{4}$ or $x = \frac{-7 + \sqrt{33}}{4}$ 27. $x = \frac{-5 - \sqrt{10}}{3}$ or $x = \frac{-5 + \sqrt{10}}{3}$ 29. $x = -\frac{1}{2}$ or $x = 1$ 31. $y = \frac{3 - \sqrt{41}}{4}$ or $y = \frac{3 + \sqrt{41}}{4}$ 33. $x = \frac{3 - \sqrt{37}}{14}$ or $x = \frac{3 + \sqrt{37}}{14}$ 35. $n = \frac{-7 - \sqrt{113}}{16}$ or $n = \frac{-7 + \sqrt{113}}{16}$ 37. $b = 1\frac{1}{2}$ 39. $t = \frac{1 - \sqrt{33}}{4}$ or $t = \frac{1 + \sqrt{33}}{4}$ 41. $x = -0.8$ or $x = 1.2$ 43. $n = -0.8$ or $n = 1.3$ 45. $b = -1.4$ or $b = -0.2$ 47. $x = \frac{-cd - c\sqrt{d^2 + 8}}{2}$ or $x = \frac{-cd + \sqrt{d^2 + 8}}{2}$ 49. $x = -1$ or $x = 1$ 51. $a = \frac{11 - \sqrt{17}}{2}$ or $a = \frac{11 + \sqrt{17}}{2}$ 53. $\left(\frac{-b + \sqrt{b^2 - 4ac}}{2a}\right)\left(\frac{-b - \sqrt{b^2 - 4ac}}{2a}\right) = \frac{b^2 - (\sqrt{b^2 - 4ac})^2}{4a^2} = \frac{b^2 - b^2 + 4ac}{4a^2} = \frac{4ac}{4a^2} = \frac{c}{a}$ 55. $x^2 - 4x - 1 = 0$

Page 478   Review Capsule for Section 13-4   1. $n, n + 1, n + 2$ 2. $n, n + 2$ 3. Let n = the number, then $\frac{1}{n}$ = the reciprocal.   4. Let n = the number, then $\frac{1}{n} - 5$ = five less than the reciprocal.   5. Let n = number of rows, then $n - 10$ = the number of seats.   6. Let n = the numerator, then $2n + 1$ = the denominator.

Page 479   Classroom Exercises   1. a. Let w = width, then $w + 3$ = length.   b. $w(w + 3) = 40$ 3. a. Let n = first integer, then $n + 2$ = second integer.   b. $n(n + 2) = 35$ 5. a. Let a = number, then n^2 = square of number.   b. $n^2 = 3n + 10$

Page 479   Word Problems   1. 27 seats   3. width: 5 cm; length: 8 cm   5. 8, or -7 7. length: 9 m; width: 6 m   9. $\frac{2}{3}$, or $\frac{1}{3}$ 11. 10 cm   13. 13 and 15, or -13 and -15 15. width: 20 m; length: 50 m   17. numerator: 3, denominator: 4; or numerator: $-\frac{8}{5}$, denominator: $-\frac{3}{5}$ 19. 3.39 m   21. 42 mi/hr

Page 481   Review   1. $x = -8$ or $x = 8$ 2. $y = -1$ or $y = 1$ 3. $x = -2\sqrt{3}$ or $x = 2\sqrt{3}$ 4. $n = -\sqrt{5}$ or $n = \sqrt{5}$ 5. $x = 4$ 6. $a = 9$ 7. $x = -3$ or $x = 5$ 8. $x = -3$ or $x = -2$ 9. $n = -2$ or $n = 4$ 10. $a = -1$ or $a = 2$ 11. $t = -2$ or $t = 1\frac{1}{2}$ 12. $s = \frac{3 - 2\sqrt{3}}{3}$ or $s = \frac{3 + 2\sqrt{3}}{3}$ 13. $a = -3$ or $a = 7$ 14. $c = 0$ or $c = 4$ 15. $y = -2$ or $y = 4$ 16. $b = \frac{-1 - \sqrt{10}}{3}$ or $b = \frac{-1 + \sqrt{10}}{3}$ 17. $x = \frac{-2 - \sqrt{6}}{2}$ or $\frac{-2 + \sqrt{6}}{2}$ 18. $y = \frac{1 - \sqrt{17}}{4}$ or $y = \frac{1 + \sqrt{17}}{4}$ 19. 12   20. 6.4 m

Page 481   Review Capsule for Section 13-5   1. 12, 8, 6, 6, 8, 12   2. 79, 37, 11, 1, 7, 29

Page 482   Career Applications   1. $3°F$ 3. $-27°F$ 5. $-36°F$ 7. $-62°F$ 9. $-21.6°C; 16.4°C$ 11. $-29.2°C; 18.4°C$ 13. $-27.6°C; 21.8°C$

Page 485   Classroom Exercises   1. No   3. Yes   5. Yes   7. No

Page 485   Written Exercises   For Exercises 1-12, the coordinates of seven points are given.   1. $(-8, 12)$, $(-7, 5)$, $(-6, 0)$, $(-4, -4)$, $(-2, 0)$, $(-1, 5)$, $(0, 12)$ 3. $(0, 8)$, $(1, 3)$, $(2, 0)$, $(3, -1)$, $(4, 0)$, $(5, 3)$, $(6, 8)$ 5. $(-3, 7)$, $(-2, 0)$, $(0, -8)$, $(1, -9)$, $(2, -8)$, $(4, 0)$, $(5, 7)$ 7. $(-5, 9)$, $(-4, 0)$, $(-2, -12)$, $(0, -16)$, $(2, -12)$, $(4, 0)$, $(5, 9)$ 9. $(-3, 6)$, $(-2, 0)$, $(0, -6)$, $(\frac{1}{2}, -6\frac{1}{4})$, $(1, -6)$, $(3, 0)$, $(4, 6)$ 11. $(0, 8)$, $(1, 3)$, $(2, 0)$, $(3, -1)$, $(4, 0)$, $(5, 3)$, $(6, 8)$ 13. a. -4 b. -4 15. a. none   b. none   17. a. $-1\frac{1}{2}$ and 2   b. $-1\frac{1}{2}$ and 2   For Exercises 19-33, the zeros and the coordinates of several points are given.   19. Zeros: -3 and 2; $(-4, 6)$, $(-2, -4)$, $(-\frac{1}{2}, -6\frac{1}{4})$, $(1, -4)$, $(3, 6)$ 21. Zeros: -3 and 3; $(-4, 7)$, $(-1, -8)$, $(0, -9)$, $(1, -8)$, $(5, 7)$ 23. Zero: -1; $(-4, 9)$, $(-2, 1)$, $(-1, 0)$, $(0, 1)$, $(2, 9)$ 25. Zeros: -1 and 13; $(-2, 15)$, $(3, 40)$, $(6, 49)$, $(9, 40)$, $(14, -15)$ 27. Zeros: -5 and 1; $(-6, -7)$, $(-4, 5)$, $(-2, 9)$, $(0, 5)$, $(2, -7)$ 29. Zeros: $-\frac{2}{3}$ and 1; $(-2, 12)$, $(\frac{1}{6}, -2\frac{1}{12})$, $(2, 8)$ 31. Zeros: $-\frac{3}{4}$ and $\frac{1}{2}$; $(-2, 3)$, $(-\frac{1}{8}, -\frac{21}{64})$, $(2, 4)$ 33. Zeros: $-2\frac{1}{2}$ and $1\frac{1}{2}$; highest point: $(-\frac{1}{2}, 16)$

Page 486   Review Capsule for Section 13-6   1. rational   2. irrational   3. rational   4. rational   5. irrational   6. irrational   7. $a = -11$ or $a = 11$ 8. $x = -\frac{3}{4}$ or $x = \frac{3}{4}$ 9. $y = -\frac{2}{3}$ or $y = -\frac{1}{4}$ 10. $b = \frac{1}{3}$ or $b = 3$ 11. $d = -7$ or $d = -\frac{1}{4}$ 12. $t = 2\frac{1}{2}$ 13. $x = 5$ 14. $b = 3 - 3\sqrt{2}$ or $b = 3 + 3\sqrt{2}$ 15. $r = -\sqrt{5}$ or $r = \sqrt{5}$ 16. $z = \frac{3 - \sqrt{29}}{10}$ or $z = \frac{3 + \sqrt{29}}{10}$ 17. $q = \frac{3 - \sqrt{17}}{4}$ or $q = \frac{3 + \sqrt{17}}{4}$ 18. $d = \frac{-7 - \sqrt{249}}{10}$ or $d = \frac{-7 + \sqrt{249}}{10}$

Page 487   Classroom Exercises   1. 17; two real solutions   3. 0; one real solution   5. -3; no real solutions

Page 488   Written Exercises   1. 61   3. 0   5. -47 7. 36   9. -48 11. -56 13. no real solutions   15. two real solutions   17. two real solutions   19. two real solutions   21. no real solutions   23. two real solutions   25. 10, -10 27. $k > \pm 2\sqrt{3}$ 29. one real solution   31. two real solutions

Page 488 Calculator Exercises 1. 0.72 **3.** 1.85 **5.** −1.62

Page 491 Classroom Exercises 1. minimum **3.** maximum **5.** maximum

Page 491 Written Exercises 1. a. x = 0 **b.** (0, 0) **3. a.** x = 0 **b.** (0, 4) **5. a.** x = −4 **b.** (−4, −9)
7. a. x = $1\frac{1}{2}$ **b.** $(1\frac{1}{2}, -2\frac{1}{4})$ **9. a.** x = 1 **b.** (1, −1) **11. a.** x = 0 **b.** (0, 1) **13. a.** x = −1 **b.** (−1, 9)
15. a. x = $1\frac{1}{2}$ **b.** $(1\frac{1}{2}, \frac{1}{4})$ **17.** 5 **19.** −25 **21.** 625 ft^2 **23.** second width: x; length: 60 − 2x
25. 450 ft^2 **27.** maximum, or minimum, $= \left[-\frac{b}{2a}, f(-\frac{b}{2a})\right]$

Page 493 Classroom Exercises 1. a. D **b.** inside **3. a.** S **b.** outside **5. a.** S **b.** outside **7. a.** D
b. outside

Page 493 Written Exercises For Exercises 1-16, the coordinates of several points are given. D represents a
dashed curve and S represents a solid curve. The terms inside and outside indicate whether the graph includes
the region inside or outside the curve. **1.** (−2, 4), (−1, 1), (0, 0), (1, 1), (2, 4); S; outside **3.** (−2, 8),
(−1, 5), (0, 4), (1, 5), (2, 8); S; inside **5.** (−2, −8), (−1, −2), (0, 0), (1, −2), (2, −8); D; outside
7. (−1, 4), (0, 0), $(1\frac{1}{2}, -2\frac{1}{4})$, (3, 0), (4, 4); S; outside **9.** (0, 4), (1, 1), (2, 0), (3, 1), (4, 4); S; outside
11. (−2, −2), (−√2, 0), (0, 2), (√2, 0), (2, −2); D; inside **13.** (−4, 0), (−3, −5), (−1, −9), (1, −5),
(2, 0); S; inside **15.** (−3, −3), (−√6, 0), (3, −3), (0, 6), (√6, 0); S; outside
17.   **19.**   **21.**   **23.**

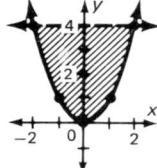 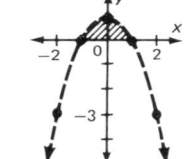 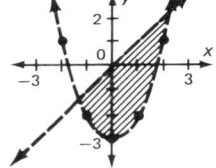 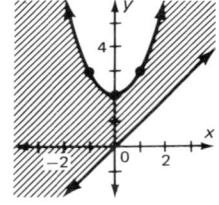

25.   **27.**   **29.** (0, 0) is the   **31.**
                                 solution.

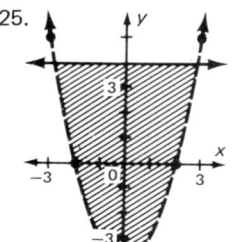 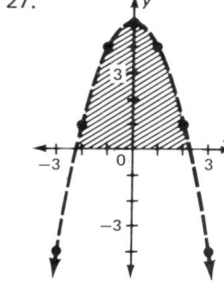 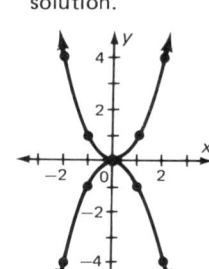 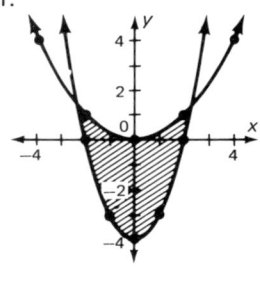

Page 495 Computer Exercises See Solution Key.
Page 496 Review 1. Parabola opens upward; vertex: (−2.5, −0.5); y intercept: (0, 6); zeros: −3, −2.
2. Parabola opens upward; vertex and y intercept: (0, −1); zeros: −1, 1. **3.** Parabola opens downward;
vertex: (2, 0); y intercept: (0, −4); zero: 2. **4.** two distinct, real solutions **5.** no real solutions **6.** no
real solutions **7. a.** x = 0 **b.** (0, 0); maximum **8. a.** x = 0 **b.** (0, 6); minimum **c.** zeros: (−√6, 0),
(√6, 0) **9. a.** x = 4 **b.** (4, −9); minimum **c.** zeros: (1, 0), (7, 0) **10.** The graph consists of all points
outside the parabola, opening downward, with vertex at (0, 0). **11.** The graph consists of all points outside
the parabola, opening upward, with vertex at (0, 2). **12.** The graph consists of all points on and outside the
parabola, opening downward, with vertex at (1, 1).

Page 497 Chapter Objectives and Review 1. x = −11 <u>or</u> x = 11 **3.** y = −3 <u>or</u> y = 3 **5.** t = −5 <u>or</u> t = −1
7. y = $-\frac{2}{3}$ <u>or</u> y = $-\frac{1}{3}$ **9.** x = $2\frac{3}{5}$ <u>or</u> x = $3\frac{2}{5}$ **11.** a = −1 <u>or</u> a = 7 **13.** x = −5 <u>or</u> x = 6 **15.** b = −2 <u>or</u>

$b = 5$ 17. $c = -1\frac{2}{3}$ or $c = -1$ 19. $y = -8$ or $y = 2$ 21. $b = -5$ or $b = 1$ 23. $x = -5$ or $x = -\frac{1}{2}$
25. $c = -\frac{2}{3}$ or $c = -\frac{1}{3}$ 27. $d = \frac{1}{3}$ or $d = 5$ 29. 6 and 7   31. width: 2.9 m; length: 3.9 m   33. The
graph is a parabola, opening upward, with vertex at (1.5, −2.25) and y intercept at the origin; zeros: 0, 3.
35. The graph is a parabola, opening upward, with vertex at (2.5, −2.25) and y intercept at (0, 4); zeros:
1, 4.   37. The graph is a parabola, opening downward, with vertex at (3, 0) and y intercept at (0, −9);
zero: 3.   39. two distinct, real solutions   41. two distinct, real solutions   43. no real solutions
45. no real solutions   47. $k = -16$ or $k = 16$

Page 498   Chapter Test 1. $x = -2$ or $x = 2$ 3. $x = -8$ or $x = 0$ 5. $x = 3$ or $x = 6$ 7. $y = -4$ or $y = 1$
9. $c = 2 - \sqrt{2}$ or $c = 2 + \sqrt{2}$ 11. $x = 4$ 13. −3, 1   15. one distinct, real solution   17. two distinct,
real solutions   19. width: 6 ft; height: 4 ft

Page 499   Additional Practice 1. $y = -9$ or $y = 9$ 3. $x = -5\sqrt{3}$ or $x = 5\sqrt{3}$ 5. $x = -4$ or $x = 2$
7. $x = 0$ or $x = 4$ 9. $x = -1 - \sqrt{5}$ or $x = -1 + \sqrt{5}$ 11. $x = 0$ or $x = 5$ 13. $x = -5$ or $x = 8$
15. $a = -1$ or $a = 1\frac{1}{2}$ 17. $p = -\frac{1}{4}$ or $p = 1$ 19. Parabola opens upward; vertex: $(1\frac{1}{2}, -6\frac{1}{4})$; y intercept:
(0, −4); zeros: −1, 4.   21. Parabola opens upward; vertex: (0, −36); y intercept: (0, −36); zeros: −6, 6.
23. Parabola opens upward; vertex: (2, 0); y intercept: (0, 4); zero: 2.   25. two distinct, real solutions
27. no real solution   29. no real solutions   31. 26 seats   33. smaller garden: 4 ft; larger garden: 7 ft

Page 500   Review of Word Problems: Chapters 1-13 1. $230   3. $136   5. 6   7. painter: $736;
assistant: $552   9. Linda: 73 km/hr; Bob: 68 km/hr   11. 15 m   13. $1\frac{1}{2}$ m   15. 25 and 45, or −17
and −40

Page 501   Cumulative Review: Chapters 1-13 1. b   3. c   5. a   7. d   9. b   11. d   13. b   15. b
17. c   19. b   21. c   23. b   25. d   27. c   29. c   31. b   33. a   35. a   37. b   39. a   41. b
43. c   45. a   47. a   49. a   51. b   53. b   55. c   57. d   59. b   61. a

Page 505   Preparing for College Entrance Tests 1. b   3. a   5. a   7. b

Page 506   Preparing for College Entrance Tests 1. a   3. d   5. d

CHAPTER 14: OTHER APPLICATIONS OF ALGEBRA

Page 509   Word Problems 1. angle: 60°; complement: 30°   3. 120°   5. 45°   7. 135°   9. angle:
120°; supplement: 60°   11. $180 - x$ 13. x

Page 511   Classroom Exercises 1. 50°   3. 60°   5. $\sqrt{2}$ 7. 4   9. $2\sqrt{3}$

Page 511   Word Problems 1. ∠G: 100°; ∠H: 40°; ∠K: 40°   3. ∠A: 50°; ∠B: 55°; ∠C: 75°   5. ∠A:
74°; ∠B: 90°; ∠C: 16°   7. $4\sqrt{2}$ m   9. 13 ft   11. $15\sqrt{3}$ ft   13. $\frac{4\sqrt{14}}{3}$ dm

Page 514   Classroom Exercises 1. $\frac{8}{4}$ 3. $\frac{9}{n} = \frac{12}{8}$

Page 514   Written Exercises 1. 30 m   3. 4.2 m   5. 3.8 m

Page 515   Review 1. angle: 17.5°; complement: 72.5°; supplement: 162.5°   2. angle: $51\frac{3}{7}°$;
complement: $38\frac{4}{7}°$; supplement: $128\frac{4}{7}°$ 3. ∠A: 25°; ∠B: 75°; ∠C: 80°   4. $30\sqrt{3}$ cm   5. $6\frac{3}{4}$ 6. $6\frac{2}{3}$

Page 518   Classroom Exercises 1. tan A = .7500; tan B = 1.3333   3. tan A = $\frac{y}{x}$; tan B = $\frac{x}{y}$ 5. .1763

Page 518   Written Exercises 1. .3640   3. .4040   5. 1.4281   7. .0875   9. .7536   11. 11.4301
13. 30°   15. 7°   17. 58°   19. increases; 57.2900   21. 15.4   23. 1; 1; 1.0000   25. 27°   27. 21 cm
29. 72 m   31. 201 m

Page 522   Classroom Exercises 1. .2079   3. .7071   5. sin A = .8660; cos A = .5000

Page 522   Written Exercises 1. sin: .5736; cos: .8192   3. sin: .8090; cos: .5878   5. sin: .9511;

cos: .3090 7. 8° 9. 41° 11. 66° 13. increase 15. 40° 17. 80° 19. 9° 21. 40.146 m
23. 13.6 m 25. 127.0 m 27. 163.6 m 29. 9.5 cm 31. 81.9 m 33. 2.47485 cm

Page 525 Classroom Exercises 1. tan 3. sin 5. cos

Page 525 Word Problems 1. about 175 m 3. about 37° 5. about 68° 7. $\overline{BD}$: about 124 cm;
$\overline{BC}$: about 137 cm 9. length of wire: about 87 m; distance: about 71 m

Page 526 Review 1. .6249 2. 1.0724 3. .2679 4. 14.3007 5. 22° 6. 65° 7. 83° 8. 52 m
9. .4226 10. .4540 11. .9945 12. .9744 13. 18° 14. 33° 15. 74° 16. 5747 m

Page 530 Written Exercises 1. 1 + 1 = 2; 1 + 2 = 3; 1 + 3 = 0; 2 + 2 = 0; 2 + 3 = 1; 3 + 1= 0; 3 + 2 = 1
3. No; each element does not have a multiplicative inverse; there is no number by which to multiply 0 or 2 to
get the identity element, 1 5. 1 X 1 = 1; 1 X 3 = 3; 1 X 4 = 4; 1 X 5 = 5; 2 X 1 = 2; 2 X 2 = 4; 2 X 3 = 0;
2 X 4 = 2; 2 X 5 = 4; 3 X 1 = 3; 3 X 2 = 0; 3 X 3 = 3; 3 X 5 = 3; 4 X 2 = 2; 4 X 3 = 0; 4 X 4 = 4; 5 X 1 = 5;
5 X 3 = 3; 5 X 4 = 2 7. Yes; a "two-hour clock" is a field 9. 1 X 1 = 1; 1 X 2 = 2; 2 X 1 = 2; 2 X 2 = 1
11. Yes

Page 532 Classroom Exercises 1. Conditional: If a triangle is a right triangle, then it has one right angle.
Converse: If a triangle has one right angle, then it is a right triangle. 3. Conditional: If a number is an odd
number, then it is not divisible by two. Converse: If a number is not divisible by two, then it is an odd
number.

Page 533 Written Exercises 1. If you have no more than 2 errors, then you do not get an A. 3. If I
drive over the speed limit, then I do not break the law. 5. False 7. True 9. True 11. If 15 is not a
real number, then 15 is not a rational number; If 15 is not a real number, then 15 is a rational number;
If 15 is a real number, then 15 is a rational number 13. If I get tired, then I work hard. 15. If Q has
exactly 3 sides and 3 angles, then Q is a triangle. 17. Conditional: If a number is an irrational number,
then it cannot be expressed as the ratio of an integer and a natural number. Converse: If a number cannot
be expressed as the ratio of an integer and a natural number, then it is an irrational number.
19. Conditional: If an angle is an obtuse angle, then its measure is greater than 90° and less than 180°.
Converse: If the measure of an angle is greater than 90° and less than 180°, then the angle is an obtuse
angle. 21. Conditional: If two equations are equivalent, then they have the same solution set. Converse:
If two equations have the same solution set, then they are equivalent. 23. Conditional: If a polynomial
is a binomial, then it has two terms. Converse: If a polynomial has two terms, then it is a binomial.

Page 535 Written Exercises For Exercises 1-27, the Reason appears in parentheses following each Statement.
1. Hypothesis: x is any number. Conclusion: $2x + 3x = 5x$ Proof: 1. x is any number. (Given)
2. $2x + 3x = (2 + 3)x$ (Dist. post.) 3. $(2 + 3)x = 5x$ (Addition) 4. $2x + 3x = 5x$ (Substitution)
3. Hypothesis: x and y are any numbers. Conclusion: $3x + (5y + 7x) = 10x + 5y$ Proof: 1. x and y are
any numbers. (Given) 2. $3x + (5y + 7x) = 3x + (7x + 5y)$ (Comm. post. for add.) 3. $3x + (7x + 5y)$
$= (3x + 7x) + 5y$ (Assoc. post. for add.) 4. $(3x + 7x) + 5y = 10x + 5y$ (Add. of like terms) 5. $3x$
$+ (5y + 7x) = 10x + 5y$ (Substitution)
5. Hypothesis: a is any number. Conclusion: $(-2a)(-3a) = 6a^2$ Proof: 1. a is any number. (Given)
2. $(-2a)(-3a) = (-2 \cdot -3)(a \cdot a)$ (Assoc. and comm. post. for mult.) 3. $(-2 \cdot -3)(a \cdot a) = 6(a \cdot a)$
(Pos. prod. theorem) 4. $6(a \cdot a) = 6a^2$ (Def. of exponents) 5. $(-2a)(-3a) = 6a^2$ (Substitution)
7. Hypothesis: x is any number. Conclusion: $(x + 3)(x + 4) = x^2 + 7x + 12$ Proof: 1. x is any number.
(Given) 2. $(x + 3)(x + 4) = (x + 3)x + (x + 3)4$ (Dist. post.) 3. $(x + 3)x + (x + 3)4 = x(x) + 3(x) + x(4)$
$+ 3(4)$ (Dist. post.) 4. $x(x) + 3(x) + x(4) + 3(4) = x^2 + 3(x) + x(4) + 3(4)$ (Def. of exponents)
5. $x^2 + 3(x) + x(4) + 3(4) = x^2 + (3x + 4x) + 3(4)$ (Comm. and assoc. post. for mult.) 6. $x^2 + (3x + 4x)$
$+ 3(4) = x^2 + 7x + 3(4)$ (Add. of like terms) 7. $x^2 + 7x + 3(4) = x^2 + 7x + 12$ (Multiplication)
8. $(x + 3)(x + 4) = x^2 + 7x + 12$ (Substitution)
9. Hypothesis: x is an even number. Conclusion: x^2 is an even number. Proof: 1. x is an even number.
(Given) 2. Let x = 2n. Then $x^2 = (2n)^2$ when n is an integer. (Def. of an even number.)
3. $(2n)^2 = (2n)(2n)$ (Def. of exponents) 4. $(2n)^2 = 2(n \cdot 2n)$ (Assoc. post. for mult.) 5. $2(n \cdot 2n)$
$= 2(2n^2)$ (Comm. post. for mult.; Def. of exp.) 6. $2n^2$ is an integer (Closure post. for mult.) 7. $2(2n^2)$

is even (Def. of even numbers) 8. x^2 is even (Substitution)

11. Hypothesis: a and b are even numbers. Conclusion: a + b is an even number. Proof: 1. a and b are even. (Given) 2. Let a = 2n, b = 2k. Then a + b = 2n + 2k (n and k are integers) (Def. of even number) 3. 2n + 2k = 2(n + k) (Dist. post.) 4. n + k is an integer (Closure post. for add.) 5. 2(n + k) is an even number (Def. of even number) 6. a + b is an even number (Susbtitution)

13. Hypothesis: a and b are any odd numbers. Conclusion: ab is odd Proof: 1. a and b are odd (Given) 2. Let a = 2k + 1, b = 2p + 1 (k and p are integers.) Then a · b = (2k + 1)(2p + 1) (Def. of odd number) 3. (2k + 1)(2p + 1) = 4kp + 2k + 2p + 1 (Mult. of binomials) 4. 4kp + 2k + 2p + 1 = 2(2kp + k + p) + 1 (Dist. post.) 5. 2kp + k + p is an integer (Closure post. for add. and mult.) 6. 2(2kp + k + p) + 1 is an odd number (Def. of odd number) 7. ab is odd (Substitution)

15. Hypothesis: a is any odd number. b is any even number. Conclusion: ab is even Proof: 1. a is odd, b is even (Given) 2. Let a = 2k + 1, b = 2p. Then ab = 2p(2k + 1). (k and p are integers) (Def. of even and odd numbers) 3. 2p(2k + 1) = 2[p(2k + 1)] (Assoc. post. for mult.) 4. 2[p(2k + 1)] = 2(2kp + p) (Dist. post.) 5. 2kp + p is an integer (Closure post. for add. and mult.) 6. 2(kp + p) is an even number (Def. of even number) 7. ab is an even number (Substitution)

17. Hypothesis: a and b are multiples of 3. Conclusion: ab is a multiple of 3 Proof: 1. a and b are mult. of 3 (Given) 2. Let a = 3n, b = 3k, where n and k are integers. Then ab = (3n)(3k). (Def. of mult. of 3) 3. (3n)(3k) = 3(n · 3k) (Assoc. post. for mult.) 4. 3(n · 3k) = 3(3kn) (Comm. post.) 5. 3kn is an integer (Closure post. for mult.) 6. 3(3kn) is a mult. of 3 (Def. of mult. of 3) 7. ab is a mult. of 3 (Substitution)

19. Hypothesis: a is divisible by 6. Conclusion: a is divisible by 2 Proof: 1. a is divisible by 6. (Given) 2. Let a = 6k, where k is an integer (If a is divisible by 6, then 6 is a factor of a.) 3. 6k = (2 · 3)k (Factors of 6) 4. (2 · 3)k = 2(3 · k) (Assoc. post. for mult.) 5. 3k is an integer (Closure post. for mult.) 6. 2(3k) is divisible by 2 (Even numbers are divisible by 2) 7. a is divisible by 2 (Substitution)

21. Hypothesis: a and b are any multiples of 5. Conclusion: ab is a multiple of 5 Proof: 1. a and b are mult. of 5 (Given) 2. Let a = 5n, b = 5k, where n and k are integers. Then ab = (5n)(5k) (Def. of mult. of 5) 3. (5n)(5k) = 5(n · 5k) (Assoc. post. for mult.) 4. 5(n · 5k) = 5(5nk) (Comm. post.) 5. 5nk is an integer (Closure post. for mult.) 6. 5(5nk) is a mult. of 5 (Def. of mult. of 5) 7. ab is a mult. of 5 (Substitution)

23. Hypothesis: a and b are any real numbers. Conclusion: (a − b) and (b − a) are opposites Proof: 1. a and b are real numbers. (Given) 2. (a − b) + (b − a) = [a + (−b)] + [b + (−a)] (Def. of subtraction) 3. [a + (−b)] + [b + (−a)] = a + (−b + b) + (−a) (Assoc. post. for add.) 4. a + (−b + b) + (−a) = [a + (−a)] + (−b + b) (Comm. post.) 5. a + (−a) + (−b + b) = 0 + 0 = 0 (Add. inverse post.) 6. (a − b) + (b − a) = 0 (Substitution) 7. a − b and b − a are opposites (Def. of opposites)

25. Hypothesis: a is any even number, b is any odd number. Conclusion: $(a + b)^2$ is an odd number Proof: 1. a is even. b is odd. (Given) 2. a + b is odd (Ex. 12) 3. $(a + b)^2$ is odd (Ex. 10)

27. Hypothesis: x is not a multiple of 4. Conclusion: x^2 is not a multiple of 8. Proof: 1. x is not a mult. of 4. (Given) 2. x may be represented as 4n + 1, 4n + 2, 4n + 3 where n is an integer (4 cannot be a factor of x, since x is not a mult. of 4) 3. $(4n + 1)^2 = 16n^2 + 8n + 1$; $(4n + 2)^2 = 16n^2 + 16n + 4$; $(4n + 3)^2 = 16n^2 + 24n + 9$ (Mult.; (Ex. 8)) 4. $16n^2 + 8n + 1 = 8(2n^2 + n) + 1$; $16n^2 + 16n + 4 = 8(2n^2 + 2n) + 4$; $16n^2 + 24n + 9 = 8(2n^2 + 3n) + 9$ (Dist. post.) 5. $(2n^2 + n)$, $(2n^2 + 2n)$ and $(2n^2 + 3n)$ are integers (Closure post. for add. and mult.) 6. $8(2n^2 + 1) + 1$, $8(2n^2 + 2n) + 4$, $8(2n^2 + 3n) + 9$ are not multiples of 8 (They do not have 8 as a factor.) 7. x^2 is not a multiple of 8. (Substitution)

Page 536 Review 1. No; 2 and 4 do not have multiplicative inverses. 2. No; 2, 3, and 4 do not have multiplicative inverses. 3. Yes 4. No; 2, 4, and 6 do not have multiplicative inverses. 5. If a number is an odd number, then the number is a rational number. 6. If the sky is not cloudy, then it is sunny outside. 7. If the electricity is working, then the lights are shining. **8.** 5. If a number is a rational number, then it is an odd number; False 6. If it is sunny outside, then the sky is not cloudy; True 7. If the lights are shining, then the electricity is working; True For Exercises 9 and 10, the Reason appears in parentheses following each Statement.

9. Hypothesis: a is any odd number. Conclusion: a^3 is an odd number Proof: 1. a is an odd number. (Given) 2. Let a = 2n + 1, where n is an integer. Then $a^3 = (2n + 1)^3$ (Def. of odd number) 3. $(2n + 1)^3 = (2n + 1)^2(2n + 1)$ (Factoring) 4. $(2n + 1)^2$ is an odd number (The square of an odd number is odd.)

(Ex. 10, page 535)   5. $(2n + 1)^2(2n + 1)$ is an odd number.   (The product of 2 odd numbers is odd.) (Ex. 13, page 535)   6. a^3 is an odd number. (Substitution)

10. Hypothesis: a, b, c are any odd numbers. Conclusion: $a + b + c$ is an odd number   Proof: 1. a, b, c are any odd numbers. (Given)   2. Let $a = 2k + 1$, $b = 2n + 1$, $c = 2p + 1$, where k, n and p are integers. Then $a + b + c = 2k + 1 + 2n + 1 + 2p + 1$ (Def. of odd number)   3. $2k + 1 + 2n + 1 + 2p + 1 = 2k + 2n + 2p + 3$ (Comm. and assoc. postulates; addition)   4. $2k + 2n + 2p + 3 = 2(k + n + p) + 3$ (Dist. post.)
5. $k + n + p$ is an integer (Closure post. for add.)   6. $2(k + n + p) + 3$ is odd (Def. of odd number)
7. $a + b + c$ is an odd number (Substitution)

Page 537   Chapter Objectives and Review   1. angle: $50°$; complement: $40°$; supplement: $130°$
3. $\angle G$: $100°$; $\angle F$: $50°$; $\angle H$: $30°$ 5. $90\sqrt{2}$ ft   7. $\frac{12}{5}$ 9. $\frac{12}{13}$ 11. $\frac{5}{13}$ 13. $x = 14.0$; $y = 24.4$ 15. $49°$
17. $53°$ 19. Yes   21. Yes   23. If 6 is a factor of 12, then 6 is a factor of 24.   25. If a number is an odd number, then it is a natural number that is not divisible by 2. If a number is a natural number that is not divisible by 2, then it is an odd number.
27. In the following proof, the Reason appears in parentheses following each Statement.
Hypothesis: a and b are any multiples of 4. Conclusion: $a + b$ is a multiple of 4   Proof: 1. a and b are multiples of 4. (Given)   2. Let $a = 4n$, $b = 4k$, where n and k are integers. Then $a + b = 4n + 4k$. (Def. of mult. of 4)   3. $4n + 4k = 4(n + k)$ (Dist. post.)   4. $n + k$ is an integer (Closure post. for add.)
5. $4(n + k)$ is a mult. of 4 (Def. of mult. of 4)   6. $a + b$ is a mult. of 4 (Substitution)

Page 540   Chapter Test   1. angle: $60°$; complement: $30°$; supplement: $120°$ 3. 12.7 cm   5. 2.625
7. $\frac{3}{4}$ 9. $\frac{4}{3}$ 11. $\frac{3}{5}$ 13. If 5 is a whole number, then 5 is a rational number.   15. If a figure is a square, then the figure is a rectangle.   17. 13. If 5 is a rational number, then 5 is a whole number; True   14. If Saturday is the last day of the week, then today is Saturday; False   15. If a figure is a rectangle, then the figure is a square; False   16. If his father's name is Joe, then his name is Joe Junior; False   19. No. There is no inverse element $\frac{1}{a}$, such that $a \cdot \frac{1}{a} = 1$.

A 3
B 4
C 5
D 6
E 7
F 8
G 9
H 0
I 1